Organic chemistry

ORGANIC
CHEMISTRY

methane to macromolecules

JOHN D. ROBERTS
California Institute of Technology

ROSS STEWART
University of British Columbia

MARJORIE C. CASERIO
University of California, Irvine

W. A. BENJAMIN, INC.
Menlo Park, California • Reading, Massachusetts
London • Amsterdam • Don Mills, Ontario • Sydney

Organic chemistry: Methane to macromolecules

Portions of this book appeared previously in
Modern Organic Chemistry
by John D. Roberts and Marjorie C. Caserio,
published by W. A. Benjamin, Inc.

Second printing, August 1971

ISBN 0-8053-8332-8
HIJKLMNOPQ-MA-79876

W. A. BENJAMIN, INC., Menlo Park, California

preface

The success achieved by this book's forerunners, *Basic Principles of Organic Chemistry* and *Modern Organic Chemistry*, was to a considerable extent due to the rigor with which the subject of organic chemistry was presented. In the present work we have tried to paint an interesting, relevant, and up-to-date picture of organic chemistry while retaining the rigorous approach of the earlier books.

Organic chemistry sometimes appears to be enormously complex to the beginning student, particularly if he must immediately grapple with the subjects of structural isomerism and nomenclature. We have attempted to avoid this difficulty in the following way. Chapter 1 briefly relates carbon to its neighbors in the Periodic Table and reviews some fundamental concepts. Chapter 2 deals with the four C_1 and C_2 hydrocarbons—methane, ethane, ethene, and ethyne—and discusses their conformational and configurational properties and some of their chemical reactions. The reader thus makes an acquaintance with the properties of some important organic compounds before dealing in an open-ended way with families of compounds—alkanes, alcohols, etc.

A heavy emphasis on spectroscopy is retained but the subject is introduced somewhat later than in the earlier books. Important additions are chapters dealing with enzymic processes and metabolism and with cyclization reactions. Many of the exercises of the earlier books have been retained and have been supplemented with drill-type problems.

It seems a shame to burden the mind of the beginning student with trivial names, some of them quite illogical, and throughout we have stressed IUPAC nomenclature, which is both logical and easy to learn. The instructor, who may well carry lightly the excess baggage of redundant names, may occasionally find this irritating but we ask him to consider the larger good. As a further aid to the student, each chapter concludes with a summary of important points.

The simple introduction to the subject and the emphasis on relevance, particularly to living systems, should make the book appealing to the general student. At the same time we hope that the up-to-date and more advanced topics that are included—the effect of orbital symmetry on cyclization reactions, for example—will also appeal to the chemistry specialist.

We should like to acknowledge the help of many persons who read all or parts of the manuscript and offered sound advice. Professor George E. Hall read the manuscript at several stages of revision and we are particularly grateful to him. Others who helped us were Drs. E. Caress, L. D. Hall, D. N. Harpp, J. P. Kutney, T. Money, M. Smith, T. Spencer, and L. S. Weiler.

We conclude this preface on a mildly philosophical note. The world of tomorrow will result from the interplay of powerful forces—some social, some technological. Responsible public action requires public knowledge and there are few areas of science that impinge more on the life around us than does organic chemistry. We hope that those who study this book will utilize their knowledge responsibly for the benefit of all who come after.

JOHN D. ROBERTS
ROSS STEWART
MARJORIE C. CASERIO

Pasadena, California
Vancouver, British Columbia
Irvine, California

contents

Chapter 6 Bonding in conjugated unsaturated systems 125

Chapter 7 Isolation and identification of organic compounds 151

Chapter 8 Nucleophilic displacement and elimination reactions 185

chapter 1
introduction

Twenty-two centuries ago the Greek mathematician Euclid wrote a textbook on geometry that is still in use today. Some 300 years ago Isaac Newton discovered the principles of mechanics that can still be applied with great precision to most macroscopic systems. By contrast, chemistry, and in particular organic chemistry, is in its infancy as a precise science. The study of molecular science—because this is what chemistry essentially is—depends on inferences about submicroscopic bodies drawn from observations of macroscopic behavior. The speculations of the early chemists are best described as "haywire" rather than as "incorrect" and it was only in the last century that the foundations of chemical theory became firmly established. Since that time enormous strides have been made in extending chemical knowledge. And today, some 1,100,000 organic compounds alone (compounds containing carbon) have been prepared, their structures elucidated, and their properties examined.

The flowering of organic chemistry in the past hundred years followed two events during the last century. The first occurred in 1828, when the German chemist Wöhler discovered that ammonium cyanate ($NH_4^{\oplus}CNO^{\ominus}$) could be converted to the compound urea ($NH_2 \overset{\overset{\displaystyle O}{\|}}{C} NH_2$). The former was a typical salt and is considered part of the mineral world, whereas urea was a product of animal metabolism and therefore part of the living or organic world. The realization gradually followed that the boundary between living and nonliving systems could be crossed, and this provided the impetus for intensive investigation of the substances found in nature: the term "organic" was thus applied to all compounds of carbon whether they were found in nature or were prepared in the laboratory.

The second important occurrence in the last century as far as organic chemistry was concerned was the recognition, achieved between 1858 and 1872, that unique, three-dimensional structures could be drawn for the molecules of every known compound of carbon. This realization followed essentially the work of six men: Avogadro, Cannizzaro, Kekulé, Couper, LeBel, and van't Hoff. Avogadro and Cannizzaro distinguished between what we would now call empirical and molecular formulas. Avogadro's hypothesis that equal volumes of gases contained equal numbers of molecules was actually made in 1811 but it was not until 1860 that the Italian chemist Cannizzaro made use of this idea to distinguish between different compounds having the same composition. Thus, the distinction between the molecules C_2H_4 and C_4H_8 became clear, and it was realized that neither had the molecular formula CH_2, though both had this empirical formula. At about the same time Kekulé, a German, and Couper, a Scot, suggested that carbon was tetravalent, always forming four bonds. Two young chemists, LeBel and van't Hoff, then independently provided convincing proof that these four bonds are tetrahedrally arranged around the carbon atom (Section 14·6).

Part of the fascination of organic chemistry comes from the knowledge that the whole complex edifice has been built up from indirect study of molecular behavior, that is, microscopic understanding from macroscopic observation. The advent in recent years of sophisticated instrumental techniques for examining structure has confirmed the vast majority of the structures assigned to organic compounds in the late nineteenth century. Spectroscopy and X-ray crystallography, in particular, have become powerful tools for checking previously assigned structures and for elucidating structures of compounds newly prepared in the laboratory or found in nature.

Considerable use will be made in this book of spectroscopy—the study of how "light" (to be more exact, electromagnetic radiation) is absorbed by matter. The infrared, ultraviolet, and nuclear magnetic resonance spectra may permit the correct structure of a fairly complex compound to be assigned in a matter of hours. If, at this point, a search of the chemical literature reveals that the compound with the suspected structure has been previously prepared, it is only necessary to compare the reported physical or spectroscopic properties with those of the substance being examined. However, if the compound has not been previously reported, it must be synthesized from starting materials of known structure before its structure is really considered to be proven.

Organic chemistry occupies a central position in the undergraduate science curriculum. It is, of course, an important branch of knowledge in its own right, but in addition it is the foundation for basic studies in botany, zoology, microbiology, nutrition, forestry, agricultural sciences, dentistry, and medicine. Antibiotics, vitamins, hormones, sugars, and proteins are only a few of the important classes of chemical substances that are organic. In addition, many industrially important products are organic—plastics, rubber, petroleum products, most explosives, perfumes, flavors, and synthetic fibers. It is little wonder that there are more organic chemists than chemists of any other kind. Of the 2000 or so Ph.D.'s awarded each year in chemistry in North America, about half go to those whose research has been in organic chemistry. The research may have involved the synthesis of a new compound of unusual structure, the elucidation of the structure of a new compound extracted from a plant, or the discovery of the reaction path that is followed when one compound is converted to another.

Only a few years ago most people regarded the effects of chemical technology as being wholly beneficial. Pesticides, herbicides, plastics, and synthetic drugs all seemed to contribute in large or small measure to human welfare. Recently we have come to realize, however, that our environment cannot indefinitely accommodate all the products that are being added to it without being damaged. A pesticide may be extremely effective at eradicating some of man's enemies but may seriously endanger some of man's friends. A cogent example is the way the potent insecticide DDT (Section 24·7) causes bird egg shells to become thin. Further, a synthetic plastic may be immune to sunlight, rain, and bacterial decay but this is a doubtful benefit after the object made from it has been discarded in a park.

Many of the substances that have been added in large amounts to our environment in recent years are synthetic organic chemicals. Some are harmful to man and to life in general; some are not. An understanding of the properties and reactions of organic compounds will help us assess the possible perils associated with new processes or products and will help us develop suitable control procedures. The grave consequences of a polluted environment can only be avoided by the wise application of chemical knowledge.

1·1   bonding in organic compounds

Why is carbon unique? What accounts for the apparently limitless number of carbon compounds that can be prepared? The answer is that bonds between carbon atoms are stable, allowing chains of carbon atoms to be formed, with each carbon atom of a chain being capable of joining to other atoms such as hydrogen, oxygen, sulfur, nitrogen, and the halogens. Neighboring atoms in the periodic table, such as boron, silicon, sulfur, and phosphorus, can also bond to themselves to form chains in the elemental state, but the resulting compounds are generally quite unstable and highly reactive when atoms of hydrogen or halogen, for example, are attached to them. The elements at the right or left of the periodic table do not form chains at all—their electron-attracting or electron-repelling properties are too great.

The forces that hold atoms and groups of atoms together are the electrostatic forces of attraction between positively charged nuclei and negatively charged electrons on different atoms. We usually recognize two kinds of binding. The first is the familiar **ionic bond** that holds a crystal of sodium chloride together. Each $Na^{\oplus}$ in the crystal feels a force of attraction to each $Cl^{\ominus}$, the force decreasing as the distance increases. (Repulsion between ions of the same sign of charge is also present, of course, but the stable crystal arrangement has more attraction than repulsion.) Thus, you cannot identify a sodium chloride pair as being a molecule of sodium chloride. Similarly, in an aqueous solution of sodium chloride, each sodium ion and chloride ion move in the resultant electric field of all the other ions in the solution. Sodium chloride, like other salts, can be vaporized at high temperatures. The boiling point of sodium chloride is 1400°.[1] For sodium chloride vapor, you can at last speak of sodium chloride molecules which, in fact, are pairs of ions, $Na^{\oplus}Cl^{\ominus}$. Enormous energy is required to vaporize the salt because in the vapor state each ion interacts with just one partner instead of many.

The second kind of bonding referred to above results from the simultaneous interaction of a pair of electrons (or, less frequently, just one electron) with two nuclei, and is called the **covalent bond**. Whereas metallic sodium reacts with chlorine by completely transferring an electron to it to form $Na^{\oplus}$ and $Cl^{\ominus}$, the elements toward the middle of the rows of the periodic table tend to react with each other by sharing electrons.

Transfer of an electron from a sodium atom to a chlorine atom produces two ions, each of which now possesses an octet of electrons. This means of achieving an octet of electrons is not open to an element such as carbon, which has two electrons in a filled inner K shell and four valence electrons in the outer L shell. A quadrinegative ion $C^{4\ominus}$ with an octet of electrons in the valence shell would have an enormous concentration of charge and be of very high energy. Similarly, the quadripositive ion $C^{4\oplus}$, which would have a filled K shell like helium, would be equally unstable. Carbon (and to a great extent boron, nitrogen, oxygen, and the halogens) completes its valence-shell octet by sharing electrons with other atoms.

---

[1] In this book all temperatures are given in degrees centigrade unless otherwise noted.

In compounds with shared electron bonds (or covalent bonds) such as methane (CH_4) or tetrafluoromethane (CF_4), carbon has its valence shell filled, as shown in these Lewis structures:

$$
\begin{array}{c}
\text{H} \\
\text{H:}\overset{\cdot\cdot}{\text{C}}\text{:H} \\
\text{H}
\end{array}
\qquad\qquad
\begin{array}{c}
:\!\overset{\cdot\cdot}{\text{F}}\!: \\
:\!\overset{\cdot\cdot}{\text{F}}\text{:}\overset{\cdot\cdot}{\text{C}}\text{:}\overset{\cdot\cdot}{\text{F}}\!: \\
:\!\overset{\cdot\cdot}{\text{F}}\!:
\end{array}
$$

methane　　　　　　tetrafluoromethane
　　　　　　　　　　(carbon tetrafluoride)

For convenience, these molecules are usually written with each bonding pair of electrons represented by a dash:

$$
\begin{array}{c}
\text{H} \\
| \\
\text{H}-\text{C}-\text{H} \\
| \\
\text{H}
\end{array}
\qquad\qquad
\begin{array}{c}
\text{F} \\
| \\
\text{F}-\text{C}-\text{F} \\
| \\
\text{F}
\end{array}
$$

1·2 methane, ammonia, water, and hydrogen fluoride

The elements in the first main row of the periodic table are

	Li	Be	B	C	N	O	F	Ne
Atomic number	3	4	5	6	7	8	9	10
Number of valence electrons								
	1	2	3	4	5	6	7	(8)

Lithium and beryllium are able to form positive ions by loss of one or two electrons, respectively. Boron is in an intermediate position and its somewhat unusual bonding properties are considered later in the book (Section 19·5). Carbon, nitrogen, oxygen, and fluorine all have the ability to form covalent bonds because each can complete its octet by sharing electrons with other atoms. (Fluorine or oxygen can also exist as stable anions in compounds such as $Na^{\oplus}F^{\ominus}$ or $Na^{\oplus}OH^{\ominus}$.)

The degree of sharing of electrons in a covalent bond will not be exactly equal if the elements being linked are different. The relative attractive power exerted by an element on the electrons in a covalent bond can be expressed by its **electronegativity**. In one quantitative definition of electronegativity we have an increase in electronegativity along the series toward fluorine as follows:

C	N	O	F
2.5	3.0	3.5	4.0

The electronegativity of hydrogen is 2.0, close to that for carbon. Each covalent bond between elements with different electronegativities will have the bonding electrons unequally shared between them, which leads to what is called polar character. In a carbon-fluorine bond the pair of electrons are attracted more to the fluorine nucleus than to the carbon nucleus. The regions of space occupied by electrons are called **orbitals** and, in a molecule such as CF_4, the pair of electrons in the orbital that represents each covalent bond will not be divided equally between the carbon and fluorine but will be polarized towards fluorine.

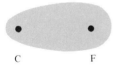

We say that such a bond is dipolar and it can be represented, when necessary, by the symbols

$$-\overset{|}{\underset{|}{C}}-\overset{\delta\oplus\ \delta\ominus}{F} \quad \text{or} \quad -\overset{|}{\underset{|}{C}}\rightarrow F$$

The electronegativity of oxygen is less than that of fluorine and closer to that of carbon; therefore the polarity of a C—O bond will be less than that of a C—F bond. Clearly the polarity of a C—N bond will be smaller still.

Even though a molecule contains polar bonds, the molecule itself may be nonpolar, that is, not possess a dipole moment. This will occur when the molecule has a shape (or symmetry) such that the dipoles of the individual bonds cancel each other. Thus, molecules such as F—O—F and H—O—H will have dipole moments (as they do) if the angle between the two F—O (or H—O) bonds is different from 180°, and zero dipole moment if the angle is 180°. To predict whether a molecule has a dipole moment, it is therefore

$$\underset{\underset{F}{\delta\ominus}\diagup\underset{F}{\overset{2\delta\oplus}{O}}\diagdown\underset{}{\delta\ominus}}{}\qquad \overset{\delta\ominus\ 2\delta\oplus\ \delta\ominus}{F-O-F}\qquad \underset{\underset{H}{\delta\oplus}\diagup\underset{H}{\overset{2\delta\ominus}{O}}\diagdown\underset{}{\delta\oplus}}{}\qquad \overset{\delta\oplus\ 2\delta\ominus\ \delta\oplus}{H-O-H}$$

necessary to know its shape, and in the next section the principles governing the shapes of covalently bound molecules are considered, with special reference to the series CH_4, NH_3, H_2O, and HF.

If a substance is a liquid, it is an easy matter to show experimentally whether its molecules are polar and have a dipole moment. All you have to do is to hold an object carrying an electrostatic charge near a fine stream of the falling liquid and note whether the stream is deflected. The charged object can be as simple as a glass rod rubbed on silk or an amber rod rubbed on cat's fur, the charge being positive in the first case and negative in the second. A fine stream of water is sharply deflected by such an object and this shows that the individual molecules in the liquid have positive and negative ends. The molecules tend to orient themselves so that the appropriately charged end is directed towards the charged object (for example, the negative end, oxygen, toward the positively charged rod) and then the electrostatic attraction draws the molecules toward the rod. A fine stream of carbon tetrachloride (tetrachloromethane), CCl_4, cannot be deflected at all. This shows that the CCl_4 molecule is sufficiently symmetrical in its arrangement of the four carbon-chlorine bonds so that the polarities of these bonds cancel each other.

A. MOLECULAR SHAPES

It is important to recognize that an understanding of the shapes of organic compounds is absolutely vital to understanding the physical, chemical, and biochemical properties of organic compounds. We present in this section a few simple concepts which will turn out later to be of great utility in predicting and correlating the shapes of complex organic molecules.

The compounds CH_4, NH_3, H_2O, and HF are all **isoelectronic**: they have the same number of electrons, 10. Two are in the inner K shell of the central atom and eight are in the valence, or bonding, shell. The bonding arrangements can be indicated by Lewis structures:

$$\begin{array}{cccc} \text{H} & & & \\ \text{H:C:H} & \text{H:N:H} & \text{H:O:H} & \text{H:F:} \\ \text{H} & \text{H} & & \end{array}$$

Carbon, nitrogen, oxygen, and fluorine have, respectively, contributed four, five, six, and seven of the electrons that make up the octet. Because no more than two electrons can occupy an orbital, we will expect that the electrons in the octet can be treated as four distinct pairs. The electron pairs repel one another and, if the four pairs are to get as far away from each other as possible, we will expect to find the four orbitals directed toward the corners of a tetrahedron, because this provides the maximum separation between the

tetrahedral
arrangement of
electron pairs

tetrahedral angle

109.5°

electrons. Methane, CH_4, is in fact tetrahedral, as is tetrafluoromethane, CF_4. The three bonds in ammonia and the two bonds in water are directed at slightly different angles, 106.6° and 104.5°, respectively. This is reasonable because the repulsions between the four pairs of electrons in each of these

bond angle 106.6°

bond angle 104.5°

molecules will not be the same. Thus, for water, two of the four orbitals contain protons and two do not. We expect somewhat greater repulsions between the nonbonding pairs than between bonding pairs, and this results in the angle of the bonding pairs being somewhat less than the tetrahedral value.

Replacement of any of the hydrogen atoms in the three molecules CH_4, NH_3, and H_2O with another kind of group will alter the bond angles to some extent. Replacement of one or more such hydrogens by the methyl group (methane minus a hydrogen atom), $CH_3—$, gives the structures shown in Table 1·1. The methyl group is an especially important **substituent group** and can be conveniently represented in three ways, the last being a three-dimensional representation.

$CH_3—$

$$H-\underset{\underset{H}{|}}{\overset{\overset{H}{|}}{C}}-$$

The four derivatives of methane shown in Table 1·1 are all **hydrocarbons**— that is, they contain only carbon and hydrogen. Hence their physical and chemical properties will resemble those of methane itself. (The molecular *shapes* are not well represented by the structures in the table because each of the carbon atoms in these molecules will have a tetrahedral arrangement of bonds connected to it. The three-dimensional shapes of such hydrocarbons are considered in more detail in Chapter 3.) The three derivatives of ammonia are called **amines** and share many of the properties of ammonia; for example, like ammonia, they have dipole moments and are weak bases. A different situation exists with the derivatives of water; *each* of them is representative of a class of compounds The structure $CH_3—OH$ is an **alcohol** while $CH_3—O—CH_3$ is an **ether**. The reason that water is considered to give two classes of compounds on methyl substitution can be traced to the great importance of the hydroxyl (OH) group in chemistry. Alcohols, like water, contain a

Table 1·1   Some simple derivatives of methane, ammonia, and water

CH_4	NH_3	H_2O
$CH_3—CH_3$	$CH_3—NH_2$	$CH_3—OH$
$CH_3—CH_2—CH_3$	$CH_3—NH$ $\quad\quad\;\;\|$ $\quad\quad CH_3$	$CH_3—O—CH_3$
$CH_3—CH—CH_3$ $\quad\quad\;\|$ $\quad\quad CH_3$	$CH_3—N—CH_3$ $\quad\quad\;\|$ $\quad\quad CH_3$	
$\quad\quad CH_3$ $\quad\quad\;\|$ $CH_3—C—CH_3$ $\quad\quad\;\|$ $\quad\quad CH_3$		

hydroxyl group whereas ethers do not. Hydroxyl groups have a great influence on molecular properties (see next section), and the properties of alcohols (ROH) and ethers (R—O—R) are quite different. (The symbol R is usually used in organic chemistry for an alkyl group, a connected group of atoms formed by removing a hydrogen atom from a hydrocarbon; a methyl group is one kind of R group.)

The bond angles at oxygen in the two compounds CH_3—O—H and CH_3—O—CH_3 are somewhat greater than those found in water. This is expected because the CH_3 group is larger than hydrogen, and interference between the CH_3 groups in CH_3—O—CH_3 is lessened by opening the C—O—C bond angle in the ether. A compromise angle is allowed in which the interference between the CH_3 groups is reduced at the expense of moving the pairs of electrons on oxygen to less favorable arrangements with respect to one another. A common description of the overall change is "*relief of steric hindrance between the* CH_3 *groups by opening the* C—O—C *bond angle.*"

O	O	O
H H	CH_3 H	CH_3 CH_3
bond angle 104.5°	bond angle 106°	bond angle 112°

B. PHYSICAL PROPERTIES

The four compounds methane, ammonia, water, and hydrogen fluoride have the physical constants shown in Table 1·2. In each of these compounds the atoms are held together to form molecules by strong covalent bonds. The melting and boiling points are governed not by these powerful forces but rather by the weaker interactions that exist between molecules—*intermolecular* forces. Everything else being the same, the weaker such intermolecular interactions, the lower the temperature which will usually be required, first to break down the crystal lattice of the solid by melting, and then to separate the molecules to relatively large distances by boiling.

What is the origin of these weak, secondary forces that exist between neutral molecules? We shall consider two here: **van der Waals forces** and **hydrogen bonding**. Van der Waals forces, sometimes called London forces, depend in an important way on the numbers of electrons in a molecule. This means that, in general, the bigger the molecule the greater will be the various

Table 1·2   Physical properties of methane, ammonia, water, and hydrogen fluoride

	CH_4	NH_3	H_2O	HF
boiling point	−161.5°	−33°	100°	20°
melting point	−183°	−78°	0°	−84°
solubility in water	very low	high	∞	∞
solubility in CCl_4	high	very low	very low	very low

Table 1·3   Boiling and melting points of some methane derivatives

	CH_4	CH_3-CH_3	$CH_3-CH_2-CH_3$	$CH_3-\underset{\underset{CH_3}{\mid}}{CH}-CH_3$	$CH_3-\underset{\underset{CH_3}{\overset{\overset{CH_3}{\mid}}{C}}}{\mid}-CH_3$
boiling point	$-161.5°$	$-88.6°$	$-42.1°$	$-10.2°$	$9.5°$
melting point	$-183°$	$-172°$	$-188°$	$-145°$	$-20°$

possible intermolecular attractions and the higher the melting and boiling points will tend to be. Boiling points tend to increase regularly within a series of compounds as the molecular weight increases. Melting points, however, usually show much less regularity. This is because the stability of a crystal lattice depends so much on molecular symmetry, which largely determines the ability of the molecules to pack well in the lattice. Thus, the five hydrocarbons shown in Table 1·1 have the boiling and melting points shown in Table 1·3.

In addition to experiencing van der Waals forces (dispersion forces), molecules containing certain groups are attracted to one another by **hydrogen bonding**. To be effective, hydrogen bonding requires the presence of an $-OH$, $-N-H$, or $F-H$ group; in other words, a hydrogen atom joined to a small electronegative atom. The covalent bonds to such hydrogen atoms are strongly polarized toward the electronegative atom, for example, $R-\overset{\delta\ominus}{O}-\overset{\delta\oplus}{H}$, and the partially positive hydrogen will be attracted toward the partially negative oxygen atom in a neighboring molecule. In the liquid state a number

of molecules may be linked together this way at any given time. These liaisons are not permanent because thermal energies of the molecules are sufficient to cause these bonds to break very rapidly (usually within milliseconds or less). Such bonds are continually being formed and broken and this leads to the description of such temporary aggregates in a hydrogen-bonded liquid as "flickering clusters."

By far the most important of the groups responsible for hydrogen bonding is the hydroxyl group, $-OH$. The strength of $O-H \cdots O$ hydrogen bonds may be as much as one-tenth that of an ordinary carbon-carbon covalent bond.[2] (See Section 2·4 on bond strengths.) The highest boiling point in the

[2] Recently, minute quantities of what is claimed to be a new form of water, sometimes called "polywater," have been isolated, in which very strong hydrogen bonds are believed to exist, indeed stable to temperatures above 400°. It is not yet known to what degree one should expect to find a multiplicity of bond strengths for hydrogen bonds to a specific molecule or indeed whether "polywater" is in fact even a compound of formula $(H_2O)_n$.

Table 1·4   Boiling and melting points of some oxygen compounds

	H_2O	CH_3OH	CH_3OCH_3
boiling point	100°	65°	−24°
melting point	0°	−89°	−139°

series CH_4, NH_3, H_2O, HF belongs to water and the lowest to methane, in which hydrogen bonding is completely absent (Table 1·2).

The three oxygen compounds shown in Table 1·1 have melting and boiling points as shown in Table 1·4.

The trends are exactly opposite to those expected on the basis of molecular weight alone and are the result of having two hydrogens bonded to oxygen in each molecule of water, one in the alcohol, CH_3OH, and none in the ether, CH_3OCH_3.

The hydroxyl group also has an important influence on solubility characteristics. The alcohol CH_3OH is completely miscible with water because the two kinds of molecule can form hydrogen bonds to one another. On the other hand, the ether CH_3OCH_3 is only partly soluble in water. Its oxygen atom can interact with the protons of water but it has no OH protons itself to continue the operation. Hydrocarbons have extremely low solubilities in water. Hydrocarbon molecules would tend to interfere with the hydrogen bonding between water molecules and could offer in exchange only the much weaker van der Waals forces.

The nitrogen compounds shown in Table 1·1 have boiling and melting points as shown in Table 1·5. There is not a great deal of difference between the values for the three amines. Hydrogen bonding $N—H \cdots N$ is not as effective as $O—H \cdots O$ and the reduction in hydrogen bonding in going from $CH_3—NH_2$ to $CH_3—\underset{\underset{CH_3}{|}}{N}—CH_3$ is roughly compensated by the increase in van der Waals forces caused by increasing molecular size.

C. ACIDITY AND BASICITY

The acidity of the four compounds methane, ammonia, water, and hydrogen fluoride increases regularly as the central atom becomes more electronegative.

Table 1·5   Boiling and melting points of some nitrogen compounds

	NH_3	CH_3NH_2	$CH_3—\underset{\underset{CH_3}{|}}{NH}$	$CH_3—\underset{\underset{CH_3}{|}}{N}—CH_3$
boiling point	−33°	−6.5°	7°	4°
melting point	−78°	−93°	−96°	−124°

Thus the acid dissociation constants for these compounds in water solution are:

	CH_4	NH_3	H_2O	HF
K_{HA}, 25°	$\sim 10^{-55}$	$\sim 10^{-35}$	1.8×10^{-16}	3.5×10^{-4}

The ionization constant used here for water is the customary value of 10^{-14} divided by the concentration of water in pure water (55 M). The symbol K_{HA} denotes the equilibrium constant for dissociation of a neutral acid HA, that is, $HA \rightleftarrows H^{\oplus} + A^{\ominus}$ and $K_{HA} = [H^{\oplus}][A^{\ominus}]/[HA]$. The values refer to water solution whether actually measurable in water or not and the symbol $H^{\oplus}$ represents the oxonium ion $H_3O^{\oplus}$.

Methane, like most other hydrocarbons, has a negligible acidity in water. Amines resemble ammonia in being very feeble acids. Alcohols are somewhat stronger and have acidities similar to that of water.

The basicities of these four compounds follow a different pattern which is not simply the reverse of that for acidity:

	CH_4	NH_3	H_2O	HF
K_B 25°	$< 10^{-30}$	1.8×10^{-5}	1.8×10^{-16}	$\sim 10^{-25}$

The symbol K_B denotes the equilibrium constant for ionization of a neutral base B, that is, $B + H_2O \rightleftarrows BH^{\oplus} + OH^{\ominus}$ and $K_B = [BH^{\oplus}][OH^{\ominus}]/[B]$. Base strengths are sometimes taken to be indicated by the acid strengths of the corresponding conjugate acids. When this is done the symbol $K_{BH^{\oplus}}$ should be used to denote the process being referred to; that is, $K_{BH^{\oplus}} = [H^{\oplus}][B]/[BH^{\oplus}]$ represents the acid dissociation $BH^{\oplus} \rightleftarrows H^{\oplus} + B$. Ordinary basic ionization constants, K_B, will be used in this book.

The increase in basicity from HF to H_2O to NH_3 is readily understandable in terms of the decreasing electronegativity of the central atom along the series. Why then is the basicity of methane so low? The reason is that this molecule has no unshared pairs of electrons available for bonding to a proton as do ammonia and the other compounds with which we have compared it.

$$H_3N: + H_2O \rightleftarrows NH_4^{\oplus} + OH^{\ominus}$$

If methane is to accept a proton to form the ion $CH_5^{\oplus}$ the carbon atom must hold five hydrogen atoms with four pairs of electrons. (There is evidence that $CH_5^{\oplus}$ can be generated and detected in the gas phase in a mass spectrometer. It may also be a transient intermediate in solutions of methane in the so-called "super acids." Examples of the latter are mixtures of FSO_3H and SbF_5; their protonating power far exceeds that of concentrated sulfuric acid.)

summary

Carbon is unique among the elements: it is able to form an enormous number of compounds by bonding to itself and to the atoms of other elements, principally hydrogen, oxygen, nitrogen, sulfur, and the halogens. Such bonding is almost always covalent, with each carbon atom having four bonds, each bond resulting from a pair of electrons in an orbital which encloses both the bonded nuclei. Repulsions between the four electron pairs in CH_4, NH_3, and H_2O determine the shapes of these molecules; CH_4 is tetrahedral with bond angles of 109.5° and NH_3 and H_2O have slightly smaller bond angles. Of these compounds only methane, CH_4, because of its symmetry, has no dipole moment.

The hydrogen atoms in CH_4, NH_3, and H_2O can be replaced by alkyl groups such as methyl, CH_3—. Compounds formed from CH_4 this way are hydrocarbons like CH_4 itself. Those from NH_3 are called amines, CH_3NH_2 or CH_3NHCH_3. Those from H_2O are alcohols if only one hydrogen is replaced, CH_3OH; and ethers if both hydrogens are replaced, CH_3OCH_3.

The physical properties of such compounds are determined chiefly by *inter*molecular forces, van der Waals forces and hydrogen bonds, which are normally much weaker than those involved in covalent bond formation. In general, the larger the molecule, the greater the van der Waals forces and the higher the boiling point. The presence of one or more hydroxyl groups (or other good hydrogen-bonding groups) will raise the boiling point considerably and will tend to make the compound soluble in water.

Acidity increases in the order $CH_4 < NH_3 < H_2O < HF$; basicity in the order $CH_4 < HF < H_2O < NH_3$.

exercises

1·1 Write Lewis structures for each of the following compounds using dots for the electrons. Mark any atoms which are not neutral with charges of the appropriate sign.

a.	ammonia	*e.*	ozone ($\angle\, O—O—O = 120°$)
b.	ammonium bromide	*f.*	hydroxylamine, H_2NOH
c.	carbon dioxide	*g.*	hydrogen cyanide
d.	hydrogen peroxide	*h.*	boron trifluoride

1·2 Tetramethyllead, $Pb(CH_3)_4$, is a volatile liquid, bp 106°, while lead fluoride, PbF_2, is a high-melting solid, mp 824°. What kinds of bonding forces are present in the two compounds?

1·3 Which of the following substances are expected to possess a dipole moment? Why?

$(CH_3)_3N$, O_3, CO_2, BF_3, CH_2F_2, CF_4, CH_3OCH_3, CH_3CH_3

1·4 Do you expect the compound hydrazine, NH_2NH_2, to be more or less basic than ammonia? Explain your answer.

1·5 Which of the compounds in the following list are expected to be more soluble in water than in carbon tetrachloride?

D_2O, CH_3NH_2, CH_3CH_3, $CH_3CO_2{}^{\ominus}Na^{\oplus}$, HCl, CCl_4

1·6   Why is hydrogen peroxide a stronger acid than water?

1·7   Arrange the following compounds in the order of increasing acidity in water solution.

$\overset{\oplus}{N}H_3-\overset{\oplus}{N}H_3$ $SO_4{}^{2\ominus}$, CH_3OH, CH_4, $NH_4{}^{\oplus}Cl^{\ominus}$, CH_3OCH_3

1·8   The term **autoprotolysis** means self-ionization by proton transfer, that is, $2\,H_2O \rightleftharpoons H_3O^{\oplus} + OH^{\ominus}$. Write autoprotolysis reactions for the following liquids: NH_3, CH_3OH, H_2SO_4, $HOOH$, CH_3NH_2.

1·9   Addition of 17.9 g of water to 100 g of pure liquid perchloric acid, $HClO_4$, produces a crystalline solid. What is its formula?

1·10   There is evidence to suggest that the form of the solvated proton in water solution is better represented by the formula $H_9O_4{}^{\oplus}$ than $H_3O^{\oplus}$. Draw a structural formula for $H_9O_4{}^{\oplus}$ and identify the kinds of bonds that might hold it together.

1·11   On pp. 8–9 it is suggested that the repulsions between the bonded pairs of electrons in water will be less than between the nonbonded pairs, thus making the $H-O-H$ angle less than 109.5°. Explain why this should be so.

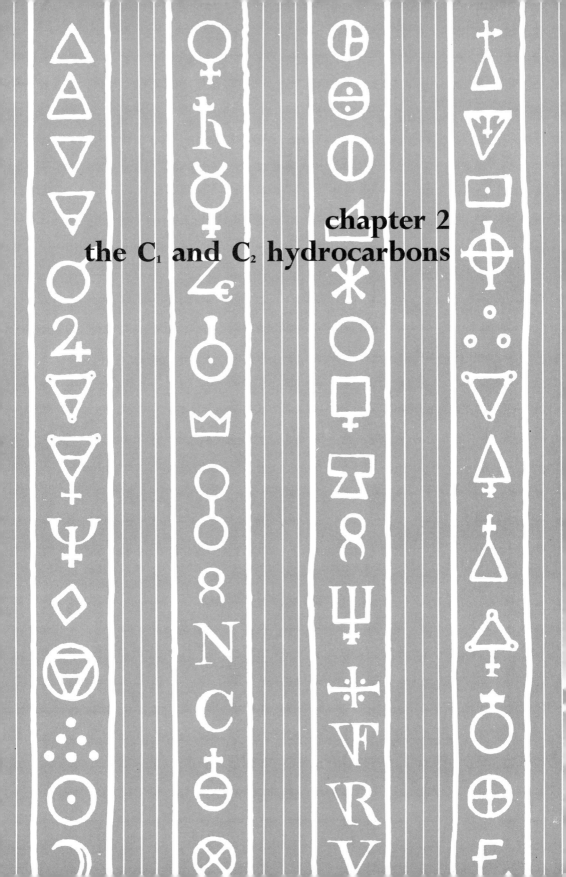

chapter 2
the C_1 and C_2 hydrocarbons

Hydrocarbons are compounds that contain only carbon and hydrogen. We shall consider in this chapter the four simplest known hydrocarbons— those with the lowest molecular weights—and we shall see that they represent *three* classes of compounds: the **alkanes**, in which each carbon atom has four single bonds; the **alkenes**, in which two carbon atoms are joined by a double bond (two electron pairs); and the **alkynes**, in which two carbon atoms are joined by a triple bond (three electron pairs). We shall also see that these classes of compounds are physically similar but chemically rather different.

There are four stable hydrocarbons of molecular weight 30 or less. They are all gases at room temperature, and analyses for carbon and hydrogen content coupled with determinations of their molecular weights show them to have the formulas CH_4, C_2H_6, C_2H_4, and C_2H_2. The first of these is methane, CH_4, whose physical properties and molecular shape were discussed in Chapter 1. The other three are all C_2 compounds and are called, respectively, *ethane, ethene, and ethyne* (ethyne rhymes with brine). These are the systematic names approved by the International Union of Pure and Applied Chemistry, IUPAC.[1] However, ethene is often called ethylene and ethyne called acetylene. It is to be hoped that both of these older names will pass out of use in time.

If the carbon atoms in each of the three C_2 compounds are tetravalent, then there is only one possible way to bond the atoms together in each case:

ethane

$$\begin{array}{ccc} H\,H & & H\ \ H \\ H\!:\!\overset{\cdot\cdot}{C}\!:\!\overset{\cdot\cdot}{C}\!:\!H & \text{or} & H-\overset{\mid}{C}-\overset{\mid}{C}-H \\ H\,H & & H\ \ H \end{array}$$

ethene
(ethylene)

$$\begin{array}{ccc} H\quad H & & H\quad\quad H \\ \quad:\!C\!:\!:\!C\! & \text{or} & \ \ C=C \\ H\quad H & & H\quad\quad H \end{array}$$

ethyne
(acetylene) $H:C:::C:H$ or $H-C\equiv C-H$

The tendency of carbon to form bonds at the tetrahedral angle results in compounds such as methane and ethane being nonplanar. The two-dimensional representation of ethane, above, is thus misleading and it is just as informative (and quicker) to write the formula as CH_3-CH_3. (Or, indeed, as C_2H_6, since there is only one stable compound known with this formula. We shall see that with some C_3 hydrocarbons and with all hydrocarbons having four or more carbons, some indication of structure is necessary because a designation such as C_4H_8 is ambiguous, there being five known compounds with this formula.)

[1]IUPAC, with headquarters at Zürich, Switzerland, is an international organization concerned with creating worldwide standards in nomenclature, analytical procedures, purity, atomic weights, and so on. It is governed by a Congress of delegates from many countries, the number of delegates depending partly on a country's financial resources and partly on its scientific maturity. The following countries have the maximum number of delegates (six): Australia, Belgium, Canada, Denmark, France, Germany, Italy, Japan, Netherlands, Sweden, Switzerland, United Kingdom, United States, U.S.S.R. IUPAC was founded in 1918 at the famous Coq d'Or restaurant in London.

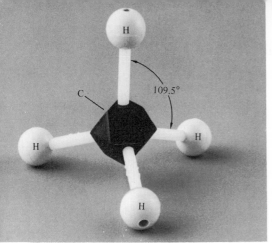

Figure 2·1   Ball-and-stick model of CH_4.

Because of the importance of molecular structure in organic chemistry, we shall consider the three-dimensional shapes of these compounds in the next section.

2·1 *molecular shape of* CH_4, C_2H_6, C_2H_4, *and* C_2H_2

You can illustrate the shape of a tetrahedral molecule such as methane with ball-and-stick models (Figure 2·1).

With ethene and ethyne, the model's carbon-to-carbon bonds are constructed from stiff metal springs or flexible or curved plastic connectors because more than one bond exists between the carbon atoms (Figure 2·2).

These simple mechanical models are surprisingly good for predicting the shapes of molecules and, indeed, their reactivity. Ethene is known from spectroscopic measurements to be planar, and this is the shape the model naturally takes. The electronic analogy here is that the orbitals for each pair of electrons extend as far away from one another as possible. Ethyne, likewise, is known to be linear. The strain involved in making " bent bonds " for these models is reflected in a higher degree of chemical reactivity for these compounds than for ethane.

Figure 2·2   Ball-and-stick models of ethene and ethyne.

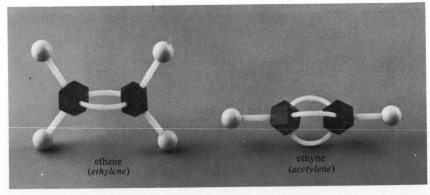

ethene
(*ethylene*)

ethyne
(*acetylene*)

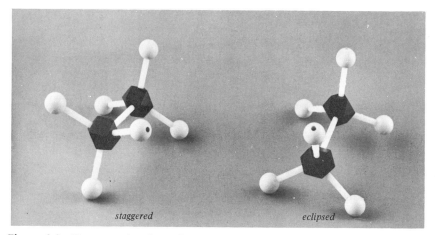

staggered   eclipsed

Figure 2·3   Two rotational conformations of ethane.

The arrangement of the linkages in the ethene model suggests that one CH_2 group cannot twist with respect to the other CH_2 group without gross distortion from the favored geometry. We shall see that this conclusion, too, is borne out by chemical evidence (Section 2·6B). By contrast, the model of the saturated compound, ethane, suggests that free rotation should be possible about the single bond joining the two carbon atoms if the sticks representing the bonds are allowed to rotate in the holes of the balls representing the atoms. Such rotation is considered in more detail in the next section.

2·2 rotational conformations of ethane

In organic chemistry, the word **structure** has a specific meaning; It designates the order in which the atoms are joined to each other. A structure does not necessarily specify the exact shape of a molecule because rotation about single bonds could lead, even for a molecule as simple as ethane, to an infinite number of different arrangements of the atoms in space. These are called **conformations** and depend on the angular relationship between the hydrogens on each carbon. Two extreme arrangements are shown in Figure 2·3.

In end-on views of the models, the *eclipsed* conformation is seen to have the hydrogens on the forward carbon directly in front of those on the back carbon. The *staggered* conformation has each of the hydrogens on the forward carbon set between each of the hydrogens on the back carbon. It has not been possible to obtain separate samples of ethane which correspond to these or intermediate arrangements because actual ethane molecules appear to have essentially "free rotation" about the single bond joining the carbons.

Free, or at least rapid, rotation is possible around all single bonds, except under special circumstances, as when the groups attached are so large that they cannot pass by one another, or when the attached groups are connected together by chemical bonds (e.g., in ring compounds). For ethane and its derivatives, the staggered conformation is always more stable than the eclip-

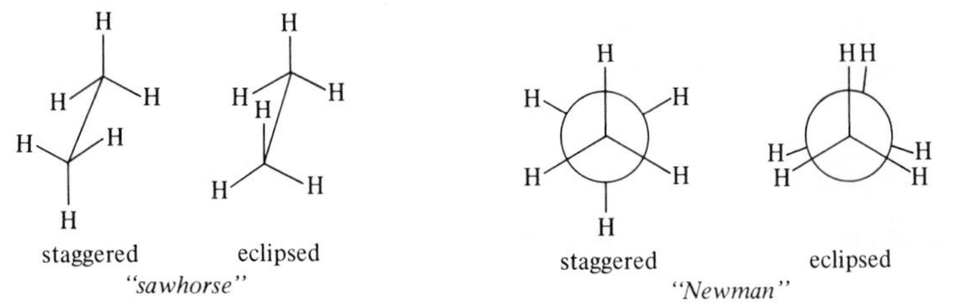

Figure 2·4   Conventions for showing the staggered and eclipsed conformations of ethane. In " saw-horse " drawings the lower left-hand carbon is always taken to be towards the front. In " Newman " drawings the view is along the C—C bond axis with the most exposed bonds being towards the front.

sed conformation because in the staggered conformation the atoms are as far away from one another as possible and offer the least interaction.

Many problems in organic chemistry require consideration of structures in three dimensions, and it is very helpful to be able to use ball-and-stick models for visualizing the relative positions of the atoms in space. Unfortunately, we are very often forced to communicate three-dimensional concepts with drawings in two dimensions, and not all of us are equally gifted in making or visualizing such drawings. Obviously, communication by means of drawings of the models shown in Figure 2·3 would be impractically difficult and time consuming—some form of abbreviation is necessary.

Two styles of abbreviating the eclipsed and staggered conformations of ethane are shown in Figure 2·4. Of these, we strongly favor the " sawhorse " convention because, although it is perhaps the hardest to visualize and the hardest to master, it is the only three-dimensional convention which is suitable for complex compounds, particularly natural products. With the sawhorse drawings, we always consider that we are viewing the molecule slightly from above and from the right, just as we have shown in Figure 2·4.

2·3 space-filling models

Ball-and-stick models of molecules are very useful for visualizing the relative positions of the atoms in space but are unsatisfactory whenever we also want to show how large the atoms are. Actually, atomic radii are so large relative to the lengths of chemical bonds that when a model of a molecule such as chloromethane is constructed with atomic radii and bond lengths, both to scale, the bonds connecting the atoms are not clearly evident. Nonetheless, this type of "space-filling" model, made with truncated balls held together with snap fasteners, is widely used to determine the possible closeness of approach of groups to each other and the degree of crowding of atoms in various arrangements (see Figure 2·5).

A defect of both the ball-and-stick and space-filling models is their motionless character. The atoms in molecules are in constant motion, even at absolute zero, and the frequencies of these vibrations give valuable information about molecular structure and shape. This subject is considered in greater detail in the section on infrared spectroscopy (Section 7·4).

chemical reactions of the C_1 and C_2 hydrocarbons

Two of the four simple hydrocarbons we have been considering are saturated (contain only single bonds) and two are unsaturated (contain multiple bonds). All four are rather similar physically, being low-boiling, colorless gases that are insoluble in water, Chemically, however, they are rather different, the unsaturated compounds being much the more reactive. The three kinds of reactions we shall consider in the following sections are combustion (shared by all hydrocarbons), substitution reactions (more important for saturated compounds), and addition reactions (confined to the unsaturated compounds).

2·4 combustion

The rapid reaction of a chemical substance with oxygen to give an oxide, usually carbon dioxide, is called combustion. The burning of a candle, the explosion of a gasoline–air mixture in the cylinder of an automobile engine, and the oxidation of glucose in a living cell are all examples of this process. In all of these cases, the result is liberation of energy.

Water and carbon dioxide, the products of complete combustion of organic compounds, are very stable substances, relative to oxygen and hydrocarbons. This means that large amounts of energy are given out when combustion occurs. Most of the energy of combustion shows up as heat, and the heat liberated in a reaction occurring at constant pressure is called the **enthalpy** change, ΔH, or simply heat of reaction. By convention, ΔH is given a *negative* sign when heat is evolved (**exothermic reaction**) and a *positive* sign when heat is absorbed (**endothermic reaction**). Some examples are given below, with the state of the reactants and products being indicated by subscripts (g) for gas and (s) for solid.

For each of these examples, ΔH can be visualized as the total heat given off when a mixture of gaseous hydrocarbon and excess oxygen at 1 atm pressure is exploded in a bomb at 25°, the contents allowed to expand or contract by

Figure 2·5   Space-filling models of organic compounds.

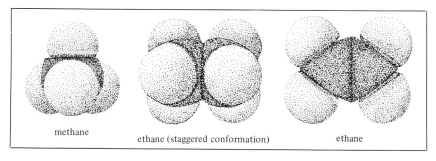

methane   ethane (staggered conformation)   ethane means of a piston to maintain the pressure at 1 atm, and allowed to cool to 25°.

$CH_4(g) + 2 O_2(g) \rightarrow CO_2(g) + 2 H_2O(g)$ $\quad\quad \Delta H = -192$ kcal per mole of methane (-11.95 kcal per gram)

$CH_3-CH_3(g) + \frac{7}{2} O_2(g) \rightarrow 2 CO_2(g) + 3 H_2O(g)$ $\quad \Delta H = -341.3$ kcal per mole of ethane (-11.35 kcal per gram)

$H-C\equiv C-H(g) + \frac{5}{2} O_2(g) \rightarrow 2 CO_2(g) + H_2O(g)$ $\quad \Delta H = -300.1$ kcal per mole of ethyne (-11.50 kcal per gram)

$C_8H_{18}(g) + \frac{25}{2} O_2(g) \rightarrow 8 CO_2(g) + 9 H_2O(g)$ $\quad \Delta H = -1222$ kcal per mole of octane (-10.71 kcal per gram)

$C_6H_{12}O_6(s) + 6 O_2(g) \rightarrow 6 CO_2(g) + 6 H_2O(g)$ $\quad \Delta H = -610$ kcal per mole of glucose (-3.39 kcal per gram)

You can see that the amount of heat liberated per gram of fuel is not greatly different in the case of the four hydrocarbons, but is much lower for the compound $C_6H_{12}O_6$ (glucose), which is already in a partly oxidized state. In the next section, we shall consider how you can estimate heats of reaction, with particular reference to combustion.

A. ESTIMATION OF HEAT OF COMBUSTION OF METHANE

The experimental value for the heat of combustion of methane obtained as described above does not depend on speed of the reaction. Slow oxidation of methane over many years would liberate as much heat as that obtained in an explosion, provided the reaction were complete in both cases, and the initial and final temperatures and pressures are the same. At 25°, combustion of each mole of methane to carbon dioxide and water vapor produces 192 kcal of heat.

We can estimate the heat of this and many other reactions by making use of the **bond energies** given in Table 2·1. Bond energies for diatomic molecules represent the energy required to dissociate completely the gaseous substances to gaseous atoms at 25° or, alternatively, the heat evolved when the bonds are formed from such atoms. For polyatomic molecules the bond energies are average values. They are selected to work with a variety of molecules and reflect the fact that the bond energy of any particular bond is likely to be influenced to some extent by other groups in the molecule.

It turns out that what is called conjugation (alternation of double and single bonds) can have a relatively large effect on bond strengths. We will see in Chapter 6 that this effect normally operates to increase bond energies; that is, the bonds are harder to break and the molecule is made more stable. However, the effects of conjugation are so special that they are not normally averaged into bond energies, but are treated separately instead.

To calculate ΔH for the combustion of methane, first we calculate the energy to break the four C—H bonds as follows (using the average value of 99 kcal for the energy of a C—H bond):

$$\overset{H}{\underset{H}{H:\overset{..}{C}:H}}(g) \longrightarrow \cdot\overset{..}{C}\cdot (g) + 4 \, H\cdot(g) \quad \Delta H = +4 \times 99 \text{ kcal} = +396 \text{ kcal}$$

Table 2·1 Bond energies (kcal/mole at 25°)[a]

<table>
<tr><td colspan="12" align="center">diatomic molecules</td></tr>
<tr><td>H—H</td><td>104.2</td><td>F—F</td><td>36.6</td><td>H—F</td><td>134.5</td></tr>
<tr><td>O=O</td><td>119.1</td><td>Cl—Cl</td><td>58.0</td><td>H—Cl</td><td>103.2</td></tr>
<tr><td>N≡N</td><td>225.8</td><td>Br—Br</td><td>46.1</td><td>H—Br</td><td>87.5</td></tr>
<tr><td>C=O</td><td>255.8</td><td>I—I</td><td>36.1</td><td>H—I</td><td>71.4</td></tr>
<tr><td colspan="12" align="center">bonds in polyatomic molycules[b]</td></tr>
<tr><td>C—H</td><td>99</td><td>C—C</td><td>83</td><td>C—F</td><td>116</td></tr>
<tr><td>N—H</td><td>93</td><td>C=C</td><td>146</td><td>C—Cl</td><td>81</td></tr>
<tr><td>O—H</td><td>111</td><td>C≡C</td><td>200</td><td>C—Br</td><td>68</td></tr>
<tr><td>S—H</td><td>83</td><td>C—N</td><td>73</td><td>C—I</td><td>51</td></tr>
<tr><td>P—H</td><td>76</td><td>C=N</td><td>147</td><td>C—S</td><td>65</td></tr>
<tr><td>N—N</td><td>39</td><td>C≡N</td><td>213</td><td>C=S</td><td>128</td></tr>
<tr><td>N=N</td><td>100</td><td>C—O</td><td>86</td><td>N—F</td><td>65</td></tr>
<tr><td>O—O</td><td>35</td><td>C=O[c]</td><td>192</td><td>N—Cl</td><td>46</td></tr>
<tr><td>S—S</td><td>54</td><td>C=O[d]</td><td>176</td><td>O—F</td><td>45</td></tr>
<tr><td>N—O</td><td>53</td><td>C=O[e]</td><td>179</td><td>O—Cl</td><td>52</td></tr>
<tr><td>N=O</td><td>145</td><td></td><td></td><td>O—Br</td><td>48</td></tr>
<tr><td colspan="12" align="center">intermolecular forces</td></tr>
<tr><td>hydrogen bonds</td><td>3-10</td></tr>
</table>

[a] The bond energies in this table are derived from those of T. C. Cottrell, *The Strengths of Chemical Bonds*, 2nd Ed., Butterworths, London, 1958, and L. Pauling, *The Nature of the Chemical Bond*, 3rd Ed., Cornell Univ. Press, Ithaca, N.Y., 1960.
[b] Average values.
[c] For carbon dioxide.
[d] Aldehydes.
[e] Ketones.

Then 119 kcal is used for the energy required to cleave a molecule of oxygen (rounded off from the exact value of 119.1):

$$2 \; O_2(g) \longrightarrow 4 \cdot \ddot{O} \cdot \; (g) \qquad \Delta H = + 2 \times 119 \text{ kcal}$$
$$= + 238 \text{ kcal}$$

Then we make bonds, using 192 kcal for each C=O bond in carbon dioxide.

$$\cdot \dot{C} \cdot \; (g) + 2 \cdot \ddot{O} \cdot (g) \longrightarrow :\ddot{O}::C::\ddot{O}:(g) \qquad \Delta H = - 2 \times 192 \text{ kcal}$$
$$= - 384 \text{ kcal}$$

We use 111 kcal for each of the H—O bonds of water:

$$2 \cdot \ddot{O} \cdot (g) + 4 \; H \cdot \; (g) \longrightarrow 2 \; H : \ddot{O} : H(g) \qquad \Delta H = - 4 \times 111 \text{ kcal}$$
$$= - 444 \text{ kcal}$$

The net of these ΔH changes is $396 + 238 - 384 - 444 = -194$ kcal, which is reasonably close to the value of 191.8 kcal for the heat of combustion of methane determined experimentally.

The same type of procedure can be used to estimate ΔH values for many other kinds of reactions of organic compounds in the vapor phase at 25°.

Moreover, if appropriate heats of vaporization or solution are available, it is straightforward to compute ΔH for liquid, solid, or dissolved substances.

The steps shown above are not intended to depict the actual mechanism of methane combustion. The overall heat of reaction is independent of the way that combustion occurs and so the above calculations are just as reliable as (and more convenient than) those based on the actual reaction path. Some of the general questions posed by the reaction mechanism are taken up in Section 2·5B.

2·5 substitution reactions of saturated hydrocarbons

Of the four simple hydrocarbons we are considering in this chapter, only ethene and ethyne are unsaturated, meaning they have a multiple bond to which reagents may add. The other two compounds, methane and ethane, have their atoms joined together by the minimum number of electrons and can react only by substitution—replacement of a hydrogen by some other atom or group.

There are only a few reagents which are able to effect the substitution of a hydrogen atom in a saturated hydrocarbon (an alkane). The most important of these are easily the halogens, and the mechanism and energetics of halogen substitution will be discussed in detail later. (Although the hydrogen atoms in alkenes such as ethene and alkynes such as ethyne are also subject to substitution, these reactions under normal conditions tend to be much slower than addition to the multiple bond and are therefore usually not important when compared to addition.)

A complete description of a chemical reaction would include the structures of the reactants and products, the position of equilibrium of the reaction, its rate, and its mechanism. These four characteristics fall nicely into two groups. The equilibrium constant for a reaction depends only on the energies of the reactants and products, not on the rate of reaction nor on the mechanism. The rate of the reaction, on the other hand, is intimately related to the reaction mechanism and, in particular, to the energy of the least stable state along the reaction path. The subjects of equilibrium constants and reaction rates are treated in the next two sections.

A. EQUILIBRIUM CONSTANTS

In Section 2·4A we considered bond energies and showed how heats of reaction could be calculated. Reactions which give out large amounts of heat (highly exothermic processes) usually proceed to completion. Consequently it is reasonable to ask if the equilibrium constant, K, for a reaction is determined only by the heat of reaction, ΔH. The study of **thermodynamics** tells us that the answer to this question is no. The equilibrium constant is, in fact, a function of the quantity **free energy** (ΔG), which is made up of ΔH and a second quantity called **entropy** (ΔS). These relations are

$$\Delta G = -RT \ln K$$
$$\Delta G = \Delta H - T \Delta S$$

where

ΔG = Free energy change for the reaction
R = The gas constant (1.986 cal/deg mole)
T = Temperature in degrees Kelvin
K = Equilibrium constant
ΔH = Heat of reaction
ΔS = Entropy of reaction

The heat of reaction term, ΔH, is readily understood but the meaning of the entropy term, ΔS, is more elusive. It is related to the difference in the numbers of vibrational, rotational, and translational states available to reactants and products (see Sections 7·3 and 7·4). As we have seen, molecules are not lifeless objects but are in constant motion, each undergoing vibrational, rotational, and translational motions. These states of motion are **quantized**—that is, they can have certain energies only. The more of these states or degrees of freedom available to a molecule, the higher its entropy and the more favorable the equilibrium constant for its formation. Thus, a *positive entropy change* in a reaction tends to make the free energy change more negative and *increase* the equilibrium constant, hence moving the reaction toward completion.

In simple terms, a negative entropy change (a ΔS that is unfavorable for the reaction as written) means that the freedom of the atoms in the products (including the environment) is restricted more than in the reactants. A positive entropy change (favorable for the reaction as written) means a greater freedom in the products.

In practice, reactions which are fairly exothermic ($-\Delta H > 15$ kcal/mole) almost always proceed far to the right; that is, K is large. An unfavorable entropy term will seldom overcome such a ΔH value at ordinary temperatures because a ΔG that is negative by only a few kilocalories per mole will still have a large K. This follows from the logarithmic relation between ΔG and K.

The thermodynamic values for the chlorination of methane are

$$CH_4 + Cl_2 \longrightarrow CH_3Cl + HCl$$

$\Delta H = -27$ kcal/mole

(measurable experimentally or calculable from the data in Table 2·1);

$\Delta S = -6$ cal/deg mole

(estimated from the spectroscopic properties of reactants and products);

$\Delta G = -25$ kcal/mole

(calculated from above values of ΔH and ΔS and the equation $\Delta G = \Delta H - T \Delta S$);

$K = 10^{18}$

(calculated from above value of ΔG and the equation $\Delta G = -RT \ln K$).

In some cases, you can experimentally check an equilibrium constant calculated as above by measuring the concentrations of reactants and products when the system has come to equilibrium. Here, however, K is so large that no trace of the reactants can be detected at equilibrium, a situation often encountered in organic chemistry.

Suppose bond energy calculations for a certain reaction indicate that the equilibrium strongly favors the desired products. Can we be assured that the reaction is a practical one to perform in the laboratory? Unfortunately, no, because first, side reactions may occur (other reactions which also have favorable equilibrium constants); and second, the rate of the desired reaction may be far too low for the reaction to be a practical one.

In the chlorination of methane, whose equilibrium constant we have seen overwhelmingly favors the products, the first of these two matters of concern is whether the substitution process may proceed further to give dichloromethane, CH_2Cl_2.

$$CH_3Cl + Cl_2 \longrightarrow CH_2Cl_2 + HCl$$

In fact, given sufficient chlorine, complete substitution may occur to give tetrachloromethane (carbon tetrachloride), CCl_4. Indeed, if the rate of chlorination of chloromethane greatly exceeds that of the first step, methane chlorination, there will be only traces of the monosubstituted product in the mixture at any time. Using an excess of methane will help encourage monosubstitution only if the rates of the first two chlorination steps are comparable.

With compounds and reagents that are more complex than methane and chlorine, you can imagine side reactions taking other forms. When devising synthetic schemes you must always consider possible side reactions that may make the proposed route an impractical one.

The second question about the chlorination of methane that is left unanswered by the calculation of the equilibrium constant is whether or not the reaction will proceed at a reasonable rate. The subject of reaction rates is bound up intimately with the question of reaction mechanism and this subject is explored in the next section.

B. REACTION RATES AND MECHANISM

Despite the enormously favorable equilibrium constant for the formation of chloromethane and hydrogen chloride from methane and chlorine, this reaction does not occur at a measurable rate at room temperature in the dark. An explosive reaction may occur, however, if such a mixture is irradiated with strong violet or ultraviolet light. Evidently, light makes possible a very effective reaction path by which chlorine may react with methane.

Any kind of a theoretical prediction or rationalization of the rate of this or other reactions must inevitably take into account the details of how the reactants are converted to the products—in other words, the reaction mechanism. One possible path for methane to react with chlorine would have a chlorine molecule collide with a methane molecule in such a way that hydrogen chloride and chloromethane are formed directly (see Figure 2·6). The failure of methane to react with chlorine in the dark at moderate temperatures is strong evidence against this path, and indeed four-center reactions of this type are rather rare.

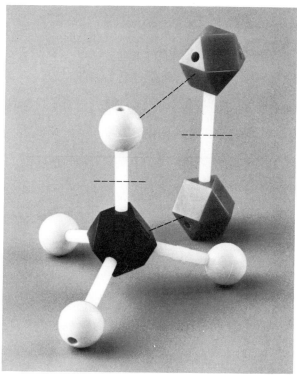

Figure 2·6 Possible four-center collision of chlorine with methane, as visualized with ball-and-stick models.

If concerted four-center mechanisms for formation of chloromethane and hydrogen chloride from chlorine and methane are discarded, the remaining possibilities are all stepwise mechanisms. A slow stepwise reaction is dynamically analogous to the flow of sand through a succession of funnels with different stem diameters. The funnel with the smallest stem will be the most important bottleneck, and if its stem diameter is much smaller than the others, it alone will determine the flow rate. Generally, a multistep chemical reaction will have a slow *rate-determining step* (analogous to the funnel with the small stem) and other, relatively *fast steps* which may occur either before or after the slow step. The prediction of the rate of a reaction proceeding by a stepwise mechanism then involves, as the central problem, a decision as to which step is rate determining and an analysis of the factors which determine the rate of that step.

A possible set of steps for the chlorination of methane follows:

(1) $Cl_2 \xrightarrow{\text{slow}} 2 : \overset{..}{\underset{..}{Cl}} \cdot$

(2) $CH_4 \xrightarrow{\text{slow}} CH_3 \cdot + H \cdot$

(3) $: \overset{..}{\underset{..}{Cl}} \cdot + CH_3 \cdot \xrightarrow{\text{fast}} CH_3Cl$

(4) $: \overset{..}{\underset{..}{Cl}} \cdot + H \cdot \xrightarrow{\text{fast}} HCl$

Reactions (1) and (2) involve dissociation of chlorine into chlorine atoms, and the breaking of a C—H bond of methane to give a methyl radical and a hydrogen atom. The methyl radical, like chlorine and hydrogen atoms, has one odd electron not involved in bond formation. Atoms and free radicals are usually highly reactive, so that formation of chloromethane and hydrogen chloride should proceed readily by (3) and (4). The crux then will be whether steps (1) and (2) are reasonable under the reaction conditions.

Our plan in evaluating the reasonableness of these steps is to determine how much energy is required to break the bonds. This will be helpful because, in the absence of some *external* stimulus, only collisions due to the usual thermal motions of the molecules can provide the energy needed to break the bonds. Below 100°C, it is very rare indeed that thermal agitation alone can supply sufficient energy to break any significant number of bonds stronger than 30 to 35 kcal/mole. Therefore, we can discard as unreasonable any step, such as the dissociation reactions (1) and (2), if the ΔH's for breaking the bonds are greater than 30 to 35 kcal.

In most reactions, new bonds form as old bonds break and it is usually incorrect to consider bond strengths alone in evaluating reaction rates. (The appropriate parameters, the heat of activation, $\Delta H^{\ddagger}$, and the entropy of activation, $\Delta S^{\ddagger}$, are discussed in Section 8·9.) However, the above rule of thumb of 30 to 35 kcal is a useful one for *thermal dissociation reactions* such as (1) and (2), and we can discard these as unreasonable if their heats of dissociation are greater than this amount.

For reaction (1) we can reach a decision on the basis of the Cl—Cl bond energy from Table 2·1, which is 58.0 kcal and clearly too large to lead to bond breaking as the result of thermal agitation at or below 100°. The C—H bonds of methane are also too strong to break at 100° or less.

The promotion of the chlorination reaction by light must be due to light being absorbed by one or the other of the reacting molecules to produce a highly reactive species. Since a Cl—Cl bond is much weaker than a C—H bond, it is reasonable to suppose that the former is split by light to give two chlorine atoms. We shall see in Section 7·3 that the energy which can be supplied by ultraviolet light is high enough to do this; photolytic rupture of the more stable C—H bonds requires radiation with much higher energy. It should now be clear why a mixture of methane and chlorine does not react in the dark at moderate temperatures.

$$Cl_2 \xrightarrow{\ h\nu\ } 2:\overset{\cdots}{\underset{\cdots}{Cl}}\cdot$$

Once produced, a chlorine atom can remove a hydrogen atom from a methane molecule and form a methyl radical and a hydrogen chloride molecule (as will be seen from Table 2·1, the strengths of C—H and Cl—H bonds are quite close):

$$CH_4 + :\overset{\cdots}{\underset{\cdots}{Cl}}\cdot \longrightarrow CH_3\cdot + HCl$$

The methyl radical resulting from the attack of atomic chlorine on a hydrogen of methane can then remove a chlorine atom from molecular chlorine and form chloromethane and a new chlorine atom:

$$CH_3\cdot + Cl_2 \longrightarrow CH_3Cl + :\overset{\cdot\cdot}{\underset{\cdot\cdot}{Cl}}\cdot$$

An important feature of the mechanistic sequence postulated for the chlorination of methane is that the chlorine atom consumed in the first step is replaced by another chlorine atom in the second step. This type of process is

$$CH_4 + :\overset{\cdot\cdot}{\underset{\cdot\cdot}{Cl}}\cdot \longrightarrow CH_3\cdot + HCl$$
$$CH_3\cdot + Cl_2 \longrightarrow CH_3Cl + :\overset{\cdot\cdot}{\underset{\cdot\cdot}{Cl}}\cdot$$

$$\overline{}$$

$$CH_4 + Cl_2 \longrightarrow CH_3Cl + HCl$$

called a **chain reaction** since, in principle, one chlorine atom can induce the chlorination of an infinite number of methane molecules through operation of a "chain" or cycle of reactions. In practice, chain reactions are limited by so-called termination processes, where chlorine atoms or methyl radicals are destroyed by reacting with one another, as shown in these equations:

$$CH_3\cdot + :\overset{\cdot\cdot}{\underset{\cdot\cdot}{Cl}}\cdot \longrightarrow CH_3Cl$$
$$2\ CH_3\cdot \longrightarrow CH_3CH_3$$

Chain reactions may be considered to involve three phases. First, chain initiation must occur, which for chlorination of methane is activation and conversion of chlorine molecules to chlorine atoms by light. In the second phase, the chain-propagation steps convert reactants to products with no net consumption of atoms or radicals. The propagation reactions occur in competition with chain-terminating steps, which result in destruction of atoms or radicals.

$$Cl_2 \xrightarrow{\text{light}} 2:\overset{\cdot\cdot}{\underset{\cdot\cdot}{Cl}}\cdot \qquad \text{chain initiation}$$

$$CH_4 + :\overset{\cdot\cdot}{\underset{\cdot\cdot}{Cl}}\cdot \longrightarrow CH_3\cdot + HCl$$
$$CH_3\cdot + Cl_2 \longrightarrow CH_3Cl + :\overset{\cdot\cdot}{\underset{\cdot\cdot}{Cl}}\cdot \qquad \text{chain propagation}$$

$$CH_3\cdot + :\overset{\cdot\cdot}{\underset{\cdot\cdot}{Cl}}\cdot \longrightarrow CH_3Cl$$
$$CH_3\cdot + CH_3\cdot \longrightarrow CH_3CH_3 \qquad \text{chain termination}$$

The two chain-termination reactions for methane chlorination as shown might be expected to be exceedingly fast, because they involve combination of unstable atoms or radicals to give stable molecules. Actually, combination of chlorine atoms does not occur readily in the gas phase because there is almost no way for the resulting molecule to lose the energy of reaction except by redissociating or colliding with some third body, including the container wall. The products in the other termination steps shown above, by contrast, can take care of this energy by redistributing it as vibrational excitation of their C—H bonds. Collisions with other molecules then disperse the excess vibrational energy throughout the system in the form of heat.

If much chain propagation is to occur before the termination steps destroy the active intermediates the propagation steps must themselves be very fast. However, propagation is favored over termination when the concentrations of radicals (or atoms) are low because then the chance of two radicals meeting (*termination*) is much less likely than encounters of radicals with molecules which are present at relatively *high* concentrations (*propagation*).

The overall rates of chain reactions are usually slowed significantly by substances which can combine with atoms or radicals and convert then into species incapable of participating in the chain-propagation steps. Such substances are often called radical traps, or inhibitors. Oxygen acts as an inhibitor in the chlorination of methane by rapidly combining with a methyl radical to form the comparatively stable (less reactive) peroxymethyl radical, $CH_3OO\cdot$. This effectively terminates the chain. Under favorable conditions, the methane-chlorination chain may go through 100 to 10,000 cycles before termination occurs by a radical or atom combination. The efficiency (or quantum yield) of the reaction is thus very high in terms of the amount of chlorination that occurs relative to the amount of the light absorbed.

C. REACTIVE INTERMEDIATES

We have seen that the chlorination of methane proceeds stepwise via highly unstable intermediate species such as chlorine atoms ($Cl\cdot$) and methyl radicals ($CH_3\cdot$). Are there other molecules or ions which are too unstable for isolation but which might exist as transient intermediates in organic reactions? If we examine simple C_1 species we find the possibilities:

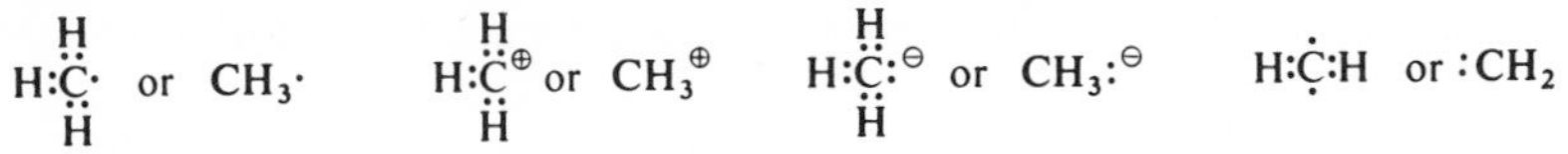

$$H:\overset{H}{\underset{H}{\overset{}{C}}}\cdot \quad \text{or} \quad CH_3\cdot \qquad H:\overset{H}{\underset{H}{\overset{}{C}}}{}^{\oplus} \text{ or } CH_3{}^{\oplus} \qquad H:\overset{H}{\underset{H}{\overset{}{C}}}:^{\ominus} \text{ or } CH_3:{}^{\ominus} \qquad H:\overset{\cdot}{C}:H \text{ or } :CH_2$$

| | methyl cation (a carbonium ion) | methyl anion (a carbanion) | methylene (a carbene) |

Each of these C_1 entities possesses some serious structural defect that makes it much less stable than methane itself. The methyl radical is unstable because it has only seven electrons in its valence shell. It exists for only brief periods of time at low concentrations before dimerizing to ethane:

$$CH_3\cdot + CH_3\cdot \longrightarrow CH_3—CH_3$$

The methyl cation, $CH_3{}^{\oplus}$, is an example of a **carbonium ion**. This species has only six valence electrons; moreover, it carries a positive charge. Methyl cations react with most species that contain an unshared pair of electrons— for example, a chloride ion, $CH_3{}^{\oplus} + Cl^{\ominus} \rightarrow CH_3—Cl$. We shall see later, however, that the replacement of the hydrogens of the methyl with other groups, such as CH_3- or C_6H_5-, can provide sufficient stability to make carbonium ions important reaction intermediates. In fact, they can sometimes be isolated as stable salts (Section 24·5). Having only three pairs of electrons about the central carbon atom, carbonium ions tend toward planarity with bond angles of 120°. This gives the maximum separation of the three pairs of electrons.

$$\overset{\displaystyle H}{\underset{\displaystyle H \diagup \overset{\oplus}{C} \diagdown H}{\big|}} \quad 120°$$

methyl cation (a carbonium ion)

The methyl anion, $CH_3{}^\ominus$, does possess an octet of electrons but bears a negative charge, for which it is ill suited by virtue of carbon's low electronegativity. Such **carbanions** react rapidly with any species that will accept a share in an electron pair—any proton donor, $CH_3{}^\ominus \xrightarrow{H^\oplus} CH_4$, for example. We shall see later that carbanions can be stabilized and rendered less reactive by having strongly electron-withdrawing groups, such as nitro $(-NO_2)$, attached to them, and we shall encounter such carbanions as reaction intermediates in subsequent chapters. Carbanions have four pairs of electrons about the central carbon atom. The mutual repulsion of the electrons gives the ion a pyramidal shape. The methyl anion, for example, is isoelectronic with ammonia and is believed to have a similar shape:

$$\underset{\displaystyle H}{H \diagup \overset{\displaystyle \overset{..}{C}{}^\ominus}{\diagup} \diagdown H} \qquad \underset{\displaystyle H}{H \diagup \overset{\displaystyle \overset{..}{N}}{\diagup} \diagdown H}$$

The nonbonding electron pairs in each of the above molecules are expected to repel the bonding pairs more than the bonding pairs repel each other (see pp. 8–9 and Exercise 1·11). This accounts for the fact that the $H-N-H$ bond angles in ammonia (Section 1·2A) are slightly less than the tetrahedral value.

Methylene, $:CH_2$, like a carbonium ion, possesses only a sextet of electrons in its valence shell and tends to react rapidly with electron donors (Section 9·7).

It is important to be able to deduce the overall charge of a species from its electronic arrangement and vice versa. A carbonium ion, such as $H : \overset{\displaystyle H}{\underset{\displaystyle H}{\overset{..}{C}{}^\oplus}}$, is positively charged because, although the hydrogens are formally neutral, the carbon atom has a half-share of six valence electrons. It thus has, effectively, only three electrons in its own outer shell instead of the four electrons that a neutral carbon atom possesses. By contrast, a carbanion such as $H : \overset{\displaystyle H}{\underset{\displaystyle H}{\overset{..}{C} :}{}^\ominus}$ is negatively charged because the carbon has an unshared electron pair in addi-

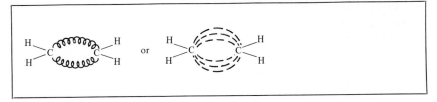

Figure 2·7   Bent bonds in ethene.

tion to its half-share of the six bonding electrons, giving it effective possession of five valence electrons, one more than that of a neutral carbon atom.

2·6 addition reactions of unsaturated hydrocarbons

The two simplest unsaturated compounds (those containing a multiple bond) are ethene ($CH_2=CH_2$) and ethyne ($HC\equiv CH$). The generally lower stability of multiply bonded compounds arises from the restriction that only one electron pair can occupy a given orbital. Because the most effective region for interaction between an electron pair and the two nuclei it links is along the bond axis, we expect to find this to be the region of highest electron density in a single bond. Bonds that run symmetrically along the bond axis are called **sigma bonds** (σ bonds).

In a molecule such as ethene, though, the two carbon atoms are linked by two electron pairs and it is quite clear that only one pair can occupy the prime space along the bond axis. There are two ways of looking at the electronic arrangement of ethene. The first, and simplest, is to consider the two orbitals used to link the carbons together as being identical, both being bent, somewhat like the arrangement taken up by springs in the ball-and-stick model of ethene (Figure 2·7). This simple view of the bonding of ethene accounts for its molecular geometry (repulsion between the electron pairs produces a planar molecule) and its chemical reactivity (the electron pairs are not bound as tightly to the nuclei as in the case of ethane where space along the bond axes can be used).

The alternative way of looking at the bonding of ethene is to consider the double bond as being made up of an ordinary single-type bond along the bond axis, a σ bond, and a second bond occupying the regions of space above and below the plane of the molecule, a π **bond** (pi bond). (A π bond is not cylindrically symmetrical along the bond axis.) The shaded regions above and below the plane of the molecule (see Figure 2·8) represent just *one* bonding orbital:

Figure 2·8 σ and π bonding in ethene.

that which corresponds to the π bond. This model also accounts for the geometry of ethene and for its high chemical reactivity. Despite being less simple than the bent-bond model, it is extensively used by chemists to describe the bonding in unsaturated systems. In the case of ethyne, two π bonds and one σ bond can be said to link the two carbons together.

Neither model can be called *correct* or *incorrect*. And, indeed, refined theory suggests that they represent equivalent approximations. Each is useful according to the degree of clarity it gives the user and according to its ability to predict molecular behavior. The language of chemistry (particularly the theory of spectroscopy and bonding) is based to a great extent on the σ, π model, and it must be considered by anyone wishing to explore organic chemistry in depth. Paradoxically, it is only recently that the simple bent-bond model has received much attention from theorists.

Both models account for the shortening of the carbon-carbon bond distance as the number of bonds between the carbons increases—the greater the forces, the shorter the bond distance. We shall see that the analogy of springs and bonds also accounts for the vibrational energies of these compounds. A greater amount of energy is required to increase the vibration in the strong triple bond of ethyne than in the double bond in ethene or the single bond in ethane.

ethane   ethene   ethyne

A. HYDROGENATION OF MULTIPLE BONDS

The reaction of hydrogen with ethyne is highly exothermic:

$$H-C{\equiv}C-H + H_2 \longrightarrow CH_2{=}CH_2$$

$\Delta H_{exp} = -42.2$ kcal
$\Delta H_{calc} = -40$ kcal (from bond energies in Table 2·1)

Likewise, the further reduction of ethene to ethane is highly exothermic:

$$CH_2{=}CH_2 + H_2 \longrightarrow CH_3-CH_3$$

$\Delta H_{exp} = -32.8$ kcal
$\Delta H_{calc} = -30$ kcal (from bond energies in Table 2·1)

However, mixtures of either compound with hydrogen are indefinitely stable under ordinary conditions, and this again reminds us that reaction rates cannot be deduced from heats of reaction. Both ethyne and ethene, however, react rapidly and completely with hydrogen at low temperatures and pressures in the presence of metals such as nickel, platinum, and palladium. For maximum catalytic effect, the metal is usually obtained in a finely divided state. This is achieved for platinum and palladium by reducing the metal oxides with hydrogen before hydrogenating the alkene or alkyne. A specially active form of nickel ("Raney nickel") is prepared from a nickel-aluminum alloy; sodium hydroxide is added to dissolve the aluminum, and the nickel remains as a black, pyrophoric powder.

$$2\,Ni-Al + 2\,OH^{\ominus} + 2\,H_2O \longrightarrow 2\,Ni + 2\,AlO_2{}^{\ominus} + 3\,H_2$$

Highly active platinum, palladium, and nickel catalysts can also be prepared by reducing metal salts with sodium borohydride.

Besides having synthetic applications, catalytic hydrogenation is useful for analytical and thermochemical purposes. The analysis of a compound for the number of double bonds is carried out by measuring the uptake of hydrogen for a given amount of sample.

The reaction occurs on the surface of the catalyst to which the reacting substances may be held loosely by van der Waals forces or, more tightly, by chemical bonds. The relatively loosely held electrons in a double or triple bond participate in forming carbon-metal bonds to the surface while hydrogen combines with the surface to give metal-to-hydrogen bonds (see Figure 2·9). The new bonds are much more reactive than the old ones and allow combination to occur readily. The hydrogenated compound is then replaced on the surface by a fresh molecule of unsaturated compound, which has a stronger attraction for the surface.

This is an example of **heterogeneous catalysis**—a type of reaction which involves adsorption on a surface of a solid or liquid and is often hard to describe in precise terms because the chemical nature of a surface is hard to define in precise terms. **Homogeneous catalysis** occurs in solution or in the vapor state. For such reactions, it is usually easier to trace the path from reactants to products in terms of intermediates with discrete structures. The light-induced chlorination of methane is an example of a homogeneous reaction.

Ethene will add one mole of hydrogen while ethyne can add either one or

Figure 2·9   Schematic representation of the hydrogenation of ethene on the surface of a nickel crystal.

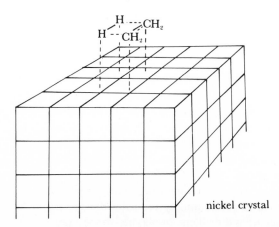

nickel crystal

two. Special catalysts are available which will convert ethyne to ethene much faster than they convert ethene to ethane.

B. ADDITION OF BROMINE TO MULTIPLE BONDS

When ethene is treated with bromine (or with chlorine), a rapid addition occurs to give the 1,2-dihaloethane. The name given to the reaction product can be

$$Br_2 + CH_2{=}CH_2 \longrightarrow BrCH_2{-}CH_2Br$$

$$\text{1,2-dibromoethane}$$

understood as follows. First, it is saturated (no double or triple bonds) and contains *two carbon atoms* and therefore is a derivative of *ethane*. The positions of two of the hydrogen atoms of ethane have been taken by *two bromine* atoms; hence it is a *dibromo*ethane. The two bromines are located on different carbon atoms. We call one of the carbon atoms number 1 and the other number 2, hence the name 1,2-dibromoethane. This naming system can be used to name the vast majority of organic compounds. In using it one should remember these points.

1. Pick out the parent hydrocarbon. Here it is ethane, not ethene, because we are interested in designating the structure, not the way the compound is formed in any particular reaction.

2. Pick out those groups or atoms that replace any of the hydrogens of the parent compound and join their names to the front of the name of the parent hydrocarbon. If there are two such groups, as in the case we are working with, designate them with the prefix *di*; three such groups, *tri*; and so on. The name at this stage should be all one word—for example, *dibromoethane*.

3. Locate the substituent groups by counting the carbon atoms from the end of the carbon chain. One can start numbering at either end in the example above, but this will not be generally true. The numbers designating the carbon atoms that bear substituents are separated from one another by commas and from the rest of the name by a hyphen—for example, 1,2-*dibromoethane*.

Remember that the *number* of substituents is designated by the prefixes *di*, *tri*, and so on, but that their *locations* are designated by the numerals that identify particular carbon atoms.

We shall examine nomenclature further in the next chapter, which deals with alkanes.

The rapidity of the reaction of ethene with bromine illustrates the high reactivity of carbon-carbon double bonds. It would be natural to suppose that this reaction occurs by a simple simultaneous addition of both atoms of bromine to the double bond:

$$\underset{\displaystyle {>}C{-}C{<}}{\overset{\displaystyle Br{\cdots}Br}{}}$$

It will be recalled from the discussion of the methane-chlorine reaction, however, that four-center reactions are rare, and in fact the addition of bromine to alkenes is known to occur in a stepwise manner, usually (but not always) to involve ionic intermediates, and usually to proceed by addition of the two bromines from *opposite* sides of the double bond. The evidence for this course of reaction is described in detail in Chapter 4 on alkenes. Suffice it to say here that an examination of the product of the ethene-bromine addition reaction will not tell us whether addition occurred from the same or the opposite side of the double bond, since rotation about the C—C bond converts one product into the other and thus obliterates the distinction between the two possible products (Equation 2·1). Both products are different conformations of the same compound, 1,2-dibromoethane.

$$(2·1)$$

Addition of bromine to ethyne also occurs readily to give the compound 1,2-dibromoethene. (Note that the parent compound is now *ethene*, not *ethyne*.) The product of this reaction is a liquid, bp 108°, mp −6.5°. It is

$$Br_2 + H-C\equiv C-H \longrightarrow BrCH=CHBr$$

1,2-dibromoethene

immiscible with water and easily can be shown to possess no dipole moment. However, there is another known compound that has the same structure —that is, possesses two carbon atoms joined by a double bond and has a bromine and hydrogen atom on each carbon. This second compound is a liquid, bp 110°, mp −53°. It is also immiscible with water but has a large dipole moment. The two isomers arise because of a lack of rotation about the double bond. The molecule with the bromine atoms on the opposite side is called the **trans** isomer, and the other the **cis** isomer.

trans-1,2-dibromoethene   *cis*-1,2-dibromoethene

These two compounds are said to have different **configurations**. It is worth reviewing here the meanings of the terms *structure, conformation,* and *configuration*. *Structure* designates the atoms that are linked together and the bonds that do this. Compounds with the same formula, $C_2H_4Br_2$ for example, but different structures, such as Br_2CH-CH_3 and $BrCH_2-CH_2Br$, are called *structural isomers*. If the compound contains one or more carbon-

carbon single bonds, rotation can usually occur freely about these and give rise to different *conformations*. If the compound contains double bonds (or a ring of atoms), rotation is prevented and different *configurations* may then be possible. Compounds with different configurations are called stereoisomers —for example, *cis-* and *trans-*1,2-dibromoethene—and they can only be interconverted by the rupture of chemical bonds. We shall encounter later in the book (Chapter 14) a more subtle form of stereoisomerism. The form of stereoisomerism we are discussing here is called either **cis-trans isomerism** or **geometrical isomerism** and, harking back to our ball-and-stick models, it is easy to rationalize why interconversion between geometrical isomers does not take place readily (Equation 2·2). For rotation to occur, one of the C—C

$$\tag{2·2}$$

bonds of the double bond must be broken. For this, the necessary energy input would be roughly equal to the difference in energy between a double and a single bond—63 kcal/mole (see Table 2·1). Such an amount of energy is not available from molecular collision at ordinary temperatures.

It is a simple matter to assign configurations to the two geometrical isomers of BrCH=CHBr. The one formed by the addition of bromine to ethyne has no dipole moment and hence must be the *trans* isomer. The boiling points of these compounds are nearly the same, but the melting points are vastly

different. *Trans* compounds often have somewhat higher melting points than the corresponding *cis* isomers, reflecting greater ease of crystal packing of their somewhat more symmetrical molecules. Dihaloethenes are exceptional in that the *cis* isomers tend to be slightly more stable than the *trans*. This is because the distances between the halogens in these compounds (but not usually between other substituents) are just right for operation of favorable van der Waals attractive forces. With most other substituents, particularly if they are bulky, the *trans* arrangement is preferred. Where three or four different groups are attached to the double bond, you must define what you mean by the terms *cis* and *trans*, and the generalizations given here about melting points and stabilities do not apply.

Will 1,1-dibromoethene (CH_2=CBr_2), which is a structural isomer of the above compounds, also exist in *cis* and *trans* forms? Clearly not, because interchange of the two bromines on one carbon or interchange of the two hydrogens on the other produces the same molecule. The requirement for the existence of geometrical isomers of an alkene is that the two groups on one end of the double bond be different from each other *and* the two groups on the other end be different from each other.

Geometrical isomerism does not arise with triply bonded compounds, because the $-C\equiv C-$ bonds in these molecules are linear.

summary

There are four C_1 and C_2 hydrocarbons: methane (CH_4) and ethane (CH_3-CH_3) are alkanes, ethene ($CH_2=CH_2$) is an alkene, and ethyne ($HC\equiv CH$) is an alkyne. Ethene is a planar molecule, ethyne is linear, and ethane nonplanar. Rotation around the single bond in ethane can be seen to give rise to an infinite number of arrangements called conformations, two extreme forms of which are designated eclipsed and staggered.

All hydrocarbons undergo combustion—complete oxidation to carbon dioxide and water. Heats of combustion and of other reactions can be calculated from bond energy data.

The hydrogens in alkanes can be replaced by halogen atoms via a substitution process—for instance, $CH_4 + Cl_2 \rightarrow CH_3Cl + HCl$. The position of equilibrium of this reaction is far to the right, the equilibrium constant K being determined by the free energy of reaction, ΔG, which in turn is related to the heat of reaction, the entropy factor, and the absolute temperature: $\Delta G = -RT \ln K = \Delta H - T \Delta S$. Reactions that are fairly exothermic ($-\Delta H > 15$ kcal) usually have large K values.   The rate of a reaction cannot be related in a simple way to its overall ΔH or K. It depends on the reaction path. For the chlorination of methane, this involves a chain reaction with the following steps: Cl_2 is cleaved by light to give $Cl\cdot$ atoms (initiation); a hydrogen atom is abstracted from CH_4 by $Cl\cdot$ to give $CH_3\cdot$, a methyl radical; the radical, in turn, abstracts a chlorine atom from Cl_2.

$$CH_4 + Cl\cdot \longrightarrow CH_3\cdot + HCl$$
$$CH_3\cdot + Cl_2 \dashrightarrow CH_3Cl + Cl\cdot$$

These two steps are the propagation steps in the chain reaction, $Cl\cdot$ being consumed in the first step and regenerated in the second; the chain is terminated when radicals or atoms combine.

Some important intermediate species that will be encountered in other reactions, in addition to radicals such as $CH_3\cdot$, are carbonium ions, such as $CH_3^{\oplus}$; carbanions, such as $CH_3^{\ominus}$; and carbenes, such as $:CH_2$.

The double bonds in alkenes can be considered as two identical bent bonds, or as one bond along the bond axis (a σ bond) and a second bond above and below the plane of the molecule (a π bond).

Unsaturated hydrocarbons undergo addition reactions, as with hydrogen or halogens. Addition of bromine is often very fast while the addition of hydrogen requires the presence of a heterogeneous catalyst such as finely divided nickel:

$$HC{\equiv}CH \xrightarrow[\text{Ni}]{\text{H}_2} H_2C{=}CH_2 \xrightarrow[\text{Ni}]{\text{H}_2} CH_3{-}CH_3$$

$$HC{\equiv}CH \xrightarrow{\text{Br}_2} BrCH{=}CHBr \xrightarrow{\text{Br}_2} Br_2CH{-}CHBr_2$$

Compounds such as 1,2-dibromoethene ($BrCH{=}CHBr$) can exist as two geometrical isomers, designated *cis* and *trans*. These two compounds have

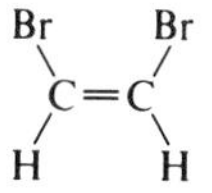

cis-1, 2-dibromoethene 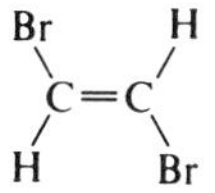   trans-1, 2-dibromoethene

different physical properties and, because of the restricted rotation about the double bond, are quite stable to interconversion. The requirements for geometrical isomerism at a double bond are that two different groups be attached to one carbon atom *and* two different groups be attached to the other. *Cis* and *trans* isomers (geometrical isomers) have the same structure but different configurations. (The many arrangements that arise because of rotation about a single bond, as in ethane, are called conformations.)

exercises

2·1   Show how the two conventions of Figure 2·4 can be used to represent the possible staggered conformations of the following substances:

    a. CH_3CH_2Cl (chloroethane)
    b. CH_2ClCH_2Cl (1,2-dichloroethane)
    c. $CH_3CH_2CH_2CH_3$ (butane); consider rotation about the middle two carbon atoms in this compound.

2·2   Use the bond-energy table to calculate ΔH for the following reactions in the *vapor* phase at 25°:

    a. $CH_3CH_2CH_3 + 5\ O_2 \rightarrow 3\ CO_2 + 4\ H_2O$
    b. $CH_4 + \frac{3}{2}\ O_2 \rightarrow CO + 2\ H_2O$
    c. $CO + 3\ H_2 \rightarrow CH_4 + H_2O$
    d. $CH_4 + 4\ Cl_2 \rightarrow CCl_4 + 4\ HCl$
    e. $CH_4 + I_2 \rightarrow CH_3I + HI$

2·3   Calculate ΔH for $C(s) \rightarrow C(g)$ from the heat of combustion of 1 gram-atom of solid carbon (94.05 kcal) and the bond energies in Table 2·1.

2·4   Write balanced equations for the complete and incomplete combustion of ethane to give, respectively, carbon dioxide and carbon monoxide. Use the table of bond energies to calculate the heats evolved in the two cases from 10 g of ethane.

2·5   A possible mechanism for the reaction of chlorine with methane would be to have collisions where a chlorine molecule removes a hydrogen according to the following scheme:

$$CH_3\!:\!H + :\!\ddot{C}l\!:\!\ddot{C}l\!: \xrightarrow{\text{slow}} CH_3\!\cdot + H\!:\!\ddot{C}l\!: + :\!\ddot{C}l\!\cdot$$

$$CH_3\!\cdot + :\!\ddot{C}l\!\cdot \xrightarrow{\text{fast}} CH_3\!:\!\ddot{C}l\!:$$

Use appropriate bond energies to assess the likelihood of this reaction mechanism. What about the possibility of a similar mechanism with elemental fluorine and methane?

2·6   Write the steps of a chain reaction for the light-catalyzed chlorination of ethane.

2·7   Calculate ΔH for each of the propagation steps of methane chlorination by a mechanism of the type

$$Cl_2 \xrightarrow{hv} 2\,Cl\cdot \qquad \text{initiation}$$
$$\left.\begin{array}{l} Cl\cdot + CH_4 \longrightarrow CH_3Cl + H\cdot \\ H\cdot + Cl_2 \longrightarrow HCl + Cl\cdot \end{array}\right\} \text{propagation}$$

Discuss the relative energetic feasibilities of these chain-propagation steps in comparison with those of other possible mechanisms.

2·8   How many dichloro substitution (not addition) products are possible with (a) methane, (b) ethane, (c) ethene, (d) ethyne?

2·9   Show that the methyl radical, CH_3, has no charge. Show that the carbons of the neutral molecules CH and CH_2 are electron deficient, that is, they do not possess an octet of valence electrons.

2·10   Which of the following molecules or ions contain a carbon atom that lacks an octet of electrons: $CH_3CH_2\cdot$, $CH_3^{\oplus}$, $CH_3^{\ominus}$, CH_3CH_3, $HC\equiv CH$, $CH_2\!:$?

2·11   Consider the feasibility of a free-radical chain mechanism for hydrogenation of ethene in the vapor state at 25° by the following propagation steps:

$$CH_3\!\!-\!\!CH_2\cdot + H_2 \longrightarrow CH_3\!\!-\!\!CH_3 + H\cdot$$
$$CH_2\!\!=\!\!CH_2 + H\cdot \longrightarrow CH_3\!\!-\!\!CH_2\cdot$$

2·12   Name the following compounds:

a. $ClCH_2CCl_3$

b. $Cl_2CHCHCl_2$

c. $BrCH\!=\!CH_2$

d. $ClC\equiv CCl$

e. $Br_2C\!=\!CBr_2$

2·13   Provide structures for the following compounds:

    a. 1,1,1-tribromoethane
    b. 1,1,2-tribromoethane
    c. 1-chloro-2-fluoroethene
    d. bromoethyne

2·14   Is geometrical isomerism possible in the following cases? Draw formulas to show the configurations of the *cis* and *trans* isomers where appropriate.

    a. $Br_2C=CHCl$ *d.* $ClC≡CCl$

    b. $BrClC=CHBr$ *e.* $CHF=CHF$

    c. $Cl_2CH—CHCl_2$

2·15   How many grams of bromine will react with (a) 20 g of ethene, (b) 20 g of ethyne?

2·16   What volume of carbon dioxide (dry, at 20° and 1 atm) will be obtained by the complete combustion of (a) 20 g of ethene, (b) 20 g of ethyne?

2·17   The reaction $HC≡CH(g) + H_2(g) → CH_2=CH_2(g)$ has the following thermodynamic parameters at 25°C.

    $\Delta G = -33.7$ kcal
    $\Delta H = -41.7$ kcal
    $\Delta S = -26.8$ cal

    a. Does the position of equilibrium favor reactants or product?
    b. Does the entropy term favor formation of reactants or product? Explain the significance of your answer about the entropy in terms of the relative freedom of the atoms in the reactants and product.

chapter 3
alkanes

In the previous two chapters we have studied in some detail the properties of the two simplest saturated hydrocarbons, methane and ethane, and have shown how their simple derivatives are named using the rules of the International Union of Pure and Applied Chemistry (IUPAC rules). In this chapter we shall examine the larger alkanes, including those that are cyclic (**cycloalkanes**). Open-chain, or acyclic, alkanes have the general formula C_nH_{2n+2}, whereas cycloalkanes have the formula C_nH_{2n}. It is *essential* that one be able to name compounds correctly and we will begin our discussion of alkanes with a survey of nomenclature.

3·1   nomenclature

The IUPAC rules for naming alkanes are simple and easy to apply. However, few people adhere strictly to these rules and it is necessary to be familiar with some other commonly used naming terms; these are often simple and convenient when applied to simple compounds but become cumbersome or ambiguous with more complex compounds. The IUPAC name for a compound is always acceptable; hence, when asked to supply a name to a compound whose structure is given, it is best to follow the IUPAC rules. You should become familiar enough with other common terms, however, so you can supply the correct structure to a compound whose name is given in non-IUPAC terminology.

The alkanes are classified as "continuous chain" (i.e., unbranched) if all the carbon atoms in the chain are linked to no more than two other carbons, or "branched chain" with one or more carbon atoms linked to three or four other carbons. Branching is only possible with alkanes C_4 and up.[1]

$$CH_3-CH_2-CH_2-CH_2-CH_2-CH_3$$

continuous–chain hydrocarbon

$$CH_3-\overset{\overset{\displaystyle H_3C}{|}}{\underset{\underset{\displaystyle H}{|}}{C}}-\overset{\overset{\displaystyle CH_3}{|}}{\underset{\underset{\displaystyle H}{|}}{C}}-CH_3 \qquad CH_3-\overset{\overset{\displaystyle CH_3}{|}}{\underset{\underset{\displaystyle CH_3}{|}}{C}}-CH_2-CH_3$$

branched–chain hydrocarbons

The first four continuous-chain hydrocarbons have nonsystematic names:

$$CH_4 \qquad CH_3-CH_3 \qquad CH_3-CH_2-CH_3 \qquad CH_3-CH_2-CH_2-CH_3$$

methane   ethane   propane   butane

The higher members, beginning with pentane, are named systematically with a numerical prefix (pent-, hex-, hept-, etc., to denote the number of carbon atoms) and with the ending -ane to classify the compound as a saturated hydrocarbon. Examples are listed in Table 3·1. These names are generic of

---

[1] The notation C_4 means a compound containing four carbon atoms whereas C-4 means the fourth carbon atom in a chain.

Table 3·1   Continuous-chain alkanes (C_nH_{2n+2})

no. of carbons, n	name	no. branched-chain of isomers
1	methane	0
2	ethane	0
3	propane	0
4	butane	1
5	pentane	2
6	hexane	4
7	heptane	8
8	octane	17
9	nonane	34
10	decane	74
20	eicosane	366,318
30	triacontane	4.11×10^9

both branched and unbranched hydrocarbons and, to specify a continuous-chain hydrocarbon, the prefix n- (for normal) is often attached. In the absence of any qualifying prefix the hydrocarbon is considered to be "normal" or unbranched.

$$CH_3-CH_2-CH_2-CH_2-CH_3$$
pentane
(n-pentane)

The possibility of branched-chain hydrocarbons isomeric with the continuous-chain hydrocarbons begins with butane ($n = 4$). The total number of theoretically possible isomers for each alkane up to $n = 10$ is given in Table 3·1, and is seen to increase very rapidly with n. All 75 possible alkanes from $n = 1$ to $n = 9$ inclusive have now been synthesized.

There are two structural isomers of C_4H_{10}, one the continuous-chain compound called butane (or n-butane to emphasize its lack of branching) and the other called 2-methylpropane (or, in common terminology, isobutane).

$$CH_3-CH_2-CH_2-CH_3$$

$$CH_3-CH-CH_3$$
$$|$$
$$CH_3$$

butane
(n-butane)

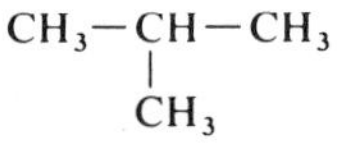

2-methylpropane
(isobutane)

The name 2-methylpropane is appropriate because the longest continuous chain in the molecule is made up of three carbons; it is thus a derivative of propane. The second carbon (from either end) has one of its hydrogens replaced by a methyl group, hence the prefix 2-methyl. It should be remembered that the shape of this molecule is not as depicted in the formula shown. The tetrahedral arrangement about the central carbon atom makes *all three* methyl groups equivalent (Figure 3·1).

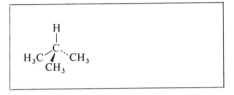

Figure 3·1 Shape of 2-methylpropane.

There are three known compounds with the formula C_5H_{12}, and this is the number of isomers expected on the basis of carbon being tetravalent and hydrogen monovalent:

$$CH_3-CH_2-CH_2-CH_2-CH_3$$

pentane
(*n*-pentane)

$$CH_3-\underset{\underset{}{|}}{\overset{\overset{CH_3}{|}}{CH}}-CH_2-CH_3$$

2-methylbutane
(isopentane)

$$CH_3-\underset{\underset{CH_3}{|}}{\overset{\overset{CH_3}{|}}{C}}-CH_3$$

2,2-dimethylpropane
(neopentane)

The prefix iso denotes a compound with two methyl groups at the end of a chain, and neo means three methyl groups at the end of a chain.

When we come to the C_6 alkanes we find that there are five isomeric compounds, C_6H_{14}. Clearly, trivial prefixes become less and less useful as the length of the chain grows and the number of possible isomers increases. Accordingly, hexane and its four branched-chain isomers are here only given IUPAC names. (The second compound in the list might be called isohexane and the fourth neohexane.)

$$CH_3-CH_2-CH_2-CH_2-CH_2-CH_3$$

hexane

$$CH_3-\underset{\underset{}{|}}{\overset{\overset{CH_3}{|}}{CH}}-CH_2-CH_2-CH_3$$

2-methylpentane

$$CH_3-CH_2-\underset{\underset{}{|}}{\overset{\overset{CH_3}{|}}{CH}}-CH_2-CH_3$$

3-methylpentane

$$CH_3-\underset{\underset{CH_3}{|}}{\overset{\overset{CH_3}{|}}{C}}-CH_2-CH_3$$

2,2-dimethylbutane

$$CH_3-\underset{\underset{}{|}}{\overset{\overset{CH_3}{|}}{CH}}-\underset{\underset{}{|}}{\overset{\overset{CH_3}{|}}{CH}}-CH_3$$

2,3-dimethylbutane

The branched-chain compounds considered so far all contain the simplest group, methyl, as substituent. Alkyl groups such as methyl are obtained by writing the alkane minus one of its hydrogens. Thus, we have methyl (CH_3-) and ethyl (CH_3-CH_2-). A problem arises when we come to the alkyl groups of propane, $CH_3-CH_2-CH_3$. The hydrogen atoms in this molecule are not all equivalent. Removing one of the six terminal hydrogens produces the *n*-propyl group, $CH_3-CH_2-CH_2-$; removing one of the two central hydrogens produces the isopropyl group, $CH_3-CH-CH_3$ (usually written

$$\begin{array}{c} H_3C \\ \\ H_3C \end{array}\!\!\!\diagdown\!\!\! CH- \text{ or } (CH_3)_2CH-).$$

Additional examples are listed in Table 3·2. These have been further classi-

Table 3·2   Typical alkyl groups (C_nH_{2n+1})

primary (RCH_2-)		
CH_3-	CH_3CH_2-	$CH_3CH_2CH_2-$
methyl	ethyl	n-propyl
$CH_3CH_2CH_2CH_2-$	$\begin{array}{c}CH_3\\ \diagdown\\ CH-CH_2-\\ \diagup\\ CH_3\end{array}$	
n-butyl	isobutyl	
$CH_3CH_2CH_2CH_2CH_2-$	$\begin{array}{c}CH_3\\ \diagdown\\ CH-CH_2-CH_2-\\ \diagup\\ CH_3\end{array}$	$\begin{array}{c}CH_3\\ \mid\\ CH_3-C-CH_2-\\ \mid\\ CH_3\end{array}$
pentyl (n-amyl)	isopentyl (isoamyl)	neopentyl
$CH_3CH_2CH_2CH_2CH_2CH_2-$	$\begin{array}{c}CH_3\\ \diagdown\\ CH-CH_2-CH_2-CH_2\\ \diagup\\ CH_3\end{array}$	$\begin{array}{c}CH_3\\ \mid\\ CH_3-C-CH_2CH_2-\\ \mid\\ CH_3\end{array}$
n-hexyl	isohexyl	neohexyl
secondary (R_2CH-)		
	$\begin{array}{c}CH_3\\ \diagdown\\ CH-\\ \diagup\\ CH_3\end{array}$	$\begin{array}{c}CH_3CH_2\\ \diagdown\\ CH-\\ \diagup\\ CH_3\end{array}$
	isopropyl	s-butyl
tertiary (R_3C-)		
	$\begin{array}{c}CH_3\\ \mid\\ CH_3-C-\\ \mid\\ CH_3\end{array}$	$\begin{array}{c}CH_3\\ \mid\\ CH_3CH_2-C-\\ \mid\\ CH_3\end{array}$
	t-butyl	t-pentyl (t-amyl)

fied according to whether they are primary, secondary, or tertiary. An alkyl group is described as **primary** if the carbon at the point of attachment is bonded to only *one* other carbon, as **secondary** if bonded to *two* other carbons, and **tertiary** if bonded to *three* other carbons. The methyl group is a special case and is regarded as a primary group.

In a few cases, where there is a high degree of symmetry, hydrocarbons are conveniently named as derivatives of methane or ethane.

$$
\begin{array}{cc}
\underset{\displaystyle \text{triisopropylmethane}}{
\begin{array}{c}
\text{H}_3\text{C} \quad\ \text{CH}_3 \\
\diagdown\ \diagup \\
\text{H}_3\text{C}\quad\ \text{CH} \\
\diagdown\quad\ | \\
\text{CH}-\text{C}-\text{H} \\
\diagup\quad\ | \\
\text{H}_3\text{C}\quad\ \text{CH} \\
\diagup\ \diagdown \\
\text{H}_3\text{C}\quad \text{CH}_3
\end{array}}
&
\underset{\displaystyle \text{hexamethylethane}}{
\begin{array}{c}
\text{H}_3\text{C}\ \ \text{CH}_3 \\
|\quad\ | \\
\text{CH}_3-\text{C}-\text{C}-\text{CH}_3 \\
|\quad\ | \\
\text{H}_3\text{C}\ \ \text{CH}_3
\end{array}}
\end{array}
$$

In naming complex compounds, you must pick out the longest consecutive chain of carbon atoms. The longest chain may not be obvious from the way in which the structure has been drawn on paper. Thus the hydrocarbon [1] is a pentane rather than a butane derivative, since the longest chain is one with five carbons.

$$
\begin{array}{c}
\text{CH}_3 \\
| \\
\text{H}_3\text{C}\quad \text{CH}_2 \\
| \\
\text{CH}_3-\text{CH}-\text{CH}-\text{CH}_3
\end{array}
$$

[1]
(dotted lines enclose longest chain of successive carbon atoms)

The parent hydrocarbon is numbered starting from the end of the chain, and the substituent groups are assigned numbers corresponding to their positions on the chain. The direction of numbering is chosen to give the lowest sum for the numbers of the side-chain substituents. Thus, hydrocarbon [1] is 2,3-dimethylpentane rather than 3,4-dimethylpentane. Although the latter name would enable one to write the correct structure for this compound, it would not be found in any dictionary or compendium of organic compounds.

$$
\begin{array}{ccc}
\begin{array}{c}
^5\text{CH}_3 \\
| \\
\text{H}_3\text{C}\quad {}^4\text{CH}_2 \\
| \\
\underset{1}{\text{CH}_3}-\underset{2}{\text{CH}}-\underset{3}{\text{CH}}-\text{CH}_3
\end{array}
&
\textit{not}
&
\begin{array}{c}
^1\text{CH}_3 \\
| \\
\text{H}_3\text{C}\quad {}^2\text{CH}_2 \\
| \\
\underset{5}{\text{CH}_3}-\underset{4}{\text{CH}}-\underset{3}{\text{CH}}-\text{CH}_3
\end{array} \\[2mm]
\text{2.3-dimethylpentane} & & \text{3,4-dimethylpentane}
\end{array}
$$

Where there are two identical substituents at one position, as in [2], numbers are supplied for each. Remember that the numerals represent positions and the prefixes di-, tri-, and so on represent the number of substituents. Note that there should always be as many numerals as there are substituents, that is, 2,2,3 (three numerals) and trimethyl (three substituents).

$$
\begin{array}{ccc}
& H_3C & CH_3 \\
& | & | \\
CH_3 & -C- & CH-CH_3 \\
& | & \\
& CH_3 &
\end{array}
$$

2,2,3-trimethylbutane

[2]

Branched-chain substituent groups are given appropriate names by a simple extension of the system used for branched-chain hydrocarbons. The longest chain of the substituent is numbered starting with the carbon attached directly to the parent hydrocarbon chain. Parentheses are used to separate the numbering of the substituent and the main hydrocarbon chain. The IUPAC rules

$$
\overset{2}{CH_2}-\overset{3}{CH_3}
$$
$$
H_3C \diagdown \diagup
$$
$$
\overset{1}{CH}
$$
$$
|
$$
$$
\underset{1}{CH_3}-\underset{2}{CH_2}-\underset{3}{CH_2}-\underset{4}{CH_2}-\underset{5}{CH}-\underset{6}{CH_2}-\underset{7}{CH_2}-\underset{8}{CH_2}-\underset{9}{CH_2}-\underset{10}{CH_3}
$$

5-(1-methylpropyl)decane
(5-s-butyldecane)

permit use of the substituent group names in Table 3·2, so that s-butyl can be used in place of (1-methylpropyl) for this example.

When there are two or more different substituents present, the question arises as to what order they should be cited in naming the compound. Two systems are commonly used which cite the alkyl substituents (1) in order of increasing complexity or (2) in alphabetical order. We shall adhere to the latter system mainly because it is the practice of *Chemical Abstracts.*[2] Examples are given below.

$$
\begin{array}{cc}
CH_3-CH_2 & CH_3 \\
| & | \\
\underset{7}{CH_3}-\underset{6}{CH_2}-\underset{5}{CH_2}-\underset{4}{CH}-\underset{3}{CH}-\underset{2}{CH_2}-\underset{1}{CH_3}
\end{array}
$$

4-ethyl-3-methylheptane
(i.e., ethyl is cited before methyl)

$$
\begin{array}{c}
CH_3 \\
| \\
CH_3-C-CH_3 \\
| \\
\underset{1}{CH_3}-\underset{2}{CH_2}-\underset{3}{CH_2}-\underset{4}{C}-\underset{5}{CH_2}-\underset{6}{CH_2}-\underset{7}{CH_2}-\underset{8}{CH_2}-\underset{9}{CH_2}-\underset{10}{CH_3} \\
| \\
CH_3-CH \\
| \\
CH_3
\end{array}
$$

4-t-butyl-4-isopropyldecane

[2] Biweekly publication of the American Chemical Society: an index to, and a digest of, recent chemical publications throughout the world.

Derivatives of alkanes, such as haloalkanes (R—Cl) and nitroalkanes (R—NO₂), where R denotes an alkyl group, are named similarly by the IUPAC system. Definite orders of precedence are assigned substituents of different types when two or more are attached to a hydrocarbon chain. Thus, alkanes with halogen and alkyl substituents are generally named as haloalkylalkanes (not as alkylhaloalkanes); alkanes with halogen and nitro substituents are named as halonitroalkanes (not as nitrohaloalkanes).

$$CH_3-CH_2-CH_2-CH_2-Cl$$

1-chlorobutane
(*n*-butyl chloride)

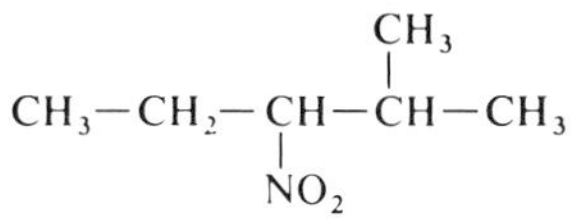

$$CH_3-CH_2-\overset{\overset{\textstyle CH_3}{|}}{CH}-\underset{\underset{\textstyle NO_2}{|}}{CH}-CH_3$$

3-nitro-2-methylpentane

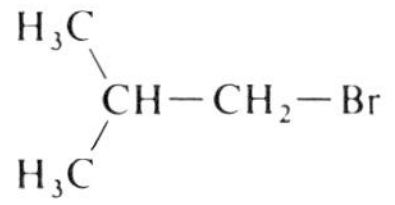

$$\begin{matrix} H_3C \\\ \diagdown \\\ \quad\ CH-CH_2-Br \\\ \diagup \\\ H_3C \end{matrix}$$

1-bromo-2-methylpropane
(isobutyl bromide)

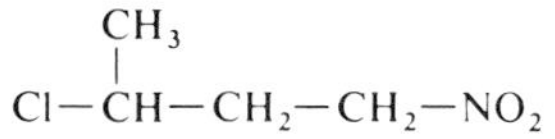

$$Cl-\overset{\overset{\textstyle CH_3}{|}}{CH}-CH_2-CH_2-NO_2$$

3-chloro-1-nitrobutane

Note that 1-chlorobutane is written as one word whereas the alternate name *n*-butyl chloride is written as two words. In the former the chloro group is substituted for one of the hydrogens of butane and the position of substitution is indicated by the numeral. The latter name is formed by simply combining names for the two parts of the compound just as one would do for NaCl, sodium chloride.

3·2   physical properties of alkanes—concept of homology

The series of continuous-chain alkanes, $CH_3(CH_2)_{n-2}CH_3$, shows a remarkably smooth gradation of physical properties (see Table 3·3 and Figure 3·2). As you go up the series, each additional CH_2 group contributes a fairly constant increment to the boiling point and density and, to a lesser extent, to the melting point. This makes it possible to estimate the properties of an unknown member of the series from those of its neighbors. For example, the boiling points of hexane and heptane are 69° and 98°, respectively; a difference in structure of one CH_2 group therefore makes a difference in boiling point of 29°. This places the boiling point of the next higher member, octane, at 98° + 29°, or 127°, which is close to the actual boiling point of 126°.

Members of a group of compounds with similar chemical structures and graded physical properties and which differ from one another by the number of atoms in the structural backbone, such as the *n*-alkanes, are said to constitute a homologous series. The concept of homology, when used to forecast the properties of unknown members of the series, works most satisfactorily for the higher-molecular-weight members. For these members, the introduction of additional CH_2 groups makes a smaller relative change in the overall composition of the molecule. This is better seen from Figure 3·2,

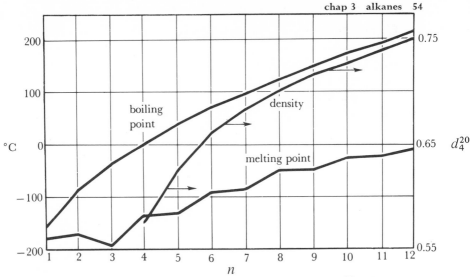

Figure 3·2   Dependence on n of melting points, and densities (d_4^{20}) of straight-chain alkanes, $CH_3(CH_2)_{n-2}CH_3$.

which shows how the boiling points and melting points of the homologous series of normal alkanes change with the number of carbons, n. See also Figure 3·3.

Branched-chain alkanes do not exhibit the same smooth gradation of physical properties as the n-alkanes. Usually, there is too great a variation in

Figure 3·3   Dependence of ΔT (difference in boiling and melting points between consecutive members of the series of normal alkanes) on n (number of carbon atoms).

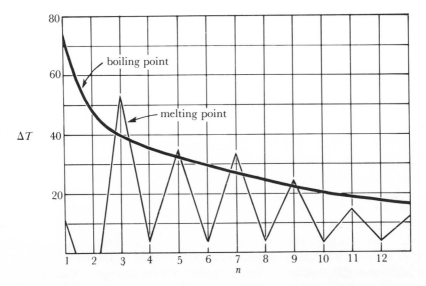

Table 3·3   Physical properties of *n*-alkanes, $CH_3(CH_2)_{n-2}CH_3$

n	name	bp, °C (760 mm)	mp, °C	density, d_4^{20}	refractive index, $n^{20}{}_D$
1	methane	−161.5	−183	0.424[a]	
2	ethane	−88.6	−172	0.546[a]	
3	propane	−42.1	−188	0.501[b]	
4	butane	−0.5	−135	0.579[b]	1.3326[b]
5	pentane	36.1	−130	0.626	1.3575
6	hexane	68.7	−95	0.659	1.3749
7	heptane	98.4	−91	0.684	1.3876
8	octane	125.7	−57	0.703	1.3974
9	nonane	150.8	−54	0.718	1.4054
10	decane	174.1	−30	0.730	1.4119
11	undecane	195.9	−26	0.740	1.4176
12	dodecane	216.3	−10	0.749	1.4216
15	pentadecane	270.6	10	0.769	1.4319
20	eicosane	342.7	37	0.786[c]	1.4409[c]
30	triacontane	446.4	66	0.810[c]	1.4536[c]

[a] At the boiling point.
[b] Under pressure.
[c] For the supercooled liquid.

molecular structure for regularities to be apparent. Nevertheless, in any one set of isomeric hydrocarbons, volatility increases with increased branching. This can be seen from the data in Table 3·4, in which are listed the physical

Table 3·4   Physical properties of hexane isomers

isomer	structure	bp, °C	mp, °C	density at 20°, d_4^{20}
hexane	$CH_3(CH_2)_4CH_3$	68.7	−94	0.659
3-methylpentane	CH_3 | $CH_3CH_2CHCH_2CH_3$	63.3	−118	0.664
2-methylpentane (isohexane)	CH_3 | $CH_3CHCH_2CH_2CH_3$	60.3	−154	0.653
2,3-dimethylbutane	CH_3 CH_3 | | $CH_3CH-CHCH_3$	58.0	−129	0.661
2,2-dimethylbutane (neohexane)	CH_3 | $CH_3CCH_2CH_3$ | CH_3	49.7	−98	0.649

properties of the five hexane isomers; the most striking feature is the 19° difference between the boiling points of hexane and neohexane.

3·3 alkanes and their chemical reactions

As a class, alkanes are singularly unreactive. The name saturated hydrocarbon (or "paraffin," which literally means "little affinity" [L. *par(um)*, little, + *affins*, affinity]) arises because their chemical affinity for most common reagents may be regarded as saturated or satisfied. Thus none of the C—H or C—C bonds in a typical saturated hydrocarbon such as ethane are attacked at ordinary temperatures by a strong acid such as sulfuric, or by powerful oxidizing agents such as potassium permanganate, or by vigorous reducing agents such as lithium aluminum hydride ($LiAlH_4$).

We have seen that methane and other hydrocarbons are attacked by oxygen *at elevated temperatures* and, if oxygen is in excess, complete combustion occurs to give carbon dioxide and water with the evolution of large amounts of heat. Vast quantities of hydrocarbons from petroleum are utilized as fuels for the production of heat and power, as will be described in the next section.

A. PETROLEUM AND COMBUSTION OF ALKANES

The liquid mixture of hydrocarbons delivered by oil wells is called **petroleum.** Its composition varies according to the location of the field but the major components are invariably alkanes. Natural gas is found in association with petroleum and also alone as trapped pockets of underground gas. Natural gas is chiefly methane, while crude petroleum is an astonishing mixture of hydrocarbons up to C_{50} in size. This dark, viscous oil is present in interstices in porous rock and is usually under great pressure.

Petroleum is believed to arise from the decomposition of the remains of marine organisms over the ages and new fields are continually sought to satisfy the enormous world demand. The effect of advanced technology on our environment is shown by the fact that combustion of fossil fuels, chiefly petroleum, has increased the carbon dioxide content of the atmosphere by 10% in the past century and an increase of 25% has been predicted by the year 2000. These increases would be even more marked were it not for the fact that the rate of photosynthesis by plants becomes more efficient at utilizing carbon dioxide as the concentration increases.

In addition to serving as a source of power—and being the only natural sources of suitable fuel for the internal combustion engine—petroleum and natural gas are extremely useful as starting materials for the synthesis of other organic compounds. These are often called petrochemicals to indicate their source but they are, of course, identical with compounds prepared in other ways or found in nature.

Petroleum refining involves separation into fractions by distillation. Each of these fractions with the exception of the first, which contains only a few components, is still a complex mixture of hydrocarbons. The main petroleum fractions are given below in order of decreasing volatility.

1. *Natural Gas.* Natural gas varies considerably in composition depending on the source but methane is always the major component, mixed with smaller amounts of ethane, propane, butane, and 2-methylpropane (isobutane). These are the only alkanes with boiling points below 0°C. Methane and ethane cannot be liquefied by pressure at room temperature (their critical temperatures are too low) but propane, butane, and isobutane can. Liquid propane (containing some of the C_4 compounds) can be easily stored in cylinders and is a convenient source of gaseous fuel. It is possible to separate natural gas into its pure components for sale as pure chemicals although the mixture is, of course, perfectly adequate as a fuel.

2. *Gasoline.* Gasoline is a complex liquid mixture of hydrocarbons composed mainly of C_5 to C_{10} compounds. Accordingly, the boiling range of gasoline is usually very wide, from approximately 40° to 180°. Because of the large number of isomers possible with alkanes of this size, it is much more difficult to separate gasoline into its pure components by fractional distillation than is the case with natural gas. Using a technique known as gas chromatography (Section 7·1), this separation can be done on an analytical scale. It has been shown that well over 100 compounds are present in appreciable amounts in ordinary gasoline. These include, besides the open-chain alkanes, cyclic alkanes (cycloalkanes, Section 3·4) and alkylbenzenes (arenes, Section 20·1).

The efficiency of gasoline as a fuel in modern high-compression internal combustion engines varies greatly with composition. Gasolines containing large amounts of branched-chain alkanes such as 2,2,4-trimethylpentane have high octane ratings and are in great demand, while those containing large amounts of continuous-chain alkanes such as octane or heptane have low octane ratings and perform poorly in a modern high-compression automobile engine. The much greater efficiency of branched-chain alkanes is not the result of greater heat of combustion but of the smoothness with which they burn. The heats of combustion of octane and 2,2,4-trimethylpentane can be calculated from the data in Table 2·1 and, since each contains the same number of carbon-carbon bonds (seven) and carbon-hydrogen bonds (18), we would expect their heats of combustion to be identical. The calculated value is -1218 kcal/mole, and the experimental values are close to this.

$$CH_3CH_2CH_2CH_2CH_2CH_2CH_2CH_3 + \frac{25}{2} O_2 \longrightarrow 8\ CO_2 + 9\ H_2O \quad \Delta H = -1222.8\ \text{kcal}$$

$$CH_3{-}\underset{\underset{CH_3}{|}}{\overset{\overset{CH_3}{|}}{C}}{-}CH_2{-}\underset{\overset{CH_3}{|}}{CH}{-}CH_3 + \frac{25}{2} O_2 \longrightarrow 8\ CO_2 + 9\ H_2O \quad \Delta H = -1220.6\ \text{kcal}$$

The combustion of vaporized branched-chain alkanes is slower and less explosive than that of continuous-chain compounds. In an automobile engine, too rapid combustion leads to dissipation of the combustion energy as heat to the engine block, rather than as movement of the piston. You can clearly hear the "knock" in an engine that is undergoing too rapid combustion of the fuel vapor in the cylinders. The problem is aggravated in high-compression engines. These will often continue to run (though inefficiently) on low-octane gasoline even when the ignition switch has been turned off, the heat of compression in the cylinder being sufficient to ignite the fuel mixture.

Combustion of hydrocarbons occurs by a complex chain reaction (Section 2·5B). It is possible to slow the propagation of the chain by adding volatile compounds such as tetraethyllead, $(CH_3CH_2)_4Pb$, to gasoline. The fine particles of solid lead oxide formed by oxidation of tetraethyllead moderate the chain-carrying reactions and reduce the tendency for knock to occur.[3] The **octane rating** of a gasoline is measured by comparing its knock with that of blends of 2,2,4-trimethylpentane whose octane rating is set at 100, and heptane whose octane rating is set at zero. Octane itself has a rating of -20. The higher the octane rating, the smoother the ignition and, with high-compression engines, the more efficient the gasoline. With low-compression engines the effect is negligible and it is wasteful or worse (see footnote) to use gasoline of higher rating than is needed to eliminate knocking.

The steadily increasing use of hydrocarbons in internal combustion engines has led to increasingly serious pollution problems. Some of these are associated with waste products from the refining operations used to produce suitable fuels from crude petroleum, others with spillage of petroleum in transit to the refineries, but possibly the worst is atmospheric pollution from carbon monoxide and of the type known as "smog." The chemical processes in the production of smog are complex but appear to involve hydrocarbons (especially branched-chain hydrocarbons), sunlight, and oxides of nitrogen. The products of the reactions are ozone, which produces rubber cracking and plant damage, particulate matter, which produces haze, oxides of nitrogen, which color the atmosphere, and virulent eye irritants (one being acetyl pernitrite, $CH_3-\overset{\overset{\displaystyle O}{\|}}{C}-O-O-N=O$). The hydrocarbons in the atmosphere which produce smog come principally from incomplete combustion in gasoline engines, although sizable amounts arise from evaporation and spillage. Whether smog can be eliminated without eliminating the internal combustion engine is not yet known, but the prognosis is rather unfavorable.

Pollution of the atmosphere from carbon monoxide is already so severe in heavy downtown traffic in large cities as to pose immediate health problems. The main reason for high concentrations of carbon monoxide in automobile exhaust is that the modern gasoline engine runs most efficiently on a slight deficiency in the ratio of oxygen to hydrocarbon which would produce complete combustion. A current solution to this problem is to introduce air and complete the combustion process in the exhaust manifold.

---

[3] Accumulation of lead oxide in a motor would rapidly damage the cylinder walls and valves. Tetraethyllead is normally used in conjunction with 1,2-dibromoethane in gasoline and this combination forms volatile lead bromide which is swept out with the exhaust gases. An unfortunate consequence of this means of improving octane rating is the addition of toxic lead compounds to the atmosphere. Isomerizing normal alkanes or cracking kerosene to produce branched-chain compounds would seem to be better solutions to the problem. The manufacture of engines capable of running on nonleaded gasoline is also being undertaken.

3. *Kerosene.* Kerosene consists chiefly of C_{11} and C_{12} hydrocarbons, compounds that do not vaporize well in automobile engines. It now finds considerable use as fuel for jet engines. It is also used in small heating units and can, if necessary, be converted to gasoline by a process known as **cracking**. This involves catalytic decomposition to smaller molecules, one of which is an alkene:

$$C_{11}H_{24} \xrightarrow[\text{catalyst}]{\text{heat}} C_9H_{20} + CH_2{=}CH_2$$

4. *Diesel Oil.* The petroleum fraction which boils between about 250° and 400° (C_{13} to C_{25}) is known as diesel oil or fuel oil. Large amounts are used in oil-burning furnaces, some is cracked to gasoline, and much is used as fuel for diesel engines. These engines operate with a very high compression ratio and no spark system, so that they depend on compression to supply the heat for ignition of the fine spray of liquid fuel that is injected into the cylinder near the top of the compression stroke. Branched-chain compounds turn out to be too unreactive to ignite and for this reason diesel and automobile engines have quite different fuel requirements.

5. *Lubricating Oils and Waxes.* The high-molecular-weight hydrocarbons (C_{26} to C_{28}) in petroleum have very high boiling points and can only be obtained in a reasonably pure state by distillation at reduced pressure. Thermal decomposition (pyrolysis) occurs if distillation is attempted at atmospheric pressure because the thermal energy acquired by collision of these compounds at their boiling points (400°) is sufficient to rupture carbon-carbon bonds. Almost all alkanes higher than C_{20} are solids at room temperature, and you might be wondering why lubricating oil is liquid. This is because it is a complex mixture whose melting point is much below that of its pure components. Indeed, as the temperature is lowered, its viscosity simply increases although this undesirable property can often be corrected by special additives such as chlorinated hydrocarbons.

Paraffin wax used in candles is a mixture of very high-molecular-weight hydrocarbons similar enough in structure to pack together to give a semi-crystalline solid. Vaseline is a mixture of paraffin wax and low-melting oils.

6. *Residue.* After removal of all volatile components from petroleum, a black, tarry material remains which is a mixture of minerals and complex high-molecular-weight organic compounds; it is known as **asphalt**.

B. SUBSTITUTION OF HALO AND NITRO GROUPS IN ALKANES

The chlorination of methane was discussed in considerable detail in the previous chapter. This reaction actually occurs with all alkanes and can also be performed satisfactorily with bromine (but not with fluorine or iodine). For the general reaction $-\overset{|}{\underset{|}{C}}-H + X_2 \rightarrow -\overset{|}{\underset{|}{C}}-X + H-X$, where $X = F$, Cl, Br, or I, the calculated ΔH value is negative and very large for fluorine,

Table 3·5   Calculated heats of reaction for halogenation of hydrocarbons

$$-\overset{\displaystyle |}{\underset{\displaystyle |}{C}}-H + X_2 \longrightarrow -\overset{\displaystyle |}{\underset{\displaystyle |}{C}}-X + HX$$

X	ΔH, kcal/mole
F	−115
Cl	−27
Br	−10
I	12

negative and moderate for chlorine and bromine, and positive for iodine (see Table 3·5). With fluorine, the reaction evolves so much heat that it is difficult to control, and products from cleavage of carbon-carbon as well as of carbon-hydrogen bonds are obtained. Indirect methods for preparation of fluorine-substituted hydrocarbons will be discussed later. Bromine is generally much less reactive toward hydrocarbons than chlorine, both at high temperatures and with activation by light. Nonetheless, it is usually possible to brominate saturated hydrocarbons successfully. Iodine is unreactive.

As we have seen, the chlorination of methane does not have to stop with the formation of chloromethane, and it is possible to obtain the higher chlorination products: dichloromethane (methylene chloride), trichloromethane (chloroform), and tetrachloromethane (carbon tetrachloride). In practice, all the substitution products are formed to some extent, depending on the

$$CH_4 \longrightarrow CH_3Cl \longrightarrow CH_2Cl_2 \longrightarrow CHCl_3 \longrightarrow CCl_4$$

	chloro-methane	dichloro-methane	trichloro-methane	tetrachloro-methane

chlorine-to-methane ratio employed. If monochlorination is desired, a large excess of hydrocarbon is advantageous.

For propane and higher hydrocarbons, where more than one monosubstitution product is generally possible, difficult separation problems may arise when a particular product is desired. For example, the chlorination of 2-methylbutane at 300° gives all four possible monosubstitution products, [3], [4], [5], and [6]. On a purely statistical basis, we might expect the ratio of products to correlate with the number of available hydrogens at the various positions of substitution; that is, [3], [4], [5], and [6] would be formed in the ratio 6 : 3 : 2 : 1. However, in practice, the product composition is substantially different, because the different kinds of hydrogens are not attacked at equal rates. Actually, the approximate ratios of the rates of attack of chlorine atoms on hydrogens located at primary, secondary, and tertiary positions are 1.0 : 3.3 : 4.4 at 300°. These results indicate that dissociation energies of C—H bonds are not exactly the same but decrease in the order primary > secondary > tertiary.

$$CH_3-\underset{\underset{H}{|}}{\overset{\overset{CH_3}{|}}{C}}-CH_2-CH_3 \xrightarrow[300°]{Cl_2} ClCH_2-\underset{\underset{H}{|}}{\overset{\overset{CH_3}{|}}{C}}-CH_2-CH_3 + CH_3-\underset{\underset{H}{|}}{\overset{\overset{CH_3}{|}}{C}}-CH_2-CH_2Cl$$

1-chloro-2-methylbutane   1-chloro-3-methylbutane
[3]   [4]

$$+ CH_3-\underset{\underset{H}{|}}{\overset{\overset{CH_3}{|}}{C}}-CHCl-CH_3 + CH_3-\underset{\underset{Cl}{|}}{\overset{\overset{CH_3}{|}}{C}}-CH_2-CH_3$$

3-chloro-2-methylbutane   2-chloro-2-methylbutane
[5]   [6]

Bromine atoms are far more selective than chlorine atoms, and bromine attacks only tertiary hydrogens, and these not very efficiently. Thus, photochemical (light-induced) monobromination of 2-methylbutane proceeds slowly and gives quite pure 2-bromo-2-methylbutane. Bromine atoms might be expected to be more selective than chlorine atoms, because bond energies indicate that the process $-\overset{|}{\underset{|}{C}}-H + :\ddot{B}r\cdot \rightarrow -\overset{|}{\underset{|}{C}}\cdot + HBr$ is distinctly endothermic while the corresponding reaction with a chlorine atom is exothermic. In such circumstances it is not surprising to find that bromine only removes those hydrogens which are less strongly bonded to a carbon chain.

Another reaction of commercial importance is the nitration of alkanes to give nitroalkanes. Reaction is usually carried out in the vapor phase at elevated temperatures using nitric acid or nitrogen tetroxide as the nitrating agent. All available evidence points to a radical-type mechanism for nitration

$$RH + HNO_3 \xrightarrow{\sim 425°} RNO_2 + H_2O$$

but many aspects of the reaction are not fully understood. Mixtures are obtained—nitration of propane gives not only 1- and 2-nitropropanes but nitroethane and nitromethane.

$$CH_3CH_2CH_3 + HNO_3 \longrightarrow \begin{cases} CH_3CH_2CH_2NO_2 & CH_3\underset{\underset{NO_2}{|}}{C}HCH_3 \\ \text{1-nitropropane (25\%)} & \text{2-nitropropane (40\%)} \\ CH_3CH_2NO_2 & CH_3NO_2 \\ \text{nitroethane (10\%)} & \text{nitromethane (25\%)} \end{cases}$$

In commercial practice, the yield and product distribution in nitration of alkanes are controlled as far as possible by the judicious addition of catalysts (e.g., oxygen and halogens) which are claimed to raise the concentration of alkyl radicals. The product mixtures are separated by fractional distillation.

3·4 cycloalkanes

An important and interesting group of hydrocarbons, known as cycloalkanes, contain rings of carbon atoms linked together by single bonds. The simple unsubstituted cycloalkanes of the formula $(CH_2)_n$ make up a particularly important homologous series in which the chemical properties change in a much more striking way than do the properties of the open-chain hydrocarbons, $CH_3(CH_2)_{n-2}CH_3$. The reasons for this will be developed with the aid of two concepts, steric hindrance and angle strain, each of which is simple and easy to understand, being essentially mechanical in nature.

The conformations of the cycloalkanes, particularly cyclohexane, will be discussed in some detail, because of their importance to the chemistry of many kinds of naturally occurring organic compounds.

Cyclohexane is a typical cycloalkane and has six methylene (CH_2) groups joined together to form a six-membered ring. Cycloalkanes with one ring have the general formula C_nH_{2n} and are named by adding the prefix cyclo to

$$
\begin{array}{c}
\overset{\displaystyle H_2}{\underset{\displaystyle}{C}} \\
H_2C \diagup \quad \diagdown CH_2 \\
\mid \qquad\qquad \mid \\
H_2C \diagdown \quad \diagup CH_2 \\
\underset{\displaystyle H_2}{C}
\end{array}
$$

cyclohexane

the name of the corresponding *n*-alkane having the same number of carbon atoms as in the ring. Substituents are assigned numbers consistent with their positions in such a way as to keep the sum of the numbers to a minimum.

$$
\begin{array}{c}
CH_3 \\
\mid \\
CH \\
H_2C \diagup \quad \diagdown CH_2 \\
\mid \qquad\qquad \mid \\
H_2C \diagdown \quad \diagup CH_2 \\
CH \\
\mid \\
CH_3
\end{array}
$$

1,4-dimethylcyclohexane
(not 3,6-dimethylcyclohexane)

$$
\begin{array}{c}
CH_3 \\
\mid \\
CH \\
H_2C \diagup \quad \diagdown CH_2 \\
\mid \qquad\qquad \mid \\
H_2C - CH \\
\diagdown \\
C_2H_5
\end{array}
$$

1-ethyl-3-methylcyclopentane
(not 1-methyl-4-ethylcyclopentane)

The substituent groups derived from cycloalkanes by removing one hydrogen are named by replacing the ending -ane of the hydrocarbon with -yl to give cycloalkyl. Thus cyclohexane becomes cyclohexyl; cyclopentane, cyclopentyl; and so on.

$$
\begin{array}{c}
CH_2 \\
H_2C \diagup \quad \diagdown \\
\mid \qquad\qquad CHCl \\
H_2C \diagdown \quad \diagup \\
CH_2
\end{array}
$$

cyclopentyl chloride
(or chlorocyclopentane)

Frequently it is convenient to write the structure of a cyclic compound in an abbreviated form as in the following examples. Each line junction represents a carbon atom and the normal number of hydrogens on each carbon atom is understood.

cyclobutane   2-methylcyclohexyl bromide   cyclooctane
(1-bromo-2-methylcyclohexane)

A. PHYSICAL PROPERTIES OF CYCLOALKANES

The melting and boiling points of cycloalkanes (Table 3·6) are somewhat higher than for the corresponding alkanes. The general "floppiness" of open-chain hydrocarbons makes them harder to fit into a crystal lattice (hence lower melting points) and less hospitable to neighboring molecules of the same type (hence lower boiling points) than the more rigid cyclic compounds.

B. CONFORMATIONS OF CYCLOHEXANE

If cyclohexane existed as a regular *planar* hexagon with carbon atoms at the corners, the C—C—C bond angles would be 120° instead of the normal

Table 3·6 Physical properties of alkanes and cycloalkanes

compounds	bp, °C	mp, °C	d_4^{20}
propane	−42	−187	0.580[a]
cyclopropane	−33	−127	0.689[a]
n-butane	− 0.5	−135	0.579[b]
cyclobutane	13	− 90	0.689[b]
n-pentane	36	−130	0.626
cyclopentane	49	− 94	0.746
n-hexane	69	− 95	0.659
cyclohexane	81	7	0.778
n-heptane	98	− 91	0.684
cycloheptane	119	− 8	0.810
n-octane	126	− 57	0.703
cyclooctane	151	15	0.830
n-nonane	151	− 54	0.718
cyclononane	178	11	0.845

[a] At −40°.
[b] Under pressure.

Figure 3·4 Two conformations of cyclohexane with 109.5° bond angles (hydrogens omitted).

valence angle of carbon, 109.5°. Thus, a cyclohexane molecule with a planar structure could be said to have an **angle strain** of 10.5° at each of the carbon atoms. Puckering of the ring, however, allows the molecule to adopt conformations that are free of angle strain.

Inspection of molecular models reveals that there are actually two extreme conformations of the cyclohexane molecule that may be constructed if the

Figure 3·5 Boat form of cyclohexane showing interfering and eclipsed hydrogens. Top, scale model; center, ball-and-stick models; bottom, sawhorse representations.

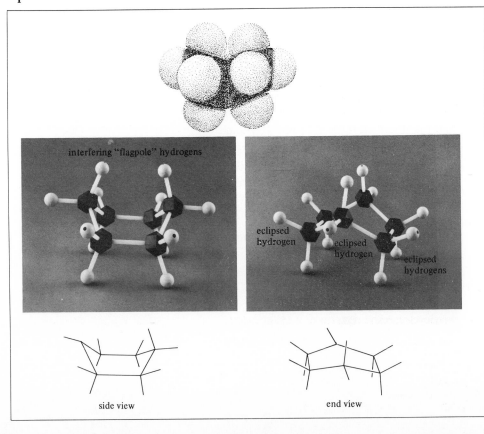

carbon valence angles are held at 109.5°. These are known as the "chair" and "boat" conformations (Figure 3·4). These two forms are so rapidly interconverted at ordinary temperatures that they cannot be separated. It is known, however, that the chair conformation is considerably more stable and comprises more than 99% of the equilibrium mixture at room temperature.

The higher energy of the boat form is not due to angle strain because all the carbon atoms in both forms have their bond angles near the tetrahedral angle of 109.5°. It is caused, instead, by relatively unfavorable interactions between the hydrogen atoms around the ring. If we make all the bond angles normal and orient the carbons in the ring to give the *extreme* boat conformation shown in Figure 3·5, we see that a pair of 1,4 hydrogens (the so-called flagpole hydrogens) have to be so close together (1.83 A) that they repel one another. This is an example of steric hindrance.

There is still another factor which makes the extreme boat form unfavorable; namely, that the eight hydrogens around the "sides" of the boat are eclipsed, which brings them substantially closer together than they would be in a staggered arrangement (about 2.27 A compared with 2.50 A). This is in striking contrast with the chair form (Figure 3·6) for which adjacent hydrogens are seen to be in staggered positions with respect to one another all the way around the ring. The chair form is therefore expected to be the more stable of the two. Even so, its equilibrium with the boat form produces inversion about 10^6 times per second at room temperature. If you make a molecular model of

less stable

cyclohexane you will find that the chair form has a considerable rigidity and the carbon-carbon bonds have to be slightly bent in going to the boat form. You will find that the boat form is extremely flexible and even if the bond angles are held exactly at 109.5°, simultaneous rotation around all the carbon-carbon bonds at once permits the ring to twist one way or the other to reduce the repulsions between the flagpole hydrogens and between the eight hydrogens around the sides of the ring. These arrangements are called **twist-boat** (sometimes **skew-boat**) conformations (Figure 3·7) and are believed to be only about 5 kcal less stable than the chair form.

It will be seen that there are two distinct kinds of hydrogens in the chair form of cyclohexane. Six are almost contained by the "average" plane of the ring (called equatorial hydrogens) and three are above and three below this average plane (called axial hydrogens). This raises an interesting question in connection with substituted cyclohexanes: For example, is the methyl group in methylcyclohexane equatorial or axial?

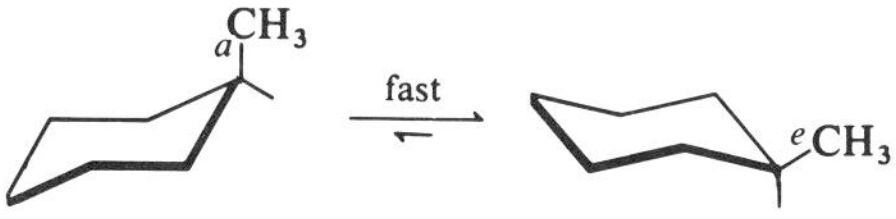

(axial)   (equatorial)

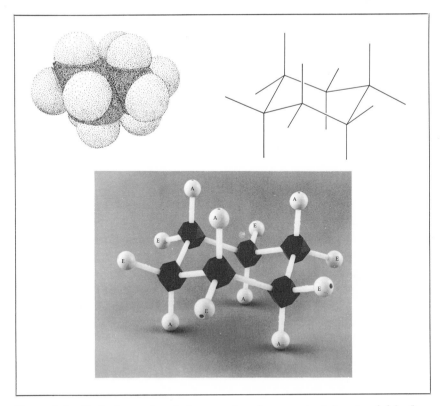

Figure 3·6   Chair form of cyclohexane showing equatorial and axial hydrogens. Top left, scale model; bottom, ball-and-stick model; top right, sawhorse representations. Note that all the axial positions are equivalent and all the equatorial positions are equivalent.

There is considerable evidence which shows that the equatorial form of methylcyclohexane predominates in the equilibrium mixture ($K \sim 15$), and the same is generally true of all monosubstituted cyclohexane derivatives. The reason can be seen from scale models which show that a substituent group has more room in an equatorial conformation than in an axial conformation (see Figure 3·8). The bigger the substituent, the greater the tendency for it to occupy an equatorial position.

The forms with axial and equatorial methyl are interconverted about 10^6

Figure 3·7   Drawings of the twist-boat conformations of cyclohexane.

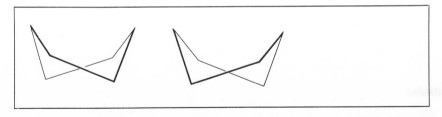

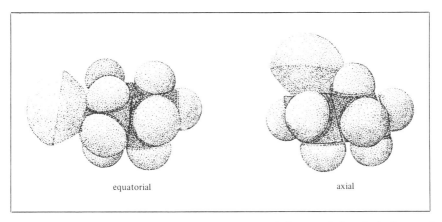

Figure 3·8   Scale models of equatorial and axial forms of the chair form of bromocyclohexane.

times/second at room temperature. The rate decreases as the temperature is lowered. If one cools the normal mixture of chlorocyclohexane conformations dissolved in a suitable solvent to very low temperatures ($-150°$), the pure equatorial conformation crystallizes out. This conformation can then be dissolved in solvents at $-150°$ and, when warmed to $-60°$, is converted to the equilibrium mixture in a few tenths of a second. However, the calculated half-time of the conversion of the equatorial to the axial form is 22 years at $-160°$.

C. OTHER CYCLOALKANE RINGS

The three cycloalkanes with smaller rings than cyclohexane are cyclopentane, cyclobutane, and cyclopropane, each with bond angles less than the tetrahedral value of 109.5°. If you consider a carbon-carbon double bond as a two-membered ring, then ethene, C_2H_4, is the simplest cycloalkane ("cyclo-ethane") and, as such, has carbon bond angles of 0° and, therefore, a very large degree of angle strain.

	cyclopentane	cyclobutane	cyclopropane	ethene
bond angle if planar:	108°	90°	60°	0°
angle strain (109.5° − bond angle):	1.5°	19.5°	49.5°	109.5°

Table 3·7 shows how strain decreases stability and causes the heat of combustion per methylene group (or per gram) to rise.

The idea that cyclopropane and cyclobutane should be strained because their C—C—C bond angles cannot have the normal tetrahedral value of 109.5° was advanced by Baeyer in 1885. It was also suggested that the diffi-

Table 3·7   Strain and heats of combustion of cycloalkanes

cycloalkane, $(CH_2)_n$	n	angle strain at each CH_2 for planar molecules, deg	heat of combustion,[a] ΔH, kcal/mole	heat of combustion per CH_2, $\Delta H/n$, kcal	total strain,[b] kcal/mole
ethene	2	109.5	337.23	168.6	22.4
cyclopropane	3	49.5	499.83	166.6	27.6
cyclobutane	4	19.5	655.86	164.0	26.4
cyclopentane	5	1.5	793.52	158.7	6.5
cyclohexane	6	(10.5)[c]	944.48	157.4	0.0
cycloheptane	7	(19.0)[c]	1108.2	158.3	6.3
cyclooctane	8	(25.5)[c]	1269.2	158.6	9.6
cyclononane	9	(30.5)[c]	1429.5	158.8	11.2
cyclodecane	10	(34.5)[c]	1586.0	158.6	12.0
cyclopentadecane	15	(46.5)[c]	2362.5	157.5	1.5
open-chain, n-alkane	∞			157.4	

[a] For gaseous hydrocarbons to give liquid water at 25°, data from S. Kaarsemaker and J. Coops, *Rec. Trav. Chim.* **71**, 261 (1952), and J. Coops, H. Van Kamp, W. A. Lambgrets, B. J. Visser, and H. Dekker, *Rec. Trav. Chim.* **79**, 1226 (1960).

[b] Calculated by subtracting ($n \times 157.4$) from the observed heat of combustion.

[c] Angle strain calculated for *planar* ring as per the Baeyer theory. The strain that is present in the C_7 to C_{10} compounds is not the result of angle strain (the molecules are puckered) but of eclipsing or interfering of hydrogen atoms.

culties encountered up to that time in synthesizing cycloalkane rings from C_7 upward was the direct result of the angle strain which would be expected if the large rings were regular planar polygons (see again Table 3·7).

We now know that the Baeyer strain theory cannot be applied to large rings because cyclohexane and the higher cycloalkanes have puckered rings with normal or nearly normal bond angles. Much of the difficulty in synthesizing large rings from open-chain compounds is due to the low probability of having reactive groups on the two fairly remote ends of a long hydrocarbon chain come together to effect cyclization. Usually, coupling of reactive groups on the ends of *different* molecules occurs in preference to cyclization, unless the reactions are carried out in very dilute solutions.

For cyclopentane, a planar structure would give bond angles of 108°, very close to the natural bond angle of 109.5°. Actually, the angle strain is believed to be somewhat greater than 1.5° in this molecule; the eclipsing of all of the hydrogens causes the molecule to distort substantially even though this increases the angle strain. Cyclobutane is also not completely flat for the same reason. (It should be remembered that molecules such as these are in vibrational motion at all times and the shapes that have been described refer to the mean atomic positions averaged over a period of time corresponding to several vibrations.)

D. CHEMICAL PROPERTIES OF CYCLOALKANES

We have already observed how strain in the small-ring cycloalkanes affects their heats of combustion. We can reasonably expect other chemical properties also to be affected by ring strain, and indeed cyclopropane and cyclobutane are considerably more reactive than saturated, open-chain hydrocarbons. In fact, they undergo some of the reactions which are typical of compounds with carbon-carbon double bonds, their reactivity depending on the degree of angle strain and the vigor of the reagent.

The result of these reactions is always opening of the ring by cleavage of a C—C bond to give an open-chain compound having normal bond angles. Relief of angle strain may therefore be considered to be an important part of the driving force of these reactions. A summary of a number of ring-opening reactions is given in Table 3·8. Ethene is highly reactive, while cyclopropane and cyclobutane are less so (in that order). The C—C bonds of the larger, relatively strain-free cycloalkanes are inert, so that these substances resemble the *n*-alkanes in their chemical behavior. Substitution reactions of these cycloalkanes are generally less complex than those of the corresponding alkanes because there are fewer possible isomeric substitution products. Thus, cyclohexane can give only one monochlorination product while *n*-hexane can give three.

E. *Cis-Trans* ISOMERISM OF SUBSTITUTED CYCLOALKANES

The form of stereoisomerism (isomerism caused by different spatial arrangements) called geometrical isomerism or *cis-trans* isomerism was discussed in the preceding chapter. This type of isomerism arises when rotation is prevented by, for example, the presence of a double bond. A ring prevents rotation equally well and we find that *cis* and *trans* isomers can also exist with appropriately substituted cycloalkanes. Thus, when a cycloalkane is disub-

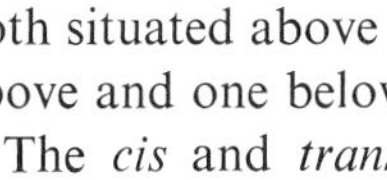

$$CH_2$$
$$CH_3CH\!\!-\!\!CHCH_3$$
1,2-dimethylcyclopropane

stituted at different ring positions, as in 1,2-dimethylcyclopropane, two isomeric structures are possible according to whether the substituents are both situated above (or both below) the plane of the ring (*cis* isomer), or one above and one below (*trans* isomer), as shown in Figure 3·9.

The *cis* and *trans* isomers of 1,2-dimethylcyclopropane cannot be interconverted without breaking one or more bonds. One way of doing this is to break open the ring and then close it again with a substituent on the opposite side from where it started. Alternatively, the bond to the substituent (or the hydrogen) can be broken and reformed on the opposite side of the ring. Examples of both processes will be discussed in later chapters.

Cis and *trans* isomers of cyclohexane derivatives have the additional possibility of different conformational forms. For example, 4-*t*-butylcyclohexyl chloride can theoretically exist in four stereoisomeric chair forms,

Table 3·8 Reactions of cycloalkanes, $(CH_2)_n$

reaction	"cycloethane" $(CH_2{=}CH_2)$	cyclo-propane	cyclo-butane	cyclo-pentane	cyclo-hexane
$\begin{array}{c}CH_2\\(CH_2)_{n-2}\mid\\CH_2\end{array}$ + Br$_2$ $\longrightarrow$ $\begin{array}{c}CH_2Br\\(CH_2)_{n-2}\\CH_2Br\end{array}$	very readily	slowly	inert	inert	inert
+ H$_2$SO$_4$ $\longrightarrow$ $\begin{array}{c}CH_3\\(CH_2)_{n-2}\\CH_2OSO_3H\end{array}$	readily	readily	?	inert	inert
+ KMnO$_4$ $\longrightarrow$ $\begin{array}{c}CH_2OH\\(CH_2)_{n-2}\\CH_2OH\end{array}$	readily	inert	inert	inert	inert
+ H$_2$ $\xrightarrow{\text{Ni}}$ $\begin{array}{c}CH_3\\(CH_2)_{n-2}\\CH_3\end{array}$	readily at room temp.	120°	200°	inert	inert

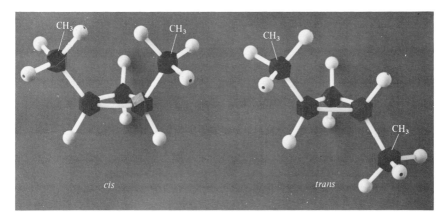

Figure 3·9 Ball-and-stick models of *cis* and *trans* isomers of 1,2-dimethyl-cyclopropane.

[7], [8], [9], and [10].

Structures [7] and [8] have the substituents *trans* to one another, but in [7] they are both equatorial while in [8] they are both axial. Structures [9] and [10] have the *cis* relationship between the groups, but the *t*-butyl and chlorine are equatorial-axial in [9] and axial-equatorial in [10]. *t*-Butyl groups are very large and bulky and much more steric hindrance results when a *t*-butyl group is in an axial position than when chlorine is in an axial position (Figure 3·10). Hence the equilibrium between the two conformational forms of the *trans* isomer strongly favors structure [7] over structure [8] because both *t*-butyl and chlorine are equatorial. For the *cis* isomer, structure [9] is favored over [10] to accommodate the *t*-butyl group in the equatorial position.

When there are two substituents in the *cis*-1,4 arrangement on a cyclohexane ring, neither of which will go easily into an axial position, then it

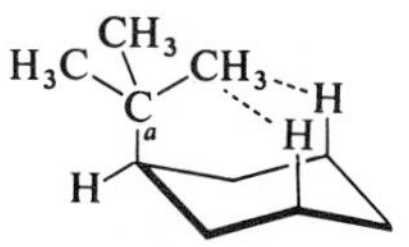

Figure 3·10   1,3 Interactions in a cyclohexane ring with an axial *t*-butyl group.

appears that the twist-boat conformation (Section 3·4B) is most favorable (Figure 3·11).

summary

Alkanes are hydrocarbons possessing only single bonds. The open-chain alkanes have the formula C_nH_{2n+2}. The IUPAC names for alkanes are based on the longest continuous carbon chain with substituents being indicated by their position along the chain. The alkane names from C_1 to C_{10} are methane, ethane, propane, butane, pentane, hexane, heptane, octane, nonane, and decane. Structural isomerism appears at C_4, there being two compounds of formula C_4H_{10}—the continuous-chain compound $CH_3CH_2CH_2CH_3$ (butane) and the branched-chain compound
$$CH_3-\overset{\overset{\displaystyle CH_3}{|}}{CH}-CH_3$$
(2-methylpropane or isobutane). The larger the number of carbon atoms in a continuous-chain alkane, the larger the number of branched-chain isomers of it that will exist.

Alkyl groups are obtained by removing a hydrogen atom from an alkane, and structural isomerism appears here at the C_3 level. The group $CH_3-CH_2-CH_2-$ is called the *n*-propyl group and $CH_3-\underset{|}{CH}-CH_3$ the isopropyl group.

The physical properties of the alkanes show a smooth gradation. At room temperature the C_1 to C_4 compounds are gases, the C_5 to C_{18} continuous-chain (normal) alkanes are liquids, and higher-molecular-weight compounds are solids. The normal alkanes which are liquids often have branched-chain isomers which are solids. All alkanes are less dense than water and all are immiscible with water.

Petroleum is a complex mixture of hydrocarbons which can be separated into fractions, according to volatility: natural gas, gasoline, kerosene, diesel

Figure 3·11   Twist-boat conformation of *cis*-1,4-di-*t*-butylcyclohexane.

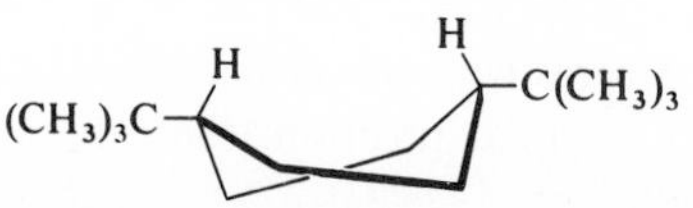

oil, lubricating oils and waxes, and residual material (asphalt). The heats of combustion of the alkanes with the same molecular weights in the gasoline fraction are all very close but their efficiencies in producing power in high-compression internal combustion engines vary widely with structure. The normal alkanes, which knock in the cylinder, have low octane ratings; the branched alkanes, which burn less rapidly, have high octane ratings.

In addition to combustion, alkanes undergo substitution reactions with halogens or nitric acid. These three reactions are illustrated using propane as the alkane:

$$CH_3CH_2CH_3 \quad
\begin{cases}
\xrightarrow{\;O_2\;} & 3\,CO_2 \;+\; 4\,H_2O \\[4pt]
\xrightarrow{\;Cl_2\;} & CH_3CHClCH_3 \;+\; CH_3CH_2CH_2Cl \quad (+\,HCl) \\[4pt]
\xrightarrow{\;HNO_3\;} & \underset{\displaystyle CH_3CHCH_3}{\overset{NO_2}{\big|}} \;+\; CH_3CH_2CH_2NO_2 \quad (+\,H_2O)
\end{cases}$$

With higher alkanes, more complex mixtures of substitution products result, although the major products are usually those in which a tertiary hydrogen has been replaced.

The cycloalkanes have similar physical and chemical properties to those of the open-chain alkanes except that the small-ring compounds such as cyclo-propane,
$$\begin{array}{c} CH_2 \\ \diagup\;\diagdown \\ H_2C\!-\!CH_2 \end{array}$$
are more reactive because of bond-angle strain. Cyclohexane exists in two principal conformations that are rapidly inter-converted, the more stable and rather rigid chair form and the less stable and flexible twist-boat form. The twelve carbon-hydrogen bonds in the chair

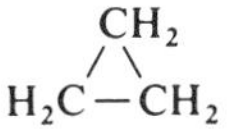

chair form
of cyclohexane

twist-boat form
of cyclohexane

form are of two types, six axial bonds parallel to the vertical axis of the ring and six equatorial bonds pointing out from the equator of the ring. Of the two kinds of positions, the equatorial provides more room for bulky substituent groups and, therefore, a substituent group will normally prefer to take an equatorial position. Some of the principal conformational forms of methylcyclohexane are shown here (all are in rapid equilibrium, with the form on the far right being the most stable).

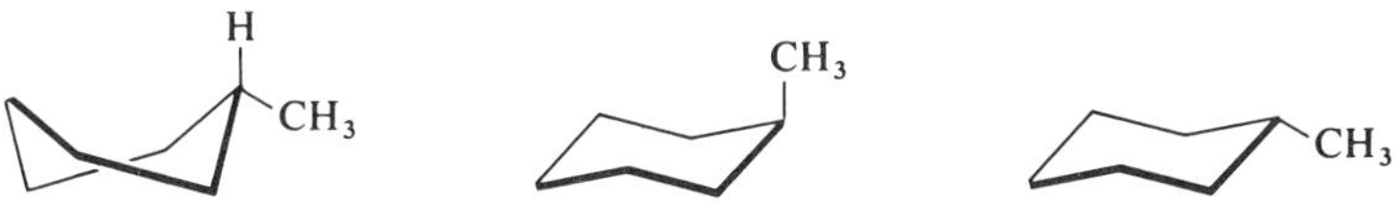

a twist-boat form

chair form
methyl group axial

chair form
methyl group equatorial

Geometrical isomers can exist with appropriately substituted cycloalkanes since rotation about the C—C bonds in the ring is prevented by the ring itself. *Cis* isomers have the substituent groups on the same side of the ring and *trans* isomers on the opposite side. A number of forms are possible in cycloalkanes because of the combination of geometrical isomerism and conformational equilibria.

exercises

3·1 Name each of the following hydrocarbons by the IUPAC system and in example *e* as an alkyl-substituted methane.

a. 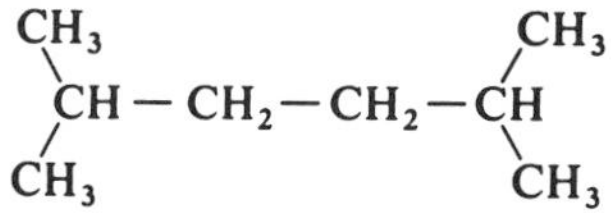
$$CH_3\!-\!CH-CH_2-CH_2-CH-CH_3$$
with CH_3 groups

$$\begin{array}{c} CH_3 \\ | \\ CH-CH_2-CH_2-CH \\ | \\ CH_3 \end{array} \quad \begin{array}{c} CH_3 \\ \\ CH_3 \end{array}$$

b.
$$CH_3-\overset{\overset{\displaystyle CH_3}{|}}{\underset{\underset{\displaystyle CH_3}{|}}{C}}-CH_2-\overset{\overset{\displaystyle CH_3}{|}}{CH}-CH_3$$

c.
$$\begin{array}{c} CH_3CH_2 \\ \\ CH-CH_2-CH \\ | \\ CH_3 \end{array} \quad \begin{array}{c} CH_3 \\ \\ CH_3 \end{array}$$

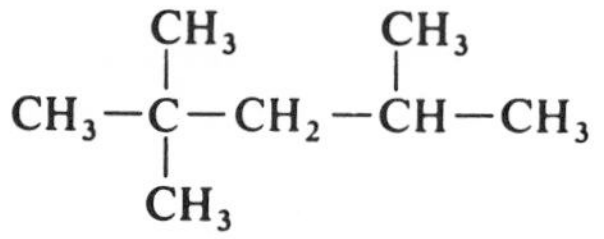

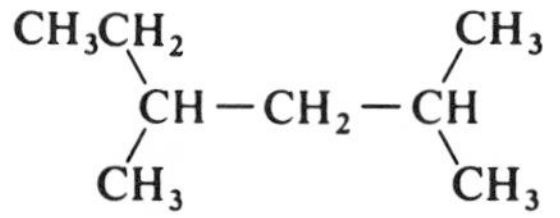

d. 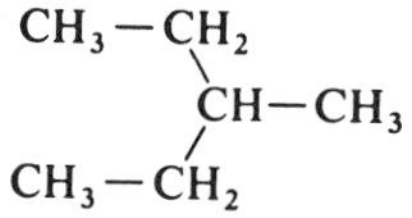
$$\begin{array}{c} CH_3-CH_2 \\ \\ CH-CH_3 \\ \\ CH_3-CH_2 \end{array}$$

e. $(CH_3-CH_2-CH_2\,\overline{)}_4\,C$

f. 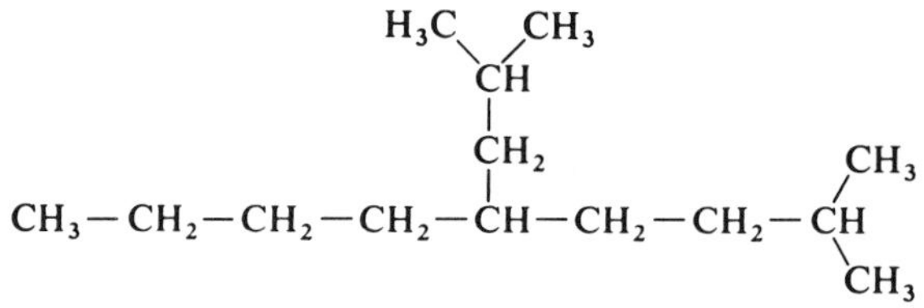
$$\begin{array}{c} H_3C \qquad CH_3 \\ CH \\ | \\ CH_2 \qquad\qquad\qquad CH_3 \\ | \qquad\qquad\qquad\quad / \\ CH_3-CH_2-CH_2-CH_2-CH-CH_2-CH_2-CH \\ \qquad\qquad\qquad\qquad\qquad\qquad\qquad CH_3 \end{array}$$

3·2 Write the structures of the eight branched-chain isomers of heptane $CH_3CH_2CH_2CH_2CH_2CH_2CH_3$. Name each by the IUPAC system.

3·3 What is the IUPAC name for (*a*) triethylmethane, (*b*) hexamethylethane?

3·4 Each of the names given below violates the rules of organic nomenclature. Supply the correct name in each case.

　　a. 2,3-diethylbutane
　　b. 2,4,4-trichlorohexane
　　c. 1,4-diisopropylbutane
　　d. 2,4,5-trimethyl-3-*n*-propylheptane

3·5 Fill in the appropriate prefix in the names given below and draw the structural formula in each case.

    a.   2,3- _____ methylpentane

    b.   1,1,1- _____ chloroethane

    c.   1,2,3,4,5,6- _____ iodohexane

3·6 Write structures for all seventeen possible monochlorohexanes and name them by the IUPAC system.

3·7 Use the data of Tables 3·3 and 3·4 to estimate the boiling points of tetra-decane, heptadecane, 2-methylhexane, and 2,2-dimethylpentane.

3·8 Is "neoheptane" an unambiguous name? Explain.

3·9 Write structural formulas for each of the following and name each by the IUPAC system:

    a.   *t*-butyl-isobutyl-*s*-butyl-*n*-butylmethane
    b.   isononane
    c.   the monochloropentane isomers; also name each as best as you can as an alkyl chloride.

3·10 Calculate ΔH for the following reactions in the vapor state at 25°:

    a. $2\,CH_4 + 7\,Cl_2 \longrightarrow CCl_3 - CCl_3 + 8\,HCl$
    b. $CH_3CH_3 + \frac{7}{2}\,O_2 \longrightarrow 2\,CO_2 + 3\,H_2O$
    c. $CH_3CH_3 + H_2 \longrightarrow 2\,CH_4$
    d. $CH_3CH_3 + Br_2 \longrightarrow 2\,CH_3Br$
    e. $CH_4 + 2\,Cl_2 \longrightarrow C(g) + 4\,HCl$

3·11 *a.*   Would the calculated ΔH in Exercise 3·10*e* be greater or less if C (solid) were the reaction product? Explain.
    b.   What are the implications of the heats of reaction determined in Exercise 3·10*c* and *d* to the "saturated" character of ethane?

3·12 The C—F bond energy in Table 2·1 was computed from recent thermo-chemical studies of the vapor-phase reaction,

$$CH_4 + 4\,F_2 \longrightarrow CF_4 + 4\,HF \qquad \Delta H = -460 \text{ kcal}$$

Show how the ΔH value for this reaction may be used to calculate the energy of the C—F bond if all the other required bond energies are known.

3·13 Investigate the energetics (ΔH) of possible chain mechanisms for the light-induced monobromination of methane and make a comparison with those for chlorination. What are the prospects for iodination of methane?

3·14 The heat of combustion of cyclopropane $(CH_2)_3$ to give carbon dioxide and water vapor is 468.6 kcal. Show how this value can be used to calculate the average C—C bond energies of cyclopropane.

3·15   Combustion of a pure sample of a gaseous alkane produced a quantity of carbon dioxide whose weight and volume (under the same conditions) were exactly three times that of the gaseous alkane. What is the latter's formula?

3.16   Combustion of natural gas is generally a "cleaner" process (in terms of atmospheric pollution) than combustion of either gasoline or fuel oil. Explain why this is so.

3·17   Write a mechanism in harmony with that usually written for hydrocarbon chlorination which would lead to production of hexachloroethane as in Exercise 3·10a. (This reaction is used for commercial production of hexachloroethane.)

3·18   Show the configurations of all of the possible *cis-trans* isomers of the following compounds:

   a.   1,2,3-trimethylcyclopropane
   b.   1,3-dichlorocyclopentane
   c.   1,1,3-trimethylcyclohexane

3·19   Would you expect *cis-* or *trans*-1,2-dimethylcyclopropane to be the more stable? Explain.

3·20   Write expanded structures showing the C—C bonds for each of the following condensed formulas. Name each substance by an accepted system.

   a. $(CH_2)_{10}$
   b. $(CH_2)_5CHCH_3$
   c. $(CH_3)_2C(CH_2)_6CHC_2H_5$
   d.   The isomers of trimethylcyclobutane
   e. $(CH_2)_6CHCH_2C(CH_3)_2CH_2Cl$
   f. $[(CH_2)_2CH]_2C(CH_3)C_2H_5$

3·21   Draw structural formulas for all C_4H_8 and all C_5H_{10} compounds that contain a ring. Designate those that exist in *cis* and *trans* forms.

3·22   The energy barrier for rotation about the C—C bond in ethane is about 3 kcal, which suggests that the energy required to bring one pair of hydrogens into an eclipsed arrangement is 1 kcal. Calculate how many kilocalories the planar form and extreme boat form of cyclohexane would be unstable relative to the chair form on account of H—H eclipsing interactions alone.

3·23   Use the sawhorse convention and draw all the possible conformations of cyclohexyl chloride with the ring in the chair and in the boat forms. Arrange these in order of expected stability. Show your reasoning.

3·24   Formation of a cycloalkane $(CH_2)_n$ by reactions such as $Br(CH_2)_n ZnBr \rightarrow (CH_2)_n + ZnBr_2$ occurs in competition with other reactions such as

2 Br$\leftarrow$(CH$_2$$\rightarrow_n$ZnBr $\rightarrow$ Br$\leftarrow$CH$_2$)$_n$(CH$_2$$\rightarrow_n$ ZnBr $+$ ZnBr$_2$. Explain why cyclization reactions of this kind carried out in *dilute* solutions are likely to give better yields of (CH$_2$)$_n$ than in *concentrated* solutions.

3·25   Use the data of Table 3·7 and other needed bond energies to calculate ΔH for the following reaction in the vapor state at 25° with $n = 3$, 4, and 5.

$$(CH_2)_n \longrightarrow CH_3(CH_2)_{n-3}CH{=}CH_2$$

3·26   What can you conclude about the stability of the cycloalkanes with $n = 3$, 4, and 5 with respect to corresponding open-chain compounds with double bonds?

3·27   Use the heats of combustion (to liquid water) given in Table 3·7 and appropriate bond energies to calculate ΔH (vapor) for ring opening of the cycloalkanes with bromine over the range $n = 2$ to $n = 6$:

$$(CH_2)_n + Br_2 \longrightarrow (CH_2)_{n-2}(CH_2Br)_2$$

3·28   Show how the reactions described in Table 3·8 could be used to tell whether a hydrocarbon of formula C$_4$H$_8$ is methylcyclopropane, cyclobutane, or 1-butene (CH$_3$CH$_2$CH$=$CH$_2$). Write equations for the reactions used.

3·29   Draw the possible chair conformations of *trans*- and *cis*-1,3-dimethylcyclohexane. Is the *cis* or the *trans* isomer likely to be the more stable? Explain.

3·30   An empirical rule known as the von Auwers-Skita rule was used to assign configurations of pairs of *cis* and *trans* isomers in cyclic systems at a time when *cis* isomers were thought to be always less stable than *trans* isomers. The rule states that the *cis* isomer will have the higher boiling point, density, and refractive index. However, the rule fails for 1,3-disubstituted cyclohexanes, where the *trans* isomer has the higher boiling point, density, and refractive index. Explain how the von Auwers-Skita rule might be restated to include such 1,3-systems.

3·31   Would you expect cyclohexene oxide to be more stable in the *cis* or *trans* configuration? Give your reasons.

 cyclohexene oxide

3·32   Write structural formulas for substances (one for each part) which fit the following descriptions. Make sawhorse drawings of the substances where conformational problems are involved.

   a.   a compound of formula C$_4$H$_8$ which reacts slowly with bromine and sulfuric acid but not with potassium permanganate solution
   b.   the most highly strained isomer of C$_5$H$_{10}$
   c.   the possible products from treatment of 1-ethyl-2-methylcyclopropane with bromine

d. the least stable chair and the least stable boat conformations of *trans*-1,4-dichlorocyclohexane

e. the most stable geometrical isomer of 1,3-di-*t*-butylcyclobutane

f. a compound with a six-membered ring which is most stable with the ring in a boat form

g. the most stable possible conformation of *trans*-1,3-di-*t*-butylcyclohexane

chapter 4
alkenes

In the early days of organic chemistry, when it was found that the alkenes, but not the alkanes, readily undergo addition reactions with substances such as halogens, hydrogen halides, sulfuric acid, and oxidizing agents, the chemical affinity of alkanes was said to be "saturated" while that of the alkenes was said to be "unsaturated." Now, even though we recognize that no chemical entity (even the noble gases such as helium and xenon) can surely be classified as saturated, the description of alkanes and alkenes as saturated and unsaturated is still commonly used. However, in place of a nebulous chemical affinity, we ascribe the unsaturation of alkenes to the ease of cleaving half of a carbon-carbon double bond in an addition reaction. Additions occur with alkenes much more easily than with alkanes because (1) the carbon-carbon bonds of a double bond are individually weaker (more strained) than a normal carbon-carbon single bond and (2) the double-bond electrons are generally more accessible than single-bond electrons to an attacking reagent (see Section 2·6).

The great variety and specificity of the addition reactions that compounds with double bonds undergo make these substances extremely important as intermediates in organic syntheses. We have already examined two of these reactions (addition of halogens and hydrogen) in connection with our study of ethene, the simplest alkene, in Chapter 2.

4·1   nomenclature

Open-chain alkenes containing one double bond have the general formula C_nH_{2n} and are sometimes called olefins. According to the IUPAC system for naming alkenes, the longest continuous chain containing the double bond is given the name of the corresponding alkane with the ending -ane changed to -ene. This chain is then numbered so that the position of the *first* carbon of the double bond is indicated by the lowest possible number.

$$\overset{4}{C}H_3\overset{3}{C}H_2\overset{2}{C}H=\overset{1}{C}H_2$$

1-butene
(not 3-butene)

$$CH_3-CH_2-CH_2-\overset{3}{C}H-\overset{4}{C}H_2-\overset{5}{C}H_2-\overset{6}{C}H_2-\overset{7}{C}H_3$$

with $\overset{1}{C}H_2$ ‖ $\overset{2}{C}H$

3-propyl-1-heptene
(the dotted lines indicate longest continuous
chain containing the double bond)

Other, less systematic names are often used for the simpler alkenes. By one method, alkenes are named as substituted ethylenes. This nomenclature,

$$CH_2=CH_2 \qquad (CH_3)_2C=C(CH_3)_2 \qquad Cl_2C=CHCl$$

ethylene   tetramethylethylene   trichloroethylene

based on the older name "ethylene," is given here because, even though not in accord with modern practices, it has been widely used in the literature. A

little reflection will show that attempts to name alkenes as derivatives of pro-
pylene (propene) or butylene (as will be seen, there are four open-chain C_4H_8
isomers) will require special rules or be hopelessly ambiguous.

The hydrocarbon groups derived from alkenes carry the suffix -enyl, as in
alkenyl, and numbering of the group starts with the carbon atom with the
free bond:

$$\overset{4}{C}H_3-\overset{3}{C}H=\overset{2}{C}H-\overset{1}{C}H_2- \qquad \overset{4}{C}H_2=\overset{3}{C}H-\overset{2}{C}H_2-\overset{1}{C}H_2-$$

   2-butenyl   3-butenyl

However, there are a few alkenyl groups for which trivial names are commonly
used in place of systematic names. These are vinyl, allyl, and isopropenyl
groups:

$$CH_2=CH- \qquad CH_2=CH-CH_2- \qquad \overset{\displaystyle CH_3}{\overset{\displaystyle |}{CH_2=C-}}$$

   vinyl   allyl   isopropenyl
  (ethenyl)   (2-propenyl)   (1-methylethenyl)

Cycloalkenes with double bonds in the ring (**endocyclic** double bonds) are
named by the system used for the open-chain alkenes, except that the numbering is always started at one of the carbons of the double bond and continued on around the ring *through* the double bond so as to keep the sum of the
index numbers as small as possible.

1,3-dimethylcyclohexene
(not 1,5-dimethylcyclohexene)

More complex nomenclature systems are required when the double bond
is **exocyclic** to the ring, especially if a ring carbon is one terminus of the
double bond. Usually the parent compounds of this type are called methylene-
cycloalkanes.

methylenecyclobutane

Many compounds contain two or more double bonds and are known as
alkadienes, alkatrienes, alkatetraenes, and so on, the suffix denoting the number of double bonds. The location of each double bond is specified by appropriate numbers.

$$CH_2=C=CH-CH_3 \qquad CH_2=CH-CH=CH_2 \qquad CH_2=C=C=CH_2$$

   1,2-butadiene   1,3-butadiene   1,2,3-butatriene

A further classification is used according to the relationships of the double bonds, one to the other. Thus, 1,2-alkadienes and similar substances are said to have cumulated double bonds. 1,3-Alkadienes and other compounds

$$CH_2=C=CH_2 \qquad\qquad \diagup\!\!\!\diagdown C=C=C\diagdown\!\!\!\diagup$$

allene
(propadiene) 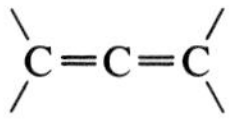
     cumulated double bonds

with alternating double and single bonds are said to have conjugated double bonds, and this arrangement leads, as we shall see in Chapter 6, to compounds having rather special properties.

$$CH_3-CH=CH-CH=CH_2 \qquad C=C-C=C \qquad CH_2=CH-\overset{\displaystyle CH_3}{\underset{\displaystyle |}{C}}=CH_2$$

1,3-pentadiene 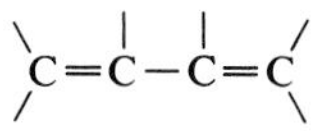
    conjugated
double bonds 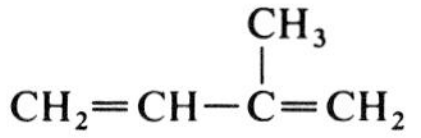
    2-methyl-1,3-butadiene
(isoprene)

Compounds with double bonds that are neither cumulated nor conjugated are classified as having isolated double-bond systems.

$$CH_2=CH-CH_2-CH=CH_2 \qquad C=C+C+_{\overline{n}}C=C$$

1,4-pentadiene 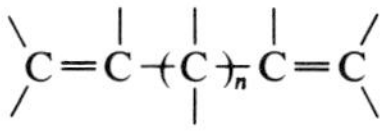
     isolated double bond system ($n \geq 1$)

4·2 isomerism in C_4H_8 compounds

In the homologous series of alkanes, isomerism first appears at the C_4 level, two compounds of formula C_4H_{10} being known. These are structural isomers:

$$CH_3-CH_2-CH_2-CH_3 \qquad\qquad CH_3-\overset{\displaystyle CH_3}{\underset{\displaystyle |}{CH}}-CH_3$$

butane, bp -0.5 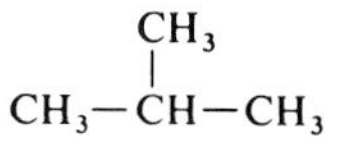
     2-methylpropane, bp $-12°$

There are in all six isomers of C_4H_8. Some are structural isomers and some stereoisomers (see Section 2·6B). Their boiling points and general physical properties are similar to those of butane and 2-methylpropane. Four of these compounds react quickly with bromine; one reacts slowly, and one not at all. The latter two compounds must be methylcyclopropane and cyclobutane, respectively (Section 3·4D), and these compounds are cycloalkanes, not alkenes. Note that the 2-butene structure is the only one that can exist in

$$CH_3-HC\begin{smallmatrix} \diagup CH_2 \\ \mid \\ \diagdown CH_2 \end{smallmatrix}$$

methylcyclopropane, bp 4°

$$\begin{matrix} H_2C-CH_2 \\ \mid \quad \mid \\ H_2C-CH_2 \end{matrix}$$

cyclobutane, bp 11°

$$CH_3-CH_2-CH=CH_2$$

1-butene, bp −6.3°

$$\begin{matrix} CH_3 \quad CH_3 \\ \diagdown \quad \diagup \\ C=C \\ \diagup \quad \diagdown \\ H \quad\quad H \end{matrix}$$

cis-2-butene, bp 3.7°

$$\begin{matrix} CH_3 \quad\quad H \\ \diagdown \quad \diagup \\ C=C \\ \diagup \quad \diagdown \\ H \quad\quad CH_3 \end{matrix}$$

trans-2-butene, bp 0.9°

$$\begin{matrix} CH_3 \\ \mid \\ CH_3-CH=CH_2 \end{matrix}$$

2-methylpropene, bp −6°

two different configurational arrangements. The other two isomers, 1-butene and 2-methylpropene, have at least one carbon atom of the double bond with identical groups attached to it. Thus, a rotation about the double bond, even if it could occur, would produce an identical arrangement.

It is worth reviewing once again the meanings of the terms *structure*, *configuration*, and *conformation* (Sections 2·2 and 2·6B). Of the six known compounds of formula C_4H_8, there are five different *structures*. These are cyclobutane, methylcyclopropane, 1-butene, 2-butene, and 2-methylpropene. One of these structures, 2-butene, has two different stable configurations or spatial arrangements. All of these substances have many different possible conformations because rotation can occur to at least some degree about their single bonds. Putting it another way, the C_4H_8 compounds illustrate structural isomerism, geometrical isomerism, and conformational variation. Structural and geometrical isomers (but not conformational isomers), because of their stability to interconversion and their somewhat different physical constants, can be separated by physical techniques such as fractional distillation or, better, by chromatography (Section 7·1).

4·3 cis and trans isomers

By convention, the configuration of complex alkenes is taken to correspond to the configuration of the *longest continuous* chain as it passes through the double bond. Thus the following compound is 4-ethyl-3-methyl-*trans*-3-heptene, despite the fact that two identical groups are *cis* with respect to each

$$\begin{matrix} CH_3-CH_2 \quad CH_2-CH_3 \\ \diagdown \quad\quad \diagup \\ C=C \\ \diagup \quad\quad \diagdown \\ H_3C \quad\quad CH_2-CH_2-CH_3 \end{matrix}$$

4-ethyl-3-methyl-*trans*-3-heptene

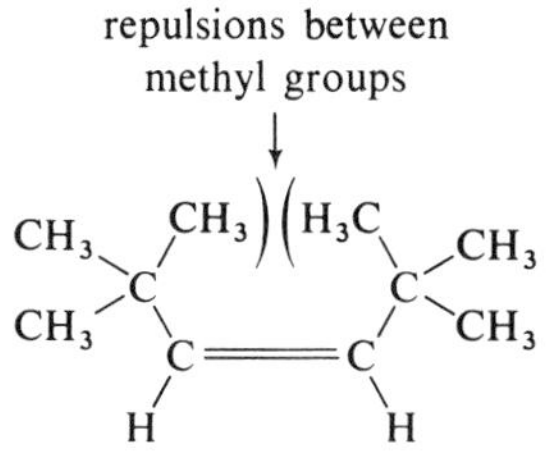

Figure 4·1   Repulsive interactions between the methyl groups of *cis-sym-di-t-butylethylene* (2,2,5,5-tetramethyl-*cis*-3-hexene).

other, because the longest continuous chain is *trans* as it passes through the double bond.

The *trans* isomers of the simple alkenes are usually more stable than the corresponding *cis* isomers. The methyl groups in *trans*-2-butene are far apart; in *cis*-2-butene, they are much closer to one another. Scale models, which reflect the sizes of the methyl groups, indicate some interference between the methyl groups of the *cis* isomer. The *cis* alkenes with large groups have very considerable repulsive interactions (steric hindrance) between the substituents, and are much less stable than the corresponding *trans* isomers (see Figure 4·1).

The generally greater stability of *trans* over *cis* isomers (see, however, Section 2·6B) is reflected in their *lower* heats of combustion. Table 4·1 compares the heats of combustion and the boiling and melting points of some *cis* and *trans* isomers. The data also reveal that *trans* isomers tend to have higher melting points and lower boiling points than *cis* isomers. Although the differences are not large, they may be of some help in assigning configurations. When electron-withdrawing groups such as halogens are attached to the

Table 4·1   Comparison of properties of *cis* and *trans* isomers

alkene	formula	bp, °C	mp, °C	heat of combustion, ΔH, kcal
cis-2-butene	$CH_3-CH=CH-CH_3$	3.7	−139	−606.4
trans-2-butene	$CH_3-CH=CH-CH_3$	0.9	−106	−605.4
cis-2-pentene	$CH_3-CH_2-CH=CH-CH_3$	37.9	−151	−752.6
trans-2-pentene	$CH_3-CH_2-CH=CH-CH_3$	36.4	−140	−751.7
cis-3-hexene	$CH_3-CH_2-CH=CH-CH_2-CH_3$	66.4	−138	−899.7
trans-3-hexene	$CH_3-CH_2-CH=CH-CH_2-CH_3$	67.1	−113	−898.1

double bond, the dipole moments of *cis* and *trans* isomers are different (Section 2·6B), allowing an assignment of configuration to be made. Infrared spectroscopy (Section 7·4) is also useful for distinguishing *cis* and *trans* isomers.

Occasionally, a chemical method, ring closure, can be used to determine the configuration of *cis-trans* isomers. In general, *cis* isomers can undergo ring closure much more readily than the corresponding *trans* isomers because it is not possible to prepare a five- or six-membered ring compound with a *trans* double bond in the ring. The kind of difference which is observed is well illustrated by maleic acid, which has a *cis* double bond and, on heating to 150°, loses water to give maleic anhydride. The corresponding *trans* isomer, fumaric acid, does not give an anhydride at 150°. In fact, fumaric anhydride, which would have a *trans* double bond in a five-membered ring, has never been prepared. Clearly, of this pair, maleic acid has the *cis* configuration and

| maleic acid | maleic anhydride | fumaric acid | fumaric anhydride (unknown) |

fumaric acid the *trans* configuration.

4·4 chemical reactions of alkenes

We have previously examined briefly two addition reactions of ethene, the first member of the homologous series of alkenes. These were addition of hydrogen, catalyzed by surfaces of finely divided metals such as nickel, and the addition of bromine. These reactions also occur with the higher homologs. For example, the colorless, volatile liquid 4-methyl-2-hexene reacts as follows:

Note that in the names of the three compounds shown, the number 1 carbon atom in one case is at the opposite end of the chain to that for the other two compounds. This is necessary to make the names conform to systematic usage (Sections 3·1 and 4·1).

The ease with which addition reactions to alkenes occur is the result of the repulsions between the two pairs of electrons that make up the double bond. Cleavage of one half of a carbon-carbon double bond requires 63 kcal, while cleavage of a carbon-carbon single bond requires 83 kcal (Table 2·1). Furthermore, because the repulsions push the electrons to average positions further from the bond axis than the electron positions of a single bond, the alkenes will be more readily attacked by **electrophiles**, that is, reagents that act to acquire electrons. On the other hand, **nucleophiles** ("nucleus-loving" reagents) are rather poor at reacting with carbon-carbon double bonds, unless one or more groups with a high degree of electron-withdrawing power are attached to one of the carbon atoms.

Of the two reagents so far considered, H_2 and Br_2, the latter, like all the halogens, is electrophilic, as we shall see when the mechanism of the reaction is considered in the next section. We have already noted that the addition of hydrogen to alkenes occurs on activated surfaces, and the availability of the electrons in the double bond is here reflected in part in the ease of adsorption of the alkene on the metallic surface.

A. ELECTROPHILIC ADDITION TO ALKENES. THE STEPWISE POLAR MECHANISM

Reagents such as the halogens (Cl_2, Br_2, and, to a lesser extent, I_2), hydrogen halides (HCl, HBr, and HI), hypohalous acids (HOCl and HOBr), water, and sulfuric acid commonly add to the double bonds of alkenes to give

saturated compounds. These reactions have much in common in their mechanisms and have been much studied from this point of view. They are also of
considerable synthetic and analytical utility. The addition of water to alkenes
(hydration) is particularly important for the preparation of a number of commercially important alcohols. Thus ethyl alcohol and *t*-butyl alcohol are made
on a very large scale by hydrating the corresponding alkenes (ethene and 2-
methylpropene), using sulfuric or phosphoric acids as catalysts.

$$CH_2{=}CH_2 \xrightarrow[240°]{H_2O,\ 10\%\ H_2SO_4} CH_3CH_2OH$$

ethene   ethyl alcohol

$$\begin{array}{c} H_3C \\ \diagdown \\ \diagup \\ H_3C \end{array} C{=}CH_2 \xrightarrow[25°]{H_2O,\ 10\%\ H_2SO_4} \begin{array}{c} H_3C \quad CH_3 \\ \diagdown \diagup \\ C \\ \diagup \diagdown \\ H_3C \quad OH \end{array}$$

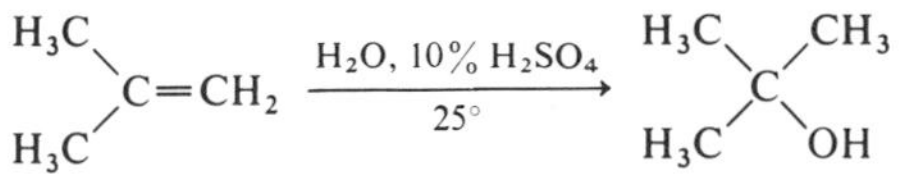

2-methylpropene   *t*-butyl alcohol

We shall pay particular attention here to addition of bromine to alkenes.
This reaction is conveniently carried out in the laboratory and illustrates a
number of important points about addition reactions. The characteristics of
bromine addition are best understood through consideration of the reaction
mechanism. A particularly significant observation concerning the mechanism
is that bromine addition (and the other additions listed above) proceeds in the
dark and in the presence of radical traps (reagents such as oxygen that react
rapidly with radicals to produce reasonably stable compounds). This is evidence against a radical chain mechanism analogous to the chain mechanism
involved in the halogenation of alkanes (Section 2·5B). It does not, however,
preclude operation of radical addition reactions under other conditions. In
fact, there are light-induced radical-trap inhibited reactions of bromine and
hydrogen bromide with alkenes which we shall describe later.

The alternative to a radical-type chain reaction is an ionic, or polar, reaction
in which electron-pair bonds are regarded as being broken in a heterolytic
manner in contrast to the radical, or homolytic, processes discussed previously.

$$X \!:\! Y \longrightarrow X^{\oplus} + :Y^{\ominus} \quad \text{heterolytic bond-breaking}$$

$$X \!\cdot\!\! \cdot Y \longrightarrow X\cdot + \cdot Y \quad \text{homolytic bond-breaking}$$

Most polar addition reactions do not seem to be simple four-center, one-
step processes for two important reasons. First, it should be noted that such
mechanisms require the formation of the new bonds to be on the same side
of the double bond and hence produce *cis* addition (Figure 4·2). However,
there is ample evidence to show that bromine and many other reagents give
trans addition. For example, cyclohexene adds bromine and hypochlorous
acid to give *trans*-1,2-dibromocyclohexane and *trans*-2-chlorocyclohexanol.
Such *trans* additions can hardly involve simple four-center reactions between

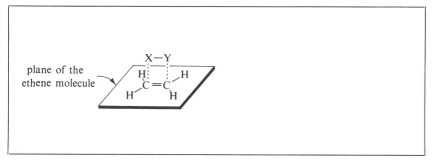

Figure 4·2 Schematic representation of *cis* addition of a reagent X—Y to ethene by a four-center mechanism. (**Most reagents do *not* add in this manner.**)

one molecule of alkene and one molecule of an addend X—Y, because the X—Y bond would have to be stretched impossibly far to permit the formation of *trans* C—X and C—Y bonds at the same time.

$$Br_2 + H_2C \underset{CH=CH}{\overset{CH_2-CH_2}{\diagdown}} CH_2 \longrightarrow$$

$$HOCl + H_2C \underset{CH=CH}{\overset{CH_2-CH_2}{\diagdown}} CH_2 \longrightarrow$$

The second piece of evidence against the four-center mechanism is that mixtures of products are often formed when addition reactions are carried out in the presence of reagents able to react by donation of a pair of electrons (nucleophilic reagents). Thus, the addition of bromine to an alkene in methyl alcohol solution containing lithium chloride leads not only to the expected dibromoalkane, but also to products resulting from attack by chloride ions and by the solvent. This intervention of extraneous nucleophilic agents in the reaction mixture is evidence against a one-step mechanism.

$$CH_2=CH_2 + Br_2 \quad
\begin{array}{l}
\xrightarrow{\quad Br_2 \quad} BrCH_2CH_2Br \\[4pt]
\xrightarrow[Cl^{\ominus}]{\quad Br_2 \quad} ClCH_2CH_2Br + Br^{\ominus} \\[4pt]
\xrightarrow[CH_3-O-H]{\quad Br_2 \quad} CH_3OCH_2CH_2Br + HBr
\end{array}$$

A somewhat oversimplified two-step mechanism that accounts for most of the facts is illustrated for the addition of bromine to ethene. (The curved arrows are not considered to have real mechanistic significance but are used primarily to show which atoms can be regarded as nucleophilic — donating electrons — and which as electrophilic — accepting electrons. The arrowheads point to the atoms that accept electrons.)

$$H_2C::CH_2 + :\ddot{B}r:\ddot{B}r: \longrightarrow {}^{\oplus}CH_2-CH_2Br + :\ddot{B}r:^{\ominus} \qquad \text{electrophilic attack} \qquad (4\cdot1)$$

$$:\ddot{B}r:^{\ominus} + {}^{\oplus}CH_2-CH_2Br \longrightarrow BrCH_2CH_2Br \qquad \text{nucleophilic attack} \qquad (4\cdot2)$$

1.2-dibromoethane
(ethylene dibromide)

The first step (which involves electrophilic attack on the double bond and heterolytic breaking of both a carbon-carbon and a bromine-bromine bond) as shown in Equation 4·1) produces a bromide ion and carbonium ion. The latter is electron deficient (Section 2·5C) and, in the second step of the postulated mechanism shown in Equation 4·2, it combines rapidly with an available nucleophile ($:\ddot{B}r:^{\ominus}$) to give the reaction product.

Clearly, if other nucleophiles (e.g., $:\ddot{C}l:^{\ominus}$, CH_3OH) are present in solution, they may compete with the bromide ion for the carbonium ion, as in Equations 4·3 and 4·4, and mixtures of products will result.

$$:\ddot{C}l:^{\ominus} + {}^{\oplus}CH_2-CH_2Br \longrightarrow ClCH_2CH_2Br \qquad (4\cdot3)$$

$$CH_3:\ddot{O}: + {}^{\oplus}CH_2-CH_2Br \longrightarrow CH_3:\overset{\oplus}{\ddot{O}}:CH_2-CH_2Br \xrightarrow{H^{\oplus}} CH_3OCH_2CH_2Br$$
$$\quad H \qquad\qquad\qquad\qquad\qquad\qquad H \qquad\qquad\qquad\qquad\qquad (4\cdot4)$$

In short, we must conclude that the reagents mentioned add across the double bond in a *trans* and stepwise manner and that the two steps take place from *opposite ends of the double bond.*

B. WHY TRANS ADDITION?

The simple carbonium-ion intermediate of Equation 4·1 does not account for formation of the *trans*-addition product. For one thing, there is no obvious reason why free rotation should not occur about the C—C bond of the cation $-\overset{|}{C}-\overset{|}{C}{}^{\oplus}$ derived from an open-chain alkene; if such occurs, all stereospecificity is lost. In the case of cyclic alkenes, addition of $Br^{\ominus}$ might be expected to occur from either side of the ring.

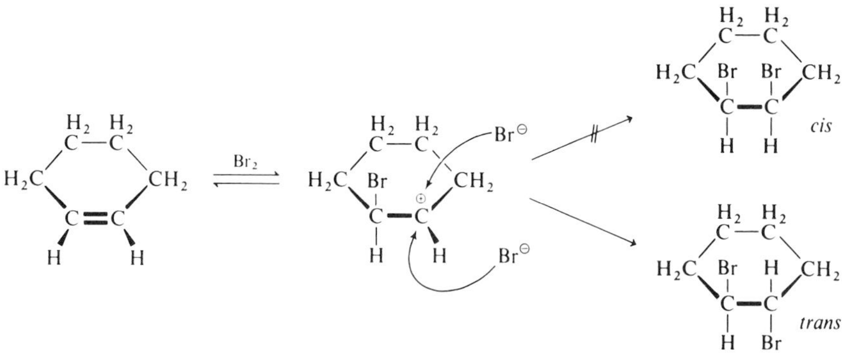

To account for the stereospecificity of bromine addition to alkenes, it has been suggested that a cyclic intermediate is formed in which bromine is bonded to both carbons of the double bond. This "bridged" ion is called a bromonium ion because the bromine formally carries the positive charge.

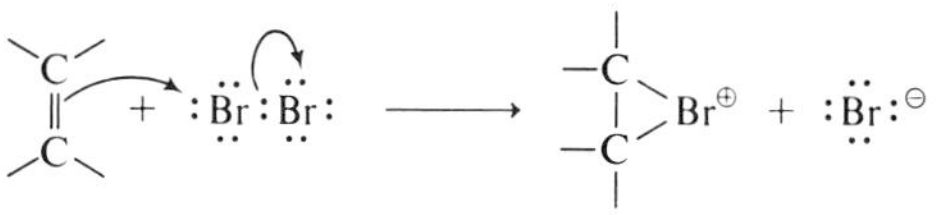

bromonium ion

Attack of a bromide ion, or other nucleophile, at the carbon on the side opposite the bridging group results in formation of the *trans*-addition product.[1]

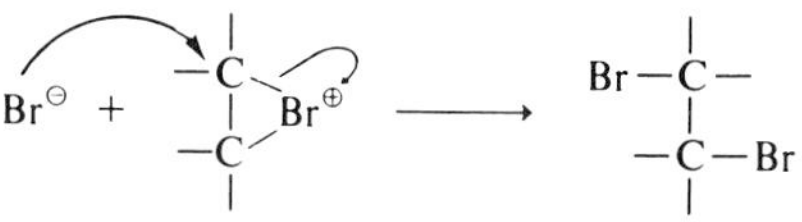

By analogy, a hydrogen-bridged intermediate can be used to account for *trans* addition of acids such as HBr, HCl, $H_3O^\oplus$, and H_2SO_4, to alkenes. These intermediates are sometimes called protonium ions and might appear to violate the usual generalization that hydrogen can form only one stable

protonium ion

[1] It is clear that the *cis* and *trans* addition routes can be distinguished in the case of addition to cycloalkenes on the basis of the stereochemistry of the product. You might wonder, however, how this can possibly be done for open-chain alkenes because free rotation can occur about the C—C bond of the product. This will be made clear when we examine optical isomerism in Chapter 14.

bond. It should be emphasized, however, that the bonding between the bridging hydrogen and the two carbon atoms is not considered to be normal electron-pair covalent bonding. It is different in that one electron pair effects the bonding of three atomic centers rather than the usual two. Protonium ions of this structure may be regarded as examples of "electron-deficient bonding," there being insufficient electrons with which to form all normal electron-pair bonds.

During the past few years, a number of species having electron-deficient bonds to hydrogen have been carefully investigated. The simplest example is the $H_2^\oplus$ ion, which may be regarded as a combination of a proton and a hydrogen atom. This ion has been detected and studied spectroscopically in the gaseous state. Another and very striking example is afforded by the stable compound diborane (B_2H_6), which has been shown to have a hydrogen-bridged structure. The bonds to each of the bridge hydrogens in diborane, like those postulated to the bridge hydrogen of an alkene-protonium ion, are examples of three-center electron-pair bonds. Spectroscopic evidence is also

diborane

available for the stable existence of alkylhalonium ions, $(CH_3)_2X^\oplus$, in solutions containing extremely weak nucleophiles.

Whether the intermediates in alkene-addition reactions are correctly formulated with bridged bromonium, chloronium, or protonium structures is still a controversial matter. Certainly, there are many other reactions of carbonium ions that are known to be far from being stereospecific, and therefore carbonium ions are not to be considered as necessarily, or generally, having bridged structures. It should also be remembered that all ions in solution, even those with only transitory existence, are strongly solvated, and this in itself may have important stereochemical consequences. In subsequent discussion, we shall most frequently write carbonium ions with the charge fully localized on one carbon atom, but it should be understood that this may not always be either the most accurate or the most desirable representation.

C. ORIENTATION IN ADDITION TO ALKENES; MARKOWNIKOFF'S RULE

Addition of an unsymmetrical substance such as HX to an unsymmetrical alkene can theoretically give two products:

$$(CH_3)_2C{=}CH_2 + HX \longrightarrow (CH_3)_2\underset{\underset{X}{|}}{C}{-}\underset{\underset{H}{|}}{C}H_2 \quad \text{and/or} \quad (CH_3)_2\underset{\underset{H}{|}}{C}{-}\underset{\underset{X}{|}}{C}H_2$$

One of the most important early generalizations in organic chemistry was Markownikoff's rule (1870), which may be stated as follows: *During the addition of HX to an unsymmetrical carbon-carbon double bond, the hydrogen of HX goes to that carbon of the double bond that carries the greater number of hydrogens.* Thus, Markownikoff's rule predicts that hydrogen chloride will add to propene to give 2-chloropropane (isopropyl chloride) and to 2-methylpropene to give 2-chloro-2-methylpropane (*t*-butyl chloride). These are, in fact, the products that are formed. The rule by no means has universal

$$CH_3-CH=CH_2 + HCl \longrightarrow CH_3-\underset{\underset{\displaystyle Cl}{|}}{C}H-CH_3$$

$$(CH_3)_2C=CH_2 + HCl \longrightarrow (CH_3)_2\underset{\underset{\displaystyle Cl}{|}}{C}-CH_3$$

additions in accord with Markownikoff's rule

application, but it is of considerable utility for polar additions to hydrocarbons with only one double bond.

D. A THEORETICAL BASIS FOR MARKOWNIKOFF'S RULE

To understand the reason for Markownikoff's rule, it will be desirable to discuss further some of the principles that are important to intelligent prediction of the course of an organic reaction. Consider the addition of hydrogen bromide to 2-methylpropene. Two different carbonium-ion intermediates could be formed by attachment of a proton to one or the other of the double-bond carbons. Subsequent reaction of the cations so formed with bromide

t-butyl cation   *t*-butyl bromide

isobutyl cation   isobutyl bromide

ion gives *t*-butyl bromide and isobutyl bromide. In the usual way of running these additions, the product is, in fact, quite pure *t*-butyl bromide.

How could we have predicted which product would be favored? The first step is to decide whether the prediction is to be based on which of the two products is the more stable, or which of the two products is formed more rapidly. If we make a decision on the basis of product stabilities, we take into account ΔH and ΔS values to estimate an equilibrium constant K between the reactants and each product. When the ratio of the products is determined by the ratio of their equilibrium constants, we say the overall reaction is subject to equilibrium (or thermodynamic) control. This will be the case when the reaction is carried out under conditions that make it readily reversible.

When a reaction is carried out under conditions in which it is *not reversible,* the ratio of the products is determined by the relative rates of formation of the products. Such reactions are said to be under kinetic control. To predict relative reaction rates, we take into account steric hindrance, stabilities of possible intermediates, and so on.

Addition of hydrogen bromide to 2-methylpropene is predicted by Markownikoff's rule to give *t*-butyl bromide. It turns out that the equilibrium constant connecting *t*-butyl bromide and isobutyl bromide is 4.5 at 25°, meaning that 82% of an equilibrium mixture is *t*-butyl bromide and 18% is isobutyl bromide.

$$K = \frac{[\textit{t-butyl bromide}]}{[\textit{isobutyl bromide}]} = 4.5$$

Addition of hydrogen bromide to 2-methylpropene actually gives 99+% *t*-butyl bromide in accord with Markownikoff's rule. This means that the rule is a *kinetic-control* rule and may very well be invalid under conditions where addition is reversible.

If Markownikoff's rule depends on kinetic control of the product ratio in the polar addition of hydrogen bromide to 2-methylpropene, then it is proper to try to explain the direction of addition in terms of the ease of formation of the two possible carbonium-ion intermediates. There is abundant evidence that tertiary carbonium ions are more easily formed than secondary carbonium ions and these, in turn, are more easily formed than primary carbonium ions. A number of carbonium salts have been prepared, and the tertiary ones are by far the most stable. Thus, the theoretical problem presented by Markownikoff's rule is reduced to predicting which of the two possible carbonium-ion intermediates will be most readily formed. With the simple alkenes, formation of the carbonium ion accords with the order of preference *tertiary > secondary > primary*.

E. ADDITIONS OF UNSYMMETRICAL REAGENTS OPPOSITE TO MARKOWNIKOFF'S RULE

The early chemical literature concerning the addition of hydrogen bromide to unsymmetrical alkenes is rather confused, and sometimes the same alkene was reported to give addition both according to and in opposition to Markownikoff's rule under very similar conditions. Much of the uncertainty about the addition of hydrogen bromide was removed by the classical researches of Kharasch and Mayo (1933), who showed that there must be two reaction mechanisms, each giving a different product. Under polar conditions, Kharasch and Mayo found that hydrogen bromide adds to propene in a rather *slow* reaction to give pure 2-bromopropane (isopropyl bromide):

$$CH_3CH{=}CH_2 + HBr \xrightarrow[\substack{\text{polar} \\ \text{conditions}}]{\text{slow}} CH_3\underset{\underset{Br}{|}}{C}HCH_3$$

With light or peroxides (radical initiators) and in the absence of radical traps, a rapid radical chain addition of hydrogen bromide occurs to yield 80% or more of 1-bromopropane (*n*-propyl bromide):

$$CH_3CH{=}CH_2 + HBr \xrightarrow[\text{peroxides}]{\text{fast}} CH_3CH_2CH_2Br$$

Similar effects have been occasionally noted with hydrogen chloride but never with hydrogen iodide or fluoride. A few substances apparently add to alkenes only by radical mechanisms and always give addition opposite to Markownikoff's rule.

The polar addition of hydrogen bromide was discussed in the previous section and will not be further considered now. Two questions with regard to the so-called abnormal addition will be given special attention: why the radical mechanism should give a product of different structure from the polar addition, and why the radical addition occurs readily with hydrogen bromide but rarely with the other hydrogen halides (see Exercise 4·17).

The abnormal addition of hydrogen bromide is strongly catalyzed by peroxides, which have the structure R—O—O—R and decompose thermally to give radicals:

$$R{-}\overset{..}{\underset{..}{O}}{:}\overset{..}{\underset{..}{O}}{-}R \longrightarrow 2\ R{-}\overset{..}{\underset{..}{O}}{\cdot} \qquad \Delta H = +35\ \text{kcal}$$

The RO· radicals can react with hydrogen bromide in two ways:

$$RO\cdot + HBr \begin{cases} \longrightarrow ROH + Br\cdot & \Delta H = -23\ \text{kcal} \\ \longrightarrow ROBr + H\cdot & \Delta H = +39\ \text{kcal} \end{cases}$$

Clearly, the formation of ROH and a bromine atom is energetically more favorable. The overall process of decomposition of peroxide and attack on hydrogen bromide, which results in the formation of a bromine atom, can initiate a radical chain addition of hydrogen bromide to an alkene:

Chain propagation:

$$CH_3CH{=}CH_2 + Br\cdot \longrightarrow CH_3\overset{\cdot}{C}H{-}CH_2Br \qquad \Delta H = -5\ \text{kcal}$$

$$CH_3\overset{\cdot}{C}H{-}CH_2Br + HBr \longrightarrow CH_3CH_2CH_2Br + Br\cdot \qquad \Delta H = -11\ \text{kcal}$$

Chain termination:

$$R'\cdot + R'\cdot \longrightarrow R'{-}R' \qquad R'\cdot = \text{atom or radical}$$

The chain-propagating steps, taken together, are exothermic by 16 kcal and have a fairly reasonable energy balance between the separate steps, which means that one is not highly exothermic and the other highly endothermic. Both steps are, in fact, comparably exothermic. The reaction chains appear to be rather long, since only traces of peroxide catalyst are needed and the addition is strongly inhibited by radical traps.

The direction of addition of hydrogen bromide to propene clearly depends on which end of the double bond the bromine attacks. The choice will depend on which of the two possible carbon radicals that may be formed is the

$$CH_3-\overset{\cdot}{C}H-CH_2-Br \qquad\qquad CH_3-\underset{\underset{Br}{|}}{C}H-CH_2\cdot$$

[1]   [2]

more stable, the 1-bromo-2-propyl radical [1] or the 2-bromo-1-propyl radical [2]. As with carbonium ions, the ease of formation and stabilities of carbon radicals follow the sequence *tertiary > secondary > primary*. Therefore, the *secondary* 1-bromo-2-propyl radical [1] is expected to be more stable and more easily formed than the *primary* 2-bromo-1-propyl radical [2]. The product of radical addition should be, and indeed is, 1-bromopropane.

It may seem strange to refer to certain radicals or ions as being stable and therefore more likely to be reaction intermediates than other *less stable* radicals or ions. Would not the *unstable* radicals or ions actually be more likely as intermediates because they would react more rapidly to give products? "Stable" is used here only in a relative sense. All of the radicals and ions which we are invoking as intermediates react very quickly to give products and never attain high concentrations in the reaction mixture. This means that the reactions will go more readily by way of the relatively more stable intermediates because these are formed most easily and react rapidly to give products. The less stable intermediates are not formed as readily and the fact that they would react more rapidly does not increase the overall reaction rate in processes which would involve them. This point will be considered in other connections later. The important thing to recognize is that there may be large differences in the ease of formation of different kinds of reaction intermediates—so much so that mechanisms which imply that primary carbonium ions or radicals ($RCH_2^{\oplus}$ or $RCH_2\cdot$) are formed in preference to secondary or tertiary carbonium ions and radicals should be regarded as suspect.

F. ADDITION OF BORON HYDRIDES TO ALKENES

A recently developed and widely used reaction is that of diborane (B_2H_6) with alkenes. Diborane (Section 19·5) is the dimer of the electron-deficient species BH_3, and it is as BH_3 that it adds to the double bond to give trialkylboron compounds (organoboranes). With ethene, triethylborane results:

$$6\ CH_2{=}CH_2 + B_2H_6 \xrightarrow{\ 0^\circ\ } 2\,(CH_3CH_2)_3B$$

This reaction is called hydroboration; it proceeds in three stages, but the intermediate mono- and dialkylboranes are not generally isolated, as they react rapidly by adding further to the alkene.

$$CH_2{=}CH_2 + BH_3 \longrightarrow CH_3CH_2BH_2$$
$$CH_2{=}CH_2 + CH_3CH_2BH_2 \longrightarrow (CH_3CH_2)_2BH$$
$$CH_2{=}CH_2 + (CH_3CH_2)_2BH \longrightarrow (CH_3CH_2)_3B$$

With an unsymmetrical alkene such as propene, hydroboration occurs so that boron becomes attached to the less substituted end of the double bond—with propene forming tri-*n*-propylborane.

$$6\ CH_3CH=CH_2 + B_2H_6 \longrightarrow 2\ (CH_3CH_2CH_2)_3B$$

Hydroborations have to be carried out with some care, since diborane and alkylboranes are highly reactive substances; in fact, they are spontaneously inflammable in air. For most synthetic purposes it is not necessary to isolate the addition products, and diborane can be generated either *in situ* or externally through the reaction of boron trifluoride with sodium borohydride.

$$3\ \overset{\oplus}{Na}\overset{\ominus}{BH_4} + 4\ BF_3 \longrightarrow 2\ B_2H_6 + 3\ \overset{\oplus}{Na}\overset{\ominus}{BF_4}$$

Boron trifluoride is conveniently used in the form of its stable complex with diethyl ether, $(C_2H_5)_2O:BF_3$, the reactions usually being carried out in ether solvents such as diethyl ether, $(C_2H_5)_2O$; diglyme, $(CH_3OCH_2CH_2)_2O$; or tetrahydrofuran, $(CH_2)_4O$.

The most common synthetic reactions of the resulting alkylboranes are oxidation with alkaline hydrogen peroxide to the corresponding primary alcohol, and cleavage with aqueous acid (or, better, anhydrous propanoic acid, $CH_3CH_2CO_2H$) to give alkanes. Thus, for tri-*n*-propylborane:

$$(CH_3CH_2CH_2)_3B + 3\ H_2O_2 \xrightarrow[25-30°]{OH^{\ominus}} 3\ CH_3CH_2CH_2OH + B(OH)_3$$

n-propyl alchohol
(a primary alcohol)

$$(CH_3CH_2CH_2)_3B + 3\ H_2O \xrightarrow[reflux]{H^{\oplus}} 3\ CH_3CH_2CH_3 + B(OH)_3$$

The first of these processes achieves "anti-Markownikoff" addition of water to a carbon-carbon double bond as the overall result of the two steps. The second reaction provides a method of reducing carbon-carbon double bonds without using hydrogen and a metal catalyst. Both of these conversions are difficult to do any other way and this accounts for the extensive use that organic chemists have made of diborane in recent years.

G. OXIDATION OF ALKENES

Most alkenes react readily with ozone, even at low temperatures, to cleave the double bond and yield cyclic peroxide derivatives known as **ozonides**.

$$CH_3CH=CHCH_3 \xrightarrow[-80°]{O_3} H_3CHC\overset{\displaystyle O}{\underset{\displaystyle O-O}{\diagup\ \diagdown}}CHCH_3$$

2-butene ozonide

Considerable evidence exists to indicate that the overall reaction occurs in three main steps, the first of which involves a *cis*-cycloaddition reaction that produces an unstable addition product called a **molozonide**.

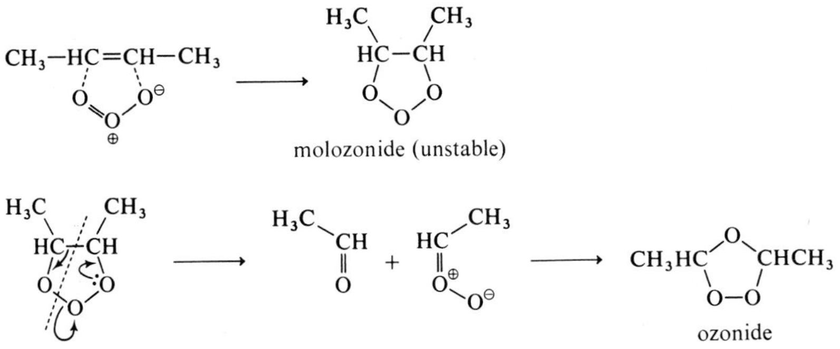

$$CH_3-HC=CH-CH_3$$

molozonide (unstable)

ozonide

Ozonides, like most substances with peroxide (O—O) bonds, may explode violently and unpredictably. Ozonizations must therefore be carried out with due caution. The ozonides are not usually isolated but are destroyed by hydrolysis with water and reduction with zinc to yield carbonyl compounds that are generally quite easy to isolate and identify. (In the absence of zinc, hydrogen peroxide is formed which may degrade the carbonyl products by oxidation). The overall reaction sequence provides an excellent means for

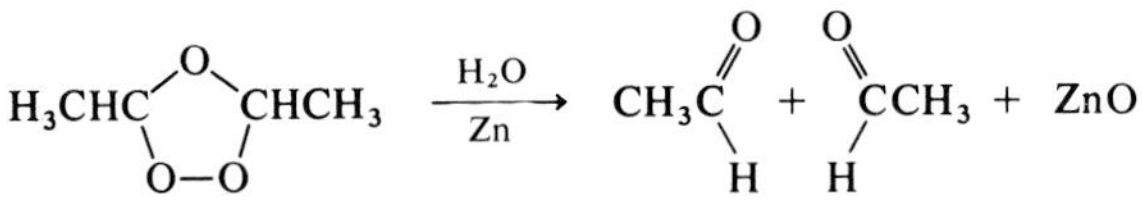

locating the positions of double bonds in alkenes. The potentialities of the method may be illustrated by the difference in reaction products between the 1- and 2-butenes:

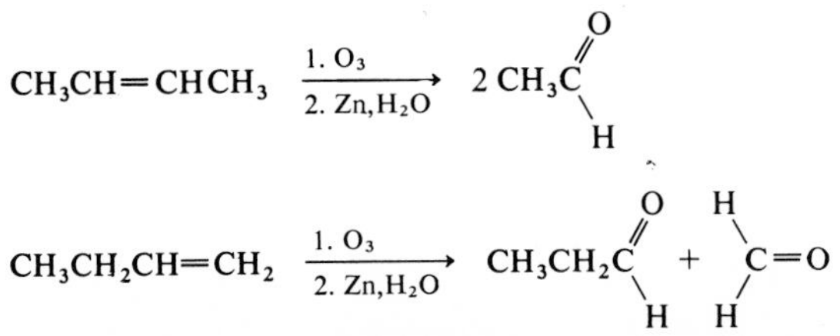

Natural rubber (polyisoprene, Section 28·2) is a substance with many double bonds, and ozone formed in the atmosphere by sunlight or by smog-producing reactions (Section 3·3A) combines with the double bonds of the rubber and causes the rubber to crack. This destructive action can be reduced by antioxidants mixed with the rubber, or by use of rubberlike materials without double bonds (see Section 4·4H).

Several other oxidizing reagents react with alkenes under mild conditions to give, overall, addition of hydrogen peroxide as HO—OH. Of particular importance are permanganate ion and osmium tetroxide, both of which react in an initial step by a *cis*-cycloaddition mechanism like that postulated for ozone:

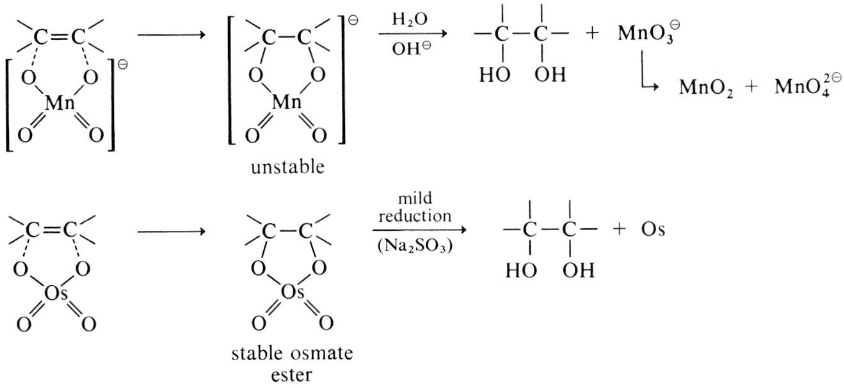

unstable

Each of these reagents produces *cis*-dihydroxy compounds (diols) with cycloalkenes:

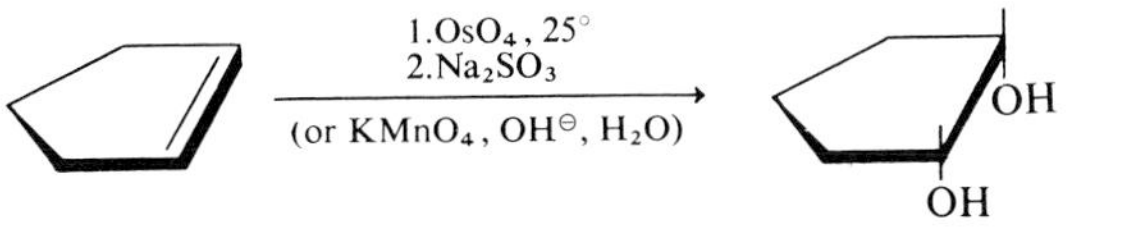

cis-1,2-cyclopentanediol

An alternate scheme for oxidation of alkenes with hydrogen peroxide in formic acid follows a different course in that *trans* addition occurs. (The mechanism of this reaction is analogous to the addition of bromine to a carbon-carbon double bond, which also takes place by *trans* addition.)

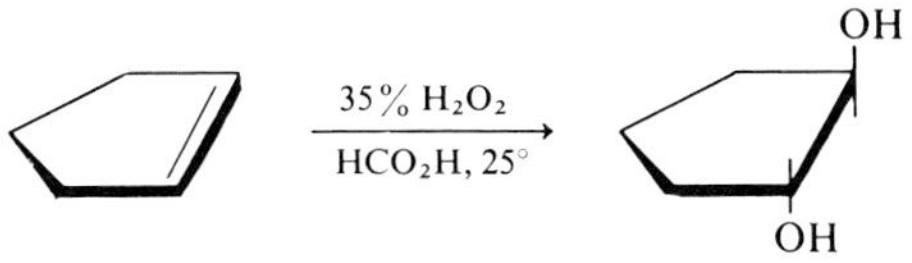

trans-1,2-cyclopentanediol

H. POLYMERIZATION OF ALKENES

One of the most important industrial reactions of alkenes is their conversion to higher-molecular-weight compounds (polymers). A polymer is here defined as a long-chain molecule with recurring structural units. Polymerization of propene, for example, gives a long-chain hydrocarbon with recurring $-\overset{\displaystyle CH_3}{\underset{\displaystyle}{\overset{\displaystyle |}{CH}}}-CH_2-$ units. Most industrially important polymerizations of alkenes

$$CH_3CH{=}CH_2 \longrightarrow \left[\begin{matrix} CH_3 \\ | \\ CH{-}CH_2 \end{matrix}\right]_n \quad \Delta H = -n \cdot 20 \text{ kcal}$$

propene   polypropene

(polypropylene)

occur by chain mechanisms and may be classed as anion, cation, or radical-type reactions, depending upon the character of the chain-carrying species. In each case, the key steps involve successive additions to molecules of the alkene. The differences are in the number of electrons that are supplied by the attacking agent for formation of the new carbon-carbon bond. For simplicity, these steps will be illustrated by using ethene, even though it does not polymerize very easily by any of them:

$$R{-}CH_2{-}\ddot{C}H_2^{\ominus} \ + \ CH_2{=}CH_2 \longrightarrow R{-}CH_2{-}CH_2{-}CH_2{-}\ddot{C}H_2^{\ominus}, \text{ etc.}$$

$$R{-}CH_2{-}\overset{\oplus}{C}H_2 + CH_2{=}CH_2 \longrightarrow R{-}CH_2{-}CH_2{-}CH_2{-}\overset{\oplus}{C}H_2, \text{ etc.}$$

$$R{-}CH_2{-}\dot{C}H_2 \ + \ CH_2{\cdot\cdot}CH_2 \longrightarrow R{-}CH_2{-}CH_2{-}CH_2{-}\dot{C}H_2$$

Anionic Polymerization. Initiation of alkene polymerization by the anion-chain mechanism may be formulated as involving an attack by a nucleophilic reagent $Y:^{\ominus}$ on one end of the double bond and formation of a carbanion. Attack by the carbanion on another alkene molecule gives a four-

$$Y:^{\ominus} + CH_2{=}CH_2 \longrightarrow Y:CH_2{-}\ddot{C}H_2^{\ominus}$$

carbanion

carbon carbanion, and subsequent additions to further alkene molecules lead to a high-molecular-weight anion. The growing chain can be terminated

$$Y:CH{-}\ddot{C}H_2^{\ominus} \ + \ CH_2{=}CH_2 \longrightarrow Y:CH_2{-}CH_2{-}CH_2{-}\ddot{C}H_2^{\ominus}$$

$$\xrightarrow{n\,(CH_2{=}CH_2)} Y:CH_2{-}CH_2{+}CH_2{-}CH_2{\overset{}{)}_n}CH_2{-}CH_2^{\ominus}$$

by any reaction (such as the addition of a proton) that would destroy the carbanion on the end of the chain:

$$Y:CH_2{-}CH_2{+}CH_2{-}CH_2{\overset{}{)}_n}CH_2{-}\ddot{C}H_2^{\ominus} \xrightarrow{\ H^{\oplus}\ } Y:CH_2{-}CH_2{+}CH_2{-}CH_2{\overset{}{)}_n}CH_2{-}CH_3$$

Anionic polymerization of alkenes is quite difficult to achieve, since few anions (or nucleophiles) are able to add readily to alkene double bonds (see p. 87). Anionic polymerization occurs readily only with ethenes substituted with sufficiently powerful electron-attracting groups to expedite nucleophilic attack.

Cationic Polymerization. Polymerization of an alkene by acidic reagents can be formulated by a mechanism similar to the addition of hydrogen halides to alkene linkages. First, a proton from a suitable acid adds to an alkene to yield a carbonium ion. Then, in the absence of any other reasonably strong nucleophilic reagent, another alkene molecule donates an electron pair and forms a longer chain cation. Continuation of this process can lead to a high-molecular-weight cation. Termination can occur by loss of a proton.

$$CH_2=CH_2 \;\overset{H^{\oplus}}{\rightleftharpoons}\; CH_3-CH_2^{\oplus} + CH_2 = CH_2 \longrightarrow$$

$$CH_3-CH_2-CH_2-CH_2^{\oplus} \xrightarrow{n(CH_2=CH_2)} CH_3-CH_2 (CH_2-CH_2)_n CH_2-CH_2^{\oplus}$$

$$\xrightarrow{-H^{\oplus}} CH_3-CH_2 (CH_2-CH_2)_n CH=CH_2$$

Ethene does not polymerize by the cationic mechanism, because it does not have groups that are sufficiently electron donating to permit ready formation of the intermediate growing-chain cation. 2-Methylpropene has electron-donating alkyl groups and polymerizes much more easily than ethene by this type of mechanism.

The usual catalysts for cationic polymerization of 2-methylpropene are sulfuric acid, hydrogen fluoride, or boron trifluoride plus small amounts of water. Under nearly anhydrous conditions, a very long-chain polymer is formed called "polyisobutylene." Polyisobutylene fractions of particular

$$n \cdot CH_2=C\overset{CH_3}{\underset{CH_3}{\big\langle}} \xrightarrow[\text{tr. } H_2O]{BF_3} CH_3-\underset{\underset{CH_3}{|}}{\overset{\overset{CH_3}{|}}{C}}-\left[CH_2-\underset{\underset{CH_3}{|}}{\overset{\overset{CH_3}{|}}{C}}\right]_{n-2} CH_2-C\overset{CH_3}{\underset{CH_2}{\big\langle}}$$

polyisobutylene

molecular weights are very tacky and are used as adhesives for pressure-sealing tapes.

In the presence of 60% sulfuric acid, 2-methylpropene is not converted to a long-chain polymer, but is **dimerized** to a mixture of C_8 alkenes. The mechanism is like the polymerization reaction described for polyisobutylene, except that chain termination occurs after only one alkene molecule has been added. The short chain length is due to the high water concentration; the intermediate carbonium ion loses a proton to water before it can react with

$$CH_2=C\overset{CH_3}{\underset{CH_3}{\big\langle}} \xrightarrow[70°]{60\% \ H_2SO_4} CH_3-\underset{\underset{CH_3}{|}}{\overset{\overset{CH_3}{|}}{C}}-CH_2-C\overset{CH_2}{\underset{CH_3}{\big\langle}} + CH_3-\underset{\underset{CH_3}{|}}{\overset{\overset{CH_3}{|}}{C}}-CH=C\overset{CH_3}{\underset{CH_3}{\big\langle}}$$

$$\qquad\qquad\qquad\qquad\quad 80\% \qquad\qquad\qquad\qquad 20\%$$

"diisobutylene"

another alkene molecule. Because the proton can be lost two different ways, a mixture of alkene isomers is obtained. The alkene mixture is known as "diisobutylene" and has a number of commercial uses. Hydrogenation gives 2,2,4-trimethylpentane (often erroneously called "isooctane"), which is used as the standard "100 antiknock rating" fuel for internal-combustion gasoline engines (Section 3·3A).

$$CH_2=C\begin{array}{c}CH_3\\CH_3\end{array} + H_2SO_4 \rightleftharpoons CH_3-\overset{\oplus}{C}\begin{array}{c}CH_3\\CH_3\end{array} \xrightarrow{\quad CH_2=C\begin{array}{c}CH_3\\CH_3\end{array}\quad} CH_3-\overset{CH_3}{\underset{CH_3}{C}}-CH_2-\overset{\oplus}{C}\begin{array}{c}CH_3\\CH_3\end{array}$$

$$\xrightarrow{-H^{\oplus}} CH_3-\overset{CH_3}{\underset{CH_3}{C}}-CH_2-C\begin{array}{c}CH_2\\CH_3\end{array} + CH_3-\overset{CH_3}{\underset{CH_3}{C}}-CH=C\begin{array}{c}CH_3\\CH_3\end{array}$$

diisobutylene isomers $\xrightarrow[50°]{H_2(Ni)}$ $CH_3-\overset{CH_3}{\underset{CH_3}{C}}-CH_2-\overset{CH_3}{CH}-CH_3$

2,2,4-trimethylpentane

Radical Polymerization. Ethene may be polymerized with peroxide catalysts under high pressure (1000 atmospheres or more, literally in a cannon barrel) at temperatures in excess of 100°. The initiation step involves formation of RO· radicals, and chain propagation entails stepwise addition of radicals to ethene molecules.

Initiation: $R:\ddot{O}:\ddot{O}:R \longrightarrow 2\,R:\ddot{O}\cdot$

Propagation:
$$\begin{cases} R:\ddot{O}\cdot + CH_2=CH_2 \longrightarrow R:\ddot{O}:CH_2-\dot{C}H_2 \\ R:\ddot{O}:\dot{C}H_2-CH_2 + n(CH_2=CH_2) \longrightarrow RO(CH_2-CH_2)_n CH_2-\dot{C}H_2 \end{cases}$$

Termination: $2RO(CH_2-CH_2)_n CH_2-\dot{C}H_2 \longrightarrow$ $[RO(CH_2-CH_2)_n CH_2-CH_2]_2$
combination

$RO(CH_2-CH_2)_n CH=CH_2 + RO(CH_2CH_2)_n-CH_2-CH_3$
disproportionation

Chain termination may occur by any reaction resulting in combination or disproportionation of two radicals. (Disproportionation means that two identical molecules react with one another to give two different product molecules.) The polymer produced this way has from 100 to 1000 ethene units in the hydrocarbon chain. The polymer, called Polythene (or sometimes polyethylene), possesses a number of desirable properties as a plastic and is widely used for electrical insulation, packaging films, piping, and a variety of molded particles. The very low cost of ethene (a few cents a pound) makes Polythene a commercially competitive material despite the practical difficulties involved in the polymerization process. Propene and 2-methylpropene do not polymerize satisfactorily by radical mechanisms.

Coordination Polymerization. A relatively low-pressure low-temperature ethene polymerization has been achieved with an aluminum-molybdenum oxide catalyst, which requires occasional activation with hydrogen (Phillips Petroleum). Ethene also polymerizes quite rapidly at atmospheric pressure and room temperature in an alkane solvent containing a suspension of the insoluble reaction product from triethylaluminum and titanium tetrachloride (Ziegler). Both the Phillips and Ziegler processes produce a very high-molecular-weight polymer with exceptional physical properties. The unusual characteristics of these reactions indicate that no simple anion, cation, or radical mechanism can be involved. It is believed that the catalysts act by coordinating with the alkene molecules in somewhat the way hydrogenation catalysts combine with alkenes.

Polymerization of propene by catalysts of the Ziegler type gives a most useful plastic material. It can be made into durable fibers or molded into a variety of shapes. Copolymers (polymers with more than one kind of monomer unit in the polymer chains) of ethene and propene made with Ziegler catalysts have highly desirable rubberlike properties and are potentially the cheapest useful elastomers (elastic polymers). A Nobel Prize was shared in 1963 by K. Ziegler and G. Natta for their work on alkene polymerization.

summary

Alkenes are hydrocarbons possessing a carbon-carbon double bond. Simple open-chain alkenes have the formula C_nH_{2n}. The IUPAC names for alkenes are obtained by finding the longest continuous carbon chain containing the double bond and giving it the name of the corresponding alkane with the ending changed from -ane to -ene. The numbering of the carbon chain is started at the end that will provide the lowest number for the position of the first carbon of the double bond. Thus,

$$CH_3-\overset{\overset{\displaystyle CH_3}{|}}{CH}-CH_2-CH=CH-CH_3$$

is 5-methyl-2-hexene. Some common alkenyl groups (an alkene minus a hydrogen atom) are vinyl (CH_2=$CH-$), allyl (CH_2=$CH-CH_2-$), and isopropenyl (CH_2=$\overset{\displaystyle C}{\underset{|}{}}-CH_3$). Compounds with two carbon-carbon double bonds are named as alkadienes; if the double bonds are adjacent they are called cumulated; if they are separated by a single bond they are conjugated; and if they are separated by more than one single bond they are isolated.

Both structural and geometrical isomerism appear at the C_4 level in the alkene series, there being three structural isomers. One of these (2-butene) exists in *cis* and *trans* forms. *Trans* isomers have the substituents on the

$$
\begin{array}{cc}
\underset{\text{H}}{\overset{\text{H}_3\text{C}}{\diagdown}}\text{C}=\text{C}\underset{\text{H}}{\overset{\text{CH}_3}{\diagup}} & \underset{\text{H}}{\overset{\text{H}_3\text{C}}{\diagdown}}\text{C}=\text{C}\underset{\text{CH}_3}{\overset{\text{H}}{\diagup}} \\
\textit{cis}\text{-2-butene} & \textit{trans}\text{-2-butene}
\end{array}
$$

opposite side of the double bond and usually are of lower energy (more stable) than their *cis* isomers. *Trans* isomers usually have the higher melting points, lower boiling points, lower dipole moments (often zero) and, because their substituent groups are far apart, they do not undergo ring closure reactions which may occur with some *cis* compounds.

The physical properties of alkenes are similar to those of the corresponding alkanes, but alkenes are much more reactive chemically. Because of the concentration of electrons in the double bond, alkenes are subject to attack by electrophiles (reagents that seek electrons). These addition reactions can be illustrated with a typical alkene such as propene:

$$CH_3CH{=}CH_2 \xrightarrow[\text{Ni}]{H_2} CH_3CH_2CH_3$$

$$\xrightarrow[\substack{\text{(other halogens}\\\text{behave similarly)}}]{Br_2} CH_3CHBrCH_2Br$$

$$\xrightarrow{HOCl} CH_3CHOHCH_2Cl$$

$$\xrightarrow{H_2SO_4} \underset{CH_3\overset{|}{C}HCH_3}{\overset{OSO_3H}{}}$$

$$\xrightarrow[\substack{\text{(HI behaves}\\\text{similarly)}}]{HCl} CH_3CHClCH_3$$

$$\xrightarrow[\text{(peroxide-free, in dark)}]{HBr} CH_3CHBrCH_3$$

$$\xrightarrow[\text{(peroxides)}]{HBr} CH_3CH_2CH_2Br$$

$$\xrightarrow[H^\oplus]{H_2O} CH_3CHOHCH_3$$

$$\xrightarrow{B_2H_6} (CH_3CH_2CH_2)_3B \underset{\substack{H_2O\\H^\oplus}}{\overset{\substack{H_2O_2\\OH^\ominus}}{\diagup\diagdown}} \begin{array}{l}CH_3CH_2CH_2OH\\[1em]CH_3CH_2CH_3\end{array}$$

$$\xrightarrow{O_3} CH_3\underset{O-O}{\overset{O}{C}H}CH_2 \xrightarrow[\text{Zn}]{H_2O} CH_3CHO + CH_2O$$

$$\xrightarrow{MnO_4{}^\ominus} \underset{CH_3\overset{|}{C}HCH_2OH}{\overset{OH}{}} \quad (\textit{cis} \text{ addition})$$

$$\xrightarrow[\text{H}_2\text{O}_2]{\text{HCO}_2\text{H}} \quad \underset{\text{CH}_3\overset{|}{\text{C}}\text{HCH}_2\text{OH}}{\overset{\text{OH}}{}} \quad \textit{(trans addition)}$$

$$\xrightarrow[\text{RO}\cdot]{\overset{\text{R}^{\ominus}}{}} \quad \underset{-\overset{|}{\text{C}}\text{H}-\text{CH}_2-\overset{|}{\text{C}}\text{H}-\text{CH}_2-\overset{|}{\text{C}}\text{H}-}{\overset{\text{CH}_3 \quad\quad \text{CH}_3 \quad\quad \text{CH}_3}{}} \quad \begin{array}{l}\text{(polymer; none of}\\\text{these reactions works}\\\text{very well for ethene}\\\text{or propene)}\end{array}$$

The reactions shown involve attack by electrophilic reagents at the double bond with the following four exceptions: the metal-induced reaction with H_2; hydrogen bromide with peroxides; and polymerization initiated by radicals, R·, or anions, $Y^{\ominus}$, both of which are difficult to achieve.

Addition of most electrophiles occurs stepwise by way of ionic intermediates (heterolytic bond breaking), with the groups being connected to the carbons in the *trans* manner.

When unsymmetrical electrophilic reagents add to unsymmetrical alkenes, Markownikoff's rule can be used to predict the principal product. Thus, during the addition of HX, the hydrogen goes to that carbon of the double bond that carries the greater number of hydrogens—for example, $CH_3CH= CH_2 + HX \rightarrow CH_3CHXCH_3$. The basis for this rule is the tendency for that part of the electrophile that initiates the reaction ($H^{\oplus}$ from HX) to add in such a way as to produce the lowest-energy carbonium ion. (Tertiary carbonium ions are of lowest energy and primary carbonium ions are of highest energy.) For this reason, the first step of the HX addition is $CH_3CH=CH_2 + H^{\oplus} \rightarrow CH_3\overset{\oplus}{C}HCH_3$, to give the secondary carbonium ion (not $CH_3CH= CH_2 + H^{\oplus} \rightarrow CH_3CH_2CH_2^{\oplus}$ to give the primary carbonium ion); the final step involves addition of $X^{\ominus}$, $CH_3\overset{\oplus}{C}HCH_3 + X^{\ominus} \rightarrow CH_3CHXCH_3$.

The ratios of products in such reactions show that they are governed by the rates of the two possible reaction paths, not by the stabilities of the final products. This is called kinetic control of the reaction as opposed to equilibrium (or thermodynamic) control.

exercises

4·1   Name each of the following substances by the IUPAC system and, if straightforward to do so, as in examples *a* and *e*, as a derivative of ethylene:

a. $(CH_3)_2C=CHCH_3$

b. $Cl_2C=C(CH_3)_2$

c. $(CH_3)_3CCH_2C(CH_3)=CH_2$

d. $(CH_3)_2C=C=CHBr$

e. $[(CH_3)_2CH]_2C=C[CH(CH_3)_2]_2$

f. $(CH_3)_2C\overset{\nearrow \text{CH}}{\underset{\searrow \text{CH}}{\Big\|}}$

g.
$$\underset{\text{HC}\underset{\diagdown \text{CH}}{\diagup}{\overset{\text{C}}{\diagdown \text{CH}_3}}}{\overset{\overset{\displaystyle \text{CH}_3}{|}}{\text{H}_2\text{C}\overset{\diagup \text{CH} \diagdown \text{CH}}{\underset{|}{\Big\|}}}}$$

4·2   Write structural formulas for each of the following substances:

    a.   trifluorochloroethylene   *d.*   1,1-di-(1-cyclohexenyl)-ethene
    b.   1,1-dineopentylethylene   *e.*   trivinylallene
    c.   1,4-hexadiene

4·3   The *trans* alkenes are generally more stable than the *cis* alkenes. Give one or more examples of unsaturated systems where you would expect the *cis* form to be more stable and explain the reason for your choice.

4·4   Write structural formulas for each of the following:

    a.   The thirteen hexene structural isomers; name each by the IUPAC system. Show by suitable formulas which isomers can exist in *cis* and *trans* forms and correctly designate each.
    b.   All *trans*-1,18-di-(2,6,6-trimethyl-1-cyclohexenyl)-3,7,12,16-tetramethyl 1,3,5,7,9,11,13,15,17-octadecanonaene ($C_{40}H_{56}$).

4·5   Calculate, from the data in Table 3·7 and any necessary bond energies, the minimum thermal energy that would be required to break one of the ring carbon-carbon bonds and interconvert *cis*- and *trans*-1,2-dimethylcyclo-butanes (see pp. 67–69).

4·6   What volume of hydrogen gas (STP) is required to hydrogenate 100 g of a mixture of 1-hexene and 2-hexene?

4·7   Supply the structure and a suitable name for the products of the reaction of 2-methyl-2-pentene with each of the following reagents:

    a. H_2, Ni   *d.*   HBr (plus peroxide)
    b. Cl_2 *e.* B_2H_6 followed by aqueous acid
    c. Cl_2 in presence of NH_4F

4·8   How could bromoethane be prepared starting with ethyne?

4·9   Show how each of the following compounds could be prepared starting with 1,5-hexadiene.

    a.   1,2,5,6-tetrabromohexane
    b.   2,5-diiodohexane
    c.   2-iodohexane

4·10   Write the structures of the products of the reaction of 3,4-dimethyl-2-octene with each of the following reagents.

    a.   diborane followed by hydrogen peroxide and base
    b.   dilute aqueous sulfuric acid
    c.   hypobromous acid
    d.   aqueous potassium permanganate
    e.   ozone followed by zinc and steam

4·11   Calculate ΔH (vapor) for addition of fluorine, chlorine, bromine, and iodine to an alkene. What can you conclude from these figures about the kind of problems that might attend practical use of each of the halogens as a reagent to synthesize a 1,2-dihalide?

4·12   *a.*   Write as detailed a mechanism as you can for the *trans* addition of hypochlorous acid (HOCl) to cyclopentene.

      b.   How does the fact that HOCl is a weak acid (K_{HA} in water $= 7 \times 10^{-10}$) make formation of CH_3CH_2OCl from ethene unlikely?

4·13   Calculate ΔH for the addition of water to ethene in the vapor state at 25°. Why are alkenes not hydrated in aqueous sodium hydroxide solutions?

4·14   When *t*-butyl bromide is allowed to stand at room temperature for long periods, the material becomes contaminated with isobutyl bromide. Write a reasonable mechanism for the formation of isobutyl bromide under the influence of traces of water and/or oxygen from the atmosphere.

4·15   Arrange ethene, propene, and 2-methylpropene in order of expected ease of hydration with aqueous acid. Show your reasoning.

4·16   Write two different radical chain mechanisms for addition of hydrogen chloride to alkenes and consider the energetic feasibility for each.

4·17   Calculate the ΔH values for initiation and chain propagation steps of radical addition of hydrogen fluoride, hydrogen chloride, and hydrogen iodide to an alkene. Would you expect these reagents to add easily to double bonds by such a mechanism?

4·18   Bromotrichloromethane, $CBrCl_3$, adds to 1-octene by a radical chain mechanism on heating in the presence of a peroxide catalyst. Use bond energies (Table 2·1) to devise a feasible mechanism for this reaction and work out the most likely structure for the product. Show your reasoning.

4·19   Determine from the general characteristics of additions to double bonds whether the direction of addition of B_2H_6 to propene is consistent with a polar mechanism.

4·20   The following physical properties and analytical data pertain to two isomeric hydrocarbons, A and B, isolated from a gasoline:

	bp	mp	%C	%H
A	68.6°	−141°	85.63	14.34
B	67.9°	−133°	85.63	14.34

Both A and B readily decolorize bromine and permanganate solutions and give the same products on ozonization. Suggest possible structures and configurations for A and B. What experiments would you consider necessary to further establish the structure and configuration of A and B?

4·21   *a.*   Write a mechanism for the sulfuric acid-induced dimerization of trimethylethylene, indicating the products you expect to be formed.

      b.   Ozonization of the mixture that is actually formed gives, among other carbonyl products $\left(-\overset{\overset{\displaystyle O}{\|}}{C}-\right)$, substantial amounts of 2-butanone

$\left(\text{CH}_3-\overset{\overset{\displaystyle O}{\|}}{C}-\text{CH}_2-\text{CH}_3\right)$, Write a structure and reaction mechanism for formation of a C_{10} alkene that might reasonably be formed in the dimerization reaction and that, on ozonization, would yield 2-butanone and a C_6 carbonyl compound. (Consider how sulfuric acid might cause the double bond in trimethylethylene to shift its position.)

4·22 A pure hydrocarbon of formula C_6H_{12} does *not* decolorize bromine water. Draw structures for at least six possible compounds that fit this description (including geometrical isomers, if any).

4·23 Calculate the heats $(-\Delta H)$ of the following reactions in the gas phase at $25°$:

$$\text{H}_2\text{O}_2 + (\text{CH}_2)_2 \longrightarrow \text{HO}-\text{CH}_2-\text{CH}_2-\text{OH}$$
$$\text{H}_2\text{O}_2 + (\text{CH}_2)_6 \longrightarrow \text{HO}-(\text{CH}_2)_6-\text{OH}$$

a. What conclusion as to the rates of the above reactions can be made on the basis of the ΔH values? Explain.
b. What change in the heats of the reactions would be expected if they were carried out in the liquid phase? Why?
c. What agents might be effective in inducing the reactions in the liquid phase? Explain.

4·24 Evaluate (show your reasoning) the possibility that the following reaction will give the indicated product:

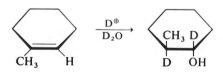

If you do not think the indicated product would be important, write the structure(s) of the product(s) you think most likely to be found.

4·25 Investigate the energetic feasibility of adding ammonia (NH_3) to an alkene by a radical chain mechanism with the aid of a peroxide (ROOR) catalyst. Would such a mechanism give addition in accord with Markownikoff's rule? Why? What practical difficulties might be encountered in attempts to add ammonia to 2-methylpropene with a sulfuric acid catalyst?

4·26 It has been found possible to synthesize two isomeric cycloalkenes of formula C_8H_{14}. Both of these compounds react with hydrogen in the presence of platinum to give cyclooctane, and each, on ozonization followed by reduction, gives

$$\text{H}-\overset{\overset{\displaystyle O}{\|}}{C}-\text{CH}_2-\text{CH}_2-\text{CH}_2-\text{CH}_2-\text{CH}_2-\text{CH}_2-\overset{\overset{\displaystyle O}{\|}}{C}-\text{H}$$

a. What are the structures and configurations of the two compounds?
b. Would the two substances give the same compound on hydroxylation with potassium permanganate?

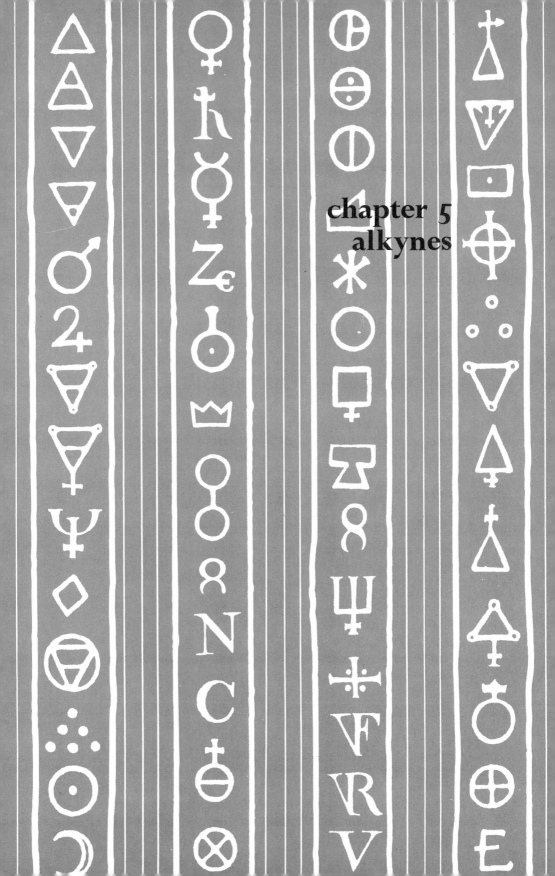

chapter 5
alkynes

Alkynes are hydrocarbons with carbon-carbon triple bonds. The simplest alkyne is ethyne, $H-C\equiv C-H$, usually called acetylene, an important starting material for organic syntheses, especially on an industrial scale. We have previously discussed the geometry of ethyne and its addition reactions with hydrogen and bromine (Section 2·6).

5·1   nomenclature

The IUPAC system for naming alkynes employs the ending *-yne* in place of the *-ane* used for the name of the corresponding, completely saturated, hydrocarbon. Many alkynes are conveniently named as substitution products of acetylene, as shown in parentheses in these examples.

$H-C\equiv C-H$ $CH_3-C\equiv C-CH_3$

ethyne   2-butyne
(acetylene)   (dimethylacetylene)

The numbering system for location of the triple bond and substituent groups is analogous to that used for the corresponding alkenes.

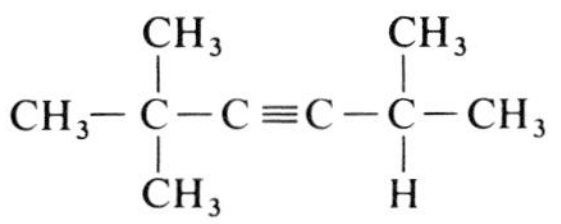

$$
\begin{array}{c}
\quad\;\; CH_3 \quad\;\; CH_3 \\
\quad\;\; | \qquad\;\; | \\
CH_3-\underset{\underset{CH_3}{|}}{C}-C\equiv C-\underset{\underset{H}{|}}{C}-CH_3
\end{array}
$$

2,2,5-trimethyl-3-hexyne
(isopropyl-*t*-butylacetylene)

Open-chain hydrocarbons with more than one triple bond are called alkadiynes, alkatriynes, and so on, according to the number of triple bonds. Hydrocarbons with both double and triple bonds are called alkenynes, alkadienynes, alkendiynes, and so on, also according to the number of double and triple bonds. The order *enyne* (not *ynene*) is used when both double and triple bonds are present:

$HC\equiv C-C\equiv CH$ $H_2C=CH-C\equiv CH$
     butadiyne   butenyne

$HC\equiv C-CH=CH-CH=CH_2$ $HC\equiv C-C\equiv C-CH=CH_2$
     1,3-hexadien-5-yne   1-hexen-3,5-diyne

The hydrocarbon substituents derived from alkynes are called alkynyl groups:

$HC\equiv C-$ $HC\equiv C-CH_2-$
ethynyl   2-propynyl
                          (propargyl)

5·2 physical properties of alkynes

Alkynes generally have physical properties rather similar to the alkenes and alkanes, as can be seen by comparing the boiling points of C_2 and C_6 representatives of these three classes of hydrocarbon:

CH_3-CH_3 $\quad\quad$ $CH_2=CH_2$ $\quad\quad$ $HC\equiv CH$ $\quad\quad$ $CH_3CH_2CH_2CH_2CH_2CH_3$
bp $-88.6°$ $\quad\quad$ bp $-105°$ $\quad\quad$ bp $-84°$ $\quad\quad\quad\quad$ bp $68.7°$

$CH_3CH_2CH_2CH_2CH=CH_2$ $\quad\quad$ $CH_3CH_2CH_2CH_2C\equiv CH$
$\quad\quad$ bp $63.5°$ $\quad\quad\quad\quad\quad\quad$ bp $71.5°$

Alkynes, like other hydrocarbons, are almost completely insoluble in water.

5·3 ethyne

The simplest alkyne, $HC\equiv CH$, is of considerable industrial importance and usually goes by the trivial name *acetylene*, rather than by the systematic name *ethyne*, which will be used here. Ethyne is customarily obtained on a commercial scale by hydrolysis of calcium carbide (CaC_2) or, in low yield, by high-temperature cracking (or partial combustion) of petroleum gases, particularly methane. Calcium carbide is obtained from the reaction of calcium oxide with carbon at about $2000°$:

$$CaO + 3\,C \xrightarrow{\;2000°\;} CaC_2 + CO$$

It is cleaved by water (acting as an acid) to give ethyne and calcium hydroxide:

$$CaC_2 + 2\,H_2O \longrightarrow HC\equiv CH + Ca(OH)_2$$

Ethyne is much less stable with respect to the elements than ethene or ethane:

$HC\equiv CH$ (g) $\longrightarrow$ $2\,C\,(s) +$ $\;H_2\,(g)$ $\quad\quad \Delta H = -54.2$ kcal
$H_2C=CH_2\,(g)$ $\longrightarrow$ $2\,C\,(s) + 2\,H_2\,(g)$ $\quad\quad \Delta H = -12.5$ kcal
$H_3C-CH_3\,(g)$ $\longrightarrow$ $2\,C\,(s) + 3\,H_2\,(g)$ $\quad\quad \Delta H = +20.2$ kcal

An explosive decomposition of ethyne to carbon and hydrogen may occur if the gas is compressed to several hundred pounds per square inch (psi). Even liquid ethyne (bp $-83°$) must be handled with care. Ethyne is not used commercially under substantial pressures unless it is mixed with an inert gas and handled in rugged equipment with the minimum amount of free volume. Large-diameter pipes for transmission of compressed ethyne are often packed with metal rods to cut the free volume. Ethyne for welding is dissolved under

200 psi in acetone ($CH_3-\overset{\overset{\displaystyle O}{\|}}{C}-CH_3$, bp $56.5°$) and contained in cylinders packed with diatomaceous earth.

$\quad$ Flame temperatures of about $2800°$ can be obtained by combustion of ethyne with pure oxygen. It is interesting that ethyne gives higher flame temperatures than ethene or ethane even though ethyne has a substantially lower heat of combustion than these hydrocarbons. The higher temperature of ethyne flames, compared with those of ethene or ethane, is possible despite the smaller molar heat of combustion:

$$C_2H_2\,(g) + \tfrac{5}{2}\,O_2\,(g) \longrightarrow 2\,CO_2\,(g) + H_2O\,(l) \quad \Delta H = -311 \text{ kcal}$$
$$C_2H_4\,(g) + 3\,O_2\,(g) \longrightarrow 2\,CO_2\,(g) + 2\,H_2O\,(l) \quad \Delta H = -337 \text{ kcal}$$
$$C_2H_6\,(g) + \tfrac{7}{2}\,O_2\,(g) \longrightarrow 2\,CO_2\,(g) + 3\,H_2O\,(l) \quad \Delta H = -373 \text{ kcal}$$

This is because the heat capacity of the products is less. Less water is formed and less of the reaction heat is used to bring the combustion products up to the flame temperatures. Alternatively, what this means is more heat liberated per unit volume of stoichiometric hydrocarbon-oxygen mixture. The comparative figures are ethyne, 3.97; ethene, 3.76; and ethane, 3.70 kcal/liter of gas mixture at standard temperature and pressure.

5·4 addition reactions of alkynes

That ethyne (acetylene) undergoes addition reactions with one or two moles of hydrogen or with halogens such as bromine was discussed in Chapter 2. The higher alkynes react similarly as can be illustrated with 4,4-dimethyl-1-pentyne:

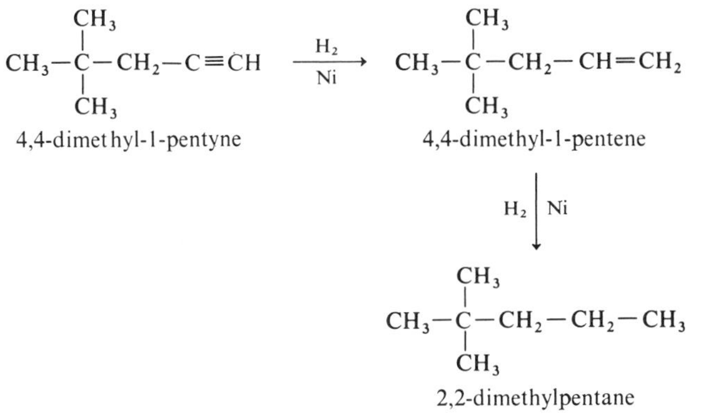

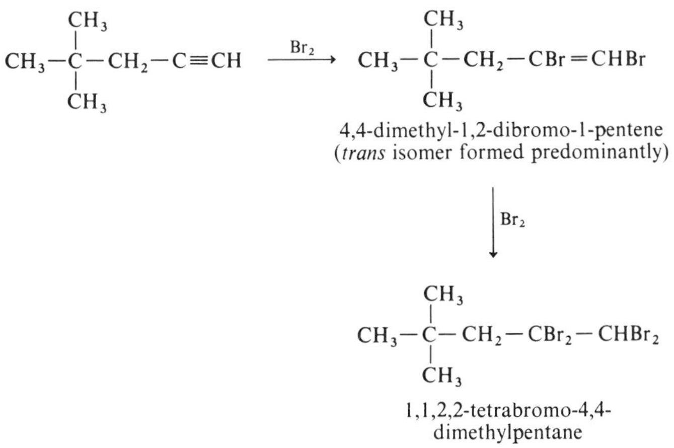

4,4-dimethyl-1-pentyne

4,4-dimethyl-1-pentene

2,2-dimethylpentane

4,4-dimethyl-1,2-dibromo-1-pentene
(*trans* isomer formed predominantly)

1,1,2,2-tetrabromo-4,4-dimethylpentane

Alkynes undergo addition reactions with many other reagents which add to alkenes, particularly those which are electrophilic. The susceptibility of alkenes to electrophilic reagents was explained earlier on the basis of repulsions between the electrons in the double bond (Section 4·4), and you might reasonably expect alkynes, with triple bonds, to be even more susceptible to electrophilic attack. Actually, however, the reaction rates of alkynes with electrophilic reagents are rather less than those of alkenes. Whereas the deep color of liquid bromine is almost instantly discharged when it is added to an alkene, the bromine color persists for a few minutes with most alkynes. Similarly, the addition of water (hydration) to alkynes not only requires the catalytic assistance of acids (as do alkenes), but also mercuric ions:

$$HC{\equiv}CH \ + \ H_2O \ \xrightarrow[\text{HgSO}_4]{\text{H}_2\text{SO}_4} \ \left[CH_2{=}C\begin{smallmatrix}H\\ \\OH\end{smallmatrix} \right] \ \longrightarrow \ CH_3{-}C\begin{smallmatrix}O\\ \\H\end{smallmatrix}$$

vinyl alcohol (unstable)   acetaldehyde

Mercuric, cuprous, and nickel ions are often specific catalysts for reactions of alkynes, perhaps because of their ability to form complexes with triple bonds.

$$R{-}C{\equiv}C{-}R \ + \ Hg^{2\oplus} \ \rightleftarrows \ R{-}C{\overset{\overset{\displaystyle Hg^{2\oplus}}{\uparrow}}{\equiv}}C{-}R$$

The product of addition of one molecule of water to ethyne is unstable and rearranges to a carbonyl compound, acetaldehyde. With an alkyl-substituted ethyne, addition of water always occurs in accord with Markownikoff's rule:

$$CH_3{-}C{\equiv}CH \ + \ H_2O \ \xrightarrow[\text{HgSO}_4]{\text{H}_2\text{SO}_4} \ \left[CH_3{-}\overset{\overset{\displaystyle OH}{|}}{C}{=}CH_2 \right] \ \longrightarrow \ CH_3{-}\overset{\overset{\displaystyle O}{\|}}{C}{-}CH_3$$

propyne   acetone

Alkynes react with potassium permanganate with formation of manganese dioxide and discharge of the purple color of the permanganate ion just as do alkenes but, again, the reaction is generally not quite as fast with alkynes. Hydrogen halides also add to the triple bond. These additions, like the ones to alkenes, occur in accord with Markownikoff's rule:

$$HC{\equiv}CH \ \xrightarrow{\text{HF}} \ H_2C{=}CHF \ \xrightarrow{\text{HF}} \ CH_3{-}CHF_2$$

fluoroethene   1,1-difluoroethane
(vinyl fluoride)

Ethyne dimerizes under the influence of aqueous cuprous ammonium chloride. This reaction is formally analogous to the dimerization of 2-methyl-propene under the influence of sulfuric acid (see Section 4·4H), but the details of the reaction mechanism are not known:

$$2 \ HC{\equiv}CH \xrightarrow{Cu(NH_3)_2{}^{\oplus}Cl^{\ominus}} \underset{H}{\overset{H \quad H}{C{=}C{-}C{\equiv}CH}}$$

butenyne
(vinylacetylene)

Alkynes, like alkenes, react with boron hydrides by addition of B—H across the carbon-carbon triple bond (Section 4·4F) and give vinylboranes:

$$CH_3CH_2{-}C{\equiv}C{-}H \ + \ BH_3 \longrightarrow \underset{H \qquad BH_2}{\overset{CH_3CH_2 \quad H}{C{=}C}}$$

(a vinylborane)

Vinylboranes react readily with acetic acid under mild conditions to give alkenes. The overall process is quite stereospecific, for a disubstituted alkyne gives only a *cis* alkene. Evidently the boron hydride adds in a *cis* manner to the triple bond, and the vinylborane produced then reacts with acid to give the corresponding *cis* alkene.

3-hexyne   90% *cis*-3-hexene

Whereas nucleophilic reagents do not generally add to alkenes, they add readily to alkynes, particularly to conjugated diynes and triynes. For example, 1,3-butadiyne adds methanol in the presence of a basic catalyst such as sodium hydroxide. The mechanism of this type of reaction resembles the

$$HC{\equiv}C{-}C{\equiv}CH + CH_3OH \xrightarrow{NaOH} CH_3OCH{=}CH{-}C{\equiv}CH$$

1,3-butadiyne   1-methoxy-1-buten-3-yne

ionic addition reactions discussed previously (Section 4·4A) except that the initial step involves attack of the nucleophile ($CH_3O^{\ominus}$) on a terminal carbon to form a carbanion intermediate. The nucleophile is initially formed by the reaction of methanol with the basic catalyst. The carbanion intermediate is a

$$CH_3OH + NaOH \rightleftharpoons CH_3O^{\ominus}Na^{\oplus} + H_2O$$

$$CH_3O^{\ominus} + HC{\equiv}C{-}C{\equiv}CH \longrightarrow CH_3O{-}CH{=}\overset{\ominus}{\underset{..}{C}}{-}C{\equiv}CH$$

very strong base and reacts rapidly with methanol to remove a proton and reform the nucleophile, $CH_3O^{\ominus}$, and generate the product, 1-methoxy-1-buten-3-yne.

$$CH_3O{-}CH{=}\overset{\ominus}{\underset{..}{C}}{-}C{\equiv}CH + CH_3OH \longrightarrow CH_3OCH{=}CH{-}C{\equiv}CH + CH_3O^{\ominus}$$

5·5 alkynes as acids

A characteristic and synthetically important reaction of 1-alkynes is salt (or "alkynide") formation with very strong bases. Calcium carbide, CaC_2, can be regarded as the calcium salt of ethyne with both hydrogens removed, $Ca^{2\oplus}\left(\overset{\ominus}{C}\equiv\overset{\ominus}{C}\right)$. Thus, the alkynes behave as acids in the sense that they give up protons to suitably strong bases:

$$R-C\equiv C{:}H + \overset{\oplus}{K}{:}\overset{\ominus}{N}H_2 \underset{\text{liquid}}{\overset{\text{liquid}}{\rightleftharpoons}} R-C\equiv \overset{\ominus}{C}{:}\overset{\oplus}{K} + {:}NH_3$$

R = H or alkyl   a potassium alkynide

Alkynes are much less acidic than water. In other words, water is much too weakly basic to accept protons from 1-alkynes; consequently, even if alkynes were soluble in water, no measurable hydrogen-ion concentration would be expected from the ionization of 1-alkynes in dilute aqueous solutions. However, 1-alkynes are roughly 10^{13} times more acidic than ammonia, and alkynide salts are readily formed from 1-alkynes and metal amides in liquid ammonia.

Alkynes are at least 10^{18} times more acidic than ethene or ethane. The high acidity of ethyne and 1-alkynes relative to other hydrocarbons can be simply explained in terms of lower repulsion between the electron pair of the C—H bond of 1-alkynes and the other carbon electrons. In the triple bond, three pairs of bonding electrons are constrained to orbitals between the two carbon nuclei. As a result, they are, on the average, farther away from the C—H electron pair than are the C—C electrons from the C—H electron pairs in alkenes or alkanes.

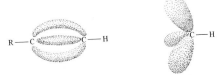

Consequently, less electron repulsion is expected for the C—H electron pair of a 1-alkyne: the less the electron repulsion, the more closely the C—H electrons will be held to the carbon nucleus; and the more strongly they are held to carbon, the more easily the hydrogen can be removed as a proton by a base. By this reasoning, 1-alkynes are expected to be stronger acids than alkenes or alkanes. It should be clear from this discussion that the ability of an atom to attract bonding electrons—its electronegativity (Section 1·2)—will depend on whether it is singly, doubly, or triply bonded. For carbon, a triply bonded atom will have the highest electronegativity, and a saturated carbon the lowest.

In terms of degree, the very much larger acidity of alkynes, compared with alkanes, is easily understood if you remember that electrostatic forces depend upon the inverse square of the distance. A small displacement of electrons will cause a very large electrostatic effect at the short distances which correspond to atomic diameters.

A simple and useful chemical test for a 1-alkyne is provided by its reaction with silver ammonia solution. Alkynes with a terminal triple bond give solid silver salts, while disubstituted alkynes do not react:

$$R-C\equiv C-H \ + \ \overset{\oplus}{Ag}(NH_3)_2 \ \longrightarrow \ R-C\equiv C-Ag(s) \ + \ NH_3 \ + \ \overset{\oplus}{NH_4}$$

$(R = H \text{ or alkyl})$ silver alkynide

The silver alkynides appear to have substantially covalent carbon-metal bonds and are not true salts like calcium, sodium, and potassium alkynides. Silver ammonia solutions may be used to precipitate terminal alkynes from mixtures with disubstituted alkynes. The monosubstituted alkynes are easily regenerated from the silver precipitates by treatment with mineral acids or sodium cyanide:

$$R-C\equiv C-Ag \ + \ NaCN \ + \ H_2O \ \longrightarrow \ R-C\equiv C-H \ + \ NaOH \ + \ AgCN(s)$$

It should be noted that dry silver alkynides may be quite shock sensitive and can decompose explosively.

5·6 synthesis of organic compounds

In this chapter we have described the chemistry of one of the important reactive groups (or "*functional groups*") in organic chemistry, the carbon-carbon triple bond. The previous chapter covered another important functional group, the carbon-carbon double bond. The numerous reactions of these groups are part of the complex web of reactions that allows us to convert one compound to another, often to one which has a quite different structure, by utilizing a number of reactions in sequence. Choosing the best route to convert compound A to compound Z is the forte of the synthetic organic chemist and, when he combines a high degree of intellectual skill in sifting through the many possible reactions with a high degree of skill in the laboratory, his work can fairly be described as both elegant and creative.

The purposes of syntheses are widely divergent: Thus one might desire to confirm by synthesis the structure of a naturally occurring substance, and at the same time, develop routes whereby analogs of it could be prepared for comparisons of chemical and physiological properties. Another aim might be to make available previously unreported substances that would be expected on theoretical grounds to have unusual characteristics because of abnormal steric or electronic effects, for example, the following compounds:

$\begin{array}{c} \text{C(CH}_3)_3 \\ | \\ \text{(CH}_3)_3\text{C}-\text{C}-\text{C(CH}_3)_3 \\ | \\ \text{C(CH}_3)_3 \end{array}$	$\begin{array}{c} \text{C}\equiv\text{C} \\ \diagdown \ \diagup \\ \text{CH}_2 \end{array}$	C(CN)_4	tetrahedrane

tetra-*t*-butylmethane   cyclopropyne   tetracyanomethane

Much research is also done to develop or improve processes for synthesizing commercially important compounds: in such work, economic considerations are obviously paramount.

Regardless of why a compound is synthesized, the goal is to make it from available starting materials as efficiently and economically as possible. Naturally, what is efficient and economical in a laboratory-scale synthesis may be wholly impractical in industrial production; and, while we shall emphasize laboratory methods, we shall also indicate industrial practices in connection with the preparation of many commercially important substances.

An essential difference between industrial and laboratory methods is that the most efficient industrial process is frequently a completely continuous process, in which starting materials flow continuously into a reactor and products flow continuously out. By contrast, research in a laboratory is usually unconcerned with sustained production of any single substance, and laboratory preparations are therefore normally carried out in batches. Another difference concerns by-products. In laboratory syntheses, a by-product such as the sulfuric acid used to hydrate an alkene is easily disposed of. But, on an industrial scale, the problem of disposal or recovery of millions of pounds per year of spent impure acid might well preclude use of an otherwise satisfactory synthesis.

We believe that it is important in writing out projected syntheses to specify reagents and reaction conditions as closely as possible because different sets of products are sometimes formed from the same mixture of reagents, depending upon the solvent, temperature, and so on. The addition of hydrogen bromide to alkenes (Section 4·4E) provides a cogent example of how a change in conditions can change the course of a reaction.

Most syntheses involve more than one step—indeed, in the preparation of complex natural products, it is not uncommon to have 30 or more separate steps. The planning of such syntheses can be a real exercise in logistics. The reason is that the overall yield is the product of the yields in the separate steps; thus, if each of any three steps in a 30-step synthesis gives only 20% of the desired product, the overall yield is limited to $(0.20)^3 \times 100 = 0.8\%$ even if all the other yields are 100%. If 90% yields could be achieved in each step, the overall yield would still be only $(0.90)^{30} \times 100 = 4\%$. Obviously in a situation of this kind, one should plan to encounter the reactions that have the least likelihood of succeeding in the earliest possible stages of the syntheses.

In planning multistep syntheses, you must have a knowledge of how compounds are formed and how they react. For example, if asked to convert compound A to compound C, one would quickly check the reactions of compounds of type A and the preparations of the compounds of type C to see if any of them coincide. If they do not, the next step is to see if there is a compound B that can be prepared from A which could itself give C. In this, one is guided by the changes, if any, that are required in the carbon skeleton. Some simple examples are shown.

Possible starting materials:

$$HC{\equiv}CH \qquad CH_3{-}\underset{\underset{\displaystyle CH_3}{|}}{CH}{-}C{\equiv}C{-}H \qquad \text{any inorganic reagents}$$

Desired products:

$$CH_3-CH_2-CH_2-CH_3 \qquad \underset{\underset{CH_3}{|}}{CH_3-CH-CH_2-CH_2Br} \qquad \underset{\underset{CH_3}{|}\quad\underset{Br}{|}}{CH_3-CH-C=CH_2}$$

A quick glance at the carbon skeletons of the starting materials and the desired products shows that the product listed first, butane, has a different carbon skeleton than that of either of the possible organic starting materials but that the other two, 1-bromo-3-methylbutane and 2-bromo-3-methyl-1-butene, have the same skeleton as one of the possible starting materials, 3-methyl-1-butyne. Let us then begin with an example where no change in carbon skeleton is necessary and try to think of reactions which will in one step convert 3-methyl-1-butyne to the desired products.

In going back over the previously discussed addition reactions, we note that addition of hydrogen bromide to a triple bond gives a bromoalkene (Section 4·4). Furthermore, if this addition occurs in the Markownikoff manner, the third product would be obtained in one step:

$$\underset{\underset{CH_3}{|}}{CH_3-CH-C\equiv CH} \;+\; HBr \xrightarrow{\text{dark}} \underset{\underset{CH_3}{|}\quad\underset{Br}{|}}{CH_3-CH-C=CH_2}$$

With regard to the second desired product, the bromoalkane, there is no reaction that we have thus far encountered (nor does one exist) that will convert a triple bond to this arrangement in one step. Alkenes, however, can be made by the catalytic hydrogenation of alkynes and one could thus convert the alkyne to the desired product by the following route:

$$\underset{\underset{CH_3}{|}}{CH_3-CH-C\equiv CH} \xrightarrow[\text{Ni}]{H_2} \underset{\underset{CH_3}{|}}{CH_3-CH-CH=CH_2} \xrightarrow[\text{peroxides}]{HBr} \underset{\underset{CH_3}{|}}{CH_3-CH-CH_2-CH_2-Br}$$

The other desired product, butane, requires a change in the carbon skeleton. The only such synthetic reaction that we have thus far encountered is the dimerization of ethyne under the influence of cuprous ion. Thus, butenyne can be made from ethyne and this, when hydrogenated, gives butane:

$$2\,HC\equiv CH \xrightarrow{Cu(NH_3)_2^{\oplus}} CH_2=CH-C\equiv CH \xrightarrow[\text{Ni}]{3\,H_2} CH_3-CH_2-CH_2-CH_3$$

Each of the reactions used in the above syntheses gives reasonably high yields of products so that troublesome separation of isomers is not necessary. We have met one reaction thus far which is *not* specific and which usually leads to the production of isomeric mixtures—the halogenation of alkanes. If we had included 2-methylbutane in the list of available starting materials for the above syntheses one might have been tempted to try to prepare 1-bromo-3-methylbutane by light-catalyzed bromination because the carbon skeletons of these two compounds are the same:

$$\underset{\underset{CH_3}{|}}{CH_3-CH-CH_2-CH_3} \;+\; Br_2 \xrightarrow{h\nu} \underset{\underset{CH_3}{|}}{CH_3-CH-CH_2-CH_2Br} \;+\; HBr$$

Unfortunately, there is no way to ensure that substitution will occur at the desired place in the alkane. Indeed, you can be sure that a mixture of bromoalkanes will be produced with the principal product being $CH_3 - \overset{\overset{\displaystyle CH_3}{\displaystyle |}}{\underset{\underset{\displaystyle Br}{\displaystyle |}}{C}} - CH_2 - CH_3$, resulting from substitution at the tertiary carbon atom. Thus, it is important to consider the practicality of synthetic schemes that you devise. The extremely important matters of identification and purification of products are considered in Chapter 7.

It should be clear that a reaction of one type of compound may well be a method of preparation of another. So far, we have considered the reactions of alkanes, alkenes, and alkynes and have not listed separately their methods of preparation. There are two reasons for this. First, some of these compounds, particularly alkanes, can be obtained quite pure by careful fractionation of petroleum and we would seldom need to prepare them in the laboratory. Second, and more important, we have as yet encountered only a few of the many functional groups which can efficiently be converted to alkanes, alkenes, and alkynes. However, when we discuss a new functional group we shall list for purposes of convenience the common preparative methods that lead to it even though they may involve reactions or types of compounds to be described later in the book.

In the interest of completeness, some useful methods of forming carbon-carbon single, double, and triple bonds are summarized below.

C—C bonds:
  Addition, as of hydrogen to C=C or C≡C bonds (Sections 4·4, 5·4)
C=C bonds:
  a. Dehydration of alcohols (Section 10·5B)
  b. Elimination of hydrogen halides from haloalkanes and related compounds (Sections 8·12, 8·13)
  c. Partial additions, such as catalytic hydrogenation, to C≡C bonds (Section 5·4)
C≡C bonds:
  a. Elimination of two moles of hydrogen halide from 1,2-dihaloalkanes (Section 9·5)
  b. Elimination of one mole of hydrogen halide from haloalkenes (Section 9·5)

summary

Alkynes possess carbon-carbon triple bonds. Simple open-chain alkynes have the formula C_nH_{2n-2} and, in the IUPAC system, are named the same way as alkenes except that the -*ene* ending becomes -*yne*. Ethyne, HC≡CH, is usually called acetylene. The physical properties of alkynes, alkenes, and alkanes are similar. Chemically, alkynes resemble alkenes in undergoing addition reactions with electrophilic reagents although they do not usually react as rapidly as alkenes. However, they will undergo additions with nucleophilic reagents more readily than alkenes. Several typical addition reactions of alkynes are illustrated with propyne as an example.   The final reaction produces *cis* alkenes when nonterminal triple bonds are reduced.

$$CH_3C\equiv CH \xrightarrow[\text{Ni}]{H_2} CH_3CH=CH_2$$

Ethyne can be dimerized to butenyne (vinylacetylene) by the action of ammoniacal cuprous ion:

$$2\ HC\equiv CH \xrightarrow{Cu(NH_3)_2{}^\oplus} CH_2=CH-C\equiv CH$$

1-Alkynes are feebly acidic and can be converted to anions (alkynide ions) by the action of powerful bases.

$$RC\equiv CH + NH_2{}^\ominus \longrightarrow RC\equiv C^\ominus + NH_3$$

Insoluble silver salts are produced by the action of ammoniacal silver ion on 1-alkynes and this is a useful means of detecting terminal triple bonds.

Some of the principles of organic synthesis have been discussed with the aid of several specific examples.

exercises

5·1   Name each of the following substances by the IUPAC system and as a substituted acetylene.

a. $CH_3C\equiv CCl$

b. $(CH_3)_3CC\equiv CCH_2C(CH_3)_3$

c. $CH_2=CHCH_2C\equiv CCH=CH_2$

d. $HC\equiv CCH_2C\equiv C-C(CH_3)=CH_2$

e.

f. $(CH_2)_8 \overset{C}{\underset{C}{\Vert}}$

5·2 Write structural formulas for each of the following, showing possible geometrical isomers:

    a. 1,2-dibromocyclopropane
    b. 2,4-hexadiene
    c. cyclooctyne
    d. dibromoethyne
    e. 1,5-hexadien-3-yne

5·3 Calculate ΔH values from the bond-energy table in Chapter 2 for the following reactions in the vapor state at 25°:

    a. $HC\equiv CH + Br_2 \longrightarrow CHBr=CHBr$
    b. $CHBr=CHBr + Br_2 \longrightarrow CHBr_2-CHBr_2$
    c. $HC\equiv CH + H_2O \longrightarrow CH_2=CHOH$

    d. $CH_2=CHOH \longrightarrow CH_3C\overset{\displaystyle O}{\underset{\displaystyle H}{\big\|}}$

    e. $2\,HC\equiv CH \longrightarrow H_2C=CH-C\equiv CH$
    f. $CH_3-C\equiv C-H \longrightarrow CH_2=C=CH_2$
    g. Calculate also a ΔH for reaction f from the experimental ΔH values for the following reactions:

$$CH_3C\equiv CH + 2\,H_2 \longrightarrow CH_3CH_2CH_3 \qquad \Delta H = -69.7\,\text{kcal}$$
$$CH_2=C=CH_2 + 2\,H_2 \longrightarrow CH_3CH_2CH_3 \quad \Delta H = -71.3\,\text{kcal}$$

Explain why the value of ΔH calculated from bond energies might be unreliable for the last reaction.

5·4 Ethyne has an acid ionization constant (K_{HA}) of $\sim 10^{-20}$ in water.

    a. Calculate the concentration of ethynide ion expected to be present in 1 M solution of aqueous potassium hydroxide that is $10^{-4}M$ in ethyne (assuming ideal solutions).
    b. Outline a practical method (or methods) that you think might be suitable to determine an approximate experimental value of K_{HA} for ethynes, remembering that water has a K_{HA} of about 10^{-16}.
    c. Would you expect $H-C\equiv N$ to be a stronger acid than $H-C\equiv C-H$? Why?

5·5 Suppose you were given four unlabeled bottles, each of which is known to contain one of the following compounds: *n*-pentane, 1-pentene, 2-pentyne, and 1-pentyne. Explain how you could use simple chemical tests (preferably test tube reactions that produce visible effects) to identify the contents of each bottle. (Note that all four compounds are low-boiling liquids.)

5·6 How would you distinguish between the compounds in each of the following pairs using chemical methods (preferably test tube reactions).

    a. $CH_3CH_2C\equiv CH$ and $CH_3C\equiv CCH_3$
    b. $CH_3CH_2C\equiv CH$ and $CH_2=CH-CH=CH_2$
    c. $C_6H_5C\equiv CC_6H_5$ and $C_6H_5CH_2CH_2C_6H_5$

5·7 Write balanced equations for the reaction of 3,3-dimethyl-1-butyne with each of the following reagents and, in the first three cases, name the product.

    a. H$_2$ (two moles), Ni   *c.* Cl$_2$ (one mole)
    b. HCl (two moles)   *d.* H$_2$O, H$^\oplus$, Hg$^{2\oplus}$

5·8   Show how each of the following compounds could be synthesized from the indicated starting material and appropriate inorganic reagents. Specify the reaction conditions, mention important side reactions, and justify the practicality of any isomer separations.

                 Cl
                 |
    a. CH$_2$=CH$-$C=CH$_2$ from ethyne (the product is an intermediate in the synthesis of the artificial rubber, neoprene)
    b. CH$_3$CHFCH$_2$Br from propyne
    c. CH$_3$CH$_2$COCH$_3$ from 1-butyne

          CH$_3$ CH$_3$
            \\   /
    d.   C=C   from 2-butyne
         /   \\
       H   H

        CH$_3$CH$_2$ H   from 1-butyne and
            \\   /   deuteroacetic acid
    e.   C=C   (CH$_3$CO$_2$D)
         /   \\
       H   D

5·9   Starting with ethyne, 3-methyl-1-butyne, and any inorganic reagents (the same starting materials used in the examples on pp. 118–119) show how you could prepare the following compounds.

             CH$_3$
             |
    a. CH$_3$$-CH-$CHBr$-CH_3$

             CH$_3$
             |
    b. CH$_3$$-CH-CCl_2$$-CH_2$Cl

             CH$_3$ O
             | ||
    c. CH$_3$$-CH-C-CH_3$
    d. CH$_3$CH$_2$CHOHCH$_3$

5·10   When 0.100 g of an unsaturated hydrocarbon was treated with an excess of hydrogen in the presence of a platinum catalyst, 90.6 ml of hydrogen was absorbed at atmospheric pressure and 25°. Furthermore, the compound gave a precipitate with ammoniacal silver nitrate. What is its structural formula?

5·11   Indicate how you would synthesize each of the following compounds from any one of the given organic starting materials and inorganic reagents. Specify reagents and the reaction conditions, and justify the practicality of any isomer separations. If separations are not readily possible, estimate the proportion of the desired compound in the final product. Starting materials: ethene, propene, isobutane, 2-methylpropene.

            CH$_3$
            |
    a. CH$_3$$-C-CH_3$
            |
           OH

b. $CH_3-\underset{\underset{F}{|}}{\overset{\overset{CH_3}{|}}{C}}-CH_3$

c. $\underset{\underset{OH}{|}}{CH_3CH}-\underset{\underset{Br}{|}}{CH_2}$

d. $CH_3-\underset{\underset{CH_3}{|}}{\overset{\overset{CH_3}{|}}{C}}-CH_2-\underset{\underset{I}{|}}{\overset{\overset{CH_3}{|}}{C}}-CH_3$

e. $CH_3-\underset{\underset{H}{|}}{\overset{\overset{CH_3}{|}}{C}}-CH_2Br$

f. $ClCH_2-\underset{\underset{CH_3}{|}}{\overset{\overset{CH_3}{|}}{C}}-CH_2-\underset{\overset{CH_3}{|}}{CH}-CH_3$

g. $CH_3-CH_2-CH_2OH$

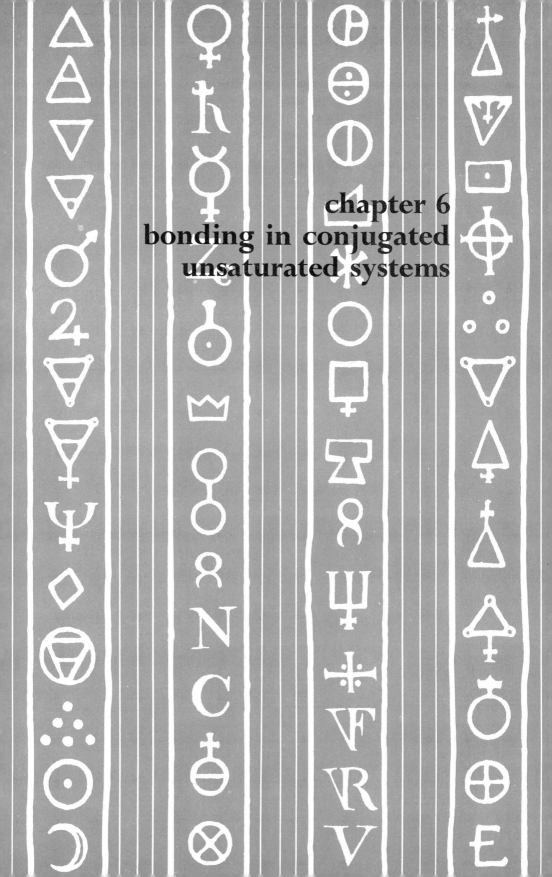

chapter 6
bonding in conjugated
unsaturated systems

The nomenclature of alkenes, including those with more than one carbon-carbon double bond, was discussed in Chapter 4. The compounds with two double bonds separated by just one single bond were categorized as *conjugated* dienes; those with double bonds separated by more than one single bond, as *isolated* dienes. Dienes with isolated double bonds have properties similar to those of simple alkenes except that there are two reactive groups instead of one. Thus, 1,5-hexadiene reacts with one mole of bromine to form 5,6-dibromo-1-hexene and with two moles to give 1,2,5,6-tetrabromohexane.

$$CH_2{=}CH{-}CH_2{-}CH_2{-}CH{=}CH_2 \xrightarrow{Br_2} CH_2{=}CH{-}CH_2{-}CH_2{-}CHBr{-}CH_2Br$$

$$\xrightarrow{Br_2} BrCH_2{-}CHBr{-}CH_2{-}CH_2{-}CHBr{-}CH_2Br$$

Furthermore, the heat of hydrogenation of 1,5-hexadiene is almost exactly double that of the heat of hydrogenation of 1-hexene, indicating the normalcy of each of the double bonds.

On the other hand, 2,4-hexadiene, the conjugated isomer, has properties which indicate that two double bonds are not wholly independent of one another. Addition of one mole of bromine produces a mixture of products.

$$CH_3{-}CH{=}CH{-}CH{=}CH{-}CH_3 + Br_2 \quad\Big\langle$$

$$\overset{\text{Br}\quad\quad\text{Br}}{CH_3{-}CH{-}CH{=}CH{-}CH{-}CH_3}$$
2.5-dibromo-3-hexene   (major product)

$$\overset{\quad\quad\text{Br}\quad\text{Br}}{CH_3{-}CH{=}CH{-}CH{-}CH{-}CH_3}$$
4.5-dibromo-2-hexene   (minor product)

The major product results from addition not to adjacent positions (1,2 addition) but to positions separated by two intervening carbon atoms (1,4 addition, or conjugate addition). Furthermore, hydrogenation of one mole of 2,4-hexadiene liberates about 6 kcal less heat than hydrogenation of one mole of 1,5-hexadiene.

A more striking anomaly is the case of benzene. This compound is a liquid hydrocarbon of formula C_6H_6. It is now known from a variety of experimental studies to be a cyclic molecule in the shape of a flat hexagon. The only way that carbon can preserve a tetravalent bonding arrangement here is by having three double bonds in the ring; for example,

or   (where a carbon and hydrogen atom are understood to be at each corner of the hexagon)

This structure for benzene was advanced in 1865 by August Kekulé, only a few years after his postulate of tetravalent carbon. Those were the years in which enormous strides were made in establishing structural organic chemistry as a sound branch of science. The objections to Kekulé's structure that were soon put forward centered on the lack of reactivity of benzene toward reagents such as bromine. A number of alternative proposals were made in the following five years, of which the structures proposed by Ladenburg, Claus, and Dewar received the most attention. The Ladenburg and Dewar

Ladenburg (1869)   Claus (1867)   Dewar (1867)

formulas will be met again later in the book. The Claus structure is difficult to formulate in modern electronic theory and must be regarded as an attempt to formulate a substance with formula C_6H_6 (no carbon is implied at the center of the ring) with all saturated tetravalent carbons. Actually, another 40 years were to pass before the electron was discovered and an additional 20 before the need would be recognized to identify bonds with pairs of electrons.

Over this period, Kekulé's structure for benzene was generally accepted, despite the dissimilarity between the reactivities of benzene and the alkenes. It was thought that the conjugated arrangement of the bonds must somehow be responsible for its inertness. Whereas the orange color of bromine vanishes instantly when cyclohexene and bromine are mixed, a benzene–bromine mixture remains colored for hours. When the mixture eventually becomes colorless, an examination of the reaction product shows it to be not the addition compound, but a *substitution* compound.[1] Clearly benzene is much more

cyclohexene
(C_6H_{10})

1,2-dibromocyclohexane
($C_6H_{10}Br_2$)

benzene
(C_6H_6)

bromobenzene
(C_6H_5Br)

resistant to addition than cyclohexene, which means that its three conjugated double bonds constitute an unusually stable system for a triene. The stabilization of benzene is further indicated by a 37 kcal/mole lower heat of combustion than calculated for a molecule containing three ordinary double bonds. The heat of combustion of cyclohexene, on the other hand, is quite close to

---

[1] The general formula for a monosubstituted benzene is C_6H_5X. The group $C_6H_5—$ is known as the **phenyl** group and the hydrocarbon $C_6H_5CH=CH_2$ is by the IUPAC system phenylethene, although commonly called styrene.

that calculated using the standard table of bond energies (Table 2·1). The

$$\text{C}_6\text{H}_6 + \frac{15}{2} \text{O}_2 \longrightarrow 6 \text{CO}_2 + 3 \text{H}_2\text{O} \qquad \begin{aligned} \Delta H_{\text{exp}} &= -759.1 \text{ kcal} \\ \Delta H_{\text{calc}} &= -796.5 \text{ kcal} \end{aligned} \qquad \begin{aligned} &37 \text{ kcal} \\ &\text{difference} \end{aligned}$$

$$\text{C}_6\text{H}_{10} + \frac{17}{2} \text{O}_2 \longrightarrow 6 \text{CO}_2 + 5 \text{H}_2\text{O} \qquad \begin{aligned} \Delta H_{\text{exp}} &= -849.6 \text{ kcal} \\ \Delta H_{\text{calc}} &= -851.5 \text{ kcal} \end{aligned} \qquad \begin{aligned} &2 \text{ kcal} \\ &\text{difference} \end{aligned}$$

degree of stabilization of benzene compared to what might be expected for cyclohexene, about 35 kcal/mole, is a large quantity of energy. This is, of course, much larger than the 6 kcal/mole stabilization of 2,4-hexadiene; but even 6 kcal/mole can give rise to important chemical effects because energies are related to equilibrium constants (and, in a crude way, to rate constants) logarithmically (Sections 2·5A and 8·9).

What is the origin of the stabilization associated with these conjugated systems and how does 1,4 addition occur? A qualitative answer to these questions is given in the next two sections.

6·1 bonding in benzene

Formation of an ordinary covalent bond between atoms A and B results in release of energy (stabilization) because the electrons that were localized on A and B can now interact with *two* nuclei instead of *one*:

$$\text{A·} + \text{B·} \longrightarrow \text{A:B}$$

The atomic orbitals on A· and B· occupied by the single electrons are designated by symbols (s, p, d, f) that are relics of the early days of atomic spectroscopy and serve now to indicate energy levels and orbital shapes. For example, s orbitals are spherical and an electron in an s orbital is of lower energy than an electron in a p orbital, which is dumbbell shaped (Figure 6·1).

Quantum theory tells us that only certain total energies are allowed of a system made up of a nucleus and an electron. The diffuse regions of space in which the electrons move are called orbitals, and the system has a specific energy when an orbital is occupied by one electron. An orbital can be described qualitatively by its approximate shape and quantitatively by rather

Figure 6·1   Shapes of s and p orbitals.

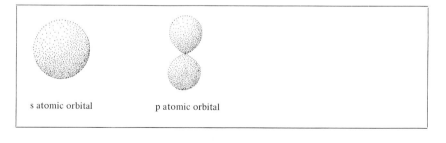

s atomic orbital   p atomic orbital

complex mathematical expressions that give the exact energies when the orbital is occupied by electrons. Because electrons have some of the characteristics of waves, the equations which define the electron distributions and their energies are called **wave equations**. While the equations describing one electron and one nucleus are not unduly complex, no rigorous solutions have so far been possible for molecules as simple as methane.

Chemistry is almost entirely devoted to the study of molecules and, except for the noble gases, it is difficult to obtain a stable system for study of isolated atoms. Thus, elemental carbon exists not as an assemblage of isolated atoms but in the form of diamond or graphite, the atoms of which are covalently bonded together just as tightly as are the carbons in ethane and benzene. It is therefore preferable to direct attention not to orbitals for electrons in atoms but orbitals for electrons in molecules, **molecular orbitals**. There is a stable molecular orbital for each C—H bond in methane; they are all equivalent and point to the corners of a regular tetrahedron.[2] The eight valence electrons of these atoms assume the configuration of lowest energy regardless of the shape of the orbitals occupied by electrons on the isolated atoms. Only two electrons can occupy the same orbital[3] and there will then be two electrons in each of the C—H molecular orbitals. The repulsion between the four pairs of electrons makes the tetrahedral arrangement the one of lowest energy or greatest stability. The resulting bonds are equivalent and those like them in other saturated compounds are often called sp^3 bonds, on the basis of a mathematical analysis of the relations of the molecular orbitals to the orbitals occupied by electrons on atomic carbon.

With carbon-carbon double bonds, a dilemma arises. Should we regard the two bonds as equivalent with both being bent or should we imagine that one of them—the σ (sigma) bond—occupies the prime space along the bond axis and the other—the π (pi) bond—the space above and below the plane defined by the other bonds to the double-bonded carbons? We saw earlier (Section 2·6) that either of these models accounts for the geometry of ethene although the second of these is less straightforward and harder to visualize than the first. However, most theoretical treatments of conjugated systems make use of the idea of clouds of π electrons above and below the σ bond. The popularity of this approach stems to a great extent from the fact that if we ascribe the unusual properties of benzene exclusively to the π electrons, we

[2]Strictly speaking, a molecular orbital describes the interaction of an electron with every nucleus in the molecule. In the case of molecules such as alkanes, however, the pair of electrons in a C—H bond appears to interact almost entirely with the carbon and hydrogen nuclei that make up the bond. To put it in other terms, the electrons in the orbitals of the C—H bonds of methane can be called "*localized*" bonding electrons.

[3]Why only two electrons to an orbital? The reasons are not simple or very intuitively reasonable. That only two electrons can occupy a given orbital is a statement of the Pauli exclusion principle. The basic idea is that only two *nonidentical* electrons can occupy an orbital. How can electrons be nonidentical? By having different spins. For electrons there are only two different possibilities, corresponding to right handed or left handed. Two right-handed electrons or two left-handed electrons cannot occupy the same orbital—only a right-handed and left-handed pair, like the nonidentical pairs of animals allowed on Noah's ark.

Figure 6·2   Diagram of the diradical ·CH$_2$—CH$_2$· with the planes of the CH$_2$ groups set at right angles to one another. Each carbon atom has a p orbital containing one electron.

greatly reduce the number of electrons we have to deal with. We shall make use of this approach (which should be regarded as a matter of convenience and not as revealed truth) in the subsequent discussion. The three σ bonds to carbon in an alkene, often designated sp^2 bonds, are taken to be spread at angles of 120° to one another.

The π bonding in ethene can be thought to arise as follows. Imagine the diradical ·CH$_2$—CH$_2$· with the carbon atoms joined only by a single bond. A reasonable electronic formulation would be the one in which the carbons are **trigonal**, that is to say, the three covalent bonds to each carbon lie in a plane at angles of 120° to one another (the maximum bond angle). The two extra electrons are considered to be placed in dumbbell-shaped p orbitals, one on each carbon atom. If the planes of the two CH$_2$ (methylene) groups are set at right angles to one another, the interaction between the electrons in the p orbitals is minimized (Figure 6·2) because the electrons are as far away from one another as they can be. If the methylene groups are now rotated with respect to one another until the carbons and hydrogens all lie in the same plane, the p orbitals will became parallel to one another (indeed, *overlap* with each other) and interaction between the electrons will be at a maximum. If the electrons have the *same* spin they cannot occupy a molecular orbital made up of the two p atomic orbitals; they repel each other and give an arrangement less stable than the one with the CH$_2$ groups at right angles. The setup with unpaired electrons does not give a stable π bond. On the other hand, if the spins are paired, they form a π bond—both electrons have the same energy, occupy the same region of space (π molecular orbital), and interact with both nuclei (see Figure 6·3).

Benzene can be described by a similar orbital arrangement. Imagine a hexagon of carbon atoms joined by single bonds (σ bonds, localized along each bond axis) with a singly occupied p orbital on each. π-Bond formation between adjacent pairs of p orbitals as in ethene would give a triene (Figure 6·4). The high degree of symmetry in this molecule, however, allows π-bond formation between each carbon and *both* its neighbors. The result is a system where the π electrons are associated with more than two nuclei and can be fairly called delocalized. Association of a pair of electrons with *two nuclei* results in stabilization with formation of a localized bond; association with *more than two nuclei* leads to still greater stabilization and delocalized bonds. The extra degree of stabilization that can be ascribed to delocalized π bonds is

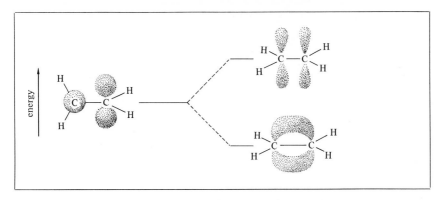

Figure 6·3   The energy levels that result from rotating the CH₂ groups of ·CH₂—CH₂· into the same plane. The lowest energy form, above, is CH₂=CH₂, ethene, with a π bond.

reflected in benzene's inertness to bromine addition and in its low heat of combustion. The stabilization energy, often called delocalization or resonance energy, amounts to more than 30 kcal/mole (the difference between the heat of combustion calculated on the basis of "normal" localized bonds and the experimental heat of combustion).

How should we draw the bonding arrangement in benzene? The following notations are often used to indicate the symmetry of the molecule and the delocalized character of some of the bonds:

It is difficult, however, to determine the number of π electrons by inspection of such structures. Indeed, with some derivatives of benzene one can be seriously misled by such notation (Section 20·1B). A more revealing representation of the structure of benzene is achieved by drawing the following resonance structures:

Figure 6·4   Electron-pairing arrangements for benzene.

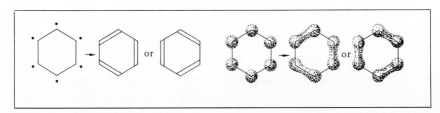

The double-headed arrow bears no relation to the symbol $\rightleftarrows$ used to describe chemical equilibrium. Rather, it indicates the two directions in which π bonds can be formed by showing the separate structures we would write if delocalization were not considered and each pair of electrons was restricted to binding only two nuclei (see Figure 6·4). Because the orbital arrangement permits extensive delocalization, we know that benzene is not the structure represented by either formula but is actually a hybrid which embodies some of the character expected of each and is more stable than either of the structures would be, if each were to correspond to a real substance. For convenience, we draw just one of these structures

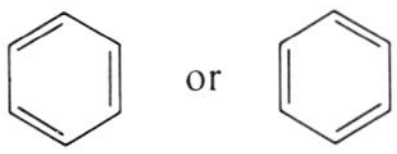

to indicate benzene whenever there is no need to represent the bonding more precisely.

There are many advantages to writing the various possible structures of a delocalized molecule or ion. You can account for all the electrons in a system at a glance and determine whether a given structure is that of a cation, an anion, or a neutral molecule, and whether or not it is a radical. Furthermore, the description is in terms of structures usually with ordinary valences of carbon, oxygen, nitrogen, and so on. This way of describing molecules with delocalized electrons, the **resonance method**, as it is usually called, has been extraordinarily successful at predicting molecular geometries and behavior, notwithstanding its apparent artificiality in using more than one structural formula to describe a single compound and its occasional failures (Section 6·7).

6·2   conjugate addition

How does conjugate addition (1,4 addition; see p. 127) occur? 1,3-Butadiene, a typical conjugated diene, exists in two important planar conformations, the

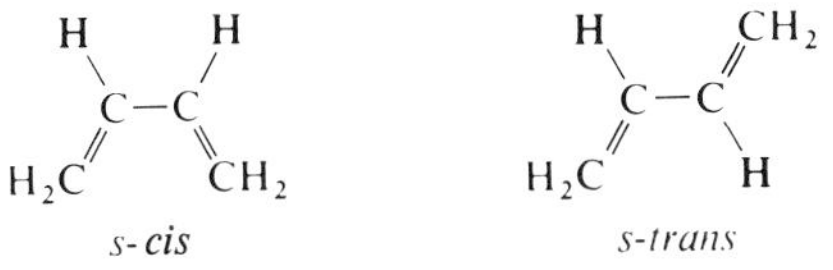

s-cis and the s-trans forms. Although rotation occurs rather rapidly about the central bond, these are the two favored conformations because they permit some degree of π-bond formation across what is normally written as a single carbon-carbon bond.

We have seen that addition of bromine to double bonds can occur by way of ionic intermediates (Section 4·4B). If we examine the bonding in the ion produced by the attack of bromine on a conjugated diene, we can see how conjugate addition takes place with 1,3-butadiene, and that an intermediate bromonium cation can be produced as follows:

$$CH_2{=}CH{-}CH{=}CH_2 \ + \ Br_2 \quad \longrightarrow \quad CH_2{=}CH{-}\overset{\oplus}{CH}{-}CH_2Br \ + \ Br^{\ominus}$$

(In the earlier discussion, the possibility was raised that bridged bromonium ions are intermediates in addition of bromine to alkenes. Such species may also be formed here but do not vitiate the following argument.) Neither the double-bond π electrons nor the cationic charge will be localized as shown above. There will be π bonding between three carbons as indicated by the resonance structures [1]. In accord with these structures, the positive charge will be divided between the 2 and the 4 carbon. The charge will not be expected to be significant on the third carbon from the bromine because any resonance structure which puts the charge there will preclude π-bond formation between *adjacent* carbons. We sometimes speak of the spreading of the charge as "delocalization of the charge." It should, however, be clear from what we have said that delocalization of charge is a consequence of the delocalization of the electrons by π-bond formation between two different pairs of carbons;

$$\underset{4321}{CH_2{=}CH{-}\overset{\oplus}{CH}{-}CH_2Br} \quad \longleftrightarrow \quad \overset{\oplus}{CH_2}{-}CH{=}CH{-}CH_2Br$$

$$[1]$$

that is, delocalization of positive charge and electron delocalization are two sides of the same coin.

Addition of bromide ion can occur at either of the two partially positively charged carbon atoms in ion [1],[4] which accounts for the mixture of products that is, in fact, formed. If initial addition of the $Br^{\oplus}$ ion were to take place at

$$BrCH_2{-}CH{=}CH{-}CH_2Br$$
$$\nearrow$$
$$[CH_2{=}CH{-}\overset{\oplus}{CH}{-}CH_2Br \quad \longleftrightarrow \quad \overset{\oplus}{CH_2}{-}CH{=}CH{-}CH_2Br] \ + \ Br^{\ominus}$$
$$\searrow$$
$$CH_2{=}CH{-}CHBr{-}CH_2Br$$

the 2 position of the diene, the charge would be localized at the 1 position and the π electrons between atoms 3 and 4 so that no resonance stabilization of the carbonium ion intermediate $(CH_2{=}CH{-}CHBr{-}CH_2{}^{\oplus})$ would be expected. On the other hand, the carbonium ion formed by addition of a $Br^{\oplus}$ ion to a terminal position of the diene has a substantial degree of resonance stabilization.

If we could prepare separate ions corresponding to the two localized structures that we have written to represent the hybrid, we would expect them to have similar bond energies and similar arrangements of the atoms in space.

---

[4]Note the singular form *ion*, not *ions*. In the resonance hybrid shown above we have used two structures, each with localized bonding, to represent as nearly as we can the true structure of the single ion which is the reaction intermediate.

The reason for the similar geometries is that the cationic carbons of carbonium ions tend to have their three bonds planar (Section 2·5C), as do alkenic carbon atoms. Thus, delocalized π-bond formation in the hybrid ion [2] can be seen to occur in a completely natural way for the two structures. This is an especially important point to which we will return later. (The ion formed from the s-cis conformation of the diene is shown here.)

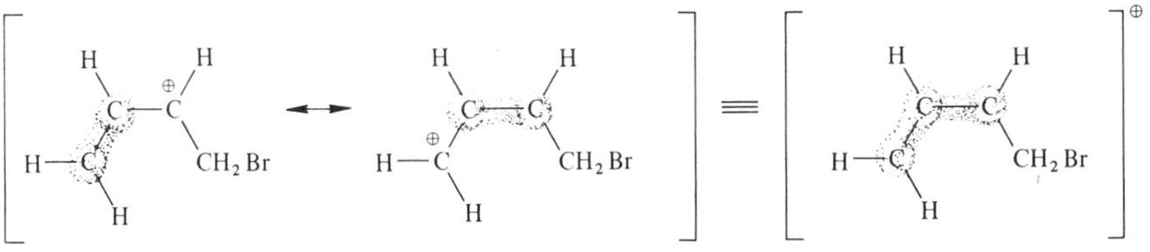

[2]

A cationic carbon atom, such as those depicted in each of the structures making up the hybrid, possesses only a sextet of electrons (the six in the three σ bonds) and hence has an empty p orbital available to interact with the adjacent pair of π electrons. These electrons thus spread over three atoms instead of two, providing a delocalized π bond. The consequence is a more stable system than would be represented by either resonance structure alone. In the next section we shall see that the electron system of 1,3-butadiene, although conjugated, is delocalized to a much smaller extent.

6·3 stabilization of conjugated dienes

The special character of conjugated dienes is manifest in their tendency to undergo 1,4 addition and in their lower heats of combustion. Conjugate addition has been accounted for on the basis of resonance stabilization (and preferential formation) of an intermediate cation which gives rise to the 1,4 product. This reaction does not tell us whether or not resonance stabilization is important in the diene. However, its low heat of combustion can be attributed to resonance in the diene because here we are dealing with the overall stabilization of the diene itself, not of a product to which it may be converted. The stabilization of 1,3-butadiene, as determined by the difference between calculated and experimental heats of combustion, is only about 6 kcal as compared to more than 30 kcal for benzene. Why should this be so? Cannot π electrons of the two adjacent double bonds bind together all of the carbons in the same way as in benzene? Such an orbital arrangement for the s-cis conformation is shown in [3].

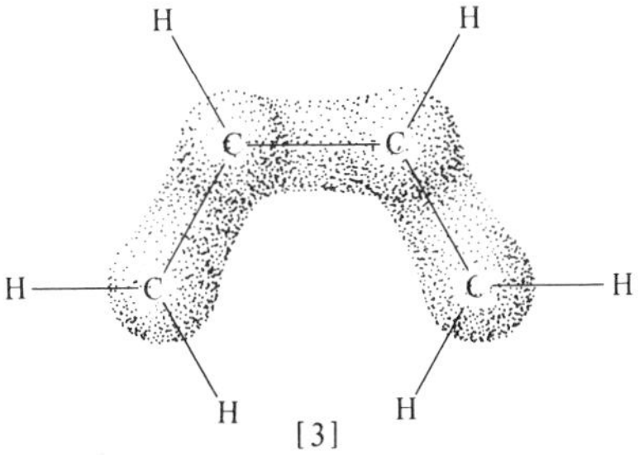

[3]

The reason for the resonance stabilization being small is readily apparent when you compare the possible ways of getting π bonding in butadiene with those for benzene. First, we write the basic structure with four singly occupied p orbitals:

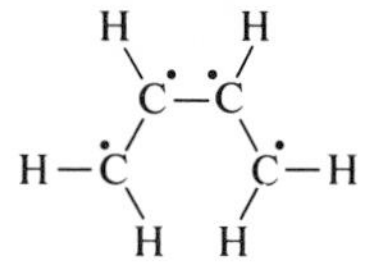

Now we consider π bonds to be made by pairing the electrons two different

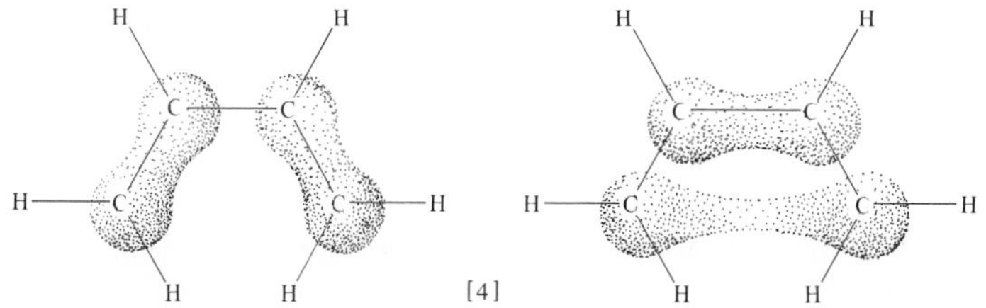

[4]

ways [4]. The first way corresponds to normal double bonds between the 1,2 and 3,4 carbons while the second corresponds to a double bond between the 2,3 carbons but essentially no binding between the 1,4 carbons, which are impossibly far apart to participate in effective binding, even though the 1,4 electrons are paired. Any attempt to increase the stabilization of *s-cis*-butadiene by bringing the 1,4 atoms closer together, thus increasing the 1,4 interaction, would run afoul of increasing angle strain and increasing interaction between the inside 1,4 hydrogens. The 2,3 π bonding does seem to increase the stability of butadiene to some extent. That it does not do more can be ascribed to the fact that 2,3 π bonding is associated with 1,4 "nonbonding."

The above discussion can be rephrased in terms of resonance structures as follows:

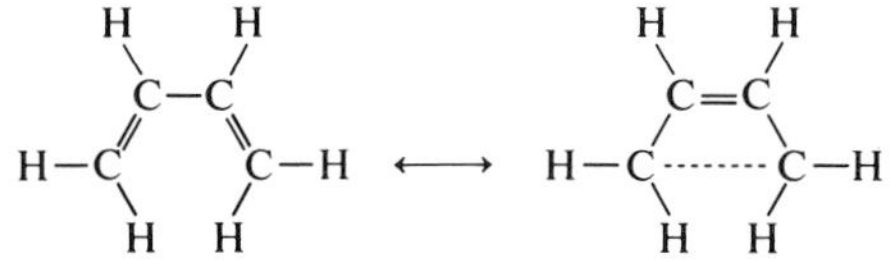

The "1,4 π bonding" is represented in the second structure by a dotted line (sometimes called a *formal bond*) to emphasize that the structure does not represent cyclobutene, which is a stable isomer of butadiene and differs from

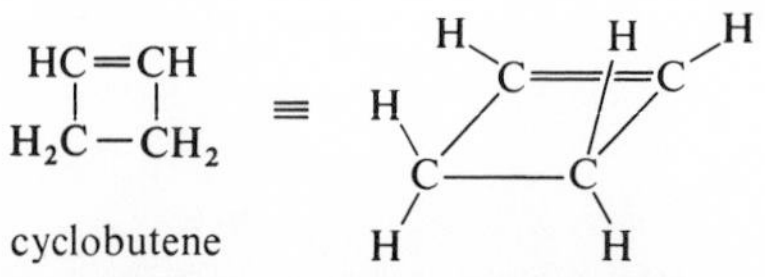

cyclobutene

butadiene in chemical behavior and in the arrangement of its atoms in space. Unlike s-cis or s-trans-butadiene, cyclobutene does not have all its carbons and hydrogens in a single plane. Also unlike butadiene, the bonding between the two methylene (CH_2) carbons results from a σ-type C—C bond of essentially normal length.

We can summarize the above discussion by noting that the resonance method considers the binding which might be produced by pairing electrons in different ways for a *given geometrical arrangement of the atoms*. The predictive power of the resonance method is derived from the fact that for a given arrangement of the atoms, important contributions will be made to the hybrid structure only by those ways of pairing the electrons which correspond to reasonably feasible ball-and-stick models.

The π bonds in the hybrid structure for butadiene can be represented by a combination of heavy and light dotted lines.

No 1,4 bonding is shown because of the large distance between the atoms.

It is important to recognize that each of the resonance structures for 1,3-butadiene (or benzene) has the same number of pairs of electrons. No structures need be considered which have a different number of paired electrons, such as $\dot{C}H_2$—CH=CH—$\dot{C}H_2$, where now the 1,4 electrons are taken to be unpaired (both right handed or both left handed; see Section 6·1). Such structures correspond to a diradical form of butadiene which is known to exist but has entirely different properties and is grossly less stable. It has a π bond only between two adjacent carbons.

6·4 stabilization of cations and anions

You might well ask why we do not consider ionic-type resonance structures for 1,3-butadiene similar to those written for the conjugate addition intermediate in the previous section.

The answer is that in the ionic structures we have substituted ionic bonding for π bonding; and just as $\overset{\oplus}{C}H_2-\overset{\overset{\ominus}{\cdot\cdot}}{C}H_2$ is far from the best structure for $CH_2=CH_2$, so the above ionic structures are less important than the wholly π-bonded $CH_2=CH-CH=CH_2$ structure for butadiene. To put it in another way, carbon is intermediate in electronegativity and has little tendency to attract electrons and become negative or give up electrons and become positive. Thus, the ionic (or dipolar) structures are less favorable than the shared electron structures. The cationic intermediate $CH_2=CH-\overset{\oplus}{C}H-CH_2Br$ $\leftrightarrow \overset{\oplus}{C}H_2-CH=CH_2-CH_2Br$ is different in that there is no way that the charge can disappear by changing the π-bond arrangements. This cation is in fact just one representative of the important class of allyl cations, the parent of which is

$$\overset{\oplus}{C}H_2-CH=CH_2 \longleftrightarrow CH_2=CH-\overset{\oplus}{C}H_2 \equiv [CH_2\text{---}CH\text{---}CH_2]^{\oplus}$$

The allyl cation is a relatively stable carbonium ion as carbonium ions go and we shall meet it again as a reaction intermediate in Chapter 8.

The bicarbonate ion is an example of an anion stabilized by resonance. Sodium bicarbonate, $NaHCO_3$, is a salt whose ionic components are sodium ion ($Na^{\oplus}$) and bicarbonate ion ($HCO_3^{\ominus}$). If you draw a structural formula for bicarbonate ion so that the carbon and oxygen atoms have octets of electrons, you obtain

$$H-O-C\overset{\displaystyle O}{\underset{\displaystyle O^{\ominus}}{\big\langle}} \quad Na^{\oplus}$$

Each of the two oxygens on the right-hand side of this formula for the bicarbonate ion is bonded only to the carbon atom. Their electronic environments appear to be different: one oxygen bears a full negative charge and the other no charge at all. There is, however, another way to arrange the electrons which reverses the roles of the two oxygens and gives additional π bonding. The actual structure is therefore that of a resonance hybrid with half of the negative charge on each of the oxygens.

$$HOC\overset{\displaystyle O}{\underset{\displaystyle O^{\ominus}}{\big\langle}} \longleftrightarrow HOC\overset{\displaystyle O^{\ominus}}{\underset{\displaystyle O}{\big\langle}} \quad or \quad HOC\overset{\displaystyle O^{\frac{1}{2}\ominus}}{\underset{\displaystyle O^{\frac{1}{2}\ominus}}{\big\langle}}$$

Since neither of these formulations is convenient to write, we usually indicate bicarbonate ion with the ambiguous formula $H-O-CO_2^{\ominus}$ or, more simply, $HCO_3^{\ominus}$. Note, however, that only two of the three oxygen atoms in the ion can bear the negative charge. The third is bonded to hydrogen and cannot participate in π bonding to carbon without giving an unfavorable dipolar type of structure:

$$\overset{\oplus}{H}O=C\overset{\displaystyle O^{\ominus}}{\underset{\displaystyle O^{\ominus}}{\big\langle}}$$

The anion of a carboxylic acid as acetic acid $\left(CH_3C \overset{\displaystyle O}{\underset{\displaystyle OH}{\Big\langle}} \right)$ is usually written

$CH_3CO_2{}^{\ominus}$ to avoid the necessity of indicating the dispersal of the negative charge to both oxygen atoms, and the same is done with many inorganic ions such as $NO_3{}^{\ominus}$, $SO_4{}^{2\ominus}$, and $N_3{}^{\ominus}$. It is important, however, to be aware that in any detailed consideration of the properties of these anions, more than one resonance structure must be taken into account.

6·5 vinyl halides and ethers

An anion that falls in the same classification as those mentioned in the previous section is the allyl anion, which can be seen to be structurally analogous to the allyl cation and involves two energetically equivalent resonance structures:

$$CH_2{=}CH{-}\overset{\ominus}{\ddot{C}H_2} \longleftrightarrow \overset{\ominus}{\ddot{C}H_2}{-}CH{=}CH_2 \equiv [CH_2{\cdots}CH{\cdots}CH_2]^{\ominus}$$

allyl anion

For many stable compounds, such as unsaturated ethers and halides, we may write electronic structures formally similar to those of the allyl anion except that there is no net charge:

$$CH_2{=}CH{-}\ddot{\ddot{O}}{-}R \qquad CH_2{=}CH{-}\ddot{\ddot{F}}{:}$$

The problem is whether we should draw resonance structures corresponding to π bonding between carbon and the attached oxygen or halogen:

$$CH_2{=}CH{-}\ddot{\ddot{O}}{-}R \longleftrightarrow \overset{\ominus}{\ddot{C}H_2}{-}CH{=}\overset{\oplus}{\ddot{O}}{-}R$$

$$CH_2{=}CH{-}\ddot{\ddot{F}}{:} \longleftrightarrow \overset{\ominus}{\ddot{C}H_2}{-}CH{=}\overset{\oplus}{\ddot{F}}{:}$$

This is a matter of controversy. Such structures lead to an increase of π bonding but with an associated separation of charge wherein electron-attracting nuclei such as oxygen and fluorine become positive, and weakly electron-attracting atoms become negative. There may be some degree of stabilization connected with resonance of this type but it is small at best. However, what is more certain is that attack of a positive reagent such as $Br^{\oplus}$ on $CH_2{=}CH{-}\ddot{\ddot{O}}R$ will occur at the 2 carbon, not at the 1 carbon, because more π bonding is possible in the resulting cationic intermediate:

$$CH_2{=}CH{-}\ddot{\ddot{O}}R + Br^{\ominus} \Bigg\langle$$

$$Br{-}CH_2{-}\overset{\oplus}{C}H{-}\ddot{\ddot{O}}{-}R \longleftrightarrow Br{-}CH_2{-}CH{=}\overset{\oplus}{O}{-}R$$

π bonding

$$\overset{\oplus}{C}H_2{-}\underset{\underset{\displaystyle Br}{|}}{CH}{-}\ddot{\ddot{O}}{-}R$$

Generally speaking, we should expect that importance of resonance of the type $CH_2{=}CH{-}\overset{..}{\underset{..}{Z}}\overset{\ominus}{} \leftrightarrow \overset{..}{\underset{..}{C}}H_2{-}CH{=}\overset{\oplus}{Z}$ will increase as Z becomes less electronegative and will, therefore, be much more important in $CH_2{=}CH{-}\overset{..}{N}(CH_3)_2$ than in $CH_2{=}CH{-}\overset{..}{\underset{..}{F}}{:}$, and all evidence indicates that this is indeed the case.

6·6 rules for the resonance method

The principles outlined in the previous sections can be reduced to a fairly precise prescription which is generally applicable for evaluating the properties of conjugated systems:

1. All resonance structures must have identical locations of the atoms in space and the same number of paired electrons. Ionic structures should be considered if atoms are present that carry unshared pairs of electrons or unfilled octets, or are substantially different in electronegativity.

2. Relative energies of the various structures are estimated by considering: (a) bond energies; (b) the degree of distortion from the geometrically favorable atomic positions (if the geometry of the actual molecule is known, then the spatial arrangements of all the resonance structures can be taken to conform with it); (c) the maximum number of valence electrons which each atom can accommodate in its outer shell—two for hydrogen and eight for first-row elements (this is particularly important).

3. Electron stabilization is expected to be greatest when structures of lowest energy are equivalent.

4. If there is only a single contributing structure of low energy, then, to a first approximation, the resonance hybrid may be expected to have properties like those predicted for the particular structure.

6·7 molecular orbital method of Hückel

We have seen that the resonance method is a very useful way of describing the behavior of delocalized systems (in which an electron may interact with three or more nuclei) in terms of localized structures (in which each electron interacts with only two nuclei). The success of the resonance method in describing the chemistry of benzene, conjugated dienes, and so on has been indicated in earlier sections of this chapter. For benzene and the intermediate cation formed in the bromine-butadiene reaction, it was shown that bonding involving delocalized electrons could be conceived as arising from electron pairing in three or more p orbitals on adjacent atoms overlapping in the π manner. These representations were designed to try to overcome the principal esthetic defect of the resonance method in that it describes conjugated molecules or ions in terms of two or more structures.

It should be recognized that the resonance method is by no means a unique approach to rationalizing the properties of conjugated molecules, and we now will consider briefly an alternative procedure, molecular orbital (MO) theory. Although this theory has many advantages it is less useful in purely qualitative structure analysis. MO theory was introduced in 1933 by the German chemist E. Hückel as a method to calculate mathematically the relative energies of unsaturated molecules. In the original Hückel treatment, the σ bonds were ignored and only the energies of the π electrons considered. To do this, ethene and 1,3-butadiene were considered to be made up of CH_2-CH_2 and $CH_2-CH-CH-CH_2$ frameworks with singly occupied parallel p orbitals on each carbon atom,

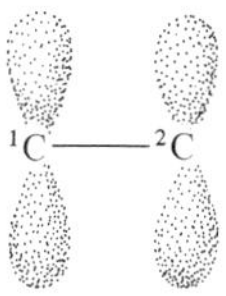

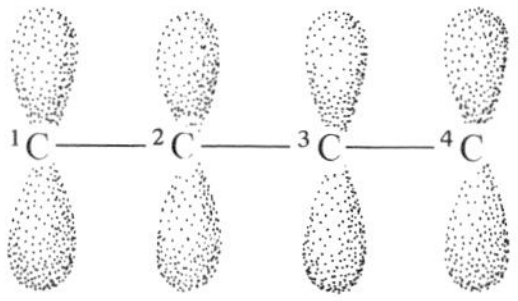

$^1C \underline{\hspace{1.5cm}} ^2C \qquad\qquad ^1C \underline{\hspace{1cm}} ^2C \underline{\hspace{1cm}} ^3C \underline{\hspace{1cm}} ^4C$

Combination of these p atomic orbitals with due regard for sign (positive or negative) gives rise to two molecular orbitals for ethene and four molecular orbitals for the diene. (The number of molecular orbitals is always equal to the number of atomic orbitals in the combinations.) The energy of an electron in each of the molecular orbitals can be calculated, giving us a set of energy levels for the π electrons.

The Hückel MO method can be applied to a wide variety of unsaturated systems.[5] It permits rather simple (though lengthy) calculations to be made of the π-electron energies of localized and delocalized conjugated systems such as benzene. Furthermore, it allows us to see which energy levels contribute to bonding and which do not. If an electron in a molecular orbital has an energy higher than that of an electron in an isolated p orbital, the orbital will, in fact, be **antibonding**. We will see later that antibonding orbitals are especially important in formulating the excited states resulting from absorption of visible or ultraviolet light (Section 26·1).

Hückel-type calculations of molecular orbital energies for the π electrons in ethene and in 1,3-butadiene reveal that they are arranged as in Figure 6·5. The "nonbonding level" is the energy of an electron in an isolated p orbital. In both these molecules, the low-lying levels are fully occupied with electrons having paired spins, as indicated by the symbol $\uparrow\downarrow$.

A disadvantage of using Hückel MO theory in an introductory study of organic chemistry is that both mathematical and artistic skills are required. Furthermore, while drawings in which p orbitals are shown combining together to form π molecular orbitals are useful in many cases (we have already used them for illustration earlier in the chapter), in others they can lead to false conclusions. The following example illustrates this point.

Consider the π-electron systems of 1,3-butadiene and trimethylenemethyl, $(CH_2)_3C$, each of which is C_4H_6 (Figure 6·6). If we arrange each system to give four molecular orbitals into which the four unsaturation electrons are placed, and draw dotted lines between the adjacent p-orbitals, we can see no

[5]J. D. Roberts, *Notes on Molecular Orbital Calculations*, Benjamin, New York, 1961.

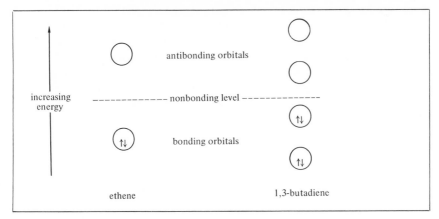

Figure 6·5   Schematic representation of MO energies of ethene and 1,3-butadiene.

reason for any pronounced difference between the two possible arrangements. But inspection of possible electron-pairing schemes (as in the resonance method) leads immediately to the conclusion that butadiene is likely to be very different from trimethylenemethyl. The latter will be a diradical if there is to be an average of one electron per carbon as can be seen from the possible forms that contribute to the resonance hybrid:

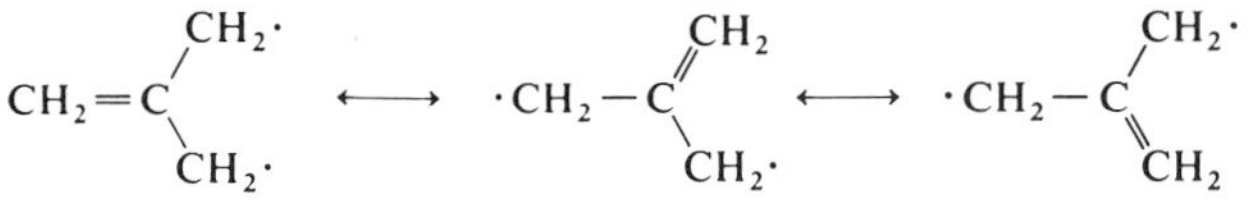

$$
CH_2=C\overset{\displaystyle CH_2\cdot}{\underset{\displaystyle CH_2\cdot}{}} \quad\longleftrightarrow\quad \cdot CH_2-C\overset{\displaystyle CH_2}{\underset{\displaystyle CH_2\cdot}{}} \quad\longleftrightarrow\quad \cdot CH_2-C\overset{\displaystyle CH_2\cdot}{\underset{\displaystyle CH_2}{}}
$$

It should be emphasized that the detailed Hückel MO calculation of energy levels leads to the same conclusion. The four energy levels (there are four p orbitals with which to construct molecular orbitals) are arranged as in Figure 6·7. The two electrons at the nonbonding energy level occupy different orbitals and have unpaired spins because this arrangement minimizes the repulsion between them (Hund's rule). Trimethylenemethyl has been characterized

Figure 6·6   Atomic orbital models of 1,3-butadiene and trimethylenemethyl.

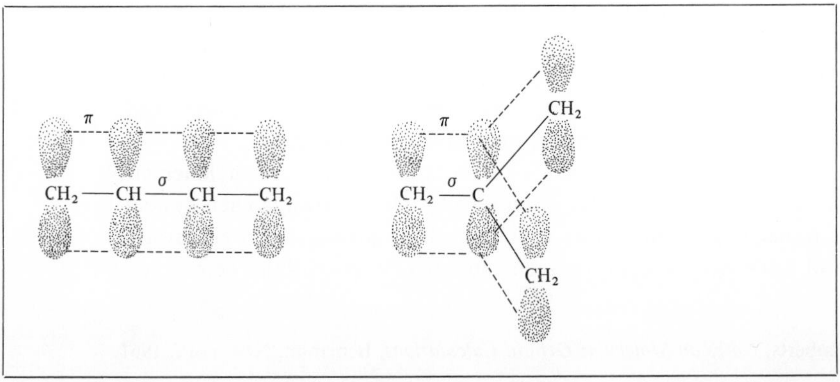

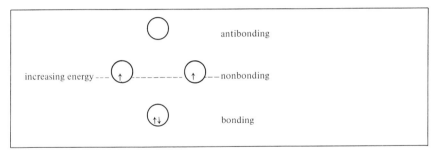

Figure 6·7   Molecular orbitals (energy levels) for trimethylenemethyl, $(CH_2)_3C$.

as a reaction intermediate and found to have the diradical character expected on the basis of the above treatments.

The greatest triumph of the Hückel MO method is in its treatment of conjugated cyclic systems. We can show diagrammatically the result of a calculation of the energy levels in any regular, planar, cyclic conjugated system made up of trigonally bonded carbon atoms such as benzene by simply inscribing a polygon of the appropriate shape within a circle such that one apex of the polygon is directly downward. The center of the circle then represents the nonbonding level and the apexes represent molecular orbital energy levels (Figure 6·8). Note that in the odd-numbered cases, such as the three-, five-, and seven-membered rings, there is a trivalent carbon atom. If you consider the p orbital on this atom, neglecting for the moment any interaction with the neighboring π orbitals, you can see that it may contain 0, 1, or 2 electrons. If the orbital is empty, the species will be a carbonium ion; if it has one electron, the species will be a neutral radical; if it has two electrons, the species will be a carbanion. Using the five-membered ring as an example, the three entities are

Figure 6·8   Energy levels of π molecular orbitals in various conjugated cyclic systems.

3-membered ring	4-membered ring	5-membered ring	6-membered ring	7-membered ring

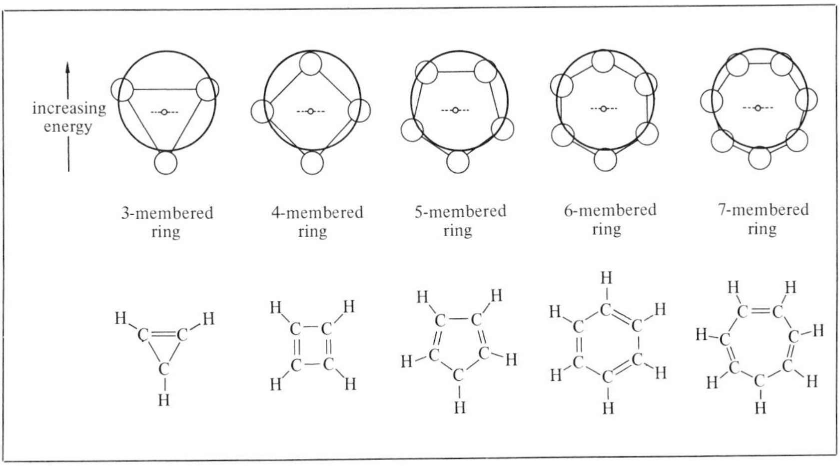

carbonium ion   radical   carbanion

The resonance method, discussed earlier, suggests that all of these species should be substantially stabilized. Thus, we can write five equivalent structures for the carbonium ion.

There are five similarly equivalent resonance structures for the radical and for the carbanion and, from what has been said so far, there would seem to be little to choose between them as far as stability is concerned. In the same way, we should expect the radical and the ions of the seven-membered ring system to be highly stabilized. Again, we show the resonance forms of the carbonium ion only, although analogous structures can be written for the radical and carbanion:

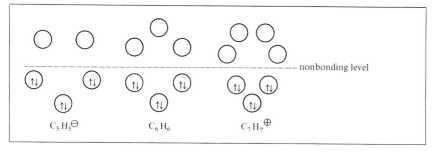

Figure 6·9 Filling of the orbitals for five-, six-, and seven-membered rings.

It turns out that there is a considerable variation in the stabilities of these six systems—the cation, radical, and anion forms of the five- and seven-membered rings. The *anion* of the five-membered ring and the *cation* of the seven-membered ring are by far the most stable and we shall encounter these later (Section 20·7). It is sufficient to point out at this stage that the Hückel MO calculations correctly predicted (in advance) that these in fact were the more stable entities. The energy levels shown in Figure 6·8 might appear to have been obtained empirically but are, in fact, the consequence of the calculations. It will be seen that there are three bonding orbitals (orbitals of lower energy than a nonbonding arrangement in which the p orbitals do not interact at all) for the five-, six-, and seven-membered rings. The six-membered ring with six π electrons filling the three bonding orbitals is the very stable compound benzene. The five- and seven-membered rings can also accommodate six π electrons by filling their bonding orbitals. The resulting electronic configurations give the anion of the five-membered ring and the cation of the seven-membered ring. Because the bonding in these species is maximized, they are expected to be particularly stable. The filling of the orbitals is shown in Figure 6·9.

A similar analysis of rings of other sizes shows that the number of electrons which suffice to fill the bonding molecular orbitals is given by the formula $4n + 2$, where n is an integer or zero. Thus, we expect planar cyclic systems containing 2, 6, 10, 14, ... π electrons to be particularly stable. This has become known as the "Hückel $4n + 2$ rule" and can be stated thus: "Regular monocyclic planar systems made up of trigonal carbon atoms will be most stable when they contain $(4n + 2)$ π electrons."

summary

Compounds with conjugated double bonds are normally more stable than their unconjugated isomers, and often undergo conjugate addition reactions. Benzene, C_6H_6, is an extreme example of stabilization by conjugation. The heat of combustion of benzene is more than 30 kcal per mole less than that calculated for a compound containing three double bonds, and it does not add bromine. The unusual degree of binding in a benzene molecule can be expressed in terms of two structural formulas, each with localized bonding (electrons interacting with only two nuclei). These correspond to the two important ways of pairing the electrons in the p orbitals perpendicular to the

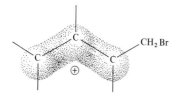

ring. Benzene is well represented as a resonance hybrid of these structures with delocalized bonding (electrons interacting with more than two nuclei).

1,4-Addition to 1,3-butadiene occurs by way of a carbonium ion intermediate which can be formulated as a resonance hybrid having the positive charge divided between two different carbon atoms:

$$CH_2=CH-CH=CH_2 \ + \ Br_2 \ \longrightarrow \ Br^\ominus \ + \ [\overset{\oplus}{C}H_2-CH=CH-CH_2-Br$$

$$\longleftrightarrow \ CH_2=CH-\overset{\oplus}{C}H-CH_2-Br \ ]$$

The π bonding in this ion can be pictured as involving pairing of the electrons in three overlapping p orbitals—two from the double bond and one from the adjacent atom:

1,3-Butadiene, $CH_2=CH-CH=CH_2$, is only slightly stabilized by resonance because there is but one favorable low-energy structure. Other possible structures are less important because they correspond to much less efficient binding. In writing resonance structures, all those to be considered for a specific molecule must have the same number of unpaired electrons. Thus, for 1,3-butadiene, we do not include structures such as $\cdot CH_2-CH=CH-CH_2\cdot$, where this structure is meant to be the one with the 1,4 electrons unpaired. Such a structure represents a different chemical entity from butadiene.

Cations such as the allyl carbonium ion, the $BrCH_2$ derivative of which is the intermediate in the 1,4 addition of bromine to butadiene, and anions such

$$CH_2=CH-\overset{\oplus}{C}H_2 \ \longleftrightarrow \ \overset{\oplus}{C}H_2-CH=CH_2 \qquad H-O-C\overset{\displaystyle O}{\underset{\displaystyle O^\ominus}{}} \ \longleftrightarrow \ H-O-C\overset{\displaystyle O^\ominus}{\underset{\displaystyle O}{}}$$

allyl carbonium ion   bicarbonate ion

as the bicarbonate ion, are stabilized by resonance which, in these cases, leads to dispersal of charge.

Vinyl halides and others have minor contributions to their hybrid structures from ionic electron-pairing schemes:

$$CH_2=CH-X \longleftrightarrow \overset{\ominus}{C}H_2-CH=\overset{\oplus}{X}$$

$$CH_2=CH-O-R \longleftrightarrow \overset{\ominus}{C}H_2-CH=\overset{\oplus}{O}-R$$

The most important of the rules for application of the resonance method (Section 6·6) are that all of the resonance structures must have the same locations of the atoms and the same number of paired electrons.

Although the resonance method generally gives very satisfactory qualitative predictions of the behavior of delocalized systems, the Hückel molecular orbital (MO) procedure for calculating molecular orbital energy levels has found many important applications, particularly in cyclic systems.

In the MO procedure, the p orbitals on each carbon atom in an unsaturated system are combined to give molecular orbitals for the π electrons. The molecular orbitals with energies less than the nonbonding level (which corresponds to isolated noninteracting p orbitals) are bonding orbitals, and those of higher energy are antibonding orbitals. In regular, planar, cyclic systems made up of trigonal carbon atoms, the number of π electrons which exactly fill the bonding orbitals is given by the expression $4n + 2$ (where n is an integer or zero).

exercises

6·1 Discuss the meaning and merit of a statement such as "compound X resonates between forms A and B" in terms of a specific example.

6·2 Evaluate the relative stabilities of actual molecules of butadiene in each of the three forms shown below from the standpoint of steric effects and the resonance method. Give your reasoning.

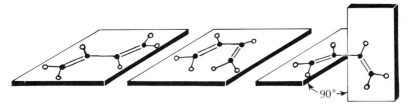

6·3 Evaluate the importance of resonance of the following types (it may be helpful to use ball-and-stick models):

c. $CH_2{=}CH{-}O^{\oplus}$ $\longleftrightarrow$ $\overset{\oplus}{C}H_2{-}CH{=}O$

d.

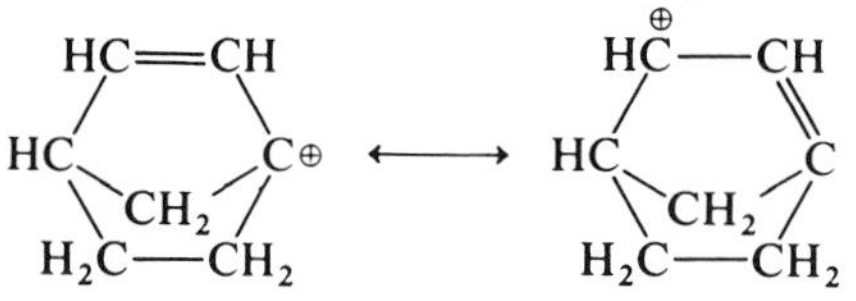

e.

f.

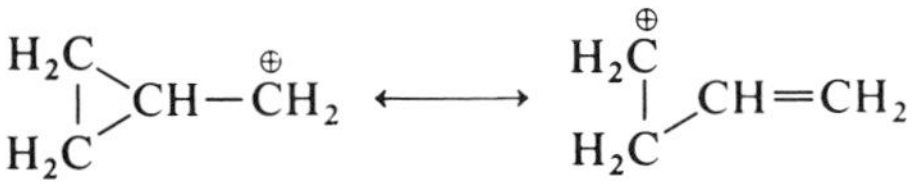

6·4 Do you expect conjugate addition of bromine to occur with

a. 1,3-cyclohexadiene
b. 1-penten-3-yne
c. 1,5-hexadiene
d. vinylbenzene

6·5 Write the structure of the intermediate cation formed by the addition of $Br^{\oplus}$ to each of the compounds in Exercise 6·4.

6·6 Write resonance structures for the ions $N_3^{\ominus}$ and $NO_2^{\ominus}$.

6·7 Consider the importance of the following resonance for cyclobutene (give your reasoning in detail):

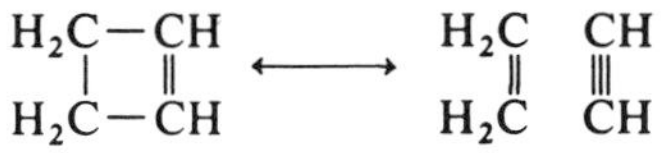

Explain what differences in geometry one would expect for a hybrid of such structures as compared with conventional cyclobutene geometry.

6·8 Write three structures for C_4H_2 with tetravalent carbon and univalent hydrogen. Decide on the most favorable geometrical configuration and evaluate the resonance energy for this configuration.

6·9 Propene reacts with chlorine at 300° to yield allyl chloride (3-chloropropene).

a. Write two chain mechanisms for this chlorination, one involving attack of a chlorine atom on the hydrogen of the $-CH_3$ group and the other an attack of a chlorine atom at the double bond.
b. Consider the relative feasibilities of the two different mechanisms on the basis either of bond energies or the stabilities of intermediate species.

6·10 Use the heats of combustion of cyclooctatetraene (1095 kcal/mole) and of cyclooctane (1269 kcal/mole), and any required bond energies (Table 2·1), to calculate the heat of hydrogenation of cyclooctatetraene to cyclooctane in the vapor phase at 25°.

6·11 Write the five Kekulé-type resonance structures of phenanthrene, and show how these can account for the fact that phenanthrene, unlike benzene, adds bromine, but only across the 9.10 positions.

phenanthrene

6·12   The compound trichlorocyclopropenium tetrachloroaluminate, $C_3Cl_3^{\oplus}$, $AlCl_4^{\ominus}$ exists as a stable salt at room temperature. Use the Hückel rule to account for the unusual stability of this carbonium salt.

6·13   An ionic derivative of cyclooctatetraene, C_8H_8, has recently been prepared. On the basis of the Hückel rule, which of the following formulas do you expect it to have: $C_8H_8^{\oplus}$, $C_8H_8^{\ominus}$, or $C_8H_8^{2\ominus}$?

6·14   In 1825, a yellow crystalline compound, named croconic acid, was prepared by the action of hot potassium hydroxide on carbon powder followed by acidification. This compound, whose formula was later shown to be $H_2C_5O_5$ and to contain a five-membered carbon ring, is quite a strong acid and gives the ion $C_5O_5^{2\ominus}$ on ionization. Suggest a structure for this acid and the ion and show how resonance stabilization of the ion accounts for the acid being strong.

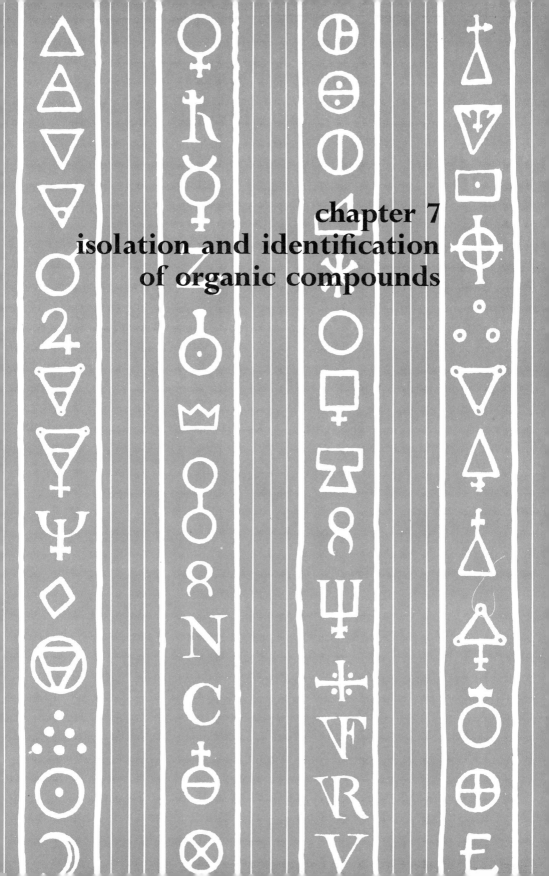

chapter 7
isolation and identification
of organic compounds

A characteristic of chemistry that is not always shared with the other sciences is a concern for purity (in the sense of molecular homogeneity) in the materials under study. Much of the time of some organic chemists working in the laboratory is devoted to isolating compounds in pure form, and the culmination of a synthetic scheme is always the purification and confirmation of the identity of the product. In this chapter we consider, first, some modern means of separating and purifying organic compounds and, second, instrumental methods which can be used to elucidate structures. There have been enormous advances in these regards over the past 20 years through introduction of new techniques. Structural or purification problems which once may have required years for solution, if they could be solved at all, can often now be solved in hours or days, but very frequently with complex and costly apparatus.

7·1   isolation and purification

Fractional distillation and crystallization are the time-honored methods for separating and purifying liquids and solids, respectively. Obviously, knowledge of the relationship between structure and boiling point will be helpful in conducting a distillation. Crystallization of solid compounds calls more for an understanding of solubilities as a function of temperature in the common solvents such as water, ethyl alcohol, benzene, and tetrachloromethane (carbon tetrachloride). The most suitable solvent for crystallizing or recrystallizing an impure compound is usually one in which the compound is slightly soluble at room temperature, for if the solubility is too high the recovery will be poor because too much of the compound will be left in solution. On the other hand, if the solubility at room temperature is too low, you can expect difficulty in trying to dissolve the compound completely in the solvent at higher temperatures.

Liquid-liquid extraction techniques, using a separatory funnel, can sometimes provide clean separations, particularly with compounds possessing a basic group such as amino ($-NH_2$) or an acidic group such as carboxyl

$$\left(-C\underset{\displaystyle OH}{\overset{\displaystyle O}{\Big\backslash}} \right)$$

The most widely used technique for separating and purifying compounds on a small scale is *chromatography*. Chromatography can be defined as the separation of components of a mixture by differences in the way they become distributed (partitioned) between two phases. By this definition, chromatography includes the simple techniques described above, such as extraction in a separatory funnel (a liquid-liquid two-phase system), fractional distillation (a gas-liquid two-phase system), and crystallization (a solid-liquid two-phase system). These techniques require fairly large amounts of material and they may give unsatisfactory separations, which may be attributed to the small degree of separation possible in any given one-stage, or even several-stage, partitioning process. We now have available what might be called super-separation chromatographic methods, which involve multistage partitioning of

very small amounts of sample, a few milligrams or less, wherein extraordinary separations can often be achieved. To this end, the most frequently
employed combinations of phases are gas-liquid and liquid-solid.

Liquid-solid chromatography was originally developed for the separation
of colored substances, hence the name chromatography (which stems from
the Greek word *chroma* meaning color). In a typical examination, a colored
substance suspected of containing colored impurities is dissolved in a suitable
solvent and the solution allowed to pass through a column packed with some
solid adsorbent (e.g., alumina), as shown in Figure 7·1. The "chromatogram"
is then "developed" by adding a suitable solvent that washes the adsorbate
down through the column. Hopefully, and this is the crux of the entire
separation, the components are adsorbed unequally by the solid phase, and
distinct bands or zones of color appear. The bands at the top of the column
contain the most strongly adsorbed components; the bands at the bottom
contain the least strongly held components. The zones may be separated mechanically, or solvent can be added to wash, or elute, the zones separately from
the column for further analysis. If all attempts to resolve a given substance
chromatographically are unsuccessful, evidence (albeit negative) is thus provided for the presence of a single pure chemical entity. Although the various
zones can be observed by eye only if the substances are colored, a variety of
other techniques can be used to detect the bands on the chromatogram and
the method is by no means limited to colored substances.

**Figure 7·1 A simple chromatographic column for liquid-solid chromatog-
raphy.**

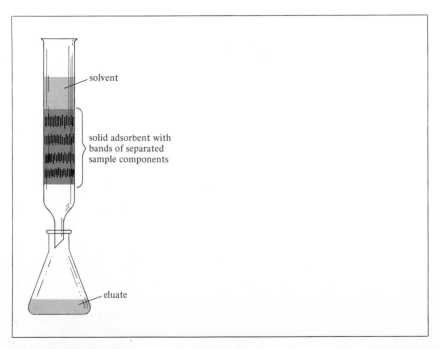

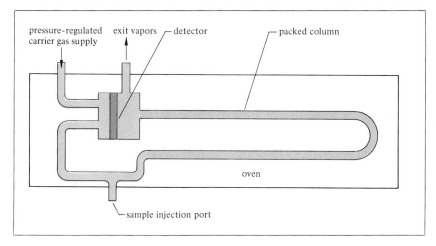

Figure 7·2   Schematic diagram of a vapor-phase chromatography apparatus. The detector is arranged to measure the difference in some property of the carrier gas alone versus the carrier gas plus effluent sample at the exit. Differences in thermal conductivity are particularly easy to measure and give high detection sensitivities.

More recently, gas-liquid phase chromatography, glpc (also called vapor-phase chromatography, vpc, or gas chromatography, gc) has added a new dimension for the analysis of volatile substances. In the usual form of vpc, a few microliters of a liquid to be analyzed are injected into a vaporizer and carried with a stream of gas (most frequently helium) into a long heated column, packed with some porous solid (such as crushed firebrick) impregnated with a nonvolatile liquid or oil. Gas-liquid partitioning occurs, and small differences between partitioning of the components can be magnified by the large number of repetitive partitions possible in a long column. Detection is usually achieved by measuring changes in thermal conductivity of the effluent gases. A schematic diagram of the apparatus and a typical separation are shown in Figures 7·2 and 7·3. While observation of a single peak in the vpc

Figure 7·3   A vapor-phase chromatogram of a mixture of isomeric butyl alcohols, C_4H_9OH.

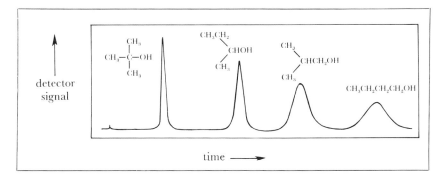

analysis of a material is, of course, only negative evidence for purity, the method is extraordinarily useful for detection of minute amounts of impurities when these are separated from the main peak. The sensitivity of vpc makes it the method of choice for analysis of volatile pesticide residues in food products, automobile exhausts, smokestack effluents, trace components of alcoholic beverages, flavors, perfumes, and so on.

Vapor-phase chromatography can be used effectively to purify materials as well as to detect impurities. To do this, the sample size and the size of the apparatus are generally increased, and the vapor of the pure component is condensed as it emerges from the column.

Two other chromatographic methods, paper chromatography and thin-layer chromatography (tlc), are described in Chapter 17.

7·2   identification of organic compounds

Distillation, crystallization, or chromatography often tells us something of the state of purity of a compound. A single chromatographic peak, a sharp boiling point, or a sharp melting point of a crystallized solid is an indication that a pure compound has been obtained. (Although melting and boiling points will be listed in this and other books as single temperatures, in practice one encounters a melting or boiling range of usually one degree or so.)

If the substance being purified is believed to be a previously known compound, it is usually a simple matter to compare its physical properties (melting point, boiling point, refractive index) or spectroscopic properties with those reported in the chemical literature for the known compound. However, if the structure of the compound is not known, you must adopt a different approach.

The traditional method, and indeed the only one really available until the second half of this century, is based on the molecular formula obtained from the molecular weight and the elemental analysis, in combination with qualitative chemical tests and degradative reactions which ultimately would lead to known compounds. The process was to a large extent highly intuitive but the conclusions drawn about structure usually proved correct. Although instrumental methods of analysis have revolutionized structure determination in the past 25 years, it would be a mistake to conclude that a wide knowledge of the transformations of organic compounds that are possible is no longer necessary for the successful elucidation of molecular structures.

The first step in the process of determining a structure is a quantitative analysis for the elements it contains.

A. ELEMENTAL ANALYSIS

The vast majority of organic substances are compounds of carbon with hydrogen, oxygen, nitrogen, or the halogens. All of these elements can be determined directly by routine procedures. Carbon and hydrogen in combustible compounds can be measured by combustion of a weighed sample in a stream of

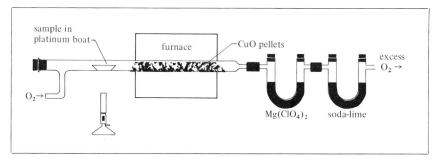

Figure 7·4   Schematic representation of a combustion train for determination of carbon and hydrogen in combustible substances.

oxygen (Figure 7·4) followed by gravimetric determination of the resulting water and carbon dioxide through absorption in anhydrous magnesium perchlorate and soda lime, respectively. Routine carbon-hydrogen analyses by combustion procedures utilize 3- to 5-mg samples and attain an accuracy of 0.1 to 0.2%. Complete elemental analyses permit computation of empirical formulas which are equal to, or are submultiples of, the molecular formulas. A knowledge of the molecular weight is needed to determine which of the multiples of the empirical formula corresponds to the molecular formula. For example, the empirical formula of the important sugar, glucose, is CH_2O, but the molecular weight defines the molecular formula as $(CH_2O)_6$ or $C_6H_{12}O_6$.

Molecular weights of gaseous organic compounds may be determined directly by vapor-density experiments. Liquid substances of moderate volatility may be vaporized, and their vapor densities determined. However, molecular weights of volatile compounds are not often determined in present-day organic research, because the molecular weight of a given substance may usually be estimated from the boiling point, to perhaps 25% accuracy, by knowledge of the boiling points of related compounds. Molecular weights of high-boiling liquids and slightly volatile solids are generally determined by measuring freezing-point depressions or boiling-point elevations of solutions in suitable solvents. Solutions in a substance such as camphor, which gives a very large freezing-point depression (37.7° per mole of solute dissolved in 1000 g of camphor), are particularly suitable for small-scale operations and can, with ordinary equipment, permit reasonably accurate molecular-weight measurements by determination of melting points.

There are many other more or less specialized techniques available, the choice depending on the problem at hand and accessibility of equipment. Thus, molecular weights of even slightly volatile substances may often be obtained by mass spectrometry, which is the method of choice, particularly since resolution is routinely achieved for masses as high as 600. The molecular weights of very high-molecular-weight compounds such as proteins and polymeric materials are frequently determined by end-group analysis, measurement of osmotic pressure, viscosity, light scattering, and sedimentation. Some of these methods will be discussed in more detail in later chapters.

B. MASS SPECTROMETRY

The application of mass spectrometry to organic molecules involves bombardment of a vaporized sample with a beam of medium-energy electrons in high vacuum and analysis of the charged particles and fragments produced.

The elements of a mass spectrometer are shown in Figure 7·5. The positive ions produced by electron bombardment are accelerated by the negatively charged accelerating plates and are swept down to the curve of the analyzer tube where they are sorted as to their mass-to-charge (m/e) ratio by the analyzing magnet. With good resolution, only the ions of a single mass number will pass through the slit and impinge on the collector, even when the mass numbers are in the neighborhood of several hundred or a thousand. The populations of the whole range of mass numbers of interest can be determined by plotting the rate of ion collection as a function of the magnetic field of the analyzing magnet.

The intense peak that is highest in mass number is of considerable importance; this corresponds to the positive ion formed from the parent molecule by the loss of just one electron and provides a highly accurate method for measuring molecular weights.

In recent years, considerable success has been achieved in the correlation of the relative abundances of various-sized fragmentation products with the molecular structures of the parent molecules. This use of mass spectrometry is discussed in more detail in Chapter 29.

Figure 7·5   Schematic diagram of a mass spectrometer.

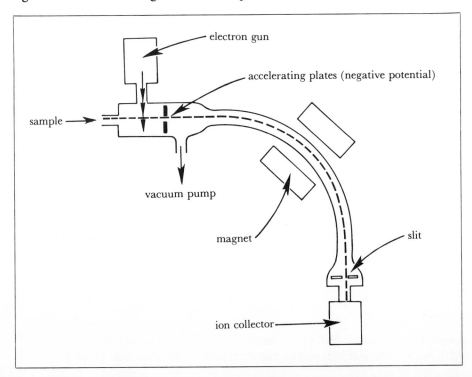

Super-resolution mass spectrometers are now available which permit distinction between ions of such molecules as $C_{43}H_{50}N_4O_6$ (mol. wt. 718.373) and $C_{42}H_{46}N_4O_7$ (mol. wt. 718.337). Such mass spectrometers can be used for elemental analysis.

spectroscopy

Virtually all parts of the spectrum of electromagnetic radiation, from X rays to radio waves, have found some practical application for the study of organic molecules. Visible light is an extremely narrow band in the spectrum characterized by the wavelength range 4000 to 7500 A; it occupies a position between ultraviolet and infrared radiation but, in terms of the way it interacts with organic molecules, it can be considered part of the ultraviolet region.

The absorption of electromagnetic radiation by molecules results in an increase in their energy. Very short-wavelength radiation, such as X rays or gamma rays, supplies so much energy that it causes covalent bonds to rupture and thus leads to drastic chemical changes. Long-wavelength radiation such as radio waves, on the other hand, may be able to induce only more rapid rotation of a molecule.

Most of the spectroscopic methods in use by organic chemists involve measuring the amount or wavelengths, or both, of radiant energy absorbed by molecules, and the principles and practice of some of these methods will be discussed. First, however, mention should be made of X-ray diffraction, because this technique has proved to be of special value in elucidating structures of organic molecules.

When a beam of X rays strikes a crystal, the result is a diffraction pattern which is characteristic of the locations of the atoms in the crystal. The diffraction pattern can usually be analyzed with the aid of a high-speed digital computer and the molecular structure may often be determined in a matter of days. (Diffraction does not itself involve absorption of radiation, although the crystal usually suffers some damage because of bond rupture caused by absorption of X rays.) Not all compounds can be examined in this way, because the compound must be crystalline and, preferably, contain at least one "heavy" atom, such as chlorine or bromine.

7·3   absorption of electromagnetic radiation

The energy, e, of a photon is related to its frequency of vibration, $\mathbf{v}$, by Planck's constant, h:

$$e = h\mathbf{v}$$

In general, you can say that a molecule will absorb incident radiation only if there is some higher energy state (with energy E_2) to which the molecule can be raised from its normal or ground state (with energy E_1) by the energy of the photon. Because not all photons have the proper energy to take a molecule from the normal to a higher energy state, we say that the energy levels are quantized, and that a specific quantum of energy separates the two states:

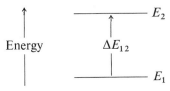

The difference in energy ΔE_{12} ($=E_2 - E_1$) is related to the frequency ($\nu \sec^{-1}$) or wavelength (λ cm) of the absorbed radiation by the equations

$$\Delta E_{12} = h\nu = \frac{hc}{\lambda}$$

where h is Planck's constant and c is the velocity of light. We generally will be interested in the energy change in kilocalories (1 kcal $= 10^3$ cal) which would result from one mole of substance absorbing light and we can rewrite the above equation in the form

$$\Delta E_{12} = \frac{286,000}{\lambda(A)} \text{ kcal}$$

where λ is now in angstrom (A) units (1 A $= 10^{-8}$ cm). As defined here, ΔE_{12} corresponds to 1 *einstein* of radiation.

The total energy (E) of a molecule (apart from nuclear and kinetic energy) can be expressed as the sum of three energy terms:

$$E = E_{\text{electronic}} + E_{\text{vibrational}} + E_{\text{rotational}}$$

The electronic energy levels correspond to the energies of the various molecular orbitals (Section 6·7) and are rather widely spaced. Ultraviolet light (and sometimes visible light) has sufficient energy to cause transitions between the electronic energy levels. Vibrational energies are also quantized but the vibrational energy levels are more closely spaced and the differences between them correspond to photons of infrared radiation. Finally, the energies of rotational states for a molecule or its parts are very closely spaced and rotational transitions result from absorption of microwaves (radar) or radio waves.

A molecule that has absorbed a photon of ultraviolet light, for example, normally remains in the resulting excited electronic state for only a very brief period. The energy may be reemitted or it may be shuffled into vibrational and rotational energy with a resulting increase in thermal energy of the system. In some cases, the excited molecules undergo chemical reactions and do not return to the original ground state. The fading of dyes is an example of this kind of behavior. The types of transition associated with absorption of radiation from the various regions of the electromagnetic spectrum are shown in Figure 7·6.

Although microwave spectroscopy can provide valuable information about bond lengths and bond angles in simple molecules, it has not so far been of

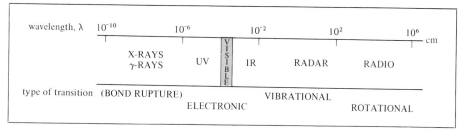

Figure 7·6   The types of transitions in molecules brought about by absorption of radiation from various regions of the electromagnetic spectrum.

general use for identification or structure proof of organic compounds. Infrared and ultraviolet spectroscopy are much more widely and routinely useful. The radio wave absorptions when used in conjunction with an applied magnetic field are also of great importance, as we shall see in a later section of this chapter.

7·4 infrared spectroscopy

Possibly the single most widely used tool for investigating organic structures and for organic chemical analyses is the infrared spectrometer. Spectra for infrared radiation over the wavelength region from 2 to 15 microns (1 micron $= \mu = 10^{-4}$ cm) are of most interest. Recording infrared spectrophotometers with excellent resolution and reproducibility are commercially available and are widely used in organic research. The operating parts of a spectrometer are shown in Figure 7·7. The sample containers (cells) and optical parts of infrared spectrophotometers are made of rock salt (NaCl) or similar materials, since glass is opaque to infrared radiation. Gaseous, liquid, or solid samples can be used. Solids are often run as finely ground suspensions (mulls) in various kinds of oils, or ground up with potassium bromide and compressed by a hydraulic press into wafers. Considerable differences are often observed between the spectra of a solid and its solutions.

In Figures 7·8, 7·9, and 7·10 are shown the infrared spectra of an alkane, an alkene, and an alkyne. In accord with current practice, the infrared spectra given here are linear in wave numbers (v cm^{-1}) that are related to radiation frequencies ($\mathbf{v}$ sec^{-1}) so that $v = \mathbf{v}/c$, where c is the velocity of light in cm/sec. A supplementary nonlinear wavelength scale in microns is shown, and to convert wave numbers v to λ in microns we use the relation $\lambda = 10^4/v$.

Considerable confusion exists as to the units used to express wavelength or frequency for various kinds of spectra. For electronic spectra, λ is most commonly expressed in angstrom units (10^{-8} cm) or millimicrons (10^{-7} cm). For infrared spectra, absorbed radiation may be defined by its wavelength λ in microns (10^{-4} cm) or by its frequency v in units of wave numbers ($10^4/\lambda$ cm^{-1}).

The infrared absorption bands between 3600 and 1250 cm^{-1} can be identified in most cases with the changes in the vibration of a particular bond.

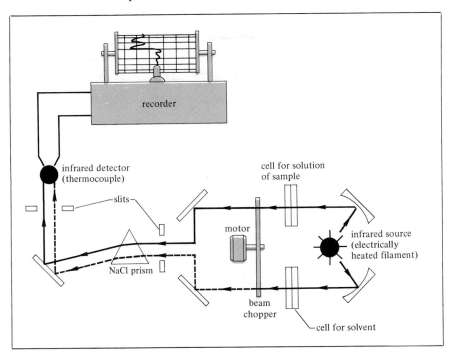

Figure 7·7 Schematic representation of a "double-beam" recording infrared spectrophotometer. The beam chopper permits radiation passing alternately through sample cell and solvent cell to reach the thermocouple. This procedure permits the difference in absorption by solute and solvent to be measured as an alternating electric current from the thermocouple. The alternating-current output is particularly desirable for electronic amplification. The usual commercial instruments operate on a "null" principle with the recorder pen linked mechanically to a "comb" (not shown here), which is placed across the solvent-cell beam and moved by a servomechanism to reduce or increase the solvent-cell-beam intensity. The servomechanism is actuated by the amplified thermocouple output to make the solvent-beam intensity equal to the solution-beam intensity—that is, to reduce the thermocouple output to zero or the null point. The spectrum can be scanned through the various wavelengths by rotation of the prism in synchronization with the motion of the recorder drum. The use of a diffraction grating in place of the prism is becoming increasingly common.

Below 1250 cm^{-1} is the so-called fingerprint region, which is associated chiefly with complex vibrational changes in the molecule as a whole.

The band at highest frequency in all three hydrocarbons is that which corresponds to changes in the C—H stretching energies. The higher the frequency of the radiation, the higher its energy, and this means that to raise the vibrational level of a C—H bond requires more energy than that for any other bond to carbon. We can regard the C—H bond to be like a spring between the two atoms, with the light hydrogen atom vibrating with respect to the much heavier carbon atom. Because vibrational energies are strictly quantized, only certain values of the stretching frequency are allowed.

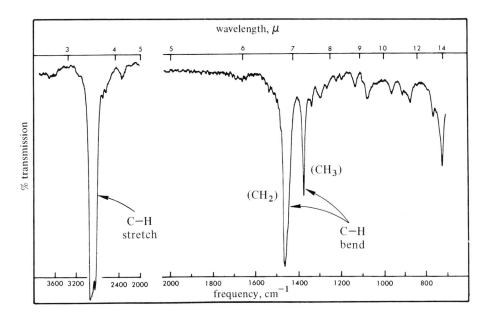

Figure 7·8   The infrared spectrum of octane, $CH_3CH_2CH_2CH_2CH_2CH_2CH_2CH_3$.

Figure 7·9   The infrared spectrum of 1-butene, $CH_3CH_2CH=CH_2$.

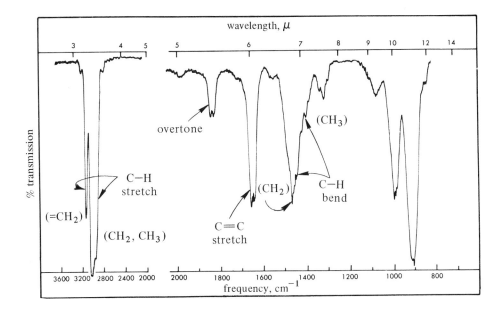

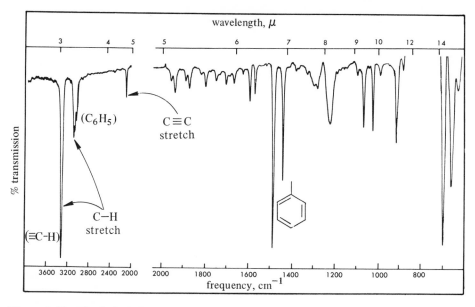

Figure 7·10   The infrared spectrum of phenylacetylene, $C_6H_5C{\equiv}CH$, in carbon tetrachloride solution. The sharp band near 1500 cm^{-1} is characteristic of a vibration of the benzene ring.

At room temperature, more than 95% of the C—H bonds of a sample of hydrocarbon are vibrating in their lowest (or zero-point) energy level. That is, the thermal energy of the system is sufficient to raise only a small fraction of the hydrogens to a higher vibrational level than that which would be found at absolute zero. The absorption bands near 3000 cm^{-1}, then, correspond to a change from the lowest vibrational state to the first excited vibrational state of the C—H bond. The slightly different locations of these bands for different kinds of C—H bond (compare Figures 7·8, 7·9, and 7·10) are of considerable use in structure identification.

The bending frequencies for C—H bonds occur at lower wave numbers showing that a smaller quantum of energy is required for excitation of bending vibrations:

$$E_{\text{C--H}} > E_{\text{C--H}}$$

The absorption of energy by changing the stretching energies of carbon-carbon bonds occurs at lower frequencies than those of carbon-hydrogen bonds and are widely separated, depending on whether the atoms are joined by a single, double, or triple bond. The carbon-carbon single-bond stretching bands occur in the complex "fingerprint" region and are difficult to identify. Carbon-carbon double and triple bonds, however, absorb at higher frequencies and can be readily identified in an infrared spectrum. The analogy of bonds to springs can be usefully applied here. The stronger the forces holding two atoms together, the greater will be the energy required to raise the system to the next vibrational level. The total binding energy of a double bond is less than that of a triple bond, and this is shown in the infrared spectra by the fact that the C$=$C stretching band in 1-butene appears at 1700 cm^{-1} and the C$\equiv$C band in phenylacetylene at 2100 cm^{-1}.

The most common positions of the easily identified stretching frequencies in hydrocarbons are

C$-$H	C$=$C	C$\equiv$C
$\sim$3000 cm^{-1}	$\sim$1650 cm^{-1}	$\sim$2200 cm^{-1}

Table 7·1 lists the characteristic infrared frequencies for many kinds of compounds that we shall subsequently meet.

The spectrum of 1-butene in Figure 7·9 shows an absorption that can trap the unwary. Thus the band at 1830 cm^{-1} falls in the region where stretching vibrations are usually observed. However, this band actually arises from an overtone (harmonic) of the $=$CH$_2$ out-of-plane bending at 915 cm^{-1}. Such overtone absorptions come at just twice the frequency of the fundamental frequency and whenever an absorption like this is observed, which does not seem to fit with the normal fundamental vibrations, the possibility of its being an overtone should be checked.

7·5 ultraviolet and visible spectroscopy (electronic spectroscopy)

The photons of visible light (4000–7500 A) are an order of magnitude higher in energy than infrared photons and the photons of ultraviolet light are of still higher energy. The type of spectroscopy that embraces these more energetic kinds of radiation is called electronic spectroscopy because the excitation that results from absorption of such photons normally involves the raising of one electron to a higher energy orbital.

We expect that electronic excitation will occur with lower-energy photons in molecules whose ground-state electrons are only loosely bound to their nuclei. Such compounds may, in fact, absorb visible light and be colored. Molecules in which all the electrons are rather tightly bound—alkanes, for instance—can only be excited electronically by the high-energy ultraviolet radiation. The valence electrons in alkanes are in C$-$C and C$-$H σ bonds, and raising one of these electrons to a higher energy, called a $\sigma \rightarrow \sigma^*$ transition, requires radiation of wavelength 1300 A or less. Such radiation is not easily accessible for routine analysis because neither air nor quartz (the best substance available for constructing cells and prisms) is transparent to such radiation. The practical lower limit for routine ultraviolet absorption spectroscopy is about 1900 A, and for this reason alkanes are transparent throughout the whole of the readily accessible ultraviolet and visible region.

The experimental arrangement for determining such spectra is usually quite similar to that of infrared spectrometers shown in Figure 7·1. The principal differences lie in the use of a tungsten lamp (3200 to 8000 A) or hydrogen arc (1800 to 4000 A) as the light source; quartz prism and sample cells; and a photoelectric cell, rather than a thermocouple, as the radiation

Table 7·1   Some characteristic infrared absorption frequencies

bond	type of compound	frequency, cm^{-1}	intensity
—C—H	alkanes	2850–2960	strong
—C—D	alkanes	~2200	strong
=C—H	alkenes and arenes	3010–3100	medium
≡C—H	alkynes	3300	strong, sharp
—C—C—	alkanes	600–1500^a	weak
C=C	alkenes	1620–1680	variable
—C≡C—	alkynes	2100–2260	variable
—C≡N	nitriles	2200–2300	variable
—C—O—	alcohols —C—OH, ethers —C—O—C—,	1000–1300	strong

carboxylic acids —C(=O)(O—H)   esters —C(=O)(O—C—)

^{a} In general, C—C single-bond stretching frequencies are not useful for identification.

detector. In these spectrometers, the prism is placed ahead of the sample.

In simple alkenes and alkynes the π electrons are, of course, less tightly bonded than are σ electrons, but the excitation energy is still too great for significant absorption to occur in the easily accessible region of the ultraviolet spectrum. Conjugated dienes, however, absorb strongly at wavelengths above 2000 A. This kind of absorption results from raising an electron from a normal π-bonding state to a π-antibonding state and is called a $\pi \rightarrow \pi^*$ transition.

The more extended the conjugated system becomes, the smaller is the energy difference between the normal and excited states. Thus, the diphenylpolyenes, $C_6H_5-(CH=CH)_n-C_6H_5$, absorb light at progressively longer wavelengths as n increases; this is apparent from the colors of these compounds, which range from colorless ($n = 1$) through yellow and orange ($n = 2$–7) to red ($n = 8$) as the wavelength increases from the ultraviolet well into the visible region of the electromagnetic spectrum. Lycopene, the red pigment in tomatoes, is a polyene with 11 conjugated double bonds (Section 29·3).

Table 7·1   Some characteristic infrared absorption frequencies *(continued)*

bond	type of compound	frequency, cm^{-1}	intensity
$\diagdown_{C=O}\diagup$	aldehydes $-\overset{\overset{\displaystyle O}{\|\|}}{C}-H$	1720–1740	strong
$\diagdown_{C=O}\diagup$	ketones $-\overset{\|}{\underset{\|}{C}}-\overset{\overset{\displaystyle O}{\|\|}}{C}-\overset{\|}{\underset{\|}{C}}-$	1705–1725	strong
$\diagdown_{C=O}\diagup$	acids $-C\overset{\diagup\!\!\diagup O}{\diagdown O-H}$ esters $-C\overset{\diagup\!\!\diagup O}{\diagdown O-\overset{\|}{\underset{\|}{C}}-}$	1700–1750	strong
$-O-H$	alcohols $-\overset{\|}{\underset{\|}{C}}-O-H$, phenols $=\overset{\|}{C}-O-H$	3590–3650	variable, sharp
$-O-H$	hydrogen-bonded, alcohols and phenols $-O-H\cdot\cdot\overset{\diagup}{O}\diagdown$	3200–3400	strong, broad
$-O-H$	hydrogen-bonded, acids $-O-H\cdot\cdot\overset{\diagup}{O}\diagdown$	2500–3000	variable, broad
$-NH_2$	amines $-\overset{\|}{\underset{\|}{C}}-NH_2$	3300–3500 (double peak)	medium
$-\overset{\|}{N}-H$	amines $-\overset{\|}{\underset{\|}{C}}-\overset{\overset{\displaystyle H}{\|}}{N}-\overset{\|}{\underset{\|}{C}}-$	3300–3500 (single peak)	medium

Electronic absorption bands are usually much broader than infrared bands for two principal reasons. First, at ordinary temperatures, molecules in either the ground or excited electronic states exist in a number of vibrational or rotational states, and the transitions which occur between the electronic states are brought about by quanta of slightly different energy. The result is to give an absorption band made up of a large number of lines which are too closely spaced to be separately distinguishable. The second reason arises from the fact that electronic spectra are usually taken of solutions, and the range of solute-solvent interactions gives a spread of energies to both the ground and excited electronic states.

We have seen that conjugated molecules, such as 1,3-butadiene, have normal or ground states (Section 6·3) which are slightly more stable than would otherwise be expected. Because conjugated molecules also have electronic absorption bands toward longer wavelengths than nonconjugated molecules (smaller energy differences between ground and excited states), the energies of the excited states of such molecules must have a higher degree of resonance stabilization than the ground state.

Can you depict excited electronic states by conventional structural formulas? Only in a rather unsatisfactory way, unfortunately. You can formulate the excited state of 1,3-butadiene associated with absorption of ultraviolet radiation by a dipolar structure such as $\overset{\oplus}{C}H_2-CH=CH-\overset{\ominus}{C}H_2$, which we have already considered in connection with the ground state of the molecule (Section 6·4). Thus, you can consider the *ground state* as being close to [1]

$$CH_2=CH-CH=CH_2 \quad \longleftrightarrow \quad \overset{\oplus}{C}H_2-CH=CH-\overset{\ominus}{C}H_2$$

$$[1] \hspace{6cm} [2]$$

$$\longleftrightarrow \quad CH_2=CH-\overset{\oplus}{C}H-\overset{\ominus}{C}H_2 \quad \longleftrightarrow \quad \text{etc.}$$

$$[3]$$

with *minor* contributions from [2], [3], and other energetically unfavorable structures. On the other hand, the *excited state* can be taken to correspond to [2] with *major* contributions from other polar forms such as [3], which can contribute in a major way because they should have comparable energies and a minor contribution from [1]. The important points are that the excited state has less total bonding than the ground state and, because it is expected to be more of a hybrid structure than the ground state, it will have a different geometry, particularly a shorter 2,3 carbon-carbon bond. In general, we will expect that the greater the degree of conjugation and the more favorable the polar forms appear, the more the excited state will be stabilized and the longer will be the wavelength of the maximum absorption, λ_{max}.

7·6 nuclear magnetic resonance spectroscopy

Nuclear magnetic resonance (nmr) spectroscopy is very useful for identification and analysis of organic compounds. The principles of this form of spectroscopy are quite simple. The nuclei of some kinds of atoms act like tiny magnets and become lined up when placed in a magnetic field. In nmr spectroscopy, we measure the energy required to change the alignment of magnetic nuclei in a magnetic field.

A schematic diagram of a very simple form of an nmr instrument is shown in Figure 7·11. When a substance such as ethyl alcohol, CH_3-CH_2-OH, (the hydrogens of which have nuclei that are magnetic) is placed in the center of the coil between the magnet pole faces, and the magnetic field is increased gradually, energy is absorbed by the sample at certain field strengths and the current flow in the coil is increased. The result is a spectrum such as the one shown in Figure 7·12. This spectrum is detailed enough to serve as a most useful fingerprint for ethyl alcohol but is also simple enough for the origin of each line to be accounted for, as we shall see.

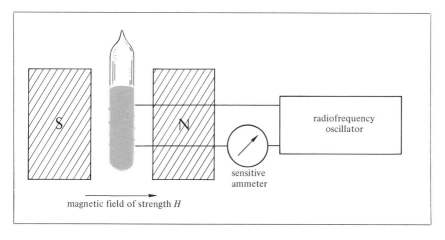

Figure 7·11   Essential features of a simple nmr spectrometer.

For what kinds of substances can we expect nuclear magnetic resonance absorption to occur? Magnetic properties are always found with nuclei of odd-numbered masses, ^1H, ^{13}C, ^{15}N, ^{17}O, ^{19}F, ^{31}P, and so on, and nuclei of even mass but odd number, ^2H, ^{10}B, ^{14}N, and so on. Nuclei such as ^{12}C, ^{16}O, ^{32}S, and so on, with even mass and atomic numbers have no magnetic properties and do not give nuclear magnetic resonance signals. For various reasons, routine use of nmr spectra in organic chemistry is confined to ^1H,

Figure 7·12   Nuclear magnetic resonance spectrum of ethyl alcohol (containing a trace of hydrochloric acid). Chemical shifts are relative to tetramethylsilane, $(CH_3)_4Si$ or TMS = 0·00 ppm. The stepped line is an integral of the areas under each of the resonance lines.

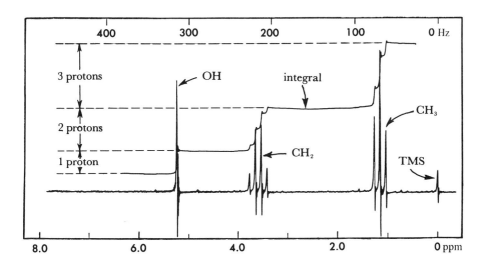

^{19}F, and ^{31}P. We shall be concerned here principally with nmr spectra of hydrogen (^{1}H), often called pmr spectroscopy (proton magnetic resonance spectroscopy).

Nuclear magnetic resonance spectra may be so simple as to have only a single absorption peak but can also be much more complex than the spectrum of Figure 7·12. On the one hand, complexity is helpful because it makes the spectra more individualistic and better suited as fingerprints for characterization of organic molecules. However, complexity can hinder the use of nmr spectra for qualitative analysis and structure proofs. Fortunately, with the aid of isotopic substitution and a technique known as "double resonance," it is now possible to analyze completely spectra that show literally hundreds of lines. The ways of doing this are beyond the scope of this book. However, it is important to recognize that no matter how complex an nmr spectrum appears to be, it can be analyzed in terms of just *three* elements: chemical shifts, spin-spin splittings, and kinetic (reaction-rate) processes.

The kind of nmr spectroscopy we shall discuss here is limited in its applications, because it can only be carried on with liquids or solutions. Fortunately, the allowable range of solvents is large, from hydrocarbons to concentrated sulfuric acid, and for most compounds it is possible to find a suitable solvent.

A. THE CHEMICAL SHIFT

Ethyl alcohol, CH_3-CH_2-OH, has three kinds of hydrogens: methyl (CH_3), methylene (CH_2), and hydroxyl (OH). In a magnetic field, the nuclei (protons) of each of these kinds of hydrogens have slightly different magnetic environments as the result of the motions of their valence electrons and those of neighboring atoms in response to the magnetic field. The magnetic field strength at a particular nucleus is usually less than the strength of the applied external magnetic field, because the motions of the electrons result in a shielding effect (the so-called diamagnetic shielding effect). The important point is that the effects arising from the motions of the electrons will be different for each kind of hydrogen and, therefore, the resonance signal produced for each kind of hydrogen will come at different field strengths. A plot of signal against field strength (Figure 7·12) thus shows three principal groups of lines for ethyl alcohol. The areas under the curves as measured by the stepped line of the chart ("the integrals") correspond to the three varieties of hydrogen.

Differences in the field strength at which signals are obtained for nuclei of the same kind, such as protons or ^{19}F, but located in different molecular environments, are called chemical shifts.

Chemical shifts are always measured with reference to a standard. For protons in organic molecules, the customary standard is tetramethylsilane, $(CH_3)_4Si$, which has the advantage of giving a strong, sharp nmr signal in a region where only a very few other kinds of protons absorb. Chemical shifts are usually expressed in hertz (Hz, or cycles per second) relative to tetramethylsilane (TMS). These may seem like odd units for magnetic field strength but since resonance occurs at a radio frequency, the use of either frequency units (hertz, cycles per second) or magnetic field units (gauss) is appropriate.

Most nmr spectrometers for routine use operate with radio frequency (rf)

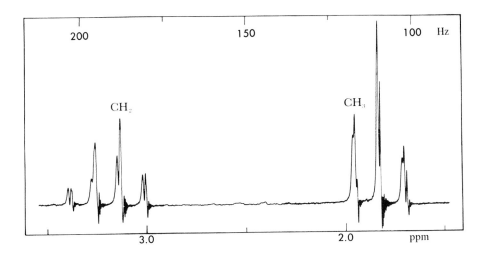

Figure 7·13   Nuclear magnetic resonance spectrum of iodoethane, CH_3CH_2I, at 60 MHz relative to TMS, 0.00 ppm.

oscillators set at 30, 60, 100, 220, or 300 megahertz (MHz). Since chemical shifts turn out to be strictly proportional to the spectrometer frequency, we expect lines 100 Hz apart at 60 MHz to be 167 Hz apart at 100 MHz. To facilitate comparisons between chemical shifts measured at different frequencies, shifts in hertz are often divided by the oscillator frequency and reported as ppm (parts per million). Thus, if a proton signal comes at 100 Hz at 60 MHz downfield (toward higher frequencies), relative to tetramethylsilane, it can be designated as being $(+100 \text{ Hz}/60 \times 10^6 \text{ Hz}) \times 10^6 = +1.67$ ppm relative to tetramethylsilane.[1] At 100 MHz the line will then be $1.67 \times 100 \times 10^6 \times 10^{-6} = 167$ Hz downfield from tetramethylsilane. A table of typical proton chemical shifts relative to TMS is given in Table 7·2. The values quoted for each type of proton may, in practice, show variations of 5 to 20 Hz. This is not unreasonable, because the chemical shift of a given proton is expected to depend somewhat on the nature of the particular molecule involved and also on the solvent, temperature, and concentration.

B. SPIN-SPIN SPLITTING

We have noted that organic molecules with protons on contiguous carbon atoms, such as ethyl derivatives $CH_3CH_2X \, (X \neq H)$, show principal resonance signals for protons of different chemical shifts (see Figure 7·12). Each of these signals is actually a group of lines that results from "spin-spin splitting." Taking as a typical example the protons of iodoethane (Figure 7·13), the

---

[1] In the past, a ppm scale was more commonly used than at present, based on so-called "τ values." The τ scale has the TMS reference at $+10$, so that most proton signals fall in the region of 0 to $+10\,\tau$. A τ value can be converted to ppm, with TMS at 0.0, by subtracting it from 10.

Table 7·2   Typical proton chemical shift values
(dilute chloroform solutions)

type of proton[a]	chemical shift[b]		type of proton[a]	chemical shift[b]	
	ppm	Hz[c]		ppm	Hz[c]
R—CH$_3$	0.9	54	O=C—CH$_3$	2.3	126
			$\quad$ | $\quad$ R		
R—CH$_2$—R	1.3	78			
			R—CH$_2$—Cl	3.7	220
R$_3$CH	2.0	120			
			R—CH$_2$—Br	3.5	210
R$_2$C=CH$_2$	~5.0	300			
			R—CH$_2$—I	3.2	190
R$_2$C=CH | R	~5.3	320			
			RCH(—Cl)$_2$[d]	5.8	350
			R—O—CH$_3$	3.8	220
HC=CH / HC \ CH \ HC=CH (ring)	7.3	440	(R—O—)$_2$CH$_2$[d]	5.3	320
			R—C—H ‖ O	9.7	580
R—C≡C—H	2.5	150			
R$_2$C=C—CH$_3$ | R	~1.8	108	R—O—H	~5[e]	300[e]
			HC=CH / HC \ C—OH \ HC=CH (ring)	~7[e]	420[e]
HC=CH / HC \ C—CH$_3$ \ HC=CH (ring)	2.3	140			
			R—C—OH ‖ O	~11[e]	660[e]

[a] The proton undergoing resonance absorption is shown in heavy type. The group R denotes a saturated hydrocarbon chain.
[b] Relative to tetramethylsilane as 0.00 ppm.
[c] Spectrometer frequency, 60 MHz (14,100 gauss magnetic field).
[d] Note how the shift produced by two chlorines or two RO— groups is greater than, but by no means double, that produced by one chlorine or RO— group.
[e] Sensitive to solvent, concentration, and temperature.

chemical-shift difference between the methyl and methylene protons gives the two main groups of lines. These are split ("first-order" effect) into *equally spaced* sets of three and four lines by mutual magnetic interactions that are called "spin-spin interactions." Several of these lines are further discernibly split as the result of "second-order" spin-spin splitting.

How do we know what we are dealing with when there are so many lines present? First, the chemical shift is easily recognizable as such by the fact that the spacing between the main groups is directly proportional to the oscillator frequency v. If we double v, the spacing doubles. In contrast, the line spacings for the first-order splitting are *independent* of v, and for this reason the first-order splitting is easily recognized, also. Finally, the second-order splitting turns out to depend on v for rather complicated reasons; it tends to disappear as v is increased. (See Figure 7·14.)

It can be shown by isotopic substitution with heavy hydrogen (deuterium, D) that the three-four pattern of lines observed for spin-spin splitting with compounds having ethyl groups (XCH_2CH_3, see Figure 7·13) arises from magnetic interaction of each group of protons with the other. Deuterons have much smaller magnetic moments than protons, and substitution of one deuteron on the methyl of an ethyl group (XCH_2CH_2D) reduces the resonance of the methylene group to a triplet (actually somewhat broadened because of the

Figure 7·14   Comparison of the pmr spectra of 2-methyl-2-butanol at rf oscillator frequencies of 60, 100, and 220 MHz. The line at 165 Hz in the 60-MHz spectrum is due to the OH protons, and this is off-scale to the left in the 220-MHz spectrum. The large single line in the center of the spectra arises from the resonances of the six methyl hydrogens.

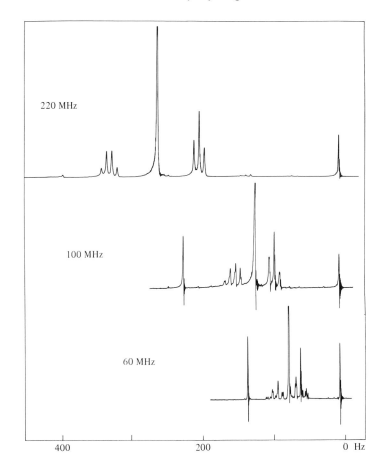

220 MHz

100 MHz

60 MHz

400   200   0 Hz

small magnetic effect of the deuteron); substitution of two deuterons (XCH_2 CHD_2) produces a doublet resonance with the splitting caused by the remaining proton. Three deuterons (XCH_2CD_3) give a one-line XCH_2 spectrum (see Figure 7·15). Thus, for this particular simple case, the multiplicity of lines can be seen to be ($n + 1$) where n is the number of protons on contiguous carbons. That the methylene resonance of an ethyl group is not complicated beyond the observed quartet by interaction of the methylene protons with each other is, for our purposes here, best condensed into a simple catechism. Protons with the *same* chemical shift do not normally split one another's absorption lines. Thus, only single resonance lines are observed for H_2, CH_4, C_2H_6, $(CH_3)_4Si$, and so on, and we say that the protons in such compounds are equivalent.

In general, the magnitude of the spin-spin splitting effect of one proton on another proton (or group of equivalent protons) depends on the number and kind of intervening chemical bonds, and on the spatial relations between the groups. For nonequivalent protons on adjacent saturated carbon atoms, the so-called *three-bond* splitting is normally about 5–8 Hz.

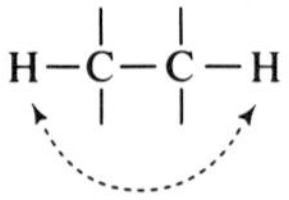

$$H-\underset{|}{\overset{|}{C}}-\underset{|}{\overset{|}{C}}-H$$

5-8
Hz

For protons separated by more than three bonds, the coupling is usually too small for observation unless a double or triple bond intervenes.

The ratios of the line intensities in spin-spin splitting patterns usually follow simple rules when the chemical shifts are large with respect to the splittings. A symmetrical doublet is produced by a single proton, a $1 : 2 : 1$ triplet by two protons in a group, a $1 : 3 : 3 : 1$ quartet by three protons in a group, $1 : 4 : 6 : 4 : 1$ quintet by four protons, and so on. The intensities follow the binomial coefficients.

The spectrum of $(CH_3O)_2CHCH_3$ (Figure 7·16) provides an excellent example of how nmr shows the presence of contiguous protons. The symmetrical doublet and $1 : 3 : 3 : 1$ quartet are typical of interaction between a single proton and an adjacent group of three. The methyl protons of the CH_3O groups are too far from the others to give demonstrable spin-spin splitting.

C. USE OF NUCLEAR MAGNETIC RESONANCE SPECTROSCOPY IN QUALITATIVE ANALYSIS

The solution of a typical qualitative analysis problem by nmr can be illustrated with the aid of the spectrum shown in Figure 7·17. Here, we see three principal groups of lines at 9.8, 2.4, and 1.0 ppm for a compound of formula C_3H_6O. The relative heights of the principal steps of the integrated spectrum show these groups to arise from one, two, and three hydrogens, respectively. The single

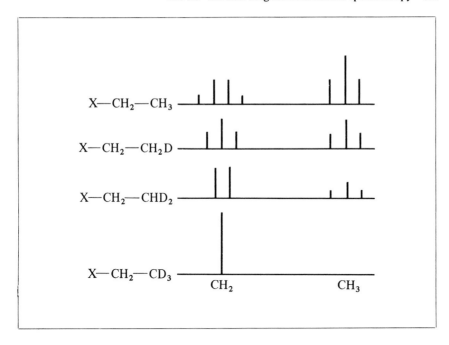

Figure 7·15 Schematic spectra of deuterated ethyl derivatives. The right-hand set of lines is always a triplet when observable because of the two protons of the X—CH₂— group.

Figure 7·16 Nuclear magnetic resonance spectrum of dimethyl acetal, $(CH_3O)_2CHCH_3$, at 60 MHz relative to TMS, 0.00 ppm.

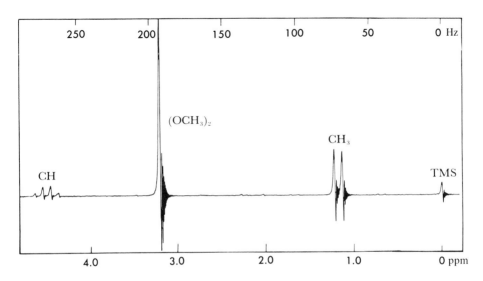

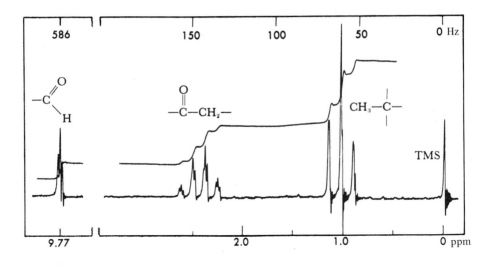

Figure 7·17   Nuclear magnetic resonance spectrum and integral for compound of formula C_3H_6O at 60 MHz relative to TMS.

hydrogen at 9.8 ppm is seen from Table 7·2 to have a chemical shift compatible with either $RCHO$ or RCO_2H. The latter possibility is, of course, excluded because the compound has only one oxygen. The only structure that can be written for C_3H_6O possessing an $RCHO$ group is CH_3CH_2CHO (propion-aldehyde), and this structure is completely compatible with the other features of the spectrum. Thus, the CH_3- resonance comes at 1.0 ppm (0.9 ppm predicted for CH_3R) and the $-CH_2-$ resonance at 2.4 ppm (2.3 ppm predicted for CH_3COR).

The spin-spin splitting pattern agrees with the assigned structure, there being the same 7 Hz spacings as in the characteristic three-four pattern of the CH_3CH_2- group shown by iodoethane (Figure 7·13). The doubling up (somewhat obscured by second-order splitting) of each of the $-CH_2-$ resonance lines is due to a small (~ 2 Hz) coupling between the $-CHO$ and $-CH_2-$ protons. This interaction also causes the $-CHO$ resonance to be split into a $1:2:1$ triplet, as expected from the $n+1$ rule. Three-bond couplings between $-CHO$ and adjacent $-CH_2-$ protons appear to be generally much smaller than $-CH_2-CH_3$ couplings.

D. NUCLEAR MAGNETIC RESONANCE AND RATE PROCESSES

An nmr spectrometer is unusual among instruments used to study molecules through absorption of electromagnetic radiation in that it acts like a camera with a relatively slow shutter speed. In fact, its "shutter speed" is quite commonly about the same as a conventional camera having exposure times of a 100th of a second or so. When we take an nmr spectrum of a molecule that is undergoing any rapid motion or reaction, the result is something like taking a picture of a turning spoked wheel with a box camera. If the wheel turns only once a minute, a photograph at a 100th of a second will show the individual spokes without much blurring. On the other hand, if the wheel turns 100 or more times a second, then a photograph does not show the individual spokes at all, but only the average outline of the rim and hub as a border to the gray of the spokes. Pictures showing blurred individual spokes result only when the wheel is turning neither very rapidly nor very slowly in relation to the camera shutter speed.

A vivid example of the use of nmr in the study of motions within molecules is given by the fluorine (^{19}F) resonance spectrum of 1-chloro-2-fluoro-1,1,2,2-tetrabromoethane. This molecule exists in three staggered rotational conformations [4–6]. Of these, [5] and [6] will have identical nmr spectra because for each the fluorine on one carbon is equivalently located with respect to the halogens on the other carbon. However, the fluorine of [4] has a different

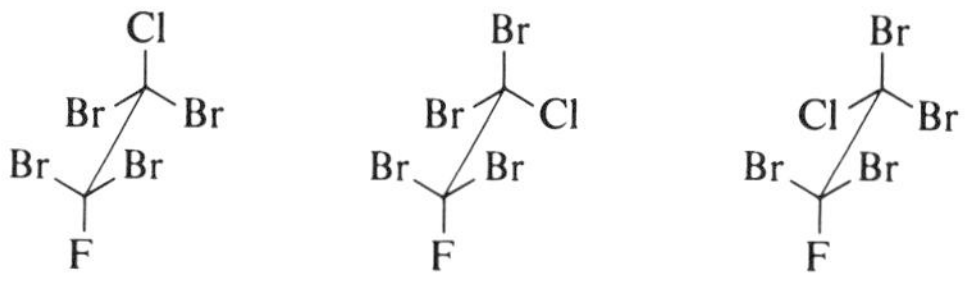

environment, being located between Br and Br, and should have a different chemical shift from the fluorines of [5] and [6]. In principle, therefore, one would expect to observe separate nmr resonances for the isomers; in fact, at 122°, rotation around the C—C bond occurs so rapidly that only a single fluorine resonance line is obtained (see Figure 7·18). The observed line position is an average position, the location of which depends on the lengths of time the molecules exist separately as [4], [5], and [6]. The rate of rotation about the C—C bond becomes slower with decreasing temperature, and is so slow at −40° that you can observe the separate resonances of [4] and the isomers [5] and [6] as shown in Figure 7·18. Studies of the changes in line shape of the nmr spectrum of 1-chloro-2-fluoro-1,1,2,2-tetrabromoethane with temperature provide a means of evaluating the amount of energy the molecules must have to allow rotation to take place. Because the halogens are large and do not move past each other easily, it takes fully 15 kcal/mole of thermal energy to interconvert [4], [5], and [6]. At 25°, the rate of interconversion is about 100 times per second.

The loss of identity of particular protons by rapid rate processes makes the nmr spectra of ethyl derivatives much simpler than they would otherwise be. Inspection of a ball-and-stick model of an ethyl derivative in the staggered conformation (see Figure 2·3) shows that one of the CH_3 hydrogens (marked here with *) should not have exactly the same chemical shift as the other two.

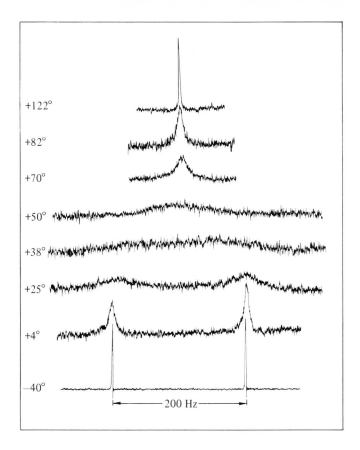

Figure 7·18 The ^{19}F spectrum at 56.4 MHz of 1-chloro-2-fluoro-1,1,2,2-tetra-bromoethane as a function of temperature.

However, rotation about the single bond in this case is sufficiently fast (10^{-6} sec) to average out the differences between the protons, and an average resonance line position is observed.

The nmr spectra of cyclohexane and substituted cyclohexanes have been extensively studied in connection with the interconversions of the boat and chair forms (Section 3·4B). The proton nmr spectrum of cyclohexane itself is a single line at room temperature because of rapid inversion ($\sim 10^6$ times per second) which averages to zero the chemical-shift differences of the equatorial and axial protons (Figure 3·6). At $-100°$, the pmr spectrum of cyclohexane is so complex as to be uninterpretable because all of the axial protons have different chemical shifts from the equatorial protons and especially complex spin-spin interactions occur. The device of substituting deuterium for hydrogen (Section 7·6B) has particular utility here. Undecadeuteriocyclohexane, $C_6D_{11}H$, gives a single proton nmr line at room temperature, while at $-100°$ and 60 MHz two equally intense lines are observed separated by 29 Hz. These lines arise from the axial and equatorial protons in [7] and [8], respectively. The rate of interconversion of [7] and [8] is on the average about

[7]   [8]

once per 10 seconds at $-100°$ so that it can be seen why separate resonance lines are obtained for the hydrogens in [7] and [8].

summary

Organic compounds can be isolated and purified by distillation, crystallization, or chromatographic techniques. The latter include (a) multistage liquid-liquid extractions; (b) column chromatography, in which a mixture is separated on a column of alumina or other solid absorbent by passage of appropriate solvents through the column; (c) vapor-phase chromatography, in which a gas stream carries the sample through a column packed with a nonvolatile liquid on a porous solid; and (d) paper and thin-layer chromatography (which will be discussed later).

A compound can often be identified by comparison of its physical and spectroscopic properties with those of known compounds published in the literature. If this is unsuccessful, elemental analysis and molecular weight determination (by freezing-point depression, etc., or by mass spectrometry) can be used to establish the molecular formula and, following this, the structure may be deduced by studies of its chemical transformation products, X-ray analysis, or spectroscopic analysis.

The three most important types of spectral analysis in routine use are infrared, electronic (ultraviolet and visible), and nuclear magnetic resonance spectroscopy. In each the absorption of a photon of electromagnetic radiation produces an excited state.

Absorption of infrared radiation causes changes in the vibrational and rotational energy levels of molecules. The stretching vibrations of C—H bonds are characterized by absorptions near 3000 cm^{-1} whereas their bending vibrations (and both kinds of vibration for other bonds to carbon) occur at lower frequencies. For carbon-carbon bonds, the greater the bond strength, the higher the frequency of vibration and the greater the energy required for excitation to a higher stretching vibrational state. Thus, C≡C absorptions occur near 2100 cm^{-1}, C=C near 1700 cm^{-1}, and C—C at still lower frequencies. The region below 1250 cm^{-1} is called the "fingerprint" region because here occur complex vibrations characteristic of the molecule as a whole rather than of specific bonds.

Absorption of ultraviolet or visible light causes electronic excitations. The usual practical short-wavelength limit for the ultraviolet region is about 1900 A. Saturated compounds and those containing isolated C=C or C≡C bonds are usually transparent down to this wavelength, but conjugated polyenes (and other unsaturated compounds) show strong absorption above 1900 A. In general, the greater the degree of conjugation, the lower will be the energy necessary for excitation and the longer will be the wavelength of absorption. Colored substances are those which absorb visible light and hence require intermediate energy photons for excitation.

Nuclear magnetic resonance spectroscopy (nmr) involves absorption of very low-energy radio-frequency photons by atomic nuclei in an applied magnetic field. The magnetic nuclei characteristic of atoms such as ^{1}H, ^{19}F, and ^{31}P can be oriented so as to be lined up with or opposed to the applied field and hence can differ very slightly in energy. This energy difference will depend, among other things, on the atom's environment in the molecule. In practice, either the frequency of the radiation or magnetic field can be kept constant while the other is varied. The chemical shift for protons is given in hertz (cycles per second) or ppm and is relative to some standard, usually tetramethylsilane (TMS). In general, the presence of electronegative groups or multiple bonds can cause large proton shifts from the standard.

When nonequivalent protons are attached to adjacent carbon atoms, there is a spin-spin splitting of 5–8 Hz. A single proton will cause a split of its neighbor's absorption into a symmetrical doublet, a pair of protons produces a 1 : 2 : 1 triplet, and so on.

Rate processes, particularly interconversion of conformational isomers, can be examined by nmr because the time interval for absorption of the radio-frequency photons used in nmr is often comparable to the rates of conformational interconversion.

exercises

7·1   Suppose you are asked to purify a compound by recrystallization from one of these solvents: water, ethanol, benzene, or heptane. The solubilities of the compound in grams per 100 ml of solvent at 20° and 80°, respectively, in the four solvents are water (0.15, 0.27), ethanol (0.70, 8.2), benzene (16, 38), heptane (36, 41). Which solvent would you choose for the purpose?

7·2   A liquid hydrocarbon, which does not decolorize bromine, has prominent bands near 1500 cm^{-1} and 3000 cm^{-1} in its infrared spectrum. Its mass spectrum shows a parent peak at 92 mass units. Suggest a likely structure for this compound.

7·3   A compound that is gaseous at room temperature was found on analysis to contain 88.9% carbon and 11.1% hydrogen. Its infrared spectrum contained a rather weak band near 2200 cm^{-1}. There are only two known compounds that fit this description. What are their names?

7·4   Explain how a mass spectrometer, capable of distinguishing between ions with m/e values differing by 1 part in 50,000, could be used to tell whether an ion of mass 29 is $C_2H_5^{\oplus}$ or $CHO^{\oplus}$.

7·5   Calculate the energy in kilocalories which corresponds to the absorption of 1 einstein of light of 5893 A (sodium D line) by sodium vapor. Explain how this absorption of light by sodium vapor might have chemical utility.

7·6   From the discussion in Section 7·5 about the structures of the ground and excited states of butadiene, see if you can rationalize why it is that the degree of π bonding between the 2,3 carbons is relatively larger in the excited state than in the ground state.

7·7   Sketch out the nmr spectrum and integral expected at 60 MHz with TMS as standard for the following substances. Show the line positions in hertz, neglecting spin-spin couplings smaller than 1 to 2 Hz and all second-order effects. Note that chlorine, bromine, and iodine (but not fluorine) act as nonmagnetic nuclei.

a. CH_3Cl
b. CH_3CH_2Cl
c. $(CH_3)_2CHCl$
d. $CH_3CD_2CH_2Cl$
e. $(CH_3)_3CCl$

f. $CHCl_2CHBr_2$
g. $CH_3(CH_2)_6CH_3$
h. $ClCH_2CH_2CH_2I$
i. $(ClCH_2)_3CH$

7·8   Figure 7·19 shows nmr spectra and integrals at 60 MHz for three simple organic compounds. Write a structure for each substance that is in accord with both its molecular formula and nmr spectrum. Explain how you assign each of the lines in the nmr spectrum.

7·9   Figure 7·20 shows the nmr spectrum of a compound, $C_5H_8O_2$. Which of the following structures fits the spectrum best? Explain.

$CH_3CH=CHCO_2CH_3$ $CH_2=CHCH_2CO_2CH_3$
$CH_2=CHCO_2CH_2CH_3$ $HCO_2CH_2CH_2CH=CH_2$
$CH_2=C(CH_3)CO_2CH_3$
$CH_2=C(OCH_3)COCH_3$ $\overline{OCH_2CH_2CH_2CH_2C=O}$
$(CH_2)_2CHCO_2CH_3$

7·10   In reasonably concentrated solutions in water, acetic acid acts as a weak acid (less than 1% dissociated). Acetic acid gives two nmr resonance lines at 2 and 11 ppm, relative to TMS, while water gives a line at 5 ppm. Nonetheless, mixtures of acetic acid and water are found to give just two lines. The position of one of these lines depends on the ratio of acetic acid to water concentration, while the other one does not. Explain and show how you would expect the position of the concentration-dependent line to change over the range of acetic acid concentrations from 0 to 100%.

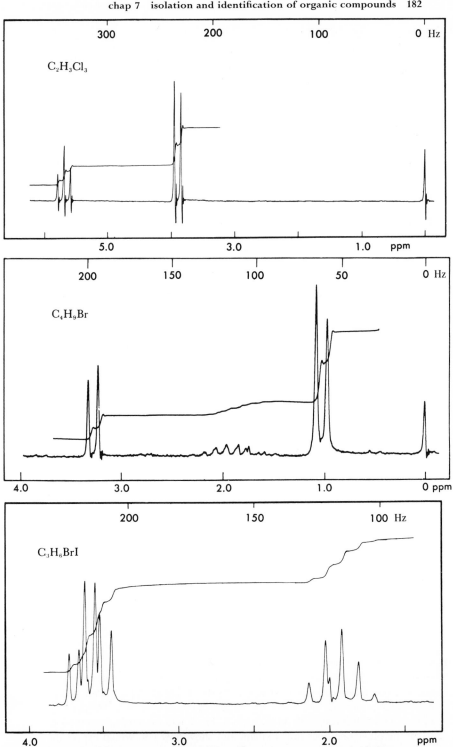

Figure 7·19   Nuclear magnetic resonance spectra and integrated spectra of some simple organic compounds at 60 MHz relative to TMS, 0.00 ppm. See Exercise 7·8.

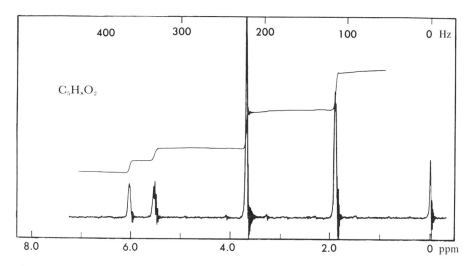

Figure 7·20 Spectrum of a compound $C_5H_8O_2$ at 60 MHz relative to TMS as standard. See Exercise 7·9.

7·11 Sketch out the principal features you would expect for the infrared and nmr spectra of the following substances. (It will be helpful to review pages 20 and 116 as well as Sections 7·4 and 7·6.)

a. $CH_3C\equiv CCH_3$

b. $CH_3C\equiv CH$ (expect a long-range nmr coupling of 3 Hz)

c. $CH_3CH_2C\equiv CCH_2CH_3$

d. $HC\equiv C-CH=CH-C\equiv CH$ (*cis* and *trans*)

e. $(CH_2)_8\ \overset{\displaystyle C}{\underset{\displaystyle C}{|||}}$

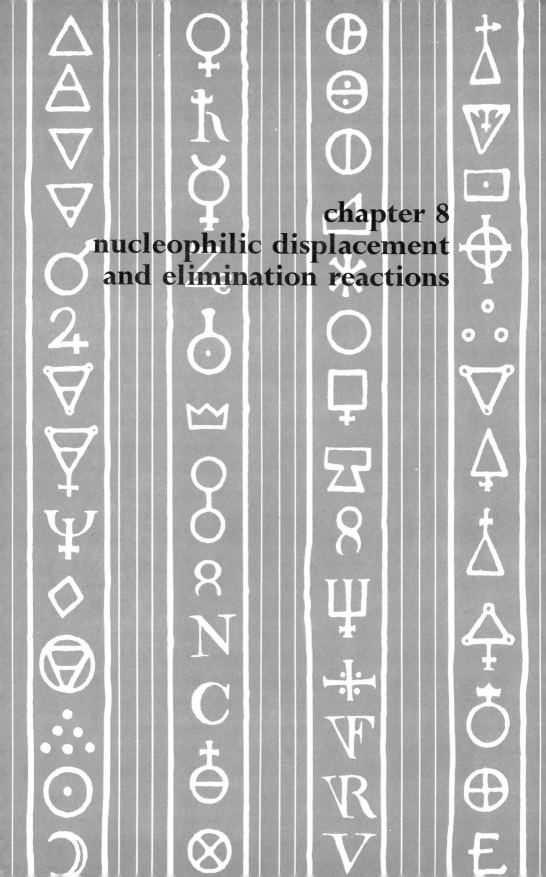

chapter 8
nucleophilic displacement
and elimination reactions

There are relatively few basic types of organic reactions. Of these, substitution, addition, and elimination are of the greatest importance. So far, we have discussed substitution of halogen for hydrogen, addition reactions of alkenes, and addition reactions of cycloalkanes with strained rings. In this chapter, the principal topics are the substitution or displacement by nucleophilic reagents of groups attached to carbon, and the formation of carbon-carbon double bonds by elimination reactions. These reactions are often profoundly influenced by seemingly minor variations in structure, reagents, solvent, and temperature. It is our purpose to show how these variations can be understood and, as far as possible, predicted in terms of the principles we have already discussed. Before proceeding, however, it will be helpful to consider the nomenclature of many of the organic reactants and products involved. The reader who is already acquainted with these nomenclature systems, or wishes to study them at a later time, can pass directly to Section 8·7.

8·1 organic derivatives of inorganic compounds

We have so far classified organic compounds by their functional groups; alkenes possess double bonds, alkynes triple bonds, and so on. Another useful classification of organic compound considers them as substitution products of water, ammonia, hydrogen sulfide, nitrous or nitric acids, and so on, through replacement of one or more hydrogens with an organic group. Reference to Table 8·1 shows how alcohols, ethers, carboxylic acids, anhydrides, and esters may be regarded as derivatives of water; mercaptans and sulfides as hydrogen sulfide derivatives; amines and amides as ammonia derivatives; alkyl nitrates as derivatives of nitric acid; alkyl nitrites as derivatives of nitrous acid; and alkyl sulfates as derivatives of sulfuric acid. For the sake of completeness, we include alkyl halides, which we have already classed as substituted alkanes, but which may also be considered as derivatives of the hydrogen halides.

8·2 alcohol nomenclature

In naming an alcohol by the IUPAC system, the ending -ol is appended to the name of the parent hydrocarbon. The latter corresponds to the longest straight chain of carbon atoms that includes the carbon carrying the hydroxyl group; it also includes the double bond when the compound is unsaturated. Note also that the -ol function normally takes precedence over a double bond, halogen, and alkyl in determining the suffix of the name. With respect to numbering, the carbon carrying the hydroxyl group is taken as number one if it terminates the chain, or the lowest number thereafter if it is attached to the nonterminal carbon.

		OH	CH₂CH₃
		$\vert$	$\vert$
CH_3-OH	CH_3CH_2-OH	$C_6H_5CH_2CHCH_2CH_3$	$ClCH_2CH=CCH_2OH$
methanol	ethanol	1-phenyl-2-butanol	4-chloro-2-ethyl-2-buten-1-ol

The most commonly used system for naming alcohols (and halides) combines the name of the appropriate alkyl group with the word *alcohol* (or

Table 8·1   Organic compounds as derivatives of common inorganic compounds

parent compound	organic derivative			
	class of compound		example	
H—O—H	R—O—H	alcohol	CH_3OH	methanol
	R—O—R′	ether	CH_3OCH_3	dimethyl ether
	$\underset{\parallel}{R—C}{}—O—H$ with O above C	carboxylic acid	$CH_3\overset{O}{\overset{\parallel}{C}}OH$	acetic acid
	$R—\overset{O}{\overset{\parallel}{C}}—O—R′$	carboxylic ester	$CH_3\overset{O}{\overset{\parallel}{C}}OCH_3$	methyl acetate
	$R—\overset{O}{\overset{\parallel}{C}}—O—\overset{O}{\overset{\parallel}{C}}—R$	carboxylic anhydride	$CH_3\overset{O}{\overset{\parallel}{C}}O\overset{O}{\overset{\parallel}{C}}CH_3$	acetic anhydride
H—S—H	R—S—H	thiol (mercaptan)	CH_3SH	methanethiol (methyl mercaptan)
	R—S—R′	thioether (sulfide)	CH_3SCH_3	methylthiomethane (dimethyl sulfide)
	$R—\overset{O}{\overset{\parallel}{C}}—S—H$	thio acid	$CH_3\overset{O}{\overset{\parallel}{C}}SH$	thioacetic acid
NH_3	RNH_2	prim. amine	CH_3NH_2	methylamine
	R_2NH	sec. amine	$(CH_3)_2NH$	dimethylamine
	R_3N	tert. amine	$(CH_3)_3N$	trimethylamine
	$R—\overset{O}{\overset{\parallel}{C}}—NH_2$	acylamine (unsubstituted amide)	$CH_3—\overset{O}{\overset{\parallel}{C}}—NH_2$	acetamide
	$R—\overset{O}{\overset{\parallel}{C}}—NHR$	(monosubstituted amide)	$CH_3—\overset{O}{\overset{\parallel}{C}}—NHCH_3$	N-methylacetamide
	$R—\overset{O}{\overset{\parallel}{C}}—NR_2$	(disubstituted amide)	$CH_3—\overset{O}{\overset{\parallel}{C}}—N(CH_3)_2$	N,N-dimethylacetamide
$H—ONO_2$ (nitric acid)	$R—ONO_2$	alkyl nitrate	$CH_3—ONO_2$	methyl nitrate
H—ONO (nitrous acid)	R—ONO	alkyl nitrite	$CH_3—ONO$	methyl nitrite
$H—NO_2$ (unknown)	$R—NO_2$	nitroalkane	$CH_3—NO_2$	nitromethane

Table 8·1   Organic compounds as derivatives of common inorganic compounds (*continued*)

parent compound	organic derivative			
	class of compound		example	
H—NO (hypo-nitrous acid, monomeric form)	R—NO	nitrosoalkane	CH$_3$—NO	nitroso-methane
$\begin{array}{c} O \\ \parallel \\ H-O-S-OH \\ \parallel \\ O \end{array}$ (sulfuric acid)	$\begin{array}{c} O \\ \parallel \\ R-O-S-OH \\ \parallel \\ O \end{array}$	alkyl hydrogen sulfate	$\begin{array}{c} O \\ \parallel \\ CH_3-O-S-OH \\ \parallel \\ O \end{array}$	methyl hydrogen sulfate
	$\begin{array}{c} O \\ \parallel \\ R-O-S-O-R \\ \parallel \\ O \end{array}$	dialkyl sulfate	$\begin{array}{c} O \\ \parallel \\ CH_3-O-S-OCH_3 \\ \parallel \\ O \end{array}$	dimethyl sulfate
H—X (X=F, Cl, Br, I)	R—X	alkyl halide (haloalkane)	CH$_3$—F	methyl fluoride (fluoro-methane)

halide). The system works well whenever the group name is simple and easily visualized:

$$\begin{array}{c} CH_3 \\ | \\ CH_3-C-OH \\ | \\ CH_3 \end{array} \qquad \begin{array}{c} CH_3 \\ | \\ CH_3-C-CH_2-OH \\ | \\ H \end{array} \qquad CH_2{=}CH-CH_2-Cl$$

t-butyl alcohol   isobutyl alcohol   allyl chloride

A prevalent but unofficial procedure names alcohols as substitution products of carbinol, CH$_3$OH, a synonym of methanol. Many alcohols that are cumbersome to name by the IUPAC system may have structures that are more easily visualized when named by the carbinol system.

$$\begin{array}{c} H_3C \quad H \quad CH_3 \\ | \quad\ | \quad\ | \\ CH_3-C-C-C-CH_3 \\ | \quad\ | \quad\ | \\ H_3C \quad OH \quad CH_3 \end{array} \qquad \begin{array}{c} H \\ | \\ C_6H_5-C-CH_2CH{=}CH_2 \\ | \\ OH \end{array}$$

di-*t*-butylcarbinol   allylphenylcarbinol
(2,2,4,4-tetramethyl-3-   (1-phenyl-3-buten-1-ol
pentanol by   by IUPAC system)
IUPAC system)

The carbinol system has been extended to include other derivatives. Alkyl halides and alkylamines, for example, are frequently called carbinyl halides and carbinylamines.

cyclohexylcarbinyl chloride

$$C_6H_5-CH-CH_2CH_3$$
$$|$$
$$NH_2$$

ethylphenylcarbinylamine

8·3 ether nomenclature

Symmetrical ethers (both R groups in R—O—R being the same) are named simply dialkyl, dialkenyl, or diaryl ethers, as the case may be. The prefix *di-* to denote disubstitution is sometimes omitted as superfluous, but most current opinion regards this form of redundancy desirable to help prevent errors. Clearly, when an ether is unsymmetrical, the names of both R groups must be included:

$CH_3CH_2-O-CH_2CH_3$

diethyl ether

$CH_3-O-CH=CH_2$

methyl vinyl ether

$C_6H_5-O-C_6H_5$

diphenyl ether

8·4 carboxylic acid nomenclature

According to the IUPAC system, carboxylic acids with saturated alkyl chains are called alkanoic acids. The suffix *-oic* is added to the name of the longest continuous-chain hydrocarbon in the molecule that includes the carbon of the carboxyl ($-CO_2H$) group. Note that the carboxyl function normally takes precedence over the hydroxyl function and that the carboxyl carbon is C-1.

$$\overset{Cl}{\underset{|}{}}$$
$$CH_3CH_2CH_2CHCO_2H$$

2-chloropentanoic acid

$$\overset{CH_3}{\underset{|}{}} \quad \overset{OH}{\underset{|}{}}$$
$$CH_3CHCH=CHCHCO_2H$$

2-hydroxy-5-methyl-3-hexenoic acid

The simple alkanoic acids have long been known by descriptive but unsystematic names that correspond variously to their properties, odors, or natural origin. It seems likely that for the following acids these trivial names will not be completely superseded by the more systematic names (shown in parentheses) for some time to come.

HCO_2H	formic acid	(methanoic acid)	(L. *formica,* ant)
CH_3CO_2H	acetic acid	(ethanoic acid)	(L. *acetum,* vinegar)
$CH_3CH_2CO_2H$	propionic acid	(propanoic acid)	(*proto* + Gr. *pion,* fat)
$CH_3CH_2CH_2CO_2H$	butyric acid	(butanoic acid)	(L. *butyrum,* butter)

$$\overset{H_3C}{\underset{H_3C}{}}\!\!\diagdown\!\!\!\!\!\diagup\!\!CHCO_2H$$ isobutyric acid   (2-methylpropanoic acid)

Esters of carboxylic acids carry the suffix *-oate* in place of *-oic* (or *-ate* in place of *-ic* for acids with descriptive names).

$$\underset{\text{methyl propionate}}{\underset{\text{(methyl propanoate)}}{CH_3CH_2\overset{\overset{\displaystyle O}{\|}}{C}OCH_3}}
\qquad
\underset{\text{ethyl phenylacetate}}{C_6H_5CH_2\overset{\overset{\displaystyle O}{\|}}{C}OCH_2CH_3}
\qquad
\underset{\text{ethyl 2-chloro-3-butenoate}}{CH_2{=}CH\overset{\overset{\displaystyle Cl}{|}}{C}H\overset{\overset{\displaystyle O}{\|}}{C}OCH_2CH_3}$$

Alkanoic acids are sometimes called **aliphatic acids** (or fatty acids) to distinguish them from those containing a benzene ring and which are called **aromatic acids.** The term aliphatic is often used for noncyclic systems in general.

8·5 the use of greek letters to denote substituent positions

Considerable use is made of the Greek letters α, β, γ, and so on to designate successive positions along a hydrocarbon chain. The carbon directly attached to the principal functional group is denoted as α, the second as β, and so on.

$$\underset{\substack{\alpha,\alpha\text{-dimethylallyl alcohol}\\(2\text{-methyl-3-buten-2-ol})}}{CH_2{=}CH{-}\overset{\overset{\displaystyle CH_3}{|}}{\underset{\underset{\displaystyle CH_3}{|}}{C}}{-}OH}
\qquad\qquad
\underset{\substack{\alpha,\beta,\beta\text{-tribromoisobutyric acid}\\(2,3,3\text{-tribromo-2-methyl-}\\ \text{propanoic acid})}}{Br_2CH{-}\overset{\overset{\displaystyle CH_3}{|}}{\underset{\underset{\displaystyle Br}{|}}{C}}{-}CO_2H}$$

Note that the α position of an acid is at the number 2 carbon atom. In general, the use of these names is to be deplored, but since it is widespread, cognizance of the system is important.

8·6 single- or multiple-word names

A troublesome point in naming chemical compounds concerns the circumstances that govern whether a compound is written as a single word (e.g., methylamine, trimethylcarbinol) or as two or more words (e.g., methyl alcohol, methyl ethyl ether). When a compound is named as a derivative of substances such as methane, ammonia, acetic acid, or carbinol because of the substitution of hydrogen for some other atom or group, its name is written

$$\underset{\text{triphenylmethane}}{(C_6H_5)_3CH}
\qquad\qquad
\underset{\text{methylethylamine}}{CH_3{-}\overset{}{\underset{\underset{\displaystyle H}{|}}{N}}{-}C_2H_5}$$

$$\underset{\text{dimethylallylcarbinol}}{CH_2{=}CH{-}CH_2{-}\overset{}{\underset{\underset{\displaystyle OH}{|}}{C}}(CH_3)_2}
\qquad\qquad
\underset{\text{vinylacetic acid}}{CH_2{=}CH{-}CH_2CO_2H}$$

$$\underset{\text{methylmagnesium iodide}}{CH_3MgI}
\qquad\qquad
\underset{\text{phenyllithium}}{C_6H_5Li}$$

as a single word. This is correct because we do not speak of "a methane" but of the compound "methane." It follows that a derivative such as $(C_6H_5)_3CH$ is called triphenylmethane and not triphenyl methane. We do speak, however, of an alcohol, an ether, a halide, acid, ester, sulfide, or ketone, for these words correspond to types of compounds rather than particular compounds. Therefore additional words are required to fully identify particular alcohols, ethers, halides, and so on. Several examples are given.

C_2H_5I
ethyl iodide

$$CH_3\overset{\overset{\textstyle O}{\|}}{C}OH$$
acetic acid

$(CH_3)_2CHOH$
isopropyl alcohol

$$CH_3\overset{\overset{\textstyle O}{\|}}{C}OCH_3$$
methyl acetate

$$CH_3\overset{\overset{\textstyle O}{\|}}{C}CH_2CH_3$$
methyl ethyl ketone

CH_3SCH_3
dimethyl sulfide

$CH_3OCH_2CH_3$
methyl ethyl ether

$$(CH_3\overset{\overset{\textstyle O}{\|}}{C})_2O$$
acetic anhydride

nucleophilic displacement reactions

8·7   general considerations

Broadly defined, a displacement reaction involves the replacement of one functional group (X) by another (Y):

$$RX + Y \longrightarrow RY + X$$

We are here concerned with *nucleophilic* displacement reactions of alkyl derivatives; these are *ionic* or *polar* reactions involving the attack by a nucleophile (i.e., an electron-pair donating reagent) at carbon. A typical example is the reaction of hydroxide ion with methyl bromide to displace bromide ion. The electron pair of the C—O bond to be formed can be regarded as

$$H\colon\!\ddot{O}\colon^{\ominus} \quad CH_3\colon\!\ddot{B}r\colon \quad\longrightarrow\quad CH_3\colon\!\ddot{O}\colon\!H \ + \ \colon\!\ddot{B}r\colon^{\ominus}$$

donated by the hydroxide ion, whereas the electron pair of the C—Br bond to be broken departs with the leaving bromide ion. The name for this type of reaction is abbreviated S_N, S for substitution and N for nucleophilic.

A number of nucleophilic reagents commonly encountered in S_N reactions are listed in Table 8·2 along with the names of the products obtained when they react with methyl chloride. The nucleophile may be an anion, $Y\colon^{\ominus}$, or a

Table 8·2   Typical S_N displacement reactions of alkyl halides, RX

1.		$R \mid :X + Y:^\ominus \rightarrow R:Y + X:^\ominus$		
nucleophilic agent	**product**	**product name, R = CH_3**	**useful solvents**	
$Cl^\ominus$	RCl	methyl chloride	acetone, ethanol	
$Br^\ominus$	RBr	methyl bromide	acetone, ethanol	
$I^\ominus$	RI	methyl iodide	acetone, ethanol	
$^\ominus OH$	ROH	methyl alcohol	water, dioxane–water	
$^\ominus OCH_3$	$ROCH_3$	dimethyl ether	methyl alcohol	
$^\ominus SCH_3$	$RSCH_3$	dimethyl sulfide	ethyl alcohol	
$CH_3-C\overset{O}{\underset{O^\ominus}{\big\langle}}$	$RO-C\overset{O}{\underset{CH_3}{\big\langle}}$	methyl acetate	acetic acid, ethanol	
$^\ominus:C\equiv N$	RCN	acetonitrile	acetone, dimethyl sulfoxide	
$HC\equiv C:^\ominus$	$RC\equiv CH$	propyne	liquid ammonia	
$^\ominus:CH(CO_2C_2H_5)_2$	$RCH(CO_2C_2H_5)_2$	diethyl methylmalonate	ethyl alcohol	
$^\ominus:NH_2$	RNH_2	methylamine	liquid ammonia	
$:\overset{\ominus}{N}=\overset{\oplus}{N}=\overset{\ominus}{N}:$	RN_3	methyl azide	acetone	
phthalimide $N:^\ominus$	RN phthalimide	N-methylphthalimide	N,N-dimethylformamide	
$NO_2^\ominus$	RNO_2	nitromethane	N,N-dimethylformamide	
2.		$R \mid :X + Y: \rightarrow R:\overset{\oplus}{Y} + \overset{\ominus}{X}:$		
nucleophilic agent	**product**	**product name, R = CH_3**	**useful solvents**	
$(CH_3)_3N:$	$R\overset{\oplus}{N}(CH_3)_3\ \overset{\ominus}{X}$	tetramethylammonium chloride	ether, benzene	
$(C_6H_5)_3P:$	$R\overset{\oplus}{P}(C_6H_5)_3\ \overset{\ominus}{X}$	triphenylmethylphosphonium chloride	ether, benzene	
$(CH_3)_2S:$	$R\overset{\oplus}{S}(CH_3)_2\ \overset{\ominus}{X}$	trimethylsulfonium chloride	ether, benzene	

Table 8·2   Typical S_N displacement reactions of alkyl halides, RX *(continued)*

3.		$R\overset{.}{:}X + H:Y: \;\rightarrow\; R:\overset{\oplus}{\underset{.}{Y}}\overset{.}{:}H + X:^{\ominus} \;\rightarrow\; R:Y: + H:X$	
nucleophilic agent	**product**	**product name, R $= CH_3$**	**useful solvents**
H_2O	ROH	methyl alcohol	water, dioxane–water
CH_3OH	$ROCH_3$	dimethyl ether	methyl alcohol
CH_3CO_2H	$RO\overset{\displaystyle O}{\overset{\|}{C}}CH_3$	methyl acetate	acetic acid
NH_3	RNH_2	methylamine	ammonia, methanol

neutral molecule, Y: or HY:, and the operation of each is illustrated in the following general equations for a compound RX:

$$R\!-\!X \;+\; Y:^{\ominus} \;\longrightarrow\; R\!-\!Y \;+\; X:^{\ominus}$$

$$R\!-\!X \;+\; Y: \;\longrightarrow\; R\!-\!\overset{\oplus}{Y} \;+\; X:^{\ominus}$$

$$R\!-\!X \;+\; HY: \;\longrightarrow\; R\overset{\oplus}{Y}H \;+\; X:^{\ominus} \;\longrightarrow\; RY: \;+\; HX$$

The wide range of products listed in Table 8·2 shows the synthetic utility of S_N reactions. Displacement can result in the formation of bonds between carbon and chlorine, bromine, iodine, oxygen, sulfur, carbon, nitrogen, and phosphorus.

Nucleophilic displacements are by no means confined to alkyl halides. Other alkyl derivatives include alcohols, ethers, esters, and "onium ions."[1] Some illustrative reactions of several different alkyl compounds with various nucleophiles are assembled in Table 8·3.

As we shall see in a later section, the mechanism of an S_N reaction and the reactivity of a given alkyl compound RX toward a nucleophile Y depend upon the nature of R, X, and Y, and upon the nature of the solvent. For reaction to occur at a reasonable rate, it is very important to select a solvent that will dissolve both the alkyl compound and the nucleophilic reagent. Furthermore, the nucleophile may require considerable assistance from the solvent in breaking the slightly polar C—X bond. However, the highly polar

---

[1] Examples of -onium cations follow:

$R_4N^{\oplus}$	$R_4P^{\oplus}$	$R_3O^{\oplus}$	$R_3C^{\oplus}$
Tetraalkylammonium	*Tetraalkylphosphonium*	*Trialkyloxonium*	*Trialkylcarbonium*

$R_3S^{\oplus}$	$R\!-\!\overset{\oplus}{N}\!\equiv\!N:$	$R_2I^{\oplus}$
Trialkylsulfonium	*Alkyldiazonium*	*Dialkyliodonium*

nucleophilic agents most used (e.g., NaBr, NaCN, H_2O) are seldom soluble in the solvents that best dissolve slightly polar organic compounds. In practice, relatively polar solvents, or solvent mixtures, such as acetone, aqueous acetone, ethanol, aqueous dioxane, and so on are found to provide the best compromise for reactions between alkyl compounds and salt-like nucleophilic reagents. A number of useful solvents for typical S_N reactions are listed in Table 8·2.

8·8 mechanisms of S_N displacements

Two mechanisms may be written for the reaction of methyl chloride with hydroxide ion in aqueous solution that differ in the timing of bond breaking in relation to bond making. In the ensuing discussion, we are not implying that these are the only possible mechanisms that one could conceive for this reaction. They appear to be the most plausible ones and by confining our attention to two possibilities we can greatly simplify the discussion. In the first mechanism, A, the reaction is written as taking place in two steps, the first of which involves a *slow* and reversible dissociation of methyl chloride

Table 8·3 S_N displacement reactions of various types of compounds, RX

type of compound, RX	reaction
alkyl chloride	$R-Cl + I^{\ominus} \rightleftharpoons RI + Cl^{\ominus}$
alkyl bromide	$R-Br + I^{\ominus} \rightleftharpoons RI + Br^{\ominus}$
alkyl iodide	$R-I + CH_3O^{\ominus} \longrightarrow ROCH_3 + I^{\ominus}$
dialkyl sulfate	$R-OSO_2OR + CH_3\overset{\ominus}{O} \longrightarrow ROCH_3 + {}^{\ominus}OSO_2OR$
benzenesulfonate ester	$R-O\overset{O}{\underset{O}{\overset{\|}{\underset{\|}{S}}}}\!\!-\!\!\bigcirc + H_2O \longrightarrow ROH + HO\overset{O}{\underset{O}{\overset{\|}{\underset{\|}{S}}}}\!\!-\!\!\bigcirc$
acetate ester	$R-O\overset{O}{\overset{\|}{C}}CH_3 + H_2O \longrightarrow ROH + HOCCH_3$
alcohol	$R-OH + HBr \longrightarrow RBr + H_2O$
ether	$R-OR' + HBr \longrightarrow RBr + R'OH$
ammonium ion	$R-\overset{\oplus}{N}R_3' + HO^{\ominus} \longrightarrow ROH + NR_3'$
iodonium ion	$R-\overset{\oplus}{I}-R' + OH^{\ominus} \longrightarrow ROH + R'I$
diazonium ion	$R-\overset{\oplus}{N}\equiv N + H_2O \longrightarrow ROH + H^{\oplus} + N_2$

to methyl cation and chloride ion. The second step involves a *fast* reaction between methyl cation and hydroxide ion (or water) to yield methanol.

Mechanism A:

$$CH_3-Cl \xrightleftharpoons{\text{slow}} CH_3^{\oplus} + Cl^{\ominus}$$

$$CH_3^{\oplus} + OH^{\ominus} \xrightarrow{\text{fast}} CH_3OH$$

$$(\text{or } CH_3^{\oplus} + H_2O \longrightarrow CH_3\overset{\oplus}{O}H_2 \xrightarrow{OH^{\ominus}} CH_3OH + H_2O)$$

In the second mechanism, B, the reaction proceeds in a single step. Attack of hydroxide ion at carbon occurs simultaneously with the loss of chloride ion; that is, the carbon-oxygen bond is formed at the same time that the carbon-chlorine bond is broken.

Mechanism B:

$$H\ddot{\text{O}}\text{:}^{\ominus} \quad CH_3\text{:}\ddot{\text{C}}\text{l:} \xrightarrow{\text{slow}} CH_3OH + \text{:}\ddot{\text{C}}\text{l:}^{\ominus}$$

Of the two mechanisms, A requires that the reaction rate be determined solely by the rate of the first step (cf. earlier discussion, Section 2·5B). This means that the rate at which methanol is formed (measured in moles per unit volume per unit time) will depend on the concentration of methyl chloride, and not on the hydroxide ion concentration, because hydroxide ion is not utilized except in a fast *secondary reaction*. In contrast, mechanism B requires the rate to depend on the concentrations of both reagents since the slow step involves collisions between hydroxide ions and methyl chloride molecules. More precisely, the reaction rate (v) may be expressed in terms of Equation 8·1 for mechanism A and Equation 8·2 for mechanism B.

$$v = k[CH_3Cl] \tag{8·1}$$
$$v = k[CH_3Cl][OH^{\ominus}] \tag{8·2}$$

Customarily, v is expressed in moles of product formed per liter of solution per unit of time (most frequently in seconds). The concentration terms $[CH_3Cl]$ and $[OH^{\ominus}]$ are in units of moles per liter, and the proportionality constant k (called the specific-rate constant) has the dimensions of sec^{-1} for mechanism A and $mole^{-1} \times liters \times sec^{-1}$ for mechanism B.

It is useful to speak of both the *order of a reaction with respect to a specific reactant* and the *overall order of a reaction*. The order of a reaction with respect to a given reactant is the power to which the concentration of that particular reagent must be raised to have direct proportionality between concentration and reaction rate. According to Equation 8·2 the rate of the methyl chloride–hydroxide ion reaction is first order with respect to both reagents. In Equation 8·1 the rate is first order in methyl chloride; the order with respect to hydroxide ion may be said to be zero since $[OH^{\ominus}]^0 = 1$. The overall order of reaction is the sum of the orders of the respective reactants. Thus, Equations 8·1 and 8·2 express the rates of first-order and second-order reactions, respectively.

We have, then, a kinetic method for distinguishing between the two possible mechanisms, A and B, that we are considering. Experimentally, the rate of formation of methyl alcohol is found to be proportional to the concentrations of both methyl chloride and hydroxide ion. The reaction rate is second order overall and is expressed correctly by Equation 8·2. From this we infer that the mechanism of the reaction is the single-step bimolecular process B. Reactions having this type of mechanism are generally classified as bimolecular nucleophilic substitutions, often designated S_N2 (S for substitution, N for nucleophilic, and 2 for bimolecular).

On the other hand, the rate of the reaction of t-butyl chloride with aqueous base depends only on the concentration of the chloride. The concentration of the base (and its strength) is irrelevant, as long as there is enough to neutralize the acid produced in the reaction. (Bicarbonate ion serves just as well as hydroxide ion for this purpose.)

$$(CH_3)_3CCl \xrightarrow{\text{slow}} (CH_3)_3C^{\oplus} + Cl^{\ominus}$$

$$(CH_3)_3C^{\oplus} + H_2O \xrightarrow{\text{fast}} (CH_3)_3\overset{\oplus}{C}OH_2 \xrightarrow{\text{B:}} (CH_3)_3COH + BH^{\oplus}$$

$$(\text{or } (CH_3)_3C^{\oplus} + OH^{\ominus} \xrightarrow{\text{fast}} (CH_3)_3COH)$$

Mechanisms such as this are designated S_N1 reactions because they are nucleophilic substitutions in which the first-order kinetics suggest that the rate-controlling step is unimolecular. That is, the rate is proportional to the concentration of alkyl halide and not to the concentration of the base.

Many S_N reactions are carried out using the solvent as the nucleophilic agent. They are called **solvolysis** reactions; specific solvents such as water, ethanol, acetic acid, and formic acid produce hydrolysis, ethanolysis, acetolysis, and formolysis reactions, respectively. The rates of all solvolysis reactions are necessarily first order since the solvent is in such great excess that its concentration does not change effectively during reaction, and hence its contribution to the rate does not change. But this does not mean that reaction is necessarily proceeding by an S_N1 mechanism, particularly in solvents such as water, alcohols, or amines, which are expected to be reasonably good nucleophilic agents.

8·9   energetics of S_N1 and S_N2 reactions

We have seen that the S_N2 reaction of methyl chloride with hydroxide is a one-step process in which no intermediate compound is formed. As the hydroxide ion begins to bond to carbon, the carbon-chlorine bond begins to break and one can formulate the course of the reaction as in Equation 8·3.

$$HO^{\ominus} \overset{H}{\underset{H}{\overset{|}{C}}}-Cl \longrightarrow \left[H-\overset{H}{\underset{H}{\overset{\delta\ominus}{O}}}\cdots\overset{|}{C}\cdots\overset{\delta\ominus}{Cl} \right]^{\ddagger} \longrightarrow HO-\overset{H}{\underset{H}{\overset{/}{C}}} + Cl \qquad (8\cdot3)$$

The transition state in Equation 8·3 which is designated by ‡ is not a molecule in the ordinary sense. It is simply a stage in the transition from reactants to products. Its importance derives from the fact that it represents the point of *highest* energy along the *lowest*-energy (most favorable) reaction path. There are many routes by which one could imagine the atoms of the reactants being rearranged so as to give the products, but most of them would involve transition states of exorbitantly high energy. (See mechanism A, Section 8·8, that involves formation of a primary carbonium ion, for one such route.) The course of any reaction—*its mechanism*— is that for which the highest energy state lying on the reaction path is lower than the lowest energy state on all other paths. Figure 8·1 shows the energy profile of the methyl chloride–hydroxide ion reaction.

The transition state is at the top of an energy barrier that must be overcome for reaction to occur but, in geographical terms, it should be considered as the highest point along the path for the most favorable *pass* between reactants and products. The transition state is not a *peak* between reactants and products.

The rate of a reaction will be expected to be determined by the height of the energy barrier to be overcome—that is, the energy difference between reactants and transition state. The energy of the final products is not relevant to the rate, although ΔG for the overall reaction must be negative for the equilibrium constant to be greater than unity (Section 2·5A).

In the so-called "theory of absolute reaction rates," the reaction rate is determined by the free-energy difference between reactants and transition

Figure 8·1   Energy profile for the reaction of a molecule of methyl chloride and a hydroxide ion. The reaction coordinate indicates the extent of reaction and might be taken as the difference in the Cl to C and C to OH distances, thus, in principle, covering the range from $-\infty$ to $+\infty$.

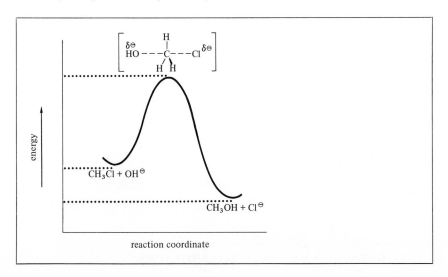

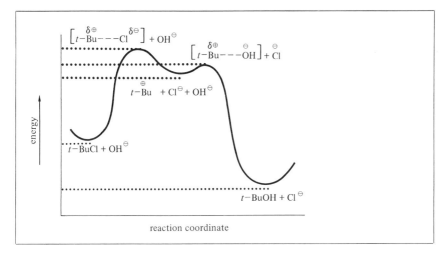

Figure 8·2   Energy profile for reaction of t-butyl chloride, $(CH_3)_3Cl$, with hydroxide ion.

state ($\Delta G^{\ddagger}$). This quantity, like ΔG, can be equated to a heat term and an entropy term:

$$\Delta G = \Delta H - T\,\Delta S$$
$$\Delta G^{\ddagger} = \Delta H^{\ddagger} - T\,\Delta S^{\ddagger}$$

The heat of activation, $\Delta H^{\ddagger}$, is usually the dominant term and can be thought of as representing the thermal energy a colliding pair of reactants must possess (in excess of the average) to reach the transition state. As the temperature is raised, more and more collisions will be between reactants having sufficient thermal energy to attain the transition state and the reaction rate will increase. Experimental values for $\Delta H^{\ddagger}$ are, in fact, determined by measuring the effect of temperature on the reaction rate.

The entropy of activation, $\Delta S^{\ddagger}$, is related to the difference in the degree of vibrational, rotational, and translational freedom of the reactants and the transition state. (Compare this with the description given previously for ΔS, in Section 2·5A.) The more freedom that the transition state possesses relative to the reactants, the more positive will be $\Delta S^{\ddagger}$ and the greater the reaction rate. Conversely, the less freedom in the transition state relative to reactants, the more negative $\Delta S^{\ddagger}$ will be and the slower the reaction rate. In simple terms, a transition state that is loose, with substantial freedom in the locations for the constituent atoms, will be favored over one in which a high degree of organization is required.

The energy profile for the S_N1 reaction of t-butyl chloride with hydroxide ion is given in Figure 8·2. This profile shows two transition states. The first leads to the formation of a discrete intermediate, $(CH_3)_3C^{\oplus}$; the second, with a low barrier, corresponds to the very rapid reaction of the intermediate carbonium ion with hydroxide ion (or water) to form the products. The overall reaction is believed to be unimolecular because the rate is independent of the concentration of hydroxide ion. Hydroxide ion is involved only in a fast following step, not in the initial slow ionization (see Section 8·8). Hydroxide ion is shown as an ingredient of the first transition state in the diagram only for the purpose of preserving the correct stoichiometry. It takes no part in the reaction until the critical ionization stage has been passed.

In Section 4·4E we discussed reaction rates in terms of energies of possible intermediates that might be formed. A more rigorous procedure is to consider not ΔG for formation of the intermediate but $\Delta G^{\ddagger}$ for formation of the transition state. In the case of the ionization of t-butyl chloride, this does not make much difference because the energy of the t-butyl cation formed as the intermediate is not likely to be greatly different from that of the transition state that precedes it. How can we expect this? Largely on the basis of intuition (tempered by experience) that an alkyl carbonium ion is likely to react very rapidly with chloride ion to form t-butyl chloride. The reaction between the more basic $OH^{\ominus}$ and t-$Bu^{\oplus}$ will be expected to have a still smaller $\Delta G^{\ddagger}$, and this is reflected in Figure 8·2 by the smaller height of the second barrier as compared to the first. The anion, $SbF_6{}^{\ominus}$, of the super acid, $HSbF_6$, (Section 1·2C), has such a small tendency to react with t-$Bu^{\oplus}$ that it is possible to prepare t-$Bu^{\oplus}$ $SbF_6{}^{\ominus}$ and determine the nmr spectrum of the cation.

8·10   stereochemistry of S_N2 displacements

If we pause to consider the S_N2 reaction of methyl chloride with hydroxide ion in more detail, we can think of two simple ways in which the reaction

Figure 8·3   Back-side (inverting) and front-side (noninverting) attack of hydroxide ion on methyl chloride, as visualized with ball-and-stick models.

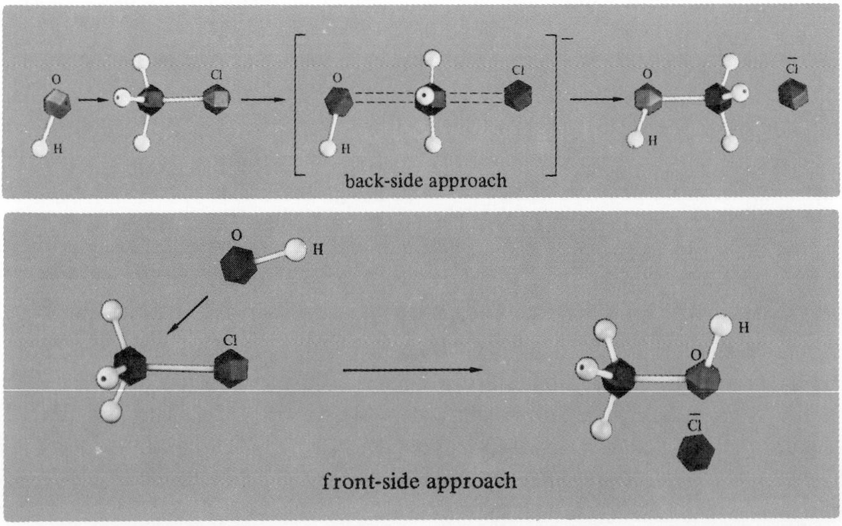

could be effected; these differ in the direction of approach of the reagents, one to the other (see Figure 8·3). The hydroxide ion might attack methyl chloride directly at the site where the chlorine is attached (i.e., front-side approach). Alternatively, hydroxide might approach the molecule from the rear to cause expulsion of chloride ion from the front (i.e., back-side approach).

There is no simple way of proving which of these paths is followed in this particular case, but the arguments in favor of the back-side approach are very strong. First, the transition state for this approach will have the oxygen and chlorine atoms well separated; that is, the charge in the transition state will be dispersed. The front-side approach would not disperse the negative charge to nearly the same extent and hence would be a less favorable arrangement. Second, in the case of cyclic compounds, the two types of displacement predict different products. For example, an S_N2 reaction between *cis*-3-chloro-1-methylcyclopentane and hydroxide ion would give the *cis* alcohol by front-side attack but the *trans* alcohol by back-side attack (Figure 8·4). The actual product is the *trans* alcohol, from which we infer that reaction occurs by back-side displacement.

Third, in the case of certain kinds of stereoisomers of open-chain compounds, back-side displacement has been conclusively proven. This is discussed later in the book (Section 14·9).

8·11 structural and solvent effects in S_N reactions

We shall consider first the relation between the structures of alkyl derivatives and their reaction rates toward a given nucleophile. This will be followed by a discussion of the relative reactivities of various nucleophiles toward a given alkyl derivative. Finally, we shall comment on the role of the solvent in S_N reactions.

Figure 8·4   Back-side and front-side displacement paths for reaction of *cis*-**3-chloro-1-methylcyclopentane with hydroxide ion.**

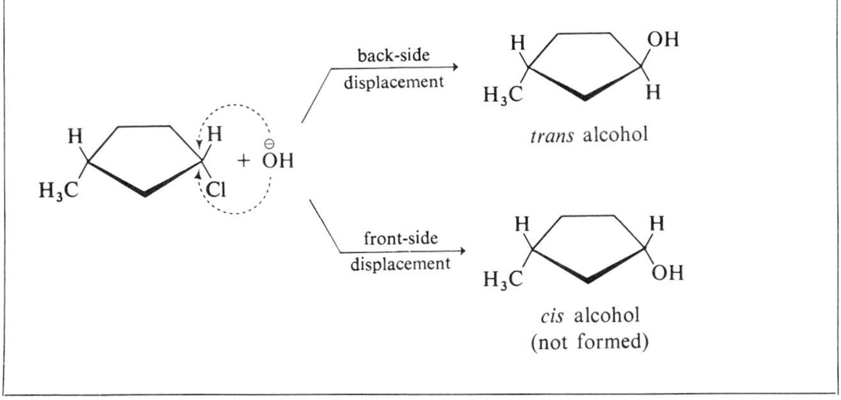

A. STRUCTURE OF THE ALKYL GROUP, R

The rates of S_N2 displacement reactions of simple alkyl derivatives, RX, follow the order *primary* R > *secondary* R > *tertiary* R. In practical syntheses involving S_N2 reactions, the primary compounds generally work very well, secondary isomers are fair, and the tertiary isomers are completely impractical. Steric hindrance appears to be particularly important in determining S_N2-reaction rates, and the slowness of tertiary halides is best accounted for by steric hindrance to the back-side approach of an attacking nucleophile by the alkyl groups on the α carbon. Neopentyl halides, which are primary halides, are very unreactive in S_N2 reactions, and scale models indicate this to be the result of their steric hindrance by the methyl groups on the β carbon.

$$CH_3-\underset{\underset{CH_3}{|}}{\overset{\overset{CH_3}{|}}{C}}-CH_2Br$$

neopentyl bromide
(slow in S_N2-type reactions)

In complete contrast to S_N2 reactions, the rates of S_N1 reactions of alkyl derivatives follow the order *tertiary* R > *secondary* R > *primary* R.

Steric hindrance is relatively unimportant in S_N1 reactions because attack by the nucleophile is not involved in the rate-determining step. In fact, *steric acceleration* is possible in the solvolysis of highly branched alkyl halides through relief of steric compression by formation of a planar cation:

$$CH_3-\underset{\underset{CH_3}{|}}{\overset{\overset{CH_3}{|}}{C}}-\underset{\underset{CH_3}{|}}{\overset{\overset{CH_3}{|}}{C}}-X \xrightarrow{-X^{\ominus}} CH_3-\underset{\underset{CH_3}{|}}{\overset{\overset{CH_3}{|}}{C}}-C^{\oplus}\underset{CH_3}{\overset{CH_3}{}}$$

steric crowding   relief of strain

The reactivity sequence *tertiary* > *secondary* > *primary* is to be expected since we know that electron-deficient centers are stabilized more by alkyl groups than by hydrogen. The reason for this is that alkyl groups are *less electron attracting* than hydrogen.

B. THE LEAVING GROUP, X

The reactivity of a given alkyl derivative, RX, in either S_N1 or S_N2 reactions is determined in part by the nature of the leaving group, X. In general, there is a reasonable correlation between the reactivity of RX and the acid strength of H—X, the X groups that correspond to the strongest acids being the best leaving groups. Thus, since H—F is a relatively weak acid and H—I is a very strong acid, the usual order of reactivity of alkyl halides is R—I > R—Br > R—Cl > R—F. Also, the greater ease of breaking a C—$OSO_2C_6H_5$ bond than a C—Cl bond in S_N2 reactions on carbon correlates with the greater acid strength of $HOSO_2C_6H_5$ in relation to HCl. A further factor influencing the rate of nucleophilic displacements is the polarizabilities of the attacking and leaving groups. A highly polarizable atom is one whose electron cloud can be easily deformed by an electric field, such as will be produced by ions in solutions. Polarizability increases as one goes down a group in the Periodic Table, and this means that iodide is not only more easily displaced than the other halogens but is itself a more reactive nucleophile. In a similar way, sulfur compounds react faster than the analogous oxygen compounds.

Alcohols are particularly *unreactive* in S_N reactions, unless a strong acid is present as a catalyst. The reason is that the $OH^\ominus$ group is a very poor leaving group. The acid functions by donating a proton to the oxygen of the alcohol, transforming the hydroxyl function into a better leaving group (H_2O in place of $OH^\ominus$). Reactions of ethers and esters are acid catalyzed for the same reasons:

$$ROH + Br^\ominus \xrightarrow{\ \ /\!/\ \ } RBr + \overset{\ominus}{O}H$$

$$R\!:\!\ddot{O}\!:\!H + H^\oplus \rightleftharpoons R\!:\!\overset{H}{\underset{}{\ddot{O}}}\!:\!H^\oplus$$

$$R\!:\!\overset{H}{\underset{}{\ddot{O}}}\!:\!H^\oplus + Br^\ominus \longrightarrow RBr + H_2O \qquad\qquad S_N2$$

$$R\!:\!\overset{H}{\underset{}{\ddot{O}}}\!:\!\overset{\oplus}{H} \longrightarrow R^\oplus + H_2O \xrightarrow{\ Br^\ominus\ } RBr \qquad S_N1$$

Heavy-metal salts, particularly those of silver, mercury, and copper, catalyze S_N1 reactions of alkyl halides in much the same way as acids catalyze the S_N reactions of alcohols. The heavy-metal ion functions by complexing with the unshared electrons of the halide, making the leaving group a metal halide rather than a halide ion. This acceleration of the rates of halide reactions is the basis for a qualitative test for alkyl halides with silver nitrate in ethanol solution. Silver halide precipitates at a rate that depends upon the structure of the alkyl group, *tertiary > secondary > primary*. Tertiary halides usually react immediately at room temperature, whereas primary halides require heating.

$$R\!:\!\ddot{X}\!: \xrightleftharpoons{\ Ag^\oplus\ } [R\!:\!\ddot{X}\!:\!\cdots Ag]^\oplus \xrightarrow[(-AgX)]{\text{slow}} R^\oplus \xrightarrow{\ HY\ } RY + H^\oplus$$

There is additional evidence for the formation of complexes between organic halides and silver ion: where the formation of carbonium ions is slow enough to permit determination of water solubility, the solubility of the halide is found to be increased by the presence of silver ion.

C. THE NUCLEOPHILIC REAGENT

The S_N2 reactivity of a particular reagent towards an alkyl derivative can be defined as its nucleophilicity, which is its ability to donate an electron pair to carbon. The nucleophilicity of a reagent does not always parallel its basicity, measured by its ability to donate an electron pair to a proton. The lack of parallelism can be seen from Table 8·4, which indicates the range of reactivities

Table 8·4   Reactivities of various nucleophiles toward methyl bromide in water at 50°

nucleophile	approximate reaction half-time, hr[a]	rate relative to water	K_B
H_2O	$1,100^b$	(1)	10^{-16}
$CH_3CO_2^{\ominus}$	2.1	5.2×10^2	10^{-11}
$Cl^{\ominus}$	1	1.1×10^3	$\sim 10^{-20}$
$Br^{\ominus}$	0.17	7.8×10^3	$< 10^{-20}$
$N_3^{\ominus}$	0.11	1.0×10^4	10^{-11}
$HO^{\ominus}$	0.07	1.6×10^4	10^0
$C_6H_5NH_2$	0.04	3.1×10^4	10^{-10}
$SCN^{\ominus}$	0.02	5.9×10^4	10^{-14}
$I^{\ominus}$	0.01	1.1×10^5	$< 10^{-22}$

[a] Time in hours required for half of methyl bromide to react at constant (1 M) concentration of nucleophile.

[b] Calculated from data for pure water, assuming water to be 55 M.

of various nucleophilic agents (toward methyl bromide in water) and their corresponding basicities. Clearly, a strong base is a good nucleophile (e.g., $OH^{\ominus}$), but a very weak base may also be a good nucleophile (e.g., $I^{\ominus}$) if it is highly polarizable.

D. THE NATURE OF THE SOLVENT

The rates of most S_N1 reactions are very sensitive to solvent changes. This is reasonable because the ionizing power of a solvent is crucial to the ease of formation of the highly ionic transition state $\overset{\oplus}{R} \cdots \overset{\ominus}{X}$ from RX.

Actually, two factors are relevant in regard to the ionizing ability of solvents. First, a high dielectric constant increases ionizing power by making it easier to separate ions, the force between charged particles depending inversely upon the dielectric constant of the medium. On this count, water with a dielectric constant of 80 should be much more effective than a hydrocarbon with a dielectric constant of 2. A related and probably more important factor is the ability of the solvent to solvate the separated ions. Cations are most effectively solvated by compounds of elements in the first row of the periodic table that have unshared electron pairs. Examples are ammonia, water, alcohols, carboxylic acids, sulfur dioxide, and dimethyl sulfoxide, $(CH_3)_2SO$. Anions are solvated most efficiently by solvents having hydrogen attached to a strongly electronegative element Y so that the H—Y bond is strongly polarized. With such solvents, hydrogen bonds between the solvent and the leaving group assist ionization in much the same way that silver ion catalyzes ionization of alkyl halides (Section 8·11B):

solvation of a cation
by a solvent with unshared
electron pairs

solvation of an anion
by a hydrogen-bonding
solvent

Water appears to strike the best compromise with regard to the structural features that make up ionizing power, that is, dielectric constant and solvating ability, and we expect *t*-butyl chloride to hydrolyze more readily in water–alcohol mixtures than in ether–alcohol mixtures. An ether can only solvate cations effectively whereas water can solvate both anions and cations. (However, the water solubility of alkyl halides is too low for pure water to be a suitable medium for these reactions.)

For S_N2 reactions, effects of changing solvents might be expected to be smaller because the reactants and the transition state each possess a full unit of negative charge: $HO^{\ominus} + RX \rightarrow (HO^{\overset{\delta\ominus}{---}} R^{\overset{\delta\ominus}{---}} X)$. No charges have been created but the charge in the transition state is less concentrated than in the reactants. Accordingly, a poor solvating solvent should raise the energy of the reactants more than it raises that of the transition state (a large diffuse ion is solvated less than a small concentrated one) and hence speed up the reaction. This hypothesis is not easily tested with solvents such as hexane or carbon tetrachloride because they do not dissolve metal hydroxides. We can, however, look for solvents with high dielectric constants but which lack hydrogen-bonding ability to solvate anions well. There are a number of such solvents and the most important of these, together with their dielectric constants, are listed here.

$$
\begin{array}{c}
O \\
\parallel \\
CH_3-S-CH_3
\end{array}
$$

dimethyl sulfoxide
(DMSO) $\varepsilon = 48$

$$
\begin{array}{c}
H_2C-CH_2 \\
| \qquad \backslash \\
H_2C \qquad CH_2 \\
\backslash \quad S \quad / \\
O \quad O
\end{array}
$$

tetramethylene sulfone
(sulfolane) $\varepsilon = 44$

$$
\begin{array}{c}
O \\
\parallel \\
H-C \\
\backslash \\
N(CH_3)_2
\end{array}
$$

dimethylformamide
(DMF) $\varepsilon = 38$

$$
\begin{array}{c}
O \\
\parallel \\
(CH_3)_2 N - P - N(CH_3)_2 \\
| \\
N(CH_3)_2
\end{array}
$$

hexamethylphosphoramide
(HMP) $\varepsilon = 30$

These solvents, called polar aprotic solvents, have a remarkable effect on the rates of many S_N2 reactions. For example, the S_N2 reaction of methyl iodide with chloride ion,

$$Cl^{\ominus} + CH_3I \longrightarrow [\overset{\delta\ominus}{Cl}^{---}CH_3^{---}\overset{\delta\ominus}{I}] \longrightarrow ClCH_3 + I^{\ominus}$$

is a million times faster in dimethylformamide than in water. Of the four solvents listed above, DMSO and HMP are usually the most effective in accelerating S_N2 reactions.

elimination reactions

The reverse of addition to alkene double bonds is elimination. Generally, an alkyl derivative will, under appropriate conditions, eliminate HX, where

X is commonly a halide, hydroxyl, ester, or onium function, and a hydrogen is located on the carbon adjacent to that bearing the X function:

$$-\overset{\displaystyle |}{\underset{\displaystyle H}{C}}-\overset{\displaystyle |}{\underset{\displaystyle X}{C}}- \longrightarrow \overset{\diagdown}{\diagup}C=C\overset{\diagup}{\diagdown} + \ HX$$

$$X = Cl, \ Br, \ I, \ -O-\overset{\displaystyle O}{\overset{\|}{C}}-CH_3, \ -\overset{\oplus}{S}R_2, \ -\overset{\oplus}{N}R_3, \ -\overset{\oplus}{O}H_2$$

Substitution and elimination usually proceed concurrently for alkyl derivatives and, in synthetic work, it is important to be able to have as much control as possible over the proportions of the possible products. As we shall see, substitution and elimination have rather closely related mechanisms, a fact which makes achievement of control much more difficult than if the mechanisms were sufficiently diverse to give very different responses to changes in experimental conditions.

8·12 the E2 reaction

Consider the reaction of ethyl chloride with sodium hydroxide:

$$CH_3CH_2Cl + OH^\ominus \overset{\displaystyle CH_3CH_2OH \ + \ Cl^\ominus \quad S_N2}{\underset{\displaystyle CH_2=CH_2 + H_2O + Cl^\ominus \quad E2}{}}$$

Elimination to give ethene competes with substitution to give ethanol. Furthermore, the rate of elimination, like the rate of substitution, has been found to be proportional to both the concentration of ethyl chloride and the concentration of hydroxide ion; thus, elimination is here a bimolecular process, appropriately abbreviated as E2. As to its mechanism, the attacking base, $OH^\ominus$, removes a proton from the β carbon simultaneously with the formation of the double bond and the loss of chloride ion from the α carbon:

$$\overset{\beta}{C}H_2\overset{\alpha}{-}CH_2\overset{..}{\underset{..}{Cl}}: \longrightarrow H_2O + CH_2=CH_2 + Cl^\ominus$$

Structural influences on E2 reactions have been studied extensively. The ease of elimination follows the order *tertiary* R > *secondary* R > *primary* R. The contrast with S_N2 reactions is strong here because E2 reactions are only slightly influenced by steric hindrance and can take place easily with tertiary

$$CH_3-\underset{\underset{CH_3}{|}}{\overset{\overset{CH_3}{|}}{C}}-Cl \quad + \quad \overset{\ominus}{OH} \quad \underset{E2}{\overset{S_N2}{\diagdown\!\!\!\diagup}}$$

$$\xrightarrow{S_N2} \quad\not\!\!\!\to \quad CH_3-\underset{\underset{CH_3}{|}}{\overset{\overset{CH_3}{|}}{C}}-OH$$

$$\xrightarrow{E2} \quad CH_2{=}C\underset{CH_3}{\overset{CH_3}{\diagup\!\!\!\diagdown}}$$

halides, unlike S_N2 reactions. Rather strong bases are generally required to bring about the E2 reaction. The effectiveness of bases parallels base strength, and the order $\overset{\ominus}{NH_2} > \overset{\ominus}{OC_2H_5} > \overset{\ominus}{OH} > \overset{\ominus}{O_2CCH_3}$ is observed for E2 reactions. This fact is important in planning practical syntheses because the E2 reaction tends to predominate with strongly basic, slightly polarizable reagents such as amide ion, $\overset{\ominus}{NH_2}$, or ethoxide ion, $\overset{\ominus}{OC_2H_5}$. On the other hand, S_N2 reactions tend to be favored with weakly basic reagents such as iodide ion or acetate ion. *Elimination is favored over substitution at elevated temperatures.*

8·13 the El reaction

Many secondary and tertiary halides undergo El type of elimination in competitition with the S_N1 reaction in neutral or acidic solutions. For example, when *t*-butyl chloride solvolyzes in 80% aqueous ethanol at 25°, it gives 83% *t*-butyl alcohol by substitution and 17% 2-methylpropene by elimination:

$$CH_3-\underset{\underset{Cl}{|}}{\overset{\overset{CH_3}{|}}{C}}-CH_3 \quad \underset{S_N1}{\overset{El}{\underset{80\% C_2H_5OH}{\diagup\!\!\!\diagdown}}}$$

$$\xrightarrow{El} \quad CH_3-\overset{\overset{CH_3}{|}}{C}{=}CH_2 \qquad 17\%$$

$$\xrightarrow{S_N1} \quad CH_3-\underset{\underset{OH}{|}}{\overset{\overset{CH_3}{|}}{C}}-CH_3 \qquad 83\%$$

The ratio of substitution and elimination remains constant throughout the reaction, which means that each process has the same kinetic order with respect to the concentration of *t*-butyl halide. Usually, but not always, the S_N1 and El reactions have a common rate-determining step—namely, slow ionization of the halide. The solvent then has the choice of attacking the intermediate carbonium ion at carbon to effect substitution, or at a β hydrogen to effect elimination.

$$CH_3-\underset{\underset{Cl}{|}}{\overset{\overset{CH_3}{|}}{C}}-CH_3 \quad \xrightarrow[\text{slow}]{H_2O} \quad CH_3-\underset{\oplus}{\overset{\overset{CH_3}{|}}{C}}-CH_3 \quad \xrightarrow[\text{fast}]{H_2O} \underset{2\,H_2O}{\overset{H_2O}{\diagup\!\!\!\diagdown}}$$

$$CH_3-\overset{\overset{CH_3}{|}}{C}{=}CH_2 \; + \; H_3\overset{\oplus}{O} \qquad El$$

$$CH_3-\underset{\underset{OH}{|}}{\overset{\overset{CH_3}{|}}{C}}-CH_3 \; + \; H_3\overset{\oplus}{O} \qquad S_N1$$

Structural influences on the E1 reaction are similar to those for the S_N1 reactions and, for RX, the rate orders are X = I > Br > Cl > F and *tertiary* R > *secondary* R > *primary* R. With halides such as *t*-pentyl chloride, which can give different alkenes depending upon the direction of elimination, the E1 reaction tends to favor the most stable, that is the most highly substituted, alkene.

$$
\begin{array}{c}
\text{CH}_3 \\
| \\
\text{CH}_3-\overset{|}{\underset{|}{\text{C}}}-\text{CH}_2-\text{CH}_3 \\
\text{Cl}
\end{array}
$$

$$
\underset{\text{slow}}{\overset{\text{H}_2\text{O}}{\nearrow}}
$$

$$
\begin{array}{c}
\text{CH}_3 \\
| \\
\text{CH}_3-\overset{|}{\underset{\oplus}{\text{C}}}-\text{CH}_2-\text{CH}_3 \\
+ \\
\text{Cl}^{\ominus}
\end{array}
\quad
\underset{\text{fast}}{\overset{\text{H}_2\text{O}}{\longrightarrow}}
\Big\langle
$$

$$
\begin{array}{c}
\text{CH}_3 \\
| \\
\text{CH}_2{=}\text{C}-\text{CH}_2-\text{CH}_3 \\
20\%
\end{array}
\qquad + \text{H}_3\text{O}^{\oplus} + \text{Cl}^{\ominus}
$$

$$
\begin{array}{c}
\text{CH}_3 \\
| \\
\text{CH}_3-\text{C}{=}\text{CH}-\text{CH}_3 \\
80\%
\end{array}
$$

Another feature of E1 reactions (and also of S_N1 reactions) is the tendency of the initially formed carbonium ion to rearrange if by so doing a more stable ion results. For example, the very slow S_N1 formolysis of neopentyl iodide leads predominantly to 2-methyl-2-butene. Here, ionization results in

$$
\begin{array}{c}
\text{CH}_3 \\
| \\
\text{CH}_3-\overset{|}{\underset{|}{\text{C}}}-\text{CH}_2\text{I} \\
\text{CH}_3
\end{array}
\underset{\text{HCO}_2\text{H}}{\overset{-\text{I}^{\ominus}}{\longrightarrow}}
\begin{array}{c}
\text{CH}_3 \\
| \\
\text{CH}_3-\overset{|}{\underset{|}{\text{C}}}-\overset{\oplus}{\text{CH}_2} \\
\text{CH}_3
\end{array}
\longrightarrow
\begin{array}{c}
\overset{\oplus}{\text{CH}_3}-\text{C}-\text{CH}_2-\text{CH}_3 \\
| \\
\text{CH}_3
\end{array}
$$

$$
\overset{-\text{H}^{\oplus}}{\longrightarrow}
\begin{array}{c}
\text{CH}_3-\text{C}{=}\text{CH}-\text{CH}_3 \\
| \\
\text{CH}_3
\end{array}
$$

migration of a methyl group with its bonding pair of electrons from the β to the α carbon transforming an unstable primary carbonium ion to a relatively stable tertiary cation. Elimination of a proton completes the reaction.

Rearrangements involving shifts of hydrogen (as $\text{H}{:}^{\ominus}$) occur with comparable ease if a more stable carbonium ion can be formed thereby.

$$
\begin{array}{c}
\text{H}_3\text{C} \quad \text{H} \\
| \quad\ | \\
\text{CH}_3-\overset{|}{\underset{|}{\text{C}}}-\overset{|}{\underset{|}{\text{C}}}-\text{CH}_3 \\
\text{H} \quad \text{Br}
\end{array}
\overset{-\text{Br}^{\ominus}}{\longrightarrow}
\begin{array}{c}
\text{CH}_3 \\
| \\
\text{CH}_3-\overset{|}{\underset{|}{\text{C}}}-\overset{\oplus}{\text{CH}}-\text{CH}_3 \\
\text{H}
\end{array}
\longrightarrow
\begin{array}{c}
\text{CH}_3 \\
| \\
\text{CH}_3-\overset{\oplus}{\text{C}}-\text{CH}_2\text{CH}_3
\end{array}
$$

$$
\overset{\text{H}_2\text{O}}{\swarrow} \qquad\qquad \overset{}{\Big\downarrow}{-\text{H}^{\oplus}}
$$

$$
\begin{array}{c}
\text{CH}_3 \\
| \\
\text{CH}_3-\overset{|}{\underset{|}{\text{C}}}-\text{CH}_2\text{CH}_3 \\
\text{OH}
\end{array}
\qquad
\begin{array}{c}
\text{CH}_3 \\
| \\
\text{CH}_3-\text{C}{=}\text{CHCH}_3
\end{array}
$$

Rearrangements of this type are also discussed in Chapter 10.

summary

Many organic compounds can be considered derivatives of the inorganic compounds water (alcohols, ethers, carboxylic acids, anhydrides), hydrogen sulfide (thiols, thioethers, thioacids), ammonia (amines and amides), nitric and nitrous acids (alkyl nitrates and nitrites), sulfuric acid (alkyl sulfates), and hydrogen halide (alkyl halides).

Three methods of naming alcohols can be illustrated using $CH_3-\overset{\overset{\displaystyle CH_3}{|}}{CH}-OH$ as an example: 2-propanol (IUPAC name), isopropyl alcohol, and dimethylcarbinol. Ethers, ROR, take their names from the two R groups. Carboxylic acids, RCO_2H, are named either as alkanoic acids (IUPAC system) in which the longest chain provides the name and -oic acid is added or, in the case of the short-chain acids, with the common names formic, acetic, propionic, or butyric (C_1 to C_4). The carboxyl carbon is taken as C-1 in the IUPAC system and the adjacent carbon is α in the common system. Thus, $CH_3-\overset{\overset{\displaystyle Cl}{|}}{CH}-CH_2CO_2H$ can be named either 3-chlorobutanoic acid or β-chlorobutyric acid.

Nucleophilic displacement reactions of the following types occur:

$$RX + Y^{\ominus} \longrightarrow RY + X^{\ominus}$$
$$RX + Y \longrightarrow RY^{\oplus} + X^{\ominus}$$
$$RX + HY \longrightarrow RY + HX \qquad \text{(a solvolysis reaction if HY is the solvent)}$$
$$RZ^{\oplus} + Y \longrightarrow RY^{\oplus} + Z$$
$$RZ^{\oplus} + Y^{\ominus} \longrightarrow RY + Z$$

Common nucleophiles are:

$$Y^{\ominus} = Cl^{\ominus}, Br^{\ominus}, I^{\ominus}, HO^{\ominus}, RO^{\ominus}, RCO_2{}^{\ominus}, CN^{\ominus}, R^{\ominus}, NH_2{}^{\ominus}, N_3{}^{\ominus}, NO_2{}^{\ominus}$$
$$Y = R_3N, R_3P, R_2S$$
$$HY = H_2O, ROH, RCO_2H, NH_3$$

Easily displaced groups are:

$$X^{\ominus} = Cl^{\ominus}, Br^{\ominus}, I^{\ominus}, RSO_3{}^{\ominus}, RCO_2{}^{\ominus}$$
$$Z = R_3N, RI, N_2$$

Nucleophilic displacements can occur by either S_N1 or S_N2 mechanisms.

S_N1 $RX \longrightarrow [R^{\delta\oplus}\text{---}X^{\delta\ominus}] \longrightarrow R^{\oplus} + X^{\ominus}$ two-step reaction, rate α [RX]
transition state
$\overset{Y^{\ominus}}{\underset{\text{fast}}{\longrightarrow}} RY$

S_N2 $RX + Y^{\ominus} \longrightarrow [Y^{\delta\ominus}\text{---}R\text{---}X^{\delta\ominus}] \longrightarrow RY + X^{\ominus}$ one-step reaction, rate α [RX][Y]
transition state

The course of such reactions can be plotted on an energy-profile diagram with energy as a function of the reaction coordinate. The activation parameters $\Delta H^{\ddagger}$ and $\Delta S^{\ddagger}$ that govern the rate of the reaction are analogous to the terms ΔH and ΔS that determine the equilibrium position of a system. The S_N2 route is favored for primary and the S_N1 route for tertiary alkyl groups.

In general, strong bases make good nucleophiles and stable molecules or ions make good leaving groups. Weak bases and less stable leaving groups may also react rapidly if their polarizabilities are high.

S_N1 reactions are greatly accelerated by highly polar solvents which promote ionization. S_N2 reactions that involve attack by an anion are greatly accelerated by polar aprotic solvents, such as dimethyl sulfoxide. The energy of the nucleophile is raised more than that of the transition state by these solvents, which solvate anions poorly.

Elimination processes are analogous to nucleophilic displacements except that the base $Y^{\ominus}$ removes a proton from the adjacent carbon. The same

$$RCH_2CH_2X + Y^{\ominus} \longrightarrow RCH{=}CH_2 + X^{\ominus} + HY$$

variations in structure and charge of X and Y are possible with elimination as with displacement and the two kinds of reaction compete with one another. Furthermore, there are two mechanisms, E1 and E2, analogous to S_N1 and S_N2. The E2 reaction is favored over S_N2 by the use of (a) powerful bases of low polarizability, (b) high temperatures, and (c) tertiary alkyl substrates.

The E1 and S_N1 reactions usually have a common first step and so the factors that govern their rates are the same. Rearrangement of the intermediate cation that is produced in both processes sometimes occurs.

exercises

8·1   Name each of the following by an accepted system:

a. $CH_3-\underset{\underset{CH_3}{|}}{\overset{\overset{CH_3}{|}}{C}}-CH_2-CH_2OH$

b. 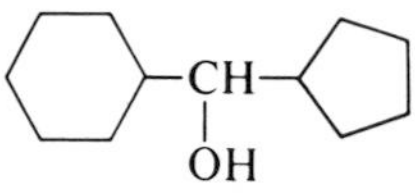   (benzene ring)$-CH-$(cyclopentane ring)
        $\underset{OH}{|}$

c. $CH_3-CH-CH-CO_2CH_3$
              $\underset{Br}{|}\ \ \underset{Br}{|}$

d. $BrCH_2CH_2OCH{=}CH_2$

e. $CH_3-CH{=}CH-\underset{\underset{SH}{}}{\overset{\overset{CH_3}{|}}{C}H}-SH$

f. 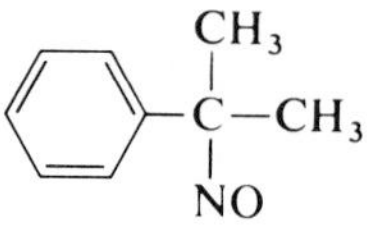   (benzene ring)$-\underset{\underset{NO}{|}}{\overset{\overset{CH_3}{|}}{C}}-CH_3$

8·2   Write structural formulas for each of the following:

a.   dimethylvinylamine
b.   allyl trimethylacetate
c.   N-methyl-N-ethylformamide
d.   formic acetic anhydride
e.   α-phenylethanol
f.   isoamyl nitrite

8·3 Name each of the following alcohols by the IUPAC method:

a. s-butyl alcohol   c. trimethylcarbinol

b. allyl alcohol   d. isobutyl alcohol

8·4 Name each of the following carboxylic acids by the IUPAC method:

a. $CH_3CH_2CHCO_2H$
$$\overset{|}{\underset{CH_3}{}}$$

c. $(C_6H_5)_2CHCH_2CO_2H$

b. $CH_2=CHCH_2CH_2CH_2CO_2H$ d. $Cl_3CCH_2CH_2CCl_2CO_2H$

8·5 Complete the following equations and provide a suitable name for each of the organic products. If additional products are likely to be formed, provide structures and names for them also.

a. $(CH_3)_2CHCH_2Br + KOH \xrightarrow{H_2O}$

b. $C_6H_5CH_2CH_2Br + NH_4I \xrightarrow{H_2O}$

c. $(CH_3)_2CHCl + NaOC_2H_5 \xrightarrow{C_2H_5OH}$

d. $C_2H_5Br + NH_3 \xrightarrow{H_2O}$

e. $(C_6H_5)_3CCH_2I + CH_3OH \xrightarrow{CH_3OH}$

8·6 Write structural formulas for the principal organic products formed by the action of each of the following reagents on $(C_6H_5)_2CHCl$: sodium cyanide, ammonia, potassium ethoxide, sodium acetate, methanol.

8·7 The numbers 1 and 2 in the symbols S_N1 and S_N2 designate the "molecularity" of the rate-controlling step; that is, the number of molecular species that are believed to react to form the transition state. This often corresponds to the kinetics of the reactions, S_N1 displacements often being first order and S_N2 displacements often being second order. Under what conditions would the molecularity and the observed kinetics not correspond?

8·8 How would you expect geometry of the transition state to be related to the entropy of activation?

8·9 The reaction of alcohols with hydrobromic acid to give alkyl bromides is an equilibrium reaction. Alkyl bromides are usually formed from alcohols and concentrated hydrobromic acid in good yields, whereas alkyl bromides hydrolyze almost completely in neutral water solution. Estimate the change in equilibrium ratio of alkyl bromide to alcohol in changing from a solution with 10 M bromide ion buffered at pH 7 to 10 M hydrobromic acid.

8·10 The S_N1 reactions of many RX derivatives that form moderately stable carbonium ions are substantially retarded by added $X^\ominus$ ions. However, such retardation is diminished, at given $X^\ominus$ concentrations, by adding another nucleophile such as $N_3^\ominus$. Explain.

The relative reactivity of water and $N_3^\ominus$ toward methyl bromide is seen from Table 8·4 to be 1 : 10,000. Would you expect the relative reactivity of these substances toward the t-butyl cation to be larger, smaller, or about the same? Why?

8·11   Classify the following solvents according to effectiveness expected for solvation of cations and anions:

a.   acetone
b.   carbon tetrachloride
c.   anhydrous hydrogen fluoride

d.   chloroform
e.   trimethylamine, $(CH_3)_3N$
f.   trimethylamine   oxide,
$(CH_3)_3\overset{\oplus}{N}-\overset{\ominus}{O}$

8·12   An alternative mechanism for E2 elimination is the following:

$$CH_3CH_2Cl + OH^{\ominus} \underset{fast}{\rightleftharpoons} \overset{\ominus}{\underset{..}{C}}H_2CH_2Cl + H_2O \xrightarrow{slow} CH_2{=}CH_2 + Cl^{\ominus}$$

a.   Would this mechanism lead to first-order kinetics with respect to the concentrations of $OH^{\ominus}$ and ethyl chloride? Explain.
b.   This mechanism has been excluded for several halides by carrying out the reaction in deuteriated solvents such as D_2O and C_2H_5OD. Explain how such experiments could be relevant to the reaction mechanism.

8·13   a.   Why is potassium t-butoxide, $K\overset{\oplus}{O}\overset{\ominus}{C}(CH_3)_3$, an excellent base for promoting elimination reactions of alkyl halides, whereas ethylamine, $CH_3CH_2NH_2$, is relatively poor for the same purpose?
b.   Potassium t-butoxide is many powers of ten more effective as an eliminating agent in dimethyl sulfoxide than in t-butyl alcohol. Explain.

8·14   The reaction of t-butyl chloride with water is strongly accelerated by sodium hydroxide. How would the ratio of elimination to substitution products be affected thereby?

8·15   Write equations and mechanisms for all the products that might reasonably be expected from the reaction of s-butyl chloride with a solution of potassium hydroxide in ethanol.

8·16   Why is apocamphyl chloride practically inert toward hydroxide ion?

8·17   Show how the following conversions may be achieved (specify reagents and conditions; note that several steps may be needed). Write a mechanism for each reaction you use. (Note that some of the steps required are described in earlier chapters.)

a.
$$CH_3-\underset{\underset{Br}{|}}{\overset{\overset{CH_3}{|}}{C}}-CH_2-CH_3 \longrightarrow CH_3-\underset{\underset{HO}{|}}{\overset{\overset{CH_3}{|}}{C}}-\underset{\underset{Br}{|}}{CH}-CH_3$$

b. 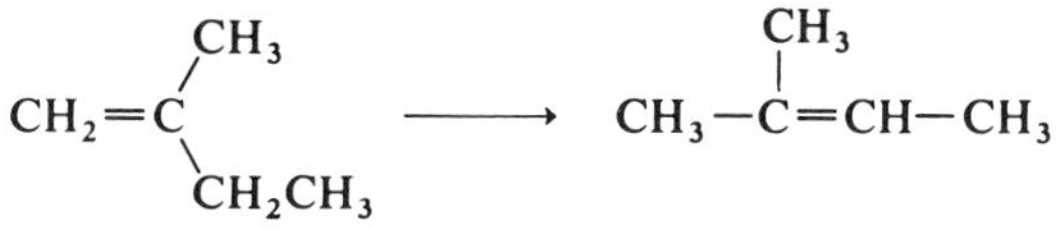 $CH_2=C\overset{\displaystyle CH_3}{\underset{\displaystyle CH_2CH_3}{}}$ ⟶ $CH_3-\overset{\displaystyle CH_3}{\overset{|}{C}}=CH-CH_3$

c. $CH_3-\overset{\displaystyle CH_3}{\underset{\displaystyle Cl}{\overset{|}{\underset{|}{C}}}}-CH_3$ ⟶ $CH_3-\overset{\displaystyle CH_3}{\underset{\displaystyle I}{\overset{|}{\underset{|}{C}}}}-CH_3$

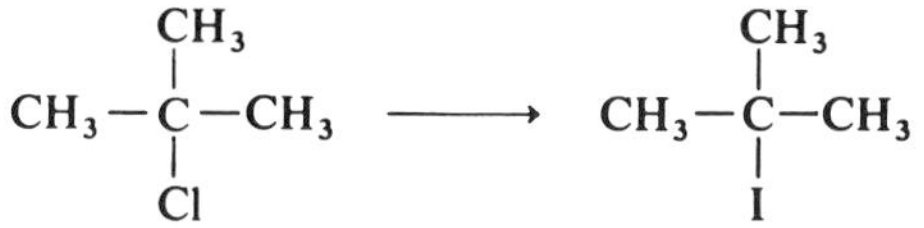

d.  $CH_3-\overset{\displaystyle CH_3}{\underset{\displaystyle Cl}{\overset{|}{\underset{|}{C}}}}-CH_3$ ⟶ $CH_3-\overset{\displaystyle CH_3}{\underset{\displaystyle H}{\overset{|}{\underset{|}{C}}}}-CH_2I$

8·18 Explain how $(CH_3)_2CDCHBrCH_3$ might be used to determine whether trimethylethylene is formed directly from the bromide in an E1 reaction, or by rearrangement and elimination as shown in Section 8·13.

8·19 Predict the products of the following reactions:

a. $CH_3CH_2CBr(CH_3)CH_2CH_3 \xrightarrow[S_N1,\ E1]{H_2O}$

b. $(CH_3)_3CCH(CH_3)CI \xrightarrow[S_N1,\ E1]{H_2O}$

c. 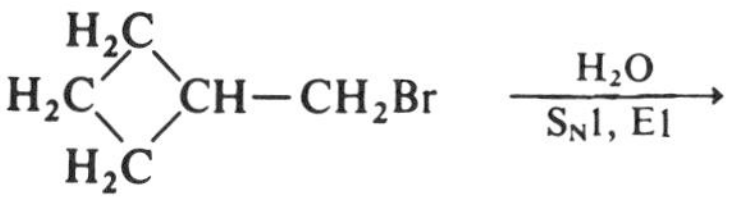 $\underset{\displaystyle H_2C}{\overset{\displaystyle H_2C}{\underset{\displaystyle H_2C}{\diagdown}}} CH-CH_2Br \xrightarrow[S_N1,\ E1]{H_2O}$

8·20 Write structural formulas for each of the following substances:

a. diisobutyl ether
b. 2-methyl-3-buten-2-ol
c. dineopentylcarbinol
d. α,β-dibromopropionic acid
e. ethyl vinyl ether
f. 9-(2,6,6-trimethyl-1-cyclohexenyl)-3,7-dimethyl-2,4,6,8-nonatetraen-1-ol

8·21 Name each of the following by the IUPAC system and, where applicable, by the carbinol (or substituted acid) system:

a. $HC\equiv C-CH_2OH$

b. 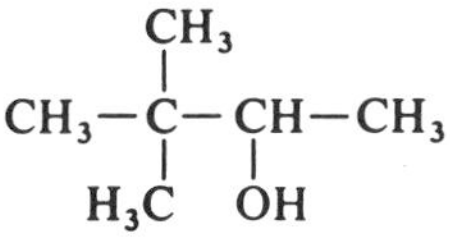 $CH_3-\overset{\displaystyle CH_3}{\underset{\displaystyle H_3C}{\overset{|}{\underset{|}{C}}}}-\overset{}{\underset{\displaystyle OH}{\underset{|}{CH}}}-CH_3$

c. $\underset{\displaystyle H_3C}{\overset{\displaystyle H_3C}{\diagup}}\diagup\hspace{-0.5em}\bigcirc\hspace{-0.5em}\underset{\displaystyle H}{\overset{\displaystyle OH}{\diagdown}}$

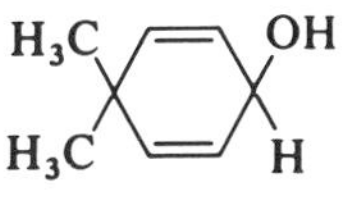

d. 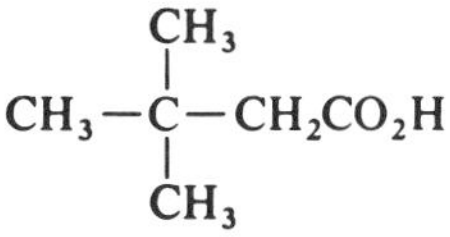 $CH_3-\overset{\displaystyle CH_3}{\underset{\displaystyle CH_3}{\overset{|}{\underset{|}{C}}}}-CH_2CO_2H$

e. 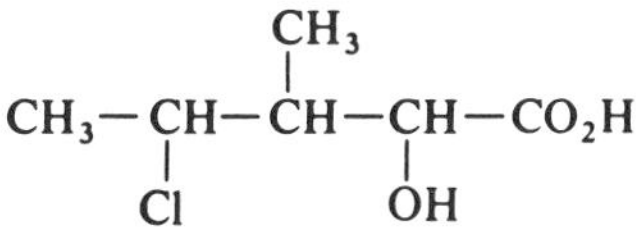 $CH_3-\underset{\displaystyle Cl}{\underset{|}{CH}}-\overset{\displaystyle CH_3}{\overset{|}{CH}}-\underset{\displaystyle OH}{\underset{|}{CH}}-CO_2H$

f. 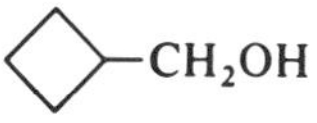 $\square-CH_2OH$

8·22   Indicate how you would synthesize each of the following substances from the given organic starting materials and any other necessary organic or inorganic reagents. Specify reagents and conditions.

    a. 2-butyne from ethyne

    b. 3-chloropropyl acetate from 3-chloro-1-propene

    c. methyl ethyl ether from ethanol

    d. methyl *t*-butyl ether from 2-methylpropene

    e. 1-iodo-2-chloropropane from propene

8·23   Which one of the following pairs of compounds would you expect to react more readily with (A) potassium iodide in acetone, (B) concentrated sodium hydroxide in ethanol, and (C) silver nitrate in aqueous ethanol? Write equations for all the reactions involved and give your reasoning with respect to the predicted orders of reactivity.

    a. methyl chloride and isobutyl chloride with A, B, and C

    b. methyl chloride and *t*-butyl chloride with A, B, and C

    c. *t*-butyl chloride and 1-fluoro-2-chloro-2-methylpropane with B and C

    d. allyl and allylcarbinyl chlorides with A, B, and C

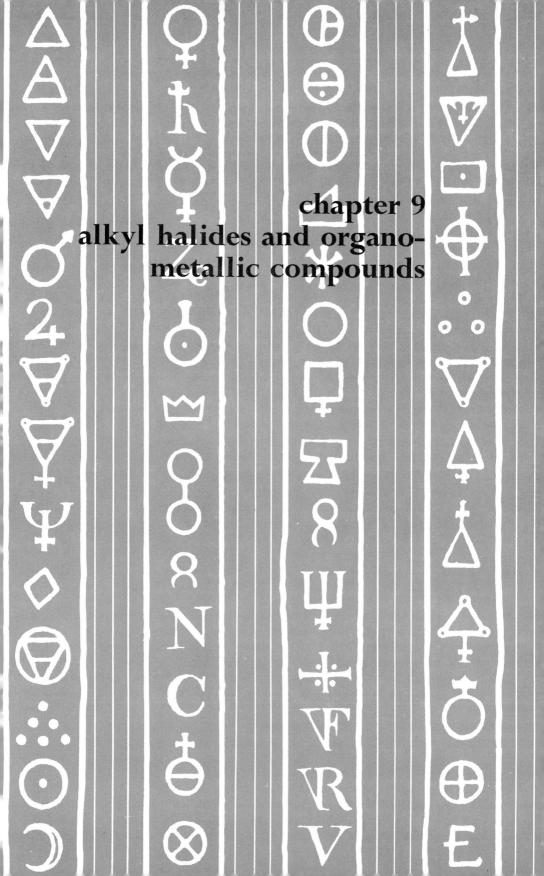

chapter 9
alkyl halides and organo-
metallic compounds

Many simple halogen derivatives of hydrocarbons have been met in earlier chapters. Their nomenclature was described in Section 3·1, the mechanism of their formation by substitution in alkanes in Sections 2·5A, 2·5B, and 3·3B, and the details of their reactions with nucleophiles (S_N1, S_N2) and bases (E1, E2) in the previous chapter.

9·1 physical properties

Methyl iodide (iodomethane), CH_3I, boils at 42° and is the only mono-halomethane that is not a gas at room temperature and atmospheric pressure. Ethyl bromide (bromoethane), CH_3CH_2Br, bp 38°, is the first monobromo-alkane in the series to be a liquid and the two chloropropanes, $CH_3CH_2CH_2Cl$ (1-chloropropane), bp 47°, and $CH_3CHClCH_3$ (2-chloropropane), bp 37°, are the first monochloroalkanes in the series to be liquids.

With the exception of the fluoroalkanes, which are discussed in a later section, the boiling points of haloalkanes tend to be near those of the alkanes of the same molecular weight.

All alkyl halides have extremely low water solubilities.

All iodo-, bromo-, and polychloro-substituted alkanes are denser than water.

9·2 spectra

The infrared spectra of alkyl halides have relatively few bands that are associated directly with the C—X bond. However, C—F bonds give rise to very intense absorption bands in the region of 1350 to 1000 cm^{-1}; C—Cl bonds absorb strongly in the region of 800 to 600 cm^{-1}; whereas C—Br and C—I bonds absorb at still lower frequencies.

Carbon tetrachloride, CCl_4, and chloroform, $CHCl_3$, are commonly used solvents for infrared work, and their spectra are shown in Figure 9·1. Carbon tetrachloride contains only one kind of bond and this makes its spectrum simpler than that of chloroform. Furthermore, the high degree of symmetry in carbon tetrachloride contributes to the simplicity of its spectrum. Absorption of a quantum of radiation can only occur if accompanied by a change in the polarity of the molecule. In many cases, changes in the vibrational energies of highly symmetrical molecules may not result in a change in polarity and thus not correspond to observable absorptions in the infrared spectrum. You should be able to deduce from this discussion why the absorption corresponding to changes in the C—H vibrational energy but not the C≡C vibrational energy can be observed in the infrared spectrum of ethyne, HC≡CH.

The nmr spectra of a number of halogen derivatives of hydrocarbons were described in Chapter 7.

The ultraviolet spectra of monohaloalkanes are unremarkable. Neither fluoroalkanes nor chloroalkanes show significant absorption in the accessible part of the spectrum. Bromo- and iodoalkanes have weak absorption maxima between 2000 A and 2500 A. Conjugation of a halogen atom with a double

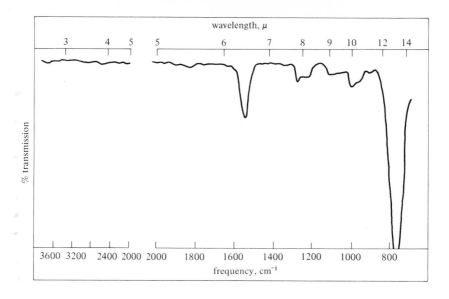

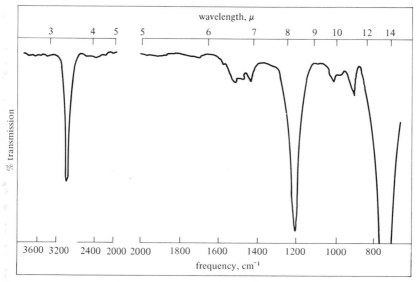

**Figure 9·1   Infrared spectra of carbon tetrachloride, CCl$_4$ (upper), and chloro-
form, CHCl$_3$ (lower); neat liquids, 0.1-mm thickness (look for overtones).**

bond, however, causes significant absorption bands to appear, as does an
accumulation of iodine on a single carbon, CHI$_3$ being yellow and CI$_4$ red.

9·3 preparation of alkyl halides

A number of ways of forming a carbon-halogen bond have been outlined
previously. These are illustrated for the production of the isomeric compounds
1-bromopropane and 2-bromopropane.

a. Halogenation of alkanes is not usually a satisfactory preparative

$$CH_3CH_2CH_3 + Br_2 \quad \xrightarrow{hv} \quad HBr + \begin{cases} CH_3CHBrCH_3 & \text{(major product)} \\ CH_3CH_2CH_2Br & \text{(minor product)} \end{cases}$$

method for bromides unless a tertiary C—H is to be substituted. With chlorine, serious mixtures of mono- and polysubstitution products may be formed.

b. Reaction of alcohols with hydrogen halides is satisfactory for most

$$CH_3CH_2CH_2OH + HBr \longrightarrow CH_3CH_2CH_2Br + H_2O$$
$$CH_3CHOHCH_3 + HBr \longrightarrow CH_3CHBrCH_3 + H_2O$$

bromides and iodides; primary alcohols (RCH_2OH) react only slowly with HCl unless $ZnCl_2$ is added (Section 10·5).

c. Addition of hydrogen halides to alkenes proceeds as follows:

$$CH_3CH{=}CH_2 + HX \longrightarrow CH_3CHXCH_3 \quad (X = F, Cl, I)$$

$$CH_3CH{=}CH_2 + HBr \quad \begin{array}{c} \nearrow CH_3CHBrCH_3 \\ \underset{\text{peroxides}}{\overset{hv}{\searrow}} CH_3CH_2CH_2Br \end{array}$$

9·4 reactions of alkyl halides

a. Displacement (S_N1, S_N2). The displacement reactions of alkyl halides with nucleophiles were listed in Table 8·2. They can be summarized as follows:

$$R{-}X + Y^{\ominus} \longrightarrow R{-}Y + X^{\ominus} \qquad Y^{\ominus} = Cl^{\ominus}, Br^{\ominus}, OH^{\ominus}, RO^{\ominus}, RS^{\ominus}, CH_3CO_2^{\ominus},$$
$$CN^{\ominus}, R^{\ominus}, NH_2^{\ominus}, N_3^{\ominus}, NO_2^{\ominus}$$

$$R{-}X + HY \longrightarrow R{-}Y + HX \qquad HY = H_2O, ROH, RCO_2H, NH_3$$

b. Elimination (E1, E2). If there is a hydrogen atom on the carbon atom adjacent to the C—X group, elimination of HX will compete with the displacement reaction:

$$RCH_2CH_2X + Y^{\ominus} \longrightarrow RCH{=}CH_2 + HY + X^{\ominus}$$

c. Formation of organometallic compounds from alkyl halides and metals is discussed in Section 9·9B.

9·5 vinyl halides

The most readily available vinyl halide is vinyl chloride, which can be prepared by a number of routes:

$$CH{\equiv}CH \;+\; HCl \qquad\qquad\qquad CH_2{=}CH_2 \;+\; Cl_2$$

$$CH_2{=}CHCl$$

high temp.

$$CH_2{=}CH_2 \;+\; Cl_2 \;\longrightarrow\; \underset{\substack{|\\Cl}}{CH_2}{-}\underset{\substack{|\\Cl}}{CH_2} \qquad\qquad CH_3{-}CHCl_2$$

$OH^{\ominus}$ E2 $OH^{\ominus}$ E2

The most feasible commercial preparation (though not convenient on a laboratory scale) is probably by way of high-temperature chlorination of ethene.

The outstanding chemical characteristic of vinyl halides is their general *inertness* in S_N1 and S_N2 reactions. Thus vinyl chloride, on long heating with solutions of silver nitrate in ethanol, gives no silver chloride, fails to react with potassium iodide by the S_N2 mechanism, and with sodium hydroxide only gives ethene by a slow E2 reaction. The haloalkynes, such as $RC{\equiv}C{-}Cl$, are not very reactive in S_N1 and S_N2 reactions.

The phenyl halides, C_6H_5X, are like the vinyl and ethynyl halides in being unreactive in both S_N1 and S_N2 reactions. The chemistry of these compounds is discussed in Chapter 21.

9·6 allyl halides

Allyl chloride is made on a commercial scale by the chlorination of propene at 400° (1,2-dichloropropane is a minor product under the reaction conditions, although at room temperature it is essentially the only product obtained).

$$CH_2{=}CH{-}CH_3 \;+\; Cl_2 \;\xrightarrow{\;400°\;}\; CH_2{=}CH{-}CH_2Cl \;+\; HCl$$

Allyl chloride is an intermediate in the commercial synthesis of glycerol (1,2,3-propanetriol) from propene.

$$CH_2{=}CHCH_3 \;\xrightarrow{Cl_2}\; CH_2{=}CHCH_2Cl \;\xrightarrow{H_2O}\; CH_2{=}CHCH_2OH$$

$$\xrightarrow{HOCl}\; \underset{\substack{|\\OH}}{CH_2}{-}\underset{\substack{|\\Cl}}{CH}{-}\underset{\substack{|\\OH}}{CH_2} + \underset{\substack{|\\Cl}}{CH_2}{-}\underset{\substack{|\\OH}}{CH}{-}\underset{\substack{|\\OH}}{CH_2} \;\xrightarrow{H_2O}\; \underset{\substack{|\\OH}}{CH_2}{-}\underset{\substack{|\\OH}}{CH}{-}\underset{\substack{|\\OH}}{CH_2}$$

glycerol

A general method for preparing allylic halides is by addition of halogen acids to conjugated dienes, which usually gives a mixture of 1,2 and 1,4 addition products (see Section 6·2).

In contrast to the vinyl halides, which are characteristically inert, the allyl

$$CH_2=CH-CH=CH_2 \quad + \quad HCl$$

$$\downarrow$$

$$\overset{\displaystyle Cl}{\underset{\displaystyle }{CH_3-\overset{|}{C}H-CH=CH_2}} \quad + \quad CH_3-CH=CH-CH_2Cl$$

3-chloro-1-butene
(α-methylallyl
chloride)

1-chloro-2-butene
(γ-methylallyl chloride)

halides are very reactive—in fact, much more reactive than corresponding saturated compounds, particularly in S_N1 reactions. Other allylic derivatives besides the halides also tend to be unusually reactive in displacement and substitution reactions, the double bond providing an activating effect on breaking the bond to the functional group. A triple bond has a comparable effect and, for example, it is found that the chlorine of 3-chloro-1-propyne is quite labile.

$$HC\equiv C-CH_2Cl \qquad \begin{array}{l} \text{3-chloro-1-propyne} \\ \text{(propargyl chloride)} \end{array}$$

The considerable S_N1 reactivity of allyl chloride compared with n-propyl chloride can be explained by reference to the electronic energies of the intermediate carbonium ions and starting halides, as shown in Figure 9·2. As we have seen previously (Section 6·2), two equivalent electron-pairing schemes may be written for the allyl cation, which suggest a stabilized hybrid structure with substantially delocalized electrons:

$$CH_2=CH-CH_2Cl \qquad \begin{array}{l} \text{(one low-energy} \\ \text{electron-pairing} \\ \text{scheme)} \end{array}$$

$$\downarrow$$

$$\left[\overset{\oplus}{CH_2=CH-CH_2} \quad \longleftrightarrow \quad \overset{\oplus}{CH_2-CH=CH_2} \quad \sim \quad \overset{\frac{1}{2}\oplus}{CH_2} = CH = \overset{\frac{1}{2}\oplus}{CH_2} \right] \quad + \quad Cl^{\ominus}$$

(two low-energy
electron-pairing
schemes)

(hybrid structure)

No such stabilized hybrid structure can be written for the n-propyl cation.

$$CH_3-CH_2-CH_2Cl \quad \longrightarrow \quad CH_3-CH_2-\overset{\oplus}{CH_2} \quad + \quad \overset{\ominus}{Cl}$$

(one low-energy
electron-pairing
scheme)

(one low-energy
electron-pairing
scheme)

Thus, we see that *less* energy is required to form the allyl cation from allyl chloride than to form the n-propyl cation from n-propyl chloride. (The ease

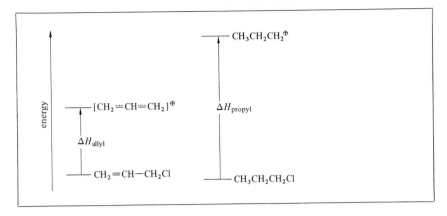

Figure 9·2   The high S_N1 reactivity of allyl chloride compared with *n*-propyl chloride is here related to the low energy of allyl-cation formation.

of reaction is actually determined by the energy differences between the starting halides and the transition states. However, the transition states must be rather close in energy to the carbonium ions, and it is convenient to deal with the latter species when developing the argument; see Section 8·9.) Figure 9·2 shows the energetics of the ionization reaction.

9·7 *polyhalogen compounds*

Polychlorination of methane affords the di-, tri-, and tetrachloromethanes

CH_2Cl_2	$CHCl_3$	CCl_4
dichloromethane	trichloromethane	tetrachloromethane
(methylene chloride)	(chloroform)	carbon tetrachloride)
bp 40°	bp 61°	bp 77°

cheaply and efficiently. These substances have excellent solvent properties for nonpolar and slightly polar substances. Chloroform was once widely used as an inhalation anesthetic but has a deleterious effect on the heart and is slowly oxidized by atmospheric oxygen to highly toxic phosgene ($COCl_2$). Commercial chloroform contains about 1 % ethanol to destroy any phosgene formed by oxidation.

Carbon tetrachloride is very commonly employed as a cleaning solvent, although its high toxicity entails some hazard in indiscriminate use. Carbon tetrachloride was once widely used as a fire extinguishing fluid for petroleum fires, although its tendency to phosgene formation makes it undesirable for confined areas. The common laboratory practice of removing traces of water from solvents with metallic sodium should never be applied to halogenated compounds. Carbon tetrachloride–sodium mixtures can detonate and are shock sensitive.

Trichloroethylene ("Triclene," bp 87°) is a widely used dry-cleaning solvent. It may be prepared from either ethene or ethyne.

$$HC\equiv CH + 2\,Cl_2 \longrightarrow CHCl_2-CHCl_2 \xrightarrow[\text{E2}]{\text{Ca(OH)}_2}$$

$$CH_2=CH_2 + 3\,Cl_2 \xrightarrow[(-3\text{ HCl})]{300°}$$

Methylene chloride reacts with hydroxide ion by an S_N2 mechanism very much less readily than does methyl chloride. The chloromethanol formed then undergoes a rapid E2 elimination to give formaldehyde, a substance that exists in water largely as dihydroxymethane (formaldehyde hydrate).

$$CH_2Cl_2 \xrightarrow[\substack{\text{slow} \\ S_N2}]{\ominus OH} \left[\substack{O-H \\ CH_2 \\ Cl}\right] \xrightarrow[\text{fast} \\ \text{E2}]{OH\ominus} H_2C=O \xrightarrow[\text{fast}]{H_2O} \left[\substack{OH \\ CH_2 \\ OH}\right]$$

Carbon tetrachloride is even less reactive than methylene chloride. One might expect chloroform to be intermediate in reactivity between methylene chloride and carbon tetrachloride, but chloroform is surprisingly reactive toward hydroxide ion and ultimately gives carbon monoxide, formate, and chloride ions. We may then infer that a different reaction mechanism is involved. Apparently, a strong base, such as hydroxide ion, attacks the chloroform molecule much more rapidly at hydrogen than at carbon. There is strong evidence to show that the carbanion so formed, $Cl_3C:\ominus$, can eliminate chloride ion to give a highly reactive intermediate of bivalent carbon, $:CCl_2$, called dichloromethylene, a **carbene** (Section 2·5C). This intermediate has only *six* valence electrons around carbon (two covalent bonds), and although it is electrically neutral it is powerfully electrophilic, and rapidly attacks the solvent to give the final products.

$$Cl_3C{:}\,H + \overset{\ominus}{O}H \rightleftharpoons Cl_3\overset{\ominus}{C}{:} + H_2O$$

$$Cl_3\overset{\ominus}{C}{:} \xrightarrow{\text{slow}} {:}CCl_2 + Cl^\ominus$$

$$:CCl_2 \begin{cases} \xrightarrow[\text{fast}]{H_2O} CO + 2\text{ HCl} \\ \xrightarrow[\text{fast}]{2\ H_2O} HC\overset{O}{\underset{O^\ominus}{\diagup}} + 2\text{ HCl} \end{cases}$$

Note the analogy between this mechanism for the hydrolysis of chloroform and the elimination mechanism of Exercise 8·12. Both reactions involve a carbanion intermediate, but subsequent elimination from a β carbon leads to an alkene, and from an α carbon to a carbene. Carbene formation is the result of 1,1 or α elimination.

The electrophilic nature of dichloromethylene, $:CCl_2$, and other carbenes, including the simplest carbene ($:CH_2$, called methylene), can be profitably used in synthetic reactions. Alkene double bonds can provide electrons, and carbenes react with an alkene by *cis* addition to the double bond to give cyclopropane derivatives, by what can be characterized as a *cis*-1,1 cycloaddition to the double bond. Activated carbenes, such as are formed

$$\text{(structure)} + :CCl_2 \longrightarrow \text{(structure)}$$

from the light-induced decomposition of diazomethane (CH_2N_2), even react with the electrons of a carbon-hydrogen bond to "insert" the carbon of the carbene between carbon and hydrogen. This transforms $C-H$ to $C-CH_3$.

$$-\overset{|}{\underset{|}{C}}:H + :CH_2 \longrightarrow -\overset{|}{\underset{|}{C}}-CH_2-H$$

The high activity of the carbene formed from diazomethane and light is because the $:CH_2$ is formed in an excited electronic state. The absorption of the photon not only cleaves the carbon-nitrogen bond but leaves the fragments in high-energy states. The $:CH_2$ generated this way is one of the most reactive reagents known in organic chemistry. More selective carbene-type reactions are possible by elimination of zinc iodide from iodomethylzinc iodide, ICH_2ZnI, which leads only to cyclopropane formation with simple alkenes.

$$\text{(structure)} + CH_2I_2 + Zn \xrightarrow{(Cu)} \text{(structure)} CH_2 + ZnI_2$$

9·8 *fluorinated alkanes*

A. FLUOROCHLOROMETHANES

Replacement of either one or two of the chlorines of carbon tetrachloride by fluorine can be readily achieved with the aid of antimony trifluoride containing some antimony pentachloride. The reaction stops after two chlorines have been replaced. The antimony trifluoride may be regenerated continuously from the antimony chloride by addition of anhydrous hydrogen fluoride.

$$3\,CCl_4 + SbF_3 \xrightarrow{SbCl_5} \underset{\text{bp } 25°}{3\,CFCl_3} + SbCl_3$$

$$3\,CCl_4 + 2\,SbF_3 \xrightarrow{SbCl_5} \underset{\text{bp } -30°}{3\,CF_2Cl_2} + 2\,SbCl_3$$

Both products have considerable utility as refrigerants, particularly for household refrigerators and air-conditioning units, under the trade name Freon. Difluorodichloromethane (Freon 12) is also employed as a propellant in aerosol bombs, shaving-cream dispensers, and other such containers. It is nontoxic, odorless, and noninflammable, and will not react with hot concentrated mineral acids or metallic sodium. This lack of reactivity is quite generally characteristic of the difluoromethylene group, provided the fluorines are not located on an unsaturated carbon. Attachment of fluorine to a carbon atom carrying one or more chlorines tends greatly to reduce the reactivity of the chlorines toward almost all types of reagents.

B. FLUOROCARBONS

Plastics and lubricating compounds of unusual chemical and thermal stability are required for many applications in the atomic energy and space programs. As one example, extraordinary chemical resistance is needed for the pumping apparatus used for separating U^{235} from U^{238} by diffusion of very corrosive uranium hexafluoride through porous barriers. The use of substances made of only carbon and fluorine (fluorocarbons) for lubricants, gaskets, protective coatings, and so on, for such equipment is suggested by the chemical resistance of the $-CF_2-$ group, and considerable effort has been spent on methods of preparing compounds such as $+CF_2+_n$.

Direct fluorination is highly exothermic and exceedingly difficult to control, but an indirect hydrocarbon-fluorination process, using cobalt trifluoride as a fluorinating intermediate, works quite well.

The radical-catalyzed polymerization of tetrafluoroethene produces the polymer called Teflon.

$$n \cdot CF_2 {=} CF_2 \xrightarrow{\text{R} \cdot} +CF_2 {-} CF_2 +_n$$

Teflon is a solid, very chemically inert substance, which is stable to around 300°. It makes excellent electrical insulation and gasket materials. It also has self-lubricating properties, which are exploited in the preparation of low-adhesion surfaces and light-duty bearing surfaces.

Tetrafluoroethene can be made on a commercial scale by the following route:

$$3 \, CHCl_3 + 2 \, SbF_3 \xrightarrow{SbCl_5} 3 \, CHClF_2 + 2 \, SbCl_3$$

$$2 \, CHClF_2 \xrightarrow[90\% \text{ yield}]{700-900°} CF_2 {=} CF_2 + 2 \, HCl$$

Radical polymerization of chlorotrifluoroethene gives a useful polymer (Kel-F) that is similar to polytetrafluoroethene (Teflon).

An excellent elastomer of high chemical resistance (Viton) can be made by copolymerizing hexafluoropropene with 1,1-difluoroethene. The product is stable to 300° and is not attacked by red fuming nitric acid.

C. PROPERTIES OF FLUOROCARBONS

The fluorocarbons have extraordinarily low boiling points relative to the hydrocarbons of comparable molecular weights and, as seen in Figure 9·3,

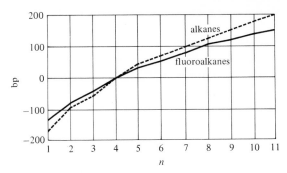

Figure 9·3   Boiling points of straight-chain fluorocarbons (C_nF_{2n+2}) and hydrocarbons (C_nH_{2n+2}).

the boiling points of fluorocarbons with the same number of carbons and about 3.5 times the molecular weight are nearly the same or even lower than those of the corresponding alkanes. Octafluorocyclobutane boils 17° lower than cyclobutane, despite a molecular weight more than three times as great. The high chemical stability, nontoxicity, and low boiling point of octafluoro-cyclobutane make it of wide potential use as a propellant in the pressure

$$\begin{array}{cc}
H_2C-CH_2 & F_2C-CF_2 \\
| \quad \ \ | & | \quad \ \ | \\
H_2C-CH_2 & F_2C-CF_2
\end{array}$$

$$\begin{array}{cc}
\text{bp} + 12° & \text{bp} - 5° \\
\text{mol. wt.} = 56 & \text{mol. wt.} = 200
\end{array}$$

packaging of food. Fluorocarbons are very insoluble in most polar solvents and are only slightly soluble in alkanes in the kerosene range. The higher-molecular-weight fluorocarbons are not even miscible in all proportions with their lower-molecular-weight homologs.

The physiological properties of organofluorine compounds vary exceptionally widely. Dichlorodifluoromethane and the saturated fluorocarbons appear to be completely nontoxic. On the other hand, perfluoro-2-methylpropene is exceedingly toxic, more so than phosgene ($COCl_2$), which was used as a toxicant in World War I. Many phosphorus-containing organic compounds are highly toxic if they also have a P—F group. The so-called "nerve gases" are of this type. Sodium fluoroacetate (CH_2FCO_2Na) and 2-fluoroethanol are toxic fluorine derivatives of oxygen-containing organic substances. The fluoroacetate salt is sold commercially as a rodenticide. Interestingly, sodium trifluoroacetate is nontoxic.

9·9   organometallic compounds

Research on the chemistry of organometallic compounds has progressed rapidly in recent years. A number of magnesium, aluminum, and lithium organometallics are now commercially available, and are used on a large scale despite their being extremely reactive to water, oxygen, and almost all organic solvents other than hydrocarbons or ethers. This high degree of reactivity is one reason for the interest in organometallic chemistry, because compounds with high reactivity generally enter into a wide variety of reactions and are therefore of value in synthetic work.

Organometallic compounds are most simply defined as substances possessing carbon-metal bonds. This definition excludes substances such as sodium acetate and sodium methoxide, since these are best regarded as having oxygen-metal bonds. Among the common metallic elements that form important organic derivatives are lithium, sodium, potassium, magnesium, aluminum, cadmium, iron, and mercury.

Less typically metallic elements (the metalloids)—boron, silicon, germanium, selenium, arsenic, and so on—also form organic derivatives, some of which are quite important, but these fall between true metallic and nonmetallic organic compounds. They are best considered separately and will not be included in the present discussion.

A. GENERAL PROPERTIES OF ORGANOMETALLIC COMPOUNDS

The physical and chemical properties of organometallic compounds vary over an extraordinarily wide range and can be well correlated with the degree of ionic character of the carbon-metal bonds present. This varies from substantially ionic, in the case of sodium acetylide, $CH\equiv C:^{\ominus}Na^{\oplus}$, to essentially covalent as in tetraethyllead, $(C_2H_5)_4Pb$. The more electropositive the metal, the more ionic is the carbon-metal bond, with carbon at the negative end of the dipole.

$$\overset{\delta\ominus}{\underset{|}{\overset{|}{-}C}}:\ \overset{\delta\oplus}{Metal}$$

The reactivity of organometallic compounds increases with the ionic character of the carbon-metal bond. It is not then surprising that organosodium and organopotassium compounds are among the most reactive organometallics. They are spontaneously inflammable in air, react violently with water and carbon dioxide, and, as might be expected from their saltlike character, are nonvolatile and do not readily dissolve in nonpolar solvents. In contrast, the more covalent compounds such as organomercurials [e.g., $(CH_3)_2Hg$] are far less reactive; they are relatively stable in air, much more volatile, and will dissolve in nonpolar solvents.

For many organometallic compounds the metal atom does not formally have a full shell of valence electrons. Thus, the usual formulation of trimethyl-aluminum will have the aluminum with six electrons in its outer valence shell. There is a tendency for such compounds to form relatively loose dimers, or more complex structures, to give the metal more nearly complete shells in a manner discussed earlier for BH_3 which forms B_2H_6 (Section 4·4B).

$$\begin{array}{c} CH_3 \\ | \\ \overset{..}{\underset{..}{Al}} \\ CH_3 \quad CH_3 \end{array}$$

(monomer)

$$\begin{array}{ccc} & \overset{H_3}{C} & \\ H_3C & | & CH_3 \\ \diagdown & & \diagup \\ & Al \quad Al & \\ \diagup & & \diagdown \\ H_3C & C & CH_3 \\ & H_3 & \end{array}$$

(dimer)

trimethylaluminum

B. PREPARATION OF ORGANOMETALLIC COMPOUNDS

Metals with Organic Halides. The reaction of a metal with an organic halide is a convenient method for preparation of organometallics derived from reasonably active metals such as lithium, magnesium, and zinc. Dialkyl ethers, particularly diethyl ether, provide an inert, slightly polar medium with unshared electron pairs on oxygen in which organometallic compounds are usually soluble. Care is necessary to exclude moisture, oxygen, and carbon dioxide, which would otherwise react with the organometallic compound, and this is usually done by using an inert atmosphere of nitrogen or helium.

$$CH_3Br + 2\ Li \xrightarrow{(CH_3CH_2)_2O} CH_3Li + LiBr$$
methyllithium

$$CH_3CH_2Br + Mg \xrightarrow{(CH_3CH_2)_2O} CH_3CH_2MgBr$$
ethylmagnesium
bromide

The reactivity order of the various halides is I > Br > Cl >> F. Alkyl fluorides do not react with lithium or magnesium. Concerning the metal, zinc reacts well with bromides and iodides, whereas mercury is satisfactory only if amalgamated with sodium.

$$2\ CH_3I + Hg(Na) \longrightarrow (CH_3)_2Hg + 2\ NaI$$

Sodium presents a special problem because of the high reactivity of organosodium compounds toward ether and organic halides. Both lithium and sodium alkyls attack diethyl ether but, whereas the lithium compounds usually react slowly, the sodium compounds react so rapidly as to make diethyl ether impractical as a solvent for the preparation of most organosodium compounds. Hydrocarbon solvents are usually necessary. Even so, special preparative techniques are necessary to avoid having organosodium compounds react with the organic halide as fast as formed to give hydrocarbons by either S_N2 displacement or E2 elimination, depending on whether the sodium derivative attacks carbon or a β hydrogen of the halide.

S_N2 displacement:

$$CH_3CH_2{:}^{\ominus}Na^{\oplus} + CH_3CH_2{:}\ddot{B}r \longrightarrow CH_3CH_2CH_2CH_3 + Na^{\oplus}Br^{\ominus}$$

E2 elimination:

$$CH_3CH_2{:}^{\ominus}Na^{\oplus} + H{-}CH_2CH_2{:}\ddot{B}r \longrightarrow CH_3CH_3 + CH_2{=}CH_2 + Na^{\oplus}Br^{\ominus}$$

Displacement reactions of this kind brought about by sodium and organic halides (often called Wurtz coupling reactions) are only of limited synthetic importance.

Organometallic Compounds with Metallic Halides. The less reactive organometallic compounds are best prepared from organomagnesium halides (Grignard reagents) and metallic halides.

$$CH_3MgCl \ + \ HgCl_2 \ \rightleftharpoons \ CH_3HgCl \ + \ MgCl_2$$

$$2\,CH_3MgCl \ + \ HgCl_2 \ \rightleftharpoons \ (CH_3)_2Hg \ + \ 2 \ MgCl_2$$

These reactions, which are reversible, actually go so as to have the most electropositive metal ending up combined with halogen. On this basis, sodium chloride can be predicted confidently *not* to react with dimethylmercury to yield methylsodium and mercuric chloride.

Organometallic Compounds and Acidic Hydrocarbons. A few organo-metallics are most conveniently prepared by the reaction of an alkylmetal derivative with an acidic hydrocarbon such as an alkyne or cyclopentadiene.

$$CH_3Mg\,Br \ + \ CH_3C\equiv CH \ \longrightarrow \ CH_4 \ + \ CH_3C\equiv CMg\,Br$$

Such reactions may be regarded as reactions of the salt of a weak acid (methane, $K_A < 10^{-40}$) with a stronger acid (propyne, $K_A \sim 10^{-22}$).

The more reactive organometallic compounds are seldom isolated from the solutions in which they are prepared. These solutions are not themselves generally stored for any length of time but are used directly in subsequent reactions. However, ether solutions of certain organomagnesium halides (phenyl-, methyl-, and ethylmagnesium halides) are obtainable commercially; also, *n*-butyllithium is available dissolved in mineral oil and in paraffin wax. Manipulation of any organometallic compounds should always be carried out with caution, owing to their extreme reactivity, and, in many cases, their considerable toxicity (particularly organic compounds of mercury, lead, and zinc).

C. ORGANOMAGNESIUM COMPOUNDS (GRIGNARD REAGENTS)

The most important organometallic compounds for synthetic purposes are the organomagnesium halides, or Grignard reagents. They are so named after Victor Grignard, who discovered them and developed their use as synthetic reagents, for which he received a Nobel Prize in 1912. As already mentioned, these substances are customarily prepared in *dry* ether solution from magnesium turnings and an organic halide. Chlorides often react

$$CH_3I \ + \ Mg \ \xrightarrow{\text{ether}} \ \underset{95\% \text{ yield}}{CH_3MgI}$$

sluggishly. In addition, they may give an unwelcome precipitate of magnesium chloride which, unlike magnesium bromide and iodide, is only very slightly soluble in ether. Very few organomagnesium fluorides are known.

Organomagnesium compounds, such as methylmagnesium iodide, are not well expressed by formulas such as CH_3MgI or $\overset{\ominus}{C}H_3\overset{\oplus}{M}gI$ because they appear to possess polar rather than purely covalent or ionic carbon-magnesium bonds. However, the reactions of Grignard reagents may often be conveniently considered as involving the carbanion, $R^{\ominus}$.

$$\overset{\delta\ominus}{R}\cdots\overset{\delta\oplus}{M}g-X \quad\longleftrightarrow\quad R:^{\ominus} + \overset{\oplus}{M}gX$$

The state of the MgX bond has not been specified here because it is not usually significant to the course of the reaction. The MgX bond may well have as much or more polar character than the RMg bond but our policy in this book will be to write structures such as $\overset{\delta\ominus}{R}\cdots\overset{\delta\oplus}{M}gX$ or $R\overset{\delta\oplus}{M}g\cdots\overset{\delta\ominus}{X}$ only when we feel that this will contribute something to understanding the reaction. Thus, CH_3MgI is usually to be understood as the composition of a substance, rather than a depiction of a structure, in the same way as we use the formulas $NaCl$ and H_2SO_4.

Grignard reagents as prepared in ether solution are very highly associated with the solvent. Not all the ether can be removed, even under reduced pressure at moderate temperatures, and the solid contains one or more moles of ether for every mole of organomagnesium compound. The ether molecules appear to be coordinated through the unshared electron pairs of oxygen to magnesium.

Reaction with Active Hydrogen Compounds. Grignard reagents react with acids, even very weak acids such as water, alcohols, alkynes, and primary and secondary amines. These reactions may be regarded as involving the neutralization of a strong base ($R:^{\ominus}$ of RMgX). The products are hydrocarbon, RH, and a magnesium salt:

$$\overset{\delta\ominus}{C}H_3\cdots\overset{\delta\oplus}{M}gI + CH_3CH_2OH \longrightarrow CH_4 + CH_3CH_2\overset{\ominus}{O}\ \overset{\oplus}{M}gI$$

This type of reaction occasionally provides a useful way of replacing a halogen bound to carbon by hydrogen as in a published synthesis of cyclobutane from cyclobutyl bromide:

$$\begin{array}{c} H_2C-CH-Br \\ | \quad\quad | \\ H_2C-CH_2 \end{array} \xrightarrow{Mg} \begin{array}{c} H_2C-CH-MgBr \\ | \quad\quad | \\ H_2C-CH_2 \end{array} \xrightarrow{H_2O} \begin{array}{c} H_2C-CH_2 \\ | \quad\quad | \\ H_2C-CH_2 \end{array}$$

Reaction with Oxygen, Sulfur, and Halogens. Grignard reagents react with oxygen, sulfur, and halogens to form substances containing C—O, C—S, and C—X bonds, respectively. These reactions are not usually impor-

$$RMgX + O_2 \longrightarrow R-O-O-MgX \xrightarrow{RMgX} 2\,ROMgX \xrightarrow{H_2O,\,H^{\oplus}} 2\,ROH$$

$$8\,RMgX + S_8 \longrightarrow 8\,RSMgX \xrightarrow{H_2O,\,H^{\oplus}} 8\,RSH$$

$$RMgX + I_2 \longrightarrow RI + MgXI$$

tant for synthetic work since the products ROH, RSH, and RX can usually be obtained more conveniently and directly from alkyl halides by S_N1 and S_N2 displacement reactions, as described in Chapter 8. However, when both S_N1 and S_N2 reactions are slow or otherwise impractical, as for neopentyl derivatives, the Grignard reactions can be very useful.

$$
\begin{array}{ccc}
\overset{\displaystyle CH_3}{\underset{\displaystyle CH_3}{CH_3-C-CH_2Cl}} & \xrightarrow{\ Mg\ } & \overset{\displaystyle CH_3}{\underset{\displaystyle CH_3}{CH_3-C-CH_2MgCl}} \xrightarrow{\ I_2\ } \overset{\displaystyle CH_3}{\underset{\displaystyle CH_3}{CH_3-C-CH_2I}}
\end{array}
$$

neopentyl chloride   neopentyl iodide

Also, oxygenation of a Grignard reagent at *low* temperatures provides an excellent method for the synthesis of hydroperoxides. To prevent formation

$$
RMgX + O_2 \xrightarrow{-70^\circ} ROOMgX \xrightarrow{H^\oplus} ROOH
$$

of excessive amounts of the alcohol, **inverse addition** is desirable (i.e., a solution of Grignard reagent is added to ether through which oxygen is bubbled rather than have the oxygen bubble through a solution of the Grignard reagent).

Additions to Carbonyl Groups. The most important synthetic use of Grignard reagents is for formation of new carbon-carbon bonds by addition to multiple bonds, particularly carbonyl bonds. (Carbon-carbon double and triple bonds, being nonpolar, are inert to Grignard reagents.) In each case, magnesium is transferred from carbon to a more electronegative element. An example is the addition of methylmagnesium iodide to formaldehyde. The

$$
CH_3\overset{\ominus}{:}\overset{\oplus}{Mg}I + H_2C{=}O \longrightarrow CH_3\overset{\ominus}{:}CH_2-\overset{\oplus}{O}\ MgI \xrightarrow[H^\oplus]{H_2O} CH_3CH_2OH
$$

new carbon–carbon bond

yields of addition products are generally high in these reactions and, with suitable variations of the carbonyl compound, a wide range of compounds can be built up from substances containing fewer carbon atoms per molecule. The products formed from a number of types of carbonyl compounds with Grignard reagents are listed in Table 9·1. (The nomenclature of carbonyl compounds is considered in Section 11·1.)

The products are complex magnesium salts from which the desired organic product is freed by acid hydrolysis:

$$
ROMgX + HOH \longrightarrow ROH + HOMgX
$$

$$
\xrightarrow{HCl} H_2O + MgXCl
$$

If the product is sensitive to strong acids, the hydrolysis may be conveniently carried out with a saturated solution of ammonium chloride; basic magnesium salts precipitate while the organic product remains in ether solution.

The reaction of carbon dioxide with Grignard reagents gives initially

Table 9·1   Products from the reaction of Grignard reagents as RMgX with carbonyl compounds

reactant	product	hydrolysis product	customary yield
formaldehyde $\begin{matrix} H \\ \diagdown \\ C=O \\ \diagup \\ H \end{matrix}$	RCH_2OMgX	*prim.* alcohol RCH_2OH	good
aldehyde $\begin{matrix} R' \\ \diagdown \\ C=O \\ \diagup \\ H \end{matrix}$	$\begin{matrix} R' \\ \mid \\ R-C-OMgX \\ \mid \\ H \end{matrix}$	*sec.* alcohol $\begin{matrix} R' \\ \mid \\ R-CHOH \end{matrix}$	good
ketone $\begin{matrix} R' \\ \diagdown \\ C=O \\ \diagup \\ R'' \end{matrix}$	$\begin{matrix} R' \\ \mid \\ R-C-OMgX \\ \mid \\ R'' \end{matrix}$	*tert.* alcohol $\begin{matrix} R' \\ \mid \\ R-C-OH \\ \mid \\ R'' \end{matrix}$	good to poor
carbon dioxide CO_2	RCO_2MgX	carboxylic acid RCO_2H	good
carboxylic acid $\begin{matrix} R' \\ \diagdown \\ C=O \\ \diagup \\ HO \end{matrix}$	$R'CO_2MgX + RH$	carboxylic acid $R'CO_2H$	good
carboxylic ester $\begin{matrix} R' \\ \diagdown \\ C=O \\ \diagup \\ R''O \end{matrix}$	$\begin{matrix} R' \\ \mid \\ R-C-OMgX \\ \mid \\ R \end{matrix}$	*tert.* alcohol $\begin{matrix} R' \\ \mid \\ R-C-OH \\ \mid \\ R \end{matrix}$	good to poor
acid chloride $\begin{matrix} R' \\ \diagdown \\ C=O \\ \diagup \\ Cl \end{matrix}$	$\begin{matrix} R' \\ \mid \\ R-C-OMgX \\ \mid \\ R \end{matrix}$	*tert.* alcohol $\begin{matrix} R' \\ \mid \\ R-C-OH \\ \mid \\ R \end{matrix}$	good to poor
N,N-dimethyl carboxamide $\begin{matrix} R' \\ \diagdown \\ C=O \\ \diagup \\ (CH_3)_2N \end{matrix}$	$\begin{matrix} R' \\ \mid \\ R-C-OMgX \\ \mid \\ N(CH_3)_2 \end{matrix}$	ketone T9-8	good to poor

RCO_2MgX. This substance is a halomagnesium salt of carboxylic acid and

$$RMgX + CO_2 \longrightarrow R-C\overset{\displaystyle O}{\underset{\displaystyle OMgX}{\diagup}} \xrightarrow{H^\oplus} R-C\overset{\displaystyle O}{\underset{\displaystyle OH}{\diagup}}$$

acidification produces the carboxylic acid itself.

Acid chlorides such as acetyl chloride, $CH_3C\overset{\displaystyle O}{\underset{\displaystyle Cl}{\diagup}}$ usually combine with two moles of Grignard reagent to give a tertiary alcohol. Presumably, the first step is addition to the carbonyl bond:

$$CH_3C \underset{Cl}{\overset{O}{\diagup}} \;+\; RMgX \longrightarrow CH_3-\underset{R}{\overset{OMgX}{\underset{|}{\overset{|}{C}}}}-Cl$$

$$CH_3-\underset{R}{\overset{OMgX}{\underset{|}{\overset{|}{C}}}}-Cl \longrightarrow CH_3-\overset{O}{\overset{\|}{C}}-R \;+\; MgXCl$$

$$CH_3-\overset{O}{\overset{\|}{C}}-R \;+\; RMgX \longrightarrow CH_3-\underset{R}{\overset{R}{\underset{|}{\overset{|}{C}}}}-OMgX$$

The reaction of acid chloride with RMgX is impractical for the synthesis of ketones because RMgX usually adds rapidly to the ketone as it is formed. However, the use of the less reactive organocadmium reagent, RCdX, usually gives good yields of ketone.

Reaction of esters with Grignard reagents is similar to the reaction of acid chlorides and is very useful for synthesis of tertiary alcohols with two identical groups attached to the carbonyl carbon:

$$CH_3-C\underset{OCH_3}{\overset{O}{\diagup}} \;+\; 2\,RMgX \longrightarrow CH_3-\underset{R}{\overset{R}{\underset{|}{\overset{|}{C}}}}-OMgX \;+\; MgX(OCH_3)$$

Many additions of Grignard reagents to carbonyl compounds proceed in nearly quantitative yields, while others give no addition product whatsoever. Trouble is most likely to be encountered in the synthesis of tertiary alcohols with bulky alkyl groups, because the R group of the Grignard reagent will be hindered from reaching the carbonyl carbon of the ketone and side reactions may compete more effectively.

Addition to Carbon-Nitrogen Triple Bonds. Nitrogen is a more electronegative element than carbon and the nitrile group is polarized in the sense $\overset{\delta\oplus}{-C}\equiv\overset{\delta\ominus}{N}$. Accordingly, Grignard reagents add to nitrile groups in much the same way as they add to carbonyl groups:

$$R'-C\equiv N \;+\; \overset{\ominus}{R}\text{---}\overset{\oplus}{Mg}X \longrightarrow \underset{R}{\overset{R'}{\diagdown}}C=\overset{\ominus}{N}\text{---}\overset{\oplus}{Mg}X$$

Hydrolysis of the adducts leads to ketimines, which are unstable under the reaction conditions and rapidly hydrolyze to ketones:

$$\underset{R}{\overset{R'}{\diagdown}}C=\overset{\ominus}{N}\text{---}\overset{\oplus}{Mg}X \;\xrightarrow{H^{\oplus},\,H_2O}\; \left[\underset{R}{\overset{R'}{\diagdown}}C=NH\right] \;\xrightarrow{H^{\oplus},\,H_2O}\; \underset{R}{\overset{R'}{\diagdown}}C=O \;+\; \overset{\oplus}{N}H_4$$

ketimine

Small-Ring Cyclic Ethers. Grignard reagents react with most small-ring cyclic ethers by S_N2 displacement. The angle strain in three- and four-membered rings facilitates ring opening, whereas the strainless five- and six-membered cyclic ethers are not attacked by Grignard reagents.

$$RMgX \;+\; H_2C\!\!-\!\!CH_2 \;\longrightarrow\; RCH_2-CH_2OMgX$$

ethylene oxide

$$RMgX \;+\; H_2C \underset{\underset{H_2}{C}}{\overset{\overset{H_2}{C}}{\diagup\!\!\diagdown}} O \;\longrightarrow\; RCH_2CH_2CH_2OMgX$$

trimethylene oxide

D. ORGANOSODIUM AND ORGANOLITHIUM COMPOUNDS

Alkylsodium and alkyllithium derivatives behave in much the same way as organomagnesium compounds, but with increased reactivity. As mentioned previously, they are particularly sensitive to air and moisture, and react with ethers, alkyl halides, active hydrogen compounds, and multiple carbon-carbon, carbon-oxygen, and carbon-nitrogen bonds. In additions to carbonyl groups they give fewer side reactions than Grignard reagents and permit syntheses of very highly branched tertiary alcohols. Triisopropylcarbinol, which has considerable steric hindrance between its methyl groups, can be made from diisopropyl ketone and isopropyllithium, but not with the corresponding Grignard reagent.

$$\begin{array}{ccc}
H_3C & O & CH_3 \\
\diagdown & \parallel & \diagup \\
CH-C-CH & \\
\diagup & & \diagdown \\
H_3C & & CH_3
\end{array}
+
\begin{array}{c}
H_3C \\
\diagdown \\
CH-Li \\
\diagup \\
H_3C
\end{array}
\longrightarrow
\left(\begin{array}{c}
H_3C \\
\diagdown \\
CH \\
\diagup \\
H_3C
\end{array} \right)_3 C-OH$$

triisopropylcarbinol

E. SOME COMMERCIAL APPLICATIONS OF ORGANOMETALLIC COMPOUNDS

Tetraethyllead, bp 202°, is the most important organometallic compound in commercial use. It greatly improves the antiknock rating of gasoline in concentrations on the order of 1 to 3 ml per gallon (Section 3·3). 1,2-Dibromoethane is added to leaded gasoline to convert the lead oxide formed in combustion to volatile lead bromide and thus diminish deposit formation. Most tetraethyllead is made by the reaction of a lead-sodium alloy with ethyl chloride. The excess lead is reconverted to the sodium alloy. Tetramethyllead shows some advantage over tetraethyllead in high-performance engines.

$$4\,C_2H_5Cl \;+\; 4\,PbNa \;\longrightarrow\; (C_2H_5)_4Pb \;+\; 4\,NaCl \;+\; 3\,Pb$$

Some alkylmercuric halides, such as ethylmercuric chloride, have fungicidal properties and are used to preserve seeds and grains. This practice, however, may be having a deleterious effect on ducks and other kinds of wildlife.

F. FERROCENE

An exceptionally stable organometallic compound of unusual structure was discovered in 1952. An orange solid, mp 174°, containing iron, it was given the name ferrocene. It can be prepared by converting cyclopentadiene to its anion and treating this with a ferrous salt.

Bonding in the ferrocene molecule results from sharing of the π electrons of the two rings with iron. The carbons are in parallel planes about 3.4 A apart with the iron between, hence the name "sandwich compound." This compound is not simply an ionic salt, $Fe^{2\oplus}(C_5H_5^\ominus)_2$, because it is insoluble in water, soluble in most organic solvents, and is not affected by boiling with dilute acid or base. In contrast, the truly ionic sodium salt of cyclopentadiene reacts rapidly with water or acids and is insoluble in most organic solvents.

Analogous sandwich compounds (metallocenes) can be formed with many other transition metals, such as nickel, cobalt, and manganese. Other sandwich compounds are known with different ring sizes—six-, seven-, and eight-membered rings with metals as diverse as chromium and uranium.

A few metals form more or less stable complexes with alkenes, which have metal-carbon bonds. Silver ion, as in solutions of silver nitrate, complexes some alkenes and alkadienes strongly enough to make them soluble in water and/or form crystalline silver nitrate complexes. Platinum, rhodium, and palladium, which in the metallic state are good hydrogenation catalysts, form some quite stable alkene complexes. A specially interesting example is stable π-cyclopentadienyldiethenerhodium,[1] a "half-sandwich" compound.

The organic groups of such compounds do not usually show much nucleophilic character. Indeed, some platinum-ethene complexes are stable in strong hydrochloric acid.

---

[1] The designation π-cyclopentadienyl means that the C_5H_5 group is bound to the metal as in ferrocene.

summary

Alkyl halides (haloalkanes) have low water solubilities and except for alkyl fluorides their boiling points are close to those of the alkanes of similar molecular weight. Other than their nmr spectra, their only striking spectral characteristics are strong infrared bands at 1350–1000 cm^{-1} (C—F stretch) and at 800–600 cm^{-1} (C—Cl stretch).

Alkyl halides can be prepared from alkanes, alkenes, and alcohols.

$$RCH_2CH_3$$
$$\Big\downarrow X_2$$

$$RCH=CH_2 \xrightarrow{\ HX\ } RCHXCH_3 \xleftarrow{\ HX\ } RCHOHCH_3 \quad (X=Cl, Br, I)$$

$$\xrightarrow{HBr} RCH_2CH_2Br$$

The reactions of alkyl halides include displacement and elimination reactions. (See summary in Chapter 8.)

Vinyl halides (RCH=CHX) are much less reactive than alkyl halides in nucleophilic displacement reactions. Allyl halides (RCH=CHCH$_2$X) are much more reactive, because of the ease of forming the resonance-stabilized cation $RCH=CH-\overset{\oplus}{CH_2} \leftrightarrow \overset{\oplus}{RCH}-CH=CH_2$.

Polyhalogen compounds are useful solvents. Di- and trihalomethanes are rather unreactive in displacement reactions with strong bases. Chloroform, however, undergoes a ready elimination with base to give a carbene, :CCl$_2$. This can add to the double bond of alkenes. Activated carbenes (as from diazomethane photolysis) also undergo insertion reactions at C—H bonds.

$$\begin{array}{c}\diagdown C \diagup \\ \| \\ \diagup C \diagdown\end{array} + :CZ_2 \longrightarrow \begin{array}{c}-\overset{|}{\underset{|}{C}}\diagdown \\ -\overset{|}{\underset{|}{C}}\diagup CZ_2\end{array} \qquad -\overset{|}{\underset{/}{C}}-H + :CZ_2^* \longrightarrow \overset{\diagdown}{\underset{/}{C}}-CHZ_2$$

Fluoroalkanes have rather different properties than the other haloalkanes; they are very much more volatile, their polymers have exceptional thermal and chemical stability (Teflon, Viton), and their toxicities vary widely.

Alkyl halides can be converted to organometallic compounds whose properties vary from the highly ionic and reactive (R$^{\ominus}$Na$^{\oplus}$) to the highly covalent and unreactive (R$_4$Pb, R$_2$Hg). Midway are organomagnesium compounds (Grignard reagents), the most important of the organometallics. Grignard

$$RX + Mg \longrightarrow RMgX \quad \text{(in dry ether)}$$

reagents react with virtually all organic compounds except alkanes, alkenes, and ethers. A summary of important Grignard reactions follows and the final step (required in all but the first example) is addition of an active hydrogen compound, such as water, to destroy a halomagnesium salt.

$$RMgX + H_2O \longrightarrow RH + MgOHX$$

ROH, RCO_2H, NH_3, and derivatives, and $R\overset{\cdot\cdot}{C}\equiv CH$ react similarly

$$+ O_2 \longrightarrow \longrightarrow ROH$$

(S_8 and I_2 react similarly)

$$+ R'CHO \longrightarrow \longrightarrow R'RCHOH$$

(HCHO reacts similarly and gives a primary alcohol)

$$+ \ R'\overset{\overset{\displaystyle O}{\|}}{-}C-R' \longrightarrow \longrightarrow R'_2\overset{\overset{\displaystyle R}{|}}{C}OH$$

$$+ \ R'\overset{\overset{\displaystyle O}{\|}}{C}-OCH_3 \longrightarrow \longrightarrow \longrightarrow R'R_2COH$$

(via $R'RC=O$; RCOCl reacts similarly)

$$+ CO_2 \longrightarrow \longrightarrow RCO_2H$$

$$+ RC\equiv N \longrightarrow \longrightarrow \longrightarrow R_2C=O$$

$$+ \ \triangledown_O \longrightarrow \longrightarrow RCH_2CH_2OH$$

$\left(\langle\!\diamond\!\rangle O \text{ reacts similarly} \right)$

Organocadmium compounds, RCdX, are less reactive than Grignard reagents. They react with acid chlorides but not with ketones.

$$RCdX + R'COCl \longrightarrow R'RC=O + CdXCl$$

The stable organoiron compound ferrocene, $Fe(C_5H_5)_2$, has a sandwich structure. Other transition metals form similar compounds.

exercises

9·1 Show how 2-bromoheptane can be prepared starting from (a) 2-heptanol, (b) 1-heptanol, (c) 1-heptyne.

9·2 When 3-ethyl-3-chloropentane reacts at room temperature with aqueous sodium carbonate solution a mixture of two compounds, one an alcohol and one an alkene, is obtained.

    a. Write the equations for these two reactions and name each of the products.

    b. Suggest changes in reaction conditions that would favor formation of the alkene.

(You may wish to review Sections 8·12 and 8·13.)

9·3   a. Write resonance structures for the transition states of S_N2 substitution for allyl and n-propyl chlorides with hydroxide ion and show how these can account for the greater reactivity of the allyl compound.

    b. Would you expect that electron-donating or electron-withdrawing groups substituted at the γ carbon of allyl chloride would increase the S_N2 reactivity of allyl chloride?

9·4 The rate of formation of the CH_2-addition product from iodomethylzinc iodide and cyclohexene is first order in each participant. Suggest a mechanism that is in accord with this fact.

9·5   What products would you expect from the reaction of bromoform, $CHBr_3$, with potassium *t*-butoxide in *t*-butyl alcohol in the presence of (*a*) *trans*-2-butene, (*b*) *cis*-2-butene?

9·6   Would you expect the same products if, instead of addition to the carbonyl group, the acyl halides were to undergo a simple S_N2 displacement of halogen with the Grignard reagent acting to furnish $R:^{\ominus}$? Explain why simple displacement is unlikely to be the correct mechanism from the fact that acid fluorides react with Grignard reagents faster than acid chlorides, which in turn react faster than acid bromides.

9·7   What products would you expect to be formed in an attempt to synthesize hexamethylethane from *t*-butyl chloride and sodium? Write equations for the reactions involved.

9·8   Write structures for the products of the following reactions involving Grignard reagents. Show the structures of both the intermediate substances and the substances obtained after hydrolysis with dilute acid. Unless otherwise specified, assume that sufficient Grignard reagent is used to cause those reactions to go to completion which occur readily at room temperatures.

  a. $C_6H_5MgBr + C_6H_5CHO$

  b. $CH_3MgI + CH_3CH_2CO_2C_2H_5$

  c. $(CH_3)_3CMgCl + CO_2$

  d. $CH_3CH_2MgBr + ClCO_2C_2H_5$

  e. $CH_3MgI + CH_3COCH_2CH_2CO_2C_2H_5$
      (1 mole)   (1 mole)

  f. $C_6H_5MgBr + CH_3O{-}\overset{\overset{\displaystyle O}{\|}}{C}{-}OCH_3$

  g. $(CH_3)_3CCH_2MgBr + CH_3\overset{\overset{\displaystyle O}{\|}}{C}{-}O{-}\overset{\overset{\displaystyle O}{\|}}{C}CH_3$

9·9   Show how each of the following substances can be prepared by a reaction involving a Grignard reagent:

  a. 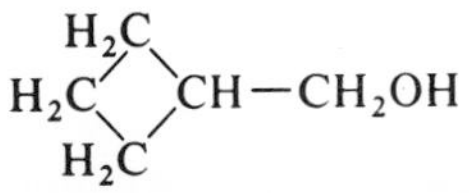 $\underset{\displaystyle H_2C}{\overset{\displaystyle H_2C}{\underset{\displaystyle H_2C}{>}}}CH{-}CH_2OH$ (two ways)

  b. $CH_2{=}CH{-}C(CH_3)_2OH$

  c. $CH_3CH_2CH(OH)CH_3$ (two ways)

  d. $(CH_3CH_2)_3COH$ (three ways)

  e. 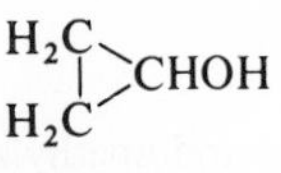 $\underset{\displaystyle H_2C}{\overset{\displaystyle H_2C}{>}}CHOH$

9·10   Complete the following equations:

  a. $C_6H_5CH_2CH_2MgBr + (CH_3)_2SO_4 \longrightarrow$

b. $C_2H_5MgBr + CH_3C\equiv C-CH_2Br \longrightarrow$

c. $CH_2=CH-CH_2Li + CH_2=CH-CH_2Cl \longrightarrow$

d. $CH_3CH_2CH_2MgBr + ClCH_2OCH_3 \longrightarrow$

9·11 Each of the following equations represents a "possible" Grignard synthesis. Consider each equation and decide whether or not you think the reaction will go satisfactorily. Give your reasoning and, for those reactions that are unsatisfactory, give the expected product or write "No Reaction" where applicable.

a. methylmagnesium iodide + butyryl chloride $\longrightarrow \longrightarrow$ n-propyl methyl ketone

b. methylmagnesium iodide + $CH_3CH=N-CH_3 \longrightarrow \longrightarrow$

$$CH_3CH_2-\overset{\overset{\displaystyle CH_3}{|}}{N}-CH_3$$

c. 2-bromoethyl acetate $\xrightarrow[\text{ether}]{\text{Mg}}$ Grignard reagent $\xrightarrow{CH_2=O} \longrightarrow$

3-hydroxypropyl acetate

d. allylmagnesium chloride + ethyl bromide $\longrightarrow$ 1-pentene

9·12 Predict the products of each of the following Grignard reactions before and after hydrolysis. Give reasoning or analogies for each.

a. $CH_3MgI + HCO_2C_2H_5 \longrightarrow$

b. $CH_3CH_2MgBr + CS_2 \longrightarrow$

c. $CH_3CH_2MgBr + NH_3 \longrightarrow$

9·13 Show how each of the following substances can be synthesized from the indicated starting materials by a route that involves organometallic substances in at least one step:

a. $(CH_3)_3C-D$ from $(CH_3)_3CCl$

b. $CH_3C\equiv C-CO_2H$ from $CH\equiv CH$

c. $CH_3-\overset{\overset{\displaystyle CH_3}{|}}{\underset{\underset{\displaystyle CH_3}{|}}{C}}-CH_2I$ from $(CH_3)_4C$

d. $CH_3-\overset{\overset{\displaystyle CH_3}{|}}{\underset{\underset{\displaystyle OH}{|}}{C}}-CH(CH_3)_2$

e. $\left(\langle\rangle\right)_3 COH$ from $\langle\rangle-Br$

f. $CH_3-\overset{\overset{\displaystyle CH_3}{|}}{\underset{\underset{\displaystyle CH_3}{|}}{C}}-CH_2CH_2CH_2CH_2OH$ from $(CH_3)_3CCH_2Cl$

9·14 Explain what inferences about the stereochemistry of the E2 reaction can be made from the knowledge that the basic dehydrohalogenation of A is exceedingly slow compared with that of B.

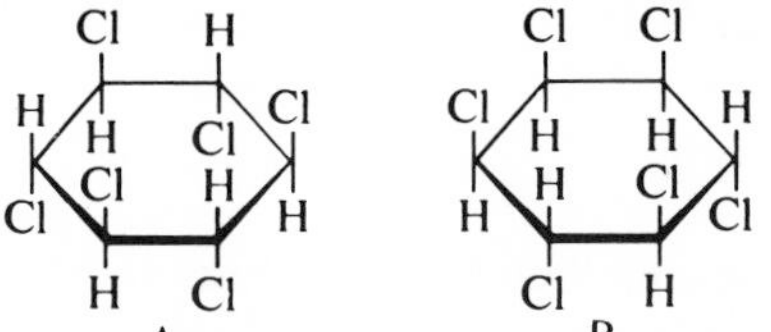

A   B

9·15   Classify each of the following reactions by consideration of yield, side reactions, and reaction rate as good, fair, or bad synthetic procedures for preparation of the indicated products under the given conditions. Show your reasoning and designate any important side reactions.

a. 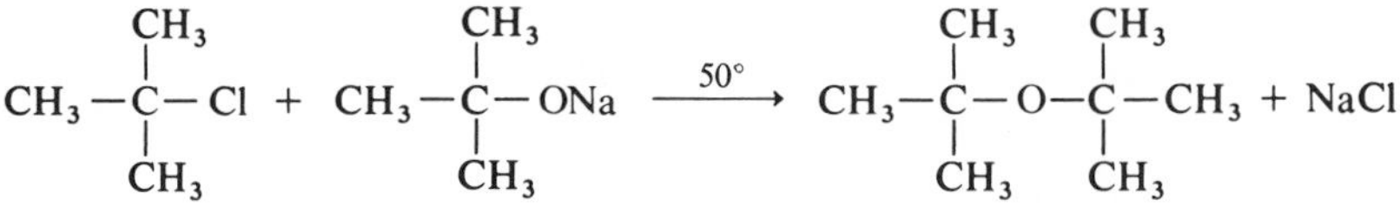 $CH_3-\underset{\underset{CH_3}{|}}{\overset{\overset{CH_3}{|}}{C}}-Cl + CH_3-\underset{\underset{CH_3}{|}}{\overset{\overset{CH_3}{|}}{C}}-ONa \xrightarrow{50°} CH_3-\underset{\underset{CH_3}{|}}{\overset{\overset{CH_3}{|}}{C}}-O-\underset{\underset{CH_3}{|}}{\overset{\overset{CH_3}{|}}{C}}-CH_3 + NaCl$

b. $CH_3-I + CH_3-\underset{\underset{CH_3}{|}}{\overset{\overset{CH_3}{|}}{C}}-OH \xrightarrow{25°} CH_4 + CH_3-\underset{\underset{CH_3}{|}}{\overset{\overset{CH_3}{|}}{C}}-O-I$

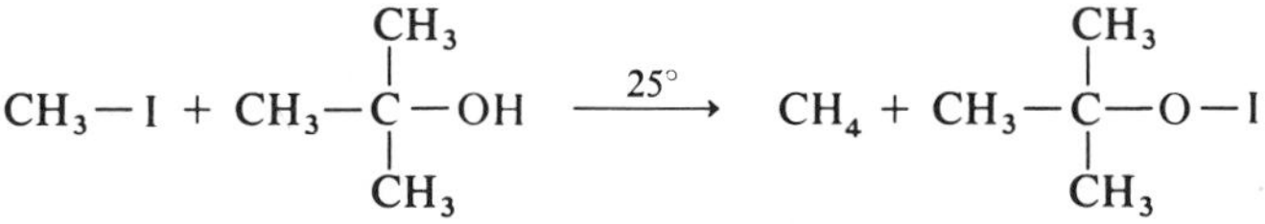

c. $CH_3-\underset{\underset{Cl}{|}}{CH}-\overset{\overset{CH_3}{|}}{CH}-CH_3 \xrightarrow[100°]{H_2O} CH_3-\overset{\overset{CH_3}{|}}{CH}-CH=CH_2 + HCl$

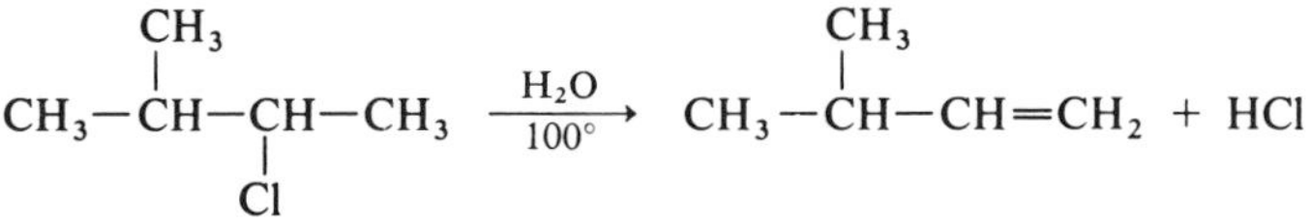

d. 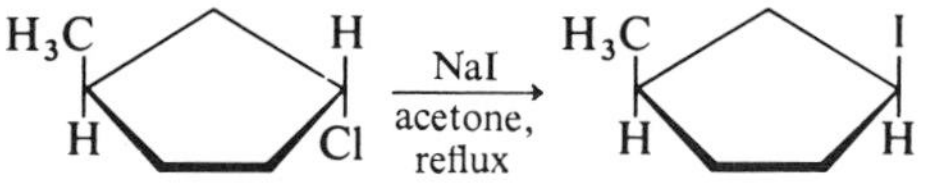 $\xrightarrow[\substack{acetone,\\reflux}]{NaI}$

e. 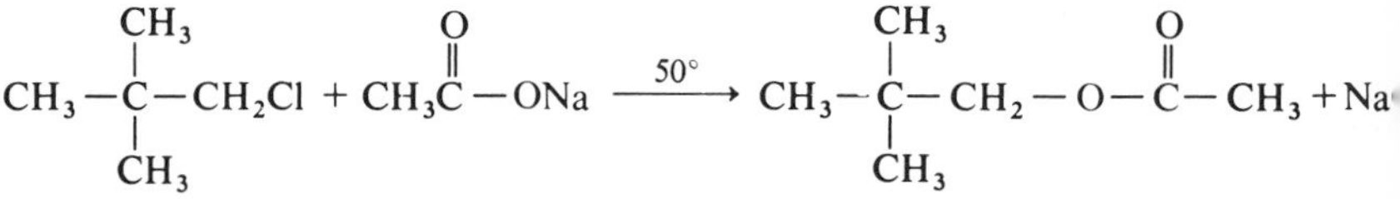 $CH_3-\underset{\underset{CH_3}{|}}{\overset{\overset{CH_3}{|}}{C}}-CH_2Cl + CH_3\overset{\overset{O}{||}}{C}-ONa \xrightarrow{50°} CH_3-\underset{\underset{CH_3}{|}}{\overset{\overset{CH_3}{|}}{C}}-CH_2-O-\overset{\overset{O}{||}}{C}-CH_3 + Na$

f. 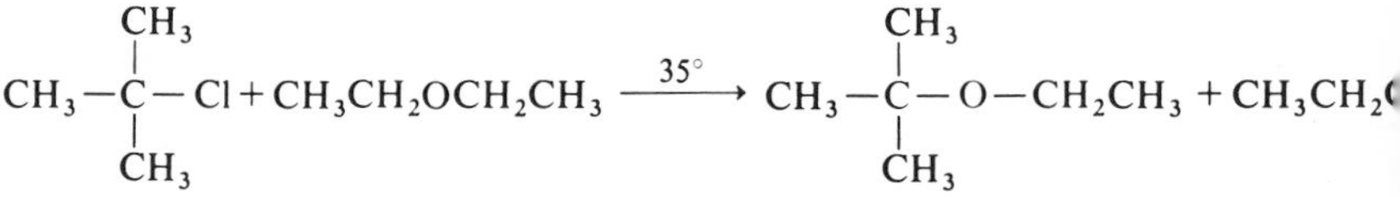 $CH_3-\underset{\underset{CH_3}{|}}{\overset{\overset{CH_3}{|}}{C}}-Cl + CH_3CH_2OCH_2CH_3 \xrightarrow{35°} CH_3-\underset{\underset{CH_3}{|}}{\overset{\overset{CH_3}{|}}{C}}-O-CH_2CH_3 + CH_3CH_2($

g. $CH_2=CHCl + CH_3\overset{\overset{O}{||}}{C}-OAg \xrightarrow[50°]{25°} CH_2=CH-O-\overset{\overset{O}{||}}{C}-CH_3 + AgCl$

h. $CH_2=CH-CH_2Cl + \frac{1}{3}SbF_3 \xrightarrow{50°} CH_2=CH-CH_2F + \frac{1}{3}SbCl_3$

9·16   Consider each of the following compounds to be in unlabeled bottles in pairs as indicated. Give for each pair a *chemical* test (preferably a test tube reaction) that will distinguish between the two substances and show what the observations will be. Write equations for the reactions expected.

	Bottle A	Bottle B
a.	$(CH_3)_3CCH_2Cl$	$CH_3CH_2CH_2CH_2Cl$
b.	$BrCH=CHCH_2Cl$	$ClCH=CHCH_2Br$
c.	$(CH_3)_3CCl$	$(CH_3)_2CHCH_2Cl$
d.	$CH_3CH=CHCl$	$CH_2=CHCH_2Cl$
e.	$(CH_3)_2C=CHCl$	$CH_3CH_2CH=CHCl$
f.	$CH_3CH_2CH=CHCl$	$CH_2=CHCH_2CH_2Cl$

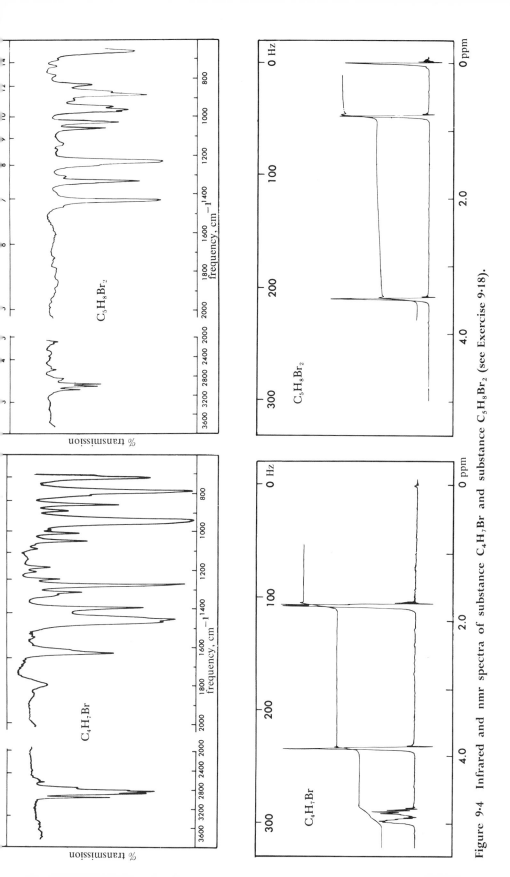

Figure 9·4 Infrared and nmr spectra of substance C_4H_7Br and substance $C_5H_8Br_2$ (see Exercise 9·18).

9·17   Show how the pairs of compounds listed in Exercise 9·16 could be distinguished by spectroscopic means.

9·18   Deduce the structures of the two compounds whose nmr and infrared spectra are shown in Figure 9·4. Assign as many of the infrared bands as you can and analyze the nmr spectra in terms of chemical shifts and spin-spin splittings.

9·19   Write balanced equations for reactions that you expect would occur between the following substances (1 mole) and 1 mole of pentylsodium. Indicate your reasoning where you make a choice between several possible alternatives.

a.	water	*f.*	allyl chloride
b.	diethyl ether	*g.*	acetic acid (added slowly to the pentylsodium)
c.	*t*-butyl chloride		
d.	pentyl iodide	*h.*	acetic acid (pentylsodium added slowly to it)
e.	propene		

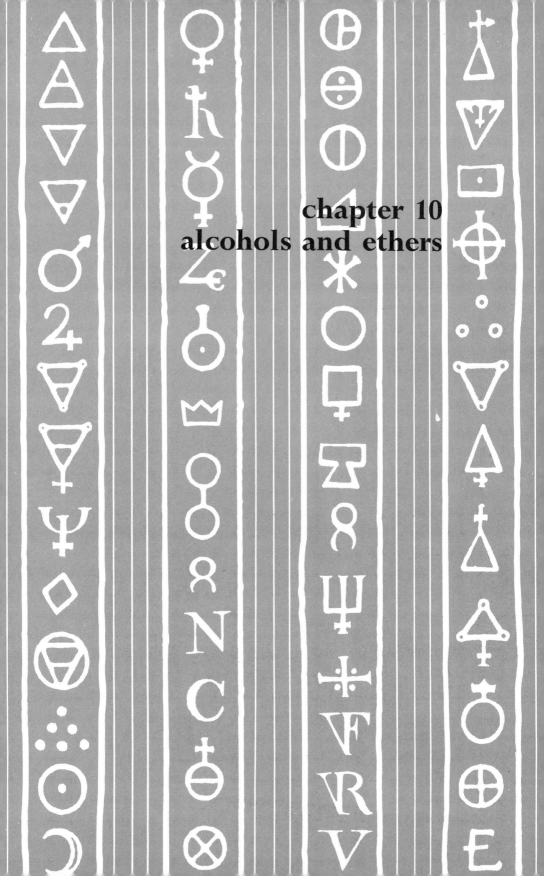

chapter 10
alcohols and ethers

Alcohols, ROH, and ethers, ROR, can be regarded as substitution products of water. With alcohols, we shall be interested on the one hand in reactions that proceed at the O—H bond without involving the C—O bond or the organic group directly, and on the other hand with processes that result in cleavage of the C—O bond or changes in the organic group. The reactions involving the O—H bond are expected to be similar to the corresponding reactions of water.

The simple ethers do not have O—H bonds, and the few reactions that they undergo involve the substituent groups.

Alcohols are classed as primary, secondary, or tertiary according to the number of hydrogen atoms attached to the hydroxylic carbon atom. This

RCH_2OH	R_2CHOH	R_3COH
primary alcohol	secondary alcohol	tertiary alcohol

classification is necessary because of the somewhat different reactions the three kinds of compounds undergo.

The nomenclature of alcohols has been discussed previously (page 187).

The first member of the alcohol series, methanol or methyl alcohol, CH_3OH, is a toxic liquid. In the past it was prepared by the destructive distillation of wood and acquired the name wood alcohol. Many cases of blindness and death have resulted from persons drinking it under the impression that it was ethyl alcohol, CH_3CH_2OH (ethanol).

Ethanol is intoxicating in small amounts but toxic in large amounts. The higher alcohols are unpleasant tasting, moderately toxic compounds which are produced in small amounts along with ethanol by fermentation of grain. A mixture of higher alcohols is called **fusel oil**. (*Fusel* means *bad liquor* in German.) One hundred proof whiskey (or whisky)[1] contains 50% ethanol by volume and 42.5% ethanol by weight. Pure ethanol (200 proof) is a strong dehydrating agent and is corrosive to the gullet.

An understanding of the chemistry of alcohols is important to understanding the functioning of biological systems which involve a wide variety of substances with hydroxyl groups. The OH group attached to a carbon chain often dramatically changes physical properties and provides a locus for chemical attack.

10·1 physical properties of alcohols

Comparison of the physical properties of alcohols with those of hydrocarbons of comparable molecular weight shows several striking differences, especially for the lower members. Alcohols are substantially less volatile and have higher melting points and greater water solubility than the corresponding hydrocarbons, although the differences become progressively smaller as molecular weight increases. The first member of the alcohol

[1] Scotch and Canadian *whisky*, but Irish and American *whiskey*.

series, CH$_3$OH (methanol or methyl alcohol), has a boiling point of 65°, whereas ethane, CH$_3$CH$_3$, with almost the same molecular weight boils at $-89°$

The profound effect of the hydroxyl group on the physical properties of alcohols is caused by hydrogen bonding. The way in which the molecules of hydroxylic compounds interact via hydrogen bonds was described earlier (Section 1·2B).

The water solubility of the lower-molecular-weight alcohols is high and is also a result of hydrogen bonding. In methanol, the hydroxyl group accounts for almost half of the weight of the molecule, and it is thus not surprising that the substance is miscible with water in all proportions. As the size of the hydrocarbon group of an alcohol increases, the hydroxyl group accounts for progressively less of the molecular weight, and hence water solubility decreases (Figure 10·1). Indeed, the physical properties of higher-molecular-weight alcohols are very similar to those of the corresponding hydrocarbons.

An interesting effect of chain branching on solubility can be seen in the four butyl alcohols. *n*-Butyl alcohol is soluble to the extent of 8 g in 100 g of water whereas *t*-butyl alcohol is completely miscible with water (Table 10·1.) Branching also affects volatility. The highly branched alcohol, *t*-butyl alcohol, has a boiling point 35° lower than that of *n*-butyl alcohol. The effect of branching on melting point is in the opposite direction because crystal packing is improved by branching. The result is that *t*-butyl alcohol has the highest melting point and the lowest boiling point of the four isomeric C$_4$ alcohols. (*t*-Butyl alcohol is liquid over a range of only 58° whereas *n*-butyl alcohol is liquid over a range of 208°.) See Table 10·1.

Figure 10·1   Dependence of melting points, boiling points, and water solubilities of continuous-chain primary alcohols (C$_n$H$_{2n+2}$O) on n. (The alcohols with C$_3$ or fewer carbons are infinitely soluble in water.)

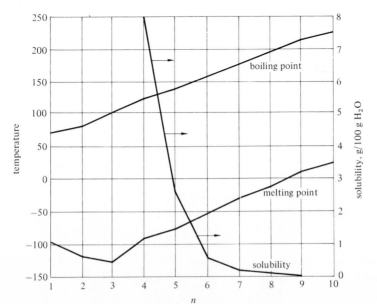

Table 10·1   Physical properties of the butyl alcohols

name	formula	mp, °C	bp, °C	solubility, g/100 g water
n-butyl alcohol (1-butanol)	$CH_3CH_2CH_2CH_2OH$	-90	118	8.0
isobutyl alcohol (2-methyl-1-propanol)	$(CH_3)_2CHCH_2OH$	-108	108	10.0
s-butyl alcohol (2-butanol)	$CH_3CH_2CHOHCH_3$	-114	100	12.5
t-butyl alcohol (2-methyl-2-propanol)	$(CH_3)_3COH$	25	83	∞

10·2   spectroscopic properties of alcohols—hydrogen bonding

The hydrogen-oxygen bond of a hydroxyl group gives a characteristic absorption band in the infrared and, as we might expect, this absorption is considerably influenced by hydrogen bonding. For example, in the *vapor state* (in which there is essentially no hydrogen bonding because of the large inter-molecular distances), ethanol gives an infrared spectrum with a fairly sharp absorption band at 3700 cm^{-1} owing to a free or unassociated hydroxyl group (Figure 10·2a). In contrast, this band is barely visible at 3640 cm^{-1} in the spectrum of a 10% solution of ethanol in carbon tetrachloride (Figure 10·2b). However, there is a relatively broad band around 3350 cm^{-1} which is characteristic of hydrogen-bonded hydroxyl groups. The shift in frequency of about 300 cm^{-1} is not surprising, since hydrogen bonding weakens the O—H bond; its absorption frequency will then be lower. The association band is broad because the hydroxyl groups are associated in aggregates of various sizes and shapes, giving rise to a variety of different kinds of hydro-gen bonds and therefore a spectrum of closely spaced O—H absorption frequencies.

In very dilute solutions of alcohols in nonpolar solvents, hydrogen bonding is minimized; but as the concentration is increased, more and more of the molecules become associated and the intensity of the infrared absorption band due to associated hydroxyl groups increases at the expense of the free hydroxyl band. Furthermore, the frequency of the association band is a measure of the strength of the hydrogen bond. The lower the frequency relative to the position of the free hydroxyl group, the stronger is the hydrogen bond. As we shall see in Chapter 13, the hydroxyl group in carboxylic acids (RCO_2H) forms stronger hydrogen bonds than alcohols and, accordingly, absorbs at lower frequencies (lower by about 400 cm^{-1}).

From the foregoing discussion of the influence of hydrogen bonding on the infrared spectra of alcohols, it should come as no surprise that the *nuclear magnetic resonance spectra* of the hydroxyl protons of alcohols are similarly affected. Thus the chemical shift of a hydroxyl proton is influenced by the degree of molecular association through hydrogen bonding and on the

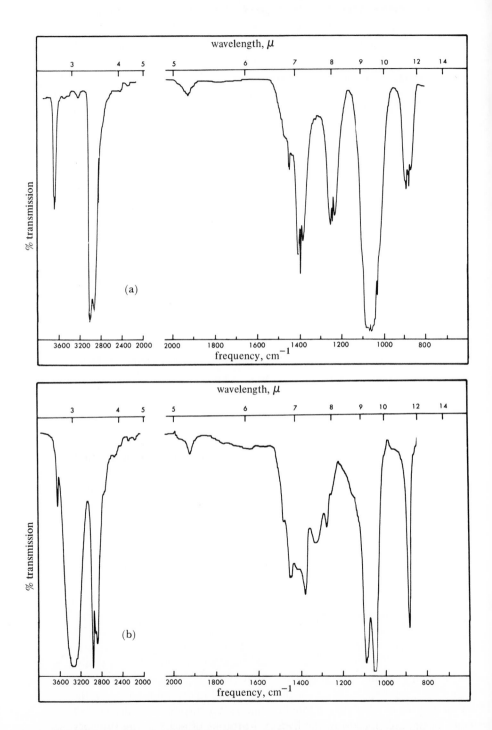

Figure 10·2   Infrared spectrum of ethanol in the vapor phase (a) and as a 10% solution in carbon tetrachloride (b).

strengths of the hydrogen bonds. Except for alcohols that form intramolecular hydrogen bonds, the OH chemical shift varies extensively with temperature, concentration, and the nature of the solvent. Also, resonance appears at lower magnetic fields (i.e., the chemical shift is larger relative to TMS) as the strengths of hydrogen bonds increase. Thus, the chemical shifts of the OH protons of simple alcohols as pure liquids generally fall between 4 and 5 ppm downfield with respect to tetramethylsilane, but when the degree of hydrogen bonding is reduced by dilution with carbon tetrachloride, the OH reso-nances move upfield. With ethyl alcohol, the shift is found to be 3 ppm between the pure liquid and very dilute solution in carbon tetrachloride.

One may well question why it is that absorptions are observed in the infra-red spectrum of alcohols which correspond both to free and hydrogen-bonded hydroxyl groups, while only one OH resonance is observed in their nmr spectra. The answer is that the lifetime of any one molecule in the free or unassociated state is long enough to be detected by infrared absorption but too short to be detected by nmr. Consequently, one sees only the average OH resonance for all species present. (For a discussion of nmr and rate processes, see Section 7·6D.)

10·3 preparation of alcohols

We have already encountered most of the important methods of preparing alcohols, which are summarized below.

1. Hydration of alkenes (Section 4·4). The direction of addition is governed

$$RCH{=}CH_2 + H_2O \xrightarrow{\ H^{\oplus}\ } RCHOHCH_3$$

by Markownikoff's rule and primary alcohols, therefore, *cannot* be made this way (except for CH_3CH_2OH).

2. Hydroboration of alkenes (Section 4·4F). The direction of addition is

$$RCH{=}CH_2 + B_2H_6 \longrightarrow (RCH_2CH_2)_3B \xrightarrow[OH^{\ominus}]{H_2O_2} RCH_2CH_2OH$$

"anti-Markownikoff" and primary alcohols, therefore, *can* be made this way.

3. Addition of hypohalous acids to alkenes (Section 4·4). The HO group

$$RCH{=}CH_2 + HOCl \longrightarrow RCHOHCH_2Cl$$

becomes bonded to the carbon atom bearing the least number of hydrogen atoms.

4. S_N2 and S_N1 hydrolyses of alkyl halides (Sections 8·7 to 8·10). Primary

$$RCH_2CH_2Cl + OH^{\ominus} \longrightarrow RCH_2CH_2OH + Cl^{\ominus} \qquad S_N2$$

$$R_3CCl \xrightarrow{H_2O} R_3COH \qquad\qquad\qquad\qquad\qquad S_N1$$

and secondary but not tertiary alkyl halides require hydroxide ion. A side reaction is elimination, which can be especially important with tertiary halides and strong bases.

5. Grignard reagents to carbonyl groups (Section 9·9C). Grignard reagents

$$RMgBr + H-\overset{\overset{O}{\|}}{C}-H \longrightarrow RCH_2\overset{\ominus}{O}\overset{\oplus}{MgBr} \xrightarrow{H_2O} RCH_2OH \qquad \text{primary alcohol}$$

$$+ R'-\overset{\overset{O}{\|}}{C}-H \longrightarrow R'CH-R \xrightarrow{H_2O} R'-\overset{OH}{\underset{}{C}H}-R \qquad \text{secondary alcohol}$$

$$+ R'-\overset{\overset{O}{\|}}{C}-R'' \longrightarrow R'-\overset{\overset{\ominus}{\underset{\overset{\oplus}{O}\overset{}{MgBr}}{}}}{\underset{R}{C}}-R'' \xrightarrow{H_2O} R'-\overset{OH}{\underset{R}{C}}-R'' \qquad \text{tertiary alcohol}$$

$$+ R'-\overset{\overset{O}{\|}}{C}-OR'' \longrightarrow R'-\overset{\overset{\ominus}{\overset{\oplus}{O}\overset{}{MgBr}}}{\underset{R}{C}}-R \xrightarrow{H_2O} R'-\overset{OH}{\underset{R}{C}}-R \qquad \text{tertiary alcohol}$$

with ketones can be used to produce tertiary alcohols in which all three R groups are different; with esters, tertiary alcohols result in which at least two of the R groups are identical.

6. Reduction of carbonyl compounds (to be described in Section 11·4F):

$$R-\overset{O}{\underset{H}{C}} \longrightarrow R-CH_2OH \qquad \text{primary alcohol}$$

$$R-\overset{O}{\underset{OR'}{C}} \longrightarrow R-CH_2OH \qquad \text{primary alcohol}$$

$$R-\overset{\overset{O}{\|}}{C}-R \longrightarrow R-\overset{OH}{\underset{}{C}H}-R \qquad \text{secondary alcohol}$$

A few of the reactions mentioned have been adapted for large-scale production. Ethanol, for example, is made in quantity by the hydration of ethene, using an excess of steam under pressure at temperatures around 300° in the presence of phosphoric acid:

$$CH_2=CH_2 + H_2O \underset{}{\overset{300°,\ H_3PO_4}{\rightleftharpoons}} CH_3CH_2OH$$

A dilute solution of ethanol is obtained which can be concentrated by distillation to a constant boiling point mixture that contains 95.6% ethanol by weight. Removal of the remaining few percent of water to give "absolute alcohol" is usually achieved either by chemical means or by distillation with benzene, which results in preferential separation of the water. Ethanol is also made in large quantities by fermentation, but this route is not competitive for industrial uses with the hydration of ethene.

Isopropyl alcohol and *t*-butyl alcohol are also manufactured by hydration of the corresponding alkenes. The industrial synthesis of methyl alcohol involves hydrogenation of carbon monoxide. Although this reaction has a favorable ΔH value of -28.4 kcal, it requires high pressures and high temperatures and a suitable catalyst; excellent conversions are achieved using a zinc oxide–chromic oxide catalyst:

$$CO + 2\,H_2 \xrightarrow[\text{ZnO–CrO}_3]{400°,\ 200\ \text{atm}} CH_3OH \qquad \Delta H = -28.4\ \text{kcal}$$

chemical reactions of alcohols

10·4 *reactions involving the O−H bond*

A.   ACIDIC AND BASIC PROPERTIES

Several important reactions of alcohols involve only the oxygen–hydrogen bond and leave the carbon–oxygen bond intact. An important example is salt formation with acids and bases.

Alcohols, like water, are amphoteric and are neither strong bases nor strong acids. The acid ionization constant (K_{HA}) of ethanol is about 10^{-18}—slightly less than that of water. Ethanol can be converted to a salt by the salt of a weaker acid such as ammonia $(K_{HA} \sim 10^{-35})$, but it is usually more convenient to employ sodium or sodium hydride. The reactions are vigorous but can be more easily controlled than the analogous reactions with water.

$$C_2H_5OH + Na^\oplus NH_2^\ominus \rightleftharpoons C_2H_5O^\ominus Na^\oplus + NH_3$$
$$\qquad\qquad \text{sodium amide} \qquad\quad \text{sodium ethoxide}$$
$$\qquad\qquad \text{(sodamide)}$$

$$C_2H_5OH + Na^\oplus H^\ominus \longrightarrow C_2H_5O^\ominus Na^\oplus + H_2$$

The order of acidity of various alcohols is generally *primary > secondary > tertiary*; *t*-butyl alcohol is therefore considerably less acidic than ethanol. The anions of alcohols are known as alkoxide ions.

$CH_3O^\ominus$ $C_2H_5O^\ominus$ $(CH_3)_2CHO^\ominus$ $(CH_3)_3CO^\ominus$
methoxide   ethoxide   isopropoxide   *t*-butoxide

Alcohols are bases comparable in strength to water and are converted to their conjugate acids by strong acids. An example is the reaction of methanol with hydrogen bromide to give methyloxonium bromide.

$$CH_3:\overset{..}{\underset{..}{O}}:H + HBr \rightleftharpoons CH_3:\overset{H\,\oplus}{\underset{..}{O}}:H + Br^\ominus$$
$$\qquad\qquad\qquad \text{methyloxonium bromide}$$

The reaction of hydrogen bromide with water proceeds in an analogous manner:

$$H:\overset{..}{\underset{..}{O}}:H + HBr \rightleftharpoons H:\overset{H\,\oplus}{\underset{..}{O}}:H + Br^\ominus$$
$$\qquad\qquad\qquad \text{hydroxonium bromide}$$

B. ETHER FORMATION

Alkoxide formation is important as a means of generating a powerful nucleophile that will readily enter into S_N2 reactions. Whereas ethanol reacts only slowly and incompletely with methyl iodide, sodium ethoxide in ethanol solution reacts rapidly with methyl iodide and gives a high yield of methyl ethyl ether.

$$CH_3I + C_2H_5O^\ominus\ Na^\oplus \xrightarrow{\text{fast}} CH_3OC_2H_5 + NaI$$

In fact, the reaction of alkoxides with alkyl halides or alkyl sulfates is an important general method for the preparation of ethers, and is known as the Williamson synthesis. Complications can occur because the increase of nucleophilicity associated with the conversion of an alcohol to an alkoxide ion is always accompanied by an even greater increase in eliminating power by the E2-type mechanism. The reaction of an alkyl halide with alkoxide may then be one of elimination rather than substitution, depending on the temperature, the structure of the halide, and the alkoxide (Section 8·12). For example, if we wish to prepare isopropyl methyl ether, better yields would be obtained if we were to use methyl iodide and isopropoxide ion rather than isopropyl iodide and methoxide ion because of the prevalence of E2 elimination with the latter combination:

$$CH_3I + (CH_3)_2CHO^\ominus \xrightarrow{S_N2} (CH_3)_2CHOCH_3 + I^\ominus$$

$$(CH_3)_2CHI + CH_3O^\ominus \xrightarrow{E_2} CH_3CH{=}CH_2 + CH_3OH + I^\ominus$$

Potassium t-butoxide is often an excellent reagent to achieve E2 elimination, since it is strongly basic but so bulky as to not undergo S_N2 reactions readily.

C. ESTER FORMATION

Esters are one of a number of compounds containing the carbonyl group $(-\overset{O}{\overset{\|}{C}}-)$ that are important to a discussion of alcohols and whose detailed chemistry will be discussed in subsequent chapters.

$R-\overset{O}{\overset{\|}{C}}-OR$	$R-\overset{O}{\overset{\|}{C}}-OH$	$R-\overset{O}{\overset{\|}{C}}-Cl$	$R-\overset{O}{\overset{\|}{C}}-H$	$R-\overset{O}{\overset{\|}{C}}-R$
esters	carboxylic acids	acyl halides	aldehydes	ketones

Esters are produced by the reactions of alcohols with either acyl halides or carboxylic acids. Acyl halides, for example, have a rather positive carbonyl carbon because of the polarization of the carbon-oxygen and carbon-halogen bonds. Addition of an electron-pair-donating agent such as the oxygen of an alcohol occurs rather easily.

$$CH_3 \overset{\delta\oplus}{\underset{\delta\oplus}{-}}\overset{\delta\ominus O}{\underset{\delta\ominus}{C}} {-}Cl \; + \; CH_3{:}\ddot{O}{:}H \; \rightleftharpoons \; CH_3 {-}\overset{O^\ominus}{\underset{CH_3\overset{}{O}H}{C}} {-}Cl$$

[1]

The complex [1] contains both an acidic group ($CH_3 - \overset{\oplus}{O} - H$) and a basic group ($-\overset{O^\ominus}{\underset{|}{C}}-$), so that one oxygen loses a proton and the other gains a proton to give [2], which then rapidly loses hydrogen chloride by either an E1 or E2 elimination to form the ester. The overall process resembles an

$$CH_3 {-}\overset{O^\ominus}{\underset{CH_3\overset{\oplus}{O}H}{C}} {-}Cl \; \rightleftharpoons \; CH_3 {-}\overset{\overset{\displaystyle H}{\underset{\displaystyle |}{O}}}{\underset{CH_3O}{C}} {\overset{\frown}{-}}Cl \; \longrightarrow \; CH_3 {-}\overset{O}{\overset{\|}{C}} {-}O {-}CH_3 \; + \; HCl$$

[1]   [2]

S_N2 reaction, but the mechanism is different in being an *addition-elimination* with three transition states rather than a one-stage displacement reaction with one transition state.

A similar but less complete reaction occurs between acetic acid and

$$CH_3 {-}\overset{O}{\overset{\|}{C}} {-}OH \; + \; CH_3{:}\ddot{O}{:}H \; \rightleftharpoons \; CH_3 {-}\overset{O^\ominus}{\underset{CH_3\overset{\oplus}{-}O{-}H}{C}} {-}OH \; \rightleftharpoons$$

$$CH_3 {-}\overset{OH}{\underset{CH_3\overset{}{-}O}{C}} {-}OH \; \rightleftharpoons \; CH_3 {-}\overset{O}{\overset{\|}{C}} {-}OCH_3 \; + \; H_2O$$

methanol. This reaction is slow in either direction in the absence of a strong mineral acid. Strong acids catalyze ester formation from the alcohol provided they are not present in large amount. The reason for the "too much of a good thing" behavior of the catalyst is readily apparent from a consideration of the reaction mechanism. A strong acid such as sulfuric acid may donate a proton to the unshared oxygen electron pairs of either acetic acid or methanol:

$$CH_3-C\overset{O}{\underset{OH}{\diagup}} + H_2SO_4 \rightleftharpoons CH_3-C\overset{\overset{\oplus}{O}H}{\underset{OH}{\diagup}} + H\overset{\ominus}{S}O_4$$

[3]

$$CH_3-O-H + H_2SO_4 \rightleftharpoons CH_3-\overset{H}{\underset{\underset{\oplus}{O}}{|}}-H + H\overset{\ominus}{S}O_4$$

Clearly, formation of methyloxonium bisulfate can only operate to *reduce* the reactivity of methanol toward the carbonyl carbon of acetic acid. However, this anticatalytic effect is more than balanced (at low concentrations of H_2SO_4) by protonation of the carbonyl oxygen of the carboxylic acid [3], since this greatly enhances the electron-pair accepting power of the carbonyl carbon:

$$\left[CH_3-\overset{\overset{\oplus}{O}H}{\underset{}{\overset{||}{C}}}-OH \longleftrightarrow CH_3-\overset{OH}{\underset{\oplus}{\overset{|}{C}}}-OH \right] + CH_3-O-H \rightleftharpoons CH_3-\overset{OH}{\underset{\underset{\oplus}{CH_3-O-H}}{\overset{|}{C}}}-OH$$

[3]   [4]

The resulting intermediate [4] is in equilibrium with its isomer [5], which can lose a water molecule to give the protonated ester [6]:

$$CH_3-\overset{OH}{\underset{\underset{\oplus}{CH_3-O-H}}{\overset{|}{C}}}-OH \rightleftharpoons CH_3-\overset{\overset{\oplus}{O}H_2}{\underset{CH_3O}{\overset{|}{C}}}-OH \rightleftharpoons CH_3-\overset{\overset{\oplus}{O}H}{\overset{||}{C}}-OCH_3 + H_2O$$

[4]   [5]   [6]

$$CH_3-\overset{O}{\overset{||}{C}}-OCH_3 + H_3\overset{\oplus}{O}$$

methyl acetate

Transfer of a proton from [6] to water gives the reaction product.

At high acid concentrations, essentially all the methanol would be converted to inert methyloxonium ion and the rate of esterification would then be very slow, even though more of the oxonium ion of acetic acid would be present.

As mentioned earlier, esterification is reversible and, with ethanol and acetic acid, has an equilibrium constant of about 4 at room temperature, which corresponds to 66% conversion to ester with equimolal quantities. Higher ester conversions can be obtained by using an excess of either the

$$CH_3\overset{O}{\overset{||}{C}}-OH + C_2H_5OH \rightleftharpoons CH_3\overset{O}{\overset{||}{C}}-O-C_2H_5 + H_2O$$

$$K = \frac{[CH_3CO_2C_2H_5]\,[H_2O]}{[CH_3CO_2H][C_2H_5OH]} \sim 4$$

alcohol or the acid. The reaction may be driven to completion by removing the ester and (or) water as they are formed.

Steric hindrance is very important in determining esterification rates, and esters with highly branched groups, in either the acid or alcohol parts, are formed at slower rates and with smaller equilibrium constants than their less highly branched analogs. In general, the ease of esterification for alcohols is *primary > secondary > tertiary* with a given carboxylic acid.

10·5 reactions involving the C—O bond of alcohols

A. HALIDE FORMATION

Alkyl halide formation from an alcohol and a hydrogen halide offers an important example of a reaction in which the C—O bond of the alcohol is

$$R\!-\!OH + HBr \rightleftharpoons RBr + H_2O$$

broken. The reaction is reversible and the favored direction depends on the water concentration (see Exercise 8·9). Primary bromides are often best prepared by passing dry hydrogen bromide into the alcohol heated to just slightly below its boiling point.

Reaction proceeds at a useful rate only in the presence of strong acid, which can be furnished by excess hydrogen bromide or, usually and more economically, by sulfuric acid. The alcohol accepts a proton from the acid to give an alkyloxonium ion, which is more reactive in subsequent displacement with bromide ion than the alcohol, since it can more easily lose a neutral water molecule than the alcohol can lose a hydroxide ion (Section 8·11B).

$$Br^{\ominus} + R\!-\!\overset{\overset{\displaystyle H}{|}}{\underset{\oplus}{O}}\!-\!H \longrightarrow RBr + H_2O \qquad S_N2$$

or

$$R\!-\!\overset{\overset{\displaystyle H}{|}}{\underset{\oplus}{O}}\!-\!H \overset{(-H_2O)}{\rightleftharpoons} R^{\oplus} \overset{Br^{\ominus}}{\longrightarrow} RBr \qquad S_N1$$

Hydrogen chloride is less reactive than hydrogen bromide or hydrogen iodide toward primary alcohols, and application of heat and the addition of a catalyst (zinc chloride) are usually required for preparation purposes.

A solution of zinc chloride in concentrated hydrochloric acid (Lucas reagent) is widely used, in fact, to differentiate between the lower primary, secondary, and tertiary alcohols. Tertiary alcohols react very rapidly to give an insoluble layer of alkyl chloride at room temperature. Secondary alcohols react in several minutes, whereas primary alcohols form chlorides only on heating.

Thionyl chloride, $SOCl_2$, is a useful reagent for the preparation of alkyl chlorides, especially when the use of zinc chloride and hydrochloric acid is undesirable. Addition of 1 mole of an alcohol to 1 mole of thionyl chloride gives an unstable alkyl chlorosulfite, which generally decomposes on mild heating to yield the alkyl chloride and sulfur dioxide.

$$\text{ROH} + \text{SOCl}_2 \xrightarrow{-\text{HCl}} \underset{\text{alkyl chlorosulfite}}{\text{R}-\text{O}-\overset{\overset{\text{O}}{\|}}{\text{S}}-\text{Cl}} \longrightarrow \text{RCl} + \text{SO}_2$$

Phosphorus tribromide, PBr_3, is an excellent reagent for converting alcohols to bromides. A disadvantage compared to thionyl chloride is the formation of involatile P(OH)_3 rather than sulfur dioxide.

$$3\,\text{ROH} + \text{PBr}_3 \longrightarrow 3\,\text{RBr} + \text{P(OH)}_3$$

B. ESTERS OF SULFURIC ACID—DEHYDRATION OF ALCOHOLS

Alkyl hydrogen sulfate formation from alcohols and concentrated sulfuric acid may occur by a reaction rather closely related to alkyl halide formation.

$$\text{ROH} + \text{H}_2\text{SO}_4 \rightleftharpoons \overset{\oplus}{\text{ROH}}_2 + \overset{\ominus}{\text{HSO}}_4 \longrightarrow \underset{\text{alkyl hydrogen sulfate}}{\text{ROSO}_3\text{H}} + \text{H}_2\text{O}$$

On heating, alkyl hydrogen sulfates readily undergo elimination of sulfuric acid to give alkenes and, in the reaction of an alcohol with hot concentrated sulfuric acid, which gives overall dehydration of the alcohol, the hydrogen sulfate may well be a key intermediate. This is the reverse of acid-catalyzed hydration of alkenes discussed previously (Section 4·4) and goes to completion if the alkene is allowed to distill out of the reaction mixture as it is formed.

$$\text{CH}_3\text{CH}_2\text{OH} + \text{H}_2\text{SO}_4 \underset{(-\text{H}_2\text{O})}{\rightleftharpoons} \text{CH}_3\text{CH}_2\text{OSO}_3\text{H} \xrightarrow[\text{--------}]{150°} \text{CH}_2{=}\text{CH}_2 + \text{H}_2\text{SO}_4$$

The mechanism of elimination of sulfuric acid from ethyl hydrogen sulfate is probably of the E2 type, with water or bisulfate ion acting as the base.

At lower temperatures, alkyl hydrogen sulfate may react by a displacement mechanism with excess alcohol in the reaction mixture with formation of a dialkyl ether. Diethyl ether is made commercially by this process. Although each step in the reaction is reversible, ether formation can be favored by distilling away the ether as fast as it forms.

$$\text{CH}_3\text{CH}_2\text{OSO}_3\text{H} + \text{CH}_3\text{CH}_2\text{OH} \xrightarrow{130°} \text{CH}_3\text{CH}_2{-}\underset{\oplus}{\overset{\overset{\text{H}}{|}}{\text{O}}}{-}\text{CH}_2\text{CH}_3 + \text{HSO}_4^{\ominus}$$

$$\Big\Updownarrow$$

$$\text{CH}_3\text{CH}_2\text{OCH}_2\text{CH}_3 + \text{H}_2\text{SO}_4$$

Most alcohols will also dehydrate at fairly high temperatures to give alkenes and (or) ethers in the presence of solid catalysts such as silica gel or aluminum oxide. The behavior of ethanol, which is reasonably typical of primary alcohols, is summarized in the following equations:

$$CH_3CH_2OH \underset{\substack{Al_2O_3 \\ 300°}}{\overset{\substack{Al_2O_3 \\ 375°}}{\huge\lessgtr}} \begin{matrix} CH_2{=}CH_2 + H_2O \\ \\ CH_3CH_2OCH_2CH_3 + H_2O \end{matrix}$$

Tertiary alcohols react with sulfuric acid at much lower temperatures than do most primary alcohols. The S_N1 and E1 reactions in Scheme I may be written for t-butyl alcohol and sulfuric acid. Di-t-butyl ether is unstable in

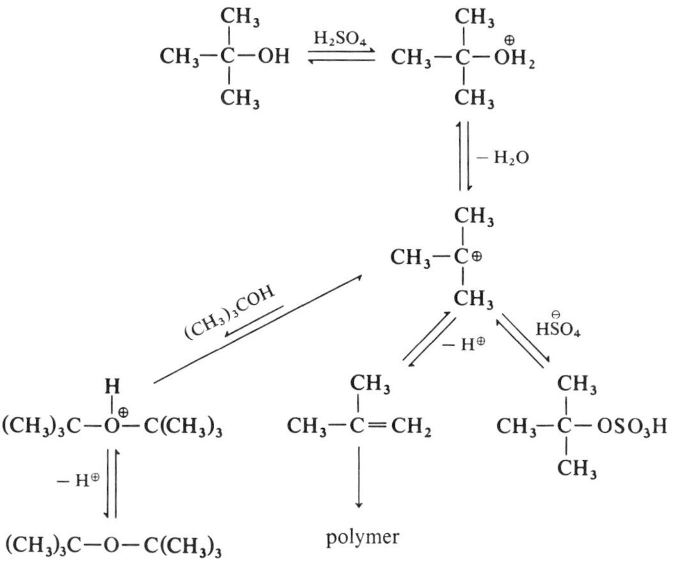

SCHEME I

sulfuric acid solution and it has never been detected in reaction mixtures of this type. Its low stability may be due to steric crowding between the alkyl groups.

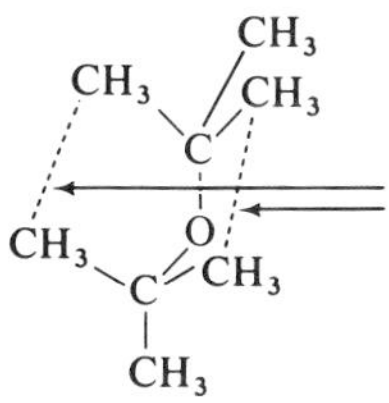

steric repulsions

2-Methylpropene can be removed from the reaction mixture by distillation and is easily made the principal product by appropriate adjustment of the reaction conditions. If the 2-methylpropene is not removed as it is formed, polymer is the most important end product. Sulfuric acid is often an unduly strenuous reagent for dehydration of tertiary alcohols. Potassium hydrogen sulfate, copper sulfate, iodine, phosphoric acid, or phosphorus pentoxide may give better results by causing less polymerization and less oxidative degradation. The oxidizing action of sulfuric acid results in formation of sulfur dioxide.

Rearrangement of the alkyl group of an alcohol is very common in dehydration, particularly in the presence of sulfuric acid, which is highly conducive to carbonium ion formation. Shown are typical examples of both methyl and hydrogen migration. The key step in each such rearrangement involves an isomerization of a carbonium ion along lines discussed in Section 8·13.

$$
\begin{array}{c}
\underset{\displaystyle\underset{\displaystyle CH_3\ OH}{|\quad\ |}}{\overset{\displaystyle CH_3}{\overset{|}{CH_3-C-CH-CH_3}}} \xrightarrow{H_2SO_4} \underset{\displaystyle CH_3\quad CH_3}{\overset{\displaystyle CH_3\quad CH_3}{C=C}} + H_2O
\end{array}
$$

$$
\underset{\displaystyle H}{\overset{\displaystyle CH_3}{\overset{|}{CH_3-C-CH_2-CH_2OH}}} \xrightarrow{H_2SO_4} \overset{\displaystyle CH_3}{\overset{|}{CH_3-C=CH-CH_3}}
$$

Except in a few circumstances where thermodynamic control dominates and leads to different results from kinetic control, the final products always correspond to rearrangement of a less stable carbonium ion to a more stable carbonium ion.

$$
\text{reactants} \longrightarrow \underset{\substack{\text{less stable}\\\text{carbonium ion}}}{\overset{\displaystyle R}{\overset{|}{-C-\overset{\oplus}{C}-}}} \longrightarrow \underset{\substack{\text{more stable}\\\text{carbonium ion}}}{\overset{\displaystyle R}{\overset{|}{-\overset{\oplus}{C}-C-}}} \longrightarrow \text{products}
$$

For the particular case of the dehydration of methyl-*t*-butylcarbinol, the sequence is

$$
\underset{\displaystyle H_3C\quad OH}{\overset{\displaystyle CH_3}{\overset{|}{CH_3-C-CH-CH_3}}} \underset{(-OH^{\ominus})}{\overset{H_2SO_4}{\rightleftharpoons}} \left[\ \underset{\substack{\text{secondary}\\\text{carbonium ion}}}{\overset{\displaystyle CH_3}{CH_3-C-\overset{\oplus}{C}H-CH_3}} \longrightarrow \underset{\substack{\text{tertiary}\\\text{carbonium ion}}}{\overset{\displaystyle H_3C\quad CH_3}{CH_3-\overset{\oplus}{C}-\underset{H}{C}-CH_3}}\ \right]
$$

$$\Big\updownarrow -H^{\oplus}$$

$$
\underset{\displaystyle CH_3\quad CH_3}{\overset{\displaystyle CH_3\quad CH_3}{C=C}}
$$

10·6 oxidation of alcohols

Primary alcohols on oxidation first give aldehydes and thence carboxylic acids, whereas secondary alcohols give ketones.

$$RCH_2OH \xrightarrow{[O]} R-C\overset{O}{\underset{H}{\diagdown}} \xrightarrow{[O]} R-C\overset{O}{\underset{OH}{\diagdown}}$$

$$\overset{R}{\underset{R}{\diagup}}CHOH \xrightarrow{[O]} \overset{R}{\underset{R}{\diagup}}C=O$$

Tertiary alcohols are oxidized with considerable difficulty and then only with degradation into smaller fragments by cleavage of carbon-carbon bonds. Similarly, oxidation of secondary alcohols beyond the ketone stage does not proceed readily and leads to degradation.

Laboratory oxidation of alcohols is most often carried out with chromic acid (H_2CrO_4), which is usually prepared as required from chromic oxide (CrO_3) or from sodium dichromate ($Na_2Cr_2O_7$) in combination with sulfuric acid. Acetic acid is the most generally useful solvent for such reactions.

$$3 \ \overset{CH_3}{\underset{CH_3}{\diagup}}CH-OH + 2 \ H_2CrO_4 + 6 \ H^\oplus \longrightarrow 3 \ \overset{CH_3}{\underset{CH_3}{\diagup}}C=O + 2 \ Cr^{3\oplus} + 8 \ H_2O$$

The mechanism of the chromic acid oxidation of isopropyl alcohol to acetone has been investigated very thoroughly and is highly interesting in that it reveals how changes of oxidation level can occur involving a typical inorganic and a typical organic compound. The initial step is reversible formation of isopropyl hydrogen chromate [7], which is quite unstable and is not usually isolated (although it can be isolated by working rapidly at low temperatures).

$$\overset{CH_3}{\underset{CH_3}{\diagup}}CH-OH + H_2CrO_4 \rightleftharpoons H_2O + \overset{CH_3}{\underset{CH_3}{\diagup}}CH-O-CrO_3H$$

$$H^\oplus \diagup\diagdown \qquad [7]$$

$$\overset{CH_3}{\underset{CH_3}{\diagup}}CH-O-CrO_3H_2^\oplus$$

The subsequent step is the slowest in the reaction and appears to involve either (a) a cyclic decomposition of the protonated ester or (b) attack of a base (water) at the α hydrogen of the protonated chromate ester concurrent with elimination of the grouping H_2CrO_3, for which there is an obvious analogy with an E2 reaction (Section 8·12).

(a)

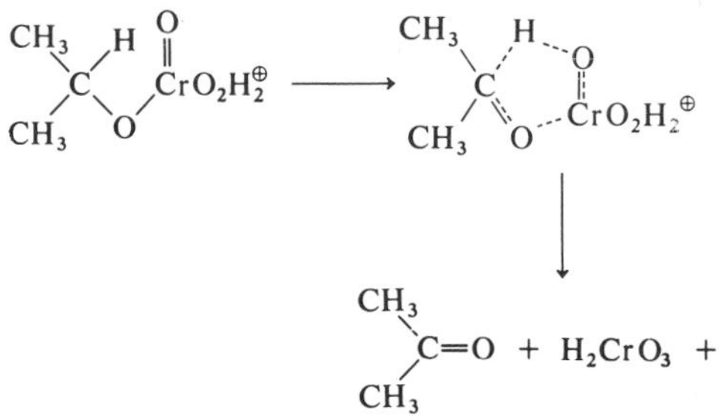

$$\underset{CH_3}{\overset{CH_3}{\diagdown}}\underset{O}{\overset{H}{\diagup}}\overset{O}{\underset{\parallel}{C}rO_2H_2^{\oplus}} \longrightarrow \underset{CH_3}{\overset{CH_3}{\diagdown}}\underset{O}{\overset{H}{\diagup}}\overset{O}{\underset{\cdots \overset{\parallel}{C}rO_2H_2^{\oplus}}{\diagup}}$$

$$\downarrow$$

$$\underset{CH_3}{\overset{CH_3}{\diagdown}}C=O \;+\; H_2CrO_3 \;+\; H^{\oplus}$$

(b)

$$\underset{CH_3}{\overset{CH_3}{\diagdown}}\underset{O-CrO_3H_2^{\oplus}}{\overset{H \leftarrow :O}{\diagup}}\overset{H}{\underset{}{}} \longrightarrow \underset{CH_3}{\overset{CH_3}{\diagdown}}C=O \;+\; H_3\overset{\oplus}{O} \;+\; H_2CrO_3$$

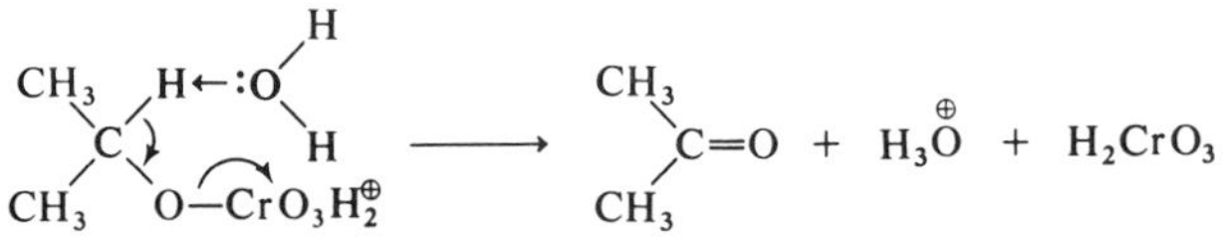

Despite intensive study, the exact mechanism of decomposition of the chromate ester remains in doubt. The Cr^{IV} shown as the reduction product (H_2CrO_3) in both (a) and (b) is a highly reactive oxidant and is rapidly converted to Cr^{III} in subsequent steps.

The Cr^{VI} oxidation of alcohols is acid catalyzed, as shown above. Indeed, neutral and basic solutions of chromate are without any effect on alcohols. Permanganate oxidation of alcohols, on the other hand, is subject to both acid and base catalysis. The acid catalysis is the result of the conversion of $MnO_4^{\ominus}$ to $HMnO_4$, a more powerful oxidant, and requires a high concentration of acid. The base catalysis, however, is the result of converting the neutral alcohol to the more easily oxidized alkoxide ion:

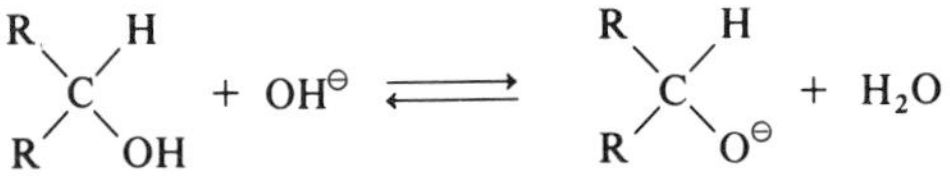

$$\underset{R}{\overset{R}{\diagdown}}\underset{OH}{\overset{H}{\diagup}}C \;+\; OH^{\ominus} \;\rightleftharpoons\; \underset{R}{\overset{R}{\diagdown}}\underset{O^{\ominus}}{\overset{H}{\diagup}}C \;+\; H_2O$$

The rate-controlling step of this reaction is transfer of hydrogen, possibly as hydride ion, to the Mn^{VII}.

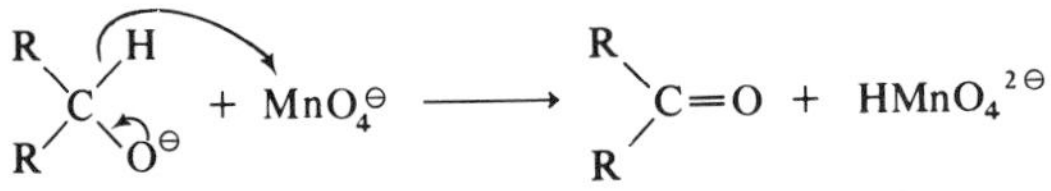

$$\underset{R}{\overset{R}{\diagdown}}\underset{O^{\ominus}}{\overset{H}{\diagup}}C \;+\; MnO_4^{\ominus} \longrightarrow \underset{R}{\overset{R}{\diagdown}}C=O \;+\; HMnO_4^{2\ominus}$$

The ion $HMnO_4^{2\ominus}$ (Mn^V) quickly disproportionates to Mn^{IV} and Mn^{VII}.

Presumably Cr^{VI} is ineffective in oxidizing alcohols by such a path because in basic solution the chromate ion, $CrO_4^{2\ominus}$, carries a double negative charge and the repulsions between the reactants would be too great.

Biological oxidation of alcohols is considered later in the book (Section 18·4).

10·7 polyhydroxy alcohols

The simplest example of an alcohol with more than one hydroxyl group is methylene glycol, $HOCH_2OH$, the term "glycol" meaning a *diol*, a substance with two alcoholic hydroxyl groups. Methylene glycol is reasonably stable in water solution but attempts to isolate it lead only to its dehydration product, formaldehyde.

$$HO-CH_2-OH \rightleftharpoons H_2C=O + H_2O$$

This behavior is typical of *gem*-diols (*gem* = geminal, i.e., with both hydroxyl groups on the same carbon atom), and the very few *gem*-diols that are isolable are those which carry strongly electron-attracting substituents, such as chloral hydrate and hexafluoroacetone hydrate.

$$\underset{\text{chloral hydrate}}{Cl_3C-\overset{\overset{\displaystyle OH}{|}}{\underset{\underset{\displaystyle H}{|}}{C}}-OH}$$

$$\underset{\text{hexafluoroacetone hydrate}}{CF_3-\overset{\overset{\displaystyle OH}{|}}{\underset{\underset{\displaystyle OH}{|}}{C}}-CF_3}$$

Polyhydroxy alcohols in which the hydroxyl groups are situated on different carbons are relatively stable and, as we might expect for substances with a multiplicity of hydrogen bonding groups, they have high boiling points, considerable water solubility, and low solubility in nonpolar solvents.

$$\underset{\substack{\text{ethylene glycol} \\ \text{1,2-ethanediol} \\ \text{bp } 197°}}{\overset{\displaystyle CH_2CH_2}{\underset{\displaystyle OH\ \ OH}{|\ \ \ |}}}$$

$$\underset{\substack{\text{tetramethylene glycol} \\ \text{1,4-butanediol} \\ \text{bp } 230°}}{\overset{\displaystyle CH_2CH_2CH_2CH_2}{\underset{\displaystyle OH\qquad\quad OH}{|\qquad\qquad |}}}$$

$$\underset{\substack{\text{glycerol} \\ \text{1, 2, 3-propanetriol} \\ \text{bp } 290°}}{\overset{\displaystyle CH_2-CH-CH_2}{\underset{\displaystyle OH\ \ \ OH\ \ \ OH}{|\qquad |\qquad |}}}$$

1,2-Diols are usually prepared from alkenes by oxidation with reagents such as osmium tetroxide, potassium permanganate, or hydrogen peroxide (Section 4·4G). However, ethylene glycol is made on a large scale commercially from ethylene oxide, which in turn is made by air oxidation of ethene at high temperatures over a silver catalyst.

$$CH_2{=}CH_2 + {\textstyle\frac{1}{2}}O_2 \xrightarrow[300°]{Ag} \underset{\text{ethylene oxide}}{CH_2{-}CH_2 \atop \diagdown\ \ \diagup \atop O} \xrightarrow{H_2O, H^\oplus} \underset{\displaystyle OH\ \ \ OH}{CH_2{-}CH_2 \atop |\qquad |}$$

Ethylene glycol has important commercial uses. It is an excellent permanent antifreeze for automotive cooling systems, because it is miscible with water in all proportions and a 50% solution freezes at $-34°$ ($-29°F$). It is also used as a solvent and as an intermediate in the production of polymers (polyesters) and other products, as shown in Section 28·4.

The trihydroxy alcohol, glycerol, is a nontoxic, water-soluble, viscous, hygroscopic liquid that is widely used as a humectant (moistening agent). It is an important component of many food, cosmetic, and pharmaceutical preparations. At one time, glycerol was obtained on a commercial scale only as a byproduct of soap manufacture through hydrolysis of fats, which are glycerol esters of long-chain alkanoic acids (see Chapter 13), but now the main source is synthesis from propene as described in Section 9·6. The trinitrate ester of glycerol (nitroglycerin) is an important but shock-sensitive explosive. Dynamite is a much safer and more controllable explosive, made by absorbing nitroglycerin in porous material like sawdust or diatomaceous earth. Smokeless powder is nitroglycerin mixed with partially nitrated cellulose.

$$
\begin{array}{l}
CH_2ONO_2 \\
| \qquad\qquad \text{nitroglycerin} \\
CHONO_2 \quad \text{(glyceryl trinitrate)} \\
| \\
CH_2ONO_2
\end{array}
$$

Glycerol plays an important role in animal metabolism as a constituent of fats and lipids.

10·8   unsaturated alcohols

The simplest unsaturated alcohol, vinyl alcohol, is unstable with respect to acetaldehyde and has never been isolated. Other simple vinyl alcohols undergo

$$
CH_2{=}CHOH \;\rightleftharpoons\; CH_3{-}C{\overset{\displaystyle O}{\underset{\textstyle H}{\big<}}}
$$

vinyl alcohol   acetaldehyde

similar transformations to carbonyl compounds. However, ether and ester derivatives of vinyl alcohols are known and the esters are used to make many commercially important polymers.

Allyl alcohol, $CH_2{=}CH{-}CH_2OH$, unlike vinyl alcohol, is a stable compound. It displays the usual double-bond and alcohol reactions but, as expected from the behavior of allylic halides (Section 9·6), it is much more reactive than saturated primary alcohols toward reagents such as Lucas reagent that cleave the C—O bond.

ethers

Substitution of both hydrogens in water by alkyl or similar groups gives compounds known as ethers, general formula R—O—R. Ethers thus lack the hydroxyl group which determines to such a great extent the physical and chemical properties of water and alcohols. Ethers are much more volatile than alcohols of the same molecular weight. Thus, diethyl ether $(C_2H_5OC_2H_5)$ boils at 35° (body temperature), which is 48° to 83° below the boiling points of the isomeric butyl alcohols. Its solubility in water, however, is 7 g per 100 g of water, about the same as n-butyl alcohol (but much less than that of t-butyl alcohol which is miscible with water). Diethyl ether is often used to extract organic substances out of water solution and it should be remembered that a considerable amount of ether can be retained in the water layer, which may release enough ether vapor to create a fire hazard.

A number of important ethers are listed here. (Nomenclature of ethers was discussed in Section 8·3.)

$CH_3CH_2OCH_2CH_3$ $CH_3OCH=CH_2$ $H_2C\underset{O}{\overset{\diagdown\diagup}{\text{—}}CH_2}$ $HOCH_2CH_2OCH_2CH_2OH$

diethyl ether   methyl vinyl ether   ethylene oxide   diethylene glycol
bp 35°   bp 8°   bp 11°   bp 245°

[benzene ring]—OCH_3

methyl phenyl ether
(anisole)
bp 155°

$\begin{matrix} H_2C-CH_2 \\ | \quad\quad | \\ H_2C\underset{O}{\quad}CH_2 \end{matrix}$

tetrahydrofuran
bp 65°

$\begin{matrix} H_2C\overset{O}{\diagup\diagdown}CH_2 \\ | \quad\quad\quad | \\ H_2C\underset{O}{\quad}CH_2 \end{matrix}$

1, 4-dioxane
bp 101.5°

10·9 preparation of ethers

There are only two generally useful ways of preparing ethers and these have been previously discussed in connection with the reactions of alcohols.

The first is the Williamson synthesis (Section 10·4B), to which the general rules governing S_N2 displacements and the competing elimination reactions apply (Sections 8·7, 8·12).

$$R\text{—}X + R'O^{\ominus}Na^{\oplus} \longrightarrow R\text{—}O\text{—}R' + Na^{\oplus}\ X^{\ominus}$$

The second is dehydration of alcohols (Section 10·5B), which can be accom-

$$2\ ROH \xrightarrow{-H_2O} R\text{—}O\text{—}R$$

plished with concentrated H_2SO_4, H_3PO_4, or at high temperatures with Al_2O_3 catalysis. Only symmetrical ethers can be made efficiently by this route; intramolecular dehydration to give alkenes is a competing reaction.

10·10 reactions of ethers

In general, ethers are low on the scale of chemical reactivity, since the carbon-oxygen bond is not cleaved readily. For this reason, ethers are frequently employed as inert solvents in organic synthesis. Particularly important in this connection are diethyl ether, diisopropyl ether, tetrahydrofuran, and 1,4-dioxane. The latter two compounds are both miscible with water.

The mono and dialkyl ethers of ethylene glycol and diethylene glycol are useful high-boiling solvents. Unfortunately, they have acquired irrational names like "polyglymes," "cellosolves," and "carbitols"; for reference, cellosolves are monoalkyl ethers of ethylene glycol; carbitols are monoalkyl ethers of diethylene glycol; polyglymes are dimethyl ethers of di- or triethylene glycol, diglyme, and triglyme, respectively.

$CH_3OCH_2CH_2OH$
methyl cellosolve
bp 124°

$C_4H_9OCH_2CH_2OCH_2CH_2OH$
butyl carbitol
bp 231°

$CH_3OCH_2CH_2OCH_2CH_2OCH_3$
diglyme
bp 161°

Unlike alcohols, ethers are not acidic and do not usually react with bases. However, exceptionally powerfully basic reagents, particularly certain alkali-metal alkyls, will react destructively with many ethers (see also Section 9·9B).

$$CH_3^{\ominus}\ Na^{\oplus} + \ H{:}CH_2{-}CH_2{-}O{-}CH_2CH_3 \longrightarrow$$

$$CH_4\ +\ CH_2{=}CH_2\ +\ CH_3CH_2\overset{\ominus}{O}\ \overset{\oplus}{Na}$$

Ethers, like alcohols, are weakly basic and are converted to oxonium ions by strong acids (e.g., H_2SO_4, $HClO_4$, and HBr) and to coordination complexes with Lewis acids (e.g., BF_3 and RMgX).

$$C_2H_5\overset{..}{O}C_2H_5\ +\ HBr\ \rightleftharpoons\ C_2H_5\overset{\overset{H}{\overset{..}{}}\ \oplus}{O}C_2H_5\ +\ Br^{\ominus}$$

diethyloxonium bromide

$$C_2H_5\overset{..}{O}C_2H_5\ +\ BF_3\ \longrightarrow\ C_2H_5\overset{\overset{F\ F\ F}{\overset{\backslash|/}{\underset{B}{}}}}{\overset{..}{O}}C_2H_5$$

boron trifluoride etherate

Dialkyloxonium ions are susceptible to nucleophilic displacement and elimination reactions just as are the conjugate acids of alcohols (Section 10·5A). Acidic conditions, therefore, are used to cleave ethers, and as appropriate to the degree of substitution either S_N2 or S_N1 (E1) reactions may occur.

$$C_2H_5-O-C_2H_5 + H^{\oplus} \rightleftharpoons C_2H_5-\overset{\overset{H}{|}}{\underset{\oplus}{O}}-C_2H_5 \xrightarrow[S_N2]{Br^{\ominus}} C_2H_5Br + C_2H_5OH$$

$$(CH_3)_3C-O-C(CH_3)_3 + H^{\oplus} \rightleftharpoons (CH_3)_3C-\overset{\overset{H}{|}}{\underset{\oplus}{O}}-C(CH_3)_3$$

$$\downarrow \quad H\overset{\ominus}{S}O_4 \; | \; E1$$

$$2(CH_3)_2C=CH_2 \longleftarrow (CH_3)_3C-OH + (CH_3)_2C=CH_2 + H_2SO_4$$

Ethers are quite susceptible to attack by radicals, and for this reason are not good solvents for radical-type reactions. In fact, ethers are potentially hazardous chemicals since, in the presence of atmospheric oxygen, a radical-chain process can occur, resulting in the formation of peroxides which are unstable, nonvolatile explosion-prone compounds. This process is called autoxidation and occurs not only with ethers but with many aldehydes and hydrocarbons. Commonly used ethers such as diethyl ether, diisopropyl ether, tetrahydrofuran, and dioxane often become contaminated with peroxides formed by autoxidation on prolonged storage and exposure to air and light. Purification of ethers is frequently necessary before use, and caution should always be exercised in their distillation as the distillation residues may contain dangerously high concentrations of explosive peroxides.

10·11   cyclic ethers

Ethylene oxide, the simplest cyclic ether, is an outstanding exception to the generalization that most ethers resist cleavage. Like that of cyclopropane, the three-membered ring of ethylene oxide is highly strained and opens readily under mild conditions. Unlike ordinary ethers it reacts with Grignard reagents (Section 9·9C), a useful way of extending a chain by two carbon atoms. For example, conversion of 1-hexanol to 1-octanol can be easily accomplished this way via the alkyl bromide.

$$CH_3CH_2CH_2CH_2CH_2CH_2OH + HBr \longrightarrow CH_3CH_2CH_2CH_2CH_2CH_2Br + H_2O$$

$$CH_3CH_2CH_2CH_2CH_2CH_2Br + Mg \xrightarrow{dry\ ether} CH_3CH_2CH_2CH_2CH_2CH_2MgBr$$

$$CH_3CH_2CH_2CH_2CH_2CH_2MgBr + \overset{CH_2-CH_2}{\underset{O}{\diagdown\diagup}}$$

$$\downarrow$$

$$CH_3CH_2CH_2CH_2CH_2CH_2CH_2CH_2\overset{\ominus}{O} \overset{\oplus}{M}gBr$$

$$\downarrow H_2O$$

$$CH_3CH_2CH_2CH_2CH_2CH_2CH_2CH_2OH + HOMgBr$$

The commercial importance of ethylene oxide lies in its readiness to form other important compounds; for example, ethylene glycol, diethylene glycol, the cellosolves and carbitols, dioxane, ethylene chlorohydrin, and polymers (Carbowax) (see Scheme II).

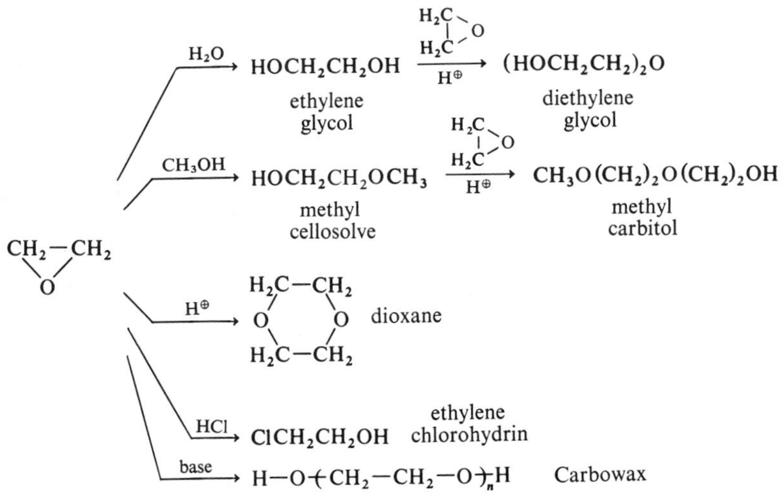

SCHEME II

The lesser-known four-membered cyclic ether, trimethylene oxide $(CH_2)_3O$, is also cleaved readily, but less so than ethylene oxide. Tetramethylene oxide (tetrahydrofuran) is relatively stable and is a water-miscible compound with desirable properties as an organic solvent. It is often used in place of diethyl ether in Grignard reactions and reductions with lithium aluminum hydride.

summary

Alcohols, whether primary (RCH_2OH), secondary (R_2CHOH), or tertiary (R_3COH), have higher melting and boiling points and much higher water solubilities than the corresponding hydrocarbons. The highest melting points and water solubilities (but not boiling points) belong to tertiary and other branched-chain alcohols.

The H—O stretching frequencies in the infrared spectra of alcohols occur near 3700 cm^{-1} (free OH) and near 3350 cm^{-1} (hydrogen-bonded OH). The nmr peaks of hydrogen-bonded OH protons occur 4–5 ppm downfield from TMS but shift upfield with dilution.

Alcohols can be prepared in the following ways for a set of typical primary, secondary, and tertiary alcohols.

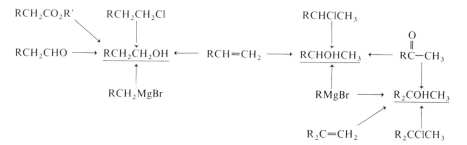

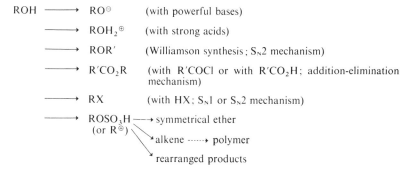

The reactions of alcohols include the following:

ROH   ⟶ $RO^{\ominus}$ (with powerful bases)

      ⟶ $ROH_2^{\oplus}$ (with strong acids)

      ⟶   ROR′   (Williamson synthesis; S_N2 mechanism)

      ⟶ $R'CO_2R$ (with $R'COCl$ or with $R'CO_2H$; addition-elimination mechanism)

      ⟶   RX   (with HX; S_N1 or S_N2 mechanism)

      ⟶ $ROSO_3H$ ⟶ symmetrical ether
          (or $R^{\oplus}$) ↘ alkene ----→ polymer
                   ↘ rearranged products

On oxidation, primary alcohols give aldehydes and secondary alcohols give ketones. Tertiary alcohols are oxidized only with degradation. The Cr^{VI} oxidation of alcohols proceeds via a chromate ester, $ROCrO_3H$, while the Mn^{VII} oxidation involves the anion of the alcohol, $RO^{\ominus}$.

Important polyhydric or unsaturated alcohols include chloral hydrate, ethylene glycol, glycerol, and allyl alcohol.

Ethers are less soluble and are more volatile than alcohols of the same molecular weight. They are prepared from alcohols by dehydration or by the Williamson synthesis (see above). Ethers are cleaved by strong acids, ROR + HX → RX + ROH, and are susceptible to attack by radicals and exceptionally powerful bases ($R^{\ominus}$).

Some important cyclic ethers include 1,4-dioxane, tetrahydrofuran, and ethylene oxide; the latter is not a typical ether because it reacts with Grignard reagents.

exercises

10·1   *cis*-1,2-Cyclopentanediol is appreciably more volatile (bp 124° at 29 mm) than *trans*-1,2-cyclopentanediol (bp 136° at 22 mm). Explain.

10·2   Suggest a likely structure for the compound of molecular formula C_4H_6O whose nmr and infrared spectra are shown in Figure 10·3a. Show your reasoning. Do the same for the compound of formula $C_3H_8O_2$ whose spectra are shown in Figure 10·3b.

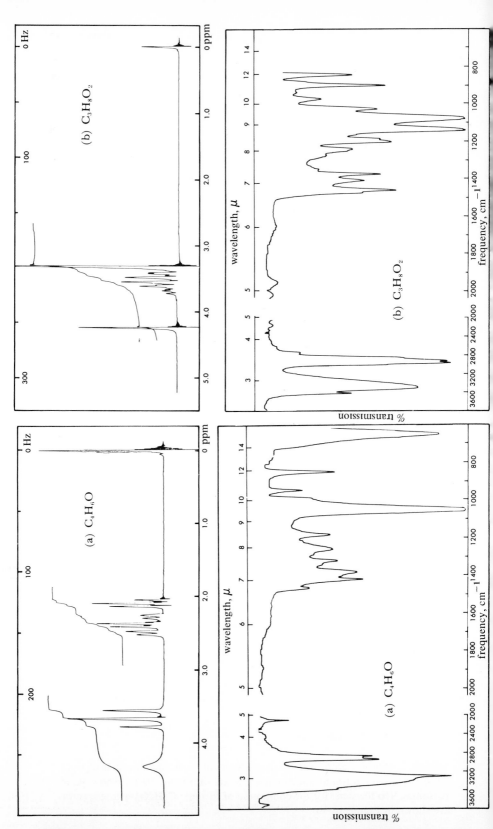

Figure 10·3 Nuclear magnetic resonance spectra and infrared spectra of C_4H_6O (a) and $C_3H_8O_2$ (b); see Exercise 10·2.

10·3 What type of infrared absorption bands due to hydroxyl groups would you expect for *trans*-1,2-cyclobutanediol and 1,2-butanediol (*a*) in very dilute solution, (*b*) in moderately concentrated solution, and (*c*) as pure liquids?

10·4 Show the reagents and conditions for the reactions used to prepare alcohols that are summarized on p. 267.

10·5 Show how you can convert 1-phenylethanol to 2-phenylethanol and 2-phenylethanol to 1-phenylethanol.

10·6 Show how you can prepare 2-methyl-2-butanol starting with (*a*) 2-butanol, (*b*) 2-propanol.

10·7 In the esterification of an acid with an alcohol, how could you distinguish between C—O and O—H cleavage of the alcohol using heavy oxygen (^{18}O) as a tracer?

$$CH_3O{+}H \ + \ RC{+}OH \ \xrightarrow{\ H^{\oplus}\ } \ RCOCH_3 \ + \ H_2O$$

or

$$CH_3{+}OH \ + \ RCO{+}H \ \xrightarrow{\ H^{\oplus}\ } \ RCOCH_3 \ + \ H_2O$$

What type of alcohols would be most likely to react by C—O cleavage, and what side reactions would you anticipate for such alcohols?

10·8 Predict the major products of the following reactions:

  a. $(CH_3)_3CCH_2I + C_2H_5O^{\ominus} \longrightarrow$

  b. $(CH_3)_3CBr \ + \ CH_3O^{\ominus} \longrightarrow$

  c. 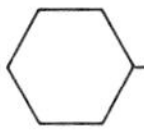 $\langle \rangle{-}Cl \ + \ (CH_3)_3CO^{\ominus} \longrightarrow$

  d. 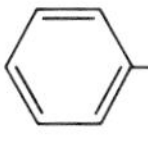 $\langle \rangle{-}CH_2Br \ + \ (CH_3)_2CHCH_2O^{\ominus} \longrightarrow$

  e. $(CH_3)_2CHCH_2Br \ + \ C_6H_5CH_2O^{\ominus} \longrightarrow$

10·9 Predict the products likely to be formed on cleavage of the following ethers with hydrobromic acid:

  a. $CH_2{=}CH{-}CH_2{-}O{-}CH_3$

  b. $CH_3CH_2{-}O{-}CH{=}CH_2$

  c. $(CH_3)_3CCH_2{-}O{-}CH_3$

  d. 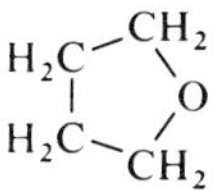 $\begin{array}{c} H_2C{-}CH_2 \\ | \qquad\ \ O \\ H_2C{-}CH_2 \end{array}$

  e. 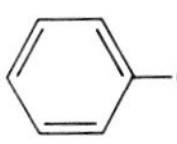 $\langle \rangle{-}O{-}CH_3$

10·10   What would be the products of the following reactions? Indicate your reasoning.

a. $(CH_3)_3COH + CH_3OH \xrightarrow[0°]{\text{conc. } H_2SO_4}$

b. 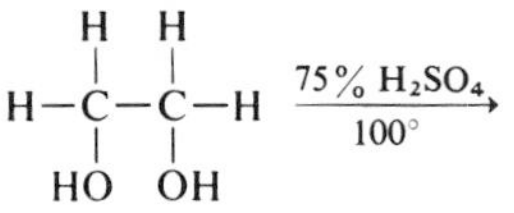 $H-\underset{\underset{HO}{|}}{\overset{\overset{H}{|}}{C}}-\underset{\underset{OH}{|}}{\overset{\overset{H}{|}}{C}}-H \xrightarrow[100°]{75\% \ H_2SO_4}$

c. $CH_3-\underset{\underset{CH_3}{|}}{\overset{\overset{CH_3}{|}}{C}}-CH_2-OH \quad \begin{array}{l} \xrightarrow[25°]{95\% \ H_2SO_4} \\ \xrightarrow[25°]{100\% \ H_2SO_4} \end{array}$

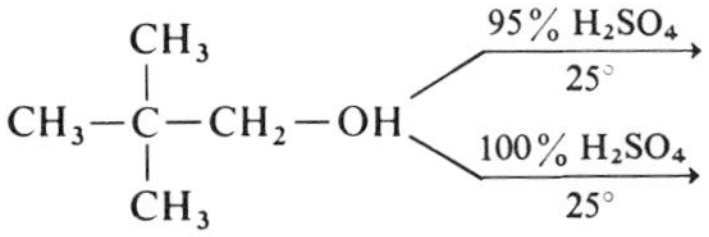

d. 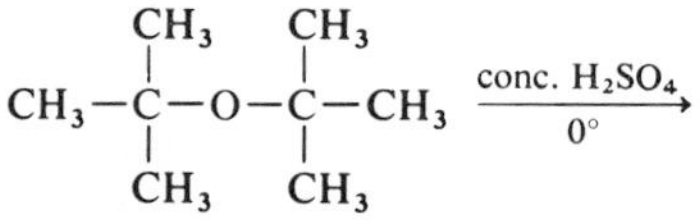 $CH_3-\underset{\underset{CH_3}{|}}{\overset{\overset{CH_3}{|}}{C}}-O-\underset{\underset{CH_3}{|}}{\overset{\overset{CH_3}{|}}{C}}-CH_3 \xrightarrow[0°]{\text{conc. } H_2SO_4}$

10·11   The reaction of methyl acetate with water to give methanol and acetic acid is catalyzed by strong mineral acids such as sulfuric acid. Furthermore, when hydrolysis is carried out in ^{18}O water, the following exchange takes place *faster* than formation of methanol.

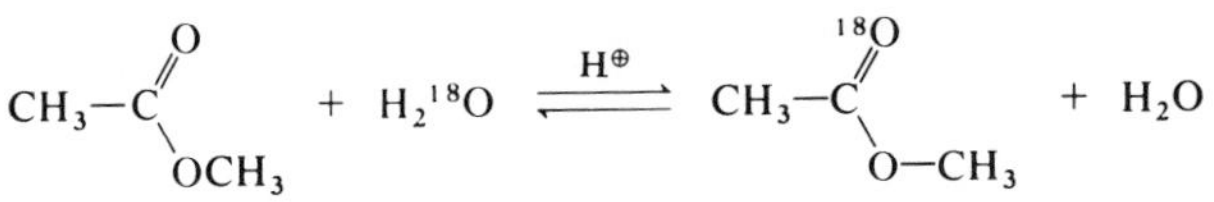

$$CH_3-C\overset{\displaystyle O}{\underset{\displaystyle OCH_3}{\diagdown}} \quad + \ H_2{}^{18}O \ \underset{\longleftarrow}{\overset{H^\oplus}{\longrightarrow}} \ CH_3-C\overset{\displaystyle {}^{18}O}{\underset{\displaystyle O-CH_3}{\diagdown}} \quad + \ H_2O$$

No methanol-^{18}O ($CH_3{}^{18}OH$) is formed in hydrolysis under these conditions.

a. Write a stepwise mechanism which is in harmony with the acid catalysis and with the results obtained in ^{18}O water. Mark the steps of the reaction that are indicated to be fast or slow.

b. The reaction depends on methyl acetate having a proton-accepting ability comparable to that of water. Why? Consider different ways of adding a proton to methyl acetate and decide which is most favorable on the basis of structural theory. Give your reasoning.

c. Explain how the reaction could be slowed down in the presence of high concentrations of sulfuric acid.

10·12   Indicate how you would synthesize each of the following substances from the given organic starting materials and other necessary organic or inorganic reagents. Specify reagents and conditions.

a. $CH_3CH_2CH_2C(CH_3)_2Cl$ from $CH_3CH_2CH_2OH$

b. 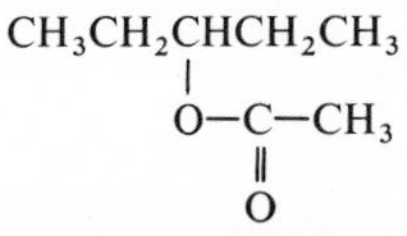 $CH_3CH_2\underset{\underset{\overset{|}{\underset{\overset{||}{O}}{C}}-CH_3}{|}}{C}HCH_2CH_3$ from CH_3CH_2OH

c. $(CH_3)_2CH-CH_2Br$ from $(CH_3)_3COH$

d. $CH_3CH_2CHCH_3$ from $CH_3CH_2CH_2CH_2OH$
$\quad\quad$ |
$\quad\quad OSO_3H$

e. $CH_3CH_2C(CH_3)_2CHO$ from $(CH_3)_2C(OH)CH_2CH_3$

f. $CH_3OCH_2CH_2OCH_3$ from   ethene

g.

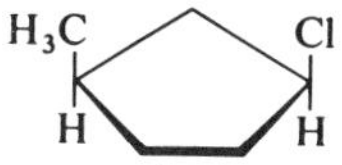

(cis)   from   (trans)

h. $CH_3-\overset{\underset{|}{CH_3}}{\underset{CH_3}{C}}-CH_2-CH_3$ from $CH_3-\overset{\underset{|}{CH_3}}{\underset{CH_3}{C}}-OH$

i. $(CH_2\!=\!CHCH_2)_2O$ from $CH_2\!=\!CHCH_2Cl$

j.

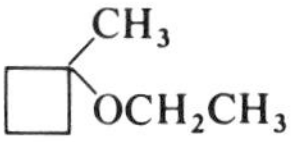

from

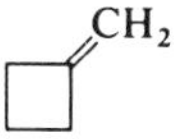

k.

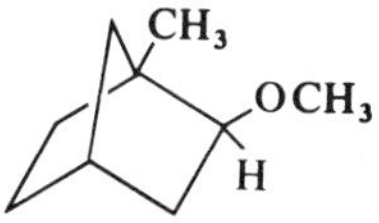

from

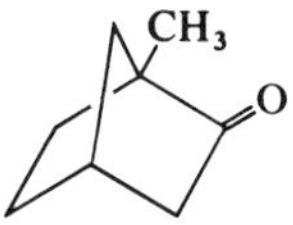

10·13   Give for each of the following pairs of compounds a chemical test, preferably a test tube reaction, which will distinguish between the two substances. Write an equation for each reaction.

a. $CH_3-\overset{\underset{|}{CH_3}}{\underset{OH}{C}}-CH_3$ and $CH_3-\overset{\underset{|}{CH_3}}{\underset{H}{C}}-CH_2OH$

b. $CH_2\!=\!CH-CH_2CH_2OH$ and $CH_3CH\!=\!CH-CH_2OH$

c. $CH_3-\overset{\underset{|}{CH_3}}{\underset{CH_3}{C}}-CH_2OH$ and $CH_3-\overset{\underset{|}{CH_3}}{\underset{}{CH}}-CH_2CH_2OH$

d. $CH_3CH_2-O-SO_2-O-CH_2CH_3$ and $CH_3CH_2CH_2CH_2-O-SO_3H$

e. $CH_3-\overset{\overset{O}{\|}}{C}-Cl$ and $ClCH_2\overset{\overset{O}{\|}}{C}-OH$

f. $CH_3-\overset{\overset{^{18}O}{\|}}{C}-OCH_3$ and $CH_3-\overset{\overset{O}{\|}}{C}-{}^{18}OCH_3$

g. $CH_3-\overset{\underset{|}{CH_3}}{\underset{CH_3}{C}}-O-CrO_3H$ and $CH_3-\overset{\underset{|}{CH_3}}{\underset{H}{C}}-CH_2-O-CrO_3H$

h. $\underset{\overset{|}{OH}\ \overset{|}{OH}}{CH_2-CH-CH_3}$ and $\underset{\overset{|}{OH}\qquad\overset{|}{OH}}{CH_2-CH_2-CH_2}$

i. $H_2C\underset{CH_2}{\overset{CH_2}{<}}O$ and $CH_3CH-CH_2 \atop \diagdown O \diagup$

j. $\underset{\overset{|}{CH_3}}{CH_3-\overset{\overset{\displaystyle CH_3}{|}}{C}-CH_2-O-CH_2-\overset{\overset{\displaystyle CH_3}{|}}{C}-CH_3}$ and $\underset{\overset{|}{CH_3}}{CH_3-\overset{\overset{\displaystyle CH_3}{|}}{C}-O-CH_2-CH_2-\overset{\overset{\displaystyle CH_3}{|}}{C}-CH_3}$

10·14   Suppose you were given unlabeled bottles, each of which is known to contain one of the following compounds: 1-pentanol, 2-pentanol, 2-methyl-2-butanol, 3-penten-1-ol, 4-pentyn-1-ol, di-*n*-butyl ether, and 1-pentyl acetate. Explain how you could use simple chemical tests (test tube reactions with a visible result) to identify the contents of each bottle.

10·15   Predict the principal features with approximate chemical shifts in the nmr spectra of the following compounds (neat liquid unless otherwise noted):

   a.   isobutyl alcohol
   b.   neopentyl alcohol
   c.   methyl β-methylvinyl ether
   d.   *t*-butyl alcohol
   e.   *t*-butyl alcohol in carbon tetrachloride

10·16   Sketch out the energy profile for the reaction of CH_3COCl with CH_3OH as discussed in Section 10·4C, following the arguments in Section 8·9. It will help, in this connection, if you calculate ΔH for the addition of ROH to a carbon-oxygen double bond to estimate the energy of [2] in Section 10·4C.

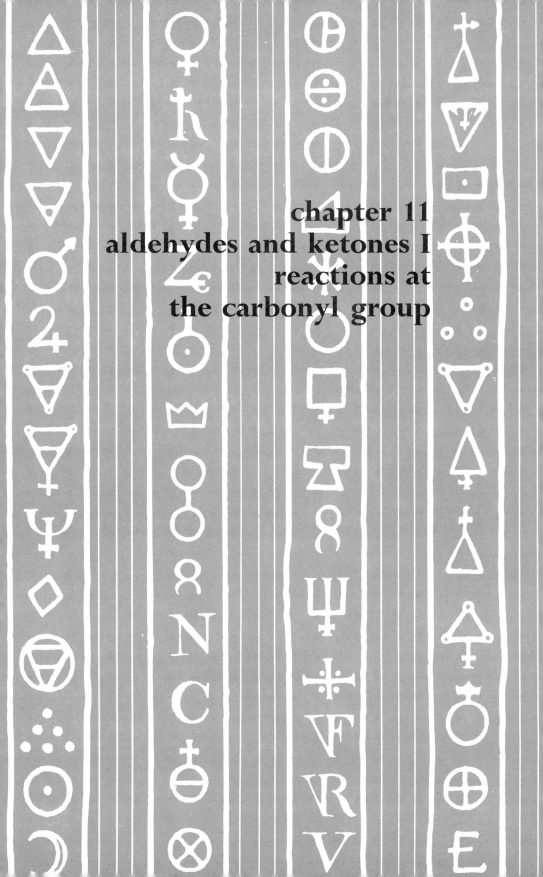

chapter 11
aldehydes and ketones I
reactions at
the carbonyl group

The carbonyl group, $-\overset{\overset{\displaystyle O}{\|}}{C}-$, is an extremely important functional group, and indeed the chemistry of carbonyl compounds is virtually the backbone of synthetic organic chemistry. We shall divide our study of these substances into three parts. In this chapter we shall consider first methods for the synthesis of simple aldehydes and ketones and then the reactions of aldehydes and ketones which involve only their carbonyl groups. In Chapter 12, consideration will be given to the way in which the carbonyl function activates groups on adjacent carbons. In Chapter 13, we shall discuss the role of the carbonyl group in reactions of carboxylic acids and their derivatives. Throughout these discussions attention will be given to the differences in behavior of various kinds of carbonyl groups—differences that may be correlated with electrical and steric effects.

11·1 nomenclature of aldehydes and ketones

Aldehydes have the general formula $R-\overset{\displaystyle O}{\underset{\displaystyle H}{\overset{\diagup}{C}_{\diagdown}}}$ and ketones $R-\overset{\overset{\displaystyle O}{\|}}{C}-R.$

Since their nomenclature follows along the lines discussed previously for other types of compounds, the most widely used naming systems are summarized in Table 11·1.

11·2 carbonyl groups of aldehydes and ketones

A. COMPARISON WITH CARBON-CARBON DOUBLE BONDS

The carbon-oxygen double bond is both a strong and a reactive bond. Its bond energy (179 kcal) is rather more than that of two carbon-oxygen single bonds (2×86 kcal) in contrast to the carbon-carbon double bond (146 kcal), which is weaker than two carbon-carbon single bonds (2×83 kcal). A typical difference in reactivity is seen in hydration:

$$CH_2{=}O + H_2O \rightleftharpoons \underset{\overset{\displaystyle |}{OH} \quad \overset{\displaystyle |}{H}}{CH_2{-}O}$$

$$CH_2{=}CH_2 + H_2O \rightleftharpoons \underset{\overset{\displaystyle |}{OH} \quad \overset{\displaystyle |}{H}}{CH_2{-}CH_2}$$

Formaldehyde adds water rapidly and reversibly at room temperature without an added catalyst; but the addition of water to ethene does not occur in the absence of a very strongly acidic catalyst, even though the equilibrium constant is considerably larger.

The reactivity of the carbonyl bond is primarily due to the difference in electronegativity between carbon and oxygen, which leads to a considerable contribution of the dipolar resonance form with oxygen negative and carbon positive.

Table 11·1   Nomenclature systems for carbonyl compounds

$$\text{Aldehydes,} \quad R-C\!\!\underset{H}{\overset{O}{\lVert}}$$

formula	IUPAC name = longest straight chain[a] + suffix -al	name as derivative of a carboxylic acid (i.e., a carboxaldehyde)
$H_2C=O$	methanal	formaldehyde
$ClCH_2CH_2CHO$	3-chloropropanal	β-chloropropionaldehyde
$\underset{\overset{\displaystyle\vert}{CH_2=CCHO}}{CH_3}$	2-methylpropenal	methacrolein (methacrylaldehyde)[b]
▷—CHO	cyclopropylmethanal	cyclopropanecarboxaldehyde[c]

$$\text{Ketones,} \quad \underset{R'}{\overset{R}{\diagdown}}C=O$$

formula	IUPAC name = longest straight chain[a] + suffix -one	name as ketone[d]
$(CH_3)_2C=O$	propanone	dimethyl ketone (acetone)[e]
$\underset{}{\overset{O}{\overset{\lVert}{CH_3CCH_2CH=CH_2}}}$	4-penten-2-one	methyl allyl ketone
⬡—C(=O)—CH_3	phenylethanone	methyl phenyl ketone (acetophenone)[e]
⬡=O	cyclohexanone	—

[a] The longest straight chain which includes the functional group is understood.
[b] Propenoic acid is commonly called *acrylic acid* and 2-methylpropenoic acid *methacrylic acid.*
[c] The acid $(CH_2)_2CHCO_2H$ is commonly called *cyclopropanecarboxylic acid.*
[d] Ketone is a separate word even though aldehyde is not. Thus $(CH_3CH_2)_2CO$ is diethyl ketone but $(CH_3CH_2)_2CHCHO$ is diethylacetaldehyde (see Section 8·6).
[e] A few ketones are named as derivatives of carboxylic acids. Names by this system stem from the synthesis (real or imagined) of the ketone by the reaction $RCO_2H + R'CO_2H \rightarrow RCOR' + CO_2 + H_2O$.

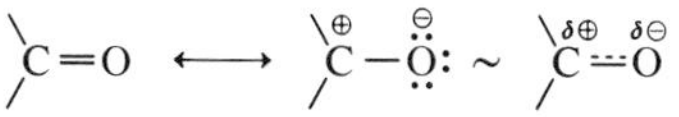

$$\overset{\diagdown}{\underset{\diagup}{C}}=O \quad \longleftrightarrow \quad \overset{\diagdown}{\underset{\diagup}{\overset{\oplus}{C}}}-\overset{\ominus}{\underset{\cdot\cdot}{O}}: \sim \quad \overset{\diagdown}{\underset{\diagup}{\overset{\delta\oplus}{C}}}\overset{\delta\ominus}{=\!=\!O}$$

The polarity of the carbonyl bond is expected to facilitate addition of water and other polar reagents such as $\overset{\delta\oplus}{H}-\overset{\delta\ominus}{X}$ and $\overset{\delta\ominus}{R}-\overset{\delta\oplus}{MgX}$ relative to addition of the same reagents to alkene double bonds. However, we must always keep in mind the possibility that, whereas additions to carbonyl groups may be rapid, their equilibrium constants may be small, because of the strength of the carbonyl bond.

The polarity of the carbonyl group is manifested in many of the other properties of aldehydes and ketones. Boiling points for the lower members of the series are 50° to 80° higher than for hydrocarbons of the same molecular weight. The water solubility of the lower-molecular-weight aldehydes and ketones is large.

Formaldehyde, $H-\overset{\overset{\textstyle O}{\|}}{C}-H$, the first member of the aldehyde series, is a gas, bp −21°. It is readily soluble in water, forming the hydrate (Section 10·7).

The second member, acetaldehyde, $CH_3-\overset{\diagup\!\!\!O}{\underset{\diagdown H}{C}}$, has a boiling point near room temperature (21°). Acetone, $CH_3-\overset{\overset{\textstyle O}{\|}}{C}-CH_3$, the first member of the ketone series, boils at 56°. It is completely miscible both with water and with benzene. As might be expected, the higher aldehydes and ketones are insoluble in water.

B. SPECTROSCOPIC PROPERTIES

The infrared stretching frequencies for the carbonyl groups of aldehydes and ketones generally fall between 1705 and 1740 cm^{-1} and the absorption intensities are much greater than for carbon-carbon double bonds.

All carbonyl compounds have absorption in the accessible part of the ultraviolet spectrum. This absorption, which is weak for ordinary carbonyl groups such as that in methyl ethyl ketone, $CH_3-\overset{\overset{\textstyle O}{\|}}{C}-CH_2CH_3$ (Figure 11·1), is designated as an $n \to \pi^*$ transition, meaning that one of the nonbonding electrons on oxygen is elevated to an antibonding π^* orbital.

Conjugation with a carbon-carbon double bond has a large effect on the spectrum of the carbonyl group. The spectrum of methyl vinyl ketone, $CH_3-\overset{\overset{\textstyle O}{\|}}{C}-CH=CH_2$, shown in Figure 11·1 reveals a significant shift toward the visible. (The tail of the band just reaches the visible part of the spectrum and imparts a slight yellow cast to the compound.) This means that less energy is required to excite a nonbonding electron in the conjugated ketone than in the saturated ketone. We can understand this behavior on the

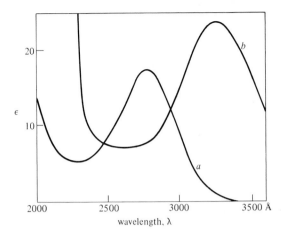

wavelength, λ

Figure 11·1   Ultraviolet spectra of methyl ethyl ketone, *a*, and methyl vinyl ketone, *b*, in cyclohexane solution.

basis of differences in the degree of resonance stabilization of the excited states of the two kinds of compounds.

More significant in practical terms is the appearance in the accessible part of the spectrum of methyl vinyl ketone of an intense absorption band that is due to a $\pi \rightarrow \pi^*$ transition. The almost vertical rise of the absorption curve in Figure 11·1 is caused by this intense absorption, whose peak is at 2190 A. A comparable band for the carbonyl group of methyl ethyl ketone is not shown in Figure 11·1 because it occurs at much shorter wavelength, about 1850 A, which is out of the range of most spectrometers.

The character of the carbonyl bond is such as to give very low-field nmr absorptions for protons of the aldehyde group (RCHO). As Table 7·2 shows, these absorptions come some 4 ppm below vinylic hydrogens. Much of this difference is probably due to the polarity of the carbonyl group. It is carried over in much smaller degree to hydrogens in the α position and we find that

protons of the type $CH_3-\overset{\displaystyle O}{\overset{\displaystyle \|}{C}}-R$ come at lower fields (0.3 ppm) than those of

$CH_3-\overset{\displaystyle R}{\overset{\displaystyle |}{C}}=CR_2$.

11·3   preparation of aldehydes and ketones

Of the six methods listed below for the preparation of aldehydes and ketones, the first four have already been met. The other two will, therefore, be described in more detail. There are a number of additional routes to aromatic aldehydes and ketones, in which the carbonyl group is directly attached to a benzene ring, and these will be encountered in Chapter 24.

1. Oxidation of alcohols (Section 10·6). The primary alcohols give alde-

primary alcohols $RCH_2OH \longrightarrow RCHO$

secondary alcohols $R_2CHOH \longrightarrow R_2C=O$

hydes readily with many oxidants but subsequent oxidation of the aldehyde to a carboxylic acid, RCO_2H (Section 11·4G), can occur; secondary alcohols give ketones in good yield; tertiary alcohols are inert unless drastic conditions are used, in which case carbon-carbon bond rupture occurs to give a mixture of cleavage products.

2. Oxidative cleavage of alkenes (Section 4·4G). The number of alkyl

$$R_2C=CHR' \xrightarrow{O_3} \xrightarrow[H_2O]{Zn} R_2C=O + R'-CHO$$

groups at the double bond determines whether aldehydes or ketones are produced; many oxidants will cleave a carbon-carbon double bond but ozone is one of the few that will not rapidly oxidize the aldehyde produced; oxidative cleavage of 1,2-glycols (Section 10·7) by HIO_4 or $Pb(OAc)_4$ produces the same products (aldehydes or ketones).

3. Hydration of alkynes (Section 5·4). This method can be used only to

$$RC{\equiv}CR + H_2O \xrightarrow[Hg^{2\oplus}]{H^\oplus} \overset{\overset{\displaystyle O}{\displaystyle \|}}{R}CCH_2R$$

prepare ketones (and acetaldehyde, CH_3CHO).

4. Organocadmium compounds react with acyl chlorides (Section 9·9C).

$$R-\overset{\overset{\displaystyle O}{\displaystyle \|}}{C}-Cl + R'CdCl \longrightarrow R-\overset{\overset{\displaystyle O}{\displaystyle \|}}{C}-R' + CdCl_2$$

Grignard reagents react the same way but, being more reactive than organo-cadmium compounds, they usually attack the ketone to give tertiary alcohols.

5. Reduction of carboxylic acids to aldehydes. Conversion of a carboxylic acid to an aldehyde by direct reduction is not easy to achieve because acids are generally difficult to reduce, whereas aldehydes are easily reduced. Thus the problem is to keep the reaction from going too far.

The most useful procedures involve conversion of the acid to a derivative that either is more easily reduced than an aldehyde, or else is reduced to a substance from which the aldehyde can be generated. The so-called **Rosenmund reduction** involves the first of these schemes; in this procedure, the acid is converted to an acyl chloride, which is reduced with hydrogen over a palladium catalyst to the aldehyde in yields up to 90%. The rate of reduction of the aldehyde to the corresponding alcohol is kept at a low level by poisoning the catalyst with sulfur.

$$R-CO_2H \xrightarrow[(-SO_2, HCl)]{SOCl_2} RCOCl \xrightarrow[Pd(S)]{H_2} RCHO + HCl$$

Reduction of an acid to a substance that can be converted to an aldehyde is usefully achieved by way of lithium aluminum hydride reduction of the nitrile corresponding to the acid. The following scheme outlines the sequence of reactions involved starting with the acid:

$$RCO_2H \xrightarrow{SOCl_2} RCOCl \xrightarrow{NH_3} RCONH_2$$

$$\xrightarrow[(-H_2O)]{POCl_3} RC{\equiv}N \xrightarrow{LiAlH_4} R-\overset{\displaystyle H}{\underset{}{C}}=N-Li$$

$$\xrightarrow{H_2O} R-\overset{\displaystyle H}{\underset{}{C}}=NH \xrightarrow{H^\oplus,\ H_2O} R-\overset{\displaystyle H}{\underset{}{C}}=O$$

The reduction step is usually successful only if *inverse* addition is used; that is, a solution of lithium aluminum hydride is added to a solution of the nitrile in ether, preferably at low temperatures.

$$\triangleright\!\!-C{\equiv}N \xrightarrow[(C_2H_5)_2O,\ -50°]{LiAlH_4} \xrightarrow{H^\oplus,\ H_2O} \triangleright\!\!-CHO$$

cyclopropanecarbonitrile   70%
cyclopropanecarboxaldehyde

If the nitrile is added to the hydride, the reduction product is a primary amine, RCH_2NH_2.

6. Rearrangements of 1,2-glycols. Many carbonyl compounds can be usefully synthesized by acid-catalyzed rearrangements of 1,2-glycols, the so-called "pinacol-pinacolone" rearrangement:

$$-\overset{\displaystyle R}{\underset{\displaystyle HO}{C}}-\overset{\displaystyle}{\underset{\displaystyle OH}{C}}- \xrightarrow{H^\oplus} -\overset{\displaystyle R}{\underset{\displaystyle O}{C}}-\overset{\displaystyle}{\underset{\displaystyle \parallel}{C}}- + H_2O$$

R = alkyl, aryl, or hydrogen

The general characteristics of the reaction are similar to those of carbonium ion rearrangements (see Section 8·13). The acid protonates one of the $-OH$ groups and makes it a better leaving group. The carbonium ion which results can then undergo rearrangement by shift of the neighboring group R with its pair of bonding electrons to give a new, more stable, species with a carbon-oxygen double bond.

An important example is provided by the rearrangement of pinacol to pinacolone, as follows:

$$CH_3-\overset{\displaystyle H_3C}{\underset{\displaystyle HO}{C}}-\overset{\displaystyle CH_3}{\underset{\displaystyle OH}{C}}-CH_3 \rightleftharpoons CH_3-\overset{\displaystyle H_3C}{\underset{\displaystyle HO}{C}}-\overset{\displaystyle CH_3}{\underset{\displaystyle \overset{\oplus}{O}H_2}{C}}-CH_3 \xrightarrow{-H_2O} CH_3-\overset{\displaystyle H_3C}{\underset{\displaystyle \overset{\oplus}{C}:OH}{C}}-\overset{\displaystyle CH_3}{\underset{}{C}}-CH_3$$

2, 3-dimethyl-2, 3-butanediol
(pinacol)

$$CH_3-\overset{\displaystyle CH_3}{\underset{\displaystyle \overset{\parallel}{O}\ \ CH_3}{C}}-CH_3 \rightleftharpoons CH_3-\overset{\displaystyle CH_3}{\underset{\displaystyle HO\ \ CH_3}{C}}-\overset{}{\underset{\oplus}{C}}-CH_3$$

3, 3-dimethyl-2-butanone
(pinacolone)

Alkenes may be converted to carbonyl compounds with the same number of carbon atoms by hydroxylation, followed by rearrangement. Isobutyralde-hyde is made on a large scale this way from 2-methylpropene.

$$
\underset{\substack{|\\CH_3}}{CH_3-C=CH_2} \xrightarrow{Cl_2} \underset{\substack{|\;\;\;|\\Cl\;\;Cl}}{\overset{\substack{CH_3\\|}}{CH_3-C-CH_2}} \xrightarrow{H_2O} \underset{\substack{|\;\;\;\;\;|\\HO\;\;OH}}{\overset{\substack{CH_3\\|}}{CH_3-C-CH_2}}
$$

$$\downarrow H^{\oplus}$$

$$
\underset{\substack{|\\H}}{\overset{\substack{CH_3\\|}}{CH_3-C-CHO}}
$$

11·4   reactions of aldehydes and ketones

The important reactions of carbonyl groups characteristically involve addition at one step or another. We have already discussed additions achieved by Grignard reagents as part of Chapter 9. It will be recalled that steric hindrance plays an important role in determining the ratio between addition and other competing reactions. Similar effects are noted in a wide variety of other reactions. We shall expect the reactivity of carbonyl groups in addition processes to be influenced by the size of the substituents thereon because when addition occurs, the substituent groups are pushed back closer to one another. On this basis, we anticipate *decreasing* reactivity with increasing bulkiness of substituents, as in the accompanying series.

$$
\underset{H}{\overset{H}{>}}C=O \;>\; \underset{CH_3}{\overset{H}{>}}C=O \;>\; \underset{CH_3}{\overset{CH_3}{>}}C=O \;\gg\; \underset{H_3C}{\overset{H_3C}{>}}C=O
$$

The term "reactivity" is often used somewhat loosely in connection with discussions of this type. Although it is probably best confined to considera-tions of reaction rate it is also rather widely employed in connection with equilibrium constants—that is, how far the reaction goes, as well as how fast it goes. If steric hindrance is high we expect equilibrium reactions to go neither very fast nor very far. In the case of carbonyl additions, this is gen-erally true, but there are exceptions which will be noted later.

Cyclic ketones almost always react more rapidly in addition processes than their open-chain analogs.

$$
\underset{\substack{|\;\;\;\;\;|\\H_2C-CH_2}}{\overset{\substack{O\\\|\\C}}{H_2C\;\;\;\;CH_2}} \;>\; \underset{\substack{|\;\;\;\;\;|\\H_3C\;\;CH_3}}{\overset{\substack{O\\\|\\C}}{H_2C\;\;\;\;CH_2}}
$$

This is because the alkyl groups of the open-chain compounds have considerably more freedom of motion and produce greater steric hindrance in transition states for addition.

Electrical effects are also important in influencing the ease of addition to carbonyl groups. Electron-attracting groups facilitate the addition of nucleophilic reagents to carbon by increasing its positive character. Thus we find that compounds such as the following add nucleophilic reagents readily:

$$CCl_3-\overset{\overset{\displaystyle O}{\|}}{C}-H \qquad HO_2C-\overset{\overset{\displaystyle O}{\|}}{C}-CO_2H$$

trichloroacetaldehyde (chloral)   oxomalonic acid

Although Grignard reagents, organolithium compounds, and the like generally add to aldehydes and ketones (Section 9·9C) rapidly and irreversibly, this is not true of many other reagents. Their addition reactions may require acidic or basic catalysts and have relatively unfavorable equilibrium constants. Some of these reactions are discussed in considerable detail in the following sections.

A. CYANOHYDRIN FORMATION

Hydrogen cyanide adds to many aldehydes and ketones to give α-cyanoalcohols, usually called cyanohydrins.

$$CH_3-\overset{\overset{\displaystyle O}{\|}}{C}-CH_3 + HCN \underset{\text{base}}{\rightleftharpoons} CH_3-\overset{\overset{\displaystyle OH}{|}}{\underset{\underset{\displaystyle C\equiv N}{|}}{C}}-CH_3$$

The products are useful in synthesis—for example, in the preparation of cyanoalkenes and hydroxy acids:

$$CH_3-\overset{\overset{\displaystyle OH}{|}}{\underset{\underset{\displaystyle C\equiv N}{|}}{C}}-CH_3$$

acetone cyanohydrin

$\xrightarrow{(-H_2O)}$ $CH_2=\overset{\overset{\displaystyle CH_3}{|}}{C}-C\equiv N$

α-methacrylonitrile

$\xrightarrow[(-NH_3)]{H_2O,\ H^\oplus}$ $CH_3-\overset{\overset{\displaystyle OH}{|}}{\underset{\underset{\displaystyle CO_2H}{|}}{C}}-CH_3$

2-hydroxy-2-methylpropanoic acid
(dimethylglycolic acid)

An important feature of cyanohydrin formation is that it requires a basic catalyst. In the absence of base, the reaction does not proceed, or is at best very slow. In principle the basic catalyst might activate either the carbonyl group or the hydrogen cyanide. With hydroxide ion as the base, one reaction to be expected is a reversible addition of hydroxide to the carbonyl group.

$$(CH_3)_2\overset{\delta\oplus}{C}\!=\!\overset{\delta\ominus}{\underset{\curvearrowleft}{O}} + \overset{\ominus}{O}H \;\rightleftharpoons\; \begin{matrix} H_3C \\ \diagdown \\ \diagup \\ H_3C \end{matrix}\!\!\overset{\displaystyle O^{\ominus}}{\underset{\displaystyle OH}{C}}$$

[1]

However, such addition is not likely to facilitate formation of cyanohydrin, because it represents a competitive saturation of the carbonyl double bond. Indeed, if the equilibrium constant for this addition were large, an excess of hydroxide ion could inhibit cyanohydrin formation by tying up acetone as the adduct [1].

Hydrogen cyanide itself has no unshared electron pair on carbon and is unable to form a carbon-carbon bond to a carbonyl carbon (indeed, the fact is that hydrogen cyanide, when it does react as a nucleophilic agent toward carbon, forms C—N rather than C—C bonds). However, an activating function of hydroxide ion is clearly possible through conversion of hydrogen cyanide to cyanide ion, which can function as a nucleophile toward carbon. A complete reaction sequence for cyanohydrin formation is shown.

$$H\!-\!C\!\equiv\!N + \overset{\ominus}{O}H \;\rightleftharpoons\; :\!\overset{\ominus}{C}\!\equiv\!N + H_2O$$

$$\begin{matrix} CH_3 \\ \diagdown\overset{\delta\oplus}{} \\ C\!=\!\overset{\delta\ominus}{O} \\ \diagup \\ CH_3 \end{matrix} + :\!\overset{\ominus}{C}\!\equiv\!N \;\rightleftharpoons\; \begin{matrix} H_3C \\ \diagdown \\ \diagup \\ H_3C \end{matrix}\!\!\overset{\displaystyle O^{\ominus}}{\underset{\displaystyle C\equiv N}{C}}$$

$$\begin{matrix} H_3C \\ \diagdown \\ \diagup \\ H_3C \end{matrix}\!\!\overset{\displaystyle O^{\ominus}}{\underset{\displaystyle C\equiv N}{C}} + H_2O \;\rightleftharpoons\; \begin{matrix} H_3C \\ \diagdown \\ \diagup \\ H_3C \end{matrix}\!\!\overset{\displaystyle OH}{\underset{\displaystyle C\equiv N}{C}} + \overset{\ominus}{O}H$$

The last step regenerates the base catalyst. All steps of the overall reaction are reversible but, with aldehydes and most nonhindered ketones, formation of the cyanohydrin is reasonably favorable. In practical syntheses of cyano-hydrins, it is convenient to add a strong acid to a mixture of sodium cyanide and the carbonyl compound, so that hydrogen cyanide is generated *in situ*. The amount of acid added should be insufficient to consume all the cyanide ion, so that sufficiently alkaline conditions are maintained for rapid addition. If sodium cyanide alone is used the reaction is rapid but does not go to completion because of the reversibility of the final step.

Table 11.2 shows the extent of reaction for some simple carbonyl compounds. The effect of introducing an isopropyl group in the 2 position of cyclohexanone is seen to be considerable and is probably steric in origin. However, in other cases where steric effects might be expected to be important, no evidence for such effects is reported. Thus virtually the same equilibrium constant is found for acetone and methyl *t*-butyl ketone. This is difficult to explain and it appears that the factors governing cyanohydrin formation require further study.

B. HEMIACETAL AND ACETAL FORMATION

Hemiacetals and acetals are products of addition of alcohols to aldehydes —thus, for acetaldehyde and methanol,

Table 11·2 Equilibrium in cyanohydrin formation in 96% ethanol solution at 20°

carbonyl compound	equilibrium constant, liters/mole	% cyanohydrin at equilibrium[a]
CH_3COCH_3	32.8	84
$CH_3COCH_2CH_3$	37.7	85
$CH_3COCH(CH_3)_2$	81.2	90
$CH_3COC(CH_3)_3$	32.3	84

carbonyl compound	equilibrium constant, liters/mole	% cyanohydrin at equilibrium[a]
	67	89
	11,000	~100
(menthone)	15.3	78

[a] Starting with 1 M concentrations of carbonyl compound and hydrogen cyanide.

a hemiacetal
(1-methoxyethanol)

acetaldehyde dimethyl acetal
(1, 1-dimethoxyethane)

First, we shall consider hemiacetal formation, which is catalyzed by *both* acids and bases. The base catalysis is similar to that involved in cyanohydrin formation. The slow step here is the addition of alkoxide ion to the carbonyl group.

Acid catalysis of hemiacetal formation might involve activation of either the alcohol or the carbonyl compound. However, the only simple reaction one would expect between various species of alcohols and proton donors is oxonium ion formation, which hardly seems the proper way to activate an alcohol for nucleophilic attack at the carbonyl group of an aldehyde.

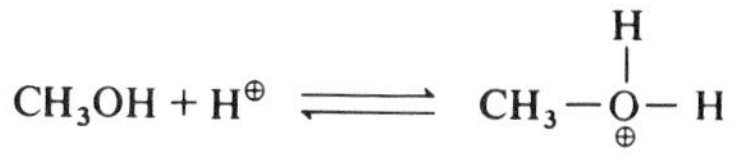

$$CH_3OH + H^\oplus \; \rightleftharpoons \; CH_3 - \overset{\overset{\displaystyle H}{|}}{\underset{\oplus}{O}} - H$$

methyloxonium ion

On the other hand, formation of the oxonium ion (or conjugate acid)[1] of the carbonyl compound is expected to provide activation for hemiacetal formation by increasing the positive character of the carbonyl carbon.

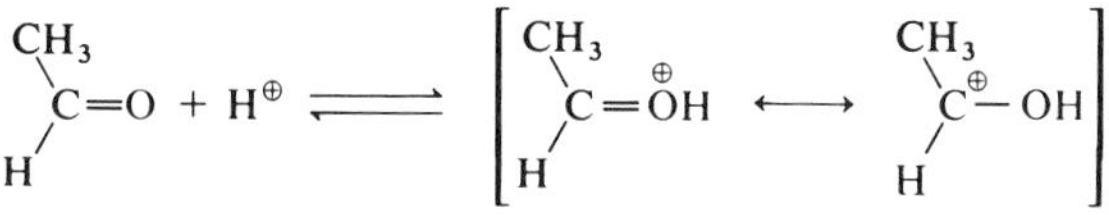

conjugate acid of acetaldehyde

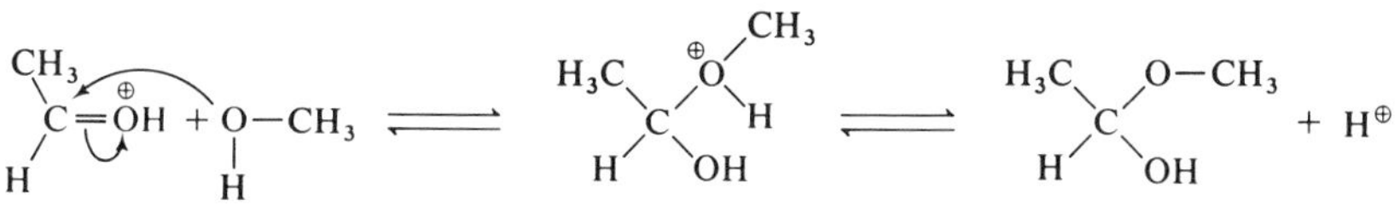

hemiacetal

In water solution most aldehydes form hydrates. This reaction is analogous

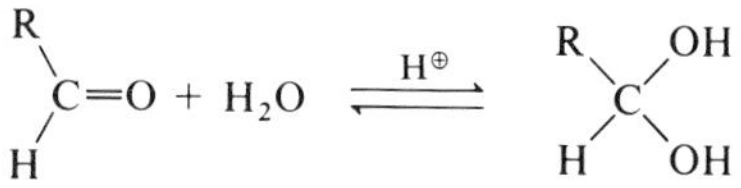

to hemiacetal formation and is catalyzed by both acids and bases. The equilibrium constant for hydrate formation depends on steric and electrical factors.

In contrast to hemiacetal formation, acetal formation is catalyzed *only* by acids. Addition of a proton to a hemiacetal can occur two ways to give either [2] or [3].

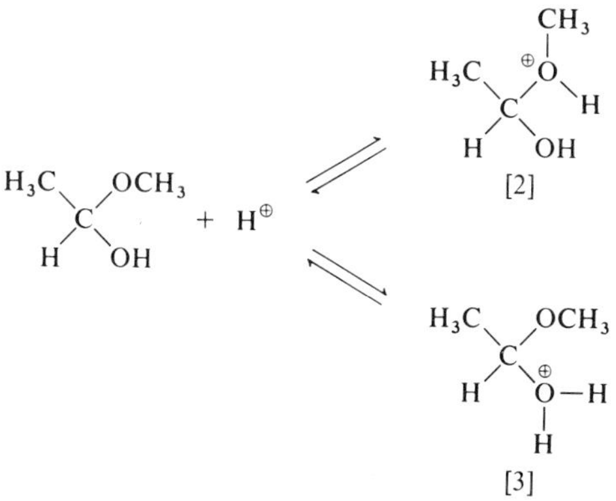

[2]

[3]

[1] The conjugate acid of X is XH$^\oplus$, while the conjugate base of HY is Y$^\ominus$.

The first of these [2] can lose CH_3OH and yield the conjugate acid of acetaldehyde. This is the reverse of acid-catalyzed hemiacetal formation.

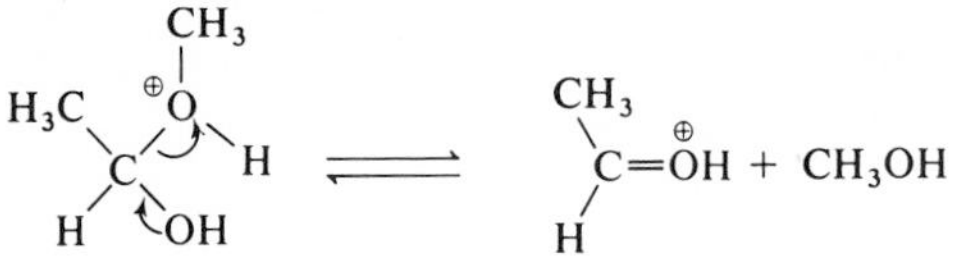

[2]

The second of these [3] can lose H_2O and give a new entity, the methyloxonium cation of the aldehyde [4].

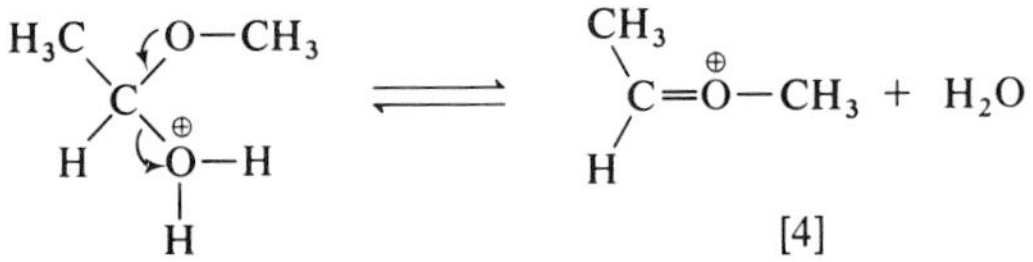

[3]   [4]

The reaction of [4] with water gives back [3], but reaction with alcohol leads to the conjugate acid of the acetal [5]. Loss of a proton from [5] gives the acetal.

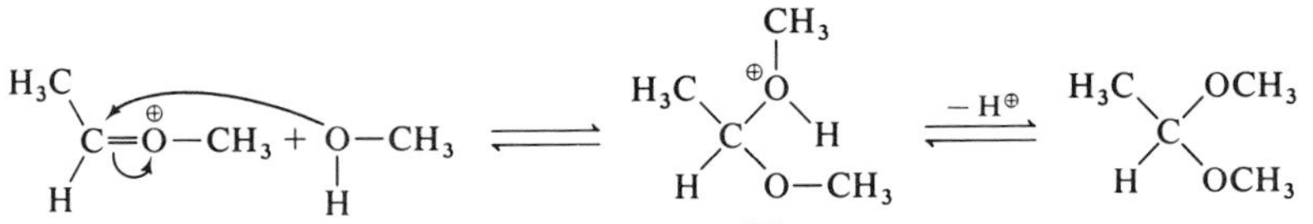

[4]   [5]

The fact that acetals are formed only in an acid-catalyzed reaction has the corollary that acetal groups are stable to base. This can be synthetically very useful, as illustrated by the following synthesis of glyceraldehyde from readily available acrolein (CH_2=CHCHO). Hydrogen chloride in ethanol adds in the anti-Markownikoff manner to acrolein to give β-chloropropion-aldehyde, which then reacts with the ethanol to give the acetal. (Markownikoff's rule does not apply when a carbon-carbon double bond is conjugated to groups such as carbonyl.)

$$CH_2=CHCHO + HCl \longrightarrow ClCH_2CH_2CHO$$
$$ClCH_2CH_2CHO + 2\,C_2H_5OH \longrightarrow ClCH_2CH_2CH(OC_2H_5)_2$$

The key step in the synthesis involves E2 dehydrochlorination of the chloroacetal without destroying the acetal group, which is stable to base.

$$ClCH_2-CH_2-CH(OC_2H_5)_2 + KOH \xrightarrow{\text{E2}} CH_2=CH-CH(OC_2H_5)_2 + KCl + H_2O$$

Hydroxylation of the double bond with neutral permanganate then gives the diethyl acetal of glyceraldehyde. This kind of step would not be possible with acrolein itself because the aldehyde group reacts with permanganate as easily

Table 11·3   Conversions of aldehydes to acetals with various alcohols (1 mole of aldehyde to 5 moles of alcohol)

aldehyde	% conversion to acetal			
	ethanol	cyclohexanol	isopropyl alcohol	*t*-butyl alcohol
CH$_3$CHO	78	56	43	23
(CH$_3$)$_2$CHCHO	71		23	
(CH$_3$)$_3$CCHO	56	16	11	
C$_6$H$_5$CHO	39	23	13	

as does the double bond.

$$CH_2{=}CH{-}CH(OC_2H_5)_2 \xrightarrow{\text{KMnO}_4} \underset{\overset{|}{OH}\ \ \overset{|}{OH}}{CH_2{-}CH{-}CH(OC_2H_5)_2}$$

Finally, mild acidic hydrolysis of the acetal function yields glyceraldehyde.

$$\underset{\overset{|}{OH}\ \ \overset{|}{OH}}{CH_2{-}CH{-}CH(OC_2H_5)_2} + H_2O \xrightarrow{H^\oplus} \underset{\overset{|}{OH}\ \ \overset{|}{OH}}{CH_2{-}CH{-}CHO} + 2\ C_2H_5OH$$

glyceraldehyde

The position of equilibrium in acetal and hemiacetal formation is rather sensitive to steric hindrance. Large groups in either the aldehyde or the alcohol tend to make the reaction less favorable. Table 11·3 shows some typical conversions in acetal formation when 1 mole of aldehyde is allowed to come to equilibrium with 5 moles of alcohol.

Hemiacetal formation occurs readily in an intramolecular manner when a five- or six-membered ring can be formed from a hydroxyaldehyde. This type

$$HOCH_2CH_2CH_2CHO \rightleftharpoons \underset{H_2C{\sim}O}{\overset{H_2C{-}\overset{CH_2OH}{\underset{|}{\diagdown}}C\diagup}{}}{}^{H}$$

of reaction is especially important for carbohydrates as will be discussed in Chapter 15.

C.   POLYMERIZATION OF ALDEHYDES

A reaction closely related to acetal formation is the polymerization of aldehydes. Both linear and cyclic polymers are obtained. For example, formaldehyde in water solution polymerizes to a solid long-chain polymer called paraformaldehyde or "polyoxymethylene." This material, when strongly heated,

$$n{\cdot}CH_2{=}O + H_2O \longrightarrow H{-}O{-}CH_2{\left(O{-}CH_2\right)}_{n-2}O{-}CH_2{-}O{-}H$$

paraformaldehyde

reverts to formaldehyde; it is therefore a convenient source of gaseous formaldehyde. When heated with dilute acid, paraformaldehyde yields the solid trimer trioxymethylene (mp 61°). The cyclic tetramer is also known.

$$\begin{array}{c} \diagup CH_2 \diagdown \\ O O \\ | | \\ H_2C \diagdown \diagup CH_2 \\ O \end{array} \quad \text{trioxymethylene}$$

Long-chain formaldehyde polymers have become very important as plastics in recent years. The low cost of paraformaldehyde (10–15 cents/lb) is highly favorable in this connection, but the instability of the material to elevated temperatures and dilute acids precludes its use in plastics. However, the "end-capping" of polyoxymethylene chains through formation of esters or acetals produces a remarkable increase in stability, and such modified polymers have excellent properties as plastics. Delrin (DuPont) and Celcon (Celanese) are stabilized formaldehyde polymers with exceptional strength and ease of molding.

D. CONDENSATIONS OF CARBONYL COMPOUNDS WITH DERIVATIVES OF AMMONIA

Ammonia adds readily to acetaldehyde to give a crystalline compound.

$$\begin{array}{c} OH \\ | \\ H_3C-C-NH_2 \\ | \\ H \end{array}$$

The corresponding adducts with most other aldehydes are not very stable, undergoing dehydration and polymerization rapidly. Amines and other derivatives of ammonia react in a similar way except that the dehydration products are usually stable compounds that do not polymerize. Reactions of this sort, in which two molecules combine and then water is split out, are often called **condensation reactions** and usually require acid or base catalysis. In the case of condensations between carbonyl compounds and amines, catalysis is normally brought about by acids.

$$\diagdown_{\diagup}C=O + H_2N-R \xrightarrow{H^{\oplus}} \diagdown_{\diagup}C=N-R + H_2O$$

Table 11·4 summarizes a number of important reactions of this type and the nomenclature of the reactants and products.

E. HYDROGEN HALIDE ADDITION AND REPLACEMENT BY HALOGEN

Addition of hydrogen halides to carbonyl groups is so easily reversible as to prevent isolation of the products.

Table 11·4   Condensation reactions of carbonyl compounds with derivatives of ammonia

reactant	typical product	class of product
H$_2$N—R (R = alkyl, aryl or hydrogen) amine	CH$_3$CH=N—CH$_3$ acetaldehyde methylimine	imine^a (Schiff's base)
NH$_2$—NH$_2$ hydrazine	$\underset{\text{CH}_3}{\overset{\text{CH}_3}{\diagdown}}$C=N—NH$_2$ acetone hydrazone	hydrazone
	$\underset{\text{CH}_3}{\overset{\text{CH}_3}{\diagdown}}$C=N—N=C$\underset{\text{CH}_3}{\overset{\text{CH}_3}{\diagup}}$ acetone azine	azine
H$_2$N—NHR (R = alkyl, aryl, or hydrogen) substituted hydrazine	=N—NH— NO$_2$ (with NO$_2$) cyclobutanone 2,4-dinitro-phenylhydrazone	substituted hydrazone^b
$\overset{\text{O}}{\overset{\|}{\text{H}_2\text{NNHCNH}_2}}$ semicarbazide	—CH=N—$\overset{\text{H}}{\text{N}}$—$\overset{\text{O}}{\overset{\|}{\text{C}}}$—NH$_2$ benzaldehyde semicarbazone	semicarbazone^b
HO—NH$_2$ hydroxylamine	CH$_2$=N—OH formaldoxime	oxime^b

^{a} Most unsubstituted imines, that is, R = H, are unstable and polymerize.
^{b} Usually these derivatives are solids and are excellent for the isolation and characterization of aldehydes and ketones.

$$\underset{\text{H}}{\overset{\text{CH}_3}{\diagdown}}\text{C=O} + \text{HCl} \rightleftharpoons \underset{\text{H}\quad\text{OH}}{\overset{\text{CH}_3\quad\text{Cl}}{\diagup\diagdown}}\text{C}$$

However, many aldehydes react with alcohols in the presence of an excess of hydrogen chloride to give α-chloro ethers:

$$\underset{\text{H}}{\overset{\text{CH}_3}{\diagdown}}\text{C=O} + \text{HCl} + \text{CH}_3\text{OH} \rightleftharpoons \underset{\text{H}\quad\text{Cl}}{\overset{\text{CH}_3\quad\text{O—CH}_3}{\diagup\diagdown}}\text{C} + \text{H}_2\text{O}$$

Replacement of the carbonyl function by two chlorines occurs with phosphorus pentachloride in ether, and by two fluorines with sulfur tetrafluoride:

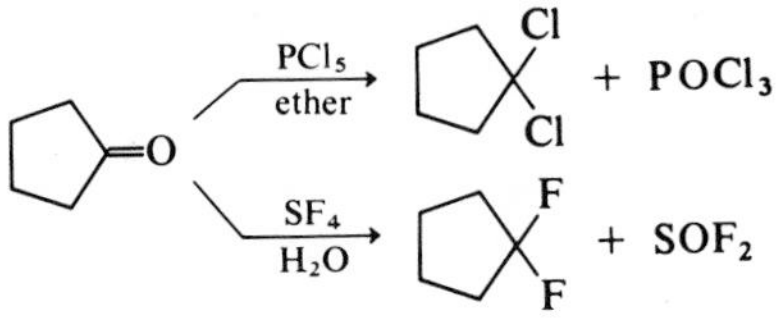

F. REDUCTION OF CARBONYL COMPOUNDS

Formation of Alcohols. The easiest large-scale reduction method for conversion of aldehydes and ketones to alcohols is by catalytic hydrogenation.

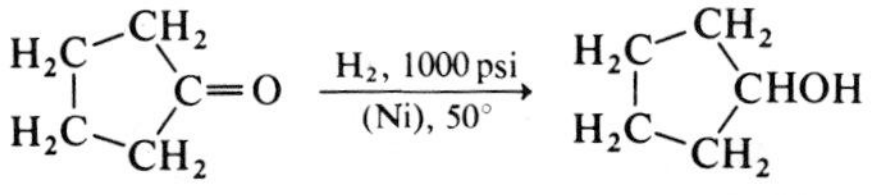

$$95–100\%$$

The advantage over most chemical reduction schemes is that usually the product can be obtained simply by filtration from the catalyst followed by distillation. The usual catalysts are nickel, palladium, copper chromite, or platinum promoted with ferrous iron. Hydrogenation of aldehyde and ketone carbonyl groups is much slower than of carbon-carbon double bonds and rather more strenuous conditions are required. This is not surprising, because hydrogenation of carbonyl groups is calculated to be less exothermic than that of double bonds. It follows that it is generally not possible to reduce a

$$\Delta H = -30 \text{ kcal}$$

$$\Delta H = -12 \text{ kcal}$$

carbonyl group with hydrogen in the presence of a double bond without also saturating the double bond.

In recent years inorganic hydrides such as lithium aluminum hydride, $LiAlH_4$, and sodium borohydride, $NaBH_4$, have become extremely important as reducing agents of carbonyl compounds. These reagents have considerable utility, especially with sensitive and expensive carbonyl compounds. The reduction of cyclobutanone to cyclobutanol is a good example:

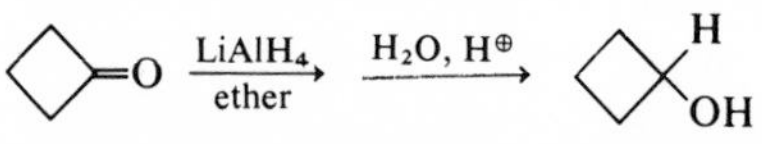

$$90\%$$

With the metal hydrides the key step is transfer of a hydride ion to the carbonyl carbon of the substance being reduced:

$$\underset{R}{\overset{R}{>}}C\!\!=\!\!\overset{\frown}{O} \;+\; H\!-\!\overset{\overset{H}{|}\ominus}{\underset{\underset{H}{|}}{Al}}\!-\!H \;\; \overset{\oplus}{Li} \longrightarrow \underset{R}{\overset{R}{>}}\underset{H}{\overset{O-\overset{\ominus}{Al}H_3\overset{\oplus}{Li}}{\underset{|}{C}}}$$

Lithium aluminum hydride is handled very much like a Grignard reagent, since it is soluble in ether and is sensitive to both oxygen and moisture. (Lithium hydride is insoluble in organic solvents and is not an effective reducing agent for organic compounds.) All four hydrogens on aluminum can be utilized.

$$\overset{\oplus}{Li} \; H\!-\!\overset{\overset{H}{|}}{\underset{\underset{H}{|}}{Al}}\!\!-\!H \;+\; 4\,CH_2\!\!=\!\!O \longrightarrow \overset{\oplus}{Li} \; CH_3O\!-\!\overset{\overset{OCH_3}{|}\ominus}{\underset{\underset{OCH_3}{|}}{Al}}\!-\!OCH_3 \;\;\xrightarrow{H_2O,\ H^{\oplus}}$$

$$4\,CH_3OH \;+\; Al^{3\oplus} \;+\; \overset{\oplus}{Li}$$

The reaction products must be decomposed with water and acid as with the Grignard complexes. Any excess lithium aluminum hydride is decomposed by water and acid with evolution of hydrogen.

$$LiAlH_4 + 4\,H^{\oplus} \longrightarrow Li^{\oplus} + Al^{3\oplus} + 4\,H_2$$

Lithium aluminum hydride usually reduces carbonyl groups without affecting carbon-carbon double bonds. It is, in addition, a strong reducing agent for carbonyl groups of carboxylic acids, esters, and other acid derivatives, as will be described in Chapter 13.

Sodium borohydride is a milder reducing agent than lithium aluminum hydride and will reduce aldehydes and ketones but not acids or esters. It reacts sufficiently slowly with water in neutral or alkaline solution so that reductions which are reasonably rapid can be carried out in water solution with only slight hydrolysis of the reagent.

$$NaBH_4 + 4\,CH_2\!\!=\!\!O + 4\,H_2O \longrightarrow 4\,CH_3OH + NaB(OH)_4$$

Reduction of Carbonyl Compounds to Hydrocarbons. There are a number of methods of transforming

$$\overset{\diagdown}{\underset{\diagup}{C}}\!\!=\!\!O \quad to \quad \overset{\diagdown}{\underset{\diagup}{C}}H_2$$

In some cases, the following sequence of conventional reactions may be useful:

This route is long, requires a hydrogen α to the carbonyl function, and may give rearrangement in the dehydration step (Section 10·5B).

More direct methods may be used depending on the character of the R groups of the carbonyl compound. If the R groups are stable to a variety of reagents there is no problem, but with sensitive R groups not all methods are equally applicable. When the R groups are stable to acid but unstable to base, the **Clemmensen** reduction with amalgamated zinc and hydrochloric acid is often very good. The mechanism of the Clemmensen reduction is not well

$$\langle \ \rangle - \overset{\overset{\displaystyle O}{\|}}{C} - CH_2CO_2C_2H_5 \quad \xrightarrow[\text{HCl}]{\text{Zn(Hg)}} \quad \langle \ \rangle - CH_2CH_2CO_2C_2H_5$$

$$59\%$$

understood. It is clear that in most cases the alcohol is *not* an intermediate, because the Clemmensen conditions do not suffice to reduce most alcohols to hydrocarbons.

When the R groups of the carbonyl compound are stable to base but not to acid, the Wolff–Kishner reduction is often very convenient. This involves treating the carbonyl compound with hydrazine and potassium hydroxide in dimethyl sulfoxide solution.

$$H_2C\overset{\overset{\displaystyle CH_2}{\diagup}}{\underset{\underset{\displaystyle CH_2}{\diagdown}}{}}C=O + NH_2-NH_2 \xrightarrow{\text{KOH}} H_2C\overset{\overset{\displaystyle CH_2}{\diagup}}{\underset{\underset{\displaystyle CH_2}{\diagdown}}{}}CH_2 + N_2 + H_2O$$

$$90\%$$

G.   OXIDATION OF CARBONYL COMPOUNDS

Aldehydes are easily oxidized by moist silver oxide or by potassium permanganate solution to the corresponding acids.

$$R-\overset{\overset{\displaystyle O}{\|}}{C}\diagdown_H \xrightarrow{\text{[O]}} R-\overset{\overset{\displaystyle O}{\|}}{C}\diagdown_{OH}$$

Ketones are much more difficult to oxidize at the carbonyl group than aldehydes. Ketones with α hydrogens can be oxidized in acidic or basic solutions because of enol formation, as will be described in Chapter 12. Thus,

$$\underset{\text{ketone}}{CH_3-\overset{\overset{\displaystyle O}{\|}}{C}-CH_3} \underset{}{\overset{\text{OH}^{\ominus}\text{(or H}^{\oplus}\text{)}}{\rightleftharpoons}} \underset{\text{enol}}{CH_3-\overset{\overset{\displaystyle OH}{|}}{C}=CH_2}$$

Enols, being unsaturated, are easily attacked by reagents which oxidize unsaturated molecules.

Methyl ketones can be oxidized to carboxylic acids with the loss of a carbon atom by the haloform reaction (Section 12·1C).

H. THE CANNIZZARO REACTION

A characteristic reaction of aldehydes without α hydrogens is the self oxidation-reduction that they undergo in the presence of strong base. Using formaldehyde as an example,

$$2\ CH_2{=}O\ +\ NaOH\ \xrightarrow[H_2O]{heat}\ CH_3OH\ +\ H{-}C\underset{ONa}{\overset{O}{\Big\langle}}$$

If the aldehyde has α hydrogens, other reactions usually occur more rapidly.

The mechanism of the Cannizzaro reaction combines many features of other processes studied in this chapter. The first step is reversible addition of hydroxide ion to the carbonyl groups.

$$\underset{H}{\overset{H}{\Big\rangle}}C{=}O\ +\ \overset{\ominus}{O}H\ \rightleftharpoons\ \underset{H}{\overset{H}{\Big\rangle}}C\underset{OH}{\overset{O^{\ominus}}{\Big\langle}}$$

The hydroxyalkoxide ion so formed can act as a hydride ion donor like lithium aluminum hydride and reduce a molecule of formaldehyde to methanol.

$$H_2C{=}O\ +\ \underset{H\ \ OH}{\overset{H}{C}}\overset{\ominus}{\underset{}{O}}\ \xrightarrow{slow}\ H_3C{-}\overset{\ominus}{O}\ +\ H{-}C\underset{OH}{\overset{O}{\Big\langle}}\ \xrightarrow{fast}\ CH_3OH\ +\ H\overset{\ominus}{C}O_2$$

I. DISTINGUISHING BETWEEN ALDEHYDES AND KETONES

Most of the reactions described in earlier sections of this chapter take place with both aldehydes and ketones. There are a number of tests, however, to distinguish between these classes of compounds, one of which is the use of ammoniacal silver ion. This is a mild reagent which oxidizes aldehydes but

$$RCHO\ \xrightarrow{Ag(NH_3)_2{}^{\oplus}}\ RCO_2H\ +\ Ag(s)$$

leaves most ketones untouched. If the reagent and substrate are carefully mixed in a test tube the metallic silver will deposit on the walls to form a mirror. A similar test for aldehydes involves the oxidizing action of complexed cupric ion (Fehling's reagent); a red precipitate of cuprous oxide indicates the oxidation of an aldehyde or other easily oxidized substance.

Another reaction that is characteristic of aldehydes and a few ketones is addition of sodium bisulfite to the carbonyl group. The resulting ionic

$$R{-}C\underset{H}{\overset{O}{\Big\langle}}\ +\ Na^{\oplus}HSO_3^{\ominus}\ \rightleftharpoons\ R{-}\underset{H}{\overset{OH}{\underset{|}{C}}}{-}SO_3^{\ominus}Na^{\oplus}$$

compound is a salt of a sulfonic acid (Section 19·2D), although it is usually called simply the bisulfite addition compound of the particular aldehyde. It contains a carbon-sulfur bond. The reaction is reversible and addition of acid regenerates the aldehyde by converting the sodium bisulfite to sulfur dioxide. Most bisulfite addition compounds are nicely crystalline and aldehydes are sometimes purified through them. The few ketones that form bisulfite addition compounds have relatively unhindered carbonyl groups—for example, acetone and cyclopentanone.

Although the carbonyl stretching frequencies of aldehydes and ketones lie close together (1705–1740 cm^{-1}) the aldehydic C—H stretching frequency occurs at somewhat lower frequency (near 2700 cm^{-1}) than the C—H absorption in ketones and most other compounds. This band is not always easy to recognize, however, and a more characteristic absorption is the nmr peak of the aldehydic proton which occurs at very low field (9.7 ppm from TMS).

summary

Aldehydes, $R-C{\overset{\displaystyle O}{\underset{\displaystyle H}{}}}$, and ketones, $R-\overset{\displaystyle O}{C}-R$, both contain the carbonyl group. The IUPAC system names aldehydes as alkanals—methanal, for example—and ketones as alkanones—propanone, for example. In addition, the simple aldehydes can be named as analogs of carboxylic acids—formaldehyde, for example—and ketones can be named by giving the names of the two groups attached to carbonyl—dimethyl ketone, for example.

The polarity of the carbonyl group accounts for aldehydes and ketones being part way between alkanes and alcohols in terms of most physical properties.

Aldehydes and ketones have characteristic infrared, ultraviolet, and nmr spectra. Strong absorption just above 1700 cm^{-1} in the infrared is due to C=O stretching. Rather weak absorption near 2750 A in the ultraviolet is due to an $n \to \pi^*$ electronic transition in saturated aldehydes or ketones; conjugation of the carbonyl group with a double bond causes an increase in both λ_{max} and ε_{max} and the appearance of powerful $\pi \to \pi^*$ absorption just above 2000 A. The aldehydic proton absorbs at very low field in the nmr.

The methods of preparing aldehydes and ketones may be summarized as follows:

$$
\begin{array}{ccccc}
RCH_2OH & & & RCH{=}CR_2 & \\
 & \searrow & \nearrow & & \searrow \\
 & & RCHO & & R_2C{=}O \longleftarrow R_2CHOH \\
 & \nearrow & \searrow & \nearrow & \\
RCO_2H & & & RC{-}Cl & \\
 & & & \overset{O}{\parallel} &
\end{array}
$$

$$
RC{\equiv}CR \longrightarrow RCCH_2R \qquad R_2C{-}CR_2 \longrightarrow RCCR_3
$$

Most of the reactions of aldehydes and ketones at the carbonyl group involve addition processes. These usually occur more readily with aldehydes or with cyclic ketones than with open-chain ketones, especially those with bulky groups attached. In almost all the reactions shown below a nucleophile attacks the carbon atom of the carbonyl group. In some cases the active nucleophile is produced by the action of base; in others, the carbonyl group is activated by protonation.

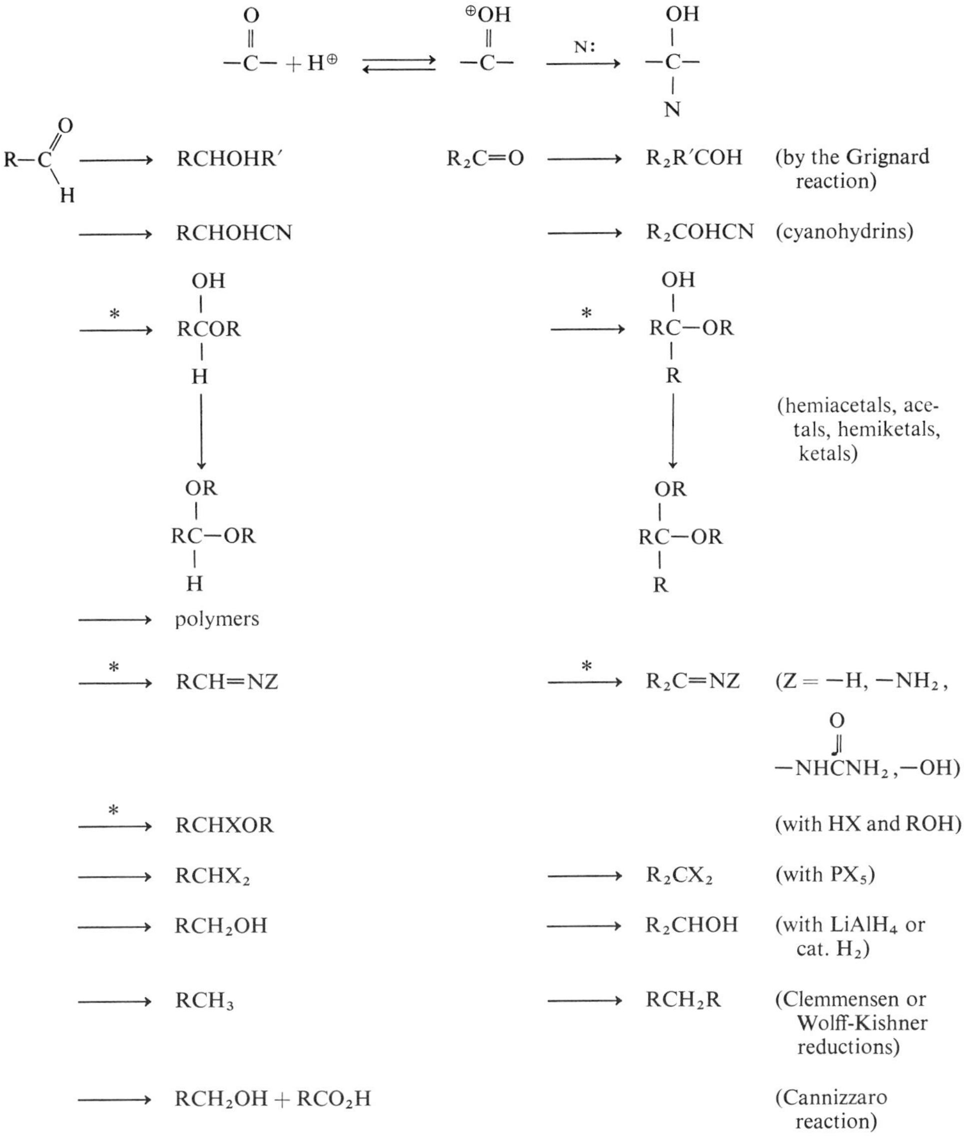

$$\underset{\overset{\|}{-\text{C}-}}{\text{O}} + \text{H}^{\oplus} \quad \rightleftharpoons \quad \underset{\overset{\|}{-\text{C}-}}{\overset{\oplus}{\text{O}}\text{H}} \quad \xrightarrow{\text{N:}} \quad \underset{\overset{|}{\underset{\text{N}}{-\text{C}-}}}{\text{OH}}$$

$$R-\overset{\overset{\text{O}}{\|}}{\underset{\text{H}}{\text{C}}}$$

$\longrightarrow$ RCHOHR′ $\qquad$ $R_2C=O$ $\longrightarrow$ $R_2R'COH$ $\quad$ (by the Grignard reaction)

$\longrightarrow$ RCHOHCN $\qquad\qquad\qquad\qquad$ $\longrightarrow$ R_2COHCN $\quad$ (cyanohydrins)

$\overset{*}{\longrightarrow}$ $\underset{\overset{|}{\text{H}}}{\overset{\overset{\text{OH}}{|}}{\text{RCOR}}}$ $\qquad$ $\overset{*}{\longrightarrow}$ $\underset{\overset{|}{\text{R}}}{\overset{\overset{\text{OH}}{|}}{\text{RC}-\text{OR}}}$

$\qquad\qquad\qquad\qquad\qquad\qquad\qquad\qquad$ (hemiacetals, acetals, hemiketals, ketals)

$\underset{\overset{|}{\text{H}}}{\overset{\overset{\text{OR}}{|}}{\text{RC}-\text{OR}}}$ $\qquad\qquad$ $\underset{\overset{|}{\text{R}}}{\overset{\overset{\text{OR}}{|}}{\text{RC}-\text{OR}}}$

$\longrightarrow$ polymers

$\overset{*}{\longrightarrow}$ RCH=NZ $\qquad$ $\overset{*}{\longrightarrow}$ $R_2C=NZ$ $\quad$ (Z = $-$H, $-NH_2$,

$$\qquad\qquad\qquad\qquad\qquad\qquad\qquad -\text{NH}\overset{\overset{\text{O}}{\|}}{\text{C}}\text{NH}_2, -\text{OH})$$

$\overset{*}{\longrightarrow}$ RCHXOR $\qquad\qquad\qquad\qquad$ (with HX and ROH)

$\longrightarrow$ $RCHX_2$ $\qquad\qquad$ $\longrightarrow$ R_2CX_2 $\quad$ (with PX_5)

$\longrightarrow$ RCH_2OH $\qquad\qquad$ $\longrightarrow$ R_2CHOH $\quad$ (with $LiAlH_4$ or cat. H_2)

$\longrightarrow$ RCH_3 $\qquad\qquad\qquad$ $\longrightarrow$ RCH_2R $\quad$ (Clemmensen or Wolff-Kishner reductions)

$\longrightarrow$ $RCH_2OH + RCO_2H$ $\qquad\qquad\qquad$ (Cannizzaro reaction)

* Acid catalyzed through prior protonation of the carbonyl group.

Aldehydes can be distinguished from most ketones by their ability to reduce Ag^I or Cu^{II}, by their ability to form bisulfite addition compounds, and by the characteristic low-field nmr absorption of the aldehydic proton.

exercises

11·1   Draw structural formulas for each of the following substances.

    a. hexanal   *d.* 3-phenyl-2-butenal
    b. divinyl ketone   *e.* cyclohexyl phenyl ketone
    c. phenylethanal

11·2   Name the following substances according to the systems developed in
      Table 11·1.

    a. $CH_3CH{=}CHCHO$ *d.* CF_3COCF_3

                                        e. $CH_3CH{-}CHCHO$

    b.   OH CH_3

                                        f. $(CH_3)_2C(CH_2)_2CHCHO$

    c. $C_6H_5COCH_2COC_6H_5$

11·3   Write structural formulas for each of the following:

    a. bromomethyl 1,2-dimethylcyclopropyl ketone
    b. diallyl ketone
    c. 4-bromo-2-methyl-3-butynal
    d. diacetylacetylene (and supply the IUPAC name;

$$\overset{\displaystyle O}{\underset{\displaystyle \quad}{\|}}$$
             acetyl $= CH_3{-}C{-}$)
    e. 3-acetyl-2-cyclohexenone

11·4   Show how you could prepare 3-hexanone using, in turn, each of the following
      compounds as starting material.

    a. butanal   *c.* 3-ethyl-2-hexene

    b. 3-hexyne   *d.* propanoyl chloride $(CH_3CH_2C\overset{\displaystyle O}{\underset{\displaystyle Cl}{}})$

11·5   A compound C_6H_{12} was treated with ozone and the reaction products
      boiled with water and zinc dust.
      A single organic product was obtained which had a strong infrared absorp-
      tion band near 1725 cm^{-1} and a low-field absorption in the nmr (almost 10
      ppm from TMS). What is the structure and name of the compound C_6H_{12}?

11·6   Identify the reagents A–F in each of the steps below:

    2-pentanol $\xrightarrow{\text{A}}$ 2-pentanone

    butanal $\xleftarrow{\text{D}}$ $\xleftarrow{\text{C}}$ butanoic acid

11·7   Predict the products to be expected from acid-catalyzed rearrangements of 1,2-propanediol and 2-methyl-2,3-butanediol.

11·8   Treatment of tetramethylethylene oxide $(CH_3)_2C\overset{\displaystyle\diagdown}{}\underset{\displaystyle O}{\overset{\displaystyle\diagup}{}}C(CH_3)_2$ with acid produces pinacolone (pp. 280–281). Explain.

11·9   How might one dehydrate pinacol to 2,3-dimethyl-1,3-butadiene without forming excessive amounts of pinacolone in the process?

11·10   Arrange the following pairs of compounds in order of expected reactivity toward addition of a common nucleophilic agent such as hydroxide ion to the carbonyl bond. Indicate your reasoning.

a. $CH_3-\overset{\displaystyle O}{\overset{\|}{C}}-CH_3$ and $CH_3-\overset{\displaystyle O}{\overset{\|}{C}}-CCl_3$

b. $(CH_3)_3C-\overset{\displaystyle O}{\overset{\|}{C}}-H$ and $CH_3-\overset{\displaystyle O}{\overset{\|}{C}}-CH_3$

c. $CH_3-\overset{\displaystyle O}{\overset{\|}{C}}-OCH_3$ and $CH_3-\overset{\displaystyle O}{\overset{\|}{C}}-CH_3$

d. $CH_3-\overset{\displaystyle O}{\overset{\|}{C}}-Cl$ and $CH_3-\overset{\displaystyle O}{\overset{\|}{C}}-CH_3$

e. $\underset{H_2C}{\overset{H_2C}{}}\!\!\!\overset{\diagup CH_2 \diagdown}{\underset{\diagdown CH_2 \diagup}{}}\!\!\!C\!=\!O$ and $H_2C\!\!\!\overset{\diagup CH_2 \diagdown}{\underset{\diagdown CH_2 \diagup}{}}\!\!\!C\!=\!O$

11·11   What should be the rate law for the formation of acetone cyanohydrin by the mechanism given on p. 283 if the first step is slow and the others fast? If the second step is slow and the others fast?

a.   Calculate ΔH for the formation of acetone cyanohydrin from hydrogen cyanide and acetone in the vapor phase at 25°. Do the same for the formation of dimethylethynylcarbinol from ethyne and acetone.

b.   What are the prospects for carrying out addition of ethyne to acetone by the same procedure used for hydrogen cyanide? Explain.

c.   What would you expect to happen if one attempted to prepare acetone cyanohydrin with acetone and a solution of sodium cyanide?

11·12   The equilibrium constant for hydration is especially large for formaldehyde, trichloroacetaldehyde, and cyclopropanone. Explain.

11·13   Write equations for the synthesis of the following substances based on the indicated starting materials. Give the reaction conditions as accurately as possible.

a. $(CH_3)_2CHCHO$ from $(CH_3)_2CHCH_2CH_2OH$

b. $\begin{array}{c} CH_2-CH-\overset{\displaystyle O}{\overset{\|}{C}}-CH_3 \\ || \\ CH_2-CH_2 \end{array}$ from $\begin{array}{c} CH_2-CHCO_2H \\ || \\ CH_2-CH_2 \end{array}$

c. 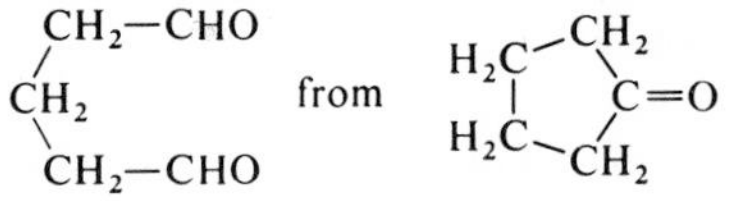
$$
\begin{array}{c}
CH_2-CHO \\
\diagup \\
CH_2 \\
\diagdown \\
CH_2-CHO
\end{array}
\quad \text{from} \quad
\begin{array}{c}
H_2C-CH_2 \\
| \quad\quad \diagdown \\
| \quad\quad\quad C{=}O \\
H_2C-CH_2
\end{array}
$$

d. 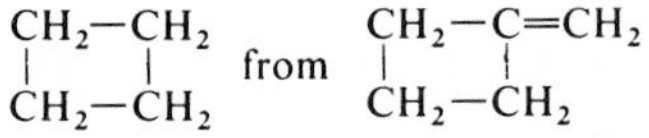
$$
\begin{array}{c}
CH_2-CH_2 \\
|\quad\quad | \\
CH_2-CH_2
\end{array}
\quad \text{from} \quad
\begin{array}{c}
CH_2-C{=}CH_2 \\
|\quad\quad\quad | \\
CH_2-CH_2
\end{array}
$$

e. 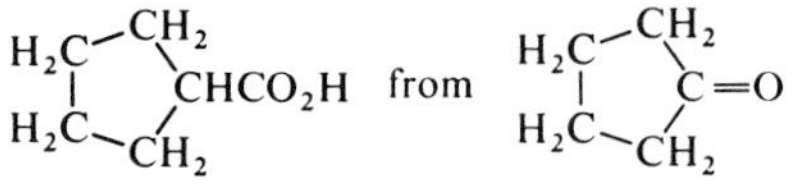
$$
\begin{array}{c}
H_2C-CH_2 \\
| \quad\quad \diagdown \\
| \quad\quad\quad CHCO_2H \\
H_2C-CH_2
\end{array}
\quad \text{from} \quad
\begin{array}{c}
H_2C-CH_2 \\
| \quad\quad \diagdown \\
| \quad\quad\quad C{=}O \\
H_2C-CH_2
\end{array}
$$

11·14 Write reasonable mechanisms for each of the following reactions. Support your formulations with detailed analogies insofar as possible.

a.
$$
\underset{\substack{\| \quad \|}}{H-C-C-H} + NaOH \xrightarrow{H_2O} HOCH_2CO_2Na
$$
$$
H-\overset{O}{\underset{}{C}}-\overset{O}{\underset{}{C}}-H
$$

b.
$$
CH_3-\underset{\substack{| \\ Br}}{\overset{\substack{H \\ |}}{C}}-\underset{\substack{| \\ OH}}{\overset{\substack{H \\ |}}{C}}-CH_3 \xrightarrow[H_2O]{Ag^{\oplus}} CH_3-\underset{\substack{\| \\ O}}{C}-CH_2CH_3
$$

11·15 The following reactions represent "possible" synthetic reactions. Consider each carefully and decide whether or not the reaction will proceed as written. Show your reasoning. If you think side reactions would be important, write equations for each.

a. $CH_3CH(OC_2H_5)_2 + 2\,NaOCH_3 \xrightarrow[50°]{\substack{\text{excess} \\ CH_3OH}} CH_3CH(OCH_3)_2 + 2\,NaOC_2H_5$

b. $(CH_3)_3CCOCH_2CH_3 + KMnO_4 \xrightarrow[KOH]{H_2O} (CH_3)_3COH + CH_3CH_2CO_2K$

c. $CH_3CCl(CH_3)CH_2Cl + 2\,NaOCH_3 \xrightarrow[50°]{CH_3OH} CH_3C(CH_3)(OCH_3)CH_2OCH_3 + 2\,NaCl$

d. $O{=}CH-CO_2H + NaBH_4 \xrightarrow{CH_3OH} O{=}CH-CH_2OH$

e. $CH_2{=}O + CH_3CO_2CH_3 + NaOH \longrightarrow HCO_2Na + CH_3CH_2OH + CH_3OH$

11·16 Name each of the following substances by an accepted system:

a. $CH_3OCH_2C(OCH_3)_3$

b. $CH_3-\underset{\substack{| \\ OH}}{CH}-SO_3Na$

c. $CH_3C(OCH_3)_3$

d. $[(CH_3)_3CO]_3Al$

e. $CH_3(CH_3CO_2)C(CN)(CH_3)$

f. $(CH_3)_2C{=}N-N(CH_3)_2$

g. $(CH_2)_2CHC(CH_3)NOH$

11·17 Show how structures may be deduced for the two substances with respective infrared and nmr spectra as shown in Figure 11·2.

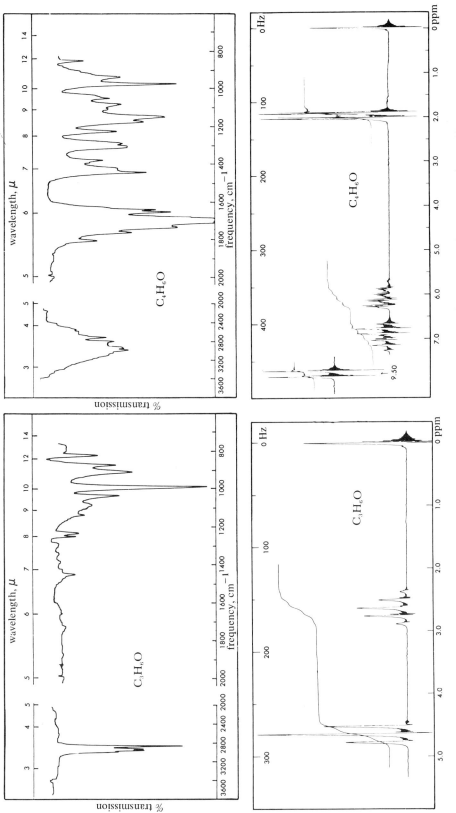

Figure 11·2 Infrared and nmr spectra of two organic compounds. See Exercise 11·17.

11·18   The mass spectra (Section 7·2B) of propanal and butanone both show strong peaks at mass 57. What is the ionic fragment that accounts for these peaks in the two cases? Propanone (acetone), on the other hand, has almost no peak at 57 but has a strong peak at mass 43. What does this suggest about the ease of bond breaking in carbonyl compounds?

11·19   Both periodic acid and lead tetraacetate are useful reagents for cleaving 1,2-diols to aldehydes or ketones. *trans*-9,10-Decalindiol, however, does not react with periodic acid at all, although it is cleaved slowly by lead tetra-acetate.

What general conclusions can you draw about the reaction pathways used by these two reagents?

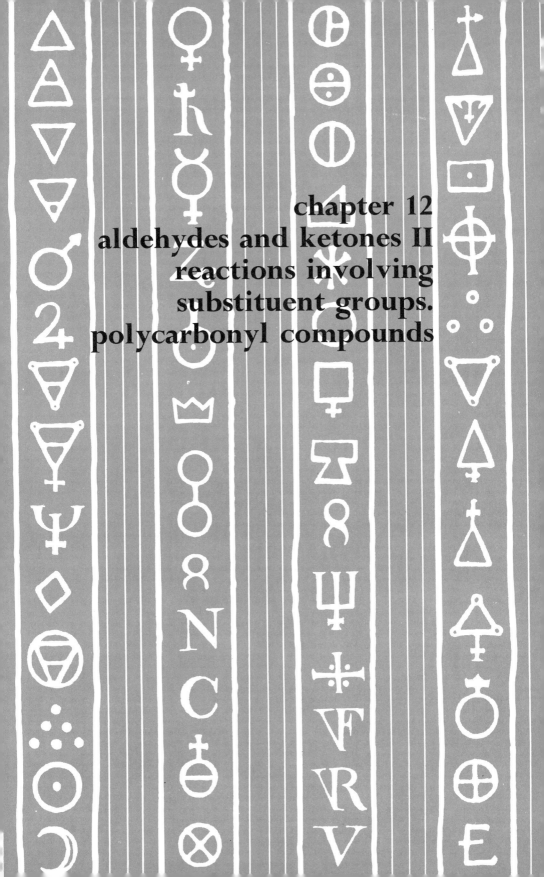

chapter 12
aldehydes and ketones II
reactions involving
substituent groups.
polycarbonyl compounds

Carbonyl groups often have a profound effect on the reactivity of their substituents. This is particularly evident when the substituents have hydrogen and halogen atoms on the carbon α to the carbonyl group, or when there is a double bond in the α,β position. In this chapter we shall consider first a number of very important synthetic reactions involving α hydrogens and later reactions of unsaturated and polycarbonyl compounds.

12·1 halogenation of aldehydes and ketones

Halogenation of saturated aldehydes and ketones usually occurs exclusively by replacement of hydrogens α to the carbonyl groups. The characteristics of

$$CH_3\overset{\overset{\displaystyle O}{\|}}{C}CH_3 + Cl_2 \longrightarrow \underset{\text{chloroacetone}}{ClCH_2\overset{\overset{\displaystyle O}{\|}}{C}CH_3} + HCl$$

2-bromocyclohexanone

such reactions are very different from those of the halogenation of alkanes (Chapter 3). Acetone has been particularly well studied and reacts smoothly with chlorine, bromine, and iodine.

An important feature of the reaction is that acetone reacts at the *same* rate with each halogen. Indeed, the rate of formation of halogenated acetone is independent of the concentration of halogen, even at quite low halogen concentrations. Furthermore, halogenation of acetone is catalyzed by both acids and bases. The rate expressions for formation of halogenated acetone in water solution are

$$v = k[CH_3COCH_3][\overset{\ominus}{O}H] \qquad \text{at moderate concentrations of } OH^{\ominus}$$
$$v = k'[CH_3COCH_3][H^{\oplus}] \qquad \text{at moderate concentrations of } H^{\oplus}$$

(The ratio of k to k' is 12,000, which means that hydroxide ion is a much more effective catalyst than hydrogen ion.)

To account for the role of the catalysts and the lack of effect of halogen concentration on the rate, the acetone must necessarily be slowly converted by the catalysts to an intermediate that reacts rapidly with halogen to give the products. This intermediate is α-methylvinyl alcohol, which is the unstable enol form of acetone.

$$CH_3-\overset{\overset{\displaystyle O}{\|}}{C}-CH_3 \xrightarrow[\text{slow}]{H^{\oplus}(\text{or } OH^{\ominus})} \underset{\substack{\text{enol} \\ (\alpha\text{-methylvinyl alcohol})}}{CH_3-\overset{\overset{\displaystyle OH}{|}}{C}=CH_2} \xrightarrow[\text{fast}]{Br_2} CH_3-\overset{\overset{\displaystyle \oplus OH}{\|}}{C}-CH_2-Br + \overset{\ominus}{Br}$$

$$\xrightarrow{\text{fast}} CH_3-\overset{\overset{\displaystyle O}{\|}}{C}-CH_2Br + H^{\oplus} + Br^{\ominus}$$

As long as the first step is slow compared with the second and third steps, the rate will be independent of both the concentration of halogen and its nature, whether chlorine, bromine, or iodine.

We shall now discuss each step in the reaction in more detail. First, there is the question of how the catalysts function to convert the ketone to its enol form.

A. BASE-CATALYZED ENOLIZATION

With a basic catalyst, the first step is removal of a proton from the α position to give the enolate anion [1]. Normally, C—H bonds are highly resistant to

$$CH_3-\overset{\overset{\displaystyle O}{\|}}{C}-CH_3 + \overset{\ominus}{O}H \underset{}{\overset{slow}{\rightleftharpoons}} \left[CH_3-\overset{\overset{\displaystyle O}{\|}}{C}-\overset{\ominus}{C}H_2: \longleftrightarrow CH_3-\overset{\overset{\displaystyle O^{\ominus}}{|}}{C}=CH_2 \right] + H_2O$$

[1]

attack by basic reagents, but removal of a hydrogen α to a carbonyl group results in the formation of a considerably stabilized anion with a substantial proportion of the negative charge on oxygen. As a result, hydrogens α to carbonyl groups have acidic character and can be removed as protons. In contrast to the dissociation of many weak acids (e.g., CH_3CO_2H, H_3BO_3, HF), the acidic proton on carbon is removed *slowly* and equilibrium between the ketone and its enolate anion [1] is not established rapidly. The reverse reaction is also slow and, as a result, the enolate anion has ample time to add a proton to oxygen to form the enol (this process is at least 10^{10} times faster than conversion to the ketone).

$$\left[CH_3-\overset{\overset{\displaystyle O}{\|}}{C}{=}CH_2 \right]^{\ominus} + H^{\oplus} \overset{fast}{\rightleftharpoons} CH_3-\overset{\overset{\displaystyle OH}{|}}{C}=CH_2$$

Both the enol and the enolate anion can combine rapidly with halogen to give the α-halo ketone.

$$\left[CH_3-\overset{\overset{\displaystyle O}{\|}}{C}{=}CH_2 \right]^{\ominus} + Br_2 \overset{fast}{\longrightarrow} CH_3-\overset{\overset{\displaystyle O}{\|}}{C}-CH_2Br + Br^{\ominus}$$

$$CH_3-\overset{\overset{\displaystyle OH}{|}}{C}=CH_2 + Br_2 \overset{fast}{\longrightarrow} CH_3-\overset{\overset{\displaystyle \oplus OH}{\|}}{C}-CH_2Br + Br^{\ominus} \overset{(-HBr)}{\longrightarrow} CH_3-\overset{\overset{\displaystyle O}{\|}}{C}-CH_2Br$$

The slowest step in the whole sequence is the formation of the enolate anion, and the overall rate is thus independent of the halogen concentration.

B. ACID-CATALYZED ENOLIZATION

Catalysis of the enolization of acetone by acids involves, first, oxonium ion formation and, second, removal of an α proton with water or other proton acceptors.

$$CH_3-\overset{\overset{\displaystyle O}{\|}}{C}-CH_3 + H^\oplus \underset{}{\overset{fast}{\rightleftharpoons}} CH_3-\overset{\overset{\displaystyle \oplus OH}{\|}}{C}-CH_3$$

$$CH_3-\overset{\overset{\displaystyle \oplus OH}{\|}}{C}-CH_3 + H_2O \overset{slow}{\longrightarrow} CH_3-\overset{\overset{\displaystyle OH}{|}}{C}=CH_2 + H_3\overset{\oplus}{O}$$

This differs from base-catalyzed enolization in that the enol is formed directly and not subsequently to the formation of the enolate anion. Also, proton addition to the carbonyl oxygen greatly facilitates proton removal from the α carbon by the electron-attracting power of the positively charged oxygen. Nevertheless, the rate of enolization (or halogenation) is determined by this last step.

The characteristics of acid- and base-catalyzed enolization, as revealed by the halogenation of acetone, are displayed in a wide variety of other, usually more complicated, reactions. For this reason the halogenation reaction has been considered in rather more detail than is consistent with its intrinsic importance as a synthetic reaction.

C. HALOFORM REACTION

The preceding discussion on the halogenation of ketones is incomplete in one important respect concerning base-induced halogenation. That is, once an α-halo ketone is formed, the other hydrogens on the same carbon are rendered more acidic by the electron-attracting effect of the halogen and are replaced much more rapidly than the first hydrogen.

$$CH_3-\overset{\overset{\displaystyle O}{\|}}{C}-CH_3 \overset{slow}{\longrightarrow} CH_3-\overset{\overset{\displaystyle O}{\|}}{C}-CH_2Br \overset{fast}{\longrightarrow} CH_3-\overset{\overset{\displaystyle O}{\|}}{C}-CHBr_2$$

$$\downarrow fast$$

$$CH_3-\overset{\overset{\displaystyle O}{\|}}{C}-CBr_3$$

The result is that if the monobromo ketone is desired, the reaction is best carried out with an acidic catalyst rather than a basic catalyst. A further complication in the base-catalyzed halogenation of a methyl ketone is that the trihalo ketone formed is readily attacked by base with cleavage of a carbon-carbon bond.

$$CH_3-\overset{\overset{\displaystyle O}{\|}}{C}-CBr_3 + \overset{\ominus}{O}H \overset{fast}{\rightleftharpoons} CH_3-\overset{\overset{\displaystyle O^\ominus}{|}}{\underset{\underset{\displaystyle OH}{|}}{C}}-CBr_3 \overset{slow}{\longrightarrow} CH_3-\overset{\overset{\displaystyle O}{\diagup\!\!\diagdown}}{C}\underset{OH}{} +$$

$$:CBr_3{}^\ominus \rightleftharpoons CH_3CO_2^\ominus + HCBr_3$$
$$\text{bromoform}$$

This sequence is often called the **haloform reaction** because it results in the production of chloroform, bromoform, or iodoform, depending on the halogen used. The haloform reaction is a useful method for detecting methyl ketones, particularly when iodine is used because iodoform is a highly insoluble, bright yellow solid. The reaction is also useful for the synthesis of carboxylic acids when the methyl ketone is more available than the corresponding acid. Because halogens readily oxidize alcohols to carbonyl com-

$$\triangleright\!\!-\!\!\overset{\overset{\textstyle O}{\|}}{C}\!\!-\!\!CH_3 \quad \xrightarrow[\text{2. H}^{\oplus}]{\text{1. Br}_2,\ OH^{\ominus},\ H_2O} \quad \triangleright\!\!-\!\!CO_2H + CHBr_3$$
$$85\%$$

pounds it follows that a positive haloform test will also be given by alcohols containing the $-CHOHCH_3$ group.

12·2   reactions of enolate anions

A. THE ALDOL ADDITION

Many of the most important synthetic reactions of carbonyl compounds involve enolate anions, either as addends to suitably activated double bonds or as participants in nucleophilic substitutions. When the addition is to a carbonyl double bond, it is often called an aldol addition. S_N reactions of enolate anions are considered in Chapter 13 with regard to synthetic applications.

The course of the aldol addition is typified by the reaction of acetaldehyde with base, and, if carried out under reasonably mild conditions, gives β-hydroxybutyraldehyde (acetaldol). If the mixture is heated, the product is dehydrated to crotonaldehyde (2-butenal).

$$2\ CH_3CHO \quad \xrightarrow{\text{dilute NaOH}} \quad \overset{\overset{\textstyle OH}{|}}{CH_3CHCH_2CHO}$$

$$\overset{\overset{\textstyle OH}{|}}{CH_3-CH-CH_2-CHO} \quad \longrightarrow \quad CH_3CH\!=\!CH\!-\!CHO$$

Formation of the enolate anion by removal of an α hydrogen by base is the first step in the aldol addition.

$$HO^{\ominus}\!\!+\!CH_3\!\!-\!\!\overset{\overset{\textstyle O}{\|}}{C}\!\!-\!\!H \ \rightleftharpoons \ \left[:\!\overset{\ominus}{C}H_2\!\!-\!\!\overset{\overset{\textstyle O}{\|}}{C}\!\!-\!\!H \ \longleftrightarrow \ CH_2\!\!=\!\!\overset{\overset{\textstyle O^{\ominus}}{|}}{C}\!\!-\!\!H \right]$$

The anion then adds to the carbonyl bond in a manner analogous to the addition of cyanide ion in cyanohydrin formation (Section 11·4A). You would expect from consideration of the two resonance forms of the enolate anion that addition might take place in either of two ways: The anion may attack to form either a carbon-carbon or a carbon-oxygen bond, leading to the aldol [2] or to α-hydroxyethyl vinyl ether [3]. Although the formation of [3] is

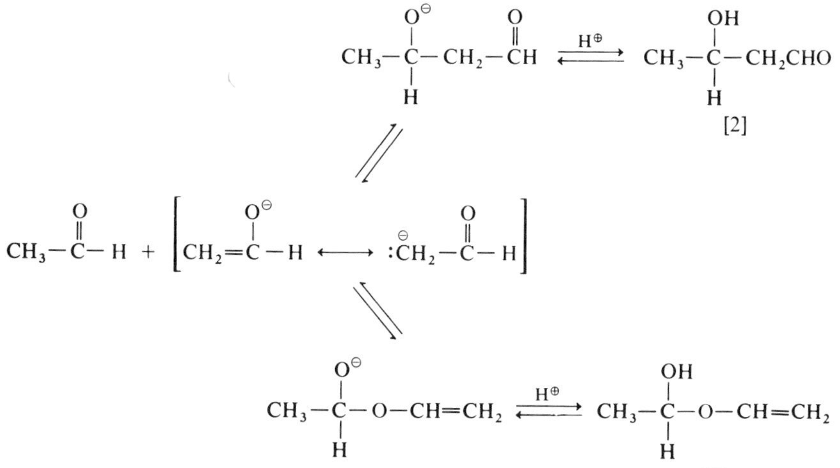

$$CH_3-\overset{\overset{\displaystyle O^{\ominus}}{|}}{\underset{\underset{\displaystyle H}{|}}{C}}-CH_2-\overset{\overset{\displaystyle O}{||}}{C}H \underset{\xleftarrow{\hspace{1cm}}}{\overset{H^{\oplus}}{\rightleftharpoons}} CH_3-\overset{\overset{\displaystyle OH}{|}}{\underset{\underset{\displaystyle H}{|}}{C}}-CH_2CHO$$

[2]

$$CH_3-\overset{\overset{\displaystyle O}{||}}{C}-H \; + \; \left[CH_2=\overset{\overset{\displaystyle O^{\ominus}}{|}}{C}-H \longleftrightarrow \overset{\ominus}{:}CH_2-\overset{\overset{\displaystyle O}{||}}{C}-H\right]$$

$$CH_3-\overset{\overset{\displaystyle O^{\ominus}}{|}}{\underset{\underset{\displaystyle H}{|}}{C}}-O-CH=CH_2 \underset{\xleftarrow{\hspace{1cm}}}{\overset{H^{\oplus}}{\rightleftharpoons}} CH_3-\overset{\overset{\displaystyle OH}{|}}{\underset{\underset{\displaystyle H}{|}}{C}}-O-CH=CH_2$$

[3]

mechanistically reasonable, it is much less so on thermodynamic grounds. Indeed, ΔH for the formation of [3] from acetaldehyde (calculated from vapor-state bond energies) is $+20$ kcal.

The equilibrium constant is favorable for the aldol addition of acetaldehyde, as in fact it is for most aldehydes. For ketones, however, the reaction is much less favorable. With acetone, only a few percent of the addition product "diacetone alcohol" [4] is present at equilibrium.

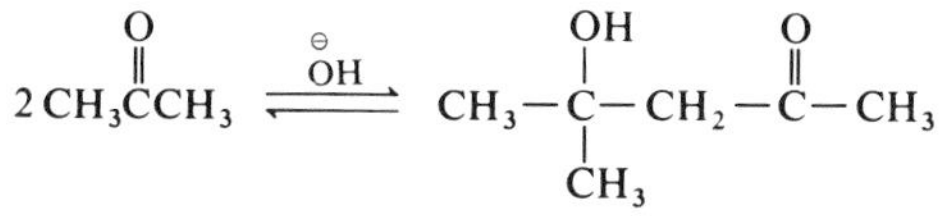

$$2\,CH_3\overset{\overset{\displaystyle O}{||}}{C}CH_3 \underset{\xrightarrow{\hspace{0.6cm}}}{\overset{\ominus}{OH}} CH_3-\overset{\overset{\displaystyle OH}{|}}{\underset{\underset{\displaystyle CH_3}{|}}{C}}-CH_2-\overset{\overset{\displaystyle O}{||}}{C}-CH_3$$

[4]

This is understandable on the basis of steric hindrance and the fact that the ketone-carbonyl bond is about 3 kcal stronger than the aldehyde-carbonyl bond. Despite the unfavorable equilibrium constant, it is possible to prepare diacetone alcohol in good yield with the aid of an apparatus such as shown in Figure 12·1.

The acetone is boiled and the hot condensate from the reflux condenser flows back through the porous thimble over the solid barium hydroxide contained therein and comes to equilibrium with diacetone alcohol. The barium hydroxide is retained by the porous thimble and the liquid phase is returned to the boiler where the acetone (boiling 110° below diacetone alcohol) is selectively vaporized and returned to the reaction zone to furnish more diacetone alcohol.

The fundamental ingredients in the key step in aldol addition are an electron-pair donor and an electron-pair acceptor. In the formation of acetaldol

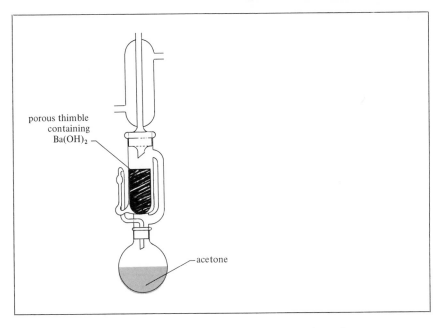

Figure 12·1   Apparatus for preparation of diacetone alcohol.

and diacetone alcohol, both roles are played by one kind of molecule, but there is no reason why this should be a necessary condition for reaction. Many kinds of mixed additions are possible. Consider the combination of formaldehyde and acetone: Formaldehyde cannot form an enolate anion because it has no α hydrogens, but it should be a particularly good electron-pair acceptor because of freedom from steric hindrance and the fact that it has an unusually weak carbonyl bond (166 kcal vs. 179 kcal for acetone). Acetone forms an enolate anion easily but is relatively poor as an acceptor. Consequently, the addition of acetone to formaldehyde should and does occur readily.

$$CH_3-\overset{\overset{\displaystyle O}{\|}}{C}-CH_3 \; + \; CH_2{=}O \; \xrightarrow{\overset{\ominus}{O}H} \; CH_3-\overset{\overset{\displaystyle O}{\|}}{C}-CH_2CH_2OH$$

The problem is not to get addition, but rather to keep it from going too far. Indeed, all six α hydrogens can be easily replaced by $-CH_2OH$ groups.

$$CH_3-\overset{\overset{\displaystyle O}{\|}}{C}-CH_3 \; + \; 6\,CH_2O \; \xrightarrow{\overset{\ominus}{O}H} \; (HOH_2C)_3C-\overset{\overset{\displaystyle O}{\|}}{C}-C(CH_2OH)_3$$

To obtain high yields of the monohydroxymethylene derivative, it is usually necessary to use an apparatus such as shown in Figure 12·2. The scheme here is to have the addition take place in the presence of a large excess of acetone to assure favorable formation of the monoadduct. The reaction is then quenched and the acetone separated and used again. This is achieved by boiling rapidly a solution of acetone containing an excess of a nonvolatile weak organic acid, such as succinic acid $(CH_2)_2(CO_2H)_2$. The vapor is condensed and then mixed with a very slow trickle of an alkaline formalde- hyde solution. The addition then occurs while the mixture flows down over a column of glass beads, and gives the monoadduct because the acetone is present in great excess. The reaction stops and reversal is prevented when the alkali is neutralized by the acid in the boiler. The excess acetone is revaporized and sent up to react with more formaldehyde.

Aldol addition products can be converted to a variety of substances by reactions that have been discussed previously. Of particular importance is the dehydration of aldols to α,β-unsaturated carbonyl compounds, which occurs spontaneously in the presence of acid. The formation of crotonaldehyde by dehydration of acetaldol has already been mentioned in this section. Another example is the dehydration of diacetone alcohol to mesityl oxide.

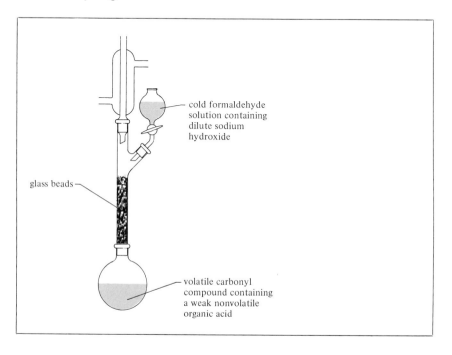

4-methyl-3-penten-2-one
(mesityl oxide)

Figure 12·2 Apparatus for preparation of monohydroxymethylene aldol-addition products from formaldehyde and carbonyl compounds with more than one α hydrogen.

glass beads

cold formaldehyde solution containing dilute sodium hydroxide

volatile carbonyl compound containing a weak nonvolatile organic acid

B. NUCLEOPHILIC SUBSTITUTION INVOLVING ENOLATE ANIONS

An enolate anion can be formed in good yield from a ketone and a power-fully basic reagent, such as sodium or potassium amide, provided that the ketone has an α hydrogen. The enolate anion so formed can theoretically undergo S_N reactions with an alkyl halide in two different ways. Thus, for *t*-butyl methyl ketone and methyl iodide, we could have the reactions shown in Scheme I, which differ only in the position of attack at the enolate anion.

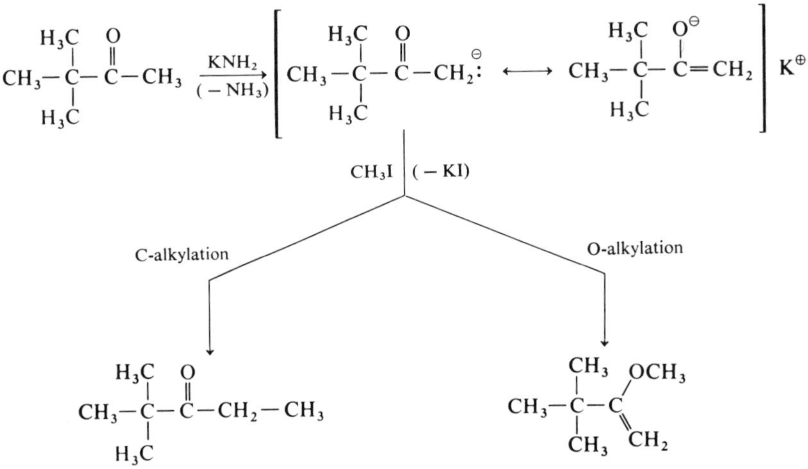

SCHEME I

The possibility of the enolate anion's acting as though its charge were effectively concentrated on carbon or on oxygen was discussed in the previous section in connection with aldol addition (Section 12·2A). However, the situation there is actually quite different from the one here, because the reaction on oxygen was indicated to be thermodynamically unfavorable over-all ($\Delta H = +20$ kcal). However, O- and C-alkylation of the *anion* are *both* thermodynamically favorable. Furthermore, alkylation, unlike the aldol addition, is not reversible under ordinary conditions, and therefore the O-alkylation product is not expected to go over to the C-alkylation product, even though the latter is considerably more stable.

Whether C- or O-alkylation occurs often depends on the reactivity of the halide; the lower the S_N2 reactivity of the halide, the more C-alkylation is favored.

Useful alkylation procedures for the preparation of α-substituted ketones will be discussed below and in Chapter 13.

unsaturated carbonyl compounds

The combination of a carbonyl function and a double bond in the same molecule leads to exceptional properties only when the groups are close to one another. The cumulated and conjugated arrangements are of particular interest. We shall consider first the conjugated or α,β-unsaturated carbonyl compounds, because their chemistry is closely related to that of the substances already discussed in this chapter and in Chapter 11.

12·3 α,β-unsaturated aldehydes and ketones

The most generally useful preparation of α,β-unsaturated carbonyl compounds is by dehydration of aldol addition products, as described in the previous section. Conjugation of the carbonyl group and double bond has a marked influence on spectroscopic properties, particularly on ultraviolet spectra, as the result of stabilization of the excited electronic states which, for $\pi \to \pi^*$ transitions, can be described in terms of important contributions by polar-resonance structures such as $\overset{\oplus}{C}-C=C-\overset{\ominus}{O}$ (see also Sections 7·5 and 11·2B).

The effect of conjugation is also reflected in nmr spectra. The protons on the β carbon of α,β-unsaturated carbonyl compounds usually come at 0.7 to 1.7 ppm lower than ordinary olefinic protons. The effect is smaller for the α proton.

α,β-Unsaturated carbonyl compounds may undergo the usual addition and condensation reactions at the carbonyl group, such as cyanohydrin and hydrazone formation and addition of organometallic compounds. These reactions, however, may be complicated, if not overshadowed, by "1,4 addition" (conjugate addition, Section 6·2) which gives as the overall result addition to the carbon-carbon double bond. The balance between the two modes of reaction is so delicate that relatively small changes in steric hindrance are sufficient to cause one or the other process to predominate.

With hydrogen cyanide, cyanohydrin formation is usually more rapid than 1,4 addition, and if the equilibrium is favorable, as with most aldehydes, only 1,2 addition is observed.

$$CH_3-CH=CH-CHO + HCN \xrightarrow{\overset{\ominus}{OH}} CH_3-CH=CH-\underset{\underset{C\equiv N}{|}}{\overset{\overset{OH}{|}}{C}}-H$$

With ketones, cyanohydrin formation is less favorable, and 1,4 addition results to give an enol intermediate which is unstable with respect to the β-cyano ketone.

$$CH_2=CH-\overset{\overset{O}{\|}}{C}-CH_3 + HCN$$

$$\overset{\ominus}{OH}$$

$$CH_2=CH-\underset{\underset{C\equiv N}{|}}{\overset{\overset{OH}{|}}{C}}-CH_3 \rightleftharpoons N\equiv C-CH_2-CH_2-\overset{\overset{O}{\|}}{C}-CH_3$$

Addition of hydrogen halides to α,β-unsaturated aldehydes, ketones, and acids occurs 1,4 and places the halogen on the β carbon atom. The mechanism of this reaction is illustrated for the reaction of hydrogen chloride with propenal (acrolein). 1,2 Addition to the carbonyl group would lead to an unstable

$$CH_2=CH-\overset{\overset{O}{\|}}{C}-H + H^{\oplus} \;\rightleftharpoons\; \left[CH_2=CH-\overset{\overset{\oplus OH}{\|}}{C}-H \;\longleftrightarrow\; ^{\oplus}CH_2-CH=\overset{\overset{OH}{|}}{C}-H\right]$$

$$\overset{Cl^{\ominus}}{\swarrow}$$

$$ClCH_2-CH=\overset{\overset{OH}{|}}{C}-H \;\rightleftharpoons\; ClCH_2-CH_2-\overset{\overset{O}{\|}}{C}-H$$

α-halo alcohol (Section 11·4E).

β,γ-Unsaturated aldehydes and ketones are usually relatively difficult to synthesize and are found to rearrange readily to the α,β-unsaturated isomers, particularly in the presence of basic reagents. (See Exercise 12·14.)

$$CH_2=CH-CH_2-CHO \;\xrightarrow{\text{base}}\; CH_3-CH=CH-CHO$$

12·4 ketenes

Substances with cumulated carbonyl and carbon-carbon double bonds,
$\overset{\diagdown}{\underset{\diagup}{}}C=C=O$, are called ketenes and, as might be expected, have interesting
and unusual properties.

There are few general preparations for ketenes although several special methods are available for ketene itself. The most convenient laboratory preparation is to pass acetone vapor over a coil of resistance wire heated electrically to a dull red heat. Air is excluded to avoid simple combustion.

$$CH_3-\overset{\overset{O}{\|}}{C}-CH_3 \;\xrightarrow{750°}\; CH_2=C=O + CH_4$$

ketene
bp − 56°

Ketene is a very useful acetylating agent for ROH and RNH_2 compounds. It reacts rapidly, and since the reactions involve additions, there are no by-products to be separated.

$$CH_2=C=O$$

$$\xrightarrow{H_2O} CH_3-C\overset{\diagup\!\!O}{\underset{\diagdown\!\!OH}{}}$$

$$\xrightarrow{CH_3CO_2H} CH_3-\overset{\overset{O}{\|}}{C}-O-\overset{\overset{O}{\|}}{C}-CH_3$$

$$\xrightarrow{CH_3CH_2OH} CH_3-\overset{\overset{O}{\|}}{C}-O-CH_2CH_3$$

$$\xrightarrow{CH_3NH_2} CH_3-\overset{\overset{O}{\|}}{C}-\overset{\overset{H}{|}}{N}-CH_3$$

The considerable convenience of ketene as an acetylating agent would make it an excellent candidate for commercial sale in cylinders except for the fact that the substance is unstable with respect to formation of a dimer known as diketene. The dimer is itself a highly reactive substance with such unusual characteristics that its structure was not firmly established until the early 1950's, some 40 years after it was first prepared.

$$CH_2=C=O \atop H_2C=C=O \longrightarrow \begin{array}{c} H_2C \\ \diagdown \\ C-O \\ | \quad | \\ H_2C-C \\ \diagdown \\ O \end{array}$$

diketene
(vinylaceto-β-lactone)

polycarbonyl compounds

12·5 1,2-dicarbonyl compounds

The structures of some typical and important members of this class are shown.

$$\begin{array}{cc} O \ O \\ \| \ \| \\ H-C-C-H \end{array} \qquad \begin{array}{cc} O \ O \\ \| \ \| \\ CH_3-C-C-CH_3 \end{array} \qquad \begin{array}{cc} O \ O \\ \| \ \| \\ C_6H_5-C-C-C_6H_5 \end{array}$$

glyoxal	biacetyl	benzil
(ethanedial)	(2, 3-butanedione)	(diphenylethanedione)

Most of the 1,2-dicarbonyl compounds are yellow in color. Glyoxal is unusual in being yellow in the liquid state, but green in the vapor state. It has very reactive aldehyde groups.

Glyoxal undergoes an internal Cannizzaro reaction (Section 11·4H) with alkali to give glycolic acid.

$$\begin{array}{cc} O \ O \\ \| \ \| \\ H-C-C-H \end{array} + \overset{\ominus}{O}H \longrightarrow \begin{array}{c} OH \\ | \\ H-C-CO_2^{\ominus} \\ | \\ H \end{array} \xrightarrow{H^{\oplus}} \begin{array}{c} OH \quad O \\ | \quad \diagup\!\!\!\!/ \\ H-C-C \\ | \quad \diagdown \\ H \quad OH \end{array}$$

An analogous reaction occurs with benzil, except that the migrating group is phenyl rather than hydrogen and this results in a rearrangement of the carbon skeleton. This is one of a very few carbon-skeleton rearrangements brought about by basic reagents, and is known as the **benzilic acid rearrangement**.

$$\begin{array}{cc} O \ O \\ \| \ \| \\ C_6H_5-C-C-C_6H_5 \end{array} + \overset{\ominus}{O}H \longrightarrow \begin{array}{c} OH \\ | \\ C_6H_5-C-CO_2^{\ominus} \\ | \\ C_6H_5 \end{array} \xrightarrow{H^{\oplus}} \begin{array}{c} OH \quad O \\ | \quad \diagup\!\!\!\!/ \\ C_6H_5-C-C \\ | \quad \diagdown \\ C_6H_5 \quad OH \end{array}$$

benzilic acid

12·6   1,3-dicarbonyl compounds

Most of the important properties of 1,3-dialdehydes, aldehyde ketones, and diketones that are characteristic of the 1,3 relationship are well illustrated by 2,4-pentanedione (acetylacetone). This substance is unusual in existing to the extent of 85% as the enol form.

$$CH_3-\overset{\overset{\displaystyle O}{\|}}{C} \dashv CH_2-\overset{\overset{\displaystyle O}{\|}}{C}-CH_3$$

2, 4-pentanedione

$$CH_3-\overset{\overset{\displaystyle O}{\|}}{C}-CH_2-\overset{\overset{\displaystyle O}{\|}}{C}-CH_3 \;\rightleftharpoons\;$$

15%   85%

The nmr spectrum of 2,4-pentanedione (Figure 12·3) is very informative about the species present in the pure liquid. Resonance lines for both the keto and enol forms can be readily distinguished. The keto form has its CH_2 resonance at 218 Hz and its CH_3 resonances at 120 Hz, whereas the enol form shows its CH_3 and vinyl-CH resonances at 110 Hz and 334 Hz, respectively. The enol-OH proton comes at the very low field value of 910 Hz with respect to tetramethylsilane. That each form may be observed separately indicates that the lifetime of each form is longer than 0.1 sec at room temperature (see Section 7·6D). However, when a basic catalyst is added, the lines broaden

Figure 12·3   Nuclear magnetic resonance spectrum of 2,4-pentanedione, $CH_3COCH_2COCH_3$, at 60 MHz. Calibrations are relative to tetramethylsilane.

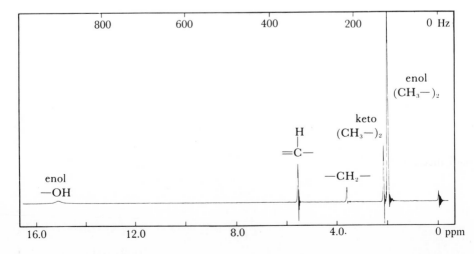

considerably; when the mixture is heated, the lines coalesce to an average spectrum as expected for rapid equilibration.

The very large chemical shift of the enol-OH proton is the consequence of internal hydrogen bonding involving the carbonyl group. This type of hydrogen bonding is also important in stabilizing the enol form, as evidenced by an increase in the percentage of enol in those solvents, such as hexane, that cannot effectively solvate the ketone groups of the keto form.

The enol form is also considerably stabilized by resonance which, in turn, increases the strength of the hydrogen bond. Such stabilization is, of course, not possible for the keto form.

The term conformer is often used to designate one of two or more stereochemical arrangements that are interconverted by rotation about single bonds. This is usually so rapid that it prevents the isolation of discrete conformers, except at very low temperatures (see Section 3·4B). The term **tautomer** is employed in exactly the same sense for *structural* isomers in rapid equilibrium, such as the keto and enol forms of 2,4-pentanedione. When tautomerization involves only the shift of a proton, as in the acetaldehyde–vinyl alcohol equilibrium (Section 10·8), it is sometimes called a **prototropic** change. While in principle the only difference between the rapid interconversion of 2,4-pentanedione on the one hand and the slow isomerization of 1,4-pentadiene on the other is a matter of relative reaction rate, rightly or wrongly, the term tautomeric change is usually applied only to the more rapid process.

2,4-Pentanedione is moderately acidic with $K_{HA} \sim 10^{-9}$ compared with K_{HA} of 10^{-5} for acetic acid and 10^{-16} for ethanol, the charge delocalization in the anion being responsible.

Alkali metal salts of the compound can be alkylated with alkyl halides of good S_N2 reactivity and generally give C-alkylation. A number of synthetically important alkylations of other 1,3-dicarbonyl compounds are discussed in Chapter 13.

Polyvalent metal cations often form very stable and slightly polar enolate salts with acetylacetone, better known as metal chelates. Cupric ion is a particularly good chelating agent. The corresponding beryllium compound is a

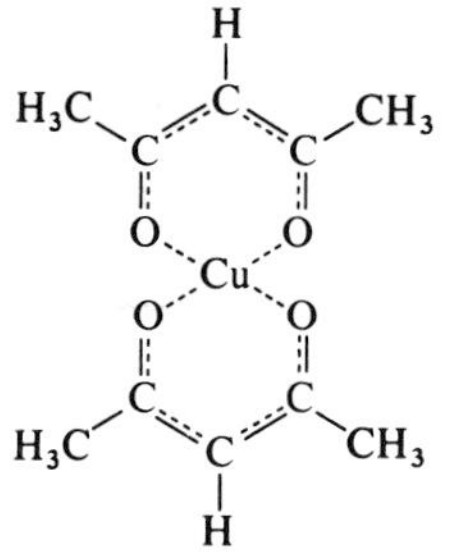

cupric acetylacetonate (dark blue)
(Cu^{II} salt of 2, 4-pentanedione)

further example of a metal chelate; it melts at 108°, boils at 270°, and is soluble in many organic solvents.

summary

Aldehydes and ketones [5] undergo a number of reactions at the α position involving either the enolate anion [6] or the enol [7]; [6] results only from the action of a base, while [7] can be generated by the action of either an acid or a base. The rates of interconversion of [7] and [5], not their equilibrium concentrations, are affected by acid or base.

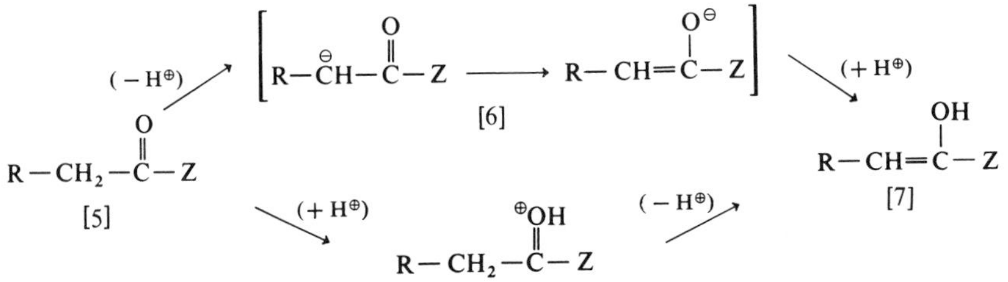

α-Halogenation can proceed via [6] or [7] with both aldehydes and ketones. Methyl ketones in basic solution undergo trisubstitution and this is followed by chain cleavage (the haloform reaction).

$$RCH_2-\overset{\overset{\displaystyle O}{\|}}{C}-CH_3 \longrightarrow RCH_2-\overset{\overset{\displaystyle O}{\|}}{C}-CX_3 \longrightarrow RCH_2-CO_2H + CHX_3$$

Aldehydes with α hydrogens undergo aldol addition in base to give products which often eliminate water to give α,β-unsaturated aldehydes. Although the equilibrium is normally unfavorable for the corresponding condensation of two molecules of a ketone, the reaction can nonetheless often be made to occur (Figure 12·1).

$$RCH_2CHO + R\overset{\ominus}{C}H-CHO \longrightarrow RCH_2\overset{\overset{\displaystyle O^{\ominus}}{|}}{C}H-CH-CHO$$
$$\underset{\displaystyle R}{|}$$

$$RCH_2\overset{\overset{\displaystyle OH}{|}}{C}H-\underset{\underset{\displaystyle R}{|}}{C}H-CHO \longrightarrow RCH_2CH=\underset{\underset{\displaystyle R}{|}}{C}-CHO$$

Ketones are alkylated (predominantly at carbon) through reaction of the enolate anions with alkyl halides.

$$R-\overset{\ominus}{C}H-\overset{\overset{\displaystyle O}{||}}{C}-R \longrightarrow R-\underset{\underset{\displaystyle R'}{|}}{C}H-\overset{\overset{\displaystyle O}{||}}{C}-R$$

α,β-Unsaturated aldehydes and ketones absorb strongly in the ultraviolet and the protons on their β-carbon atoms appear at lower field in the nmr than other alkenic protons: They are usually subject to 1,4-addition reactions of the type RCH=CHCHO + HZ → RCHZCH₂CHO.

Ketenes contain cumulated double bonds and react rapidly with hydroxylic (and amino) compounds.

$$R_2C=C=O + ZOH \longrightarrow R_2CH\overset{\overset{\displaystyle O}{||}}{C}OZ \quad \left(Z=H-,\ R\overset{\overset{\displaystyle O}{||}}{C}-,\ R-\right)$$

Ketene itself, which is prepared in the laboratory by the pyrolysis of acetone, readily dimerizes to give diketene, a β-lactone.

1,2-Dicarbonyl compounds include glyoxal (OHCCHO), biacetyl ($CH_3\overset{\overset{\displaystyle O}{||}}{C}-\overset{\overset{\displaystyle O}{||}}{C}CH_3$), and benzil ($C_6H_5\overset{\overset{\displaystyle O}{||}}{C}-\overset{\overset{\displaystyle O}{||}}{C}C_6H_5$). In basic solution, glyoxal undergoes an internal Cannizzaro reaction and benzil undergoes a carbon-skeleton rearrangement to give benzilic acid, $(C_6H_5)_2COHCO_2H$.

Two important characteristics of 1,3-dicarbonyl compounds are their acidity and their tendency to enolize. Stabilization of the anion and enol can be ascribed to resonance stabilization and hydrogen bonding, respectively.

The keto-enol forms are called tautomers (structural isomers in rapid equilibrium). Enols form complex salts called chelates with many metal cations.

exercises

12·1   At what point would the system shown in Figure 12·1 cease to produce more diacetone alcohol? What would happen if some barium hydroxide were to get through a hole in the thimble and pass into the boiler? Why is barium hydroxide more suitable for the preparation than sodium hydroxide?

12·2   What would be the products expected from aldol additions involving propanal, 2,2-dimethylpropanal, and a mixture of the two aldehydes?

12·3   Predict the principal products to be expected in each of the following reactions; give your reasoning:

a. $CH_3CHO + (CH_3)_2CO \xrightarrow{NaOH}$

b. $(CH_3)_2C(OH)CH_2COCH_3 \xrightarrow{NaOH}$

c. $CH_2O + (CH_3)_3CCHO \xrightarrow{NaOH}$

12·4   Show how the following compounds can be synthesized from the indicated starting materials by way of aldol-addition products:

a. $CH_3-CH-CH_2-CH_2$ from acetaldehyde
        | |
        OH   OH

b. $CH_3CH=CH-CH_2OH$ from acetaldehyde

c. $(CH_3)_2CHCH_2CH_2CH_3$ from acetone

d. $CH_3CH-\overset{\overset{\text{O}}{\|}}{C}-CH_2CH_3$ from propionaldehyde
        |
        CH_3

12·5   Although trivial names for organic compounds are slowly passing out of common use a few such names remain; for example, diacetone alcohol (Section 12·2A), benzilic acid (Section 12·5), and benzoin (Section 24·6 and Exercise 12·27). Provide the IUPAC names for these three compounds and suggest a reason for the reluctance of chemists to abandon the trivial names completely.

12·6   Aldol additions also occur in the presence of acidic catalysts. For example, acetone with dry hydrogen chloride slowly yields $(CH_3)_2C=CHCOCH_3$ (mesityl oxide) and $(CH_3)_2C=CHCOCH=C(CH_3)_2$ (phorone). Write mechanisms for the formation of these products giving particular attention to the way in which the new carbon-carbon bonds are formed. Review Sections 4·4H and 11·4B.

12·7   The following reactions represent "possible" synthetic reactions. Consider each carefully and decide whether or not the reaction will proceed as written. *Show your reasoning.* If you think side reactions would be important, write equations for each.

a. $CH_3COCH_3 + 6 Br_2 + 8 NaOH \longrightarrow 2 CHBr_3 + Na_2CO_3 + 6 NaBr + 6 H_2O$

b. $CH_3CHO + NaNH_2 + (CH_3)_3CCl \longrightarrow (CH_3)_3CCH_2CHO + NH_3 + NaCl$

c. $(CH_3)_2CHCOCH_3 + CH_2=O \xrightarrow{Ca(OH)_2} (CH_3)_2C(CH_2OH)COCH_3$

d. $CH_3CHO + CH_3CO_2C_2H_5 \xrightarrow{OH^\ominus} CH_3CHCH_2CO_2C_2H_5$
$\overset{|}{OH}$

12·8 Write equations for a practical laboratory synthesis of each of the following substances, based on the indicated starting materials (several steps may be required). Give reagents and conditions.

a. 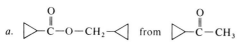 from

b. $CH_2=CHCOCH_3$ from CH_3COCH_3

c. $(CH_3)_3CCO_2H$ from $(CH_3)_2C(OH)C(CH_3)_2OH$

d. $(CH_3)_3CCOC(CH_3)_3$ from $CH_3CH_2COCH_2CH_3$

e. $(CH_3)_2CHCH_2CH(CH_3)_2$ from CH_3COCH_3

f. $(CH_3)_3CCH_2CH_2CH_3$ from $(CH_3)_3CCOCH_3$

12·9 Give for each of the following pairs of compounds a chemical test, preferably a test tube reaction, that will distinguish between the two compounds. (You may wish to review Section 11·4I in connection with some of these.)

a. $CH_3COCH_2CH_2COCH_3$ and $CH_3COCH_2COCH_3$

b. $(CH_3CH_2CH_2CH_2)_2CO$ and $[(CH_3)_3C]_2CO$

c. $(C_6H_5)_2CHCH_2CHO$ and $(C_6H_5CH_2)_2C=O$

d. $C_6H_5COCOC_6H_5$ and $C_6H_5COCH_2COC_6H_5$

e. $CH_3CH=C=O$ and $CH_2=CH-CH=O$

12·10 How might spectroscopic methods be used to distinguish between the two isomeric compounds in the following pairs:

a. $CH_3CH=CHCOCH_3$ and $CH_2=CHCH_2COCH_3$

b. $C_6H_5COCH_2COC_6H_5$ and p-$CH_3C_6H_4COCOC_6H_5$

c. $CH_3CH=C=O$ and $CH_2=CH-CHO$

d. ⬠O and $CH_3COCH_2CH_3$

12·11 Sketch out an energy profile with the various transition states for the reaction $CH_3COCH_3 + OH^\ominus + Br_2 \rightarrow CH_3COCH_2Br + H_2O + Br^\ominus$ described in Section 12·1A, using the general procedure of Section 8·9. Note that in this case the enol form, unlike the carbonium ion in Figure 8·2, is a rather stable intermediate.

12·12 Interpret the proton nmr spectra given in Figure 12·4 in terms of structures of compounds with the molecular formulas $C_6H_{10}O$ and C_9H_8O. The latter substance has a phenyl (C_6H_5) group.

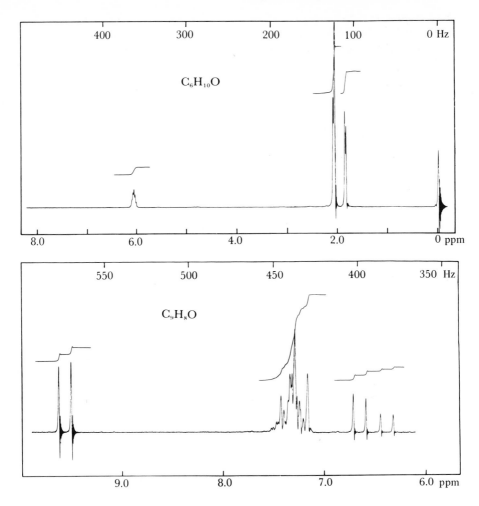

Figure 12·4   Proton nmr spectra at 60 MHz with TMS as standard. See Exercise 12·12.

12·13   Calculate ΔH for vapor-phase 1,2 and 1,4 additions of hydrogen cyanide to methyl vinyl ketone. Write a mechanism for 1,4 addition that is consistent with catalysis by bases and the fact that hydrogen cyanide does not add to an isolated carbon-carbon double bond.

12·14   Write a reasonable mechanism for the base-induced rearrangement of 3-butenal to 2-butenal. Why is 2-butenal the more stable isomer?

12·15   Write reasonable mechanisms for the reaction of ketene with alcohols and amines. Would you expect these reactions to be facilitated by acids or bases or both?

12·16   The following structures have been proposed or could be proposed for diketene. Show how infrared, ultraviolet, and nmr spectroscopy might be used to distinguish between the possibilities. (If necessary, review Chapter 7.)

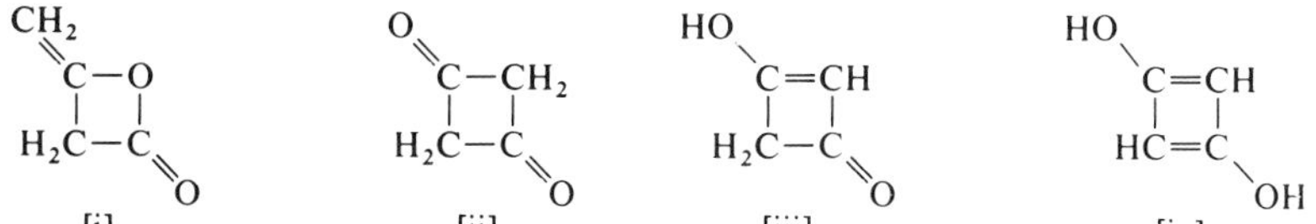

$$CH_2=C-O,\quad H_2C-C(=O)\quad [i]$$

$$O=C-CH_2,\quad H_2C-C(=O)\quad [ii]$$

$$HO-C=CH,\quad H_2C-C(=O)\quad [iii]$$

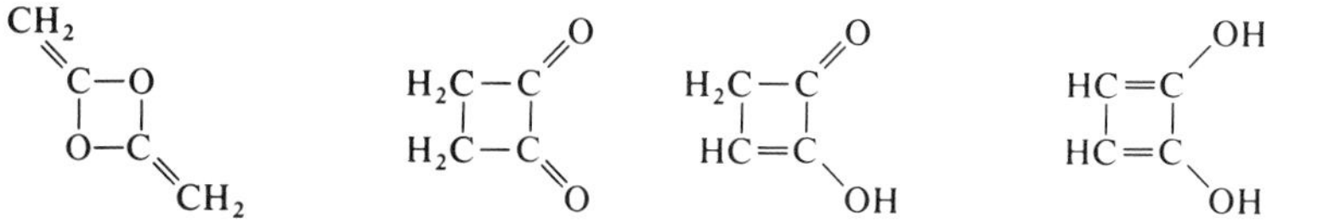

$$HO-C=CH,\quad HC=C-OH\quad [iv]$$

$$CH_2=C-O,\quad O-C=CH_2\quad [v]$$

$$H_2C-C(=O),\quad H_2C-C(=O)\quad [vi]$$

$$H_2C-C(=O),\quad HC=C-OH\quad [vii]$$

$$HC=C-OH,\quad HC=C-OH\quad [viii]$$

$$CH_3-\overset{O}{\overset{\|}{C}}-CH=C=O \quad \text{(the favored structure for many years)}$$
[ix]

12·17   2,6-Bicyclo[2.2.2]octanedione exhibits no enolic properties. Explain.

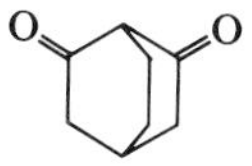

12·18   What experiments might be done to prove or disprove the following mechanism for rearrangement of glyoxal to glycolic acid?

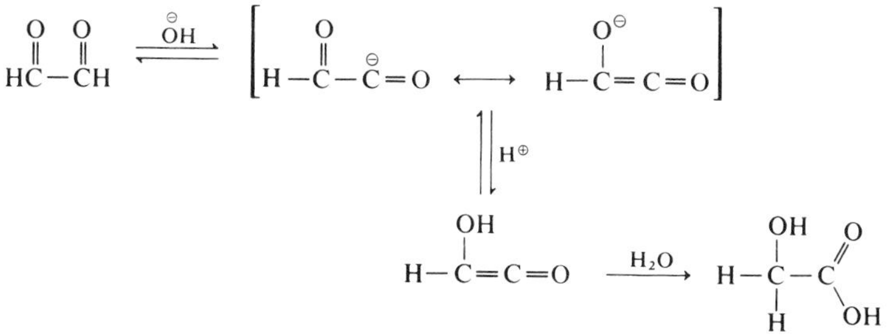

12·19   Write a mechanism analogous to that for the Cannizzaro reaction for the benzil–benzilic acid transformation. Would you expect the same type of reaction to occur with biacetyl? Why or why not?

12·20   Account for the considerable K_{HA} of the enol of acetylacetone with respect to ethyl alcohol. Arguing from the proportions of each at equilibrium, which is the stronger acid, the keto or the enol form of acetylacetone? Explain.

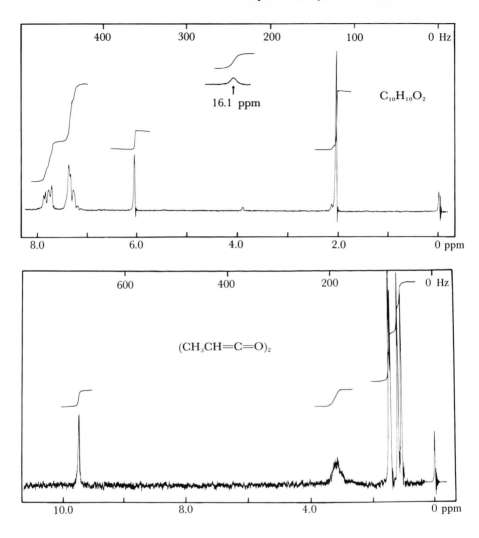

Figure 12·5   Proton nmr spectra at 60 MHz with TMS as standard. See Exercise 12·21.

12·21   Interpret the proton nmr spectra shown in Figure 12·5 in terms of structures of the compounds with molecular formulas $C_{10}H_{10}O_2$ and $(CH_3CH=C=O)_2$. See also Exercise 12·16.

12·22   Write a reasonable mechanism, supported by analogy, for the acid-catalyzed dehydration of 2,4-pentanedione to 2,5-dimethylfuran.

H₃C   O   CH₃

2, 5-dimethylfuran

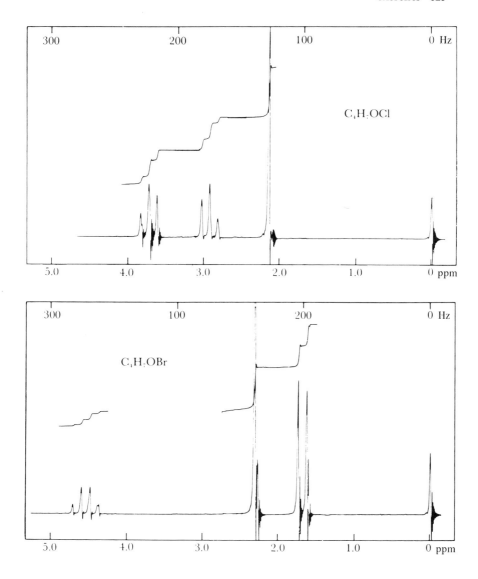

Figure 12·6   Proton nmr spectra at 60 MHz with TMS as standard. See Exercise 12·23.

12·23   The nmr spectra of two compounds of formulas C_4H_7OCl and C_4H_7OBr are shown in Figure 12·6. Assign to each compound a structure that is consistent with its spectrum. Show your reasoning. Give a concise description of the chemical properties to be expected for each compound.

12·24   When the formation of β-hydroxybutyraldehyde is carried on in D_2O containing $OD^{\ominus}$, using moderate concentrations of undeuteriated acetaldehyde, the product formed in the early stages of the reaction contains no deuterium bound to carbon. Assuming the mechanism shown in Section 12·2A to be correct, what can you conclude as to which step in the reaction is the slow step? What would then be the kinetic equation for the reaction? What would you expect to happen to the kinetics and the nature of the product formed in D_2O at *very low* concentrations of acetaldehyde?

12·25 1,2-Cyclopentanedione exists substantially as the monoenol, whereas biacetyl exists as the keto form. Suggest explanations for this behavior that take into account possible conformational differences between the two substances. How easily would you expect dione [8] to enolize? Why?

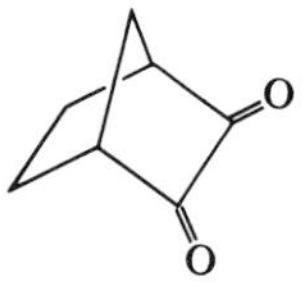

[8]

12·26 A detailed study of the rate of bromination of acetone in water, using acetic acid–acetate buffers, has shown that

$$v = \{6 \times 10^{-9} + 5.6 \times 10^{-4}[H_3O^{\oplus}] + 1.3 \times 10^{-6}[CH_3CO_2H] + 7[OH^{\ominus}] + 3.3 \times 10^{-6}[CH_3CO_2^{\ominus}] + 3.5 \times 10^{-6}[CH_3CO_2H][CH_3CO_2^{\ominus}]\}[CH_3COCH_3]$$

in which the rate is expressed in moles per liter per second when the concentrations are in moles per liter.

a. Calculate the rate of the reaction for 1 *M* acetone in water at pH 7 in the absence of acetic acid or acetate ion.

b. Calculate the rate of the reaction for 1 *M* acetone in a solution made by neutralizing 1 *M* acetic acid with sufficient sodium hydroxide to give pH 5.0 (K_{HA} of acetic acid $= 1.75 \times 10^{-5}$).

12·27 The carbon skeletons of diphenylethanedione (benzil) and benzoin are identical, as are the skeletons of benzilate ion and diphenylhydroxyethanal. Yet, diphenylethanedione rearranges under the influence of base to give benzilate ion and the aldehyde rearranges under the influence of acid to give benzoin. Explain why these two reactions proceed in the directions that they do and provide reasonable mechanisms for both processes.

$$\underset{\text{(diphenylethanedione)}}{C_6H_5-\overset{O}{\overset{\|}{C}}-\overset{O}{\overset{\|}{C}}-C_6H_5} \xrightarrow{OH^{\ominus}} \underset{\text{(benzilate ion)}}{(C_6H_5)_2COHCO_2^{\ominus}}$$

$$\underset{\text{(benzoin)}}{C_6H_5-\overset{O}{\overset{\|}{C}}-CHOHC_6H_5} \xleftarrow{H^{\oplus}} \underset{\text{(diphenylhydroxyethanal)}}{(C_6H_5)_2COHCHO}$$

12·28 Describe the course of the following reaction:

$$2\,(C_6H_5)_3C\overset{O}{\overset{\|}{C}}CH_3 \xrightarrow{(C_6H_5)_3C^{\ominus}Na^{\oplus}} (C_6H_5)_3C\overset{O}{\overset{\|}{C}}CH_2\overset{O}{\overset{\|}{C}}CH_3 + (C_6H_5)_3CH$$

What would be a suitable solvent in which to conduct this reaction?

12·29   The commercially important tetrahydroxy alcohol $C(CH_2OH)_4$ known as pentaerythritol is prepared by alkaline addition of formaldehyde and acetaldehyde according to the following equation:

$$CH_3CHO + 4CH_2O \xrightarrow{\overset{\ominus}{O}H} C(CH_2OH)_4 + HCO_2H$$

Work out a sequence of steps which reasonably accounts for the course of the reaction.

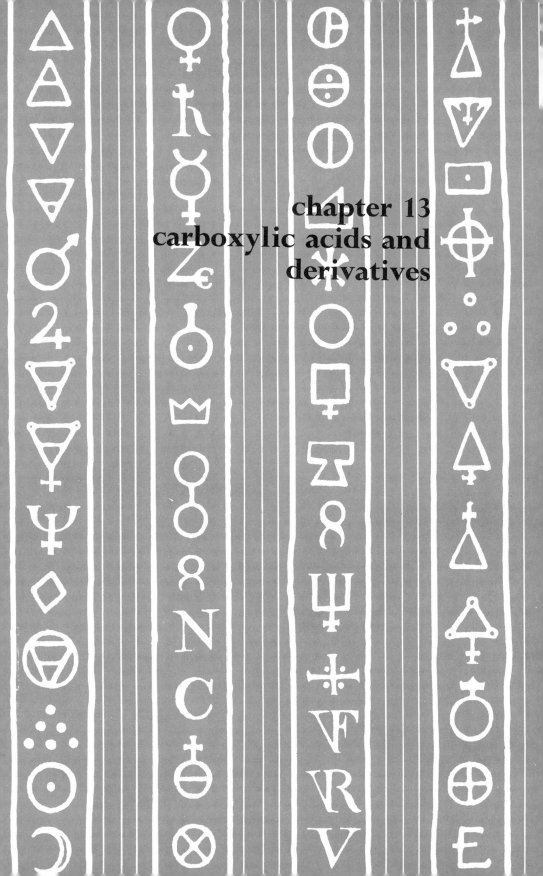

chapter 13
carboxylic acids and derivatives

We shall be concerned in this chapter with the chemistry of the carboxylic acids, RCO_2H, and some of their functional derivatives of the type RCOX.

Although the carboxyl function $-C\overset{\displaystyle O}{\underset{\displaystyle O-H}{\diagdown}}$ is a combination of a hydroxyl

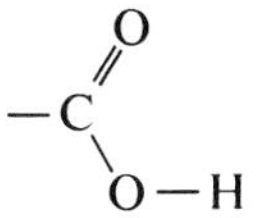

and a carbonyl group, the combination is such a close one that neither group behaves independently of the other. However, we shall be able to make a number of helpful comparisons of the behavior of the hydroxyl groups of alcohols and acids, and of the carbonyl groups of aldehydes, ketones, and acids.

The carboxyl group is acidic because of its ability to donate a proton to a suitable base. In water most carboxylic acids are only slightly dissociated ($K_{HA} \sim 10^{-5}$, degree of ionization of a 1 M solution $\sim 0.3\%$).

$$RCO_2H + H_2O \rightleftharpoons RCO_2{}^{\ominus} + H_3O^{\oplus}$$

Aqueous solutions of the corresponding carboxylate salts are basic because of the reaction of the carboxylate anion with water (hydrolysis).

$$CH_3CO_2{}^{\ominus}Na^{\oplus} + H_2O \longleftarrow CH_3CO_2H + Na^{\oplus}\,OH^{\ominus}$$
sodium acetate   acetic acid

The nomenclature of carboxylic acids, which was discussed previously (Section 8·4), is illustrated with some representative compounds in Figure 13·1.

Figure 13·1   Representative carboxylic acids. The IUPAC names are given first and some common names in parentheses.

$CH_3CH_2CO_2H$ propanoic acid (propionic acid)	$CH_2{=}CHCO_2H$ propenoic acid (acrylic acid)	$CH{\equiv}CCO_2H$ propynoic acid (propiolic acid)
$CH_3CH_2CH_2CH_2CH_2CO_2H$ hexanoic acid (caproic acid)	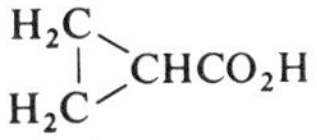 $\overset{\displaystyle H_2C}{\underset{\displaystyle H_2C}{\diagup}}CHCO_2H$ cyclopropane- carboxylic acid (same)	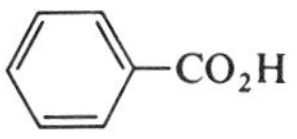 $\langle\!\bigcirc\!\rangle{-}CO_2H$ benzoic acid (same)
$BrCH_2CO_2H$ bromoethanoic acid (bromoacetic acid)	$CH_3\underset{\displaystyle OH}{CH}CO_2H$ 2-hydroxypropanoic acid (lactic or α-hydroxypropionic acid)	$NCCH_2CO_2H$ cyanoethanoic acid (cyanoacetic acid)
$CH_3\underset{\displaystyle NH_2}{CH}CO_2H$ 2-aminopropanoic acid (alanine or α-aminopropionic acid)	$CH_3\overset{\displaystyle O}{\overset{\|}{C}}CH_2CO_2H$ butan-3-on-1-oic acid (acetoacetic acid)	$\underset{\displaystyle CH_2CO_2H}{CH_2CO_2H}$ butanedioic acid (succinic acid)

Some common names are given in parentheses. The IUPAC names will be used wherever practicable in this chapter although the common names for the C_1 and C_2 compounds, formic acid and acetic acid, will be retained.

Carboxylic acids with R as an alkyl or alkenyl group are also called **fatty acids**, but this term is more correctly applied to the naturally occurring continuous chain, saturated and unsaturated aliphatic acids which, in the form of esters, are constituents of the fats, waxes, and oils of plants and animals. The most abundant of the fatty acids are palmitic, stearic, oleic, and linoleic acids; they occur as glycerides, which are esters of the trihydroxy alcohol glycerol.

$CH_3(CH_2)_{14}CO_2H$	palmitic acid
$CH_3(CH_2)_{16}CO_2H$	stearic acid
$CH_3(CH_2)_7CH=CH(CH_2)_7CO_2H$	oleic acid (*cis*)
$CH_3(CH_2)_4CH=CHCH_2CH=CH(CH_2)_7CO_2H$	linoleic acid

Alkaline hydrolysis of fats affords salts of the fatty acids, those of the alkali metals being useful as soaps. The cleansing mechanism of soaps is described in the next section.

$$
\begin{array}{c}
\overset{\overset{\displaystyle O}{\|}}{CH_2OCR} \\
\overset{\overset{\displaystyle O}{\|}}{CHOCR} \quad \xrightarrow{\text{NaOH}} \quad \overset{CH_2OH}{\underset{CH_2OH}{CHOH}} \quad + \; 3\,RCO_2^{\ominus}\,Na^{\oplus} \quad \xrightarrow{H^{\oplus}} \quad 3\,RCO_2H \\
\overset{\overset{\displaystyle O}{\|}}{CH_2OCR}
\end{array}
$$

fat	glycerol	soap	fatty acid
(a glyceride)			

13·1 physical properties of carboxylic acids

The physical properties of carboxylic acids reflect a considerable degree of association through hydrogen bonding. We have encountered such bonding previously in the case of alcohols (Section 10·1); however, acids form stronger hydrogen bonds than alcohols because their O—H bonds are more strongly polarized as $\overset{\delta\ominus}{-}O\overset{\delta\oplus}{-}H$. In addition, carboxylic acids have the possibility of forming hydrogen bonds to the rather negative oxygen of the carbonyl dipole rather than just to the oxygen of another hydroxyl group. Indeed, carboxylic acids in the solid and liquid states exist mostly as cyclic dimers. These dimeric

$$
\begin{array}{c}
\overset{\delta\ominus}{O}\cdots H{-}O \\
R{-}\overset{\delta\oplus}{C}\diagup \qquad \diagdown \overset{\delta\oplus}{C}{-}R \\
\diagdown O{-}H\cdots \overset{\delta\ominus}{O} \diagup
\end{array}
$$

structures persist in solution in hydrocarbon solvents and to some extent even in the vapor state.

The physical properties of some representative carboxylic acids are listed in

Table 13·1   Physical properties of representative carboxylic acids

acid	structure	solubility, g/100 g H_2O	mp, °C	bp, °C	$K_{HA}(H_2O)$ at 25°
formic	HCO_2H	∞	8.4	100.7	1.77×10^{-4}
acetic	CH_3CO_2H	∞	16.6	118.1	1.75×10^{-5}
propanoic	$CH_3CH_2CO_2H$	∞	−22	141.1	1.3×10^{-5}
butanoic	$CH_3CH_2CH_2CO_2H$	∞	−8	163.5	1.5×10^{-5}
2-methylpropanoic	$(CH_3)_2CHCO_2H$	20	−47	154.5	1.4×10^{-5}
pentanoic	$CH_3(CH_2)_3CO_2H$	3.3	−34.5	187	1.6×10^{-5}
palmitic	$CH_3(CH_2)_{14}CO_2H$		64	390	
stearic	$CH_3(CH_2)_{16}CO_2H$		69.4	360 d	
chloroacetic	$ClCH_2CO_2H$		63	189	1.4×10^{-3}
dichloroacetic	Cl_2CHCO_2H	8.63	5	194	5×10^{-2}
trichloroacetic	Cl_3CCO_2H	120	58	195.5	3×10^{-1}
trifluoroacetic	F_3CCO_2H	∞	−15	72.4	strong[a]
2-chlorobutanoic	$CH_3CH_2CHClCO_2H$			101^{15mm}	1.4×10^{-3}
3-chlorobutanoic	$CH_3CHClCH_2CO_2H$		44	116^{22mm}	8.9×10^{-5}
4-chlorobutanoic	$ClCH_2CH_2CH_2CO_2H$		16	196^{22mm}	3.0×10^{-5}
5-chloropentanoic	$ClCH_2(CH_2)_3CO_2H$		18	130^{11mm}	2×10^{-5}
methoxyacetic	$CH_3OCH_2CO_2H$			203	3.3×10^{-4}
cyanoacetic	$N\equiv CCH_2CO_2H$		66	108^{15mm}	4×10^{-3}
vinylacetic	$CH_2{=}CHCH_2CO_2H$		−39	163	3.8×10^{-5}
benzoic	$C_6H_5CO_2H$	0.27	122	249	6.5×10^{-5}
phenylacetic	$C_6H_5CH_2CO_2H$	1.66	76.7	265	5.6×10^{-5}

[a] The term "strong" acid means essentially complete dissociation in dilute aqueous solution; that is, the concentration of the neutral molecule is too low to be measured by any analytical technique now available.

Table 13·1. The notably high melting and boiling points of acids relative to alcohols and chlorides can be attributed to the strength and degree of hydrogen bonding. The differences in volatility are shown more strikingly by Figure 13·2, which is a plot of boiling point versus n for the homologous series

Figure 13·2   Boiling points of acids, $CH_3(CH_2)_{n-2}CO_2H$, alcohols, $CH_3(CH_2)_{n-2}CH_2OH$, and chlorides, $CH_3(CH_2)_{n-2}CH_2Cl$.

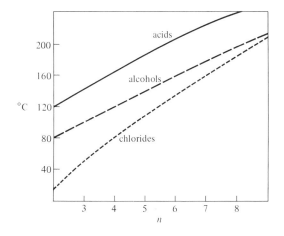

$CH_3(CH_2)_{n-2}X$, in which X is $-CO_2H$, $-CH_2OH$, and $-CH_2Cl$.

Hydrogen bonding is also responsible for the high water solubility of the simple aliphatic acids—formic, acetic, propanoic, and butanoic—which are completely miscible with water in all proportions. As the alkyl chain increases in length (and in degree of branching) the solubility decreases markedly. On the other hand, the *salts* of carboxylic acids retain their moderately high solubilities in water even when the alkyl group becomes large. This enables carboxylic acids to be extracted from solutions in benzene and other low-polarity solvents by aqueous base. Sodium bicarbonate is sufficiently basic to convert any carboxylic acid to the anion, $RCO_2H + HCO_3^{\ominus} \rightarrow RCO_2^{\ominus} + H_2O + CO_2$, and is usually used for this purpose. Separation of the liquid layers, followed by acidification of the aqueous layer, then precipitates the free carboxylic acid. The separation of a mixture of a water-insoluble alcohol and water-insoluble carboxylic acid is illustrated in Scheme I.

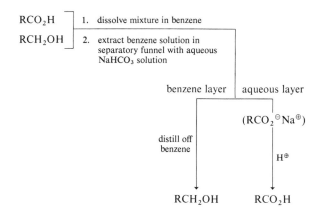

SCHEME I.   The separation of a mixture of an alcohol and
a carboxylic acid.

Though the salts of long-chain carboxylic acids are moderately soluble in water, the resulting solutions are usually opalescent as a result of the grouping together of molecules to form colloidal particles. These are called **micelles**, and their formation reflects the antipathy of the long hydrocarbon chains for the aqueous environment into which they have been drawn by the attraction of the water for the anionic group at the carboxylate end of the molecule. The alkyl groups cluster together in the micelle with the charged groups on the outside in position to be solvated by water in the usual way (Figure 13·3).

Ordinary soaps are sodium or potassium salts of C_{16} and C_{18} acids, such as palmitic and stearic acids (Table 13·1), and their cleansing action results from the abilities of their micelles to dissolve grease and other nonpolar substances that are insoluble in water alone.

In minute concentrations, salts such as sodium stearate, $C_{17}H_{35}CO_2^{\ominus}Na^{\oplus}$ (sodium octadecanoate), do not form micelles in water but, instead, concentrate at the surface of the liquid with the charged ends of the salt molecules immersed in the water and the hydrocarbon parts forming a surface layer. This results in a sharp drop in surface tension of water by even minute con-

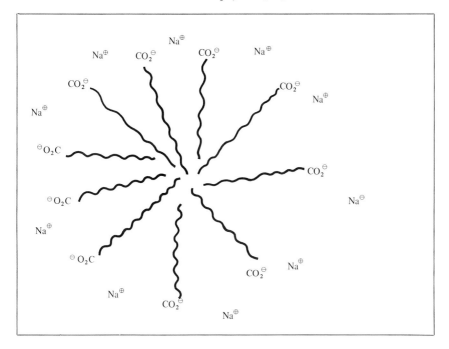

Figure 13·3   A micelle, in which long–chain carboxylate salt molecules group together in aqueous solution. The interior of the micelle is a region of very low polarity. The total negative charge on the micelle is balanced by the positive charge of sodium ions in the solution.

centrations of soap. As the concentration of long-chain carboxylate salt is increased and after the surface has become saturated, the system can either form micelles or attempt to increase its surface. Agitation will allow the latter to occur (frothing) but otherwise, at a certain concentration, micelles will begin to form. This point is called the **critical micelle concentration.**

Micelles have some interesting catalytic properties. Not only do they provide a nonpolar environment in an aqueous system, but they have a large charge concentrated at their surface. Each of these characteristics can be important in accelerating the rates of certain reactions, and the catalytic behavior of micelles is being actively investigated.

The lower-molecular-weight aliphatic acids have quite characteristic odors. Although formic, acetic, and propanoic acids have sharp odors, those of the C_4 to C_8 acids (butanoic to octanoic) are disagreeable and can be detected in minute amounts, especially by dogs.[1] It has been shown that a dog's tracking ability stems from its recognition of the particular blend of compounds, mostly aliphatic acids, released by the sweat glands in the feet of the person being followed. Each person's metabolism produces a characteristic

---

[1] A dog can detect butanoic acid at a concentration of 10^{-17} mole per liter of air, about a million times less than the concentration required by man (R. H. Wright, *The Science of Smell*, George Allen and Unwin, London, 1964).

spectrum of compounds although those from identical twins differ little from each other. The higher-molecular-weight carboxylic acids have low volatilities and hence are essentially odorless.

13·2 spectra of carboxylic acids

The infrared spectra of carboxylic acids provide clear evidence of hydrogen bonding. This is illustrated in Figure 13·4, which shows the spectrum of acetic acid in carbon tetrachloride solution, together with those of ethanol and acetaldehyde for comparison. The spectrum of ethanol has two absorption bands, characteristic of the OH bond; one is a sharp band at 3640 cm^{-1}, corresponding to free or unassociated hydroxyl groups, and the other is a broad band centered on 3350 cm^{-1} due to hydrogen-bonded groups. The spectrum of acetic acid shows no absorption due to free hydroxyl groups but, like that of ethanol, has a broad intense absorption ascribed to associated OH groups. However, the frequency of absorption, 3000 cm^{-1}, is shifted appreciably from that of ethanol and reflects a stronger type of hydrogen bonding than in ethanol. The absorption due to the carbonyl group of acetic acid (1740 cm^{-1}) is broad but not shifted significantly from the carbonyl absorption in acetaldehyde.

The carboxyl function does absorb ultraviolet radiation, but the wavelengths at which this occurs are appreciably shorter than for carbonyl compounds such as aldehydes and ketones, and, in fact, are barely in the range of most commercial ultraviolet spectrometers. Some idea of how the hydroxyl substituent modifies the absorption properties of the carbonyl group in carboxylic acids can be seen from Table 13·2, in which are listed the wavelengths of maximum light absorption (λ_{max}) and the extinction coefficients at maximum absorption (ε_{max}) of several carboxylic acids, aldehydes, and ketones.

In the nmr spectra of carboxylic acids, the carboxyl proton is found to absorb at unusually low magnetic fields. The chemical shift of carboxylic acid protons comes about 5.5 ppm toward lower magnetic fields than that of the hydroxyl proton of alcohols. This behavior parallels that of the enol hydrogens of 1,3-dicarbonyl compounds (Section 12·6) and is probably similarly related to hydrogen-bond formation.

Table 13·2   Ultraviolet absorption properties of carboxylic acids, aldehydes, and ketones

compound	λ_{max}, mμ	ε_{max}	solvent
acetic acid	204	40	water
acetic acid	197	60	hexane
acetaldehyde	293	12	hexane
acetone	270	16	ethanol
butanoic acid	207	74	water
butyraldehyde	290	18	hexane

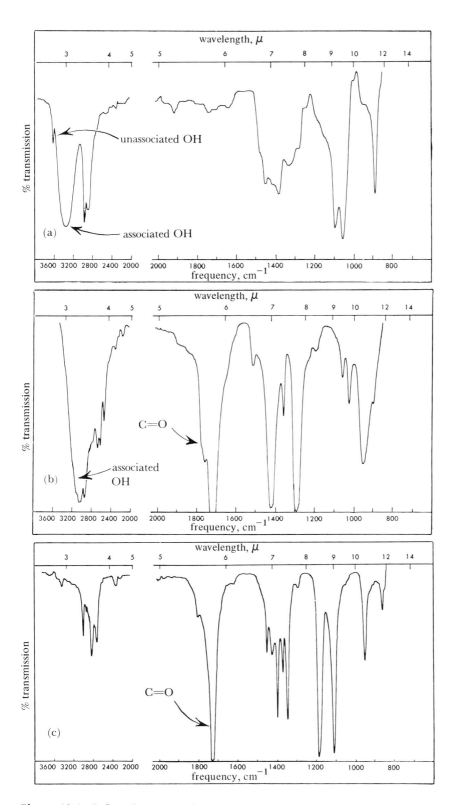

Figure 13·4   Infrared spectra of ethanol (a), acetic acid (b), and acetaldehyde (c); 10% in carbon tetrachloride.

13·3 preparation of carboxylic acids

The first three methods listed below have already been met in earlier chapters.

1. Oxidation of a primary alcohol or aldehyde (Sections 10·6 and 11·4G);

$$RCH_2OH \longrightarrow RCHO \longrightarrow RCO_2H$$

2. Cleavage of alkenes or 1,2-glycols (Sections 4·4G and 10·7). Any powerful

$$RCH{=}CHR \longrightarrow 2\,RCO_2H$$
$$RCHOHCHOHR \longrightarrow 2\,RCO_2H$$

oxidant may be used; carboxylic acids are produced only if the carbons being cleaved possess hydrogen atoms—otherwise, ketones result. Cleavage of aryl side chains can also be brought about by drastic oxidation, $ArCH_2R \rightarrow ArCO_2H$ (Section 24·1).

3. Carbonation of Grignard reagents (Section 9·9C). This is a useful method

$$RMgX + CO_2 \longrightarrow R-C\overset{\displaystyle O}{\underset{\displaystyle OMgX}{\big\backslash}} \xrightarrow[H^\oplus]{H_2O} RCO_2H$$

of extending a chain by one carbon atom.

4. Hydrolysis of nitriles (to be described in Section 16·2B):

$$RC{\equiv}N \xrightarrow[H^\oplus \text{ or } OH^\ominus]{H_2O} RCO_2H$$

5. Malonic ester synthesis (to be described in Section 13·9C): This is a

$$RX + {}^\ominus CH(CO_2Et)_2 \longrightarrow RCH(CO_2Et)_2 \longrightarrow RCH(CO_2H)_2$$

$$\downarrow$$

$$RCH_2CO_2H$$

useful method of extending a chain by two carbon atoms.

Hydrolysis of esters (RCO_2R), amides ($R\overset{O}{\overset{\|}{C}}-NH_2$), and acid chlorides ($R\overset{O}{\overset{\|}{C}}-Cl$) also gives carboxylic acids, but these compounds are usually prepared from carboxylic acids in the first place.

13·4 dissociation of carboxylic acids

A. THE RESONANCE EFFECT

Compared with mineral acids such as hydrochloric, perchloric, nitric, and sulfuric acids, the fatty acids, $CH_3(CH_2)_{n-2}CO_2H$, are weak. The extent of dissociation in aqueous solution is relatively small, the acidity constants, K_{HA}, being approximately 10^{-5} (see Table 13·1).

$$RCO_2H + H_2O \; \rightleftharpoons \; RCO_2^{\ominus} + H_3O^{\oplus}$$

$$K_{HA} = \frac{[RCO_2^{\ominus}][H_3O^{\oplus}]}{[RCO_2H]} \sim 10^{-5} \quad \text{for} \quad R = CH_3(CH_2)_n$$

Even though they are weak, the fatty acids are many orders of magnitude stronger than the corresponding alcohols, $CH_3(CH_2)_{n-2}CH_2OH$. Thus, the K_{HA} of acetic acid, CH_3CO_2H, is 10^{10} times larger than that of ethanol, CH_3CH_2OH.

The acidity of the carboxyl group can be accounted for by resonance stabilization of the carboxylate anion, $RCO_2^{\ominus}$, which has the unit of negative charge distributed to both oxygen atoms (Section 6·4).

[la]   [lb]

The neutral carboxylic acid is expected to possess some stabilization associated with the ionic resonance structure [2b], but this is a minor contributor to the hybrid compared to [2a]. For the carboxylate anion, on the other hand, the two contributing forms [la] and [lb] are equivalent:

[2a]   [2b]

Alcohols are much weaker acids than are carboxylic acids because the charge in the alkoxide ion is localized on a single oxygen atom.

B. THE INDUCTIVE EFFECT

Although unsubstituted alkanoic acids with two carbons or more vary little in acid strength, substitution in the alkyl group can cause large acid-strengthening effects to appear (Table 13·1). Formic acid and almost all the α-substituted acetic acids of Table 13·1 are stronger than acetic acid; trifluoro-acetic acid is in fact comparable in strength to hydrochloric acid. The nature of the groups which are close neighbors of the carboxyl carbon obviously has a profound effect on the acid strength, a phenomenon which is commonly called the **inductive effect** (symbolized as $\pm I$). The inductive effect is distinguished from resonance effects of the type discussed earlier by being associated with substitution on the saturated carbon atoms of the fatty acid chain. It is taken as negative $(-I)$ if the substituent is acid enhancing, and positive $(+I)$ if the substituent is acid weakening.

The high acid strength of α-halogen-substituted acids (e.g., chloroacetic), compared with acetic acid, results from the electron-attracting power (electronegativity) of the substituent halogen relative to the carbon to which it is attached. The electron-attracting power of three such halogen atoms is of course expected to be greater than that of one halogen; hence trichloroacetic acid (K_{HA}, 3.0×10^{-1}) is a markedly stronger acid than chloroacetic acid (K_{HA}, 1.4×10^{-3}).

$$Cl \leftarrow CH_2 \leftarrow C \overset{O}{\underset{O \leftarrow H}{\diagup}}$$

arrows show movement of average position of electrons toward chlorine ($-I$ effect)

As would be expected the inductive effect falls off rapidly with increasing distance of the substituent from the carboxyl group. This is readily seen by the significant difference between the K_{HA} values of the 2-, 3-, and 4-chlorobutanoic acids (see Table 13·1).

Many other groups besides halogen exhibit an acid-enhancing, electron-withdrawing ($-I$) effect. Among these are nitro ($-NO_2$); methoxyl (CH_3O-); carbonyl ($\overset{\diagdown}{\underset{\diagup}{C}} = O$, as in aldehydes, ketones, acids, esters, and amides); cyano ($-C\equiv N$); and trialkylammonio ($R_3\overset{\oplus}{N}-$). Alkyl groups— methyl, ethyl, isopropyl, etc.—are the only substituents listed in Table 13·1 that are acid weakening relative to hydrogen (as can be seen by comparing their K_{HA}'s with those of formic and acetic acids). This means that alkyl groups release electrons to the carboxyl group and thus exhibit a $+I$ effect. The magnitude of the electrical effects of alkyl groups does not appear to change greatly in going from methyl to ethyl to propyl, and so on (compare the K_{HA} values of acetic, propanoic, butanoic, and pentanoic acids).

$$CH_3 \rightarrow C \overset{O}{\underset{O \rightarrow H}{\diagup}}$$

the arrows represent shifts in the average positions of the bonding electrons from the methyl group toward the carboxyl group ($+I$ effect)

In addition to their acidic properties, carboxylic acids also can act as weak bases, the carbonyl oxygen accepting a proton from a strong acid such as H_2SO_4 or $HClO_4$ (Equation 13·1). Such protonation is an important step in acid-catalyzed esterification, as discussed in Section 10·4C.

$$RCO_2H + H_2SO_4 \rightleftharpoons RCO_2H_2{}^{\oplus} + HSO_4{}^{\ominus} \tag{13·1}$$

It requires a 12.8 M solution of sulfuric acid (74% H_2SO_4, 26% H_2O) to "half-protonate" acetic acid. This means that if a small amount of acetic acid is dissolved in 12.8 M sulfuric acid, half of the acetic acid molecules at any instant would be in the cationic form, $RCO_2H_2^{\oplus}$, whereas in 1 M sulfuric acid, only about one in a million would be. (The acidity of solutions of strong acids rises very sharply as the medium becomes less aqueous.)

The cation formed by protonation of acetic acid ("acetic acidium ion" or "conjugate acid of acetic acid") has its positive charge distributed to both oxygen atoms and, to a much lesser extent, to carbon.

$$\left[CH_3-C\overset{\overset{\oplus}{OH}}{\underset{OH}{\diagdown}} \longleftrightarrow CH_3-C\overset{OH}{\underset{\overset{\oplus}{OH}}{\diagdown}} \longleftrightarrow CH_3-\overset{OH}{\underset{OH}{C\oplus}} \right] \equiv CH_3-\overset{OH}{\underset{OH}{C\overset{..}{\oplus}}} \equiv CH_3CO_2H_2^{\oplus}$$

Although oxygen is more electronegative than carbon, the resonance forms with oxygen bearing the positive charge are expected to be more important than the one with carbon bearing the positive charge because the former have one more covalent bond than the latter.

Another cation can be reasonably formed by protonation of acetic acid,

$$CH_3-C\overset{O}{\underset{\overset{\oplus}{OH_2}}{\diagup}}$$

This ion is in rapid equilibrium with the isomer that has a proton on each oxygen, but is present in smaller amount. Note that these isomeric ions are tautomers (Section 12·6) and not resonance forms, because they are inter-converted only by changing the atomic positions.

13·5 reactions at the carbonyl carbon of carboxylic acids

Many important reactions of carboxylic acids involve attack on carbon of the carbonyl group by nucleophilic species. These reactions are frequently catalyzed by acids, since addition of a proton or formation of a hydrogen bond to the carbonyl oxygen makes the carbonyl carbon more strongly electropositive and hence more vulnerable to nucleophilic attack. The follow-ing equations illustrate an acid-catalyzed reaction involving a negatively charged nucleophile ($:Nu^{\ominus}$):

$$R-C\overset{O}{\underset{OH}{\diagup}} + H^{\oplus} \rightleftharpoons R-C\overset{OH}{\underset{OH}{C\oplus}} \overset{:Nu^{\ominus}}{\rightleftharpoons} R-\overset{OH}{\underset{Nu}{\overset{|}{\underset{|}{C}}}}-OH$$

Subsequent cleavage of a C—O bond and loss of a proton yields a displace-ment product:

$$R-\overset{OH}{\underset{Nu}{\overset{|}{\underset{|}{C}}}}-OH \overset{-OH^{\ominus}}{\rightleftharpoons} R-C\overset{\overset{\oplus}{OH}}{\underset{Nu}{\diagdown}} \overset{-H^{\oplus}}{\rightleftharpoons} R-C\overset{O}{\underset{Nu}{\diagup}}$$

An important example of this type of reaction is the formation of esters as dis-cussed in Section 10·4C. Similar addition-elimination mechanisms occur in many reactions at the carbonyl groups of acid derivatives. A less obvious example of addition to carboxyl groups involves hydride ion ($H:^{\ominus}$) and takes place in lithium aluminum hydride reduction of carboxylic acids (Section 13·5B).

A. ACID-CHLORIDE FORMATION

Carboxylic acids react with phosphorus trichloride, phosphorus pentachloride, or thionyl chloride with replacement of OH by Cl to form acid (acyl) chlorides, RCOCl.

$$(CH_3)_2CHCH_2C\overset{O}{\underset{OH}{\big\langle}} \xrightarrow{\;SOCl_2\;} (CH_3)_2CHCH_2C\overset{O}{\underset{Cl}{\big\langle}} + SO_2 + HCl$$

3-methylbutanoic acid   3-methylbutanoyl chloride
(isovaleric acid)   (isovaleryl chloride)

Formyl chloride, HCOCl, is unstable and decomposes rapidly to carbon monoxide and hydrogen chloride at ordinary temperatures.

B. REDUCTION OF CARBOXYLIC ACIDS

In general, carboxylic acids are difficult to reduce either by catalytic hydrogenation or by sodium and alcohol. Reduction to primary alcohols proceeds smoothly, however, with lithium aluminum hydride, $LiAlH_4$.

$$RCO_2H \xrightarrow{LiAlH_4} \xrightarrow{H^{\oplus},\,H_2O} RCH_2OH$$

$$CH_2{=}CHCH_2CO_2H \xrightarrow{LiAlH_4} \xrightarrow{H^{\oplus},\,H_2O} CH_2{=}CHCH_2CH_2OH$$

3-butenoic acid   3-buten-1-ol
(vinylacetic acid)   (allylcarbinol)

The first step in lithium aluminum hydride reduction of carboxylic acids is formation of a complex aluminum salt of the acid and liberation of 1 mole of hydrogen:

$$R{-}C\overset{O}{\underset{OH}{\big\langle}} + LiAlH_4 \longrightarrow R{-}C\overset{O}{\underset{\overset{\ominus}{O}AlH_3 \;\; \overset{\oplus}{Li}}{\big\langle}} + H_2$$

Reduction then proceeds by successive transfers of hydride ion, $H:^{\ominus}$, from aluminum to carbon. Two such transfers are required to reduce the acid salt to the oxidation level of the alcohol:

$$RCO_2{}^{\ominus} + 2H^{\ominus} \longrightarrow RCH_2O^{\ominus} + O^{2\ominus}$$

The anions shown as products in this equation are actually in the form of complex aluminum salts from which the product is freed in a final hydrolysis operation. The overall reaction can be shown as follows:

$$4 RCO_2H + 3 LiAlH_4 \longrightarrow [(RCH_2O)_4Al]Li + 4H_2 + 2 LiAlO_2$$

$$\downarrow H_2O, HCl$$

$$4 RCH_2OH + AlCl_3 + LiCl$$

13·6   decarboxylation of carboxylic acids

The ease of loss of carbon dioxide from the carboxyl group varies greatly with the nature of the acid. Some acids require to be heated as their sodium salts in the presence of soda lime (in general, however, this is not a good preparative procedure).

sodium acetate

Other acids lose carbon dioxide simply by being heated at moderate temperatures.

malonic acid   acetic acid

Thermal decarboxylation occurs most readily when the α carbon carries a strongly electron-attracting group (i.e., $-I$ substituent), as in the following examples:

O_2N-CH_2-COOH	nitroacetic acid	
$HOOC-CH_2-COOH$	malonic acid	
$NC-CH_2-COOH$	cyanoacetic acid	decarboxylation occurs readily at 100°–150°
CH_3CO-CH_2-COOH	acetoacetic acid	
CCl_3CO_2H	trichloracetic acid	

The mechanisms of thermal decarboxylation are probably not the same in all cases, but decarboxylation of acids having a β-carbonyl group is probably a cyclic process of elimination in which hydrogen bonding plays an important role:

malonic acid   enol form of   acetic acid
                                acetic acid

Stepwise decarboxylation also occurs, particularly in reactions in which the carboxylate radical ($RCO_2 \cdot$) is formed. This radical can decompose further to a hydrocarbon radical $R\cdot$ and CO_2. The overall decarboxylation product is determined by what $R\cdot$ reacts with: If a good hydrogen atom donor is present, RH is formed; if a halogen donor such as Br_2 is present, RBr is formed.

$$RCO_2 \cdot \longrightarrow R\cdot + CO_2$$

$$R\cdot + R'H \longrightarrow RH + R'\cdot$$

$$R\cdot + Br_2 \longrightarrow RBr + Br\cdot$$

Carboxylate radicals can be generated several ways. One is the thermal decomposition of diacyl peroxides, which are compounds with a rather weak O—O bond:

$$
\begin{array}{c}
\overset{O}{\overset{\|}{R-C}}-O \!\!+\!\! O-\overset{O}{\overset{\|}{C}}-R \longrightarrow 2\,R-\overset{O}{\overset{\|}{C}}-O\cdot
\end{array}
$$

Another method involves electrolysis of sodium or potassium carboxylate solutions, known as **Kolbe electrolysis**, in which carboxylate radicals are formed by transfer of an electron from the carboxylate ion to the anode. Decarboxylation may occur simultaneously with, or subsequent to, the formation of carboxylate radicals, leading to hydrocarbon radicals, which subsequently dimerize.

$$RCO_2{}^{\ominus} \longrightarrow RCO_2 \cdot + e \qquad \text{anode reaction}$$

$$K^{\oplus} + e + H_2O \longrightarrow KOH + \tfrac{1}{2} H_2 \qquad \text{cathode reaction}$$

$$RCO_2 \cdot \longrightarrow R\cdot + CO_2$$

$$R\cdot + R\cdot \longrightarrow RR$$

In the **Hunsdiecker reaction**, an alkyl bromide is formed when a silver salt of a carboxylic acid is treated with bromine in the absence of water. Carboxylate radicals are probably involved. This reaction provides a means for removing a carbon from the end of a chain with retention of a functional group in the product.

$$
RCO_2Ag + Br_2 \xrightarrow{-AgBr} RC\!\!\overset{O}{\underset{O-Br}{\diagdown}} \longrightarrow RC\!\!\overset{O}{\underset{O\cdot}{\diagdown}} + Br\cdot \longrightarrow RBr + CO_2
$$

13·7 reactions at the 2 position of carboxylic acids

A. HALOGENATION

Bromine reacts smoothly with carboxylic acids in the presence of small quantities of phosphorus to form 2-bromo acids. The reaction is slow in the

$$RCH_2CO_2H + Br_2 \xrightarrow{P} RCHBrCO_2H + HBr$$

absence of phosphorus, whose function appears to be to form phosphorus

tribromide which reacts with the acid to give the acid bromide, $-C\overset{\displaystyle O}{\underset{\displaystyle Br}{\diagdown}}$, a

compound known to be substituted readily by bromine. Substitution occurs exclusively at the 2 position (α position) and is therefore limited to carboxylic acids with α hydrogens. Chlorine with a trace of phosphorus reacts similarly but with less overall specificity. Concurrent radical chlorination can occur at all positions along the chain (as in hydrocarbon halogenation; see Section 3·3B).

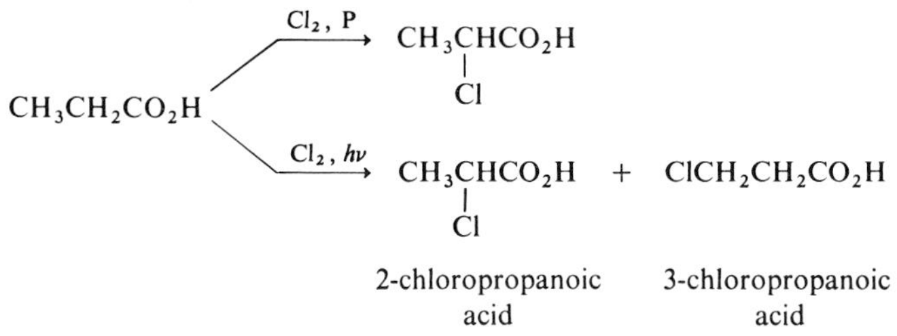

$$CH_3CH_2CO_2H \quad \begin{array}{l} \xrightarrow{Cl_2,\ P} \quad \underset{\underset{Cl}{|}}{CH_3CHCO_2H} \\[2em] \xrightarrow{Cl_2,\ h\nu} \quad \underset{\underset{Cl}{|}}{CH_3CHCO_2H} \ + \ ClCH_2CH_2CO_2H \end{array}$$

2-chloropropanoic   3-chloropropanoic
acid   acid

B. SUBSTITUTION REACTIONS OF 2-HALO ACIDS

The halogen of a 2-halo acid is activated by the adjacent electron-withdrawing carboxyl group and is readily replaced by nucleophilic reagents such as $CN^{\ominus}$, $OH^{\ominus}$, $I^{\ominus}$, and NH_3. Thus, a variety of 2-substituted carboxylic acids may be prepared by reactions that are analogous to S_N2 substitutions of alkyl halides (Scheme II).

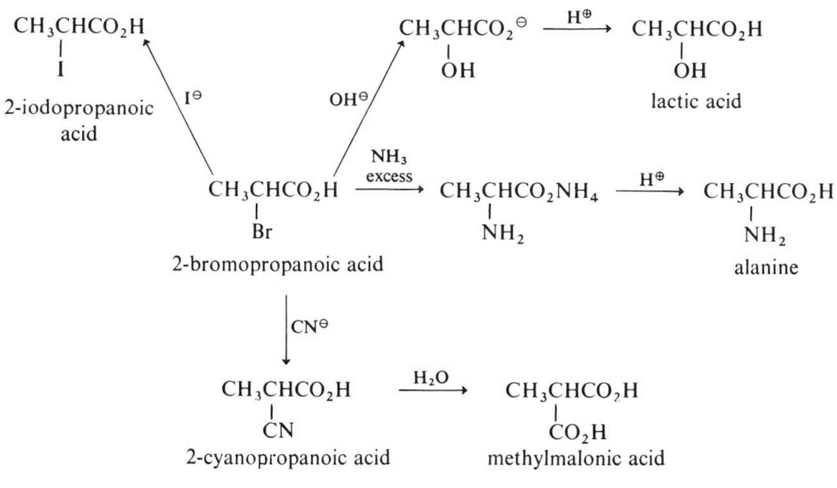

SCHEME II

functional derivatives of carboxylic acids

A functional derivative of a carboxylic acid is a substance formed by replacement of the hydroxyl group of the acid by some other group, X, that can be hydrolyzed back to the parent acid according to Equation 13·2. By this definition, an amide, $RCONH_2$, but not a ketone, $RCOCH_3$, is a functional

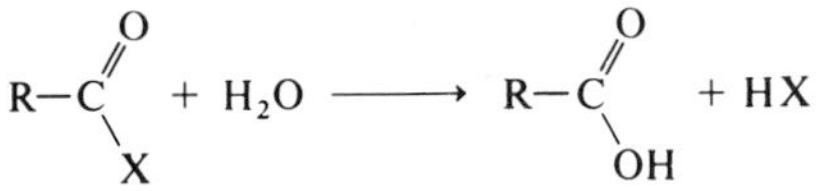

$$R-\overset{\displaystyle O}{\underset{\displaystyle X}{C}} + H_2O \longrightarrow R-\overset{\displaystyle O}{\underset{\displaystyle OH}{C}} + HX \qquad (13\cdot2)$$

derivative of a carboxylic acid. A number of types of acid derivatives are given in Table 13·3.

The common structural feature of the compounds listed in Table 13·3 is the acyl group $R-\overset{\displaystyle O}{C}$. Nitriles, $RC\equiv N$, however, are often considered to be acid derivatives, even though the acyl group is not present as such, because hydrolysis of nitriles leads to carboxylic acids. The chemistry of nitriles is discussed in Chapter 16.

$$CH_3C\equiv N \xrightarrow{\ H^\oplus,\ H_2O\ } CH_3COOH$$
acetonitrile   acetic acid

The carbonyl group plays a dominant role in the reactions of acid derivatives, just as it does for the parent acids. The two main types of reactions of acid derivatives with which we shall be concerned are the replacement of X by attack of a nucleophile $:Nu^\ominus$ at the carbonyl carbon with subsequent cleavage of the C—X bond (Equation 13·3), and substitution at the 2-carbon facilitated by the carbonyl group (Equation 13·4).

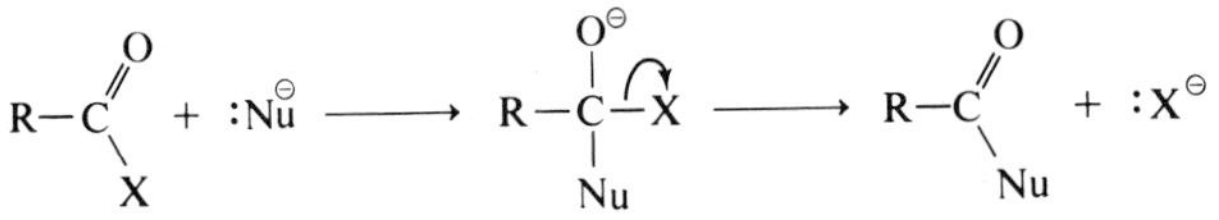

$$R-\overset{\displaystyle O}{\underset{\displaystyle X}{C}} + :Nu^\ominus \longrightarrow R-\overset{\displaystyle O^\ominus}{\underset{\displaystyle Nu}{C}}X \longrightarrow R-\overset{\displaystyle O}{\underset{\displaystyle Nu}{C}} + :X^\ominus \qquad (13\cdot3)$$

$$RCH_2-\overset{\displaystyle O}{\underset{\displaystyle X}{C}} + YZ \longrightarrow RCH-\overset{\displaystyle O}{\underset{\displaystyle Y\quad X}{C}} + HZ \qquad (13\cdot4)$$

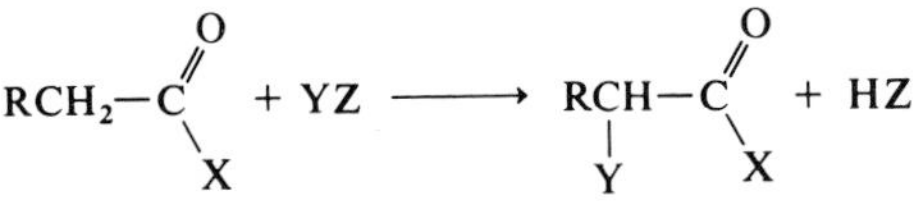

13·8 displacement reactions of acid derivatives

The following are the more important displacement reactions:

1. Acid derivatives are hydrolyzed to the parent acids. These reactions are commonly acid and base catalyzed, but acid chlorides usually hydrolyze rapidly without the agency of an acid or base catalyst:

$$R-\overset{\overset{\displaystyle O}{\|}}{\underset{\underset{\displaystyle X}{}}{C}} + H_2O \xrightarrow{\text{H}^{\oplus} \text{ or OH}^{\ominus}} R-\overset{\overset{\displaystyle O}{\|}}{\underset{\underset{\displaystyle OH}{}}{C}} + HX$$

X = −OR (ester), halogen (acid halide), −NH₂ (amide), and −O₂CR (acid anhydride)

2. Acid or base catalysts are usually required for ester interchange.

$$CH_3-\overset{\overset{\displaystyle O}{\|}}{\underset{\underset{\displaystyle OCH_3}{}}{C}} + CH_3CH_2OH \underset{}{\overset{\text{H}^{\oplus} \text{ or } ^{\ominus}\text{OR}}{\rightleftharpoons}} CH_3-\overset{\overset{\displaystyle O}{\|}}{\underset{\underset{\displaystyle OCH_2CH_3}{}}{C}} + CH_3OH$$

methyl acetate   ethanol   ethyl acetate   methanol

3. Esters are formed from acid chlorides and anhydrides.

$$R-\overset{\overset{\displaystyle O}{\|}}{\underset{\underset{\displaystyle Cl}{}}{C}} + R'OH \longrightarrow R-\overset{\overset{\displaystyle O}{\|}}{\underset{\underset{\displaystyle OR'}{}}{C}} + HCl, \quad \begin{matrix} R-\overset{\overset{\displaystyle O}{\|}}{C} \\ | \\ O \\ | \\ R-\overset{\underset{\displaystyle O}{\|}}{C} \end{matrix} + R'OH \longrightarrow R-\overset{\overset{\displaystyle O}{\|}}{\underset{\underset{\displaystyle OR'}{}}{C}} + R-\overset{\overset{\displaystyle O}{\|}}{\underset{\underset{\displaystyle OH}{}}{C}}$$

From bond energies alone, the reaction of an alcohol with an acid chloride should be endothermic by 3 kcal. Such reactions are actually exothermic because esters have stabilization energies of some 10–15 kcal through contributions of resonance structures analogous to [2b] (p. 337) for carboxylic acids. Acid chlorides are not similarly stabilized.

4. Amides are formed from esters, acid chlorides, and anhydrides.

$$\left. \begin{matrix} R-\overset{\overset{\displaystyle O}{\|}}{\underset{\underset{\displaystyle OR'}{}}{C}} \\[12pt] R-\overset{\overset{\displaystyle O}{\|}}{\underset{\underset{\displaystyle Cl}{}}{C}} \\[12pt] \begin{matrix} R-\overset{\overset{\displaystyle O}{\|}}{C} \\ | \\ O \\ | \\ R-\overset{\underset{\displaystyle O}{\|}}{C} \end{matrix} \end{matrix} \right\} \xrightarrow{\text{NH}_3} \left\{ \begin{matrix} R-\overset{\overset{\displaystyle O}{\|}}{\underset{\underset{\displaystyle NH_2}{}}{C}} + R'OH \\[12pt] R-\overset{\overset{\displaystyle O}{\|}}{\underset{\underset{\displaystyle NH_2}{}}{C}} + NH_4^{\oplus}Cl^{\ominus} \\[12pt] R-\overset{\overset{\displaystyle O}{\|}}{\underset{\underset{\displaystyle NH_2}{}}{C}} + RCO_2^{\ominus}NH_4^{\oplus} \end{matrix} \right.$$

All of these reactions are rather closely related, and we shall illustrate the principles involved mostly by the reactions of esters, since these have been particularly well studied. Acid-catalyzed hydrolysis of esters is the reverse of acid-catalyzed esterification discussed previously (Section 10·4C). In contrast, base-induced hydrolysis (saponification) is, in effect, an irreversible reaction. The initial step is the attack of hydroxide ion at the electron-deficient carbonyl carbon; the intermediate anion [3] so formed then has the choice of losing OH$^{\ominus}$ and reverting to the original ester, or of losing CH₃O$^{\ominus}$ to form the

Table 13·3   Functional derivatives of carboxylic acids

derivative	structure	example structure	example name
esters	R—C(=O)OR	CH₃—C(=O)OC₂H₅	ethyl acetate
acid halides (acyl halides)	R—C(=O)X X = F, Cl, Br, I	C₆H₅—C(=O)Br	benzoyl bromide
anhydrides	R—C(=O)—O—C(=O)—R	CH₃—C(=O)—O—C(=O)—CH₃	acetic anhydride
amides (primary)	R—C(=O)NH₂	C₆H₅—C(=O)NH₂	benzamide
amides (secondary)	RCNHR′ (O)	CH₃—C(=O)NHCH₃	N-methyl-acetamide
amides (tertiary)	RCNR′R″ (O)	H—C(=O)N(CH₃)₂	N,N-dimethyl-formamide

Table 13·3   Functional derivatives of carboxylic acids *(continued)*

derivative	structure	example structure	name
imides			succinimide
acyl azides	$R-C\overset{O}{\underset{N_3}{}}$	$CH_3-C\overset{O}{\underset{N_3}{}}$	acetyl azide
hydrazides	$R-C\overset{O}{\underset{NHNH_2}{}}$	$C_2H_5-C\overset{O}{\underset{NHNH_2}{}}$	propanoyl hydrazide
hydroxamic acids	$R-C\overset{O}{\underset{NHOH}{}}$	$ClCH_2C\overset{O}{\underset{NHOH}{}}$	chloroacetyl- hydroxamic acid
lactones (cyclic esters)	most stable with $n = 3, 4$		γ-butyrolactone
lactams (cyclic amides)	most stable with $n = 3, 4$		δ-caprolactam

acid. The overall reaction is irreversible since, once the acid is formed, it is immediately converted to the carboxylate anion, which is not further attacked

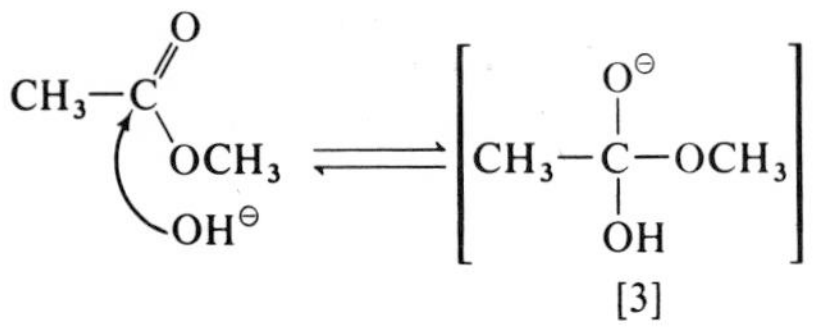

[3]

by base. As a result, the reaction goes to completion in the direction of hydrolysis.

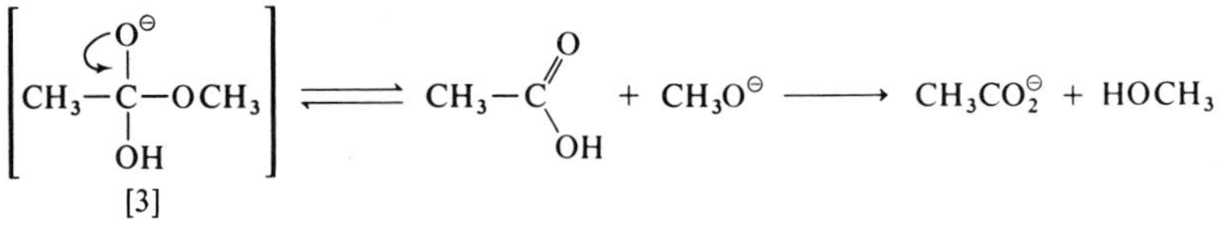

[3]

Base-catalyzed ester interchange is analogous to the saponification reaction, except that an alkoxide base is used in catalytic amounts in place of hydroxide. The equilibrium constant is much nearer to unity, however, than for saponification, because the salt of the acid is not formed.

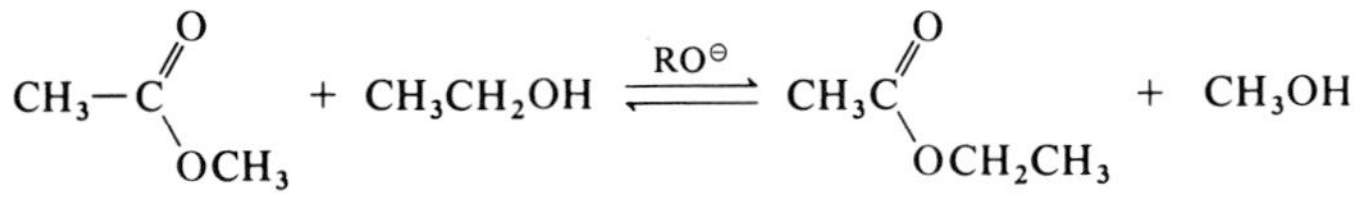

The mechanism is as shown in Equation 13·5. Either methoxide or ethoxide

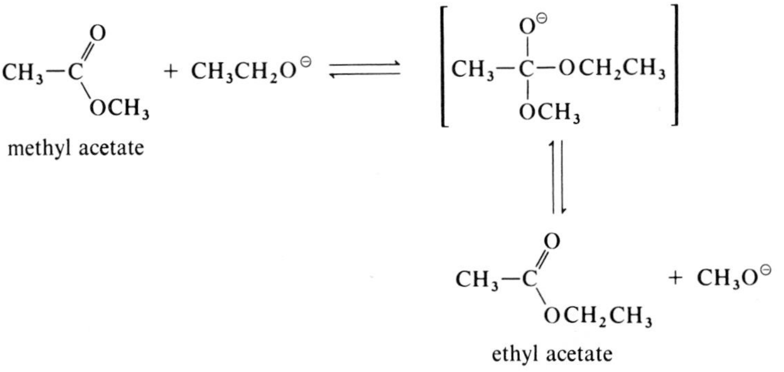

(13·5)

ion can be used as the catalyst since the equilibrium of Equation 13·6 is rapidly established.

$$CH_3O^\ominus + CH_3CH_2OH \rightleftharpoons CH_3CH_2O^\ominus + CH_3OH \tag{13·6}$$

Acid-catalyzed ester interchange is entirely analogous to acid-catalyzed esterification and hydrolysis and requires no further discussion.

The reactions of a number of carboxylic-acid derivatives with organo-magnesium and organolithium compounds were described in Chapter 9 (Section 9·9C).

Esters, acid chlorides, and anhydrides are reduced by lithium aluminum hydride in the same general way as described for the parent acids (Section 13·5B), the difference being that no hydrogen is evolved. The products are primary alcohols.

$$R-C\underset{Z}{\overset{O}{\vphantom{|}}}\quad\xrightarrow[\text{2. H}^{\oplus}\text{, H}_2\text{O}]{\text{1. LiAlH}_4}\quad RCH_2OH \qquad Z = Cl,\ OR,\ RCO_2$$

Nitriles can be reduced to amines by lithium aluminum hydride. An imine salt is an intermediate product; if the reaction is carried out under the proper conditions, this salt is the major product and provides an aldehyde on hydrolysis.

$$R-C\equiv N \xrightarrow{\text{LiAlH}_4} R-CH=N^{\ominus}Li^{\oplus} \xrightarrow{\text{LiAlH}_4} \xrightarrow{\text{H}^{\oplus}\text{, H}_2\text{O}} RCH_2NH_2$$

$$\text{(imine salt)}$$

$$H_2O \Big| H^{\oplus}$$

$$RC\underset{H}{\overset{O}{\vphantom{|}}}$$

Amides can be reduced to primary amines, and N-substituted amides to secondary and tertiary amines.

$$\left.\begin{array}{l} \overset{O}{\underset{\|}{R}C-NH_2} \\[4pt] \overset{O}{\underset{\|}{R}C-NHR'} \\[4pt] \overset{O}{\underset{\|}{R}C-NR_2'} \end{array}\right\} \xrightarrow[\text{H}^{\oplus}\text{, H}_2\text{O}]{\text{LiAlH}_4} \left\{\begin{array}{l} RCH_2NH_2 \\[4pt] RCH_2NHR' \\[4pt] RCH_2NR_2' \end{array}\right.$$

Although lithium aluminum hydride is a very useful reagent, it is sometimes too expensive to be used on a large scale. Other methods of reduction may then be necessary. Of these, the most important are reduction of esters with sodium and ethanol (acids do not reduce readily) and high-pressure hydrogenation over a copper chromite catalyst.

$$RCO_2R' + 4\,Na + 4\,C_2H_5OH \xrightarrow{C_2H_5OH} RCH_2OH + R'OH + 4\,C_2H_5O^{\ominus}Na^{\oplus}$$

$$RCO_2R' + 2\,H_2 \xrightarrow[\text{Cu(Cr)}]{200°} RCH_2OH + R'OH$$

13·9 reactions at the 2 position (α position) of carboxylic acid derivatives

A. THE ACIDIC PROPERTIES OF ESTERS WITH α HYDROGENS

Many important synthetic reactions in which C—C bonds are formed involve esters and are brought about by basic reagents. This is possible because the α hydrogens of an ester such as $RCH_2CO_2C_2H_5$ are weakly acidic, and a strong base, such as sodium ethoxide, can produce a significant concentration of the ester anion at equilibrium.

$$RCH_2CO_2C_2H_5 + C_2H_5O^{\ominus} \rightleftharpoons R\overset{\ominus}{C}HCO_2C_2H_5 + C_2H_5OH$$

The acidity of α hydrogens is attributed partly to the $-I$ inductive effects of the ester oxygens, and partly to resonance stabilization of the resulting anion.

When the 2 position of the ester carries a second strongly electron-attracting

Figure 13·5 Nuclear magnetic resonance spectrum of ethyl acetoacetate at 60 MHz; calibrations are relative to tetramethylsilane at 0.00 ppm. Peaks marked a, b, and c, are assigned respectively to the protons of the enol form, whereas peaks d and e are assigned to the α-CH₂ and methyl protons, respectively, of the keto form. The quartet of lines at 4.2 ppm and the triplet at 1.3 ppm result from the ethyl groups of both keto and enol forms.

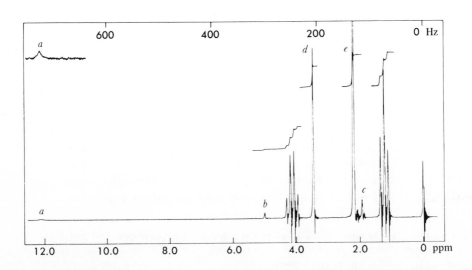

group, the acidity of an α hydrogen is greatly enhanced. Examples of such compounds follow:

$O_2NCH_2CO_2C_2H_5$ ethyl nitroacetate

$C_2H_5O_2CCH_2CO_2C_2H_5$ diethyl malonate

$NCCH_2CO_2C_2H_5$ ethyl cyanoacetate

$CH_3COCH_2CO_2C_2H_5$ ethyl acetoacetate

The stabilization of the anions of these specially activated esters is greater than for simple esters because the negative charge can be distributed over more than two centers. Thus, for the anion of ethyl acetoacetate, we can regard all three of the resonance structures [4a] through [4c] as important con-

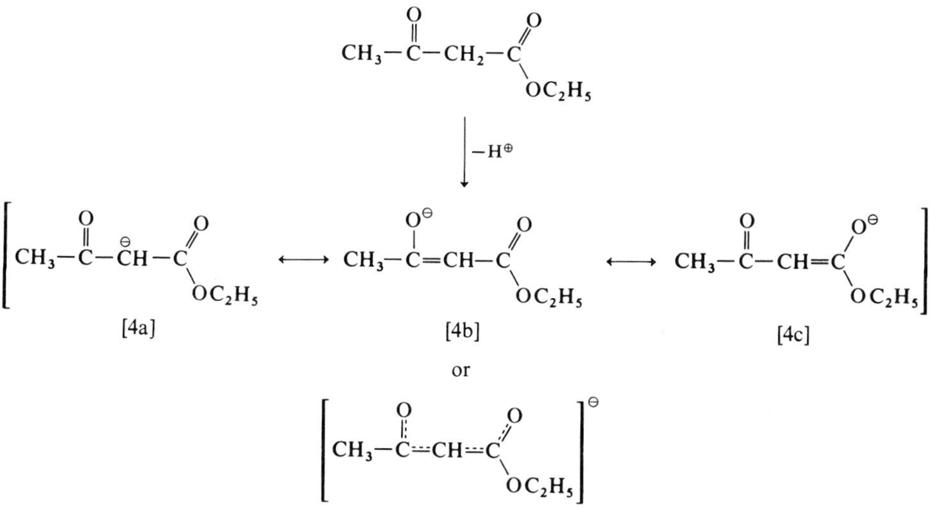

tributors to the hybrid [4]. Since the anion [4] is relatively stable, the K_{HA} of ethyl acetoacetate is about 10^{-11} in water solution. Although this compound is about 10^5 times as strong an acid as ethanol it is much more sluggish in its reaction with bases. Removal of a proton from carbon is a process with a finite energy of activation and only a small fraction of the collisions of such a molecule with hydroxide ion result in proton transfer. On the other hand, acids that have their ionizable protons attached to oxygen (even feeble acids such as ethanol) transfer their protons to strong bases on almost every collision.

Ethyl acetoacetate, like 2,4-pentanedione (Section 12·6), ordinarily exists at room temperature as an equilibrium mixture of keto and enol tautomers in the ratio of 92.5 to 7.5. This can be shown by rapid titration with bromine but is more clearly evident from the nmr spectrum (Figure 13·5), which shows absorptions of the hydroxyl, vinyl, and methyl protons of the enol form, in addition to the absorptions expected for the keto form.

$$CH_3-\overset{\overset{\textstyle O}{\|}}{C}\diagdown_{CH_2}\diagup\overset{\overset{\textstyle O}{\|}}{C}-OC_2H_5 \;\rightleftharpoons\; CH_3-\overset{\overset{\textstyle O\diagup^{H\cdots}}{|}}{C}\diagdown_{CH}\diagup\overset{\overset{\textstyle O}{\|}}{C}-OC_2H_5$$

keto form, 92.5%   enol form, 7.5%

Interconversion of the enol and keto forms of ethyl acetoacetate is powerfully catalyzed by bases through the anion [4] and less so by acids through the conjugate acid of the keto form with a proton adding to the ketone oxygen.

If contact with acidic and basic substances is rigidly excluded (to the extent of using quartz equipment in place of glass, which normally has a slightly alkaline surface), then interconversion is slow enough to enable separating the lower-boiling enol from the keto form by fractional distillation under reduced pressure. The separated tautomers are indefinitely stable when stored at $-80°$ in quartz vessels.

B.   THE CLAISEN CONDENSATION

One of the most useful of the base-induced reactions of esters is illustrated by the self-condensation of ethyl acetate under the influence of sodium ethoxide to give ethyl acetoacetate.

$$CH_3\overset{\overset{\textstyle O}{\|}}{C}\!-\!OC_2H_5 \;+\; H\!-\!CH_2CO_2C_2H_5 \;\xrightarrow{\;NaOC_2H_5\;}\; CH_3COCH_2CO_2C_2H_5 \;+\; C_2H_5OH$$

This reaction is called the **Claisen condensation** and its mechanism has some of the flavor of both the aldol addition (Section 12·2A) and the nucleophilic reactions of acid derivatives discussed earlier (Section 13·5). The first step, as shown in Equation 13·7, is the formation of the anion of ethyl acetate, which, being a powerful nucleophile, attacks the carbonyl carbon of a second ester molecule (Equation 13·8). Elimination of ethoxide ion then leads to the β-keto ester, ethyl acetoacetate (Equation 13·9).

$$C_2H_5O^{\ominus} + CH_3CO_2C_2H_5 \rightleftharpoons {}^{\ominus}CH_2CO_2C_2H_5 + C_2H_5OH \qquad (13\cdot7)$$

$$CH_3-C\overset{\displaystyle O}{\underset{\displaystyle OC_2H_5}{\big\langle}} + {}^{\ominus}CH_2CO_2C_2H_5 \rightleftharpoons CH_3-\overset{\displaystyle O^{\ominus}}{\underset{\displaystyle OC_2H_5}{\overset{\displaystyle |}{C}}}-CH_2CO_2C_2H_5 \qquad (13\cdot8)$$

$$CH_3-\overset{\displaystyle O^{\ominus}}{\underset{\displaystyle OC_2H_5}{\overset{\displaystyle |}{C}}}-CH_2CO_2C_2H_5 \rightleftharpoons CH_3-\overset{\displaystyle O}{\overset{\displaystyle \|}{C}}-CH_2CO_2C_2H_5 + C_2H_5O^{\ominus} \qquad (13\cdot9)$$

The sum of these steps represents an unfavorable equilibrium, and satisfactory yields of the β-keto ester are obtained only if the equilibrium can be shifted by removal of one of the products. One simple way of doing this is to remove the ethyl alcohol by distillation as it is formed; this may be difficult, however, to carry to completion and, in any case, is self-defeating if the starting ester is low boiling. Alternatively, one can use a large excess of sodium ethoxide. This is helpful because ethanol is a weaker acid than the β-keto ester, and excess ethoxide shifts the equilibrium to the right through conversion of the ester to the enolate salt.

$$CH_3-\overset{\displaystyle O}{\overset{\displaystyle \|}{C}}-CH_2CO_2C_2H_5 + C_2H_5O^{\ominus} \rightleftharpoons CH_3-\overset{\displaystyle O}{\overset{\displaystyle \|}{C}}-\overset{\displaystyle \ominus}{\underset{\displaystyle ..}{C}}HCO_2C_2H_5 + C_2H_5OH$$

Obviously the condensation product must be recovered from the enol salt and isolated under conditions that avoid reversion to starting materials. The best procedure is to quench the reaction mixture by pouring it into an excess of cold, dilute acid.

Claisen condensations can be carried out between two different esters but, since there are four possible products, serious mixtures often result. This objection is obviated if one of the esters has no α hydrogen and reacts readily with a carbanion according to Equations 13·8 and 13·9. The reaction then has considerable resemblance to the mixed aldol additions, discussed in Section 12·2A. Among the useful esters without α hydrogens and with the requisite electrophilic reactivity are those of benzoic, formic, oxalic, and carbonic acids. Two practical examples of mixed Claisen condensations are shown.

$$C_6H_5CO_2C_2H_5 + CH_3CO_2C_2H_5 \xrightarrow[\text{2. } H^{\oplus}]{\text{1. } C_2H_5O^{\ominus}} C_6H_5COCH_2CO_2C_2H_5 + C_2H_5OH$$

ethyl benzoate

ethyl benzoylacetate
55%

$$HCO_2C_2H_5 + C_6H_5CH_2CO_2C_2H_5$$

ethyl   ethyl
formate   phenylacetate

1. $C_2H_5O^{\ominus}$ | 2. $H^{\oplus}$

$$C_6H_5CHCO_2C_2H_5 \rightleftharpoons C_6H_5-\overset{\displaystyle }{\underset{\displaystyle \|}{C}}-CO_2C_2H_5$$
$$\underset{\displaystyle CHO}{|} \qquad\qquad \underset{\displaystyle CHOH}{}$$

ethyl formylphenylacetate
90%

An important variation on the Claisen condensation is to use a ketone as the anionic reagent. This often works well because ketones are usually more acidic than simple esters and the base-induced self-condensation of ketones (aldol addition) is thermodynamically unfavorable (Section 12·2A). A typical example is the condensation of cylclohexanone with ethyl oxalate.

$$(CO_2C_2H_5)_2 \quad + \quad \overset{\displaystyle O}{\underset{\displaystyle}{\bigcirc}} \quad \xrightarrow[\text{2. } H^\oplus]{\text{1. } C_2H_5O^\ominus} \quad \overset{\displaystyle O}{\underset{\displaystyle}{\bigcirc}}\!\!-COCO_2C_2H_5 \quad + \quad C_2H_5OH$$

ethyl oxalate   cyclohexanone   2-(ethyl oxalyl)-
cyclohexanone

C. ALKYLATION OF ACETOACETIC AND MALONIC ESTERS

Alkylation of the anions of esters such as ethyl acetoacetate and diethyl malonate is a useful way of synthesizing carboxylic acids and ketones. The ester is converted by a strong base to the enolate anion (Equation 13·10), and this is then alkylated by an S_N2 attack on the alkyl halide (Equation 13·11). Usually, C-alkylation predominates.

$$CH_3\overset{\displaystyle O}{\overset{\|}{C}}-CH_2CO_2C_2H_5 + C_2H_5O^\ominus \rightleftharpoons CH_3\overset{\displaystyle O}{\overset{\|}{C}}-\overset{\ominus}{C}HCO_2C_2H_5 + C_2H_5OH \qquad (13{\cdot}10)$$

$$CH_3I + CH_3\overset{\displaystyle O}{\overset{\|}{C}}-\overset{\ominus}{C}HCO_2C_2H_5 \longrightarrow CH_3\overset{\displaystyle O}{\overset{\|}{C}}-\underset{\underset{\displaystyle CH_3}{|}}{C}HCO_2C_2H_5 + I^\ominus \qquad (13{\cdot}11)$$

Esters of malonic acid can be alkylated similarly.

$$H_2C\!\!\begin{array}{l}{}^{\displaystyle CO_2C_2H_5}\\[-2pt]{}_{\displaystyle CO_2C_2H_5}\end{array} \xrightarrow{\text{NaOC}_2H_5} \xrightarrow{CH_3CH_2Br} CH_3CH_2\!-\!CH\!\!\begin{array}{l}{}^{\displaystyle CO_2C_2H_5}\\[-2pt]{}_{\displaystyle CO_2C_2H_5}\end{array}$$

Alkylacetoacetic and alkylmalonic esters can be hydrolyzed under acidic conditions to the corresponding acids and, when these are heated, they readily decarboxylate (see Section 13·6). Alkylacetoacetic esters thus yield methyl alkyl ketones, while alkylmalonic esters produce carboxylic acids.

$$CH_3\overset{\displaystyle O}{\overset{\|}{C}}-\underset{\underset{\displaystyle CH_3}{|}}{C}HCO_2C_2H_5 \xrightarrow{H^\oplus,\ H_2O} CH_3\overset{\displaystyle O}{\overset{\|}{C}}-\underset{\underset{\displaystyle CH_3}{|}}{C}HCO_2H \xrightarrow[-CO_2]{\text{heat}} CH_3\overset{\displaystyle O}{\overset{\|}{C}}-CH_2CH_3$$
methyl ethyl ketone

$$CH_3CH_2CH\!\!\begin{array}{l}{}^{\displaystyle CO_2C_2H_5}\\[-2pt]{}_{\displaystyle CO_2C_2H_5}\end{array} \xrightarrow{H^\oplus,\ H_2O} CH_3CH_2CH\!\!\begin{array}{l}{}^{\displaystyle CO_2H}\\[-2pt]{}_{\displaystyle CO_2H}\end{array} \xrightarrow[-CO_2]{\text{heat}} CH_3CH_2CH_2CO_2H$$
butanoic acid

13·10   reactions of unsaturated carboxylic acids and their derivatives

Unsaturated carboxylic acids of the type $RCH=CH(CH_2)_nCOOH$ usually exhibit the properties characteristic of isolated double bonds and isolated carboxyl groups when n is large and the functional groups are far apart. As expected, exceptional behavior is most commonly found when the groups are sufficiently close together to interact strongly, as in 2-alkenoic acids. These compounds are invariably called α,β-unsaturated acids, $R\overset{\beta}{C}H=\overset{\alpha}{C}HCO_2H$, and we shall use this term herein.

A.   HYDRATION AND HYDROGEN BROMIDE ADDITION

Like alkenes, the double bonds of α,β-unsaturated acids can be brominated, hydroxylated, hydrated, and hydrobrominated, although the reactions are often relatively slow. With unsymmetrical addends, the direction of addition is opposite to that observed for alkenes (anti-Markownikoff). Thus propenoic acid (acrylic acid) adds hydrogen bromide and water so that 3-bromo- and 3-hydroxypropanoic acids are formed. These additions are closely analogous to the addition of halogen acids to propenal (Section 12·3).

$$CH_2=CHCOOH \begin{cases} \xrightarrow{HBr} BrCH_2CH_2COOH \quad \text{3-bromopropanoic acid} \\ \xrightarrow[H^\oplus]{H_2O} CH_2CH_2COOH \ (OH) \quad \text{3-hydroxypropanoic acid} \end{cases}$$

propenoic acid
(acrylic acid)

B.   LACTONE FORMATION

When the double bond of an unsaturated acid lies farther down the carbon chain than between the α and β positions, conjugate addition is not possible. Nonetheless, the double bond and carboxyl group frequently interact in the presence of acid catalysts because the carbonium ion that results from addition of a proton to the double bond has a built-in nucleophile (the carboxyl group), which may attack the cationic center to form a cyclic ester (i.e., a lactone). Lactone formation usually occurs readily by this mechanism only when a five- or six-membered ring can be formed.

$$CH_2=CHCH_2CH_2C\overset{O}{\underset{OH}{\big\backslash}} \xrightarrow{H^\oplus} CH_3-\overset{\oplus}{C}HCH_2CH_2C\overset{O}{\underset{OH}{\big\backslash}} \xrightarrow{-H^\oplus}$$

4-pentenoic acid
(allylacetic acid)

(γ-valerolactone)

Five- and six-membered lactones are also formed by internal esterification when either 4- or 5-hydroxy acids are heated. Under similar conditions, 3-hydroxy acids are dehydrated to α,β-unsaturated acids, while 2-hydroxy acids undergo bimolecular esterification to substances with six-membered dilactone rings called lactides.

$$HOCH_2CH_2CH_2CO_2H \xrightarrow{\text{heat}} \overset{\displaystyle H_2C-CH_2}{\underset{\displaystyle \underset{O}{\overset{\|}{C}}}{O \diagdown \diagup CH_2}} + H_2O$$

4-hydroxybutanoic acid
(γ-hydroxybutyric acid)

γ-butyrolactone

$$\underset{\displaystyle OH}{CH_3\overset{|}{C}HCH_2CO_2H} \xrightarrow{\text{heat}} CH_3CH{=}CHCO_2H + H_2O$$

3-hydroxybutanoic acid

2-butenoic acid

$$2\,\underset{\displaystyle OH}{CH_3\overset{|}{C}HCO_2H} \xrightarrow{\text{heat}} \underset{\displaystyle O{=}\overset{|}{C}\diagdown_O\diagup\overset{|}{C}HCH_3}{CH_3HC\diagup^O\diagdown_{\displaystyle C}\diagdown^O} + 2\,H_2O$$

2-hydroxypropanoic acid
(lactic acid)

lactide

13·11 dicarboxylic acids

Acids in which there are two carboxyl groups separated by a chain of more than five carbon atoms ($n > 5$) have, for the most part, unexceptional properties, the carboxyl groups behaving more or less independently of one another.

$$\underset{\displaystyle CO_2H}{\overset{\displaystyle CO_2H}{(CH_2)_n}}$$

When the carboxyl groups are closer together, however, the possibilities for interaction increase; we shall be primarily concerned with such acids. A number of important dicarboxylic acids are listed in Table 13·4.

A. ACIDIC PROPERTIES OF DICARBOXYLIC ACIDS

The inductive effect of one carboxyl group is expected to enhance the acidity of the other and, from Table 13·4, we see that the acid strength of the dicarboxylic acids, as measured by the first acid-dissociation constant, K_1, is higher than that of acetic acid ($K_{HA} = 1.8 \times 10^{-5}$) and falls off with increasing distance between the two carboxyl groups. Two other factors operate to raise K_1 in comparison to the K_{HA} of acetic acid. First, the statistical factor:

Table 13·4   Dicarboxylic acids

acid	formula	mp, °C	$K_1 \times 10^5$ at 25°	$K_2 \times 10^5$ at 25°
oxalic (ethanedioic)	CO_2H | CO_2H	189	3500	5.3
malonic (propanedioic)	CO_2H / CH_2 \ CO_2H	136 dec.	171	0.22
succinic (butanedioic)	CO_2H / $(CH_2)_2$ \ CO_2H	185	6.6	0.25
glutaric (pentanedioic)	CO_2H / $(CH_2)_3$ \ CO_2H	98	4.7	0.29
adipic (hexanedioic)	CO_2H / $(CH_2)_4$ \ CO_2H	152	3.7	0.24
pimelic (heptanedioic)	CO_2H / $(CH_2)_5$ \ CO_2H	105	3.4	0.26
maleic (cis-butenedioic)	$HCCO_2H$ ‖ $HCCO_2H$	130	1170	0.026
fumaric (trans-butenedioic)	$HCCO_2H$ ‖ HO_2CCH	sub. 200	93	2.9
phthalic (benzene-1,2-dicarboxylic)	CO_2H CO_2H	231	130	0.39[18]

there are two carboxyl groups per molecule instead of one. Second, there can be stabilization of the monoanion by internal hydrogen bonding, when the geometry of the molecule allows it.

The second acid-dissociation constant, K_2, is smaller than K_{HA} for acetic acid in most cases, and this must also be largely due to the hydrogen-bonding effect. Comparison of K_1 and K_2 for maleic and fumaric acids is especially instructive. Only the *cis* monoanion can be stabilized by internal hydrogen bonding and we find K_1 to be larger and K_2 smaller for the *cis* acid.

B. THERMAL BEHAVIOR OF DICARBOXYLIC ACIDS

The reactions that occur when diacids are heated depend critically upon the chain length separating the carboxyl groups. Cyclization is usually favored if a strainless five- or six-membered ring can be formed. Thus adipic and pimelic acids cyclize and decarboxylate to give cyclopentanone and cyclohexanone, respectively.

adipic acid   cyclopentanone

pimelic acid   cyclohexanone

Succinic and glutaric acids take a different course. Rather than form the strained cyclic ketones—cyclopropanone and cyclobutanone—both acids form cyclic anhydrides—succinic and glutaric anhydrides—having five- and six-membered rings, respectively. Phthalic and maleic acids behave similarly giving five-membered cyclic anhydrides.

succinic   succinic   phthalic   phthalic
acid   anhydride   acid   anhydride

glutaric   glutaric   maleic   maleic
acid   anhydride   acid   anhydride

Malonic and oxalic acids behave still differently, each undergoing decarboxylation when heated (Section 13·6).

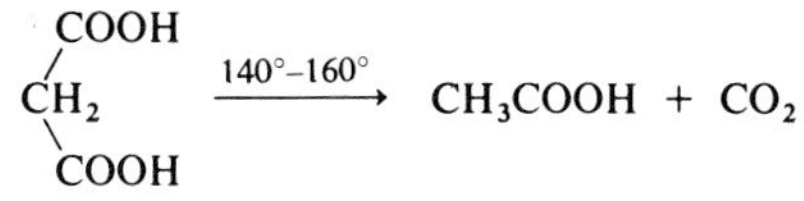

$$\underset{\text{malonic acid}}{\begin{array}{c} \text{COOH} \\ / \\ \text{CH}_2 \\ \backslash \\ \text{COOH} \end{array}} \xrightarrow{140°-160°} \text{CH}_3\text{COOH} + \text{CO}_2$$

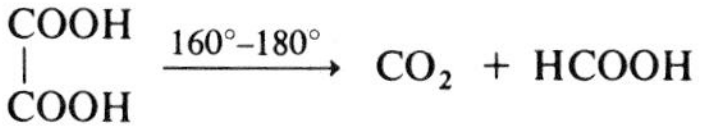

$$\underset{\text{oxalic acid}}{\begin{array}{c} \text{COOH} \\ | \\ \text{COOH} \end{array}} \xrightarrow{160°-180°} \text{CO}_2 + \text{HCOOH}$$

summary

Carboxylic acids, such as $(CH_3)_2CHCO_2H$ (2-methylpropanoic acid or isobutyric acid), have higher melting and boiling points than alcohols of the same molecular weight. They ionize weakly in aqueous solution ($K_{HA} \sim 10^{-5}$) but associate as dimers in hydrocarbon solvents.

Carboxylate salts ($RCO_2^\ominus\ Na^\oplus$) are quite soluble in water and this fact permits carboxylic acids to be separated from other organic compounds by extraction with appropriately basic solutions. Acids with long alkyl or alkenyl groups are called fatty acids. Their salts form colloidal particles in water called micelles in which the charged carboxyl end groups point outward and the hydrocarbon chains point inward. The mechanism of soap action is related to the ability of micelles to dissolve nonpolar substances; the tendency of salts of fatty acids to concentrate at interfaces is also a factor.

The C_4 to C_8 carboxylic acids have strong unpleasant odors. The infrared spectra of carboxylic acids shows broad absorption near $3000\ cm^{-1}$ (hydrogen-bonded O—H) and near $1750\ cm^{-1}$ (C=O stretch). The carboxyl proton in the nmr absorbs at very low field (> 10 ppm from TMS).

Some methods of preparing carboxylic acids are illustrated here.

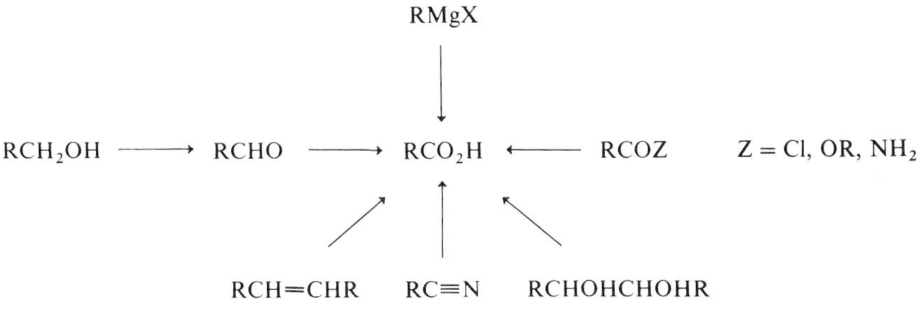

$$RMgX$$
$$\downarrow$$

$$RCH_2OH \longrightarrow RCHO \longrightarrow RCO_2H \longleftarrow RCOZ \qquad Z = Cl, OR, NH_2$$

$$RCH=CHR \quad RC\equiv N \quad RCHOHCHOHR$$

In addition to these methods RX can be converted to RCH_2CO_2H by the malonic ester synthesis (see below).

The acidity of the carboxyl group can be attributed to the inductive effects of the carbonyl group and resonance stabilization of the ion $RCO_2^{\ominus}$. Electron-withdrawing substituents such as Cl in R increase the acid strength by inductive withdrawal of charge from the carboxyl group ($-I$ effect).

Carboxyl groups can be protonated by strongly acidic systems to give

cations of formula
$$R-C\begin{cases} \overset{\frac{1}{2}\oplus}{OH} \\ OH \\ {\scriptstyle \frac{1}{2}\oplus} \end{cases}$$
These are intermediates in the esterification reaction.

In summary, the reactions of the carboxyl group are:

$$RCO_2H \longrightarrow RC\overset{\displaystyle O}{\underset{\displaystyle Cl}{\big\langle}} \qquad \text{(with } PCl_3, PCl_5, \text{ or } SOCl_2\text{)}$$

$$\longrightarrow RCH_2OH \qquad \text{(with } LiAlH_4\text{)}$$

$$\longrightarrow RH + CO_2 \qquad \text{(occurs readily only if C-2 carries a } -I \text{ substituent)}$$

$$\longrightarrow R-R \qquad \text{(Kolbe electrolysis)}$$

$$\longrightarrow R-Br \qquad \text{(Hunsdiecker reaction)}$$

The 2 position of carboxylic acids can be halogenated via the acid halide ($RCH_2CO_2H \rightarrow RCH_2COX \rightarrow RCHXCOX \rightarrow RCHXCO_2H$). A halogen at the 2 position suffers ready displacement by nucleophiles.

Derivatives of carboxylic acids include esters (RCO_2R), acid halides ($RCOX$), anhydrides (($RCO)_2O$), and amides ($RCONH_2$). They can all be hydrolyzed to carboxylic acids and the first three also react with alcohols or amines to give esters and amides.

$$\left.\begin{array}{l} R-\overset{\displaystyle O}{\overset{\|}{C}}-X \\[1em] R-\overset{\displaystyle O}{\overset{\|}{C}}-OR \\[1em] (RCO)_2O \end{array}\right\} \longrightarrow \left\{\begin{array}{l} RCO_2H \\[1em] R\overset{\displaystyle O}{\overset{\|}{C}}-OR^* \\[1em] R\overset{\displaystyle O}{\overset{\|}{C}}-NH_2 \end{array}\right.$$

*(ester interchange in case of $R\overset{\displaystyle O}{\overset{\|}{C}}-OR \rightarrow R\overset{\displaystyle O}{\overset{\|}{C}}-OR'$)

Lithium aluminum hydride reduction of carboxylic acid derivatives gives primary alcohols or amines.

$$\left.\begin{array}{l} R\overset{\displaystyle O}{\overset{\|}{C}}-Cl \\[1.5em] R\overset{\displaystyle O}{\overset{\|}{C}}-OR \end{array}\right\rangle RCH_2OH \qquad\qquad \left.\begin{array}{l} R\overset{\displaystyle O}{\overset{\|}{C}}-NH_2 \\[1.5em] RC\equiv N \end{array}\right\rangle RCH_2NH_2$$

Esters with anion-stabilizing substituents are moderately acidic and some of these, especially the β-keto esters, undergo a number of useful reactions. They can be prepared by the Claisen condensation between two molecules of ester.

$$2\,RCH_2CO_2C_2H_5 \longrightarrow RCH_2\overset{\overset{\displaystyle O}{\|}}{C}\underset{\underset{\displaystyle R}{|}}{CH}CO_2C_2H_5$$

Acetoacetic and malonic esters may be alkylated via their anions; acid hydrolysis then gives ketones and acids, respectively (acetoacetic and malonic ester syntheses).

$$CH_3\overset{\overset{\displaystyle O}{\|}}{C}CH_2CO_2C_2H_5 \longrightarrow CH_3\overset{\overset{\displaystyle O}{\|}}{C}\underset{\underset{\displaystyle R}{|}}{CH}CO_2C_2H_5 \longrightarrow CH_3\overset{\overset{\displaystyle O}{\|}}{C}CH_2R$$

$$CH_2(CO_2C_2H_5)_2 \longrightarrow RCH(CO_2C_2H_5)_2 \longrightarrow RCH_2CO_2H$$

α,β-Unsaturated acids (double-bond between C-2 and C-3) undergo typical alkene-addition reactions except that unsymmetrical addends add in the anti-Markownikoff manner. γ,δ- or δ,ε-Unsaturated acids (4- or 5-alkenoic acids) form lactones readily.

Dicarboxylic acids have exalted values of K_1 and depressed values of K_2 relative to monocarboxylic acids and this is mainly due to internal hydrogen bonding in the monoanion.

Heating of dicarboxylic acids gives five- or six-membered rings if this is possible (either ketones by decarboxylation and dehydration or anhydrides by dehydration). The C_2 and C_3 dicarboxylic acids tend to undergo simple decarboxylation.

$$HO-\overset{\overset{\displaystyle O}{\|}}{C}\sim\sim\overset{\overset{\displaystyle O}{\|}}{C}-OH \longrightarrow \bigcirc\!\!-C=O \text{ or } \bigcirc\!\!<^{C}_{C}\!\!<^{O}_{O}>O \text{ or } RCO_2H$$

exercises

13·1 Explain why the chemical shift of the acidic proton of a carboxylic acid, dissolved in a nonpolar solvent like carbon tetrachloride, varies less with concentration than that of the OH proton of an alcohol under the same conditions (see Section 13·1).

13·2 A white solid contains ammonium octanoate mixed with naphthalene ($C_{10}H_8$) and sodium sulfate. Describe the exact procedure you would follow to obtain pure octanoic acid from this mixture.

13·3 Would you expect the compound $C_{15}H_{31}\overset{\oplus}{N}(CH_3)_3Cl^{\ominus}$ to form micelles in water?

13·4 Write equations for a practical laboratory synthesis of each of the following substances from the indicated starting materials (several steps may be required). Give reagents and conditions.

    a. butanoic acid (*n*-butyric acid) from 1-propanol
    b. trimethylacetic acid from *t*-butyl chloride
    c. 2-methylpropanoic acid (isobutyric acid) from 2-methylpropene
    d. 2-bromo-3,3-dimethylbutanoic acid from *t*-butyl chloride
    e. β-chloroethyl bromoacetate from ethanol and (or) acetic acid
    f. 2-methoxypentanoic acid from pentanoic acid
    g. 3,5,5-trimethyl-3-hexanol from 2,4,4-trimethyl-1-pentene (commercially available)
    h. 3,3-dimethylbutanal from 3,3-dimethylbutanoic acid
    i. 2,3,3-trimethyl-2-butanol from 2,3-dimethyl-2-butene
    j. cyclopentane from hexanedioic acid (adipic acid)
    k. cyclopropyl bromide from cyclopropanecarboxylic acid

13.5 Give for each of the following pairs of compounds a chemical test, preferably a test tube reaction with a visible result, that will distinguish between the two substances. Write an equation for each reaction.

    a. HCO_2H and CH_3CO_2H
    b. $CH_3CO_2C_2H_5$ and $CH_3OCH_2CO_2H$
    c. $CH_2{=}CHCO_2H$ and $CH_3CH_2CO_2H$
    d. CH_3COBr and $BrCH_2CO_2H$

    e. $(CH_3CH_2CO)_2O$ and

    f.

    g. $HC{\equiv}CCO_2CH_3$ and $CH_2{=}CHCO_2CH_3$
    h. $CH_3CO_2NH_4$ and CH_3CONH_2
    i. $(CH_3CO)_2O$ and $CH_3CO_2CH_2CH_3$

13·6 Explain how you could distinguish between the pairs of compounds listed in Exercise 13·5 by spectroscopic means.

13·7 Write structural formulas for all 13 carboxylic acids and esters of formula $C_5H_{10}O_2$. Provide the IUPAC name and, if possible, one other suitable name for each compound.

13·8 Only two different products are obtained when the following four compounds are reduced with an excess of lithium aluminum hydride; what are they? $(CH_3)_2CHCO_2H$ $(CH_3)_2CHCO_2CH_3$ $(CH_3)_2CHCONH_2$ $(CH_3)_2CHC{\equiv}N$

13·9 At high current densities, electrolysis of salts of carboxylic acids in hydroxylic solvents produce (at the anode) alcohols and esters of the type ROH and RCO_2R. Explain.

13·10   Name each of the following substances by an accepted system:

a. 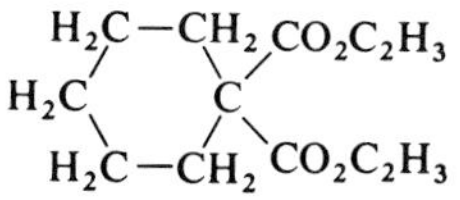 $\underset{H_2C-CH_2}{\overset{H_2C-CH_2}{\diagdown}}\underset{C}{\overset{CO_2C_2H_3}{\diagup}}$

b. $CH_3COCH[CH(CH_3)_2]CO_2C_2H_5$

c. $C_6H_5CH_2CH_2COCl$

d. $HOCH=CHCO_2C_2H_5$

e. $C_2H_5OCOCOCH_2CO_2C_2H_5$

f. $HCO_2C_2F_5$

g. 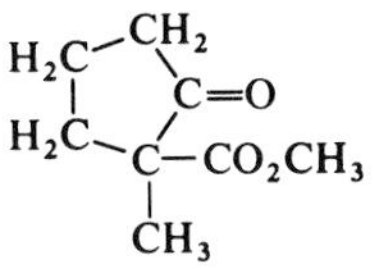 $\underset{H_2C}{\overset{H_2C}{\diagup}}\overset{CH_2}{\underset{\underset{CH_3}{|}}{\underset{C-CO_2CH_3}{|}}}C=O$

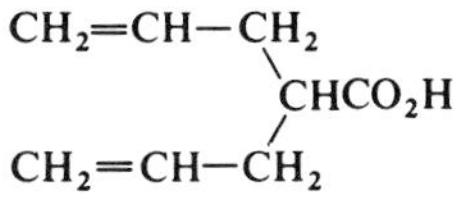

h. $\underset{CH_2=CH-CH_2}{\overset{CH_2=CH-CH_2}{\diagdown\diagup}}CHCO_2H$

i. $CH_3CH_2COCHCH_3$
          $\overset{|}{CH_2CH_2CH(CH_3)_2}$

j. $CH_3CH_2CH(CH=CH_2)CO_2H$

k. $CH_3COCH(CO_2C_2H_5)_2$

13·11   Write equations for the effect of heat on the 2, 3, 4, and 5 isomers of hydroxy-pentanoic acid.

13·12   Predict the relative volatility of acetic acid, acetyl fluoride, and methyl acetate. Give your reasoning.

13·13   By analogy with ester hydrolysis, propose a mechanism for each of the following reactions:

a. $C_6H_5CO_2CH_3 + C_2H_5OH \xrightarrow{H^\oplus} C_6H_5CO_2C_2H_5 + CH_3OH$

b. $CH_3COCl + CH_3CH_2OH \longrightarrow CH_3CO_2CH_2CH_3 + HCl$

c. $(CH_3CO)_2O + CH_3OH \xrightarrow{H^\oplus} CH_3CO_2CH_3 + CH_3CO_2H$

d. $CH_3CONH_2 + H_3O^\oplus \longrightarrow CH_3CO_2H + NH_4^\oplus$

e. $CH_3CONH_2 + {}^\ominus OH \longrightarrow CH_3CO_2{}^\ominus + NH_3$

f. $CH_3COCl + 2 NH_3 \longrightarrow CH_3CONH_2 + NH_4Cl$

13·14   Why is a carboxylate anion more resistant to attack by nucleophilic agents, such as $CH_3O^\ominus$, than the corresponding ester?

13·15 What can you conclude about the mechanism of acid-catalyzed hydrolysis of β-butyrolactone from the following equation:

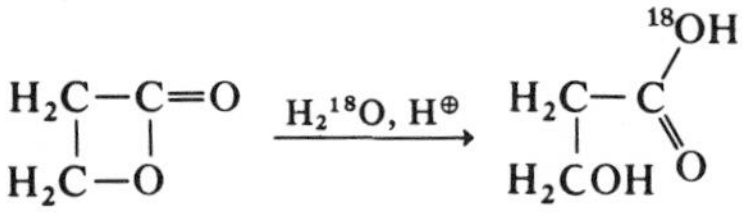

$$H_2C-C{=}O \quad \xrightarrow{H_2{}^{18}O,\ H^{\oplus}} \quad \underset{H_2COH}{\overset{{}^{18}OH}{H_2C-C}}{=}O$$

13·16 Amides of the type $R-\overset{\overset{\displaystyle O}{\|}}{C}-NH_2$ are much weaker bases (and stronger acids) than amines. Why?

13·17 Write a plausible mechanism for the following reaction:

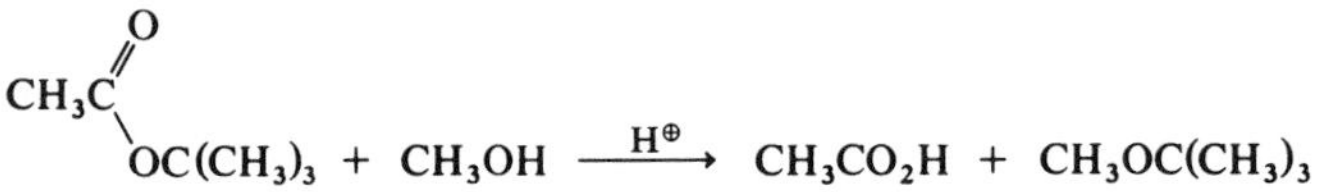

$$CH_3\overset{\displaystyle O}{\overset{\displaystyle /\!/}{C}}{-}OC(CH_3)_3 + CH_3OH \xrightarrow{H^{\oplus}} CH_3CO_2H + CH_3OC(CH_3)_3$$

13·18 Other conceivable products of the Claisen condensation of ethyl acetate are

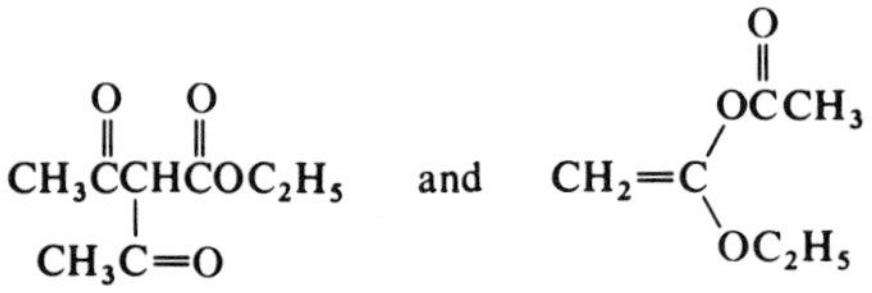

$$\underset{\underset{\displaystyle CH_3C{=}O}{|}}{CH_3\overset{O}{\overset{\|}{C}}CH\overset{O}{\overset{\|}{C}}OC_2H_5} \quad \text{and} \quad CH_2{=}\underset{\displaystyle OC_2H_5}{\overset{\overset{\displaystyle O}{\overset{\|}{OCCH_3}}}{C}}$$

Explain how these products might be formed and why they are not formed in significant amounts.

13·19 Suggest a reason why 2,4-pentanedione (acetylacetone) contains much more enol at equilibrium than ethyl acetoacetate. How much enol would you expect to find in diethyl malonate? In butan-3-on-1-al (acetylacetaldehyde)? Explain.

13·20 Write structures for all of the Claisen condensation products that may reasonably be expected to be formed from the following mixtures of substances and sodium ethoxide:

    a.   ethyl acetate and ethyl propanoate
    b.   ethyl carbonate and acetone
    c.   ethyl oxalate and ethyl trimethylacetate

13·21 Show how the substances below may be synthesized by Claisen-type condensations based on the indicated starting materials. Specify the reagents and reaction conditions as closely as possible.

    a.   ethyl 2-propanoylpropanoate from ethyl propanoate
    b. $CH_3COCH_2COCO_2C_2H_5$ from acetone
    c.   diethyl phenylmalonate from ethyl phenylacetate
    d.   2,4-pentanedione from acetone
    e.   2,2,6,6-tetramethyl-3,5-heptanedione from pinacolone (*t*-butyl methyl ketone).

13·22   Why does the following reaction fail to give ethyl propanoate?

$$CH_3CO_2C_2H_5 \ + \ CH_3I \ \xrightarrow[]{\text{NaOC}_2\text{H}_5} \ CH_3CH_2CO_2C_2H_5$$

13·23   Show how one could prepare cyclobutanecarboxylic acid starting from diethyl malonate and a suitable dihalide.

13·24   Would you expect vinylacetic acid to form a lactone when heated with a catalytic amount of sulfuric acid?

13·25   Fumaric and maleic acids give the same anhydride on heating, but fumaric acid must be heated to much higher temperatures than maleic acid to effect the same change. Explain. Write reasonable mechanisms for both reactions.

13·26   t-Butyl acetate is converted to methyl acetate by sodium methoxide in methanol about one-tenth as fast as ethyl acetate is converted to methyl acetate under the same conditions. With dilute hydrogen chloride in methanol, t-butyl acetate is rapidly converted to t-butyl methyl ether and acetic acid, whereas ethyl acetate goes more slowly to ethanol and methyl acetate.

    a.   Write reasonable mechanisms for each of the reactions and show how the relative-rate data agree with your mechanisms.

    b.   How could one use ^{18}O as a tracer to substantiate your mechanistic picture?

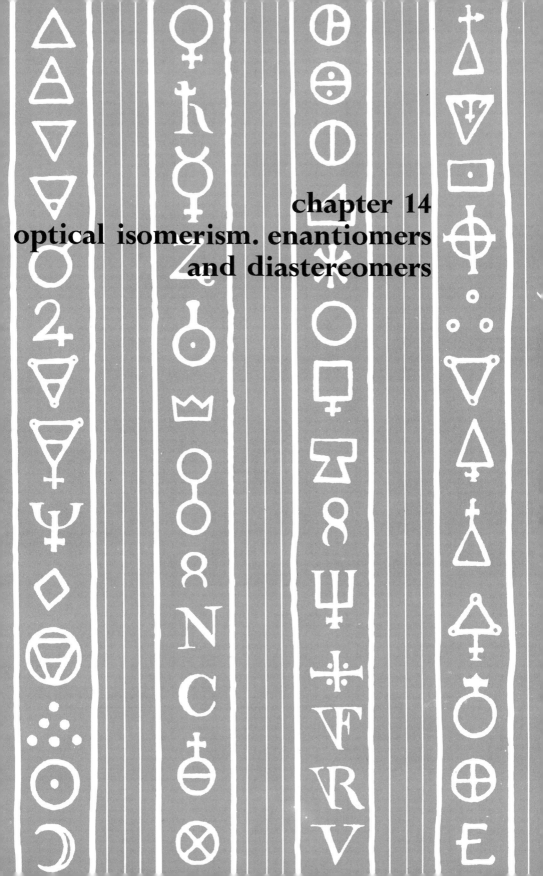

chapter 14
optical isomerism. enantiomers
and diastereomers

Isomers are compounds that have the same molecular formula (e.g., $C_4H_{10}O$) but differ in the way in which the constituent atoms are joined together. The simplest form of isomerism is structural isomerism, in which the bonding sequence differs. Two of the structural isomers of $C_4H_{10}O$ are 1-butanol, $CH_3CH_2CH_2CH_2OH$, and 2-butanol, $CH_3CH_2CHOHCH_3$. Stereoisomerism is the isomerism of compounds having the same structural formula but different arrangements of groups in space. We have already met one of the two forms of stereoisomerism, called geometrical (*cis-trans*) isomerism, and we will now encounter the other, optical isomerism. We shall see that 2-butanol, but not 1-butanol, exhibits this rather subtle form of isomerism.

Isomers, whether structural, geometrical, or optical are generally long-lived and isolable because isomerization usually requires that bonds be broken. In this way they differ from conformers, the many different spatial arrangements that result from rotations about single bonds (Section 2·2). It should be understood that isomers and conformers are not mutually exclusive. Thus while 2-butanol will be seen to have two stable optical isomers, each of these optical isomers exists as a dynamic mixture of conformations. We shall return to this point frequently in subsequent discussions.

What are optical isomers? They are stereoisomers, some or all of which have the ability to rotate the plane of polarized light, that is, exhibit optical activity. What quality do optically active molecules possess that causes them to affect polarized light this way? We shall see that it is actually a property they *lack* that is responsible for their optical activity and that this property is *symmetry*. Before going further, however, we shall examine the phenomenon of the polarization of light.

14·1 plane-polarized light and the origin of optical rotation

Electromagnetic radiation, as the name implies, involves the propagation of both electric and magnetic forces. At each point in a light beam, there is a component electric field and a component magnetic field which are perpendicular to each other and which oscillate in all directions perpendicular to the direction in which the beam is propagated. In plane-polarized light, the oscillation of the electric field is restricted to a single plane, the plane of polarization, while the magnetic field of necessity oscillates at right angles to that plane. Passing ordinary light through a split prism of calcite (a form of $CaCO_3$) known as a Nicol prism resolves the light into two beams, each of which is polarized and has half of the intensity of the original beam. (A sheet of Polaroid can also be used.) Light polarized by passage through one Nicol prism will not pass through a second Nicol prism set at right angles to the first one. Now if a transparent sample (usually a solution) of an optically active substance is placed between the two prisms, any change in the angle of the plane of polarization in the solution can be detected (Figure 14·1), because the second prism will have to be rotated a certain number of degrees to be at right angles to the new plane of polarization and stop the light from coming through. An instrument that measures optical rotation this way is called a **polarimeter** (Figure 14·2).

A clockwise rotation of the prism to produce extinction, as the observer looks toward the beam, defines the substance as **dextrorotatory** (rotates to the right), and we say that it has a positive ($+$) rotation. If the rotation is counterclockwise, the substance is **levorotatory** (rotates to the left) and the compound has a negative ($-$) rotation. The angle of rotation is designated α.

The question naturally arises as to why compounds whose molecules lack symmetry interact with polarized light in this manner. We shall oversimplify the explanation since the subject is best treated rigorously with rather complex mathematics. However, it is not difficult to understand that the electric forces in a light beam impinging on a molecule will interact to some extent with the electrons within the molecule. Although radiant energy may not actually be absorbed by the molecule to promote it to higher excited electronic-energy states (see Chapter 7), a perturbation of the electronic configuration of the molecule can occur. One can visualize this process as a polarization of the electrons brought about by the oscillating electric field associated with the radiation. This kind of interaction is important to us here because it causes the electric field of the radiation to change its direction of oscillation. The effect produced by any one molecule is extremely small, but in the aggregate may be measurable as a net rotation of the plane-polarized light. Molecules such as methane, ethane, and acetone, which have enough symmetry so that each is identical with its reflection, do not give a net rotation of plane-polarized light. This is because the symmetry of each is such that every optical rotation in one direction is canceled by an equal rotation in the opposite direction. *However, a molecule with its atoms so disposed in space that it is*

Figure 14·1 Schematic representation of the vibrations of **(a)** ordinary light, and **(b)** plane-polarized light that is being rotated by interaction with an optically active substance.

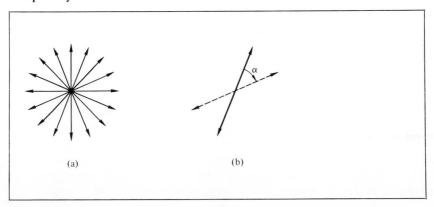

(a)   (b)

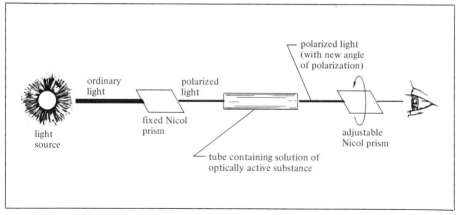

Figure 14·2   Schematic diagram of a polarimeter. The plane of polarization has been rotated by passage through the solution of the optically active substance, and extinction of the beam of polarized light can only be restored by rotating the adjustable Nicol prism.

not symmetrical to the degree of being superimposable on its mirror image will have a net effect on the incident polarized light. The electromagnetic interactions do not average to zero and such substances we characterize as being optically active. The structural characteristics of optically active molecules will be discussed beginning in Section 14·3.

14·2 specific rotation

The angle of rotation of the plane of polarized light α depends on the number and kind of molecules the light encounters—it is found that α varies with the concentration of a solution (or the density of a pure liquid) and on the distance through which the light travels in the sample. A third important variable is the wavelength of the incident light, which must always be specified even though the sodium D line (5893 A) is commonly used. (See also Section 14·10.) To a lesser extent, α varies with the temperature and with the solvent (if used), which also should be specified. Thus, the specific rotation, $[\alpha]$, of a substance is generally expressed by the following formulas:
for solutions,

$$[\alpha]_\lambda^{t°} = \frac{100\,\alpha}{l \cdot c}$$

for neat liquids,

$$[\alpha]_\lambda^{t°} = \frac{\alpha}{l \cdot d}$$

where α is measured degree of rotation; $t°$ is temperature; λ is wavelength of light; l is length in decimeters of light path through the solution; c is concentration in grams of sample per 100 ml of solution; and d is density of liquid in grams per milliliter.

For example, when a compound is reported as having $[\alpha]_D^{25°} = -100$ ($c = 2.5$, chloroform), this means that it has a specific levorotation of 100 degrees at a concentration of 2.5 g per 100 ml of chloroform solution at 25°C when contained in a tube 1 decimeter long, the rotation being measured with sodium D light, which has a wavelength of 5893 A.

Frequently, molecular rotation $[M]$ is used in preference to specific rotation. It is related to specific rotation by the following equation:

$$[M]_\lambda^{t°} = \frac{[\alpha]_\lambda^{t°} \cdot M}{100}$$

where M is the molecular weight of the optically active compound. Expressed in this form, optical rotations of different compounds can be compared directly because differences in rotation arising from differences in molecular weight are taken into account.

14·3 optically active compounds with asymmetric carbon atoms

A. ONE ASYMMETRIC CARBON

Having discussed how optical activity is measured experimentally, we shall now consider the conditions of asymmetry (lack of symmetry) which are necessary for a compound to be optically active. The inflexible condition for optical activity is: *the geometric structure of a molecule must be such that it is nonsuperimposable on its mirror image.* Unless this condition holds, the molecule cannot exist in optically active forms. Asymmetry is, of course, a property of many objects you see around you. Each of your hands is asymmetric, that is, your right hand cannot occupy the same space that its mirror image (your left hand) fits into, as can be seen by trying to put your right hand into a glove that fits your left hand. The term **chirality**[1] is often applied to asymmetric objects (or molecules); it refers to their " handedness." At the molecular level, there are a number of types of structural elements that can make a molecule asymmetric and nonidentical with its mirror image. The most common and important of these is the asymmetrically substituted carbon atom, which is a carbon atom bonded to four *different* atoms or groups. If a molecule has such an asymmetrically substituted atom, the molecule will be nonidentical with its mirror image and will therefore be optically active. A simple example is 2-butanol [1], the C-2 of which is said to be asymmetric since it carries four different groups, hydrogen, hydroxyl, methyl, and ethyl.

---

[1] Pronounced kī′raləd-ē.

$$
\begin{array}{c}
CH_3 \quad H \\
\diagdown C \diagup \\
\diagup \quad \diagdown \\
CH_3CH_2 \quad OH
\end{array}
$$

[1]

However, 2-butanol, as prepared from optically inactive materials (e.g., by the reduction of 2-butanone with lithium aluminum hydride), is optically inactive:

$$
CH_3COCH_2CH_3 \xrightarrow{\text{LiAlH}_4,\text{H}^\oplus} CH_3CH(OH)CH_2CH_3
$$

It is a mixture of two isomeric forms, [2] and [3], which are mirror images of one another.

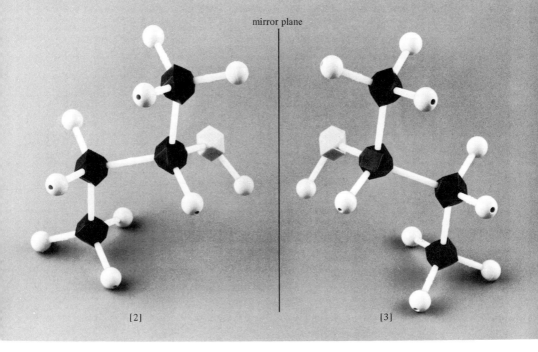

mirror plane

[2]   [3]

The chemical and physical properties of the two forms are identical, *except* that they rotate the plane of plane-polarized light equally but in opposite directions. Mirror image forms of the same compound, such as [2] and [3], are called **enantiomers**. The 2-butanol, as prepared by the reduction of inactive 2-butanone, is optically inactive because it is a mixture of equal numbers of molecules of each enantiomer; the net optical rotation is therefore zero. Such a mixture is described as **racemic** and is often designated by the symbol ($\pm$).

Separation of the enantiomers in a racemic mixture is known as **resolution**, and conversion of the molecules of one enantiomer into a racemic mixture of both is called **racemization**.

Table 14·1   Physical properties of tartaric acids

tartaric acid	specific rotation, $[\alpha]_D^{20}$ in H_2O	melting point, °C	specific gravity of solid	solubility in H_2O, g/100 g at 25°
meso[a]		140	1.666	$120^{(15°)}$
(−)	−11.98°	170	1.760	147
(+)	+11.98°	170	1.760	147
(±)		205	1.687	25

[a] *meso*-Tartaric acid is discussed in Section 14·3C.

Although all the physical properties of pure enantiomers (apart from their optical properties) are identical, their melting points, solubilities, and any other properties involving the solid state are usually different from those of the racemic mixture. This is because a mixture of enantiomers packs differently in a crystal lattice (often more efficiently) than either enantiomer in the pure form. Tartaric acid is one such compound, and the physical properties of its various forms are given in Table 14·1.

B.   PROJECTION FORMULAS

We have distinguished the two enantiomers of 2-butanol, [2] and [3], with a picture of a three-dimensional model to show the tetrahedral arrangement of the groups about the asymmetric carbon atom. Clearly it will be inconvenient to do this in every case, particularly for more complex examples. It is necessary therefore to have a simpler convention for distinguishing between optical isomers. The so-called Fischer projection formulas are widely used for this purpose and, by their use, the enantiomers of 2-butanol are represented by [4] and [5].

$$
\begin{array}{ccc}
& CH_3 & \\
& | & \\
H-&C&-OH \\
& | & \\
& CH_2CH_3 & \\
& [4] &
\end{array}
\qquad
\begin{array}{ccc}
& CH_3 & \\
& | & \\
HO-&C&-H \\
& | & \\
& CH_2CH_3 & \\
& [5] &
\end{array}
\qquad \uparrow \; \text{North}
$$

The convention of the Fischer projections is such that the east and west bonds of the asymmetric carbon are considered to extend *in front* of the plane of the paper and the north and south bonds extend *behind* the plane of the paper. This is shown more explicitly in structures [6] and [7]. Structures [2], [4], and [6] all correspond to one enantiomer while [3], [5], and [7] correspond to the other.

$$
\begin{array}{ccc}
& CH_3 & \\
& \vdots & \\
H\!\leftarrow\!&C&\!\rightarrow\!OH \\
& \vdots & \\
& CH_2CH_3 & \\
& [6] &
\end{array}
\qquad
\begin{array}{ccc}
& CH_3 & \\
& \vdots & \\
HO\!\leftarrow\!&C&\!\rightarrow\!H \\
& \vdots & \\
& CH_2CH_3 & \\
& [7] &
\end{array}
$$

With projection formulas, configuration is inverted (i.e., one enantiomer is changed into the other) each time two atoms or groups about the asymmetric atom (or asymmetric center, as it is often called) are interchanged. Clearly, if we interchange hydrogen for hydroxyl in [4], we have the enantiomer [5]. Less obvious is the interchange of methyl and hydrogen in [4] to give [8], which by our convention is equivalent to [5]. (Inspection of models may be helpful if the results of these operations are not clear.)

$$CH_3-\underset{\underset{CH_2CH_3}{|}}{\overset{\overset{H}{|}}{C}}-OH$$

[8]

It should be noted that [8] is not strictly a Fischer projection formula because, by the Fischer convention, the carbon chain is always written vertically. Note also that rotation of a Fischer projection formula 180° (but not 90° or 270°) in the plane of the paper leaves the configuration unchanged.

$$H-\underset{\underset{CH_2CH_3}{|}}{\overset{\overset{CH_3}{|}}{C}}-OH \quad \equiv \quad HO-\underset{\underset{CH_3}{|}}{\overset{\overset{CH_2CH_3}{|}}{C}}-H$$

For sake of uniformity, we normally show the carbon chain vertically with C-1 at the top.

C. COMPOUNDS WITH TWO ASYMMETRIC CARBON ATOMS. DIASTEREOMERS

We have considered how a compound with one asymmetric carbon atom can exist in two optically active forms. However, it would be incorrect to infer from this that asymmetric carbon is a *necessary* condition for optical activity, because many compounds are known that have no asymmetric atoms but still exhibit optical isomerism (Section 14·4). It would be no more correct to infer that, because a molecule has *two* or *more* asymmetric carbons, it will necessarily be optically active.

For example, consider a molecule with structure, configuration, and conformation as in [9] with two asymmetric atoms, 1 and 2, the groups attached to atom 1 being the same as for atom 2, and the structure being so oriented that atom 1 is toward the front and atom 2 toward the rear. It can be seen that [9] is identical with its mirror image [10] by simply turning [9] end for end to give [11], which, when rotated 180° about the 1,2 bond axis as shown by the arrow, superimposes on [10]. A molecule with this configuration will be optically inactive, despite the presence of two asymmetric carbons, because it is superimposable on its mirror image.

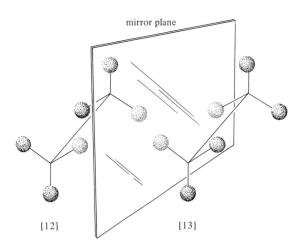

One could argue, however, that this condition does not hold for all conformations of [9]. Certainly, the conformation [12] is not superimposable on its mirror image [13].

Nevertheless, the molecule represented by [12] will not be optically active, because the asymmetric conformation [12] is rapidly converted into its enantiomer [13] by rotation about the bond joining the two asymmetric centers. Optical activity would be possible only if it were possible to "freeze" the molecule in one of the asymmetric conformations.

It will be seen that the eclipsed conformation [14] of the same system has a plane of symmetry that bisects the molecule into two halves, each half being the mirror image of the other. Molecules that possess this sort of symmetry are frequently said to be *internally compensated*, since the optical rotations contributed by each asymmetric half are equal in degree but opposite in sign; the net rotation is therefore zero.

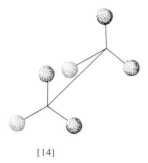

[14]

This is perhaps more easily visualized from the Fischer projection formula of the conformations [9] through [14].

(+)

(−)

zero net rotation

[14]

To generalize, if a substance has a plane of symmetry in at least one conformation, it will not be resolvable into optically active forms.

Among the many examples of compounds that have two asymmetric carbon atoms but are optically inactive because their molecules are free to pass through a conformation with a plane of symmetry are *meso*-tartaric acid [15]; *meso*-2,3-dibromobutane [16]; and *cis*-cyclohexane-1,2-dicarboxylic acid [17]. The asterisks in the formulas denote the asymmetric carbons.

$$CO_2H$$
H—C*—OH
H—C*—OH
$$CO_2H$$
[15]

$$CH_3$$
H—C*—Br
H—C*—Br
$$CH_3$$
[16]

$$CH_2—CH_2H$$
$$CH_2$$ H   C*
$$CH_2—C*   CO_2H$$
$$CO_2H$$
[17]

The prefix *meso* denotes an optically inactive optical isomer of a compound that can exist in other optically active modifications. The *meso* form is considered to be an optical isomer because it is a stereoisomer of the optically active forms and its lack of optical activity does not of itself change the type of isomerism involved. This will be clearer when we discuss *erythro* and *threo* forms later in this section.

Tartaric acid and 2,3-dibromobutane each have a total of three optical isomers, two optically active enantiomers, and one optically inactive *meso* form. These are shown in structures [18a], [18b], and [15] for tartaric acid, and [19a], [19b], and [16] for 2,3-dibromobutane.

$$
\begin{array}{cccc}
\text{CO}_2\text{H} & \text{CO}_2\text{H} & \text{CH}_3 & \text{CH}_3 \\
| & | & | & | \\
\text{H}-\text{C}-\text{OH} & \text{HO}-\text{C}-\text{H} & \text{H}-\text{C}-\text{Br} & \text{Br}-\text{C}-\text{H} \\
| & | & | & | \\
\text{HO}-\text{C}-\text{H} & \text{H}-\text{C}-\text{OH} & \text{Br}-\text{C}-\text{H} & \text{H}-\text{C}-\text{Br} \\
| & | & | & | \\
\text{CO}_2\text{H} & \text{CO}_2\text{H} & \text{CH}_3 & \text{CH}_3 \\
[18a] & [18b] & [19a] & [19b]
\end{array}
$$

Stereoisomeric structures that are not enantiomers and thus not mirror images are called **diastereomers**. *meso*-Tartaric acid [15] and either one of the optically active tartaric acids [18a or 18b] are therefore diastereomers. Only [18a] and [18b] are enantiomers. Diastereomers usually have substantially different physical properties, whereas enantiomers have identical properties apart from the direction in which they rotate the plane of polarized light. This is illustrated in Table 14·1 for the tartaric acids.

The reason for the difference in physical properties between diastereomers can be seen very simply for a substance with two asymmetric centers by noting that a right shoe on a right foot can be a mirror image and non-identical with a left shoe on a left foot, but is not expected to be a mirror image or have the same physical properties as a left shoe on a right foot or a right shoe on a left foot. In chemical terms, a pair of diastereomers have different internal distances in their molecules. If the groups about the central bonds in [15] and [18a] are rotated so that, for example, the two hydrogen atoms are at their closest, then the two hydroxyl groups will be separated by different distances in the two isomers. Although free rotation can take place about any of the single bonds in [15] and [18a], there are no conformations for which all the internal distances correspond. Enantiomers such as [18a] and [18b], on the other hand, can be arranged so that all the internal distances in one are identical with those in the other.

Many compounds have two asymmetric carbons but cannot exist in an internally compensated *meso* form. This situation occurs when the two asymmetric carbons are differently substituted so that there is no conformation in which any of the isomers has a plane of symmetry. As an example, consider the possible diastereomers of 2,3,4-trihydroxybutanal, [20] and [21], which are commonly known as erythrose and threose, respectively. They are represented below by the projection formulas [20a] and [21a], as well as by the conformational, or so-called "sawhorse," structures, [20b] and [21b]:

$$
\begin{array}{cccc}
\text{CHO} & \text{H} & \text{CHO} & \text{OH} \\
| & & | & \\
\text{H}-\text{C}-\text{OH} & \text{OHC}\diagup\text{OH} & \text{HO}-\text{C}-\text{H} & \text{OHC}\diagup\text{H} \\
| \quad \text{or} & \text{H}\diagdown\text{OH} & | \quad \text{or} & \text{H}\diagdown\text{OH} \\
\text{H}-\text{C}-\text{OH} & & \text{H}-\text{C}-\text{OH} & \\
| & \text{CH}_2\text{OH} & | & \text{CH}_2\text{OH} \\
\text{CH}_2\text{OH} & & \text{CH}_2\text{OH} & \\
& \text{erythrose} & & \text{threose} \\
[20a] & [20b] & [21a] & [21b]
\end{array}
$$

Neither diastereomer has a plane of symmetry in any conformation, and consequently there are two pairs of enantiomers, or a total of four optical isomers. In general, a compound with n asymmetric carbons will have 2^n possible optical isomers, provided there are no isomers with a plane of symmetry arising from similarly substituted asymmetric carbons as in *meso* forms. The structures assigned to erythrose and threose have been established beyond question by the finding that $(-)$-erythrose, which is a naturally occurring sugar, on oxidation with nitric acid gives *meso*-tartaric acid, whereas $(+)$-threose, which does not occur naturally, gives $(+)$-tartaric acid.

CHO		CO_2H		CHO		CO_2H
H—C—OH	$\xrightarrow{HNO_3}$	H—C—OH		H—C—OH	$\xrightarrow{HNO_3}$	H—C—OH
H—C—OH		H—C—OH		HO—C—H		HO—C—H
CH_2OH		CO_2H		CH_2OH		CO_2H
$(-)$-erythrose		*meso*-tartaric acid		$(+)$-threose		$(+)$-tartaric acid

The terms *erythro* and *threo* are often used to designate pairs of diastereomers related to threose and erythrose. The *erythro* isomers, like $(+)$ or $(-)$ erythrose, are the ones which give a *meso* compound when the end groups are made identical while the $(+)$ or $(-)$ *threo* isomers are converted to optically active forms by the same transformation.

14·4 optically active compounds having no asymmetric carbon atoms

A. ALLENES AND SPIRANES

Many compounds have no asymmetric carbon atoms, yet exhibit optical isomerism. This condition sometimes exists when there is a possibility for restricted rotation. For instance, in a molecule of allene, the two planes that contain the terminal methylene (CH_2) groups are mutually perpendicular because of the rigidity and directional character of the two cumulated double bonds.

Consequently, an allene of the type $XYC=C=CXY$, in which X and Y are different, is asymmetric and can exist in two, nonsuperimposable, optically active forms.

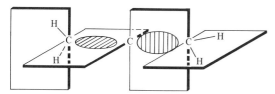

mirror plane

The optical isomerism of allenes was predicted by van't Hoff some 60 years before experiment proved him to be correct. The delay was mainly caused by practical difficulties in resolving asymmetric allenes. The first successful resolutions were achieved with the allenes [22] and [23].

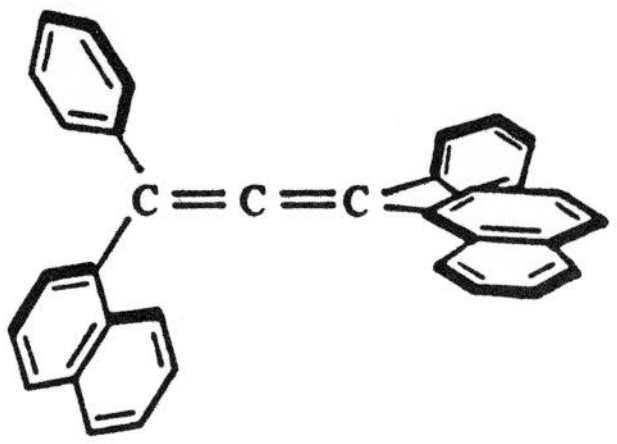

[22] 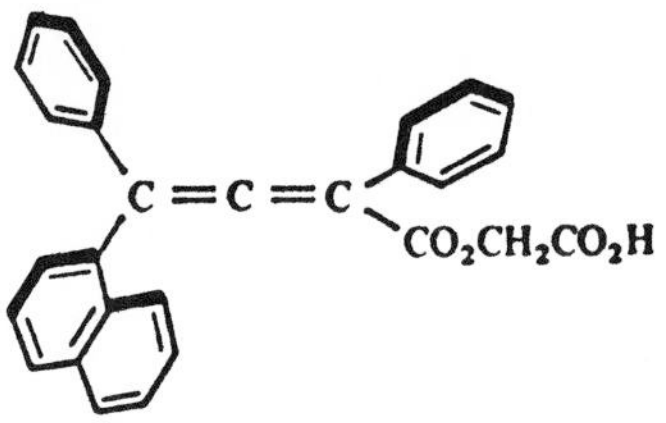   [23]

Other structures that can have the same type of asymmetry are the spiranes, which are bicyclic compounds with one atom (and only one) common to both rings. The simplest example is spiro[2.2]pentane [24].

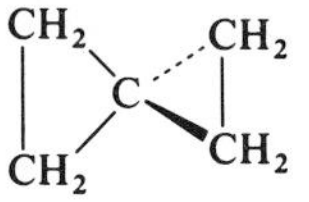

[24]

The two rings of [24], or any spirane, cannot lie in a common plane; hence, provided that each ring is substituted so that it has no plane of symmetry, the substance can exist as one or the other of a pair of optically active enantiomers. An example of a spirane that has been resolved is [25].

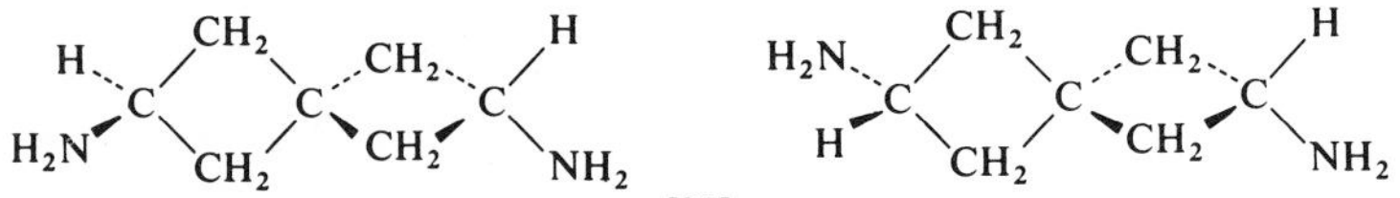

[25]

B. OPTICALLY ACTIVE BIPHENYLS

In contrast to the asymmetric allenes, optical activity in the biphenyl series was discovered before it could be explained adequately. In fact, when the first biphenyl derivative was resolved (1922), there was considerable confusion as to the correct structure of biphenyl compounds, and the source of asymmetry was not known. It was subsequently established by dipole-moment and X-ray diffraction data that the benzene rings in biphenyls are coaxial.

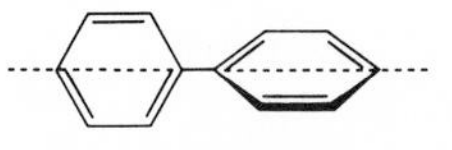

common axis

With this information, the existence of stable optical isomers of o,o'-dinitrodiphenic acid [26] can be explained only if rotation about the central bond does not occur and, in addition, the two rings lie in different planes. A molecule of [26], which fulfills these requirements, is not superimposable on its mirror image, and will therefore be optically active.

[26]

The lack of rotation about the pivot bond is caused by steric hindrance between the bulky *ortho* substituents. Evidence for this stems from the failure to resolve any biphenyl derivatives that are not substituted in *ortho* positions. Also, resolution of *ortho*-substituted derivatives can be achieved only if the *ortho* substituents are sufficiently large. Thus, *o,o'*-difluorodiphenic acid [27], like the corresponding dinitro derivative [26], is resolvable but is more easily racemized than [26]. This is due to the smaller size of the fluorine atom relative to the nitro group, and with less interference from the *ortho* substituents the rings can more easily pivot about the central bond. Once they reach the planar conformation [27b] the asymmetry is lost and racemization results.

Racemization of hindered biphenyls does not involve bond breaking and hence these compounds are exceptions to the statement made earlier (Section 2·6B) about the clear distinction between stereoisomers and conformers.

14·5   absolute and relative configuration

The sign of rotation of plane-polarized light by an enantiomer is not easily related to either its absolute or relative configuration. This is true even for substances with very similar structures, and we find that an optically active acid derivative having the same sign of rotation as the parent acid need not have the same configuration. Thus, given lactic acid (2-hydroxypropanoic acid), $CH_3CHOHCO_2H$, with a specific rotation $+3.82°$, and methyl lactate, $CH_3CHOHCO_2CH_3$, with a specific rotation $-8.25°$, we cannot tell from the rotations alone whether the acid and ester have the same or a different arrangement of groups about the asymmetric center. The relative configurations have to be obtained by other means.

If we convert $(+)$-lactic acid into its methyl ester, we can be reasonably certain that the ester will be related in configuration to the acid, because esterification should not affect the configuration about the asymmetric carbon atom. It happens that the methyl ester so obtained is levorotatory so we know that $(+)$-lactic acid and $(-)$-methyl lactate have the same *relative* configuration at the asymmetric carbon, even if they possess opposite signs of optical rotation. However, we still do not know the *absolute* configuration; that is, we are unable to tell which of the two possible configurations of lactic acid, [28a] or [28b], corresponds to the dextro or (+) acid and which to the levo or (−) acid. The term *chirality*, whose meaning was given as "handedness" in Section 14·3A, is often used for what we are calling absolute configuration. Chirality is the more general term—molecules and environments can both possess chirality.

$$CO_2H$$
$$H\!-\!\overset{|}{C}\!-\!OH$$
$$CH_3$$
[28a]

$$CO_2H$$
$$HO\!-\!\overset{|}{C}\!-\!H$$
$$CH_3$$
[28b]

Until recently, the absolute configuration of no optically active compound was known with certainty. Instead, configurations were assigned relative to a standard, glyceraldehyde, which was originally chosen for the purpose of correlating the configurations of carbohydrates but has also been related to many other classes of compounds, including α-amino acids, terpenes, and steroids, and other biochemically important substances. Dextrorotatory glyceraldehyde was arbitrarily assigned the configuration [29a] and is known as D-(+)-glyceraldehyde. The levorotatory enantiomer [29b] is designated as L-(−)-glyceraldehyde. In these names, the sign in parentheses refers only to the direction of rotation, while the small capital letter D or L denotes the absolute configuration. The sign of rotation is sometimes written as *d* for (+) and *l* for (−), or *dl* for (±).

$$CHO$$
$$H\!-\!\overset{|}{C}\!-\!OH$$
$$CH_2OH$$
[29a]
D-(+)-glyceraldehyde

$$CHO$$
$$HO\!-\!\overset{|}{C}\!-\!H$$
$$CH_2OH$$
[29b]
L-(−)-gylceraldehyde

At the time the choice of absolute configuration for glyceraldehyde was made, there was no way of knowing whether the configuration of (+)-glyceraldehyde was in reality [29a] or [29b]. However, the choice had a 50% chance of being correct and we now know that [29a], the D configuration, is in fact the correct configuration of (+)-glyceraldehyde. This was established through use of a special X-ray crystallographic technique, which permitted determination of the absolute disposition of the atoms in space of sodium rubidium (+)-tartrate. The configuration of (+)-tartaric acid [18a] had been previously shown chemically to be the same as that of (+)-glyceraldehyde. Consequently, the absolute configuration of any compound is now known once it has been correlated directly or indirectly with glyceraldehyde.[2]

[2] Relating a compound's configuration to that of glyceraldehyde works well when the compound shares two or three of the same groups with the standard (H, OH, CHO, and CH_2OH), but is rather arbitrary otherwise. For this reason a new procedure has been introduced, the Cahn-Ingold-Prelog system, in which a series of sequence rules determines configuration. The symbols R and S are used to designate configurations by this system instead of D and L. In the case of glyceraldehyde and closely related compounds D corresponds to R, and L corresponds to S. The R and S system has been extended to chiral molecules in general and it is possible, for example, to designate the optical isomers of [27] specifically as R and S.

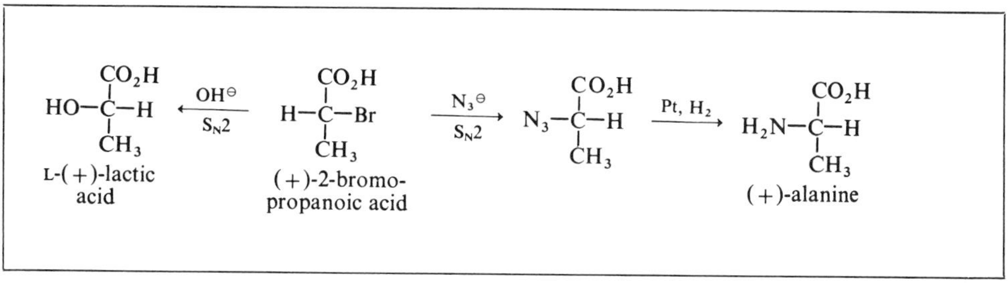

$$\underset{\substack{\text{L-(+)-lactic} \\ \text{acid}}}{\overset{\displaystyle CO_2H}{\underset{\displaystyle CH_3}{HO-C-H}}} \xleftarrow[S_N2]{OH^\ominus} \underset{\substack{\text{(+)-2-bromo-} \\ \text{propanoic acid}}}{\overset{\displaystyle CO_2H}{\underset{\displaystyle CH_3}{H-C-Br}}} \xrightarrow[S_N2]{N_3^\ominus} \overset{\displaystyle CO_2H}{\underset{\displaystyle CH_3}{N_3-C-H}} \xrightarrow{Pt, H_2} \underset{\text{(+)-alanine}}{\overset{\displaystyle CO_2H}{\underset{\displaystyle CH_3}{H_2N-C-H}}}$$

Figure 14·3   Chemical tranformations showing how the configuration of natural (+)-alanine has been related to L-(+)-lactic acid and hence to L-(−)-glyceraldehyde. The transformations shown involve two S_N2 reactions which are stereospecific and invert configuration (Section 14·9). Reduction of the azide group leaves the configuration unchanged.

In general, the absolute configuration of a substituent at an asymmetric center is specified by writing a projection formula with the carbon chain vertical and the lowest numbered carbon at the top. The D configuration is then the one that has a specified substituent on the bond extending to the *right* of the asymmetric carbon, while the L configuration has the substituent on the *left*.

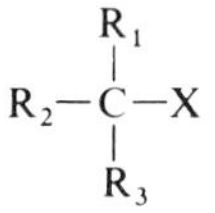

$$\underset{\text{D configuration}}{\overset{\displaystyle R_1}{\underset{\displaystyle R_3}{R_2-C-X}}} \qquad\qquad \underset{\text{L configuration}}{\overset{\displaystyle R_1}{\underset{\displaystyle R_3}{X-C-R_2}}}$$

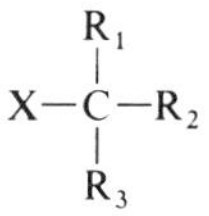

Compounds whose configurations are related to D-(+)-glyceraldehyde belong to the D series, and those related to L-(−)-glyceraldehyde belong to the L series.

Many of the naturally occurring α-amino acids have been correlated with glyceraldehyde by the type of transformations shown in Figure 14·3. Here, natural alanine (2-aminopropanoic acid) is related to L-(+)-lactic acid and hence to L-(−)-glyceraldehyde. Alanine therefore belongs to the L series, and by similar correlations it has been shown that all of the α-amino acids which are constituents of proteins are L-amino acids. Many D-amino acids are components of other biologically important substances.

When there are several asymmetric carbon atoms in a molecule, the configuration at one center is usually related directly or indirectly to glyceraldehyde, and the configurations at the other centers are determined relative to the first. Thus in the aldehyde form of the important sugar, (+)-glucose, there are four different asymmetric centers, and so there are $2^4 = 16$ possible stereoisomers. The projection formula of the isomer which corresponds to natural glucose is [30]. By convention for sugars, the configuration of the *highest* numbered asymmetric carbon is referred to glyceraldehyde to determine the overall configuration of the molecule. For glucose, this atom is C-5, next to the CH_2OH group, and has the hydroxyl on the right. Therefore, naturally occurring glucose belongs to the D series and is properly called D-glucose (see also Section 15·2).

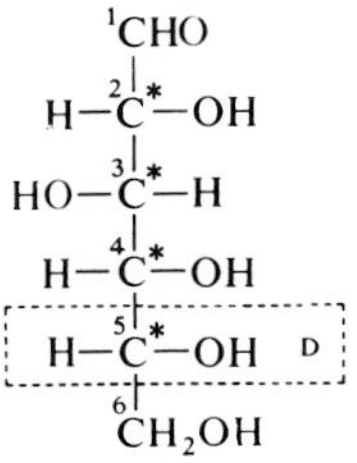

$$^1CHO$$
$$H-^2\overset{*}{C}-OH$$
$$HO-^3\overset{*}{C}-H$$
$$H-^4\overset{*}{C}-OH$$
$$H-^5\overset{*}{C}-OH \quad D$$
$$^6CH_2OH$$

[30]

On the other hand, the configurations of α-amino acids possessing more than one asymmetric center are determined by the *lowest* numbered asymmetric carbon, which is the carbon *alpha* to the carboxyl group. Thus, even though the natural α-amino acid threonine has exactly the same kind of arrangement of substituents as the natural sugar threose, threonine by the amino acid convention belongs to the L series, while threose by the sugar convention belongs to the D series.

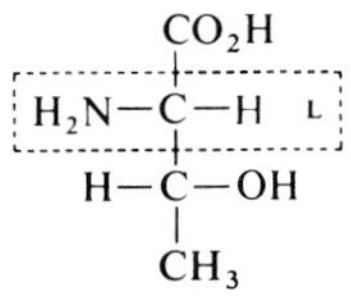

$$CO_2H$$
$$H_2N-C-H \quad L$$
$$H-C-OH$$
$$CH_3$$
L-threonine

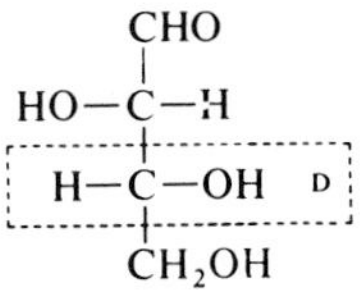

$$CHO$$
$$HO-C-H$$
$$H-C-OH \quad D$$
$$CH_2OH$$
D-(−)-threose

14·6 *separation or resolution of enantiomers*

Since the physical properties of enantiomers are identical, they cannot usually be separated by physical methods such as fractional crystallization or distillation. It is only in the presence of another optically active substance that the enantiomers behave differently, and almost all methods of resolution (and asymmetric synthesis) are based on this fact.

Perhaps the most general resolution procedure is to convert enantiomers to diastereomers, whose physical properties are *not* identical. For instance, if a racemic or D,L mixture of an acid is converted to a salt with an optically active base of the D configuration, the salt will be a mixture of two diastereomers, (D acid + D base) and (L acid + D base). These diastereomeric salts are not identical and not mirror images and will therefore differ in their physical properties. Hence, separation by physical means, such as crystallization, is in principle possible. Once separated, the acid regenerated from each salt will be either the pure D or L enantiomer:

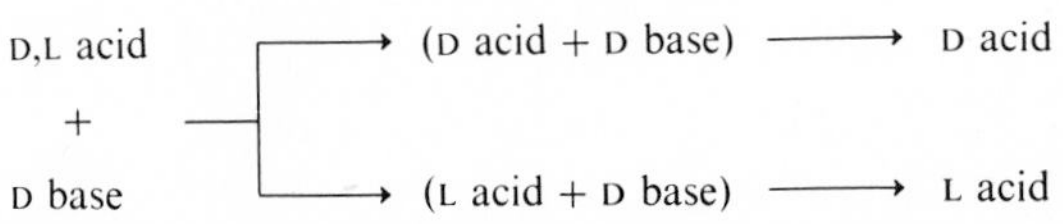

D,L acid

+

D base

⟶ (D acid + D base) ⟶ D acid

⟶ (L acid + D base) ⟶ L acid

Resolution of optically active acids through formation of diastereomeric salts requires adequate supplies of suitable optically active bases. Brucine [31a], strychnine [31b], and quinine [32] are most frequently used because they are readily available, naturally occurring, optically active bases.

brucine, R=OCH$_3$ [31a]
strychnine, R=H [31b]

quinine
[32]

For the resolution of a racemic base, optically active acids are used, such as (+)-tartaric acid, (−)-malic acid, (−)-mandelic acid, and (+)-camphor-10-sulfonic acid.

malic acid   mandelic acid   camphor-10-sulfonic acid

To resolve an alcohol, an optically active acid may be used to convert the alcohol to a mixture of diastereomeric esters. High-molecular-weight acids (~400) are advantageous since they are likely to give crystalline esters, and these may usually be separated by fractional crystallization.

Other, more specialized methods of resolution are also available. One procedure, which is excellent when applicable, takes advantage of differences in reaction rates of enantiomers with optically active substances. One enantiomer may react more rapidly, leaving an excess of the other enantiomer behind. As one example, racemic tartaric acid can be resolved with the aid of certain penicillin molds that consume the dextrorotatory enantiomer faster than the levorotatory enantiomer; as a result, almost pure (−)-tartaric acid can be recovered from the mixture.

(±)-tartaric acid + mold ⟶ (−)-tartaric acid + more mold

A crystallization procedure was employed by Louis Pasteur for his classical resolution of D,L-tartaric acid, but this technique is limited to very few cases. It depends upon the formation of individual crystals of each enantiomer. Thus, if the crystallization of sodium ammonium tartrate is carried out below 27°, the usual racemate salt does not form; a mixture of crystals of the D and L salts forms instead. The two different kinds of crystals, which are mirror images of one another, can be separated manually with the aid of a micro-scope and may be subsequently converted to the tartaric acid enantiomers by strong acid.

Optical activity had been observed in quartz crystals and in solutions of various natural substances such as sugars well before Pasteur effected the first resolution in 1848. The explanation of optical activity on a molecular basis had to await the development of structural organic chemistry in the years following 1860 (Chapter 1). In 1874, Le Bel and van't Hoff showed that all known examples of optically active organic compounds possess asym-metrically substituted carbon atoms and, if the valences of carbon are tetrahedral, then each of the known optically active compounds would have to be able to exist in two mirror-image forms. This not only explained the existence of optically active organic compounds, it strengthened belief in the tetrahedral character of carbon and nurtured the growth of structural organic chemistry.

14·7 asymmetric synthesis and asymmetric induction

If you could prepare 2-hydroxypropanonitrile from acetaldehyde and hydrogen cyanide in the absence of any optically active substance and produce an excess of one enantiomer over the other, this would constitute an **absolute asymmetric synthesis**—that is, creation of an optically active com-pound in a symmetrical environment from symmetrical reagents.

D-2-hydroxypropanonitrile
(product of attack
of $CN^{\ominus}$ from above)

L-2-hydroxypropanonitrile
(product of attack
of $CN^{\ominus}$ from below)

This is obviously unlikely for the given example because there is no reason for cyanide ion to have anything other than an exactly equal chance of attack-ing above or below the plane of the acetaldehyde molecule, thus producing equal numbers of molecules of each enantiomer.

However, when an asymmetric center is already present and a second center is created, an exactly 1:1 mixture of the two possible isomers (which are now diastereomers) is not expected because the transition states are diastereo-meric also and the reaction rates will differ. The optically active aldehyde [33] and methylmagnesium iodide react, for example, to give the two diastereo-meric alcohols [34a] and [34b] in a 2 : 1 ratio.

$$
\begin{array}{c}
\text{O} \\
\parallel \\
\text{C}-\text{H} \\
\text{H}_3\text{C} \diagdown \quad \diagup \text{H} \\
\text{C} \\
\mid \\
\text{C}_6\text{H}_5 \\
[33]
\end{array}
$$

1. CH₃MgI 2. H⊕ (left)   1. CH₃MgI 2. H⊕ (right)

$$
\begin{array}{c}
\text{OH} \\
\text{CH}_3 \diagup\!\diagdown \text{H} \\
\text{CH}_3 \text{---} \text{H} \\
\mid \\
\text{C}_6\text{H}_5 \\
[34a]
\end{array}
\qquad
\begin{array}{c}
\text{OH} \\
\text{H} \diagdown\!\diagup \text{CH}_3 \\
\text{CH}_3 \text{---} \text{H} \\
\mid \\
\text{C}_6\text{H}_5 \\
[34b]
\end{array}
$$

The formation of unequal amounts of diastereomers when a second asymmetric center is created in the presence of a first is called **asymmetric induction**. The degree of stereochemical control displayed by the first asymmetric center usually depends on how close it is to the second. The more widely separated they are, the less steric control there is. Another factor is the degree of asymmetry at the first asymmetric center. If all the groups there are very nearly the same electrically and sterically, not much stereochemical control is to be expected.

Even when the asymmetric centers are close neighbors, asymmetric induction is seldom 100% efficient in simple molecules. In biochemical systems, however, asymmetric synthesis is highly efficient. The photosynthesis of glucose [30] by plants from carbon dioxide and water gives the D enantiomer only, which means a completely specific synthesis at each of four asymmetric carbons. The L enantiomer is "unnatural" and, furthermore, is not even metabolized by animals. Similarly, all of the α-amino acids which can be asymmetric and are constituents of proteins have the L configuration.

$$
\begin{array}{c}
\text{CO}_2\text{H} \\
\mid \\
\text{NH}_2\text{---}\text{C}\text{---}\text{H} \\
\mid \\
\text{R}
\end{array}
$$

L-α-amino acid

The stereospecificity of biochemical reactions is a consequence of their being catalyzed in every case by enzymes, which are large protein molecules that possess many asymmetric centers and hence are themselves highly asymmetric. The stereospecificity of living organisms is related to their efficient operation since no organism could deal with all of the possible isomers of molecules with many asymmetric centers. Thus, if a protein molecule has 100 different asymmetric centers (a not uncommon or, in fact, large number), it will have 2^{100} or 10^{30} possible optical isomers. A vessel with a capacity of about 10^7 liters would be required to hold all of the possible stereoisomeric molecules of this structure if no two were identical. An organism so constituted as to be able to deal specifically with each one of these isomers would be very large indeed.

14·8 racemization

Racemization, which is loss of optical activity, occurs with optically active biphenyls (Section 14·4B) if the two aromatic rings at any time pass through a coplanar configuration by rotation about the central bond. This can be brought about by heat, unless the *ortho* substituents are very large.

The way in which other compounds—for example, those with asymmetric carbon atoms—are racemized is more complicated. Optically active carbonyl compounds of the type $-\overset{|}{C}H-\overset{|}{C}=O$, in which the α carbon (C-2) is asymmetric, are racemized by both acids and bases. From the discussion in Section 12·1 on halogenation of carbonyl compounds, this is surely related to enolization. Formation of either the enol or the enolate anion will destroy the asymmetry at the α carbon so that, even if only trace amounts of enol are present at any given time, eventually all of the compound will be racemized.

Base-catalyzed enolization:

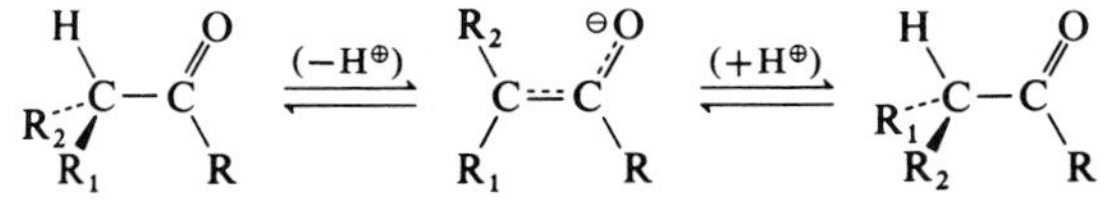

Acid-catalyzed enolization:

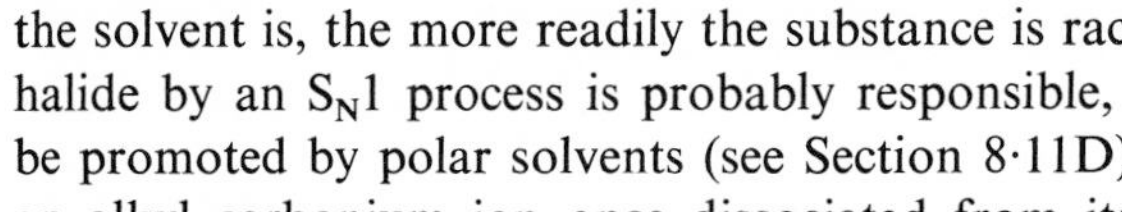

The racemization of an optically active secondary halide (e.g., 2-chlorobutane) may occur in solution. Usually, the more polar and better ionizing the solvent is, the more readily the substance is racemized. Ionization of the halide by an S_N1 process is probably responsible, and this would certainly be promoted by polar solvents (see Section 8·11D). All indications are that an alkyl carbonium ion once dissociated from its accompanying anion is planar; and, when such an ion recombines with the anion, it has equal probability of forming the D and L enantiomers.

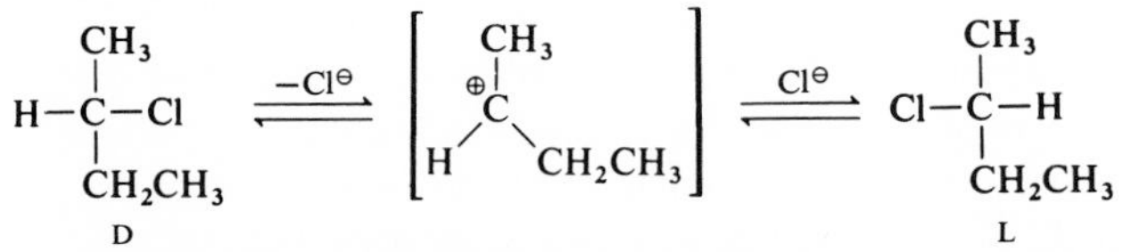

Asymmetric alcohols are often racemized by strong acids. Undoubtedly, ionization takes place, and recombination of the carbonium ion with water leads to either enantiomer.

$$
\begin{array}{ccc}
\underset{\substack{\text{D}}}{\overset{\text{CH}_3}{\underset{\text{CH}_2\text{CH}_3}{\text{H}-\overset{|}{\underset{|}{\text{C}}}-\text{OH}}}}
& \overset{\text{H}^{\oplus}}{\rightleftharpoons} &
\underset{\substack{\text{CH}_2\text{CH}_3}}{\overset{\text{CH}_3}{\text{H}-\overset{|}{\underset{|}{\text{C}}}-\overset{\oplus}{\text{O}}\text{H}_2}}
\end{array}
$$

(−H₂O)

$$
\left[\begin{array}{c} \text{CH}_3 \\ \overset{\oplus}{\text{C}} \\ \text{H} \diagup \diagdown \text{CH}_2\text{CH}_3 \end{array}\right]
$$

$$
\begin{array}{ccc}
\underset{\substack{\text{L}}}{\overset{\text{CH}_3}{\underset{\text{CH}_2\text{CH}_3}{\text{HO}-\overset{|}{\underset{|}{\text{C}}}-\text{H}}}}
& \overset{(-\text{H}^{\oplus})}{\rightleftharpoons} &
\underset{\substack{\text{CH}_2\text{CH}_3}}{\overset{\text{CH}_3}{\overset{\oplus}{\text{H}_2}\text{O}-\overset{|}{\underset{|}{\text{C}}}-\text{H}}}
\end{array}
$$

H₂O

14·9 inversion of configuration

In discussing the mechanism of S_N2 displacements we pointed out that backside attack would reduce electrostatic repulsions in the transition state to a minimum. Such a mechanism would cause inversion of configuration at

$$
\text{HO}^{\ominus} + \underset{}{\text{C}-\text{Cl}} \longrightarrow \left[\overset{\delta\ominus}{\text{HO}}\text{---}\overset{|}{\text{C}}\text{---}\overset{\delta\ominus}{\text{Cl}}\right] \longrightarrow \text{HO}-\text{C} + \text{Cl}^{\ominus}
$$

the central carbon atom. When an optically active compound such as D-(+)-2-chlorobutane is converted to 2-butanol by aqueous base the product is, indeed, found to have an inverted configuration:

$$
\underset{\substack{\text{D isomer}}}{\overset{\text{CH}_3}{\underset{\text{CH}_2\text{CH}_3}{\text{H}-\overset{|}{\underset{|}{\text{C}}}-\text{Cl}}}}
\xrightarrow{\text{HO}^{\ominus}}
\underset{\substack{\text{L isomer}}}{\overset{\text{CH}_3}{\underset{\text{CH}_2\text{CH}_3}{\text{HO}-\overset{|}{\underset{|}{\text{C}}}-\text{H}}}}
$$

The rotation of L-2-butanol is negative and that of D-2-chlorobutane is positive, but these relative rotations do not themselves prove that inversion occurs. The relative configurations of reactant and product must be determined according to the principles discussed earlier in Section 14·5. Because secondary alkyl halides can also react, though slowly, by an S_N1 mechanism (Section 8·11A) a certain amount of racemization usually accompanies this reaction.

14·10 optical rotatory dispersion

The sodium D line (5893 A) is used as the light source in most polarimeters. If we use light of a different wavelength can we expect α, the measured rotation, to change? Yes, and in many cases drastic changes occur even to the extent of a change in sign of rotation. The variation of optical activity with wavelength is known as optical rotatory dispersion (ORD).

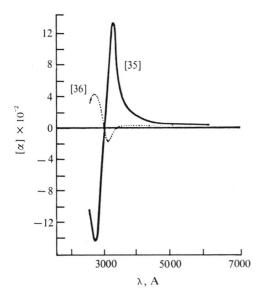

Figure 14·4   Rotatory dispersion curves for *trans*-10-methyl-2-decalone [35] and *cis*-10-methyl-2-decalone [36]. (By permission from C. Djerassi, *Optical Rotatory Dispersion*, McGraw-Hill, New York, 1960.)

Figure 14·4 shows α as a function of wavelength for the two ketones [35] and [36], the *trans* and *cis* isomers of 10-methyl-2-decalone, which have quite different stable conformations.

It can be seen that the effect of [35] on the polarization angle of the light increases as the wavelength of the light decreases, reaching a maximum just above 3000 A. A drastic drop then occurs followed by a change in sign. This type of behavior is called a **positive Cotton effect**. With some compounds, for example [36], a decrease in wavelength causes a change of sign to occur before the maximum is reached; this is the **negative Cotton effect**.

The change in sign of the optical rotation can be linked to the presence of the carbonyl chromophore in [35] and [36] since the $n \rightarrow \pi^*$ absorption maximum of nonconjugated ketones occurs near 3000 A (Section 11·2B). Light absorption and rotatory dispersion are hence associated phenomena.

We can expect that any molecular property that is highly dependent on structure and configuration will find analytical application and ORD is no exception. The quite different ORD curves that are often obtained for various members of a set of diastereomers can be highly useful in assigning configurations.

summary

Optical activity, the ability to rotate plane-polarized light, is exhibited by compounds lacking molecular symmetry and is detected and measured by an instrument called a polarimeter. The angle of rotation of a liquid or solute is expressed either in terms of α, the measured degree of rotation; $[\alpha]$, the specific rotation (adjusted for concentration and tube length); or molecular rotation $[M]$ (adjusted for molecular weight).

At the molecular level, the structural feature most commonly associated with optical activity is the asymmetrically substituted carbon atom, a carbon atom with four different groups attached, $w-\overset{\displaystyle x}{\underset{\displaystyle z}{C}}-y$. A molecule with a single such structural unit is not superimposable on its mirror image and there are two possible configurations, called enantiomers.

Optical isomers, like geometrical isomers, have the same bond structures and differ only in the spatial arrangements of the atoms and hence are stereoisomers. Unlike *cis-trans* pairs, enantiomers have identical internal distances and hence identical melting points, solubilities, and so on. A 50 : 50 mixture of enantiomers, which is called a racemic mixture and does not rotate the plane of polarized light, may have different melting or solubility characteristics than either of its components because of crystal-packing effects. Resolution is the process of separation of a racemic mixture into its components and racemization is the reverse process.

Fischer projection formulas are used to represent in two dimensions the three-dimensional configurations of enantiomers, such as 2-butanol.

$$\begin{array}{ccc} \text{CH}_3 & & \text{CH}_3 \\ | & & | \\ \text{H}-\text{C}-\text{OH} & \equiv & \text{H}-\text{C}-\text{OH} \\ | & & | \\ \text{CH}_2\text{CH}_3 & & \text{CH}_2\text{CH}_3 \end{array}$$

Compounds with two identical asymmetric carbon atoms exist in three forms, two optically active enantiomers and an optically inactive *meso* form, which possesses a plane of symmetry. In addition, the two enantiomers in equal amount form a racemic mixture. If a compound possesses two nonidentical asymmetric carbon atoms, four optical isomers are possible—two pairs of enantiomers. Molecules of different enantiomeric pairs are called diastereomers of one another and have different physical properties. (Diastereomers are stereoisomers that are not mirror images and hence a *meso* compound and one of the enantiomers of the same structure are also diastereomers.) Thus, 2,3-butanediol [1] exists in two enantiomeric forms and one *meso* form whereas 2,3-pentanediol [2] exists in four optically active forms which constitute two pairs of enantiomers.

$$CH_3CHOHCHOHCH_3 \qquad CH_3CHOHCHOHCH_2CH_3$$
$$[1] \qquad\qquad\qquad [2]$$

Optical activity results from molecular asymmetry and certain allenes, spiranes, and hindered biphenyls that do not possess asymmetric carbon atoms can exist in optically active forms.

The sign of rotation of an enantiomer, (+) or *d*, (−) or *l*, reveals neither the molecule's absolute configuration nor its configuration relative to some other compound. Chemical means, however, can be used to determine the latter and this knowledge, combined with X-ray diffraction studies, has enabled many absolute configurations to be determined. The symbols D and L are used to designate absolute configuration and configurations are assigned relative to glyceraldehyde. (+)-Glyceraldehyde is known to be the D isomer.

$$CHO$$
$$H-C-OH$$
$$CH_2OH$$

D-(+)-glyceraldehyde

The number of optical isomers possible for a compound with n different asymmetric carbon atoms is 2^n, which corresponds to $2^n/2$ pairs of enantiomers. Enantiomers A_D and A_L can be separated by appropriate combination of the racemic mixture with a second optically active compound, B_D, which thus produces a pair of diastereomers, $A_D B_D$ and $A_L B_D$. Because the members of the pair of diastereomers possess different physical properties, they can be separated and converted to the separate optical isomers.

$$A_D A_L \text{ mixture} \xrightarrow{B_D} \begin{array}{l} A_D B_D \longrightarrow A_D \\ A_L B_D \longrightarrow A_L \end{array}$$

Occasionally a racemic mixture will crystallize to give a mixture of D crystals and L crystals, which can be separated mechanically (method of Pasteur).

A chemical reaction that creates an asymmetric center in a molecule will produce equal amounts of the two enantiomers unless asymmetry is already present in the molecule, in which case unequal amounts of two diastereoisomers are expected by asymmetric induction.

Racemization occurs when a symmetrical substance is produced at any stage in a reaction undergone by an optically active compound. Inversion of configuration normally occurs during S_N2 reactions as a result of backside attack by the nucleophile.

When the wavelength of polarized light is varied the amount of rotation caused by an optically active substance changes (optical rotatory dispersion), and may even undergo a change in sign. The sign change is normally associated with the absorption of visible or ultraviolet light by a chromophore in the molecule.

exercises

14·1 Many familiar objects, such as gloves, and screws, are nonidentical with their mirror images. Is it reasonable to expect such objects to be optically active provided they are transparent to light, or are further conditions necessary?

14·2 Which of the following compounds exist in optically active forms? Identify those that have a *meso* form.

a.	3-heptanol	g.	bis(4-chlorophenyl)carbinol
b.	4-heptanol	h.	1,1-dimethylcyclobutane
c.	3,4-dibromohexane	i.	1,2-dimethylcyclobutane
d.	1,6-dimethoxy-1-hexene	j.	1,3-dimethylcyclobutane
e.	diphenylcarbinol	k.	2,3-dimethylbutanoic acid
f.	4-chlorodiphenylcarbinol (Section 20·1A)		

14·3 Identify the compounds listed in Exercise 14·2 that exhibit geometrical isomerism.

14·4 Citric acid (2-hydroxy-1,2,3-propanetricarboxylic acid) is the principal acid in citrus fruits. Can citric acid or any of its methyl esters exhibit optical activity?

14·5 The compound 1,1,1-trifluoro-2-bromo-2-chloroethane is the well-known anesthetic halothane. Can it exist in stable optically active forms? Make sawhorse drawings of the different optically active conformations of this substance.

14·6 Draw the chair form of *cis*-cyclohexane-1,2-dicarboxylic acid. Is it identical with its mirror image? Why is the compound not resolvable? How many stereoisomers are possible for cyclohexane-1,3-dicarboxylic acid and, of these, which are optical isomers and which are geometric isomers?

14·7 Draw structures similar to [9] through [13] for all the possible different staggered conformations of (+)-tartaric acid [18]. Are any of these identical with their mirror images? How many optically active forms of tartaric acid could there be altogether if rotation were not possible about the 2,3 bond and only the staggered conformations were allowed?

14·8 Write projection formulas for (+)-erythrose and (−)-threose. Which tartaric acids will they give on oxidation?

14·9 Draw projection formulas for all of the possible optical isomers of 2,3,4-trihydroxypentanoic acid.

14·10   Camphor has two asymmetric carbons, but only two optical isomers are known. Explain. (Models may be helpful.)

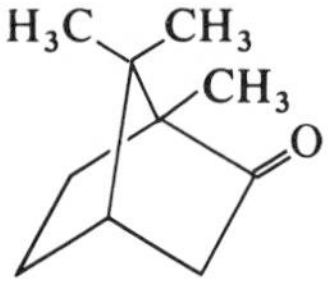

camphor

14·11   Would the following structures be resolvable into optically active isomers? Show the structures of the possible isomers.

a.

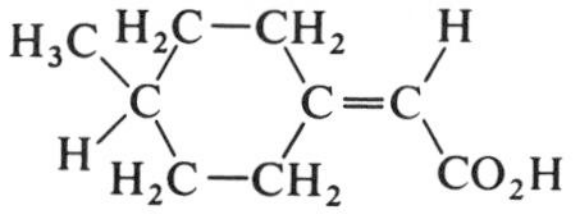

b.

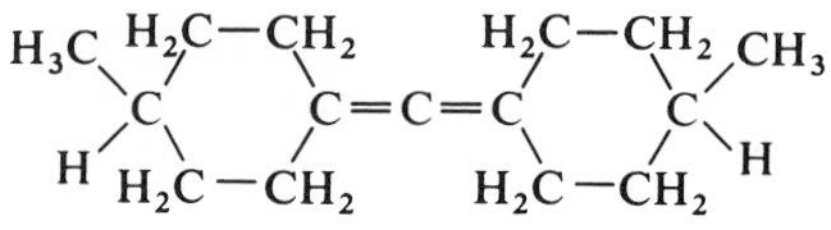

14·12   Which of the following biphenyl derivatives would you expect might give stable enantiomers? Show your reasoning.

a.

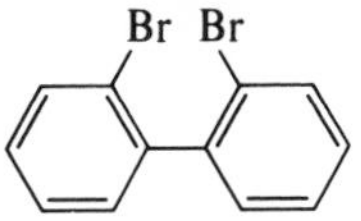

c.

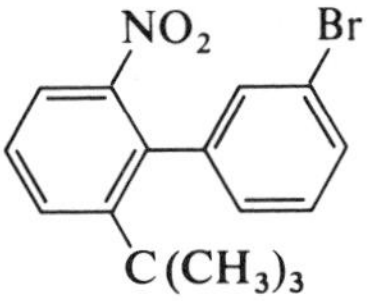

b.

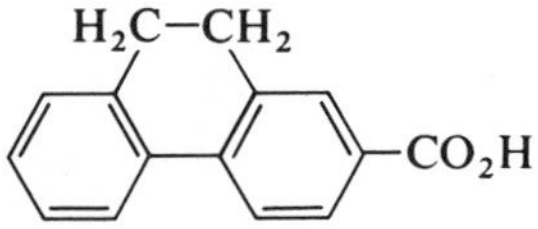

d.

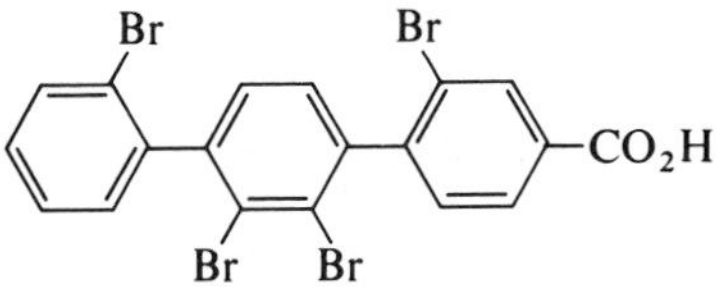

14·13   Which of the following projection formulas represent the same optical isomers? Write each in its proper form as a Fischer projection formula of 3-amino-2-butanol.

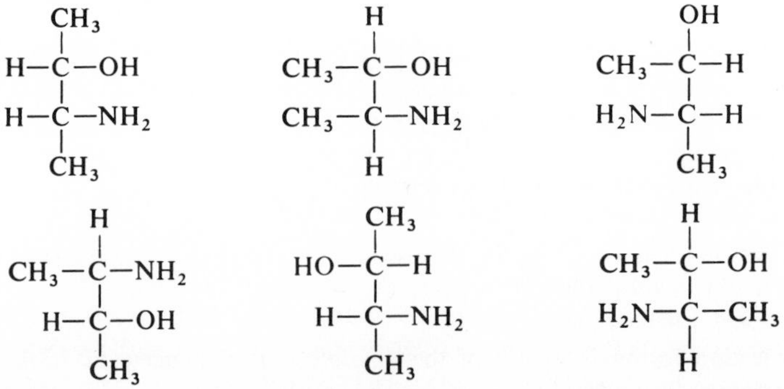

14·14 Draw Fischer projection formulas for all the possible different optical isomers of the following substances:

    a. 1,2,3,4-tetrachlorobutane
    b. methylethylpropylboron
    c. 2,3-dibromopropanoic acid
    d. triisopropylmethane
    e. 3-bromo-2,5-hexanediol

    f.

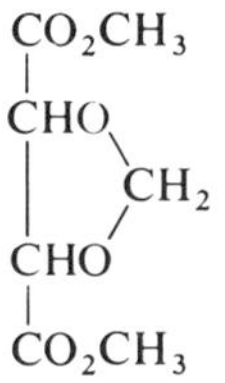

$$
\begin{array}{c}
CO_2CH_3 \\
| \\
CHO \\
\quad\diagdown \\
| \quad\quad CH_2 \\
\quad\diagup \\
CHO \\
| \\
CO_2CH_3
\end{array}
$$

    g. methyl hydrogen tartrate
    h. *s*-butyl lactate

14·15 Predict the stereochemical configuration of the products from each of the following reactions. Write projection formulas for the starting materials and products.

    a. D-2-butanol with acetic anhydride
    b. D-methylethylisobutylcarbinol with hydrochloric acid
    c. D-glycerol monoacetate with aqueous sodium hydroxide
    d. D-*s*-butyl *t*-butyl ketone with bromine and dilute base

14·16 Explain how one could determine experimentally whether hydrogen peroxide in formic acid adds *cis* or *trans* to cyclopentene, assuming the possible addition products to be unknown.

14·17 Devise a reaction scheme for relating configuration of (+)-2-butanol to glyceraldehyde. Think carefully about the reaction mechanisms involved in devising your scheme.

14·18 Discuss possible procedures for resolution of ethyl D,L-lactate (ethyl 2-hydroxypropanoate, bp 155°) into ethyl D-lactate and ethyl L-lactate.

14·19 How could you tell whether a chloroform solution of an optically active compound showing a rotation of $-100°$ was actually levorotatory by $-100°$ or dextrorotatory by $+260°$?

14·20 Solutions of optically active 2,2′-diiodobiphenyl-5,5′-dicarboxylic acid racemize at a measurable rate on heating. Racemization of active 2,3,2′3′-tetraiodobiphenyl-5,5′-dicarboxylic acid goes many thousand times more slowly. (For nomenclature see Section 20·1A.) Make a scale drawing of the transition state (planar) for racemization; deduce from it the reason for the very slow racemization of the tetraiodo diacid. Use the following bond distances (note that the benzene ring is a regular hexagon):

C—C (benzene ring) = 1.40 A
C—C (between rings) = 1.47 A
C—H   = 1.07 A
C—I   = 1.63 A

The interference radii of iodine and hydrogen are 2.15 and 1.20 A, respectively.

14·21 Compounds of the type shown below have been found to be resolvable into two optically active forms. Explain.

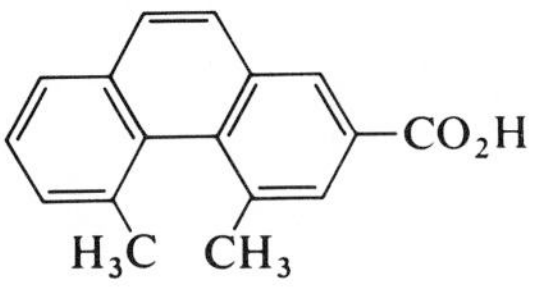

14·22 Can the structures $CH_2=C=CBr_2$ and $BrHC=C=C=CHBr$ be optically active? Explain.

14·23 Write Fischer projection formulas for each of the following substances, remembering, where necessary, that D and L isomers of substances with more than one asymmetric carbon are always enantiomers, not diastereomers.

a. L-alanine (L-2-aminopropanoic acid)
b. D-2,3-butanediol
c. D-threonine
d. L-glucose
e. D-*threo*-2,3-dihydroxybutanoic acid
f. L-*erythro*-2,3-butanediol monomethyl ether

chapter 15
carbohydrates

Carbohydrates are a major class of naturally occurring organic compounds which came by their name because they usually have the general formula $C_x(H_2O)_y$. Among the more well-known carbohydrates are the various sugars, the starches, and cellulose, all of which are important for the maintenance of life in both plants and animals.

Carbohydrates are formed in green plants as the result of **photosynthesis**, which is the chemical combination or "fixation" of carbon dioxide and water by utilization of energy gained through absorption of visible light:

$$x\ CO_2 + x\ H_2O \xrightarrow[\text{green plants}]{\text{light}} \underset{\text{carbohydrate}}{(CH_2O)_x + x\ O_2}$$

Although many aspects of photosynthesis are not yet well understood, the primary process is clearly the excitation of the green plant pigment chlorophyll-*a* (Figure 15·1) by absorption of light; the energy of the resulting activated chlorophyll-*a* molecules is used to oxidize water to oxygen and to reduce carbon dioxide. One of the first-formed products in the fixation of carbon dioxide is believed to be D-glyceric acid.

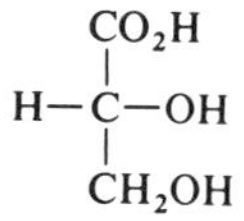

$$\begin{array}{c} CO_2H \\ | \\ H-C-OH \\ | \\ CH_2OH \end{array}$$

D-glyceric acid

From this compound, the plant carries out a series of enzyme-catalyzed reactions which result in the synthesis of simple sugars, such as glucose $(C_6H_{12}O_6)$, and polymeric substances, such as the starches and cellulose $(C_6H_{10}O_5)_n$, with $n > 1000$.

Figure 15·1 The structure of chlorophyll-*a*. The coordination of the unshared electron pairs on two of the nitrogens to the magnesium is indicated by dashed lines. Other resonance structures can also be written leading to the conclusion that all four bonds to magnesium are equivalent.

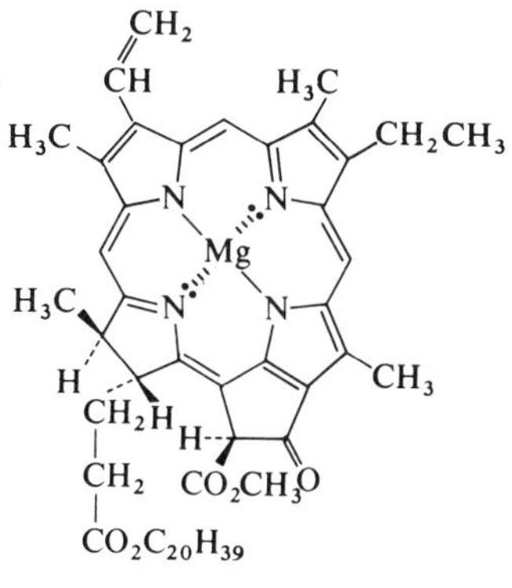

Table 15·1   Some classes and examples of naturally occurring carbohydrates

MONOSACCHARIDES

Pentoses $(C_5H_{10}O_5)$ *Hexoses* $(C_6H_{12}O_6)$

Pentoses	Hexoses
L-arabinose	D-glucose
D-ribose	D-fructose
D-xylose	D-galactose
	D-mannose

OLIGOSACCHARIDES

Disaccharides $(C_{12}H_{22}O_{11})$ *Trisaccharides* $(C_{18}H_{32}O_{16})$
sucrose (D-glucose + D-fructose)   raffinose (D-glucose + D-fructose
maltose (D-glucose + D-glucose)   + D-galactose)
lactose (D-galactose + D-glucose)

POLYSACCHARIDES $(C_6H_{10}O_5)_n$

Plants   *Animals*
starch   glycogen
cellulose

15·1   classification of carbohydrates

The simplest sugars, called **monosaccharides**, are polyhydroxy aldehydes or ketones, usually containing five or six carbon atoms. If several of these are joined together by acetal-type linkages the molecule is called an **oligosaccharide**. If 10 or more are joined this way the resulting polymer is called a **polysaccharide**. The names of all individual monosaccharides and oligosaccharides (**sugars**) end in **-ose**. Table 15·1 shows some of the important naturally occurring carbohydrates.

The aldopentoses are five-carbon sugars containing an aldehyde function. The most abundant of these are L-arabinose, D-ribose, D-xylose, and 2-deoxy-D-ribose. (*Deoxy* means without oxygen; thus, 2-deoxy-D-ribose is D-ribose in which the 2-hydroxyl group is replaced with hydrogen.) Their structures and configurations are given in Table 15·2. We shall see later that they exist predominantly in a cyclic form involving combination of the carbonyl group and a hydroxyl group further down the chain. D-Ribose is a component of ribonucleic acid (RNA) and vitamin B_{12} and some coenzymes. 2-Deoxy-D-ribose is part of the deoxyribonucleic acid (DNA) chain. Both RNA and DNA will be met again later in the book.

There are three important aldohexoses: D-glucose, D-mannose, and D-galactose. Of these D-glucose is by far the most abundant in nature and we shall examine its chemistry in detail in the next section.

There is one other important monosaccharide, D-fructose. This is a *keto-hexose* which is found in fruit juices and in honey. Linked to glucose it forms the disaccharide sucrose, which is common table sugar. The structures and

Table 15·2   Typical pentoses and hexoses

pentoses	hexoses
CHO │ H—C—OH │ HO—C—H │ HO—C—H │ CH₂OH L-arabinose	CHO │ H—C—OH │ HO—C—H │ H—C—OH │ H—C—OH │ CH₂OH D-glucose
CHO │ H—C—OH │ H—C—OH │ H—C—OH │ CH₂OH D-ribose	CH₂OH │ C=O │ HO—C—H │ H—C—OH │ H—C—OH │ CH₂OH D-fructose
CHO │ CH₂ │ H—C—OH │ H—C—OH │ CH₂OH 2-deoxy-D-ribose	CHO │ HO—C—H │ HO—C—H │ H—C—OH │ H—C—OH │ CH₂OH D-mannose
CHO │ H—C—OH │ HO—C—H │ H—C—OH │ CH₂OH D-xylose	CHO │ H—C—OH │ HO—C—H │ HO—C—H │ H—C—OH │ CH₂OH D-galactose

configurations of fructose and the three important aldohexoses are given in Table 15·2. As with the aldopentoses, these molecules exist largely in the cyclic form.

Some carbohydrates found in nature contain an amino group in place of an hydroxyl group. The antibiotic **streptomycin**, for example, contains an amino derivative of glucose, as do other compounds of structural and immunological importance (Sections 15·8 and 15·9).

15·2 *glucose*

D-Glucose, the most abundant monosaccharide, occurs free in fruits, plants, and honey, and in the blood and urine of animals, and combined in many oligosaccharides and polysaccharides. It is one of the optical isomers of the aldohexoses, all of which have structure [1].

```
  CHO
   |
 *CHOH
   |
 *CHOH
   |
 *CHOH
   |
 *CHOH
   |
  CH₂OH
```
[1]

The carbons labeled with an asterisk in [1] are asymmetric, and there are therefore 2^4, or 16, possible optically active forms. All are known—some occur naturally and others have been synthesized. The problem of identifying glucose as a particular one of the 16 possibilities was solved by Emil Fischer during the latter part of the nineteenth century. The configurations he deduced for each of the asymmetric carbons (C-2 to C-5) are shown in the projection formula [2]. (Remember that the horizontal bonds in Fischer projection formulas such as [2] are understood to extend forward out of the plane of the paper and the vertical bonds extend back behind the paper.)

```
        ¹CHO
         |
   H—²C—OH
         |
  HO—³C—H
         |
   H—⁴C—OH
         |
   H—⁵C—OH
         |
        ⁶CH₂OH
```
[2]

Fischer was well aware that natural glucose could be the enantiomer of [2]. His original guess proved to be correct, because the configuration at C-5 is that of the simplest "sugar," D-(+)-glyceraldehyde. This was arbitrarily assigned as [3] and later shown to be correct (Section 14·5). Therefore, natural glucose is specifically D-glucose.

$$
\begin{array}{l}
\text{CHO} \\
\mid \\
\text{H--C--OH} \\
\mid \\
\text{CH}_2\text{OH}
\end{array}
$$

[3]

The relationship between naturally occurring glucose, mannose, and fructose was uncovered by Fischer with the help of the phenylhydrazine reaction. Phenylhydrazine is one of the reagents used to characterize aldehydes and ketones (Table 11·4), and even though only a small fraction of the sugar molecules are in the noncyclic carbonyl form, hydrazone formation occurs and eventually all the sugar is converted to a phenylhydrazone. With 2-hydroxyaldehydes or ketones the reaction does not stop at this stage, and the adjacent alcohol group is oxidized by a second molecule of phenylhydrazine; the resulting carbonyl group then reacts with a third molecule of reagent. The reaction stops at this stage giving a crystalline derivative called an **osazone**. With glucose, the product would be named glucose phenylosazone. Although

$$
\begin{array}{l}
\text{CHO} \\
\mid \\
\text{CHOH} \\
\mid
\end{array}
\xrightarrow{\text{C}_6\text{H}_5\text{NHNH}_2}
\begin{array}{l}
\text{CH}=\text{NNHC}_6\text{H}_5 \\
\mid \\
\text{CHOH} \\
\mid
\end{array}
\longrightarrow
\begin{array}{l}
\text{CH}=\text{NNHC}_6\text{H}_5 \\
\mid \\
\text{C}=\text{O} \\
\mid
\end{array}
\longrightarrow
\begin{array}{l}
\text{CH}=\text{NNHC}_6\text{H}_5 \\
\mid \\
\text{C}=\text{NNHC}_6\text{H}_5 \\
\mid
\end{array}
$$

glucose   glucose   glucose
       phenylhydrazone   phenylosazone

glucose, mannose, and fructose all give different phenylhydrazones, *they give the same phenylosazone.*

$$
\begin{array}{l}
\text{CHO} \\
\mid \\
(\text{CHOH})_4 \\
\mid \\
\text{CH}_2\text{OH}
\end{array}
\xrightarrow[\text{excess}]{\text{C}_6\text{H}_5\text{NHNH}_2}
\begin{array}{l}
\text{CH}=\text{NNHC}_6\text{H}_5 \\
\mid \\
\text{C}=\text{NNHC}_6\text{H}_5 \\
\mid \\
(\text{CHOH})_3 \\
\mid \\
\text{CH}_2\text{OH}
\end{array}
\xleftarrow[\text{excess}]{\text{C}_6\text{H}_5\text{NHNH}_2}
\begin{array}{l}
\text{CH}_2\text{OH} \\
\mid \\
\text{C}=\text{O} \\
\mid \\
(\text{CHOH})_3 \\
\mid \\
\text{CH}_2\text{OH}
\end{array}
$$

glucose and   phenylosazone from glucose,   fructose
mannose   mannose, and fructose

This shows that the configuration at C-3, C-4, and C-5 must be the same for all three sugars. Further, glucose and mannose differ only in configuration at C-2; they are said to be **epimers**. Fischer used many pieces of evidence such as this to deduce the configuration of each asymmetric carbon atom in each of the 16 optical isomers of the aldohexoses (an amazing accomplishment in the days when instrumental analysis, other than polarimetry, was unknown).

Glucose and related sugars have the properties expected of compounds containing several alcoholic hydroxyl groups. They tend to have high water solubilities, their hydroxyl groups can be oxidized to give aldehydes and ketones, and they form esters; being glycols they are cleaved by periodic acid, and so on.

Glucose is also an aldehyde and although it has many of the reactions of aldehydes it lacks others. For example, it forms certain carbonyl derivatives (e.g., oxime, phenylhydrazone, and cyanohydrin); it can be reduced to the hexahydric alcohol sorbitol, and oxidized with bromine to gluconic acid (a monocarboxylic acid). With nitric acid, oxidation proceeds further to give the dicarboxylic acid, D-glucaric acid.

$$
\begin{array}{ccccccc}
\text{CH}_2\text{OH} & & \text{CHO} & & \text{CO}_2\text{H} & & \text{CO}_2\text{H} \\
| & & | & & | & & | \\
\text{H}-\text{C}-\text{OH} & & \text{H}-\text{C}-\text{OH} & & \text{H}-\text{C}-\text{OH} & & \text{H}-\text{C}-\text{OH} \\
| & & | & & | & & | \\
\text{HO}-\text{C}-\text{H} & \xleftarrow{\text{Na}-\text{Hg}} & \text{HO}-\text{C}-\text{H} & \xrightarrow{\text{Br}_2} & \text{HO}-\text{C}-\text{H} & \xrightarrow{\text{HNO}_3} & \text{HO}-\text{C}-\text{H} \\
| & & | & & | & & | \\
\text{H}-\text{C}-\text{OH} & & \text{H}-\text{C}-\text{OH} & & \text{H}-\text{C}-\text{OH} & & \text{H}-\text{C}-\text{OH} \\
| & & | & & | & & | \\
\text{H}-\text{C}-\text{OH} & & \text{H}-\text{C}-\text{OH} & & \text{H}-\text{C}-\text{OH} & & \text{H}-\text{C}-\text{OH} \\
| & & | & & | & & | \\
\text{CH}_2\text{OH} & & \text{CH}_2\text{OH} & & \text{CH}_2\text{OH} & & \text{CO}_2\text{H} \\
\text{sorbitol} & & \text{D-glucose} & & \text{D-gluconic acid} & & \text{D-glucaric acid}
\end{array}
$$

Glucose will also reduce Fehling's solution ($Cu^{II} \rightarrow Cu^{I}$) and Tollen's reagent ($Ag^{I} \rightarrow Ag^{0}$). However, it fails to give a bisulfite addition compound and it forms two different monomethyl derivatives (called methyl α-D-glucoside and methyl β-D-glucoside) under conditions which normally convert an aldehyde to a dimethyl acetal.

$$
\text{R}-\text{C}\underset{\text{O}}{\overset{\text{H}}{\diagup\!\!\!\diagdown}} + 2\,\text{CH}_3\text{OH} \xrightarrow{\text{H}^{\oplus}} \text{R}-\underset{\text{OCH}_3}{\overset{\text{H}}{\underset{|}{\overset{|}{\text{C}}}}}-\text{OCH}_3 + \text{H}_2\text{O}
$$

$$
\text{C}_6\text{H}_{12}\text{O}_6 + \text{CH}_3\text{OH} \xrightarrow{\text{H}^{\oplus}} (\text{C}_6\text{H}_{11}\text{O}_5)\text{OCH}_3 + \text{H}_2\text{O}
$$

methyl α- and β-D-glucoside

The above behavior suggests that the carbonyl group is not free in glucose but is tied up in combination with one of the hydroxyl groups, which turns out to be the one at C-5, to form a cyclic hemiacetal represented by [4].

$$
\begin{array}{l}
\overset{1}{\text{C}}\text{HOH} \\
| \\
\text{H}-\overset{2}{\text{C}}-\text{OH} \\
| \\
\text{HO}-\overset{3}{\text{C}}-\text{H} \\
| \\
\text{H}-\overset{4}{\text{C}}-\text{OH} \\
| \\
\text{H}-\overset{5}{\text{C}}-\text{O}- \\
| \\
\overset{6}{\text{C}}\text{H}_2\text{OH}
\end{array}
$$

[4]

A new asymmetric center is created at C-1 by hemiacetal formation, and there are therefore two stereoisomeric forms of D-glucose, α-D-glucose and β-D-glucose.

$$
\text{H}-\overset{1}{\text{C}}-\text{OH} \qquad\qquad \text{HO}-\overset{1}{\text{C}}-\text{H}
$$

α-D-glucose   β-D-glucose

A specific term is used to describe carbohydrate stereoisomers differing only in configuration at the hemiacetal carbon; they are called **anomers**. Although Fischer projection formulas are useful for indicating configuration in open-chain molecules they are less suitable for cyclic structures such as [4] because they do not clearly show the spatial relationships of the molecules.

15·3   cyclic structures

Because glucose and most other sugars exist predominantly ($>99\%$) in the cyclic hemiacetal structure we will want to draw the structures and configurations as clearly as possible. The Haworth projection formulas [5] and [7] were adopted before chemists became aware of the conformational mobility of six-membered rings. They are still used extensively but are rather less informative than conformational formulas such as [6] and [8].

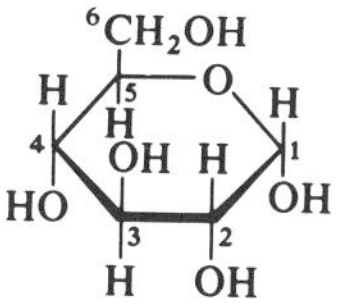

[5]
Haworth projection
formula

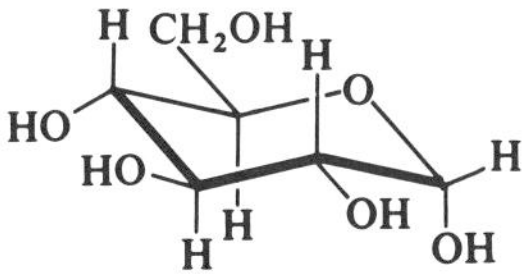

[6]
conformational
formula

α-D-glucose

X-Ray diffraction studies have shown that crystalline α-D-glucose has the chair conformation [6]. The Haworth and conformational formulas can be related to the chainlike Fischer projection formulas in the following way. A group that extends to the *right* in a Fischer projection formula extends *downward* in a Haworth projection or conformational formula. Furthermore, for D sugars the OH at C-1 will be *down* in the α form and *up* in the β form.

β-D-Glucose differs from α-D-glucose only in the configuration at C-1 and its Haworth and conformational formulas are shown in [7] and [8]. Note that all the OH and CH₂OH groups in this molecule occupy equatorial positions. This suggests that the β anomer should be of slightly lower energy because the hydroxyl at C-1 in the α anomer will suffer 1,3 interactions with the hydrogens at C-3 and C-5.

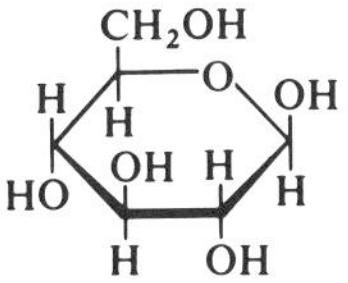

[7]
Haworth projection
formula

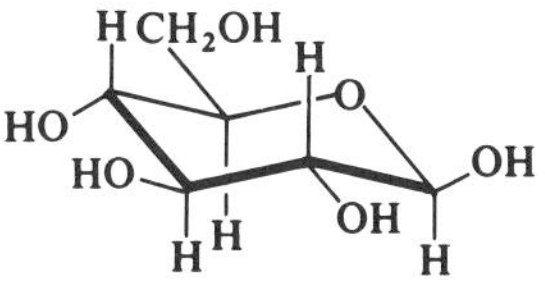

[8]
conformational
formula

β-D-glucose

Since the oxide ring is six membered in some sugars and five membered in others, it is helpful to use names that indicate the ring size. The five- and six-membered oxide rings bear a formal relationship to the cyclic ethers, furan and pyran. Hence, the terms **furanose** and **pyranose** have been coined

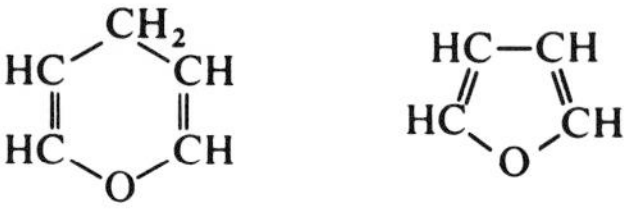

pyran   furan

to denote five- and six-membered rings, respectively, in cyclic sugars. The two forms of glucose are appropriately identified by the names α-D-gluco-pyranose and β-D-glucopyranose. Likewise, L-arabinose, D-xylose, D-galactose, and D-mannose occur naturally as pyranoses—but D-ribose and D-fructose usually occur as furanoses.

15·4 mutarotation

Although the crystalline forms of α- and β-D-glucose are quite stable, in solution each form slowly changes into an equilibrium mixture of both. The process can be readily observed as a decrease in specific optical rotation from that of the α anomer ($+112°$) or an increase from that of the β anomer ($+18.7°$) to the equilibrium value of $+52.5°$. The phenomenon is known as **mutarotation** (Figure 15·2) and is commonly observed for reducing sugars (i.e., sugars with their carbonyl function in the form of a hemiacetal). Mutarotation is catalyzed by both acids and bases and by molecules that can change from one tautomeric form to another (Section 18·1E).

At equilibrium, there is present some 64% of the β anomer and 36% of the α anomer. The amount of the free aldehyde form present at equilibrium is very small (0.024%). Preponderance of the β anomer is to be expected because the hydroxyl substituent at C-1 is equatorial in the β anomer [8] and

Figure 15·2   Mutarotation of D-glucose in solution via the open-chain aldehyde form.

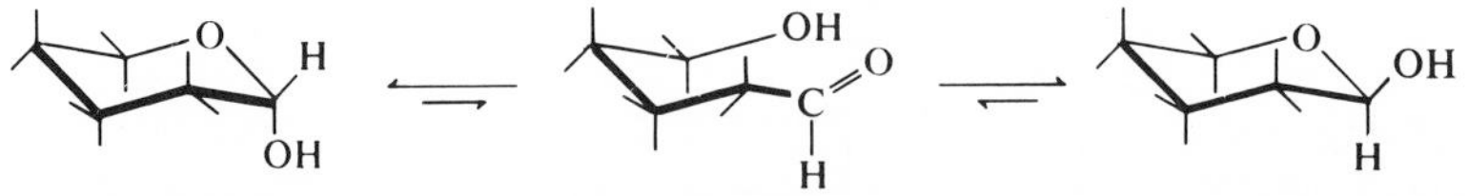

[6]   [7]   [8]
α-D-glucose   open-chain form   β-D-glucose
(chair conformation)   (one of many conformations)   (chair conformation)

axial in the α anomer [6]. Oddly enough, compounds such as those described in the next section having a methoxy group at C-1 tend to have the methoxy group axial (anomeric effect).

15·5 glycosides

Although abundant quantities of glucose and fructose occur in the free state in nature, they and the less common sugars are also found combined with various hydroxy compounds. The generic name for these combinations is **glycoside**, or, more specifically, O-glycoside, to denote that the linkage to the hydroxy compound is through oxygen. The simplest glycosides are those formed by the acid-catalyzed reaction of methanol with a molecule such as β-D-glucose; this reaction is shown in Equation 15·1. (Since the α and β forms of glucose are in equilibrium the α-glucoside will also be formed.) The cyclic sugar is a hemiacetal and the glycoside is an acetal. The additional group in the glycoside (methyl in Equation 15·1) is called the **aglycone** group. This

methyl β-D-glucoside
(plus α anomer)   (15·1)

group is another sugar in many compounds found in nature, in which case the molecule is a disaccharide. Polysaccharides are formed by the union of many sugars by such linkages.

Of particular importance biologically are the N-glycosides, in which the sugar residue is D-ribose and the aglycone is attached to the sugar by a C-N bond to a nitrogen base, usually a pyrimidine or purine derivative. These glycosides are better known as ribonucleosides and deoxyribonucleosides.

ribonucleoside
(partial structure)

deoxyribonucleoside
(partial structure)

pyrimidine

purine

Furanose rings are usually shown by a Haworth projection formula because there is less need to indicate conformational mobility than with the six-membered pyranose rings. The latter are much like cyclohexane except that the ring is not puckered to quite the same extent. The furanose rings are much like cyclopentane, one of the atoms being slightly out of the plane of the other four.

Adenosine is one example of a purine ribonucleoside, and when esterified at the 5′ position with the triphosphoryl group (a phosphoric acid anhydride)

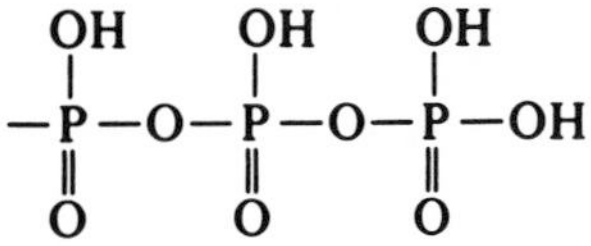

$$-\overset{\overset{\displaystyle OH}{|}}{\underset{\underset{\displaystyle O}{\|}}{P}}-O-\overset{\overset{\displaystyle OH}{|}}{\underset{\underset{\displaystyle O}{\|}}{P}}-O-\overset{\overset{\displaystyle OH}{|}}{\underset{\underset{\displaystyle O}{\|}}{P}}-OH$$

it is known as adenosine triphosphate (ATP), a so-called "energy-rich" compound present in muscle tissue.

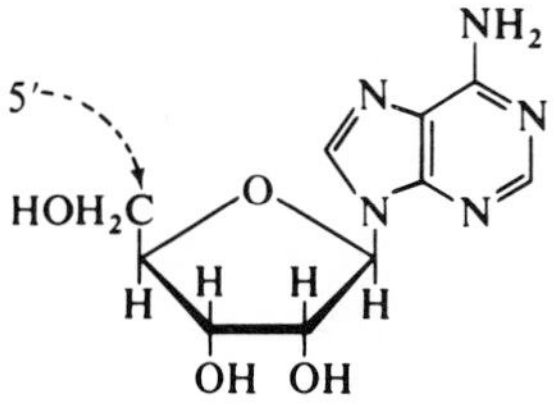

adenosine

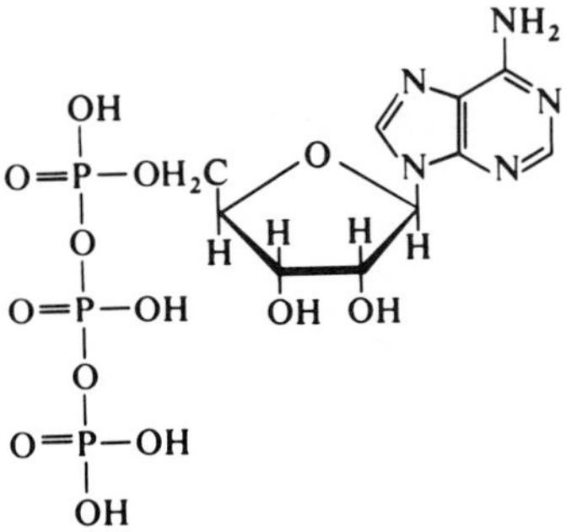

adenosine triphosphate (ATP)

15·6   disaccharides

The simplest and most important oligosaccharides are the disaccharides. These, on acid or enzymic hydrolysis, give the component monosaccharides, which are frequently hexoses. The bond between the hexoses is an O-glycoside linkage, but only one hemiacetal hydroxyl need be involved. In fact, most disaccharides have reducing properties indicating that one of the sugar residues has the easily opened hemiacetal function. However, when both hexoses are joined through their anomeric carbons, as in sucrose, the sugar is an acetal (like a methyl glycoside) and has no reducing properties, and forms no phenylosazone or other carbonyl derivative (provided that the experimental conditions do not effect hydrolysis of the acetal function).

Among the more important disaccharides are sucrose, maltose, cellobiose, and lactose (Figure 15·3). Sucrose and lactose occur widely as the free sugars, lactose in the milk of mammals and sucrose in plants, fruit, and honey (principally in sugar cane and sugar beet). Maltose is the product of enzymic hydrolysis of starch, and cellobiose is a product of hydrolysis of cellulose.

To fully establish the structure of a disaccharide we must know (1) the identity of the component monosaccharides; (2) the ring size (furanose or pyranose) in each monosaccharide, as it exists in the disaccharide: (3) the positions which link one monosaccharide with the other; and (4) the anomeric configuration (α or β) of this linkage.

The hydrolysis products of these four disaccharides are shown here.

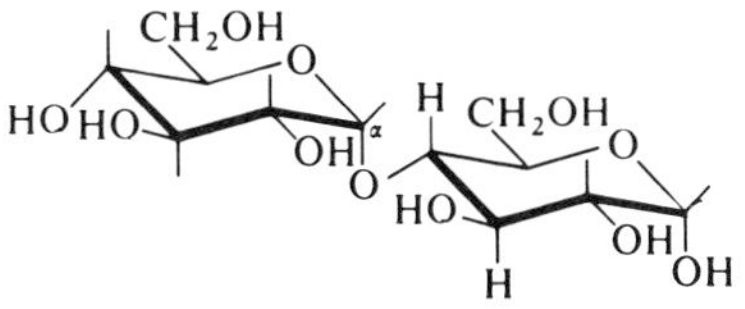

maltose
[9]

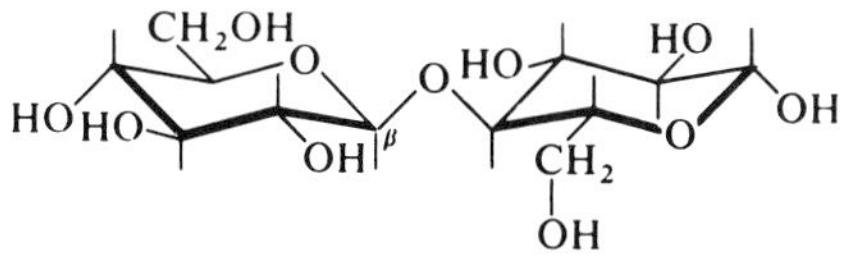

cellobiose
[10]

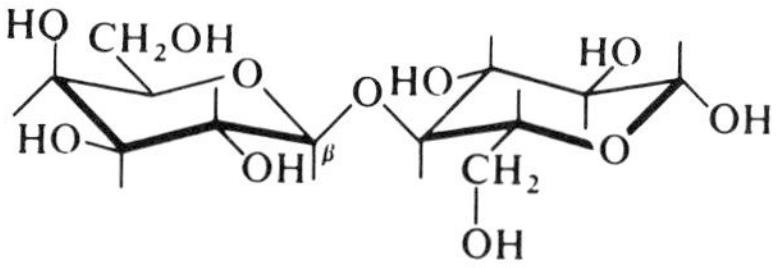

lactose
[11]

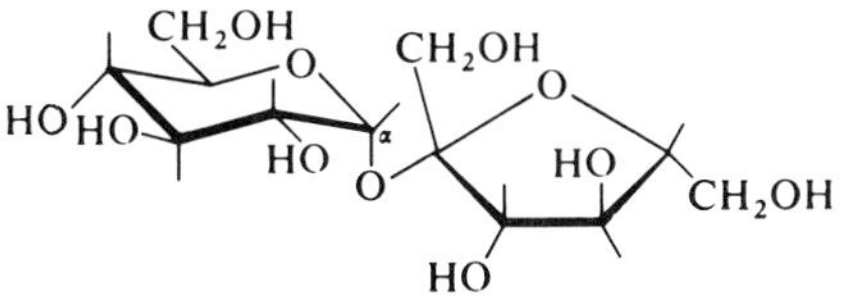

sucrose
[12]

Figure 15·3 Conformational formulas for maltose [9], cellobiose [10], lactose [11], and sucrose [12]. For maltose, cellobiose, and lactose only one of the anomeric forms of the right-hand ring is shown. In the case of cellobiose and lactose the right-hand rings have been turned upside down to permit reasonable bond angles to be shown at the oxygens between the rings.

$$C_{12}H_{22}O_{11} + H_2O \xrightarrow[\text{(or enzymes)}]{H^{\oplus}} C_6H_{12}O_6 + C_6H_{12}O_6$$

maltose ⟶ D-(+)-glucose + D-(+)-glucose

cellobiose ⟶ D-(+)-glucose + D-(+)-glucose

lactose ⟶ D-(+)-glucose + D-(+)-galactose

sucrose ⟶ D-(+)-glucose + D-(−)-fructose

The hydrolysis products of maltose and cellobiose are identical—two molecules of glucose—because these two disaccharides differ only in the configuration at the anomeric linkage (see Figure 15·3). Although both disaccharides can be hydrolyzed with acid, they are much more discriminating in their behavior toward enzymes. Hydrolysis of maltose [9] and many other α-linked oligosaccharides is catalyzed by the action of an enzyme called **maltase** whereas hydrolysis of cellobiose [10] and other β-linked compounds is catalyzed by the enzyme **emulsin**.

Sucrose [12] is a nonreducing nonmutarotating sugar because its component hexose units are joined at their anomeric carbons. Sucrose has a positive sign of rotation ($[\alpha] = +66.5°$) as does D-glucose ($[\alpha] = +52°$). D-Fructose, on the other hand, has a large negative rotation, $[\alpha] = -92°$. The complete hydrolysis of sucrose to glucose and fructose thus causes an inversion of the sign of rotation and the product is known as **invert sugar**. Honey is chiefly invert sugar because bees contain the enzyme invertase which catalyzes the hydrolysis. Sucrose has an extraordinarily high solubility in water—1.5 g of sucrose will dissolve in 1 g of water at room temperature.

The sign of rotation of naturally occurring glucose is revealed by one of the common names for this sugar: **dextrose**.

15·7 polysaccharides

The fibrous tissue in the cell walls of plants and trees contains the polysaccharide **cellulose**, which consists of long chains of glucose units, each of which is combined by a β-glucoside link to the C-4 hydroxyl of another glucose unit, as in the disaccharide **cellobiose**.

Indeed, enzymic hydrolysis of cellulose leads to cellobiose. The molecular weight of cellulose varies with the source but is usually high; cotton cellulose, for example, consists of some 3000 glucose units per molecule.

Cellulose is the natural fiber obtained from cotton, wood, flax, hemp, and jute and is used in the manufacture of textiles and paper. In addition to its use as a natural fiber, cellulose is used to make cellulose acetate (for making rayon acetate yarn, photographic film, and cellulose acetate plastics), cellulose nitrate (gun cotton and celluloid), and cellulose xanthate (for making viscose rayon fibers). The process by which viscose rayon is manufactured involves converting wood pulp or cotton linters into cellulose xanthate by treatment first with sodium hydroxide and then with carbon disulfide.

cellulose xanthate

The degree of polymerization of the original cellulose generally falls to around 300 monomer units in this process. At this degree of polymerization the cellulose is regenerated in the form of fine filaments by forcing the xanthate solution through a spinneret into an acid bath.

$$-\overset{|}{\underset{|}{C}}-O-\overset{\overset{S}{\|}}{C}-S^{\ominus} \xrightarrow{\ H^{\oplus}\ } -\overset{|}{\underset{|}{C}}-OH\ +\ CS_2$$

Wood owes its strength to the presence of lignin, a highly cross-linked polymeric substance that binds the cellulose fibers together in a rigid mass. Cellulose is obtained from wood by pulping it with various chemicals that will dissolve the lignin and leave the cellulose fibers behind. Most woods are about 50% cellulose and about 30% lignin, the remainder being other carbohydrates, fats, and terpenoid resins (Section 29·3).

Unlike cellulose there is no general agreement about the exact structure of lignin, possibly because it seems to lack the structural regularity of cellulose. There is no doubt, however, that a dioxyphenylpropyl moiety is an important part of the polymer.

a segment of lignin

Lignin can be dissolved from wood in a number of ways but the method that least damages the cellulose fiber and can be applied to most varieties of wood involves digesting the wood with a solution of sodium hydroxide and sodium sulfide. This is called the **kraft process** because of the strength of the cellulose fibers that remain. (*Kraft* means *strength* in Swedish and in German.) The length of the cellulose fiber varies greatly from one wood to another and this is important in determining the strength of paper produced from it. Douglas fir has the longest fiber of the common woods—about 4 mm.

The chemistry of lignin degradation that occurs during kraft pulping is not completely understood. A black liquor containing a wide variety of organo-sulfur compounds, some of them volatile and evil smelling, is formed. This liquor is burned to provide power and to enable the inorganic pulping chemicals to be recovered. In most other pulping methods, the waste liquor cannot be recycled.

The principal alternative to kraft pulping involves dissolving the lignin through the action of sulfite in acid solution. The waste sulfite liquor that remains after the cellulose has been removed contains pulping chemicals, degraded lignin, and other substances. These were formerly discharged directly into rivers or inlets with drastic ecological effects. Largely as a result of anti-pollution legislation but partly to obtain useful organic products the waste sulfite liquors are now generally treated before being discharged.

The per capita consumption of paper each year in North America is more than a quarter of a ton. The reader may wish to ponder the benefits and the drawbacks of this enormous rate of consumption.

A few creatures (e.g., ruminants and termites) are able to metabolize cellulose with the aid of appropriate microorganisms in their intestinal tracts;

but man cannot utilize cellulose as food because he lacks the necessary hydrolytic enzymes. However, such enzymes are widely distributed in nature and cause cellulosic materials, either textiles, paper, or wood, to deteriorate slowly.

The second very widely distributed polysaccharide is **starch**, which is stored in the seeds, roots, and fibers of plants as a food reserve—a potential source of glucose. The number of glucose units in starch varies with the source, but in any one starch there are two structurally different polysaccharides. Both consist entirely of glucose units, but one is a linear structure (**amylose**) and the other is a branched structure (**amylopectin**).

The amylose form of starch consists of repeating 1,4-glucopyranose links as in cellulose, but unlike cellulose the linkage is α rather than β. Hydrolysis by the enzyme diastase leads to maltose.

In amylopectin, amylose-like chains are apparently branched by 1,6 linkages.

Animals also store glucose in the form of starchlike substances called glycogens. These resemble amylopectin more than amylose in that they are branched chains of glucose units with 3,4- and 1,6-glucoside links.

A polysaccharide which resembles cellulose in structure and stability is chitin, which forms the hard shells of crustaceans and insects. Chitin is a polymer of N-acetyl-D-glucosamine; that is, the $-OH$ groups at C-2 of the glucose units of cellulose are replaced by $-NH\overset{\overset{\textstyle O}{\|}}{C}CH_3$ groups. Crab shells boiled with hydrochloric acid produce D-glucosamine (2-amino-2-deoxy-D-glucose) [13].

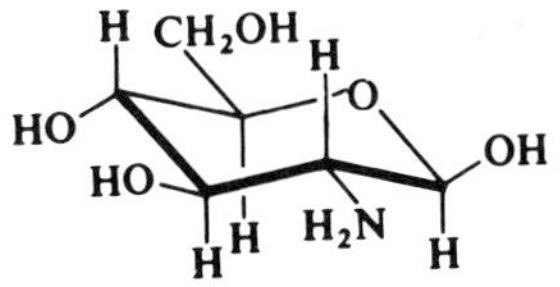

[13]

D-glucosamine (β anomer)

15·8 vitamin C

The "antiscorbutic" factor of fresh fruits which prevents the development of the typical symptoms of scurvy in man is a carbohydrate derivative known as vitamin C or ascorbic acid. This substance is not a carboxylic acid but a lactone and owes its acidic properties (and ease of oxidation) to the presence of an enediol grouping conjugate to a carbonyl group. It belongs to the L

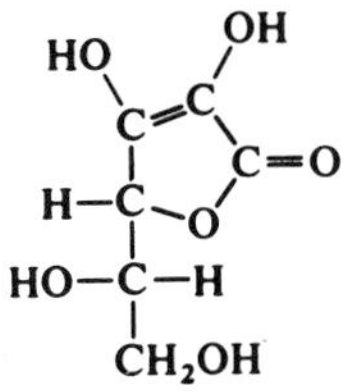

L-ascorbic acid

series by the glyceraldehyde convention. L-Ascorbic acid is formed from D-glucose in certain plants and in the liver of most animals (see Exercise 15·10).

15·9 immunologically important carbohydrates

One of the most active areas of carbohydrate chemistry at the present is the study of the polysaccharides present in microorganisms and their influence on immunological specificity. The production of antibodies in the bloodstream when foreign bacteria are introduced is a well-known phenomenon, and the extraordinarily high degree of specificity of these antibodies can be traced to the chemical composition of that part of the cell wall of bacteria called the **antigen**. The antigen is a complex combination of polysaccharides, lipids (esters of fatty acids), and proteins. The antigen can be separated into these three fractions and the carbohydrate fraction degraded.

The *Salmonella* bacteria, for example, have been intensively studied, and it has been shown that all of the 100 or more different cell-wall antigens that have been characterized contain five sugars: D-glucose; D-galactose; D-glucosamine [13]; a C_7 sugar (a heptose); and a C_8 sugar (an octose). A polysaccharide of these five sugars makes the basal chain to which are attached side chains containing a number of other pentoses and hexoses. The way in which these sugar units are arranged is evidently the source of the specificity of the antigen-antibody interaction.

summary

Carbohydrates are polyhydroxyaldehydes and polyhydroxyketones—monosaccharides—or substances that yield these on hydrolysis—oligosaccharides (two to nine components) or polysaccharides (10 or more components). The monosaccharides are further classified according to the number of carbon atoms in the chain and to whether they are aldehydes or ketones; that is, aldopentoses, ketohexoses, and so on. Most carbohydrates exist predominantly in cyclic hemiacetal or hemiketal forms.

There are four nonidentical asymmetric centers in the open-chain form of an aldohexose which means that there are 2^4 or 16 possible optical isomers (eight pairs of enantiomers), all of which are known. The most important of these is D-(+)-glucose (also called dextrose), whose Fischer projection formula is shown.

```
       CHO
        |
   H—C—OH
        |
  HO—C—H
        |
   H—C—OH
        |
   H—C—OH
        |
      CH₂OH
```
D-(+)-glucose

The relation of D-glucose to another of the aldohexoses (D-mannose) and one of the eight ketohexoses (D-fructose) was revealed by the fact that all three gave the same phenylosazone on treatment with phenylhydrazine. The configurations at C-3, C-4, and C-5 must be identical in all three compounds. The two aldohexoses are called epimers of one another since they differ only in configuration at C-2.

```
       CH=NNHC₆H₅
        |
        C=NNHC₆H₅
        |
  HO—C—H
        |
   H—C—OH
        |
   H—C—OH
        |
      CH₂OH
```
phenylosazone from D-glucose,
    D-mannose, and D-fructose

D-Glucose can be reduced to a hexahydric alcohol (sorbitol) or oxidized to a monocarboxylic acid (D-gluconic acid) or a dicarboxylic acid (D-glucaric acid). It reacts with methanol and acid to form a pair of acetal-like substances called methyl glucosides (general term—glycoside) whose structures are analogous to the two cyclic forms of D-glucose itself. The latter, designated α and β, are anomers—they differ in configuration only at C-1. Two ways of representing the cyclic structure of one of these anomers (α-D-glucose) and its methyl glucoside are shown here.

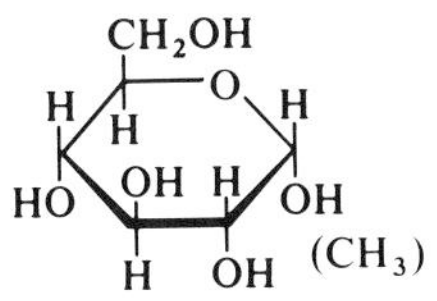

Haworth projection formula 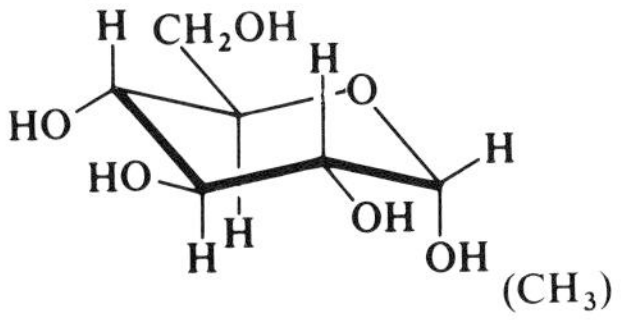   conformational formula

The equilibrium between the open-chain form and the two cyclic anomers of D-glucose strongly favors the cyclic forms. The latter, being diastereomers of one another, can be separated by crystallization. When dissolved in water, each anomer reverts at a measurable rate to the equilibrium mixture. This interconversion process is known as mutarotation.

The additional group in a glycoside (methyl in the formulas above) is called the aglycone group. Two of the important kinds of aglycones are nitrogen bases and other monosaccharides. The former leads to compounds such as the ribonucleosides—adenosine, for example—and the latter to di- and poly-saccharides.

Four important disaccharides are sucrose (D-glucose and D-fructose joined at C-1 and C-2, respectively), maltose and cellobiose (two D-glucose units joined at C-4 and C-1, respectively), and lactose. The two components of sucrose are bound together through their anomeric carbons and hence this sugar does not undergo mutarotation and is not oxidized by reagents such as Fehling's solution unless the disaccharide linkage is first hydrolyzed. The other three disaccharides have one free anomeric carbon and they can undergo mutarotation and reduce Fehling's solution. Maltose and cellobiose differ only in the configuration at the glycosidic link between the glucose units. Hydrolysis of maltose and some other α-linked compounds is catalyzed by maltase, and hydrolysis of cellobiose and some other β-linked compounds is catalyzed by emulsin.

Polysaccharides include cellulose and starch. Cellulose is a polymer of D-glucose with all the glycosidic links β and is the fibrous material in cotton, wood, flax, and so on. It can be converted to various esters, some of which are useful in their own right (cellulose acetate) and from some of which a shorter-chain cellulose can be regenerated (viscose rayon). Starch is a mixture of polymers of D-glucose with all the glycosidic links α, one a linear polymer (amylose) and the other a branched-chain polymer (amylopectin).

Vitamin C (ascorbic acid) is a carbohydrate derivative. Other important biological substances include the antigens, parts of which are polysaccharide in nature. Immunological response is related to the arrangement of monosaccharides in the polymer chain.

exercises

15·1   A naturally occurring optically active pentose ($C_5H_{10}O_5$) reduces Tollen's reagent and forms a tetraacetate with acetic anhydride. It gives an optically *inactive* phenylosazone. Write all the possible structures for this pentose which are in accord with all the experimental facts.

15·2   A hexose, $C_6H_{12}O_6$, which we shall call X-ose, on reduction with sodium amalgam gives pure D-sorbitol, and, upon treatment with phenylhydrazine gives an osazone different from that of D-glucose. Write a projection formula for X-ose and equations for its reactions.

15·3   D-Arabinose and D-ribose give the same phenylosazone. D-Ribose is reduced to the optically inactive pentahydric alcohol ribitol. D-Arabinose can be degraded by the **Ruff** method, which involves the following reactions:

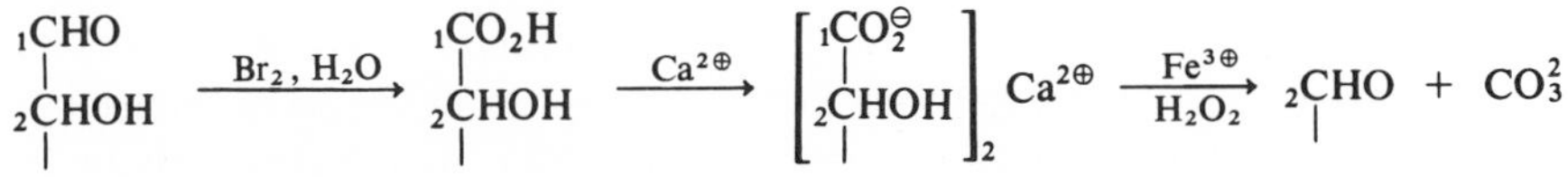

$$\begin{array}{c}\overset{1}{C}HO \\ | \\ \overset{2}{C}HOH \\ | \end{array} \xrightarrow{Br_2,\ H_2O} \begin{array}{c}\overset{1}{C}O_2H \\ | \\ \overset{2}{C}HOH \\ | \end{array} \xrightarrow{Ca^{2+}} \left[\begin{array}{c}\overset{1}{C}O_2^{\ominus} \\ | \\ \overset{2}{C}HOH \\ | \end{array}\right]_2 Ca^{2+} \xrightarrow[H_2O_2]{Fe^{3+}} \begin{array}{c}\overset{2}{C}HO \\ | \end{array} + CO_3^{2-}$$

The tetrose, D-erythrose, so obtained can be oxidized with nitric acid to *meso*-tartaric acid. What are the configurations of D-arabinose, D-ribose, ribitol, and D-erythrose?

15·4   The logic necessary to solve this problem is essentially that used by Fischer in his classic work which established the configurations of glucose, arabinose, and mannose.

   a.   Write projection formulas for all the theoretically possible D-aldopentoses, $HOH_2C(CHOH)_3CHO$.

   b.   One of the D-aldopentoses is the naturally occurring D-arabinose, enantiomeric with the more abundant L-arabinose. Oxidation of D-arabinose with nitric acid gives an *optically active* five-carbon trihydroxydicarboxylic acid. Which of the D-aldopentoses could be D-arabinose?

   c.   D-Arabinose is converted by the following transformations into D-glu-

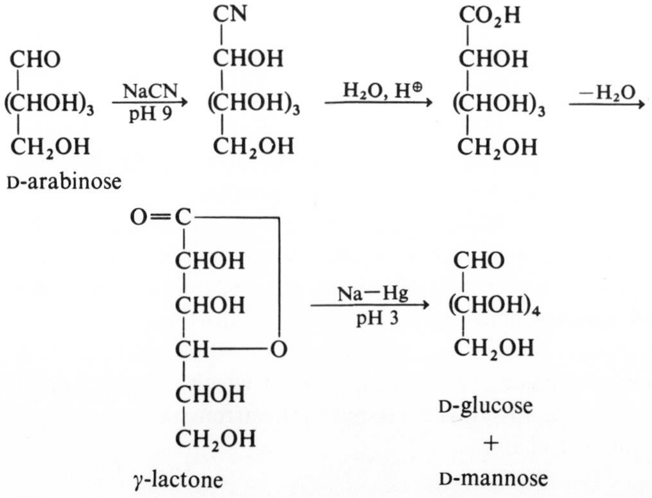

$$\begin{array}{c}CHO \\ | \\ (CHOH)_3 \\ | \\ CH_2OH \\ \text{D-arabinose}\end{array} \xrightarrow[pH\ 9]{NaCN} \begin{array}{c}CN \\ | \\ CHOH \\ | \\ (CHOH)_3 \\ | \\ CH_2OH\end{array} \xrightarrow{H_2O,\ H^{\oplus}} \begin{array}{c}CO_2H \\ | \\ CHOH \\ | \\ (CHOH)_3 \\ | \\ CH_2OH\end{array} \xrightarrow{-H_2O}$$

$$\begin{array}{c}O{=}C\text{——} \\ | \quad\quad\ \ | \\ CHOH \quad | \\ | \quad\quad\ \ | \\ CHOH \quad | \\ | \quad\quad\ \ | \\ CH\text{——}O \\ | \\ CHOH \\ | \\ CH_2OH \\ \gamma\text{-lactone}\end{array} \xrightarrow[pH\ 3]{Na-Hg} \begin{array}{c}CHO \\ | \\ (CHOH)_4 \\ | \\ CH_2OH \\ \text{D-glucose} \\ + \\ \text{D-mannose}\end{array}$$

cose and D-mannose. (This is the classic **Kiliani-Fischer cyanohydrin synthesis** of sugars). What do these transformations tell about the relationship between the configurations of mannose and glucose?

d. Oxidation of D-glucose and D-mannose gives the six-carbon, tetrahydroxydicarboxylic acids, glucaric and mannaric acids, respectively. Both are *optically active*. What then are the configurations of the D- and L-arabinoses?

e. D-Glucaric acid can form two different γ-monolactones, whereas D-mannaric acid can form only one monolactone. What then are the configurations of D-glucose and D-mannose?

15·5 Deduce possible configurations of natural galactose from the following:

a. The **Wohl degradation** is a means of reducing the chain length of a sugar by one carbon through the following reaction sequence:

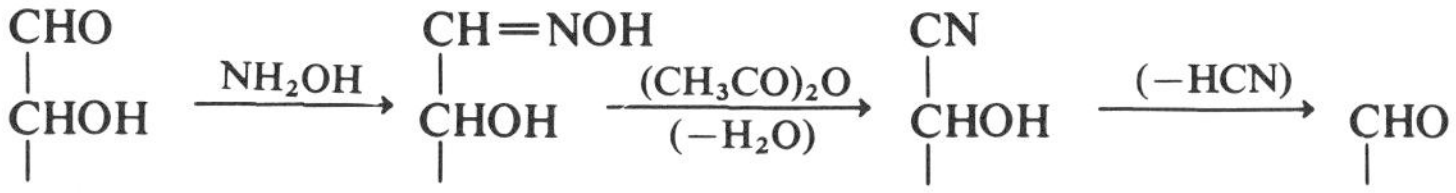

$$\underset{\text{CHOH}}{\overset{\text{CHO}}{|}} \xrightarrow{\text{NH}_2\text{OH}} \underset{\text{CHOH}}{\overset{\text{CH=NOH}}{|}} \xrightarrow[(-\text{H}_2\text{O})]{(\text{CH}_3\text{CO})_2\text{O}} \underset{\text{CHOH}}{\overset{\text{CN}}{|}} \xrightarrow{(-\text{HCN})} \underset{|}{\text{CHO}}$$

D-Galactose gives a pentose by one Wohl degradation. This pentose on nitric acid oxidation gives an optically active, five-carbon, trihydroxydicarboxylic acid.

b. The pentose by a second Wohl degradation followed by nitric acid oxidation gives D-tartaric acid.

c. Write reasonable mechanisms for the reactions involved in the Wohl degradation.

15·6 Draw Haworth- and conformation-type formulas for each of the following:

a. methyl 2,3,4,6-O-tetramethyl-α-D-glucopyranoside
b. α-L-arabinofuranose
c. L-sucrose

15·7 Sugars condense with anhydrous acetone in the presence of an acid catalyst to form isopropylidene derivatives.

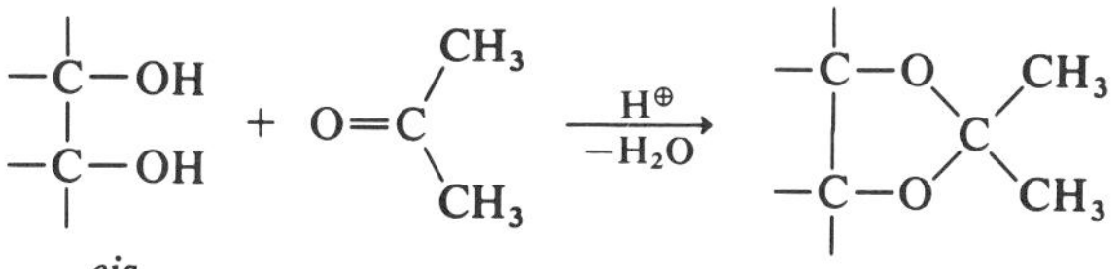

$$\begin{array}{c} -\overset{|}{\underset{|}{\text{C}}}-\text{OH} \\ -\overset{|}{\underset{|}{\text{C}}}-\text{OH} \\ \textit{cis} \end{array} + \text{O=C} \overset{\text{CH}_3}{\underset{\text{CH}_3}{\diagdown}} \xrightarrow[-\text{H}_2\text{O}]{\text{H}^\oplus} \begin{array}{c} -\overset{|}{\underset{|}{\text{C}}}-\text{O} \\ -\overset{|}{\underset{|}{\text{C}}}-\text{O} \end{array} \overset{\text{CH}_3}{\underset{\text{CH}_3}{\diagup}}$$

Predict the products of reaction of α-D-galactopyranose, α-D-glucopyranose, and α-D-glucofuranose with acetone and an acid catalyst.

15·8 How can the β-D-glucoside units of cellulose produce a polymer with a stronger, more compact physical structure than the α-D-glucose units of starch? Models will be helpful.

15·9 Complete the following sequence of reactions, writing structures for all the products, *A–I*:

a. α-D-glucofuranose $\xrightarrow[\text{HCl}]{\substack{\text{acetone} \\ (1 \text{ mole})}}$ *A* (see Exercise 15-7)

b. *A* $\xrightarrow{\text{NaIO}_4}$ *B*

c. *B* $\xrightarrow{\text{Na}^{14}\text{CN}}$ *C + D*

d. *C + D* $\xrightarrow[\text{2. H}^{\oplus},\text{ H}_2\text{O}]{\text{1. H}_2\text{O, OH}^{\ominus}}$ *E + F* + acetone

e. *E + F* $\xrightarrow[(-\text{H}_2\text{O})]{\Delta}$ *G + H*

f. *G + H* $\xrightarrow[\text{H}_2\text{O}]{\text{NaBH}_4}$ *I* + D-glucose-6-^{14}C

15·10 The following sequence of steps has been worked out for the conversion of D-glucose to L-ascorbic acid in nature.

Formulas [14], [15], and [16] are drawn to show stereochemical interrelationships and *not* stable conformations.

a. Identify the type of chemical reaction (reduction, lactone formation, etc.) that occurs in each of the steps.
b. Account for the change from the D series to the L series that accompanies the reaction.

15·11 Ascorbic acid (see Exercise 15·10) has a pK_{HA} of 4.2, making it stronger than acetic acid, p$K_{\text{HA}} = 4.7$. Identify the ionizable proton in ascorbic acid and account for the compound's acidity.

15·12 A compound called **inositol** that is widely distributed in nature bears some resemblance to simple sugars. Its formula is 1,2,3,4,5,6-hexahydroxycyclohexane and it can exist in nine possible stereoisomeric forms, two of which are optically active and seven of which are not. Draw the chair forms of the all-*cis* and all-*trans* isomers of inositol. Which of these isomers will be the more stable? Will either of these isomers rotate the plane of polarized light?

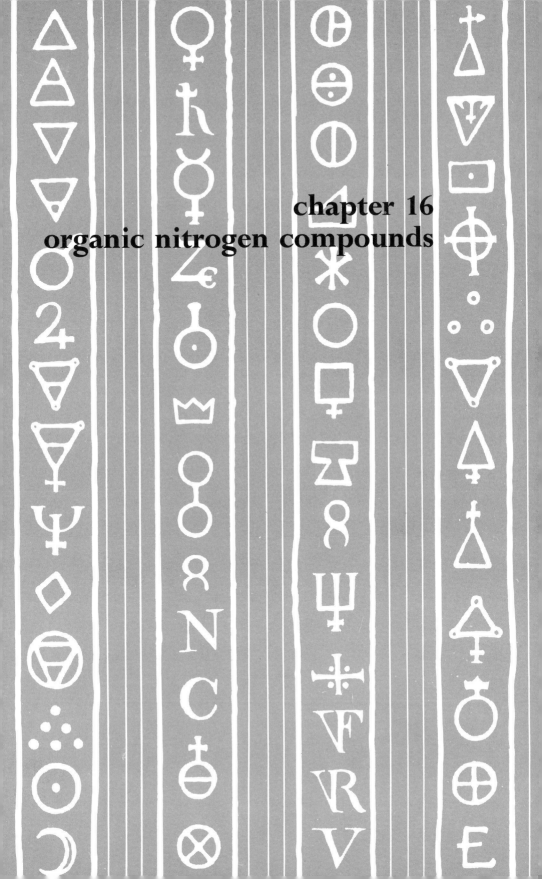

chapter 16
organic nitrogen compounds

Nitrogen is an element with many oxidation levels, ranging from the most reduced state, NH_3 or $NH_4^{\oplus}$, to the most oxidized state, HNO_3 or N_2O_5. With a compound at an intermediate oxidation level, particularly one with nitrogen-nitrogen bonds, such as HN_3, it is often not helpful to assign numerical oxidation states to the atoms. (The same situation occurs with compounds of carbon.) The important inorganic states of nitrogen are listed in Table 16·1 together with their organic analogs. The groupings there are made on the basis of bonding arrangements at the nitrogen atoms rather than on formal oxidation state.

16·1   amines

A. TYPES AND NOMENCLATURE

The nomenclature of alkyl-substituted ammonias, or amines, was considered briefly in Chapter 8. We shall give a short review here to help focus attention on the types of substitution which are commonly encountered. Classification is made according to the number of alkyl or aryl groups attached to nitrogen, since this number is important in determining the chemical reactions that are possible at the nitrogen atom.

RNH_2	R_2NH	R_3N	$\overset{\oplus\ \ominus}{R_4N\ X}$
primary amine	secondary amine	tertiary amine	quaternary ammonium salt

Amino compounds can be named either as derivatives of ammonia or as amino-substituted compounds. Thus, $HOCH_2CH_2NH_2$ can be named almost equally well as 2-hydroxyethylamine or as 2-aminoethanol, although by convention 2-aminoethanol is favored, since hydroxyl normally takes precedence over amino. With halogens the situation is reversed, and 2-chloroethylamine is favored over 2-aminoethyl chloride. Some typical amines with the names which they have in common use are listed in Table 16·2 together with their physical properties.

Salts of amines with inorganic or organic acids are usually best named as substituted ammonium salts. Often, however, the name of the corresponding

$$CH_3\overset{\oplus}{N}H_3\ \overset{\ominus}{Cl} \qquad\qquad CH_2=CH-CH_2-\overset{\overset{\displaystyle H}{|}\ \oplus}{\underset{\underset{\displaystyle CH_3}{|}}{N}}-CH_3\ \overset{\ominus}{O_2CCH_3}$$

methylammonium chloride   allyldimethylammonium
                                        acetate

amine is used in conjunction with the name of the acid, for instance, methyl-amine hydrochloride for methylammonium chloride. With quaternary salts

Table 16·1   Inorganic compounds of nitrogen and their organic analogs[a]

inorganic compound	methyl derivative	acetyl derivative
NH_3 ammonia	CH_3NH_2 methylamine	
$NH_4^{\oplus} Cl^{\ominus}$ ammonium chloride	$CH_3NH_3^{\oplus}Cl^{\ominus}$ methylammonium chloride	acetamide
NH_2NH_2 hydrazine	$CH_3NHNHCH_3$ 1,2-dimethylhydrazine	
$HN{=}NH$ diimine (unstable)	$CH_3N{=}NCH_3$ azomethane	
$H{-}\overset{\oplus}{N}{=}N{=}\overset{\ominus}{N}$ hydrazoic acid	CH_3N_3 methyl azide	 acetyl azide
$HC{\equiv}N$ hydrogen cyanide	$CH_3C{\equiv}N$ acetonitrile	acetyl cyanide
$N{\equiv}COH \leftrightarrows HN{=}C{=}O$ cyanic isocyanic acid acid	$CH_3N{=}C{=}O$ methyl isocyanate	
NH_2OH hydroxylamine	$(CH_3)_2NOH$ N,N-dimethylhydroxylamine	N-acetylhydroxylamine
$O{=}\overset{\oplus}{N}{=}\overset{\ominus}{N}$ nitrous oxide	$CH_2{=}\overset{\oplus}{N}{=}\overset{\ominus}{N}$ dizaomethane	
$\cdot N{=}O$ nitric oxide		
$HON{=}O$ nitrous acid	$CH_3{-}N{=}O$ nitrosomethane $CH_3O{-}N{=}O$ methyl nitrite	
$\cdot NO_2 \leftrightarrows NO_2{-}NO_2$ nitrogen dinitrogen dioxide tetroxide		
$HO{-}NO_2$ nitric acid	$CH_3{-}NO_2$ nitromethane $CH_3O{-}NO_2$ methyl nitrate	 acetyl nitrate

[a] Arranged according to the type of bonding at the nitrogen atoms; the alkyl or acyl group replaces a hydrogen atom in the inorganic compound in some cases and a hydroxyl group or an oxygen atom in others.

Table 16·2   Typical amines and their properties

amine	name	bp, °C	mp, °C	water solubility, g/100 ml, 25°	K_B in water[a]
NH_3	ammonia	−33	−77.7	90	1.8×10^{-5}
CH_3NH_2	methylamine	−6.5	−92.5	1156	4.4×10^{-4}
$CH_3CH_2NH_2$	ethylamine	16.6	−80.6	∞	5.6×10^{-4}
$(CH_3)_3CNH_2$	t-butylamine[b]	46	−67.5	∞	2.8×10^{-4}
$(CH_3CH_2)_2NH$	diethylamine	55.5	−50	very soluble	9.6×10^{-4}
$(CH_3CH_2)_3N$	triethylamine	89.5	−115	1.5	4.4×10^{-4}
$(CH_3CH_2CH_2CH_2)_3N$	tri-n-butylamine	214		slightly soluble	
⬡NH	piperidine	106	−9	∞	1.6×10^{-3}
⬡N	pyridine	115	−42	∞	1.7×10^{-9}
⬡—NH_2	cyclohexylamine	134		slightly soluble	4.4×10^{-4}
⬡—NH_2	aniline	184.4	−6.2	3.4	3.8×10^{-10}
$H_2NCH_2CH_2NH_2$	ethylenediamine	116	8.5	soluble	8.5×10^{-5}

[a] Usually at 20°–25°.
[b] Note that t-butylamine is a primary amine.

an extension of the same system leads to trimethylamine methiodide for tetramethylammonium iodide. Whenever possible, however, the substituted ammonium ion name should be used because a name such as trimethylamine methiodide conceals the fact that the bonds to the four methyl groups are identical.

B. PHYSICAL AND SPECTROSCOPIC PROPERTIES OF AMINES

The properties of amines depend in an important way on the degree of substitution at nitrogen. For example, tertiary amines have no N—H bonds and are thus unable to form hydrogen bonds of the type N—H···N. In general, N—H···N bonds are somewhat weaker than those of corresponding types, O—H···O and F—H···F, because the electronegativity of nitrogen is less than that of oxygen or fluorine. Even so, association of the molecules of primary and secondary amines (but not tertiary amines) through hydrogen bonding is significant and decreases their volatility relative to hydrocarbons of similar size, weight, and shape, as the accompanying examples show.

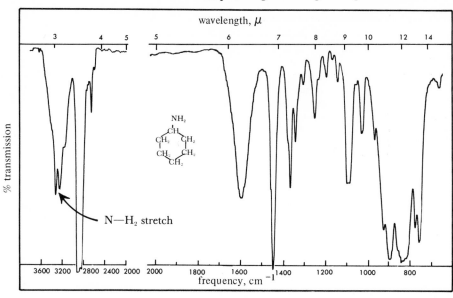

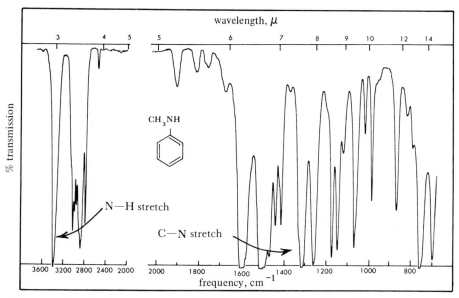

Figure 16·1 Infrared spectra of cyclohexylamine and N-methylaniline.

$CH_3CH_2CH_2CH_2CH_2NH_2$
n-pentylamine
mol. wt. 87; bp 130°

$CH_3CH_2NHCH_2CH_3$
diethylamine
mol. wt. 73; bp 55.5°

$$CH_3CH_2-\overset{\overset{\displaystyle CH_2CH_3}{|}}{N}-CH_2CH_3$$
triethylamine
mol. wt. 101; bp 89.5°

$CH_3CH_2CH_2CH_2CH_2CH_3$
hexane
mol. wt. 86; bp 69°

$CH_3CH_2CH_2CH_2CH_3$
pentane
mol. wt. 72; bp 36°

$$CH_3CH_2\overset{\overset{\displaystyle CH_2CH_3}{|}}{C}HCH_2CH_3$$
3-ethylpentane
mol. wt. 100; bp 93.3°

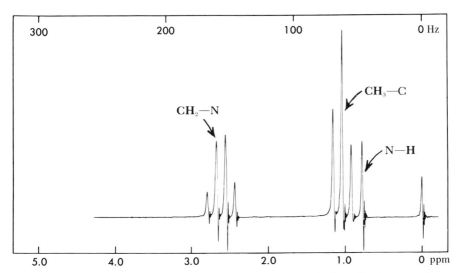

Figure 16·2 Nuclear magnetic resonance spectrum of diethylamine at 60 MHz relative to tetramethylsilane, 0.00 ppm.

The water solubilities of the lower-molecular-weight amines are generally greater than those of alcohols of comparable molecular weights. This is the result of hydrogen bonding between the amine and water, which leads to hydrogen bonds (of considerable strength) of the type $-\overset{|}{\underset{|}{N}}:\cdots H-O-H$.

A characteristic feature of the infrared spectra of primary and secondary amines is the moderately weak absorption at 3500 to 3300 cm^{-1}, corresponding to N—H stretching vibrations. Primary amines have two such bands in this region, whereas secondary amines generally show only one band. Absorption is shifted to lower frequencies on hydrogen bonding of the amine, but because NH···N hydrogen bonding is weaker than OH···O hydrogen bonding, the shift is not as great and the bands are not as intense as are the absorption bands of hydrogen-bonded O—H groups (see Table 7·1). Absorptions corresponding to C—N vibrations are less easily identifiable, except in the case of aromatic amines, which absorb fairly strongly near 1300 cm^{-1}. Spectra that illustrate these effects are shown in Figure 16·1.

The nmr spectra of amines show characteristic absorptions for $H-\overset{|}{\underset{|}{C}}-N$ protons around 2.7 ppm. The resonances of N—H protons are not so easily identifiable; considerable variability arises from differences in degree of hydrogen bonding and matters are further complicated when, as with diethylamine (Figure 16·2), the N—H resonance has nearly the same chemical shift as the resonances of C—CH$_3$ protons.

C. STEREOCHEMISTRY OF AMINES

The bond angles of nitrogen in amines and ammonia are less than tetrahedral as a consequence of electrostatic repulsion between the bonding electrons and the unshared electron pair (Section 1·2). The configuration at nitrogen is pyramidal and, if three different groups are attached, optically active forms are, in principle, possible because there is no plane or center of symmetry in the molecules.

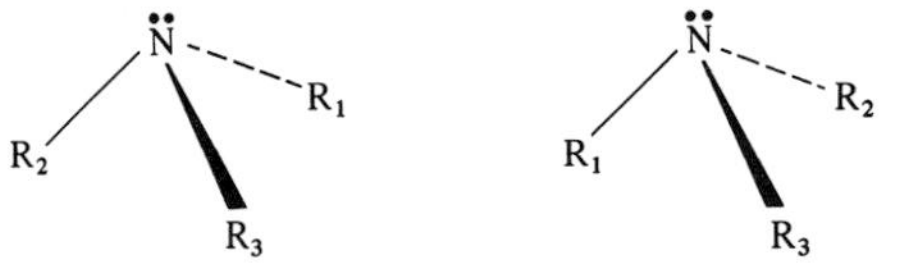

The resolution of such a mixture of forms has not as yet been achieved because they are rapidly interconverted by an inversion process involving a planar transition state.

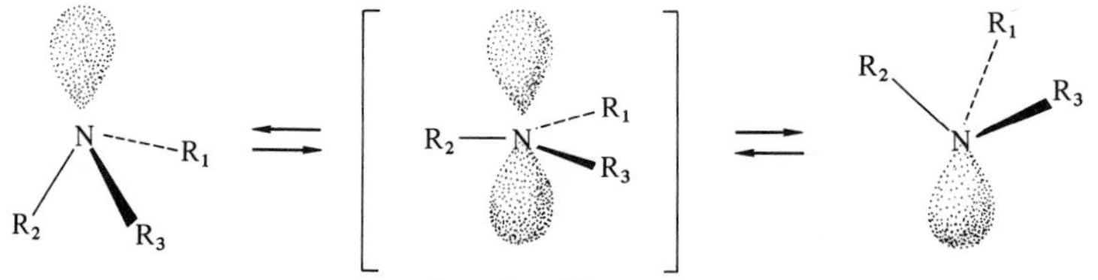

planar transition
state

With ammonia, inversion of this type occurs at about 4×10^{10} times per second at room temperature; with aliphatic tertiary amines, the rate is of the order of 10^3 to 10^5 times per second. Such inversion rates are much too great to permit separation of amines into stable optical isomers at room temperature. There are a few specially substituted amines such as [1] which invert at nitrogen sufficiently slowly at room temperature to permit isolation of the separate diastereomers [1a] and [1b].

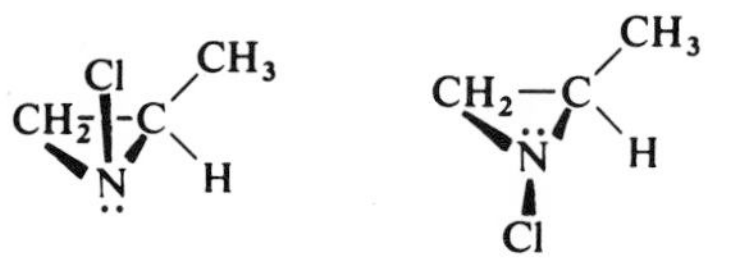

[1a]   [1b]

D. AMINES AS ACIDS AND BASES

Although perhaps the most characteristic chemical property of amines is their ability to act as bases by accepting protons from a variety of acids, it should not be forgotten that primary and secondary amines are also able to act as acids, albeit very weak acids. The lithium salts of such amines are readily preparable in ether solution by treatment of the amine with phenyllithium:

$$(C_2H_5)_2NH + C_6H_5Li \xrightarrow{ether} (C_2H_5)_2\overset{\ominus}{N} \overset{\oplus}{Li} + C_6H_6$$

lithium diethylamide

The anions from aliphatic amines, being conjugate bases of very weak acids ($K_{HA} \sim 10^{-33}$), are powerfully basic reagents and will remove protons even from many notably weak carbon acids.

The base strengths of saturated aliphatic amines, as given by K_B, are usually about 10^{-4} in water solution.

$$RNH_2 + H_2O \overset{K_B}{\rightleftharpoons} R\overset{\oplus}{N}H_3 + \overset{\ominus}{O}H$$

Ammonia and primary, secondary, and tertiary amines have the same base strengths within perhaps a factor of 50, as can be seen from the data in Table 16·2. There is no evidence for formation of undissociated amine hydroxides such as R_3NHOH, any more than there is for NH_4OH.

Unsaturated amines are often very weak bases. An example with C—N unsaturation is pyridine, C_5H_5N, which is a nitrogen analog of benzene, often called a **heterocycle** because not all of the atoms in the ring are of the same element. Pyridine, $K_B = 1.7 \times 10^{-9}$, is less basic by a factor of about 10^5 than aliphatic amines.

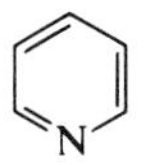

pyridine

Vinylamines or enamines, $RCH{=}CH{-}NH_2$, are not usually stable and rearrange to imines, $RCH_2CH{=}NH$. An exception of a particular sort is aniline (phenylamine, $C_6H_5NH_2$), which has an amino group attached to a benzene ring. Here, the imine structure is less favorable because of the considerable stabilization energy of the aromatic ring:

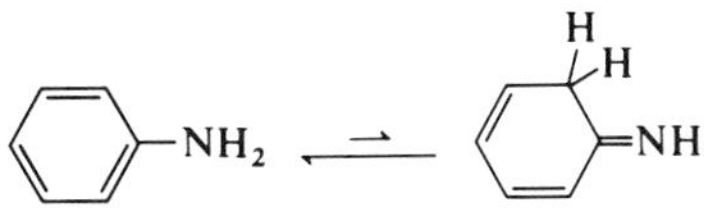

The K_B of aniline is 10^{-10}, which is less by a factor of 10^6 than that of cyclohexylamine (and is even less than that of pyridine). The decrease in stabilization associated with forming a bond to the unshared electron pair of nitrogen accounts for the difference; it prevents the electron pair from being delocalized over the benzene ring as represented by the following structures:

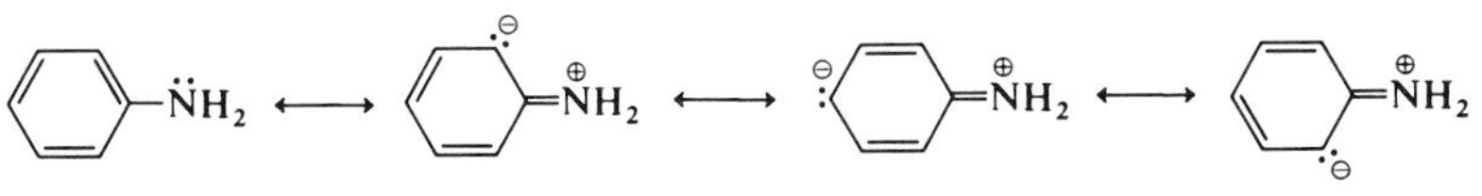

Some or all of the low basicity of aniline may also be accounted for by the electron-attracting power of unsaturated carbons relative to saturated carbons (see Section 5·5).

E. THE PREPARATION OF AMINES

1. *Alkylation.* We discussed the reactions of ammonia and amines with alkyl halides in Chapter 8. Such processes would be expected to provide straightforward syntheses of amines, at least with those halides which undergo S_N2 but not E2 reactions readily. For example,

$$CH_3I + NH_3 \longrightarrow CH_3\overset{\oplus}{N}H_3 \overset{\ominus}{I}$$

The methylamine can be recovered by treating the salt with a strong base, such as sodium hydroxide.

$$CH_3\overset{\oplus}{N}H_3 \overset{\ominus}{I} + \overset{\oplus}{Na}\overset{\ominus}{OH} \longrightarrow CH_3NH_2 + NaI + H_2O$$

In practice, such reactions lead to mixtures of products because of equilibria of the following kind and subsequent reactions to give more than mono-alkylation.

$$CH_3\overset{\oplus}{N}H_3\overset{\ominus}{I} + NH_3 \rightleftharpoons CH_3NH_2 + \overset{\oplus}{N}H_4 \overset{\ominus}{I}$$

$$CH_3NH_2 + CH_3I \longrightarrow (CH_3)_2\overset{\oplus}{N}H_2 \overset{\ominus}{I}$$

The reaction continues and ultimately gives some tetramethylammonium iodide.

$$(CH_3)_3N + CH_3I \longrightarrow (CH_3)_4\overset{\oplus}{N} \overset{\ominus}{I}$$

The latter product, of course, is not readily converted to an amine by treatment with base.

Nevertheless, the alkylation reaction is by no means hopeless as a practical method for the preparation of amines because usually the starting materials are readily available and the boiling-point differences between mono-, di-, and trialkylamines are sufficiently large to make for easy separations by fractional distillation. Separations may also be achieved by chemical means.

The tetraalkylammonium halide salts formed by exhaustive alkylation of amines resemble alkali salts and, with moist silver oxide, can be converted to tetraalkylammonium hydroxides. These compounds are strong bases and are true ammonium hydroxides.

$$(CH_3)_4\overset{\oplus}{N} \overset{\ominus}{I} \xrightarrow{Ag_2O, H_2O} (CH_3)_4\overset{\oplus}{N} OH^{\ominus} + AgI(s)$$

Tetramethylammonium hydroxide, when heated, decomposes slowly according to the following equation:

$$(CH_3)_4\overset{\oplus}{N} \overset{\ominus}{OH} \longrightarrow CH_3OH + (CH_3)_3N$$

With a higher alkylammonium hydroxide, thermal decomposition leads to the formation of an alkene. The reaction is a standard method for the preparation of alkenes.

Many of the drugs that have been used in cancer therapy are chloroalkyl-amines whose effectiveness appears to be associated with their alkylating ability. The so-called **nitrogen mustards** [2], containing two chloroethyl groups, react by a sequence of displacement steps. The chlorine is displaced

$$R-N\begin{array}{c}CH_2CH_2Cl\\ \\ CH_2CH_2Cl\end{array} \xrightarrow[(-Cl^{\ominus})]{} \begin{array}{c}CH_2-CH_2\\ \oplus\\ N\\ R\quad CH_2CH_2Cl\end{array} \xrightarrow[(-H^{\oplus})]{ZH} R-N\begin{array}{c}CH_2CH_2Z\\ \\ CH_2CH_2Cl\end{array}$$

[2]

by the neighboring amino group and the resulting ion rapidly alkylates an amino or hydroxylic compound (ZH). Alkylating agents react with many cellular constituents but there is evidence to suggest that reaction with deoxyribonucleic acid (DNA; Section 17·6) is the biologically important process.

The name nitrogen mustards arises from the structural resemblance of these compounds to the toxic agent **mustard gas** $S(CH_2CH_2Cl)_2$, and some of them share its vesicant (blistering) action on the skin. The nitrogen mustards contain two chloroethyl groups and both can undergo displacement, each reaction being aided by the neighboring amino group. It is significant that almost all the alkylating agents that exhibit tumor-inhibiting properties con-tain two or more alkyl groups, suggesting that some form of cross-linking process takes place within the cell.

Some of the more successful chemotherapeutic agents are chlorambucil [3], used extensively in treating chronic lymphocytic leukemia, and merophan [4].

[3]

[4]

Merophan has been used successfully in the treatment of Burkitt's lymphoma, a disease which mainly affects children in parts of Africa and which is often curable by chemotherapy alone.

2. *The Beckmann and Related Rearrangements.* Rearrangement of oximes of ketones (Table 11·4) by the action of concentrated sulfuric acid often pro-vides a useful synthesis of amines through formation of intermediates with positive nitrogen called nitrenium ions.[1] This reaction is called the **Beckmann rearrangement.** The nitrenium ion has only a fleeting existence at best and, indeed, may not be a true intermediate at all. The departure of the water molecule from the protonated oxime is probably accompanied by the 1,2-shift

---

[1] A more appropriate name for such an ion might be nitronium ion, analogous to car-bonium ion, but this term is already in use for the species $NO_2^{\oplus}$.

of the R group from the carbon to nitrogen. The amide is not usually hydro-

lyzed under the conditions of the reaction. If the amine is desired, a separate hydrolysis step has to be carried out. The Beckmann rearrangement is often conducted using phosphorus pentachloride instead of sulfuric acid.

Three other reactions that proceed by way of *neutral* intermediates possessing electron-deficient nitrogen and also give amines are the Schmidt, Curtius, and Hofmann reactions, shown in that order (the influence of late nineteenth century German chemists is seen in the number of reactions that bear their names).

3. *Formation of Amines by Reduction.* Excellent procedures are available for preparation of primary, secondary, and tertiary amines by the reduction of a variety of types of nitrogen compounds. Primary amines can be obtained by hydrogenation or lithium aluminum hydride reduction of nitro compounds, azides, oximes, nitriles, and unsubstituted amides.

Some care has to be exercised in the reduction of nitro compounds since reduction is highly exothermic. For example, the reaction of 1 mole (61 g) of nitromethane with hydrogen to give methylamine liberates sufficient heat to raise the temperature of a 25-lb iron bomb by 100°.

$$CH_3NO_2 + 3H_2 \longrightarrow CH_3NH_2 + 2H_2O \qquad \Delta H = -85 \text{ kcal}$$

Secondary and tertiary amines, particularly those with different R groups, are advantageously prepared by lithium aluminum hydride reduction of substituted amides (Section 13·8).

F. REACTIONS OF AMINES

1. *With Acids.* The formation of salts from amines and acids is the most characteristic reaction of amines, and, since amines are usually soluble in organic solvents, amines are often very useful when a mild base is required for a base-catalyzed reaction or when it is desirable to tie up an acidic reaction product. Pyridine has excellent properties in this regard, being a tertiary amine with a K_B of about 10^{-9}, reasonably volatile (bp 115°), and soluble in both water and hydrocarbons. When a stronger base is required, triethylamine is commonly used. The strengths of various amines as bases were considered in Section 16·1D.

2. *Acylation of Amines.* The unshared electrons on nitrogen play a key role in many other reactions of amines besides salt formation. In fact, almost all reactions of amines at the nitrogen atom have, as a first step, the formation of a bond involving the unshared electron pair on nitrogen. A typical example is acylation, wherein an amide is formed by the reaction of an acid chloride, an anhydride, or an ester with an amine (Section 13·8). The initial step in these reactions is as follows, using benzoyl derivatives and methylamine as illustrative reactants.

$$C_6H_5-\overset{O}{\overset{\|}{C}}-X + CH_3\ddot{N}H_2 \;\rightleftharpoons\; C_6H_5-\overset{\overset{\ominus}{O}}{\underset{\underset{\oplus}{H_2N-CH_3}}{\overset{|}{\underset{|}{C}}}}-X$$

$$X = \text{halogen}, \; -O-\overset{O}{\overset{\|}{C}}-C_6H_5 \text{ or } -OR$$

The reaction is completed by loss of a proton and elimination of $X^{\ominus}$.

$$C_6H_5-\overset{\overset{\ominus}{O}}{\underset{\underset{\oplus}{H_2N-CH_3}}{\overset{|}{\underset{|}{C}}}}-X \;\underset{}{\overset{-H^{\oplus}}{\rightleftharpoons}}\; C_6H_5-\overset{\overset{\ominus}{O}}{\underset{\underset{}{HN-CH_3}}{\overset{|}{\underset{|}{C}}}}-X \;\underset{}{\overset{-X^{\ominus}}{\rightleftharpoons}}\; C_6H_5-\overset{O}{\overset{\|}{C}}-NHCH_3$$

A serious disadvantage to the preparation of amides through the reaction of an amine with an acid chloride (or anhydride) is the formation of 1 mole of amine salt for each mole of amide. This is especially serious if the amine is the

$$
CH_3-\overset{\overset{\displaystyle O}{\|}}{C}-Cl \ + \ 2\ RNH_2 \ \longrightarrow \ CH_3-\overset{\overset{\displaystyle O}{\|}}{C}-\overset{\overset{\displaystyle H}{|}}{N}-R \ + \ R\overset{\oplus}{N}H_3\ \overset{\ominus}{Cl}
$$

expensive ingredient in the reaction. In such circumstances, the reaction is usually carried on in a two-phase system with the acid chloride and amine in the nonaqueous phase and sodium hydroxide in the aqueous phase. As the amine salt is formed and dissolves in the water, it is converted to amine by the sodium hydroxide and extracted back into the nonaqueous phase. This

$$
R\overset{\oplus}{N}H_3\ \overset{\ominus}{Cl} + Na\ \overset{\ominus}{OH} \ \longrightarrow \ RNH_2 + Na\overset{\oplus}{}\ \overset{\ominus}{Cl} + H_2O
$$

procedure requires an excess of acid chloride, since some of it is wasted by hydrolysis.

3. *Amines with Nitrous Acid.* Nitrous acid reacts with all amines, but the nature of the products depends very much on whether the amine is primary, secondary, or tertiary. Indeed, aqueous nitrous acid is a useful reagent to distinguish these compounds. Thus, with primary amines, nitrous acid evolves nitrogen gas; with secondary amines, an insoluble yellow liquid or solid N-nitroso compound $(R_2N-N=O)$ separates; tertiary amines dissolve in and react with aqueous nitrous acid without evolution of nitrogen, usually to give complex products. These reactions are of little preparative value with many aliphatic amines because mixtures of products result. With aromatic amines such as aniline, however, the reaction with nitrous acid is extremely useful (Section 22·6).

4. *Halogenation.* Primary amines in the presence of base react with hypochlorous acid [or t-butyl hypochlorite, $(CH_3)_3C-OCl$] to produce both mono- and disubstitution products:

$$
RNH_2 \ \xrightarrow[\text{OH}^\ominus]{\text{Cl}_2} \ R-\overset{\overset{\displaystyle H}{|}}{N}-Cl \ \xrightarrow[\text{OH}^\ominus]{\text{Cl}_2} \ R-\overset{\overset{\displaystyle Cl}{|}}{N}-Cl
$$

Secondary amines give mono-N-haloamines. These substances are rather weak bases, $K_B \sim 10^{-13}$; they are not very stable and are oxidizing agents. They hydrolyze in water, particularly in acid solution, to regenerate the halogen.

$$
R_2NCl + HCl \ \longrightarrow \ R_2NH + Cl_2
$$

5. *Oxidation of Amines.* *Oxidation with permanganate.* Potassium permanganate and most other strong oxidants oxidize amines in much the same way that they oxidize alcohols, giving aldehydes, ketones, or carboxylic acids. It should be remembered that the terms primary, secondary, and tertiary mean different things when applied to alcohols and amines. A

secondary alcohol, for example, is an alcohol with one hydrogen atom on the alcoholic *carbon atom* (R_2CHOH); a secondary amine is an amine with one hydrogen on the *nitrogen atom*, R_2NH. We should focus our attention on the alkyl groups in the two cases; a primary alkyl group, whether attached to $-OH$, $-NH_2$, $-NHR$, or $-NR_2$, will give an aldehyde or carboxylic acid on oxidation:

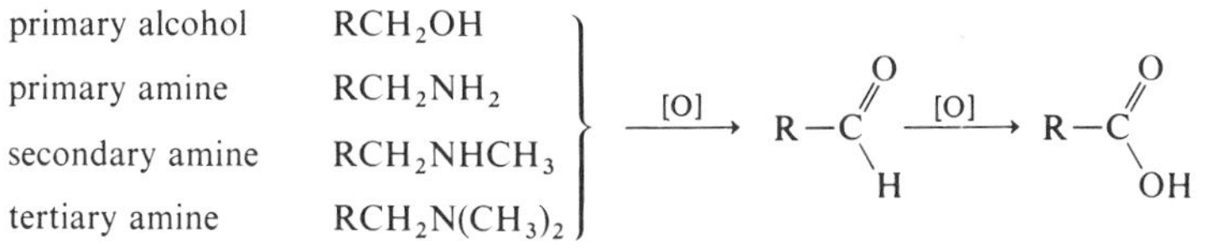

primary alcohol RCH_2OH

primary amine RCH_2NH_2

secondary amine RCH_2NHCH_3

tertiary amine $RCH_2N(CH_3)_2$

$$\xrightarrow{[O]} R-\overset{O}{\underset{H}{\overset{\|}{C}}} \xrightarrow{[O]} R-\overset{O}{\underset{OH}{\overset{\|}{C}}}$$

A secondary alkyl group will give a ketone:

secondary alcohol R_2CHOH

primary amine R_2CHNH_2

secondary amine $R_2CHNHCH_3$

tertiary amine $R_2CHN(CH_3)_2$

$$\xrightarrow{[O]} R_2C=O$$

The amino nitrogen in the above reactions is converted largely to ammonia.

A tertiary alcohol is not oxidized unless the conditions are drastic enough to cleave a carbon-carbon bond; a tertiary alkyl group in an amine is likewise stable. In this case, however, the amino group succumbs slowly and it is often possible to obtain high yields of the nitro compound:

$$(CH_3)_3C-NH_2 \xrightarrow{KMnO_4} (CH_3)_3C-NO_2$$

t-butylamine   2-nitro-2-methylpropane
                        83%

A compound such as $(CH_3)_3C-N(CH_3)_2$ will be demethylated by permanganate by rapid oxidation of the two methyl groups, producing eventually two moles of CO_2.

Acid helps protect amines from oxidation by tying up the pair of electrons on nitrogen and this is a matter of some importance because many common oxidizing agents, such as Cr^{VI}, are vigorous oxidants only in acid solution. Permanganate oxidations, however, do not require acid catalysis and amines are readily oxidized by this reagent in basic solution.

Oxidation with peracids. Oxidation of tertiary amines by peracids gives amine oxides. Thus, triethylamine can be oxidized with peracetic acid to triethylamine oxide:

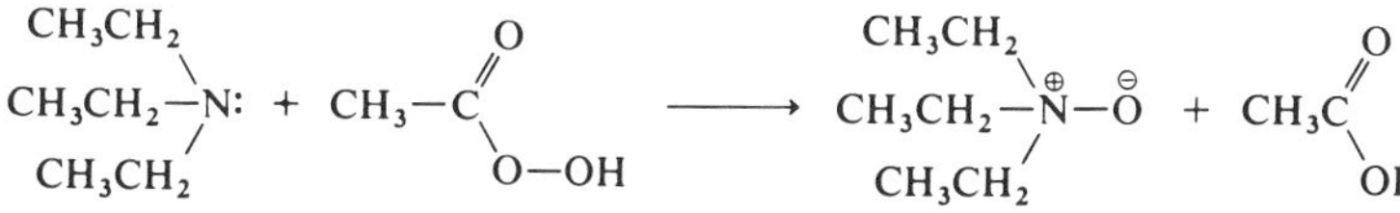

$$\underset{\underset{CH_3CH_2}{CH_3CH_2}}{CH_3CH_2}N: + CH_3-\overset{O}{\underset{O-OH}{\overset{\|}{C}}} \longrightarrow \underset{\underset{CH_3CH_2}{CH_3CH_2}}{CH_3CH_2}\overset{\oplus}{N}-\overset{\ominus}{O} + CH_3\overset{O}{\underset{OH}{\overset{\|}{C}}}$$

Peracids are excellent donors of oxygen atoms to amines (and also to alkenes;

see Section 4·4G) because bond breaking in the transition state is accompanied by bond formation, and high-energy intermediates are thus avoided:

(hydrogen bonded)   transition state

$$R-C \overset{OH}{\underset{O}{\diagdown}} + {}^{\ominus}O-\overset{\oplus}{N}{\diagup}$$

With secondary amines, peracids give hydroxylamines, presumably as the result of rearrangement of the N-oxide:

$$R_2NH \longrightarrow R_2\overset{\oplus}{N}H-\overset{\ominus}{O} \longrightarrow R_2NOH$$

Primary amines react similarly, but with an excess of peracid they go all the way to the nitro compound, though the yields are only moderate.

Unlike amines, amine oxides would not be expected to undergo inversion at the nitrogen atom, and the oxides from amines with three different R groups should be resolvable into optically active forms. This has been realized for several amine oxides, including the one from methylethylallylamine.

Amine oxides are one of the few types of organic nitrogen compounds that do not have analogs in known inorganic nitrogen compounds. The inorganic model would be $H_3\overset{\oplus}{N}-\overset{\ominus}{O}$, a surely unstable tautomer of hydroxylamine, H_2NOH.

An understanding of the chemistry of simple amides is particularly important because peptides and proteins, substances that are fundamental to all life as we know it, are polyamides.

simple amide   N,N-disubstituted amide

An important characteristic of the amide group is its planarity—the carbon, oxygen, nitrogen, and the first atoms of the R groups of an N,N-disubstituted amide all lie in the same plane. This planarity can be regarded as reflecting the importance of the following type of resonance in the amide group:

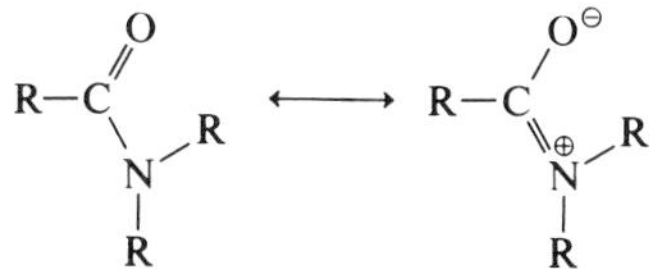

$$R-C \overset{\displaystyle O}{\underset{\displaystyle \underset{\displaystyle R}{\overset{\displaystyle |}{N}} \diagdown R}{}} \longleftrightarrow R-C \overset{\displaystyle O^{\ominus}}{\underset{\displaystyle \underset{\displaystyle R}{\overset{\displaystyle |}{\overset{\oplus}{N}}} \diagdown R}{}}$$

Coplanarity is required if the dipolar structure is to be significant. The stabilization energy of acetamide is 11 kcal/mole, a value typical of most amides.

A. PHYSICAL AND SPECTRAL CHARACTERISTICS OF AMIDES

The amides have rather high melting and boiling points as a result of extensive intermolecular hydrogen bonding. Formamide is the only simple amide that is liquid at room temperature. Acetamide (mp 82°, bp 222°) has melting and boiling points far above the values for acetic acid (mp 17° and bp 118°), which has almost the same molecular weight. Disubstituted amides such as N,N-dimethylacetamide have lower boiling and melting points because of the absence of hydrogen bonding.

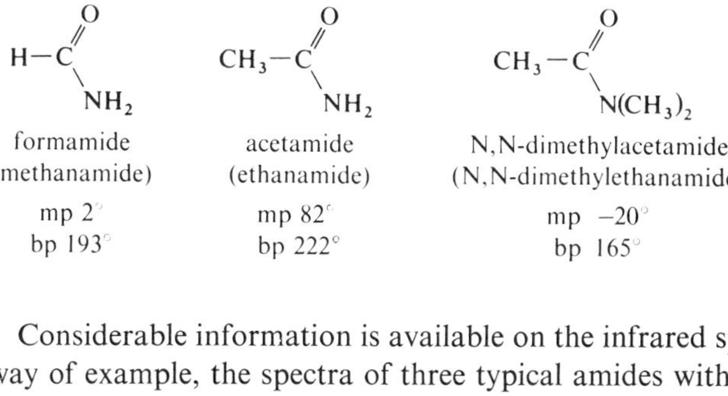

$$H-C\overset{O}{\underset{NH_2}{}} \qquad CH_3-C\overset{O}{\underset{NH_2}{}} \qquad CH_3-C\overset{O}{\underset{N(CH_3)_2}{}}$$

formamide	acetamide	N,N-dimethylacetamide
(methanamide)	(ethanamide)	(N,N-dimethylethanamide)
mp 2°	mp 82°	mp −20°
bp 193°	bp 222°	bp 165°

Considerable information is available on the infrared spectra of amides. By way of example, the spectra of three typical amides with different degrees of substitution on nitrogen are shown in Figure 16·3.

As we might expect, a strong carbonyl absorption is evident in the spectra of all amides, although the frequency of absorption varies slightly with the structure of the amide. Thus, unsubstituted amides generally absorb near 1690 cm^{-1}, whereas mono-N-substituted and di-N-substituted amides absorb at slightly lower frequencies. The N—H stretching frequencies of amides are close to those of amines and show shifts of 100 to 200 cm^{-1} to lower frequencies as the result of hydrogen bonding. Unsubstituted amides have two N—H bands of medium intensity near 3500 and 3400 cm^{-1}, whereas monosubstituted amides, to a first approximation, have only one N—H band near 3440 cm^{-1}.

The nmr resonance of the N—H protons of amides are usually somewhat different from any we have discussed so far. Customarily, these will appear as a quite broad ragged singlet absorption which may turn to a broad triplet at high temperatures. A typical example is shown by propanamide (Figure 16·4). The reason for this is associated with the special nuclear properties of ^{14}N, the abundant isotope of nitrogen. When the ^{14}N is replaced by ^{15}N, the

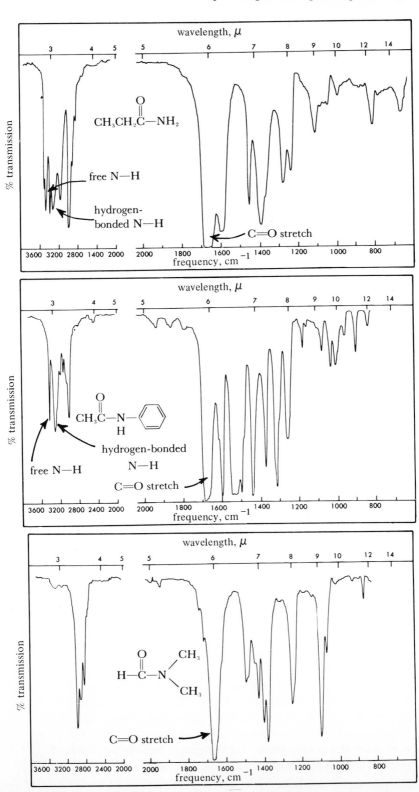

← Figure 16·3 Infrared spectra of propanamide, acetanilide, and N,N-dimethylformamide in chloroform solution. Note the appearance of both free NH bands (sharp, 3300–3500 cm⁻¹) and hydrogen-bonded N-H bands (broad, 3100–3300 cm⁻¹) for unsubstituted and monosubstituted amides.

lines become completely sharp. A more detailed explanation of this behavior is beyond the scope of this book.

The ultraviolet spectra of amides generally resemble those of carboxylic acids.

In general, the amide group is reasonably polar and the lower-molecular-weight amides are reasonably high melting and water soluble as compared to esters, amines, alcohols, and the like. N,N-Dimethylformamide and N-methylpyrrolidone have excellent solvent properties for both polar and nonpolar substances.

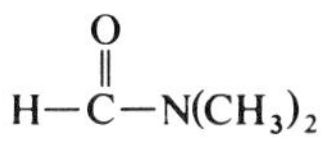

$$H-\overset{\overset{\displaystyle O}{\|}}{C}-N(CH_3)_2$$

N, N-dimethylformamide

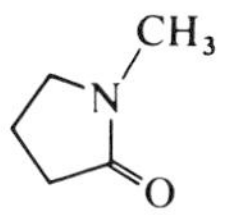

N-methylpyrrolidone
(N-methyl-γ-butyrolactam)

Amides with N—H bonds are weakly acidic, the usual K_{HA} being about 10^{-16}.

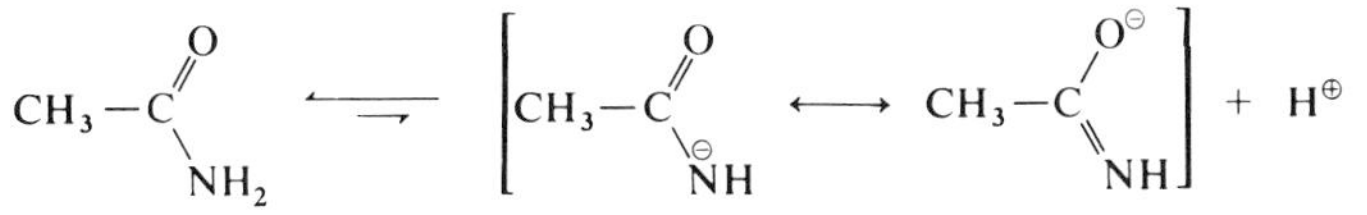

$$CH_3-C\overset{O}{\underset{NH_2}{\diagdown}} \rightleftharpoons \left[CH_3-C\overset{O}{\underset{\overset{\ominus}{N}H}{\diagdown}} \longleftrightarrow CH_3-C\overset{O^{\ominus}}{\underset{NH}{\diagdown}}\right] + H^{\oplus}$$

Amides, then, are far more acidic than ammonia with $K_{HA} \sim 10^{-33}$, and this reflects a very substantial degree of stabilization of the amide anion.

Figure 16·4 Nuclear magnetic resonance spectrum of propanamide, CH_3CH_2-$CONH_2$, in chloroform solution (solvent not shown) at 60 MHz relative to TMS at 0.00 ppm.

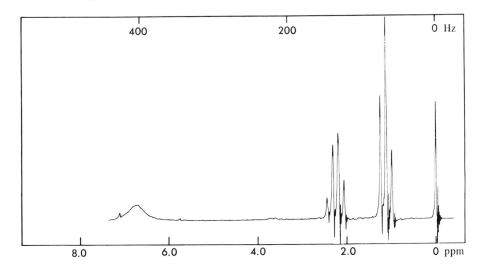

However, amides are still very weak acids and, for practical purposes, are to be regarded as essentially nonacidic in aqueous solutions.

The degree of basicity of amides is very much less than that of aliphatic amines. For acetamide, K_B is about 10^{-15} (the $K_{BH\oplus}$ of the conjugate acid is ~ 10) and acetamide is "half-protonated" in 1 M sulfuric acid.

$$CH_3-C\overset{O}{\underset{NH_2}{\big\backslash}} + H_2O \;\rightleftharpoons\; \begin{cases} CH_3-C\overset{O}{\underset{\overset{\oplus}{N}H_3}{\big\backslash}} + \overset{\ominus}{O}H \\[2em] CH_3-C\overset{OH}{\underset{\overset{\oplus}{N}H_2}{\big\backslash}} + \overset{\ominus}{O}H \end{cases}$$

The proton can become attached either to nitrogen or to oxygen. Nitrogen is, of course, intrinsically more basic than oxygen, but formation of the N-conjugate acid would cause loss of all the resonance stabilization energy of the amide. Infrared and nmr studies of amide cations reveal that the O-protonated form predominates; the equilibrium between the two is established so rapidly, however, that the N-protonated form appears to serve as an intermediate in some reactions.

B. PREPARATION OF AMIDES

Two of the three reactions given below have been discussed in some detail earlier. The third, hydrolysis of nitriles, has been met previously only as a means of preparing carboxylic acids.

1. Reaction of esters, acyl chlorides, or anhydrides with ammonia or amines (Section 13·8).

$$R-C\overset{O}{\underset{OEt}{\big\backslash}} + NH_3 \longrightarrow R-C\overset{O}{\underset{NH_2}{\big\backslash}} + EtOH$$

$$R-C\overset{O}{\underset{Cl}{\big\backslash}} + 2NH_3 \longrightarrow R-C\overset{O}{\underset{NH_2}{\big\backslash}} + NH_4^{\oplus}\,Cl^{\ominus}$$

$$\begin{matrix} R-C\overset{O}{\big\backslash} \\ \quad\;O \\ R-C\underset{O}{\big\nearrow} \end{matrix} + 2NH_3 \longrightarrow R-C\overset{O}{\underset{NH_2}{\big\backslash}} + NH_4^{\oplus}\;{}^{\ominus}O_2CR$$

If primary or secondary amines are used in place of ammonia, N-substituted amides result.

$$CH_3-C\overset{O}{\underset{Cl}{\big\backslash}} + 2CH_3NH_2 \longrightarrow CH_3-C\overset{O}{\underset{NHCH_3}{\big\backslash}} + CH_3NH_3^{\oplus}\,Cl^{\ominus}$$

N-methylacetamide

2. Beckmann rearrangement of oximes (Section 16·1E2).

$$R_2C{=}NOH \xrightarrow{H_2SO_4} RC{\equiv}\overset{\oplus}{N}R \xrightarrow{H_2O} R{-}C\overset{\displaystyle O}{\underset{\displaystyle NHR}{\big<}}$$

N-Substituted amides are formed; hydrolysis beyond the amide stage gives an amine and a carboxylic acid.

3. Hydrolysis of nitriles.

$$R{-}C{\equiv}N + H_2O_2 \xrightarrow{OH^{\ominus}} R{-}C\overset{\displaystyle O}{\underset{\displaystyle NH_2}{\big<}} + \tfrac{1}{2}O_2$$

Nitriles can be hydrolyzed to amides in strongly acidic or basic solution but a better method is to use hydrogen peroxide in mildly basic solution, thus avoiding further hydrolysis of the amide to the carboxylic acid. The effectiveness of hydrogen peroxide can in part be traced to the very high nucleophilicity of the hydroperoxide anion $HO_2{}^{\ominus}$, compared to the hydroxide ion itself (see Exercise 16·24).

C. REACTIONS OF AMIDES

In general, amides can be hydrolyzed in either acid or base solutions although the reactions are usually slow. The mechanisms are much like that of ester hydrolysis (Section 13·8).

Amides can be converted to amines by reduction (Sections 13·8 and 16·1E3), or by the Hofmann hypobromite reaction (Section 16·1E2). In the latter case the amine that is formed has one less carbon atom than the amide:

$$R{-}C\overset{\displaystyle O}{\underset{\displaystyle NH_2}{\big<}} \quad \begin{array}{l} \xrightarrow{\text{LiAlH}_4} RCH_2NH_2 \\[2mm] \xrightarrow[\text{NaOH}]{\text{Br}_2} RNH_2 \end{array}$$

D. IMIDES

Imides are N-acyl amides. Unlike amides they are considerably ionized in aqueous solution ($pK_{HA} \sim 9$) as a result of effective charge dispersal in the anion.

$$R{-}C\overset{O}{\underset{\underset{\displaystyle H}{\displaystyle N}}{\big\|}}C{-}R \rightleftharpoons H^{\oplus} + R{-}C\overset{O}{\underset{\underset{\displaystyle N}{\ominus}}{\big|}}C{-}R$$

an imide

Examples of cyclic imides are succinimide [5] (succinic acid is 1,4-butanedioic acid) and the compound [6]. The common name of [6] is thalidomide, the drug which attained notoriety when its unforeseen *teratogenic* (fetus-deforming) properties were discovered.

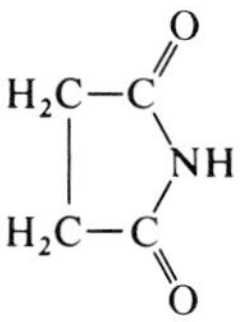

[5] 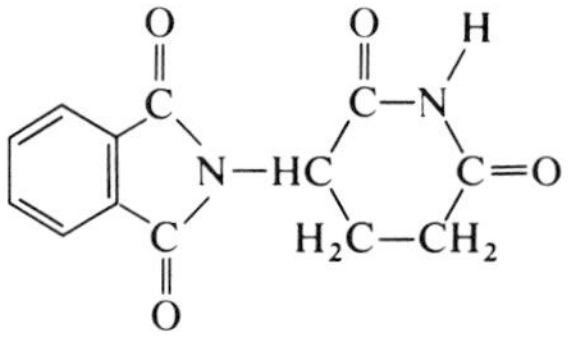   [6]

16·3 nitriles

The carbon-nitrogen triple bond differs considerably from the carbon-carbon triple bond by being stronger (213 kcal vs. 200 kcal) and much more polar. Liquid nitriles have rather high dielectric constants compared to most organic liquids and are reasonably soluble in water.

Nitriles absorb in the infrared in the region 2000 to 2300 cm^{-1}, owing to stretching vibrations of the carbon-nitrogen triple bond.

The preparation of nitriles by S_N2 reactions of alkyl or allyl halides with cyanide ion has been mentioned before (Section 8·7), and this is the method of choice where the halide is available and reacts satisfactorily. Other useful syntheses involve cyanohydrin formation (Section 11·4A) or dehydration of the corresponding amide.

The reduction of nitriles to amines and the hydrolysis of nitriles to amides have been discussed earlier (see Sections 16·1E3, 13·8, and 16·2B).

Hydrogens on the α carbons (C-2) of nitriles are about as acidic as the hydrogens α to carbonyl groups; accordingly, esters of cyanoacetic acid undergo many reactions similar to those of the esters of malonic and acetoacetic acids (Section 13·9C). The α positions of nitriles can be alkylated with alkyl halides by processes like the following:

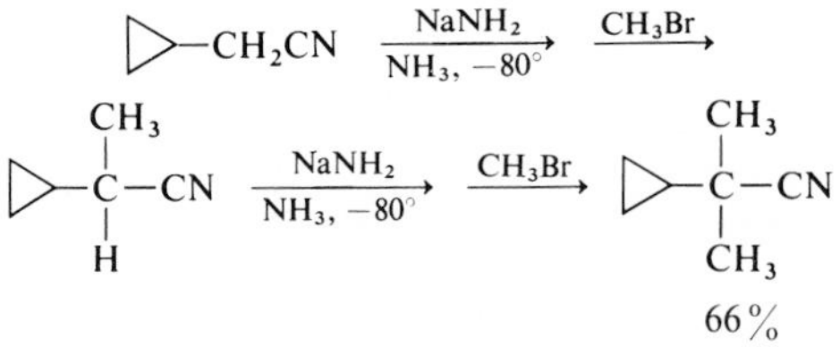

16·4 nitroso compounds

Although C-nitroso compounds, R—N=O, have no special synthetic importance at present, they do possess some interesting properties. Primary and secondary nitroso compounds are unstable and rearrange to oximes.

$$\underset{\text{2-nitrosopropane}}{\underset{H_3C}{\overset{H_3C}{>}}C\underset{N=O}{\overset{H}{<}}} \;\rightleftharpoons\; \underset{CH_3}{\overset{CH_3}{>}}C=N\overset{OH}{}$$

Tertiary and aromatic nitroso compounds are reasonably stable substances, which, although usually blue or green in the gas phase or in dilute solution, are isolated as colorless or yellow solids or liquids. The color changes are due to dimerization.

$$2\,R-N=O \;\rightleftharpoons\; \underset{\text{(yellow or orange)}}{R-\overset{\ominus O \quad O}{\underset{\oplus}{N}-N}-R}$$

(green or blue)   (yellow or orange)

16·5   nitro compounds

Nitro compounds make up a very important class of nitrogen derivatives. The nitro group ($-NO_2$), like the carboxylate anion, is well formulated as a hybrid of two equivalent resonance structures.

$$R-\overset{\oplus}{N}\overset{O}{\underset{O^\ominus}{\big<}} \;\longleftrightarrow\; R-\overset{\oplus}{N}\overset{O^\ominus}{\underset{O}{\big<}} \quad or \quad R-\overset{\oplus}{N}\overset{O^{\frac{1}{2}\ominus}}{\underset{O_{\frac{1}{2}\ominus}}{\big<}}$$

The hybrid structure is seen to have a full positive charge on nitrogen and a half-negative charge on each oxygen. The polar character of the nitro group results in lower volatility of nitro compounds than ketones of about the same molecular weight; thus the boiling point of nitromethane (mol. wt. 61) is 101°, whereas acetone (mol. wt. 58) has a boiling point of 56°. Surprisingly, the water solubility is low; a saturated solution of nitromethane in water is less than 10% by weight, whereas acetone is infinitely miscible with water.

Nitro groups of nitroalkanes can be identified by strong infrared bands at about 1580 and 1375 cm^{-1}, whereas the corresponding bands in the spectra of aromatic nitro compounds occur at slightly lower frequencies. A weak transition occurs in the electronic spectra of nitroalkanes at around 2700 A; aromatic nitro compounds, such as nitrobenzene, have extended conjugation and absorb at longer wavelengths ($\sim$ 3300 A).

Nitro compounds are quite unstable in the thermodynamic sense and the heat of decomposition of nitromethane, according to the following stoichiometry, is 67.4 kcal/mole:

$$CH_3NO_2 \;\longrightarrow\; \tfrac{1}{2}N_2 + CO_2 + \tfrac{3}{2}H_2 \qquad \Delta H = -67.4 \text{ kcal}$$

The rate of decomposition under ordinary conditions is immeasurably slow, however, and pure nitromethane is a stable, easily handled, compound. On the other hand, some polynitro compounds, such as tetranitromethane, explode on shock and require very careful handling.

2,4,6-Trinitrotoluene (TNT) is not set off easily by simple impact and is used in high-explosive shells. However, once set off, TNT explodes violently.

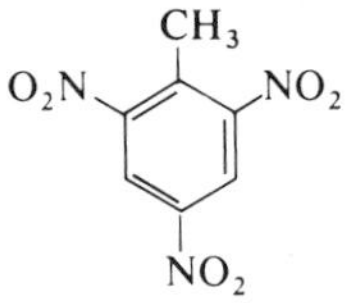

2,4,6-trinitrotoluene

The characteristics of reasonable handling stability and high thermodynamic potential make the chemistry of nitro compounds particularly interesting and useful.

Nitro compounds can be prepared in a number of ways, including the direct substitution of hydrocarbons with nitric acid. This reaction was discussed

$$RH + HONO_2 \longrightarrow RNO_2 + H_2O$$

earlier (Section 3·3B) in connection with the nitration of alkanes, and it was there noted that reaction is successful only when conducted at high temperatures in the vapor phase. Mixtures of products are invariably obtained. Direct nitration of aromatic compounds such as benzene, in contrast, takes place readily in the liquid phase. The characteristics of aromatic nitration are discussed in Chapter 22.

Other routes to aliphatic nitro compounds include the reaction of an alkyl halide (of good S_N2 reactivity) with sodium nitrite. Suitable solvents are dimethyl sulfoxide and dimethylformamide. As can be seen below, formation of the nitrite ester by O- instead of N-alkylation is a competing reaction.

$$CH_3(CH_2)_6Br + NaNO_2 \longrightarrow CH_3(CH_2)_6NO_2 + CH_3(CH_2)_6ONO$$
$$60\% \qquad\qquad 30\%$$

Tertiary nitro compounds may be prepared by the oxidation of the corresponding amine with aqueous potassium permanganate solution (Section 16·1F5).

Nitro compounds are readily reduced to amines (Section 16·1E3) and this offers a particularly useful synthesis of aromatic amines, as will be discussed in Chapter 22. Most aliphatic amines are more easily prepared other ways.

16·6 some compounds with nitrogen-nitrogen bonds

There are a number of important compounds containing nitrogen-nitrogen bonds. Among these are hydrazines, azo and diazo compounds, and azides.

A. HYDRAZINES

Organic hydrazines are substitution products of NH_2—NH_2 and have many properties similar to those of amines in forming salts and acyl derivatives as well as undergoing alkylation and condensations with carbonyl compounds (Table 11·4). Unsymmetrical hydrazines can be prepared by careful reduction of N-nitrosoamines.

$$CH_3\!\!\diagdown\!\!NH + HONO \longrightarrow \ CH_3\!\!\diagdown\!\!N-NO \xrightarrow{\ 2\,H_2\ } \ CH_3\!\!\diagdown\!\!N-NH_2$$

Aromatic hydrazines are best prepared by reduction of aromatic diazonium salts (Chapter 22).

Hydrazines of the type $R-\overset{H}{\underset{|}{N}}-\overset{H}{\underset{|}{N}}-R$ are usually easily oxidized to the corresponding azo compounds, $R-N=N-R$.

B. AZO COMPOUNDS

Azo compounds possess the $-N=N-$ grouping. Aliphatic azo compounds of the type $R-N=N-H$ are highly unstable and decompose to $R-H$ and nitrogen. Derivatives of the type $R-N=N-R$ are much more stable and can be prepared as mentioned above by oxidation of the corresponding hydrazines. Aromatic azo compounds are available in profusion from diazonium coupling reactions (Chapter 22) and are of commercial importance as dyes and coloring materials.

A prime characteristic of azo compounds is their tendency to decompose into organic radicals and liberate nitrogen:

$$R-N=N-R \longrightarrow 2\,R\cdot + N_2$$

The ease of these reactions is usually a fairly reasonable guide to the stabilities of the radicals that result. For instance, it is found that azomethane $(CH_3N=NCH_3)$ is stable to about 400°, and azobenzene $(C_6H_5N=NC_6H_5)$ is also resistant to thermal decomposition; but, when the azo compound decomposes to radicals that are stabilized by resonance, the decomposition temperature is greatly reduced. Thus 2,2′-azobis(2-methylpropanonitrile) decomposes to radicals at moderate temperatures (60° to 100°), and for this reason is a very useful agent for the initiation of polymerization of vinyl compounds.

$$CH_3-\overset{CN}{\underset{\underset{CH_3}{|}}{\overset{|}{C}}}-N=N-\overset{CN}{\underset{\underset{CH_3}{|}}{\overset{|}{C}}}-CH_3 \xrightarrow{60°-100°} 2\ CH_3-\overset{CN}{\underset{\underset{CH_3}{|}}{\overset{|}{C}}}\!\cdot\ + N_2$$

2,2′-azobis(2-methylpropanonitrile)

C. DIAZO COMPOUNDS

The parent of the diazo compounds, diazomethane $CH_2=\overset{\oplus}{N}=\overset{\ominus}{N}$, has been mentioned before in connection with formation of carbenes (Section 9·7). It is one of the most versatile and useful reagents in organic chemistry, despite the fact that it is highly toxic, dangerously explosive, and cannot be stored without decomposition.

Diazomethane is an intensely yellow gas, bp $-23°$, which is customarily prepared and used in diethyl ether or methylene chloride solution. It can be synthesized a number of ways, such as by the action of base on an N-nitroso-N-methyl amide.

$$R-C\underset{\underset{NO}{\overset{|}{\underset{}{}}}}{\overset{\overset{O}{\parallel}}{\underset{N-CH_3}{}}} + NaOH \xrightarrow{\text{ether}} R-CO_2Na + CH_2N_2 + H_2O$$

As a methylating agent for moderately acidic substances, diazomethane has nearly ideal properties. It can be used in organic solvents; it reacts very rapidly without need for a catalyst; the coproduct is nitrogen, which offers no separation problem; it gives essentially quantitative yields; and, because of its color and the appearance of bubbles of nitrogen, it acts as its own indicator to show when reaction is complete. With acids it gives esters and with enols it gives O-alkylation.

$$CH_3-\underset{\underset{CH}{}}{\overset{\overset{O-H\cdots O}{|\quad\parallel}}{C\quad\quad C}}-CH_3 + CH_2N_2 \longrightarrow CH_3-\underset{\underset{CH}{}}{\overset{\overset{OCH_3\ O}{|\quad\parallel}}{C\quad\quad C}}-CH_3 + N_2$$

Diazomethane was originally believed to possess the three-membered, *diazirine* ring structure, but this was disproved by electron-diffraction studies, which show the linear structure to be correct.

diazirine   diazomethane

Recently, a variety of authentic "cyclodiazomethanes" or, more properly, diazirines have been prepared, and these have been found to have very different properties from the diazoalkanes. The simple diazirines are colorless and do not react with dilute acids, bases, or even bromine. The syntheses of these substances are relatively simple. The route shown is one of the several possible ones.

an "isohydrazone"

summary

Organic nitrogen compounds include amines (RNH_2), amine salts ($RNH_3^{\oplus}X^{\ominus}$), amides ($RCONH_2$), nitriles ($RC\equiv N$), isocyanates ($RNCO$), hydrazines (RNHNHR), azo compounds (RN=NR), diazo compounds (RCHN$_2$), azides (RN$_3$), nitroso compounds (RNO), and nitro compounds (RNO$_2$).

Amines are associated by hydrogen bonding to a moderate extent and as a result they are more volatile than hydrocarbons but less volatile than alcohols of the same molecular weight. However, amines are more soluble in water than alcohols because they form strong hydrogen bonds with the protons of hydroxylic compounds. Amines, like ammonia, undergo rapid inversion at nitrogen. Aliphatic amines are weak bases ($K_B \sim 10^{-4}$) and are very feeble acids ($K_{HA} \sim 10^{-33}$).

Amines can be prepared as illustrated.

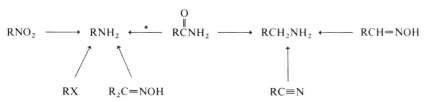

*Hofmann reaction (see also Schmidt and Curtius reactions)

Some of the reactions of amines are

RCH$_2$NH$_2$ $\longrightarrow$ RCH$_2$NH$_3{}^{\oplus}$ (with acids)

$$\longrightarrow \overset{\overset{\displaystyle O}{\|}}{\text{RCH}_2\text{NHCCH}_3}$$ (with acetyl halides)

$\longrightarrow$ N$_2$ + complex products   (with nitrous acid)

$\longrightarrow$ RCHO $\longrightarrow$ RCO$_2$H (with oxidants like Mn^{VII}; *t*-alkyl amines give nitro compounds)

$\longrightarrow$ RCH$_2$NO$_2$ (with peracids; secondary amines give oximes, tertiary amines give amine oxides)

Amides have high melting and boiling points as a result of strong hydrogen bonding. They absorb in the infrared near 3400 cm^{-1} (N—H stretch) and near 1690 cm^{-1} (C=O stretch). They are weak acids ($K_{HA} \sim 10^{-16}$) and weak bases ($K_B \sim 10^{-15}$). Their preparations and reactions are summarized here.

$\overset{\overset{\displaystyle O}{\|}}{\text{RCOCH}_3}$

$\overset{\overset{\displaystyle O}{\|}}{\text{RCCl}}$ (RCO)$_2$O $\longrightarrow$ $\overset{\overset{\displaystyle O}{\|}}{\text{RCNH}_2}$ RC≡N   R$_2$C=NOH

$\overset{\overset{\displaystyle O}{\|}}{\text{RCNH}_2}$ $\longrightarrow$ RCO$_2$H

$\longrightarrow$ RNH$_2$

$\longrightarrow$ RCH$_2$NH$_2$

Nitriles are rather polar compounds with moderate water solubility. The cyano group activates an adjacent methylene like a carbonyl group. Nitriles absorb in the infrared near 2200 cm^{-1} (C≡N stretch). Some methods of preparation and reactions of nitriles are summarized.

$$RX \longrightarrow RC\equiv N \longleftarrow R\overset{\overset{\displaystyle O}{\|}}{C}NH_2 \qquad RCHO \longrightarrow RCHOHC\equiv N$$

$$RC\equiv N \longrightarrow R\overset{\overset{\displaystyle O}{\|}}{C}NH_2 \longrightarrow RCO_2H$$
$$\searrow RCH_2NH_2$$

Nitro compounds absorb strongly in the infrared near 1580 cm^{-1} and 1375 cm^{-1}. Polynitro compounds are often explosive. Nitro compounds can be prepared by nitration of hydrocarbons (works best with arenes) or by the route $RX + NO_2^{\ominus} \rightarrow RNO_2 + X^{\ominus}$.

Azo compounds can be prepared by oxidation of their dihydro derivatives (hydrazines). They are used as sources of radicals ($RN{=}NR \rightarrow N_2 + 2\,R\cdot$). Diazo compounds also tend to lose N_2 and the simplest of them, CH_2N_2 (diazomethane), is an excellent methylating agent for carboxylic acids and enols.

exercises

16·1   Provide a suitable name for each of the following compounds:

a. $H_2N(CH_2)_7NH_2$

g. $H_2NCH_2CO_2H$

b. $(CH_3)_2CHC\overset{\displaystyle\nearrow O}{\underset{\displaystyle\searrow NHCH_3}{}}$

h. $H_2NCH_2CH_2\overset{\oplus}{N}H_3Cl^{\ominus}$

c. $C_6H_5CHClCHClCN$

i.   (benzene ring)—N with CH$_3$ and CH$_2$CH$_3$ substituents

d. $(CH_3)_3CCH_2NO_2$

e. $CH_2{=}CH\overset{\oplus}{N}(CH_3)_3Br^{\ominus}$

j.   (pyridine ring)$\overset{\oplus}{N}{-}CH_3$ $I^{\ominus}$

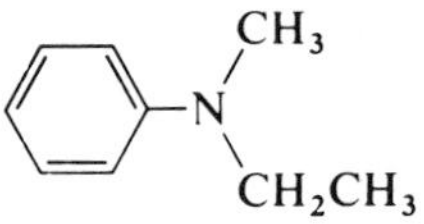

f. $(HOCH_2CH_2)_3N$

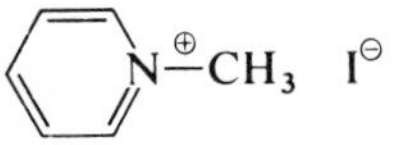

16·2   How could you show with certainty that the peak at 47 Hz with reference to tetramethylsilane in the nmr spectrum of diethylamine (Figure 6·2) is actually due to the N—H resonance?

16·3   Show how structures can be deduced for the substances (a) and (b) of molecular formulas $C_8H_{11}N$, whose nmr and infrared spectra are shown in Figure 16·5.

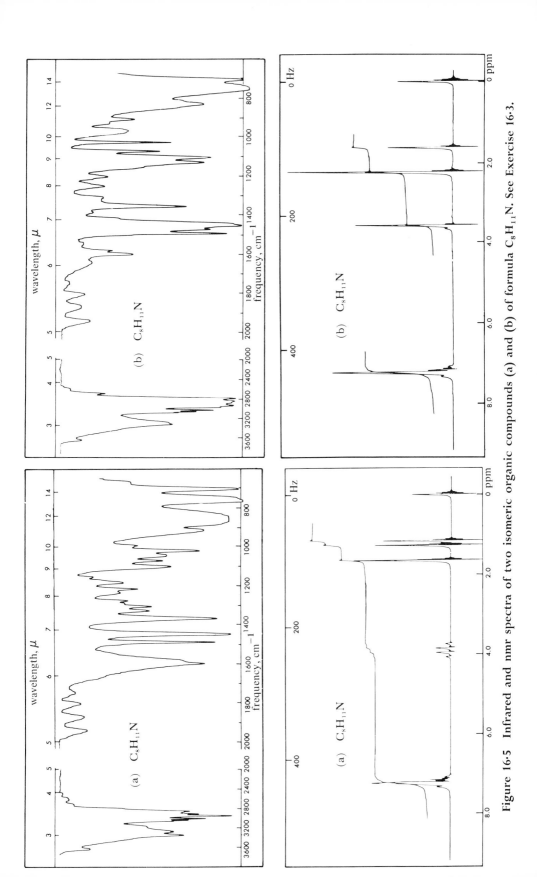

Figure 16-5 Infrared and nmr spectra of two isomeric organic compounds (a) and (b) of formula $C_8H_{11}N$. See Exercise 16-3.

16·4   Guanidine ($K_B \sim 1$) is a very strong base and an exception to the generalization that unsaturated amines are weaker bases than saturated amines.
Consider various ways of adding a proton to guanidine and the kind of
changes in stabilization energies which would be expected for each.

$$HN{=}C\begin{array}{c} \diagup NH_2 \\ \diagdown NH_2 \end{array} \quad \text{guanidine}$$

16·5   Write equations for the reaction that occurs when each of the following
compounds is refluxed with an excess of aqueous sodium hydroxide.

    a.   heptanamide
    b.   N-chlorocyclohexylamine
    c.   allyl 2,3-dimethylbutanoate
    d.   heptanonitrile

16·6   Write equations for the reaction that occurs when each of the following
compounds is treated with an excess of lithium aluminum hydride and the
resulting mixture decomposed with water and acid.

    a.   diphenylacetonitrile
    b.   1,2-dinitrocyclopentane
    c.   diphenylacetic acid
    d.   4-nitrohexanal

16·7   Write structures and provide names for the simplest amine and the simplest
nitrile that can be separated into stable optical isomers at room temperature.

16·8   Write equations for a practical laboratory synthesis of each of the following
compounds based on the indicated starting materials. Give reagents and
conditions.

    a.   dimethyl-*t*-pentylamine from 2-chloro-2-methylbutane
    b. $(CH_3)_3CCH_2NH_2$ from $(CH_3)_3CCO_2H$
    c.   1,6-diaminohexane from 1,3-butadiene
    d.   butanonitrile from 1-butanol
    e. $(CH_3CO_2CH_2)_3C{-}NO_2$ from nitromethane
    f.   N-*t*-butylacetamide from *t*-butyl alcohol
    g.   methylethyl-*n*-butylamine oxide from *n*-butylamine

16·9   *a.*   Make a chart of the mp, bp, and solubilities in water, ether, dilute
acid, and dilute base of each of the following compounds:

       n-octylamine   N,N-dimethylacetamide
       di-*n*-butylamine   1-nitrobutane
       tri-*n*-propylamine 2-nitro-2-methylbutane

    b.   Outline a practical procedure for separation of an equimolal mixture
of each of the above compounds into the *pure components*. Note that
selective reactions are *not* suitable unless the reaction product can be
reconverted to the starting material. Fractional distillation will not
be accepted here as a practical means of separation of compounds
boiling less than 25° apart.

16·10   Give for each of the following pairs of compounds a chemical test, preferably a test tube reaction, which will distinguish between the two compounds.

   a. $(CH_3)_3CNH_2$ and $(CH_3)_2NC_2H_5$
   b. $CH_3CH_2NO_2$ and CH_3CONH_2
   c. $CH_3CH_2C\equiv N$ and $CH\equiv C-CH_2NH_2$
   d. CH_3CH_2NHCl and $CH_3CH_2NH_3Cl$
   e. $CH_3OCH_2CH_2NH_2$ and $CH_3NHCH_2CH_2OH$

   f. $CH_3CH_2C\overset{O}{\underset{NH_2}{\diagup}}$ and $CH_3OCH_2CH_2NH_2$

16·11   Arrange the following pairs of substances in order of expected base strengths. Show your reasoning.

   a. $(CH_3)_3N$ and $(CF_3)_3N$

   b.   ⟨benzene⟩$-CH_2NH_2$ and CH_3-⟨benzene⟩$-NH_2$

   c. $CH_3C\equiv N\colon$ and   ⟨pyridine⟩$N\colon$

   d. $H-C\overset{NH}{\underset{NH_2}{\diagup}}$ and $H-C\overset{O}{\underset{NH_2}{\diagup}}$ (review Exercise 16·4)

   e.   ⟨N-methylpyrrole⟩   and   ⟨azepine⟩   (review Section 6·7)

16·12   Using spectroscopic methods, how could you distinguish one isomer from the other in the following pairs?

   a.   ⟨o-methyl⟩$-NH_2$ and   ⟨⟩$-NHCH_3$

   b. $CH_3CH_2-\overset{O}{\overset{\|}{C}}-NH_2$ and $H-\overset{O}{\overset{\|}{C}}-N(CH_3)_2$

   c. $CH_3CH_2-NO_2$ and CH_3CH_2-ONO

16·13   It is usually possible to obtain two different stable oximes from an unsymmetrical ketone. These so-called *syn* and *anti* isomers are related to *cis-trans* isomers of alkenes.

$\overset{R}{\underset{R'}{\diagdown}}C=N\overset{OH}{\diagup}$ $\overset{R}{\underset{R'}{\diagdown}}C=N\overset{}{\underset{OH}{\diagdown}}$

(*syn* to R, *anti* to R')   (*syn* to R', *anti* to R)

An important characteristic of these isomers is that they give *different* products in the Beckmann rearrangement. In each case, the group *anti* to the OH group migrates to nitrogen. Decide whether or not the mechanism given in Section 16·1E2 for the Beckmann rearrangement can account for this fact and, if not, how it might be modified to do so. What products might be expected from the *syn* and *anti* forms of benzaldehyde oxime?

16·14   Show how one could synthesize and resolve methylethylallylamine oxide from allylamine with the knowledge that amine oxides are somewhat basic substances having K_B values of about 10^{-11}.

16·15   The proton nmr spectrum of N,N-dimethylformamide shows a single proton resonance at 8.06 ppm and two separate three-proton resonance at 2.78 and 2.95 ppm at room temperature. At 150°, the two three-proton lines are found to have coalesced to a single six-proton line, while the single-proton line is unchanged. Explain the nmr spectrum of this compound and its behavior with temperature. What would you predict the energy barrier would be for the process by which the lines are caused to coalesce at elevated temperatures?

16·16   Amides with structures like the following are difficult to prepare and are relatively unstable. Explain.

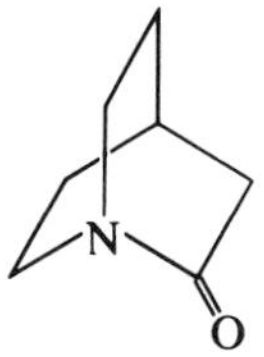

16·17   Benzamidine [7] has a pK_B of 2.4, making it about 10^{14} times as strong a base as benzamide [8].

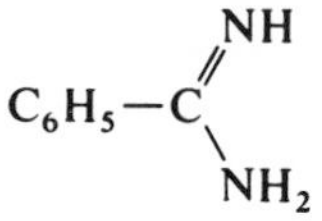

[7] 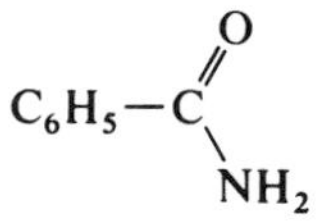   [8]

How do you account for this large difference in view of the fact that protonation produces a resonance-stabilized cation in both cases?

16·18   Show how structures can be deduced for the two substances with the molecular formula $C_5H_9NO_3$ and $C_{10}H_{13}NO$ from their infrared and nmr spectra, as given in Figure 16·6.

16·19   Nitriles of the type RCH_2CN undergo an addition reaction analogous to the aldol addition in the presence of strong bases such as lithium amide. Hydrolysis of the initial reaction product with dilute acid yields a cyano-ketone, $RCH_2-\overset{\text{O}}{\underset{\|}{C}}-\overset{\text{CN}}{\underset{|}{CH}}-R$. Show the steps that are involved in the mechanism of the overall reaction and outline a scheme for its use to synthesize large-ring ketones of the type $(CH_2)_nC=O$ from dinitriles of the type $NC(CH_2)_nCN$.

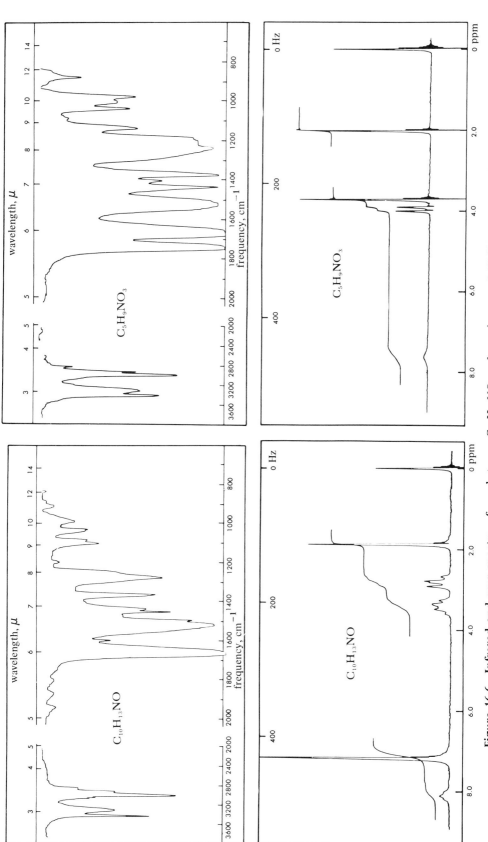

Figure 16-6 Infrared and nmr spectra of a substance $C_{10}H_{13}NO$ and a substance $C_5H_9NO_3$. See Exercise 16-18.

16·20 Show how the following substances may be synthesized from the indicated starting materials.

  a. $(CH_3)_3CCN$ from $(CH_3)_3CCl$
  b. $CH_3CH=CHCN$ from $CH_2=CHCH_2Br$
  c. $CH_2=CHCO_2H$ from CH_3CHO

16·21 Consider possible ways of formulating the electronic structures of nitroso dimers with the knowledge that X-ray diffraction studies indicate the presence of nitrogen-nitrogen bonds.

16·22 Show from the electronic structure of nitrite ion how it could react with an alkyl halide in the S_N2 manner to give either a nitrite ester or a nitro compound. What kind of properties would you expect for a nitrite ester and how could they be removed from the reaction products?

16·23 Arrange the following azo substances in order of their expected rates of thermal decomposition to produce nitrogen. Give your reasoning.

  a. $-CH_2-N=N-CH_2-$ d. $CH_3-N=N-CH_3$

  b. $(CH_3)_3C-N=N-C(CH_3)_3$ e.

  c. $-N=N-$

16·24 Nitriles are converted readily to amides with hydrogen peroxide in dilute sodium hydroxide solution. The reaction is

$$RC\equiv N\ +\ 2\,H_2O_2\ \xrightarrow{\overset{\ominus}{OH}}\ RC\underset{NH_2}{\overset{O}{\big\backslash}}\ +\ O_2\ +\ H_2O$$

The rate equation is

$$v = k[H_2O_2][\overset{\ominus}{OH}][RC\equiv N]$$

When hydrogen peroxide labeled with ^{18}O ($H_2{}^{18}O_2$) is used in ordinary water ($H_2{}^{16}O$), the resulting amide is labeled with ^{18}O ($RC^{18}ONH_2$).

   Write a mechanism for this reaction which is consistent with *all* the experimental facts. Note that hydrogen peroxide is a weak acid ($K_A \sim 10^{-12}$) and, in the absence of hydrogen peroxide, dilute sodium hydroxide attacks nitriles only very slowly.

16·25 An amine, A, forms a precipitate with chloroplatinic acid of formula $(AH^{\oplus})_2PtCl_6{}^{2\ominus}$. A sample of 0.1834 g of this salt is found to contain 0.0644 g of platinum. On treatment with nitrous acid the amine, A, gives an alcohol which gives a positive iodoform test. What is the structure of A?

16·26 The oxidation of an aldehyde to an acid and a secondary alkylamine to a ketone can be carried out as shown in the following equations, which appear to involve merely addition or removal of water. How do the oxidations arise?

$$RCHO + H_2NOH \xrightarrow{-H_2O} RCH{=}NOH \xrightarrow{-H_2O} RC{\equiv}N \xrightarrow{+H_2O} RCONH_2$$

$$\Big\downarrow {+H_2O}$$

$$RCO_2H$$

16·27 Use bond energies (Table 2·1) to evaluate qualitatively the position of the following equilibrium.

$$CH_2{=}CH{-}NH_2 \rightleftharpoons CH_3{-}CH{=}NH$$

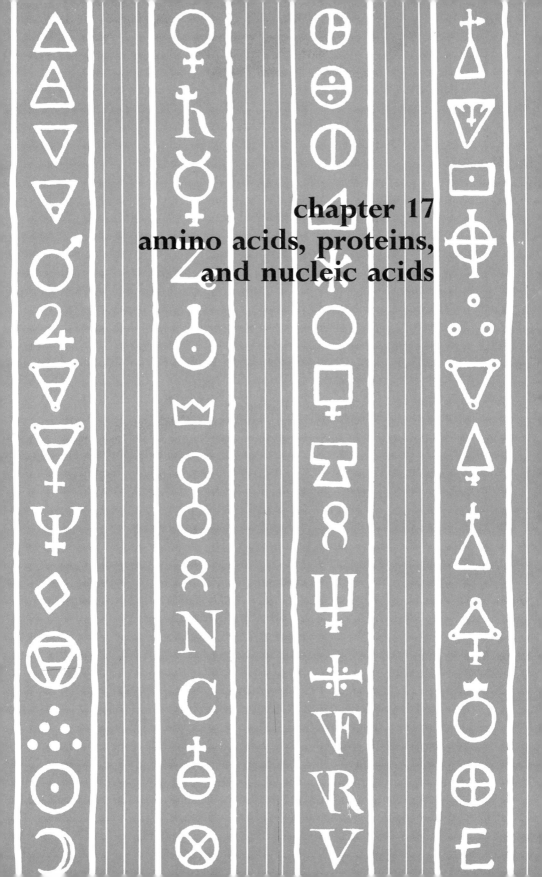

chapter 17
amino acids, proteins, and nucleic acids

The chemistry of life is largely the chemistry of polyfunctional organic compounds. The functional groups are usually of types which interact rather
strongly and are often so located with respect to one another that both
intra- and intermolecular interactions can be important. Carbohydrates offer
one example, and we have seen how the alcohol and carbonyl functions
interact in these substances, leading both to the cyclization of the simple
sugars and to the formation of bonds between sugar molecules to give polysaccharides. This chapter is devoted to the chemistry of amino acids, proteins, and nucleic acids.

Apart from water, protein is the principal component of muscle and many
other kinds of tissue. Nucleic acids, the substances which control heredity, are
just as widely distributed in living organisms although they are present in
smaller amounts. We shall see that both proteins and nucleic acids are polymeric materials built up with polyfunctional compounds as units. In proteins,
these units are amino acids and we shall begin with a discussion of their
chemistry.

17·1   amino acids

All the natural amino acids which occur as constituents of proteins are
carboxylic acids with an amino group at the α position (C-2), $RCHNH_2CO_2H$.
All, with the exception of the simplest one (glycine, R = H), have a center of
asymmetry at the α position and belong to the L series, corresponding to the
projection formula shown (see also Section 14·3B).

$$
\begin{array}{c}
CO_2H \\
| \\
H_2N-C-H \\
| \\
R
\end{array}
$$

L-amino acid

In the case of two amino acids, proline and hydroxyproline, the amino
group is secondary by virtue of being part of a ring. The structures and names
of these and other important α-amino acids are shown in Table 17·1. You
can see that the names in common use for amino acids are not very descriptive
of their structural formulas; but they do have the advantage of being shorter
than the systematic names. As you will see later, the abbreviations Gly, Glu,
and so on listed in Table 17·1 are particularly useful in designating the sequences of amino acids in proteins and peptides. Amino acids that have an
excess of amine over acid groups are called *basic* amino acids (e.g., lysine and
arginine); those with an excess of acid groups are called *acidic* amino acids
(e.g., aspartic and glutamic acids). The additional amino or carboxyl groups
that these four amino acids possess and the functional groups that amino
acids such as serine possess are important in providing points of attachment
for other groups to the protein chain. These may be covalent, ionic, or
hydrogen-bond links.

Three of the amino acids listed in Table 17·1, cysteine, cystine, and methionine, contain sulfur, and the making and breaking of S—S linkages in the

interconversion of cysteine and cystine are important processes in the bio-chemistry of sulfur-containing peptides and proteins. Further characteristics of the general reaction

$$2\,RSH \underset{2[H]}{\overset{[O]}{\rightleftharpoons}} R-S-S-R$$

are considered in Chapter 19.

Organisms differ considerably in their ability to synthesize amino acids. The eight acids that are indispensable for human beings, yet which the body cannot synthesize, are often called "essential" amino acids and are so marked in Table 17·1. Of the 24 amino acids listed in the table only 20 are fundamental building blocks. The presence in proteins of the remaining four (see Table 17·1) results from *in vivo* conversions of other amino acids *after* the protein has been synthesized. Protein synthesis, both *in vitro* and *in vivo*, is considered in more detail later in the chapter.

A. SYNTHESIS OF α-AMINO ACIDS

Many of the types of reactions useful in preparing amino acids in the labora-tory have been discussed earlier in connection with separate syntheses of carboxylic acids (Chapter 13) and amino compounds (Chapter 16). Two examples are included here.

1. Amination of chloroacetic acid to yield glycine, which works best with a large excess of ammonia.

$$3\,NH_3 + ClCH_2CO_2H \xrightarrow{50°} \overset{\ominus}{NH_2}CH_2\overset{\oplus}{CO_2}NH_4 + \overset{\oplus}{NH_4}\overset{\ominus}{Cl}$$

$$\downarrow H^{\oplus}$$

$$NH_2CH_2CO_2H$$
$$\text{glycine}$$

2. **Strecker synthesis**; in its first step, it bears a close relationship to cyano-hydrin formation.

$$\langle \text{C}_6\text{H}_5 \rangle - CHO + NH_3 + HCN \longrightarrow \langle \text{C}_6\text{H}_5 \rangle - \underset{NH_2}{\underset{|}{CH}} - C\equiv N \xrightarrow{H^{\oplus},\,H_2O} \langle \text{C}_6\text{H}_5 \rangle - \underset{NH_2}{\underset{|}{CH}} - CO_2H$$

Many amino acids are very soluble in water and it may be necessary to isolate the product either by evaporation of an aqueous solution or by precip-itation induced by addition of an organic solvent such as alcohol. Difficul-ties are often encountered in obtaining a pure product if inorganic salts are coproducts of the synthesis.

B. THE ACID-BASE PROPERTIES OF AMINO ACIDS

The behavior of glycine is typical of that of the simple amino acids. Since glycine is neither a strong acid nor a strong base, we shall expect a solution of

Table 17·1   Amino acids important as constituents of proteins

name	abbreviation	formula	$[M]_D$ of L isomer, H_2O, 25°[a]	isoelectric point, pH units	water solubility at isoelectric point,[b] g/100 g, 20°
glycine	Gly	$NH_2CH_2CO_2H$		6.0	22.5
alanine	Ala	CH_3CHCO_2H $\quad\ \ \|$ $\quad NH_2$	+1.6°	6.0	15.8
valine[c]	Val	$(CH_3)_2CHCHCO_2H$ $\qquad\qquad\ \|$ $\qquad\qquad NH_2$	+6.6°	6.0	6.8
leucine[c]	Leu	$(CH_3)_2CHCH_2CHCO_2H$ $\qquad\qquad\qquad\ \|$ $\qquad\qquad\qquad NH_2$	−14.4°	6.0	2.4
isoleucine[c]	Ile	$CH_3CH_2CH{-}CHCO_2H$ $\qquad\quad\ \|\quad\ \|$ $\qquad\quad CH_3\ NH_2$	+16.3°	6.0	2.1
phenylalanine[c]	Phe	$C_6H_5CH_2CHCO_2H$ $\qquad\qquad\ \|$ $\qquad\qquad NH_2$	−57.0°	5.5	2.7
serine	Ser	$HOCH_2CHCO_2H$ $\qquad\quad\ \|$ $\qquad\quad NH_2$	−7.9°	5.7	4.3
threonine[c]	Thr	$CH_3CH{-}CHCO_2H$ $\qquad\ \|\quad\ \|$ $\qquad OH\ NH_2$	−33.9°	5.6	1.6
lysine[c]	Lys	$NH_2(CH_2)_4CHCO_2H$ $\qquad\qquad\quad\ \|$ $\qquad\qquad\quad NH_2$	+19.7°	9.7	very sol.
5-hydroxylysine[d]	Hyl	$NH_2CH_2CH(CH_2)_2CHCO_2H$ $\qquad\quad\ \|\qquad\qquad\ \|$ $\qquad\quad OH\qquad\qquad NH_2$	+14.9°	9.15	very sol.

Table 17·1   Amino acids important as constituents of proteins (*continued*)

name	abbreviation	formula	$[M]_D$ of L isomer, H_2O, 25°[a]	isoelectric point, pH units	water solubility at isoelectric point,[b] g/100 g, 20°
arginine	Arg	$HN{=}C(H_2N){-}NH(CH_2)_3CHCO_2H$, NH_2	+21.8°	11.2	very sol.
aspartic acid	Asp	$HO_2CCH_2CHCO_2H$, NH_2	+6.7°	2.8	0.4
asparagine	Asn	$NH_2COCH_2CHCO_2H$, NH_2	−7.4°	5.4	2.4
glutamic acid	Glu	$HO_2C(CH_2)_2CHCO_2H$, NH_2	+17.7°	3.2	0.7
glutamine	Gln	$NH_2CO(CH_2)_2CHCO_2H$, NH_2	+9.2°	5.7	3.6^{18}
cysteine	CySH	$HSCH_2CHCO_2H$, NH_2	−20.0°	5.1	very sol.
cystine[d]	CyS—|—CyS	$S{-}CH_2CHCO_2H$, NH_2 / $S{-}CH_2CHCO_2H$, NH_2 $\xrightleftharpoons[{[H]}]{[O]}$	−509° (1 N HCl)	5.0	0.009
methionine[c]	Met	$CH_3S(CH_2)_2CHCO_2H$, NH_2	−14.9°	5.7	3.0

[a] For definition of $[M]_D$ see Section 14·2. Usually, the concentration $c = 1\text{--}2$ g per 100 ml of solution. For slightly soluble amino acids, the rotations are given for HCl solutions.

[b] Refers to the L isomer. The D,L mixtures are usually less soluble (see Section 14·3A).

Table 17·1 (*continued*)

name	abbreviation	formula	$[M]_D$ of L isomer, H_2O, 25°[a]	isoelectric point, pH units	water solubility at isoelectric point,[b] g/100 g, 20°
tyrosine	Tyr	HO—⟨ benzene ⟩—CH_2CHCO_2H / NH_2	−18°	5.7	0.04
thyroxine[d]	Thy	HO—⟨ I,I-ring ⟩—O—⟨ I,I-ring ⟩—CH_2CHCO_2H / NH_2	−3.8°[e]		
proline	Pro	H_2C—CH_2 / H_2C / N—$CHCO_2H$ / H	−99.2°	6.3	154.5
hydroxyproline[d]	Hyp	HOHC—CH_2 / H_2C / N—$CHCO_2H$ / H	−99.6°	5.7	34.5
tryptophan[c]	Try	⟨ indole ⟩ CH_2CHCO_2H / NH_2	−68.8°	5.9	1.1
histidine	His	HC=CCH_2CHCO_2H / N NH NH_2 / CH	−59.8°	7.5	4.0

[c] Must be included in diet of normal adult humans.
[d] Formed by conversion of the other amino acids after the protein has been synthesized.
[e] In ethanolic sodium hydroxide solution.

glycine in water to contain four species in rapid equilibrium.

$$NH_2CH_2CO_2H$$

$$\overset{\oplus}{N}H_3CH_2CO_2H \underset{+H^\oplus}{\overset{-H^\oplus}{\rightleftharpoons}} \overset{\oplus}{N}H_3CH_2\overset{\ominus}{C}O_2 \underset{+H^\oplus}{\overset{-H^\oplus}{\rightleftharpoons}} NH_2CH_2\overset{\ominus}{C}O_2$$

| conjugate acid | dipolar ion | conjugate base |
| of glycine | (zwitterion) | of glycine |

The proportions of these species are expected to change with pH, the conjugate acid being the predominant form at low pH values and the conjugate base being favored at high pH values. Since the establishment of equilibrium between the uncharged molecule and the dipolar ion (often called a "zwitterion") involves no net change in hydrogen or hydroxide ion concentrations, the *ratio* of these two substances is independent of pH. The position of equilibrium, however, strongly favors the zwitterion.

$$NH_2CH_2CO_2H \rightleftharpoons \overset{\oplus}{N}H_3CH_2\overset{\ominus}{C}O_2$$

A titration curve starting with glycine hydrochloride is shown in Figure 17·1. Two equivalents of base are required to convert $^\oplus NH_3CH_2CO_2H$ to $NH_2CH_2CO_2{}^\ominus$. The pH of half-neutralization during addition of the first equivalent of base corresponds to proton loss from the carboxyl group of the conjugate acid of glycine, $K_{BH^\oplus} = 5 \times 10^{-3}$, whereas the pH of half-neutralization during the addition of the second equivalent of base corresponds to proton loss from the ammonium group of the zwitterion, $K_{HA} = 2 \times 10^{-10}$. There will be a pH on the titration curve where the concentration of zwitterion is at a maximum and where the concentration of $\overset{\oplus}{N}H_3CH_2CO_2H$ will be just equal to the concentration of $NH_2CH_2CO_2{}^\ominus$. If these two ions conduct electric current equally well, then, in an electrolytic experiment, there

Figure 17·1 Titration curve of the conjugate acid of glycine, $\overset{\oplus}{N}H_3CH_2CO_2H$, with base.

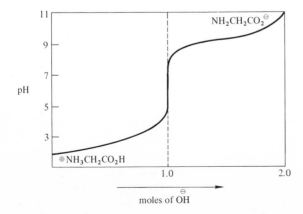

moles of $\overset{\ominus}{O}H$

will be no net migration of the ions at this particular pH, which is called the **isoelectric point.** Generally, the isoelectric point corresponds also to the pH at which the amino acid's water solubility is least. Isoelectric points are listed for most of the amino acids shown in Table 17·1.

Because the basic dissociation constant, K_B, of most aliphatic amines and the acid dissociation constant, K_{HA}, of most aliphatic acids are comparable, we expect the isoelectric point for simple amino acids like glycine to be not far from neutrality. The value of 6.0 shown in Table 17·1 indicates that the carboxyl group in glycine is actually very slightly stronger than the amino group.

A basic amino acid such as lysine exists as a neutral molecule (actually an equilibrium mixture containing one of the zwitterions as the principal component) at a somewhat higher pH. The isoelectric point of this compound is 9.7.

$$NH_2CH_2CH_2CH_2CH_2\underset{\underset{\overset{|}{\underset{\oplus}{NH_3}}}{}}{CHCO_2^{\ominus}} \;\rightleftharpoons\; \overset{\oplus}{NH_3}CH_2CH_2CH_2CH_2\underset{\underset{\overset{|}{NH_2}}{}}{CHCO_2^{\ominus}}$$

An acidic amino acid such as glutamic acid, by contrast, is only electrically neutral in the presence of enough excess acid to prevent the second carboxyl group from ionizing. Its isoelectric point is 3.2, which means that the electrically neutral forms shown here are at their highest concentrations at this pH. (The free amino or carboxyl groups in protein chains provide acidic or basic centers in these molecules in addition to serving as points of attachment for other groups.)

$$HO_2CCH_2CH_2\underset{\underset{\overset{|}{\underset{\oplus}{NH_3}}}{}}{CHCO_2^{\ominus}} \;\rightleftharpoons\; {^\ominus}O_2CCH_2CH_2\underset{\underset{\overset{|}{\underset{\oplus}{NH_3}}}{}}{CHCO_2H}$$

C. ANALYSIS OF AMINO ACIDS

Nitrous Acid Reactions. The action of nitrous acid on amino acids proceeds in a manner similar to that discussed earlier for ordinary amines (Section 16·1F3). Primary amino groups are lost as nitrogen; secondary amino groups are nitrosated, whereas tertiary amino functions react to give complex products without evolution of nitrogen. Measurement of the nitrogen evolved on treatment of amino acids or their derivatives with nitrous acid provides a useful analysis for free $-NH_2$ groups in such materials **(Van Slyke amino-nitrogen determination).** With amino acids, as with amines, the nitrous acid reaction is not to be regarded as a generally satisfactory preparative method for conversion of RNH_2 to ROH.

The Ninhydrin Test. In many kinds of research it is important to have simple means of detecting compounds in minute amounts. Detection of α-amino acids is readily achieved by the "ninhydrin color test." An alcoholic solution of the triketone hydrate called "ninhydrin," heated with a solution containing an amino acid, produces a blue-violet color. The sensitivity and reliability of this test is such that 0.01 micromole of amino acid gives a colored solution whose absorbance is reproducible to a few percent, provided that oxidation of the colored ion by dissolved oxygen is prevented by the addition of a reducing agent such as stannous chloride.

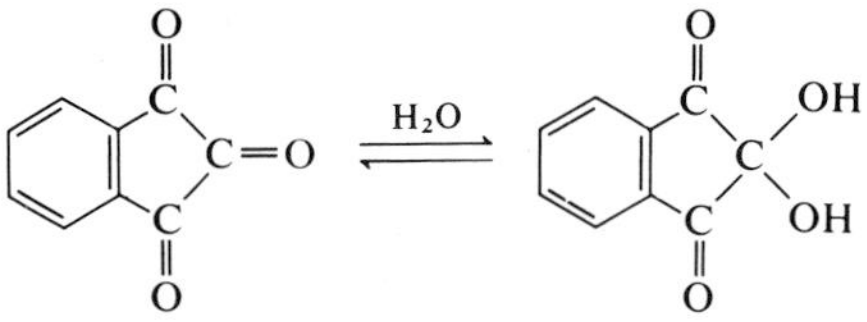

indane-1,2,3-trione   "ninhydrin"

The color-forming reaction is interesting because all amino acids except

Figure 17·2   The color-forming reaction of ninhydrin (in the trione form) with an amino acid.

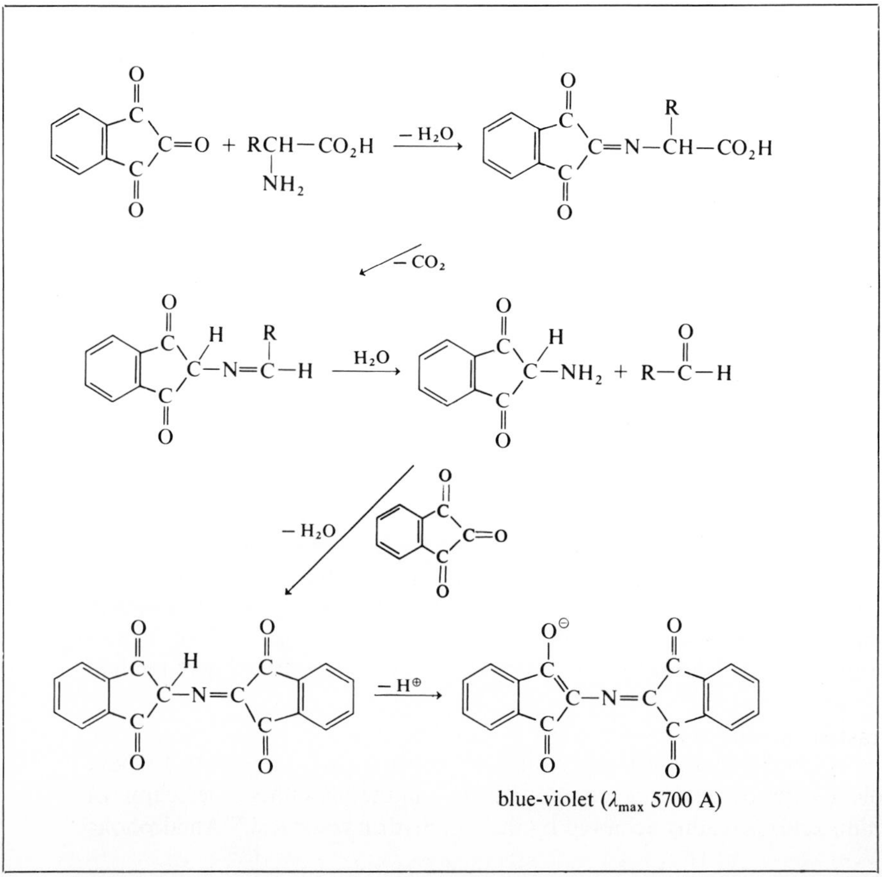

blue-violet (λ_{max} 5700 A)

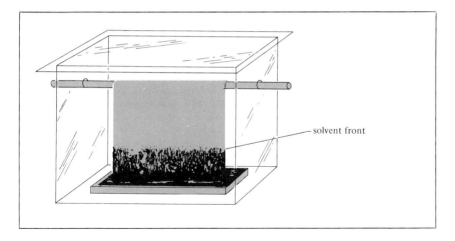

solvent front

Figure 17·3   Diagram of apparatus used to develop a paper chromatogram. Paper is suspended from its top edge within an airtight container (here a glass box closed with a glass plate) having an atmosphere saturated with solvent vapor; the lower edge of paper dips into a trough containing the liquid solvent.

proline and hydroxyproline give the same color ($\lambda_{max} = 5700$ A). The sequence of steps that leads to the color is shown in Figure 17·2. The secondary amino acids proline and hydroxyproline give a yellow color ($\lambda_{max} = 4400$ A) with ninhydrin.

Chromatography. The analysis of mixtures of amino acids (or other compounds) can be conveniently carried out by any of three chromatographic techniques—paper chromatography, column chromatography, or thin-layer chromatography (tlc). In Chapter 7 we described the principles of chromatography on which each of these methods is based.

In paper chromatography, amino acids are separated as the consequence of differences in their partition coefficients between water and an organic solvent. The aqueous phase is held stationary in the microporous structure of the paper. The differences in partition coefficients show up as differences in rates of migration on the surface of moist (but not wet) filter paper over which is passed a slow flow of water-saturated organic solvent.

We shall discuss one of several useful modes of operation. In this, a drop of the solution to be analyzed is placed on the corner of a sheet of moist filter paper, which is then placed in an apparatus such as shown in Figure 17·3, arranged so that the organic solvent can migrate upward by capillarity across the paper, carrying the amino acids with it along one edge. The acids that have the greatest solubility in the organic solvent move most rapidly and, before the fastest moving acid reaches the top of the paper, the paper is removed, dried, then turned sideways and a different solvent allowed to diffuse across the width. This double migration process gives a better separation of the amino acids than a single migration and results in concentration of the different amino acids in rather well-defined zones or spots. These spots can

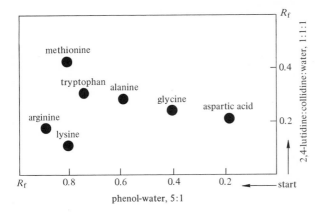

Figure 17·4 Idealized two-dimensional paper chromatogram of a mixture of amino acids. The horizontal and vertical scales represent the distance of travel of a component of the mixture in a given solvent in a given time relative to that of the solvent itself. This is known as the *Rf* value and is fairly constant for a particular compound in a given solvent. A rough identification of the amino acids present in the mixture may therefore be made on the basis of their *Rf* values

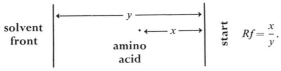

be made visible by first drying and then spraying the paper with ninhydrin solution. The final result is as shown in Figure 17·4 and is usually quite reproducible under a given set of conditions. The identities of the amino acids that produce the various spots are established by comparison with the behavior of known mixtures.

Paper chromatography has proved very useful in following the mechanisms of biological processes using radioactive tracers. For example, in the study of the fixation of carbon dioxide in photosynthesis, it was found possible to determine the rate of incorporation of radioactive carbon from carbon dioxide into various sugars, amino acids, and the like, by separating the products of photosynthesis at a succession of time intervals on paper chromatograms, then analyzing their radioactivities by scanning the paper with a Geiger counter or by simply measuring the degree of fogging of an X-ray film laid over the chromatograms.

A quantitative method of analysis of amino acids can be achieved using column chromatography (Section 7·1). The solution to be analyzed is passed through columns packed with an ion-exchange resin and this separates the amino acids according to their ability to be complexed with the highly polar sites of the resin. The effluent from the column is mixed with ninhydrin solution and the intensity of the blue color developed is measured with a photo-electric colorimeter and plotted as a function of time at constant flow rates. A typical analysis of a mixture of amino acids by a machine constructed to carry out the procedure automatically is shown in Figure 17·5.

Thin-layer chromatography (tlc) is similar to paper chromatography except that the adsorbent (usually silica gel) is applied in a thin layer to a glass plate. Silica gel is mixed with plaster of Paris ($CaSO_4$) and a small amount of water and the resulting slurry is coated on a plate which may be as small as a microscope slide or as large as a medium-sized window pane. The samples are then spotted on the adsorbent as in paper chromatography and the $\check{R}f$ values determined the same way.

Thin-layer chromatography is now very widely used because it combines the best features of paper and column chromatography—that is, the ease of locating compounds by spraying with various reagents as in paper chromatography and the wide range of adsorbents available in column chromatography. It is rapid, and more drastic reagents can be used for locating spots than is possible with paper chromatographs.

17·2   lactams

The cyclization of hydroxy acids through lactone formation has been discussed in Chapter 13. The corresponding cyclization of amino acids leads to lactams.

γ-butyrolactone
(lactone of 4-hydroxybutanoic acid)

γ-butyrolactam
(lactam of 4-aminobutanoic acid)

Figure 17·5   Section of amino acid chromatogram obtained by the method of automatic amino acid analysis from a hydrolyzed sample of the enzyme ribonuclease. The amino acids are identified by their position of elution and are quantified by integration of the area under the curve.

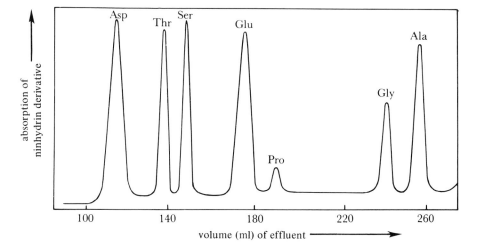

Formation of α- and β-lactams is expected to generate considerable ring strain, and other more favorable reactions usually intervene. Thus, while γ-butyrolactam can be prepared by heating ethyl 4-aminobutanoate, the corresponding α-lactam is not formed from ethyl 2-aminobutanoate but, instead, the dimeric diethyldiketopiperazine [1] with a six-membered ring results.

diethyldiketopiperazine
[1]

β-Lactams have been rather intensively investigated following the discovery that the important antibiotic penicillin G [2], produced by fermentation with *Penicillium notatum*, possesses a β-lactam ring.

penicillin G (benzylpenicillin)
[2]

The problem of determining the correct structure of penicillin was an extraordinarily difficult one because the molecule is very labile and undergoes extensive rearrangements to biologically inactive products even under very mild conditions. The β-lactam structure was finally established by X-ray diffraction analysis. Penicillin G and many closely related compounds with different groups in place of the benzyl group have been synthesized.

17·3 peptides

We saw earlier that the reaction of a carboxyl function with an amine produces an amide.

If both the reactants are bifunctional, each containing an α-amino group and a carboxyl function, the reaction can proceed further to form a poly-amide.

$$R-\overset{\displaystyle O}{\overset{\|}{C}}-NH-\underset{\displaystyle R}{\overset{\displaystyle |}{CH}}-\overset{\displaystyle O}{\overset{\|}{C}}-NH-\underset{\displaystyle R}{\overset{\displaystyle |}{CH}}-\overset{\displaystyle O}{\overset{\|}{C}}-NH-\underset{\displaystyle R}{\overset{\displaystyle |}{CH}}\text{------------}$$

Such molecules are called **peptides** (or polypeptides) and, of course, may be so constituted that all of the R groups are not the same. They are classified according to the number of amino acid groups in the chain and are named as derivatives of the amino acid with the free carboxyl group, the amide group being called the **peptide linkage**.

$$\overset{\oplus}{H_3N}-CH_2-\overset{\displaystyle O}{\overset{\|}{C}}-NH-\underset{\displaystyle CH_3}{\overset{\displaystyle |}{CH}}-CO_2^{\ominus} \qquad \overset{\oplus}{H_3N}-\underset{\displaystyle CH_3}{\overset{\displaystyle |}{CH}}-\overset{\displaystyle O}{\overset{\|}{C}}-NH-\underset{\displaystyle CH_2}{\overset{\displaystyle |}{\underset{\displaystyle |}{CH}}}-\overset{\displaystyle O}{\overset{\|}{C}}-NH-\underset{\displaystyle CH_2OH}{\overset{\displaystyle |}{CH}}-CO_2^{\ominus}$$

glycylalanine (H·Gly·Ala·OH) alanylcysteinylserine (H·Ala·CySH·Ser·OH)
a dipeptide a tripeptide

Peptides, being polyamides, can be hydrolyzed under the influence of acids or bases (or enzymes) to give their constituent amino acids.

The distinction between a protein and a peptide is not completely clear. One arbitrary choice is to call proteins only those substances with molecular weights greater than 10,000. The distinction might also be made in terms of differences in physical properties, particularly hydration and conformation. The naturally occurring peptides have relatively short flexible chains and are hydrated reversibly in aqueous solution; proteins, by contrast, have very long chains which appear to be coiled and folded in rather particular ways, with water molecules helping to fill the interstices. Under the influence of heat, organic solvents, salts, and so on, protein molecules undergo more or less irreversible changes, called **denaturation**, in which both the conformations of the chains and the degree of hydration are altered. The result is usually a decrease in solubility and loss of ability to crystallize. Proteins thus have a very high degree of conformational specificity. Recent success in synthesizing polypeptides with enzymic activity (Section 17·3C) suggests that the folding of the peptide chain to give the conformationally correct enzyme is a conse-quence of the way the amino acids are arranged in sequence.

Proteins, particularly those with hormonal or enzymic functions, often have other groups attached to the polypeptide chain. These groups are called **prosthetic groups**.

A. PEPTIDE ANALYSIS

A wide variety of peptides occur naturally. However, of those whose struc-tures have been determined, a considerable proportion contain one or more amino acids which are not found as constituents of proteins. Indeed, many peptides are cyclic, and in some even D-amino acids occur. Most of the well-characterized peptides contain 3 to 10 amino acid units.

The properties of peptides and of proteins are a critical function of not only the number and kind of their constituent amino acids but also the sequence in which the amino acids are linked together. Analyses for amino acid content can be made by complete hydrolysis and ion exchange separations, as described in Section 17·1C. Establishment of the sequence of amino acids is much more difficult but has been carried through to completion on peptide chains having more than 100 amino acid units.

The general procedure for determining amino acid sequences is to establish the nature of the end groups and then, by a variety of hydrolytic or oxidative methods, break up the chain into peptides having two to five amino acid units. The idea in using a variety of ways of cutting the chains is to obtain fragments with common units which can be matched up to one another to obtain the overall sequence.

Determination of the amino acid that supplies the terminal amino group in a peptide chain (the N-terminal acid) is best made by treatment of the peptide with 2,4-dinitrofluorobenzene, a substance which is very reactive in nucleophilic displacements with amines but not with amides. The product is a N-2,4-dinitrophenyl derivative of the peptide which, after hydrolysis of the amide linkages, yields a N-2,4-dinitrophenylamino acid. See Figure 17·6.

This substance can be separated from the ordinary amino acids resulting from hydrolysis of the peptide, owing to the low basicity of the 2,4-dinitrophenyl-substituted nitrogen, which greatly reduces the solubility of the compound in acid solution and alters its chromatographic behavior.

B. PEPTIDE SYNTHESIS

The problem of synthesizing peptides is of great importance and has received considerable attention. The major difficulty in putting together a chain of, say

Figure 17·6   Determination of the terminal amino acid possessing the free amino group in a peptide chain.

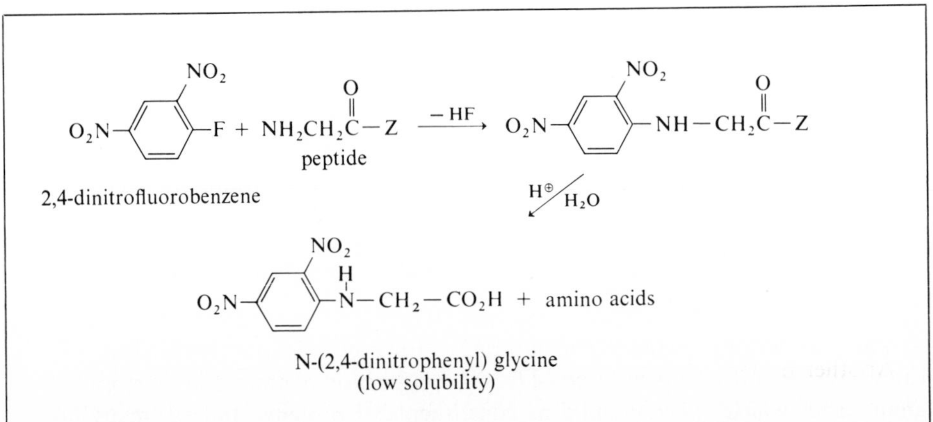

100, amino acids in a particular order is one of overall yield. At least 100 separate synthetic steps would be required and, if the yields in each step are all equal to $n \times 100\%$, the overall yield is $(n^{100} \times 100\%)$. Thus, if each yield is 90%, the overall yield is only 0.003%. Obviously, a laboratory synthesis of a peptide chain comparable in size to those which occur in proteins must be a highly efficient process. The extraordinary ability of living cells to achieve syntheses of this nature, not of just one but of a wide variety of such substances, is truly impressive.

Several methods for the formation of amide bonds have been discussed in Chapters 13 and 16. The most generally useful reactions are of the type where X is halogen, alkoxyl, or acyloxy, corresponding to acyl halides, esters, or acid anhydrides.

$$R-\overset{\overset{\displaystyle O}{\|}}{\underset{\underset{\displaystyle X}{\diagdown}}{C}} + NH_2-R' \longrightarrow R-\overset{\overset{\displaystyle O}{\|}}{\underset{\underset{\displaystyle NHR'}{\diagdown}}{C}} + HX$$

When these are applied to join up two different amino acids, difficulty is to be expected, because the same reactions can link together two amino acids of the same kind.

$$NH_2CH_2\overset{\overset{\displaystyle O}{\|}}{C}-OH \xrightarrow{PCl_3} NH_2CH_2\overset{\overset{\displaystyle O}{\|}}{C}-Cl$$

$$2\, NH_2CH_2\overset{\overset{\displaystyle O}{\|}}{C}-Cl \xrightarrow{-HCl} NH_2CH_2\overset{\overset{\displaystyle O}{\|}}{C}NHCH_2\overset{\overset{\displaystyle O}{\|}}{C}-Cl,\quad \text{etc.}$$

To avoid such reactions, a "protecting group" is substituted on the amino function of the acid that is to act as the acylating agent. A good protecting group must be easily attached to the amino group without causing racemization of an optically active acid. Moreover, it must be easily removed without affecting the peptide linkages or sensitive functional groups on the amino acid side chains, such as the sulfur-containing groups of cysteine, cystine, and methionine.

The benzyloxycarbonyl group, $C_6H_5CH_2O\overset{\overset{\displaystyle O}{\|}}{C}-$, is a useful protecting group that can be removed at the appropriate time by catalytic hydrogenolysis.

$$C_6H_5CH_2O\overset{\overset{\displaystyle O}{\|}}{C}-NHCH\overset{\overset{\displaystyle O}{\|}}{\underset{\underset{\displaystyle R}{|}}{C}}-NHCHCO_2H$$
$$\underset{R}{|}$$

$$\xrightarrow{H_2} C_6H_5CH_3 + CO_2 + \overset{\oplus}{N}H_3CH\overset{\overset{\displaystyle O}{\|}}{\underset{\underset{\displaystyle R}{|}}{C}}-NHCHCO_2^{\ominus}$$

Another protecting group that has been found to be particularly useful in solid-phase peptide synthesis, described in the next section, is the t-butoxycarbonyl group, $(CH_3)_3COC$—$\overset{\text{O}}{\overset{\|}{}}$. Treatment of an amino acid such as glycine with t-butoxycarbonyl azide [3] in basic solution produces the protected amino acid [4] after acidification.

$$(CH_3)_3COCN_3 + NH_2CH_2CO_2^{\ominus} \xrightarrow[\text{2. H}^{\oplus}]{\text{1. base}} (CH_3)_3COC-NHCH_2CO_2H$$

[3]   [4]

The product dissolved in methylene chloride can then be coupled with a second amino acid, such as alanine, by treatment with dicyclohexylcarbodiimide, $C_6H_{11}N{=}C{=}NC_6H_{11}$, an efficient, nonacidic dehydrating agent.[1]

$$(CH_3)_3COC-NHCH_2CO_2H + \underset{\underset{CH_3}{|}}{\overset{\oplus}{N}H_3CHCO_2^{\ominus}} + C_6H_{11}N{=}C{=}NC_6H_{11}$$

$$\longrightarrow (CH_3)_3COC-NHCH_2C-NH\underset{\underset{CH_3}{|}}{C}HCO_2H + C_6H_{11}NH-C-NHC_6H_{11}$$

The chain can then be extended by treating this dipeptide with a third amino acid, and so on. Cleavage of the protecting group, which occurs readily on treatment with hydrochloric acid dissolved in acetic acid, gives the polypeptide.

$$(CH_3)_3COC-NHCH_2C\text{\textasciitilde} \xrightarrow{\text{HCl}} (CH_3)_2C{=}CH_2 + CO_2 + \overset{\oplus}{N}H_3CH_2C\text{\textasciitilde}$$

C. SOLID-PHASE PEPTIDE SYNTHESIS

The difficulty with the method of peptide synthesis described in the previous section is the number of steps involved in order to make a peptide of even modest size. We have shown earlier how poor the overall yield in a multistage process can be if each stage is not highly efficient.

In recent years, R. B. Merrifield has developed an approach to peptide synthesis which permits preparation of peptides of some size (and even enzymically active substances) in acceptable yields. The advantage of the method is that it avoids the intermediate isolation steps which characterize the usual multistage synthesis. At the start, the amino acid that will ultimately be at the free-carboxyl end of the peptide is bonded to active groups on a solid polymer through its *carboxyl group*. The polymer is usually an insoluble polystyrene resin containing chloromethyl groups and is prepared as small spherical beads. The binding reaction is brought about by nucleophilic displacement between the chloride and the salt of the amino acid to give an ester.

---

[1] Great care should be exercised when working with this compound—it is a potent contact allergen.

$$NH_2CHCO_2{}^{\ominus} + ClCH_2-[POLYMER]$$
$$\qquad\quad |$$
$$\qquad\quad R_1$$

$$\xrightarrow{\hspace{2cm}} NH_2\overset{\overset{\displaystyle O}{\|}}{C}H\overset{}{C}-O-CH_2-[POLYMER] + Cl^{\ominus}$$
$$\qquad\qquad\qquad\quad |$$
$$\qquad\qquad\qquad\quad R_1$$

The resulting solid, insoluble, amino acid–polymer complex is quite porous and, when treated with a methylene chloride solution of a second amino acid (suitably protected at the amino group by a *t*-butoxycarbonyl group) and dicyclohexylcarbodiimide, yields a dipeptide, attached at one end to the solid resin.

$$(CH_3)_3CO\overset{\overset{\displaystyle O}{\|}}{C}-NH\overset{}{C}HCO_2H + NH_2\overset{\overset{\displaystyle O}{\|}}{C}H\overset{}{C}-O-CH_2-[POLYMER]$$
$$\qquad\qquad\qquad |\qquad\qquad\qquad\qquad\quad |$$
$$\qquad\qquad\qquad R_2\qquad\qquad\qquad\qquad\quad R_1$$

$$C_6H_{11}N=C=NC_6H_{11}$$
$$CH_2Cl_2$$

$$(CH_3)_3CO\overset{\overset{\displaystyle O}{\|}}{C}-NH\overset{}{C}H\overset{\overset{\displaystyle O}{\|}}{C}-NH\overset{}{C}H\overset{\overset{\displaystyle O}{\|}}{C}-O-CH_2-[POLYMER]$$
$$\qquad\qquad\qquad |\qquad\qquad\quad |$$
$$\qquad\qquad\qquad R_2\qquad\qquad\quad R_1$$

The protecting group can be removed, as described in the previous section, and the process continued. The advantage of the procedure is that the products at each stage need not be isolated and purified as would normally be required for reactions in solution. Instead, the solid resin with its attached peptide chain can be washed free of impurities and excess reagents at each stage with virtually no loss of peptide. The method lends itself beautifully to automatic control, and machines suitably programmed to add reagents and wash the product at appropriate times have been developed. At present, the chain can be extended by six or so amino acid units per day.

When the synthesis of the peptide chain has been completed, it is removed from the resin surface with hydrogen bromide in anhydrous trifluoroacetic acid. This treatment removes the final N-protecting group at the same time.

$$(CH_3)_3CO\overset{\overset{\displaystyle O}{\|}}{C}-NH\overset{}{C}H\overset{\overset{\displaystyle O}{\|}}{C}\sim\sim NH\overset{}{C}H\overset{\overset{\displaystyle O}{\|}}{C}-O-CH_2-[POLYMER]$$
$$\qquad\qquad\qquad\quad |\qquad\qquad\quad |$$
$$\qquad\qquad\qquad\quad R_x\qquad\qquad\quad R_1$$

$$HBr \Big| CF_3CO_2H$$

$$\overset{\oplus}{NH_3}\overset{}{C}H\overset{\overset{\displaystyle O}{\|}}{C}\sim\sim NH\overset{}{C}H\overset{}{C}O_2{}^{\ominus} + (CH_3)_2C=CH_2 + CO_2 + BrCH_2-[POLYMER]$$
$$\quad |\qquad\qquad\qquad |$$
$$\quad R_x\qquad\qquad\quad R_1$$

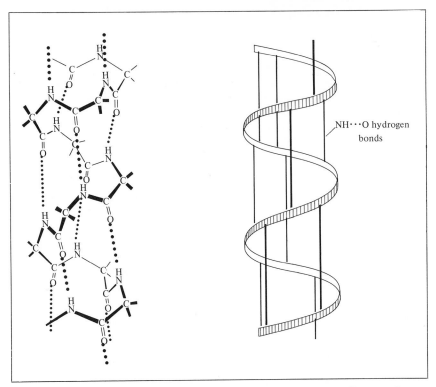

Figure 17·7 Peptide chain of a protein coiled to form an α helix. Configuration of the helix is maintained by hydrogen bonds, shown as vertical dotted (or solid) lines. The helix on the left shows the detailed atom structure of the peptide chain (the side chain groups are not shown). The helix on the right is a schematic representation without structural detail.

The Merrifield method has been used to synthesize a polypeptide with 124 amino acids arranged in the sequence present in the enzyme ribonuclease. After removal of the peptide from the resin, it was purified and then exposed to air to oxidize the SH bonds in eight cysteine units to form the four S—S bonds that are largely responsible for stabilizing the folded pattern of the peptide chains in the enzymically active state (see the next section). The product showed enzymic activity although it was less efficient than the natural enzyme, probably because minute amounts of impurities were introduced during the individual reactions. The synthesis involved 369 reactions and almost 12,000 individual operations of the automated peptide-synthesis machine without isolation of any intermediates.

17·4 protein structures

Considerable attention has been given to the possible ways in which peptide chains can be arranged to give stable conformations. An especially favorable arrangement that is found to occur in many peptides and proteins is the

α helix. The principal feature of the α helix is the coiling of peptide chains in such a way as to form hydrogen bonds between the amide hydrogens and carbonyl groups that are four peptide bonds apart. The hydrogen bonds are nearly parallel to the long axis of the coil and the spacing between the turns is about 5.4 A (see Figure 17·7). The amino acid side chains lie outside the coil of the α helix. However, proteins are not perfect α helices, because steric hindrance between certain of the amino acid side chains or the lack of hydrogen bonding is sometimes sufficient to reduce the stability of the normal α helix and allow the chain to fold.

Various levels of complexity therefore exist in any one protein structure. The *primary structure* is the specific sequence of amino acids in the polypeptide chain; the *secondary structure* is the way the chain is coiled, often to form an α helix; and the *tertiary structure* is the way in which the coiled chain(s) is folded and hydrated in the natural state. Some proteins, in fact, have a *quaternary structure* as a result of the grouping together of two or more of these folded units. Hemoglobin, for example, is a tetramer and insulin a hexamer. Ionic forces, van der Waals forces, and hydrogen bonds (but not covalent bonds) are responsible for quaternary structure.

The primary structure of the antidiabetic hormone insulin was elucidated in 1950 by Sanger, work for which he received the Nobel Prize. The sequence of the 51 amino acids in the peptide chain of beef insulin is shown in Figure 17·8. Sheep, horse, and hog insulin all have a slightly different arrangement

Figure 17·8   Amino acid sequence in beef insulin. In agreement with convention the amino acids on the left-hand side of the chain have free amino groups and the other two terminal amino acids have free carboxyl groups.

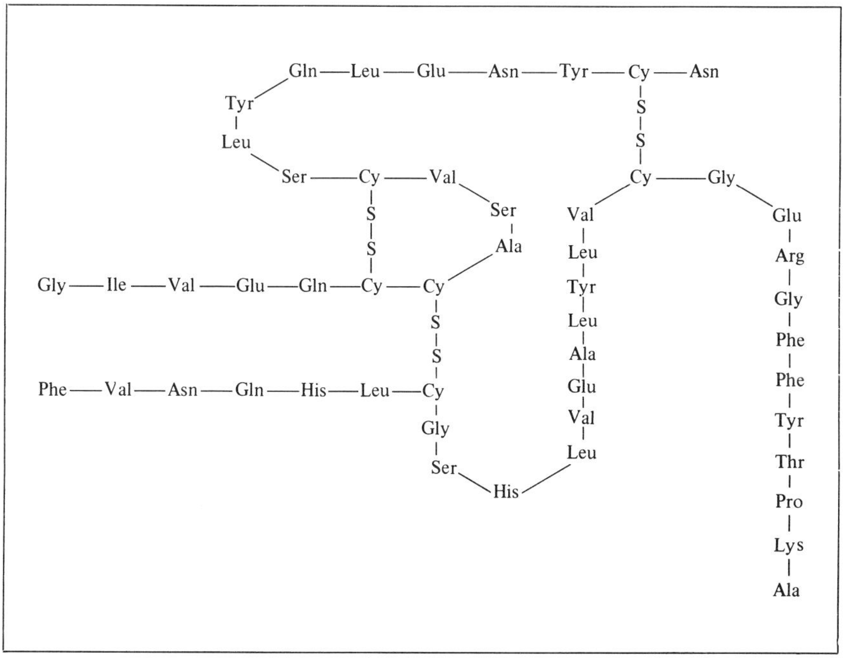

of amino acid residues at one location in the molecule, but this does not affect the hormone's physiological function, probably because substitution at this location does not greatly affect the higher structures of the protein. Insulin from man is identical with pig insulin except that threonine replaces alanine at the very end of one of the chains.

The solution to the problem of the quaternary structure of crystalline insulin has only recently been announced, almost 50 years after Banting and Best first isolated insulin and 20 years after Sanger established its primary structure. The English chemist Dorothy Crowfoot Hodgkin (already a Nobel Prize winner for earlier work) has shown by X-ray diffraction studies of crystalline insulin that the hormone is a roughly triangular ring made up of six polypeptide chains (such as that shown in Figure 17·8), two to each side of the triangle. Two zinc atoms are complexed to the inner side of the ring.

The bewildering and almost random-appearing sequences of amino acids in the peptide chains of proteins such as insulin probably have more than one role in influencing the higher structures of proteins and hence their properties. In the first place, the electrical behavior of proteins and their isoelectric points are determined by the number and location of acidic and basic amino acids. Second, the steric effects of substituent groups determine the stabilities and positions of folds in the peptide helices. The nature of the amino acid sequences may also influence the degree of intermolecular interactions and protein solubilities. Peptides of only one kind of amino acid are often highly insoluble, partly because of strong intermolecular forces. If the regularity of the chain is broken by having different amino acids in it, the intermolecular forces should diminish.

Proteins are found to occur in a very wide variety of sizes and shapes. Determination of the molecular weights and dimensions of proteins has been made with the aid of an impressive array of physical techniques. Molecular weights can be obtained by analysis for particular constituents (see Exercise 17·13), determination of diffusion rates, sedimentation velocities in the ultracentrifuge, light scattering, and even measurements of the sizes of individual, very large protein molecules by electron microscopy. The shapes are deduced from measurements of rates of molecular relaxation after electric polarization, changes in optical properties (double refraction) resulting from streaming in liquid flow, directly by electron microscopy, and perhaps most importantly by the intensities of light or X-ray scattering as a function of scattering angle. The application of all these methods is often rendered difficult by the high degree of hydration of proteins and by the fact that many proteins undergo reversible association reactions to give dimers, trimers, and so on. The molecular weights, molecular dimensions, and isoelectric points of a few important proteins are compared in Table 17·2.

It is found that many proteins contain metals such as iron, zinc, and copper, and these metal atoms turn out to be intimately involved in the biological functions of the molecules to which they are bound. The well-known oxygen-carrying property of hemoglobin and the hemocyanins is a case in point. These molecules have metal-containing heme rings as the prosthetic groups attached to the polypeptide chain. The cytochrome enzymes that are involved in biological oxidation (Chapter 18) are constructed similarly. Like many other substances we call proteins they are more than simple polymers of amino acids.

The biological functions of proteins are extremely diverse. Some act as hormones regulating various metabolic processes (e.g., insulin is responsible for the control of blood sugar levels); some act as catalysts for biological reactions (enzymes), and others as biological structural materials (e.g., collagen in connective tissue and keratin in hair). The oxygen-carrying properties of hemoglobin in mammals (and the copper-containing proteins called hemocyanins, which function similarly for shellfish) have been mentioned already. Some blood proteins function to form antibodies, which provide resistance to disease, while the so-called nucleoproteins are important constituents of the genes that supply and transmit genetic information in cell division. The viruses, such as tobacco mosaic virus, are made up of nucleoproteins, nucleic acids encased in a protein "coat." The structures of many viruses are so regular that they can be obtained in nicely crystalline form. Viruses function by invading the cells of the host and by supplying a genetic pattern that destroys the normal functions of the cells and sets the cellular enzymes to work synthesizing more virus particles.

17·5 biosynthesis of proteins

One of the most interesting and basic problems connected with the synthesis of proteins in living cells is how the component amino acids are induced to link together in the sequences which are specific for each type of protein. There is also the related problem of how the information as to the amino acid sequences is perpetuated in each new generation of cells. We now know that the substances responsible for genetic control in plants and animals are present in and originate from the chromosomes of cell nuclei. Chemical analysis of the chromosomes has revealed them to be composed of giant molecules of deoxyribonucleoproteins, which are deoxyribonucleic acids (DNA) bonded to proteins. Since it is known that DNA rather than the protein component of a nucleoprotein contains the genetic information for the biosynthesis of enzymes and other proteins, we shall be interested mainly in DNA and will first discuss its structure. Note that part or perhaps all of a particular DNA is the chemical equivalent of the Mendelian gene—the unit of inheritance.

17·6 the structure of DNA

The role of DNA in living cells is analogous to that of a punched tape used for controlling the operation of an automatic turret lathe. DNA supplies the information for the development of the cells, including synthesis of the necessary enzymes and such replicas of itself as are required for reproduction by cell division. Despite the enormous differences in gross structure of the many

Table 17·2   Some typical proteins

name	mol. wt.	shape	isoelectric point	occurrence	function
insulin[a,b]	5800[c]		5.4	pancreas	regulation of blood sugar levels
ribonuclease[a,b]	13,000		7.8	pancreas	hydrolysis of ribonucleic acids
myoglobin (horse)[a,b]	17,500	platelets		horse heart	respiratory protein
lysozyme[a,b]	14,600	prolate ellipsoid	10.7	egg white	breaks down the cell walls of bacteria by hydrolysis of $\beta(1 \to 4)$ glucose linkages
α-chymotrypsin[a,b]	25,000		8.4	pancreas	hydrolysis of ester and peptide linkages
papain[a]	21,000		8.8	latex of papaya melons	hydrolysis of peptide linkages
hemoglobin[a,b]	64,450	nearly spherical	6.7	red-blood corpuscles	respiratory protein
catalase	250,000	blocks[d]		liver and kidney	destroys H_2O_2
fibrogenin	330,000	elongated	6.8	blood plasma	blood clotting
tobacco mosaic virus (protein part)[a]	41,000,000	hexagonal prisms or rods[d]	4.1	infected tobacco or tomato plants	plant virus

[a] Complete sequence of amino acids has been established.
[b] Structure investigated by X-ray diffraction methods.
[c] Molecular weight of monomeric insulin; crystalline insulin consists of six such units complexed with two zinc atoms.
[d] From electron-microscope photographs.

varieties of plants and animals the basic structural features of DNA from all sources are surprisingly similar. We shall be mainly concerned with these basic features in the following discussion.

In the first place, DNA molecules are quite large—sufficiently so that they can be seen individually in photographs taken with electron microscopes. The molecular weights vary considerably, but values of 1,000,000 to 4,000,000,000 are typical. X-ray diffraction indicates that DNA is made up of two long-chain molecules twisted around each other to form a double-stranded helix about 20 A in diameter.

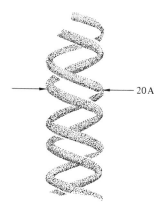
— 20 A

As we shall see, the components of the chains are such that the strands can be held together efficiently by hydrogen bonds. In agreement with the proposed structure, it has been found that, when DNA is heated to about 80° under proper conditions, the strands of the helix untwist and dissociate to two randomly coiled fragments. Furthermore, when the dissociated material is allowed to cool slowly (again, under proper conditions), the fragments recombine and regenerate the helical structure.

Chemical studies show that the strands of DNA have the structure of a long-chain polymer made of alternating phosphate and nitrogen base-substituted sugar residues [5]. The sugar is D-2-deoxyribofuranose [6], and each

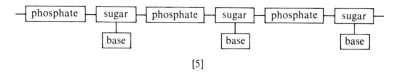

[5]

sugar residue is bonded to two phosphate groups by ester links involving the 3- and 5-hydroxyl groups.

$HOH_2\overset{5}{C}$ O   OH

2-deoxyribofuranose

[6]

The backbone of DNA is thus a polyphosphate ester of a 1,3-glycol.

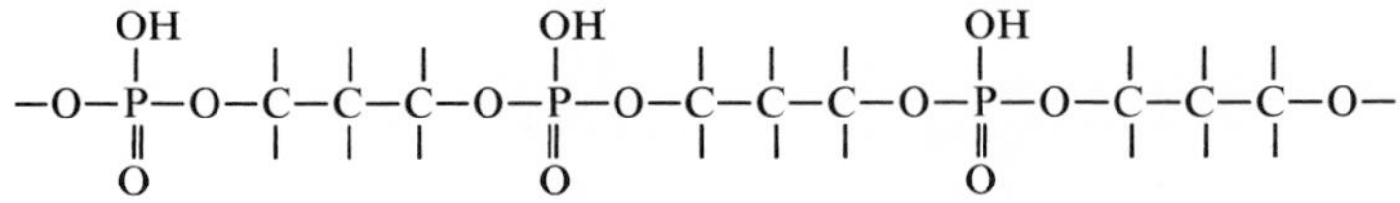

With the details of the sugar residue included, the structure of DNA becomes as shown in Figure 17·9.

Each of the sugar residues of DNA is bonded at the 1 position to one of four bases, adenine [7], guanine [8], cytosine [9], and thymine [10], through an N-glycosidic linkage. The four bases are derivatives of either 2-hydroxy-pyrimidine or purine, both of which are heterocyclic nitrogen bases.

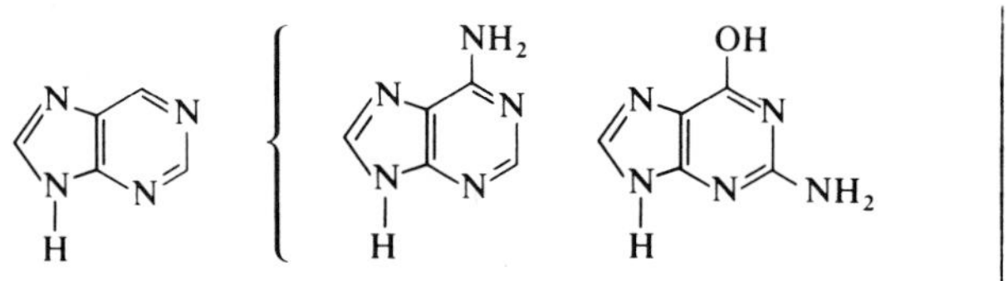

| purine | adenine [7] | guanine [8] |

| 2-hydroxypyrimidine | cytosine [9] | thymine [10] |

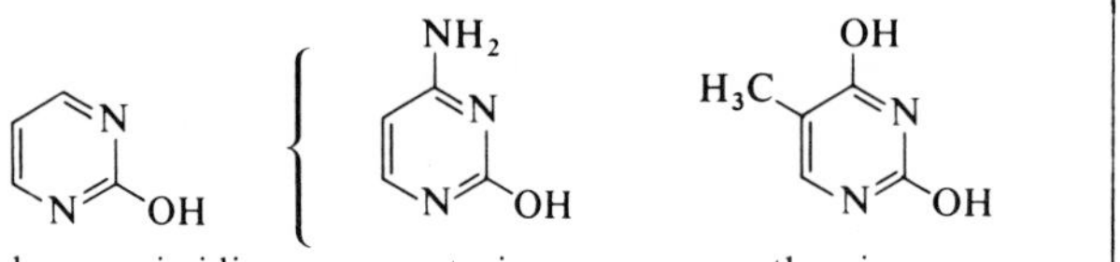

For the sake of simplicity in illustrating N-glycoside formation in DNA, we shall show the type of bonding involved for the sugar and base components only (i.e., the **nucleoside** structure). Attachment of 2-deoxyribose to the purines, adenine and guanine, is easily envisioned as involving the NH group of the five-membered ring and the C-1 of the deoxyribofuranose ring, the union always being β.

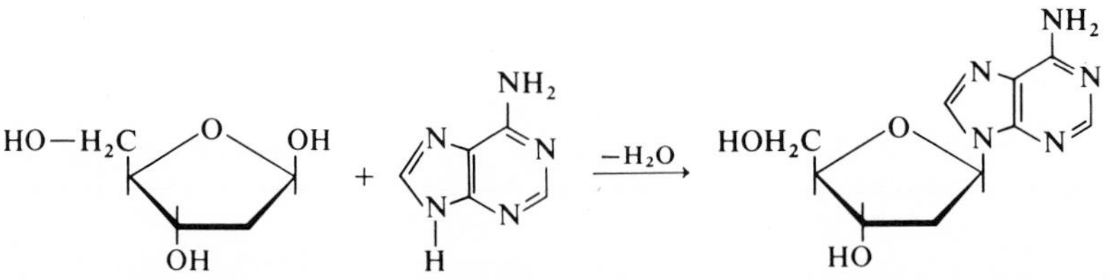

| 2-deoxyribofuranose | adenine | adenine deoxyriboside (a nucleoside) (β) |

However, an analogous process with the pyrimidines, cytosine and thymine, has to involve tautomerization of the base to an amide-type structure.

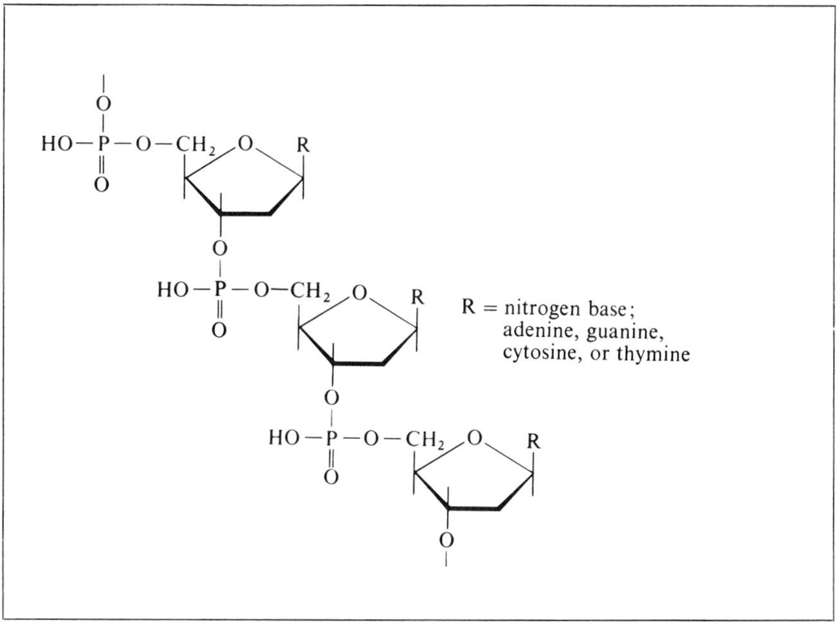
HO—P—O—CH2
R
R = nitrogen base; adenine, guanine, cytosine, or thymine

Figure 17·9 Structure of the strands of deoxyribonucleic acid (DNA).

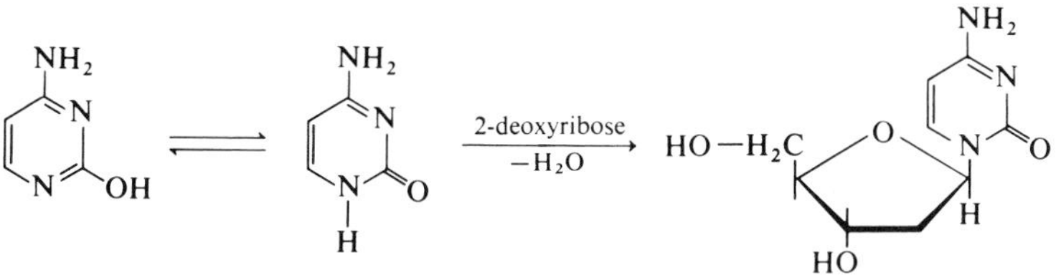
2-deoxyribose
$-H_2O$

cytosine

cytosine deoxyriboside
(a nucleoside)
(β)

Esterification of the 5-hydroxyl group of deoxyribose nucleosides, such as cytosine deoxyriboside, with phosphoric acid gives the corresponding **nucleotides**.

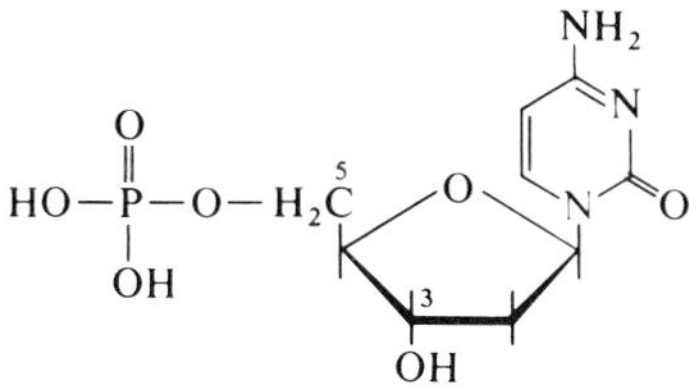

cytosine deoxyribonucleotide
(a nucleotide)

Thus DNA may be considered to be built up from nucleotide monomers by esterification of the 3-hydroxyl group of one nucleotide with the phosphate

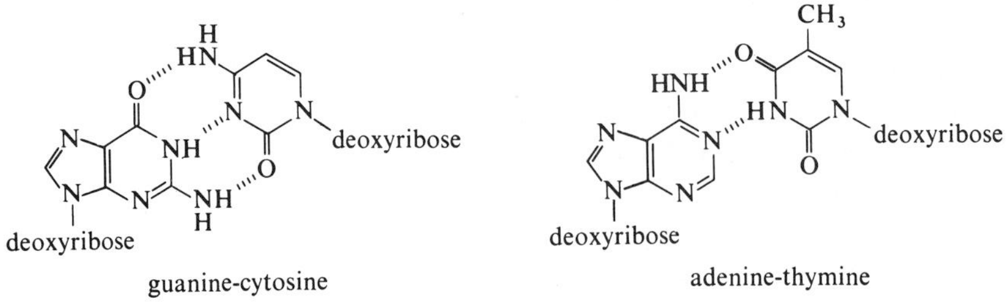

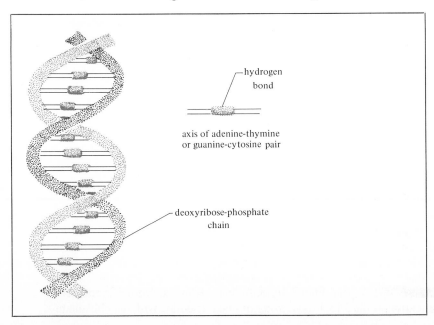

guanine-cytosine

adenine-thymine

Figure 17·10   Hydrogen bonding in the base pairs guanine-cytosine and adenine-thymine, which leads to the two strands of DNA being linked. In each case the distance between C-1 of the two deoxyribose units is 11 A and the favored geometry has the rings coplanar.

group of another. Enzymes are available which hydrolyze DNA to cleave the linkage at C-3 and give the 5-phosphorylated nucleotides. There are other enzymes which cleave DNA at C-5 to give the 3-phosphorylated nucleotides.

The number of nucleotide units in a DNA chain varies from a few thousand

Figure 17·11   Schematic representation of configuration of DNA, showing the relation between the axes of hydrogen-bonded purine and pyrimidine bases and the deoxyribose-phosphate strands. There are 10 pairs of bases per complete 360° twist of the chain. The spacing between the strands is such that there is a wide and a narrow helical "groove" which goes around the molecule. Apparently in the combination of DNA with protein, the protein is wound around the helix filling one or the other of the grooves.

to well over a million. A single DNA molecule can be isolated from the bacterium *Escherichia coli* which has a molecular weight of 2×10^9 and whose extended length is almost a millimeter.

Although the sequences of the purine and pyrimidine bases in the chains are not known, there is a striking equivalence between certain of the bases regardless of the origin of DNA. Thus the number of adenine groups equals the number of thymine groups, and the number of guanine groups equals the number of cytosine groups (i.e., $A = T$ and $G = C$). Also, the overall percentage composition of the bases is constant in a given species but varies widely from one species to another.

The equivalence between the purine and pyrimidine bases in DNA was accounted for by Watson and Crick (1953). They were the first to realize that if two strands are twisted together to form a double helix, hydrogen bonds can form between adenine in one chain and thymine in the other or cytosine in one chain and guanine in the other. Thus, each adenine occurs paired with a thymine and each cytosine with a guanine and the strands are said to have **complementary** structures. The hydrogen bonds that form the base pairs are shown in Figure 17·10, and the relation of the bases to the strands in Figure 17·11.

17·7 *genetic control and the replication of DNA*

It is now clear that DNA provides the genetic recipe that permits cell division to produce identical cells. In reproducing itself, it perpetuates the information necessary to regulate the synthesis of specific enzymes and other proteins of the cell structure. The genetic information inherent in DNA depends on the arrangement of the bases (symbolized as A, T, G, and C) along the phosphate-carbohydrate backbone—that is, on the arrangement of the four nucleotides specific to DNA.

There are 20 amino acids that become joined together to form proteins but only four nucleotide bases. A single base, therefore, cannot correspond to a single amino acid and even a pair of adjacent bases gives only 4^2 or 16 combinations. A triplet of bases, however, provides 4^3 or 64 combinations, more than enough to store the information required for the sequential addition of 20 different amino acids to form a protein of specific structure. Each of the 64 three-letter code words, called **codons** (for example, AGC, adenine-guanine-cytosine), corresponds to an amino acid and it is apparent that an individual amino acid may have several codons that direct its addition to the growing polypeptide chain.

The base sequence in DNA can be modified chemically by treatment of DNA *in vitro* (outside the cell) or *in vivo* (inside the cell) with nitrous acid, which can convert the primary amino groups of adenine, cytosine, and guanine to OH groups. This clearly changes the genetic message, since DNA modified this way leads to mutations in the organisms from which it was originally obtained. A drastic change may occur when the DNA of a bacteriophage (which is no more than a bundle of DNA enclosed in a protein coat) is introduced into a bacterium. The bacteriophage DNA acts as a primer for the synthesis of DNA and proteins of its own kind, finally causing dissolution of the host cell and liberation of new bacteriophage particles.

Other important experiments which indicate that a given organism manufactures DNA of its own kind are based on the synthesis of DNA *in vitro*. A mixture of the four DNA nucleotides, *A*, *G*, *C*, and *T*, with triphosphate groups in the 5 position, can be polymerized to DNA in the presence of the enzyme DNA-polymerase, magnesium ions, and a DNA primer. The last can come from a variety of sources, but the synthetic DNA has the composition of the primer DNA, even if the relative amounts of the nucleotides that are supplied are varied. The role of magnesium is not clear, but it behaves as a type of inorganic coenzyme, since the enzyme apparently does not function in its absence. The triphosphate grouping on the nucleotides is necessary as a source of energy to drive the reaction forward; some 7 kcal/mole is liberated in the cleavage of the triphosphoryl group to pyrophosphate (see Section 15·5).

The mechanism of replication of DNA that takes place when the cell divides probably involves the unwinding of the DNA double helix into two complementary chains. During the unwinding process, each chain serves as a template on which is built the complement of itself.

The genetic information of cells is stored in DNA but protein synthesis takes place on small subcellular particles called **ribosomes**. How does the information stored in DNA become translated into a protein molecule in the ribosome? This is accomplished through the intermediacy of ribonucleic acid (RNA), a substance similar in structure to DNA[2] but containing ribose in-

---

[2] Although DNA was first located in cell nuclei of plants and animals (hence the name *nucleic* acid), it is now known to be present outside the nucleus, as well, that is, in the cytoplasm. Indeed, bacterial cells, which contain no nuclei, use the same system of information transfer (DNA→RNA→protein) as do nucleated cells.

stead of deoxyribose (see Section 15·5). RNA contains the base sequence transcribed from DNA, but with the base uracil [11] replacing thymine [10]. In contrast to DNA most RNA molecules are single stranded.

There is a striking variation in size of RNA molecules and this seems to depend on the particular role they play. One class of RNA molecules is called **transfer RNA** (tRNA). The various molecules contain 75 or so nucleotide units and have molecular weights of about 25,000. Specific tRNA molecules are esterified enzymically with the corresponding amino acid and the amino acids then are transferred to the growing protein chain on the ribosome in a complex series of enzyme-catalyzed reactions. Because tRNA is the smallest and most soluble form of RNA, it is sometimes called soluble RNA (sRNA).

Another kind of RNA with a somewhat bigger molecular weight is called **messenger RNA** (mRNA). It carries the message from the DNA in the nucleus to the tRNA at the ribosome. Its base sequence is complementary to a portion of one strand of DNA and consequently it contains the sequence of codons defining the sequence of amino acids in the protein.

The codon(s) for a particular amino acid can be determined by experiment. For example, a synthetic RNA containing only one type of base, uracil, acts as the mRNA for a cell-free preparation of the protein-synthesizing system of the bacterium *E. coli*. The product is a polypeptide containing only phenylalanine. This suggests that the codon for phenylalanine is UUU. The messages delivered by all 64 codons are now known, at least for *E. coli*, and it is probable that the code is universal.

In some cases, the codon was determined by synthesis of the simple tri-nucleotide molecule made up of the appropriate triplet. This is often sufficient to cause amino acyl-tRNA to be bound to the ribosome. For example, the trinucleotide UUU causes only phenylalanyl tRNA, and the trinucleotide UCU only seryl tRNA, to be bound. Other trinucleotides are much less efficient in promoting binding, however, making it difficult to determine the amino acid to which they correspond. In these cases, the complex polynucleotide having the correct base sequence had to be synthesized and its effect on amino acid incorporation in polypeptides observed.

It turns out that only 61 of the 64 codons correspond to amino acids. The other three, UAA, UAG, and UGA, are so-called "nonsense" codons. Despite this name their message is clear—they stop the growth of the polypeptide chain.

A third class of RNA is called ribosomal RNA (rRNA). These molecules are components of ribosomes but their roles are not as well understood as those of tRNA and mRNA.

Phenomenal progress has been made in the past 20 years in understanding the chemical basis of heredity and we can expect in the future to learn that manipulation of human genetic material can be done on a clinical basis. It remains to be seen whether or not we possess the wisdom to use such knowledge in a wholly beneficial way.

17·8   chemical evolution

The term "chemical evolution" is used to refer to those events occurring on the primitive Earth that led to the appearance of the first living cell. There is general agreement that the Earth was formed about $4\frac{1}{2}$ billion years ago by condensation from a dust cloud. Fossil evidence shows that unicellular organisms (protozoa) existed on Earth at least 3 billion years ago, which leaves possibly a billion years for chemical evolution to produce the complex organic molecules that are the components of a living cell.

There is good reason to believe that the atmosphere of the prebiotic Earth was hydrogen dominated, rather than oxygen dominated as at present, and the principal atmospheric constituents were probably methane, ammonia, and water vapor. The change from a reducing to an oxidizing atmosphere may have been caused by radiolysis of water vapor by ultraviolet radiation followed by escape of hydrogen from the planet's atmosphere. This allowed the ozone shield to develop in the upper atmosphere—the protection required by cells from the lethal effects of high-energy ultraviolet light.

Experiments have been conducted in the laboratory which simulate "natural" but prebiotic organic syntheses. Application of ultraviolet radiation and electric discharges (the analogs of unshielded sunlight and lightning storms, respectively) to mixtures of CH_4, NH_3, H_2O, N_2, and H_2 produces both amino acids and nucleic acid bases. Other kinds of compounds, too, are formed but it is interesting that the naturally occurring amino acid 2-aminopropanoic acid (alanine) is always formed in larger amounts than its isomer 3-aminopropanoic acid.

Adenine, one of the nucleic acid bases, has the formula $C_5H_5N_5$, or $(HCN)_5$, and it has been shown that adenine is one of the compounds formed when aqueous solutions of ammonia and hydrogen cyanide (products of CH_4–N_2 irradiation) are heated at 90° for several days. One of several possible routes for this reaction begins with the stepwise trimerization of hydrogen cyanide to give aminomalononitrile:

$$2 \text{ HCN} \longrightarrow [\text{HN}{=}\text{CHCN}] \xrightarrow{\text{HCN}} \text{H}_2\text{NCH(CN)}_2$$
$$\qquad\qquad\qquad\quad \text{dimer} \qquad\qquad\qquad \text{aminomalononitrile}$$

This compound, which has been detected in the reaction mixture, is known to be able to condense with one mole of formamidine (formed by addition of ammonia to hydrogen cyanide) to give the imidazole [12]. The imidazole [12]

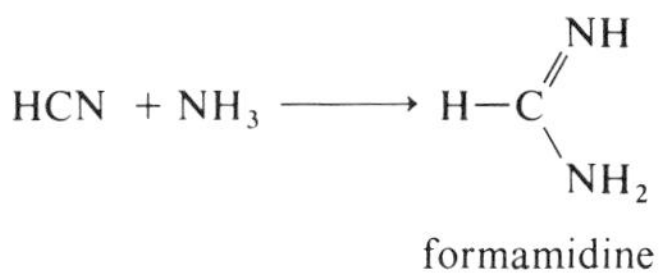

$$HCN + NH_3 \longrightarrow H-C\begin{array}{c} \nearrow NH \\ \searrow NH_2 \end{array}$$

formamidine

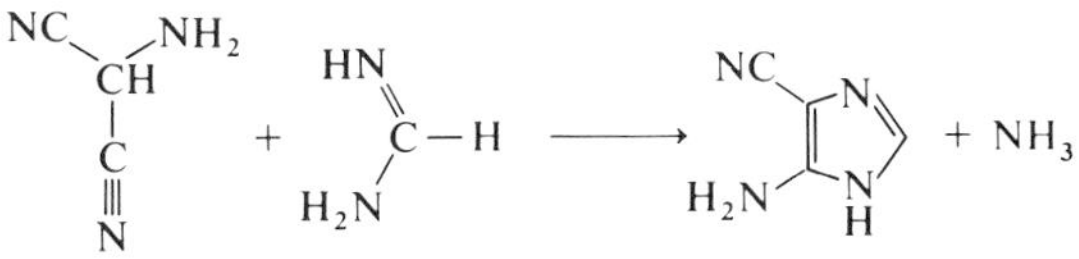

[12]

can react with a second mole of formamidine to give adenine. All of the

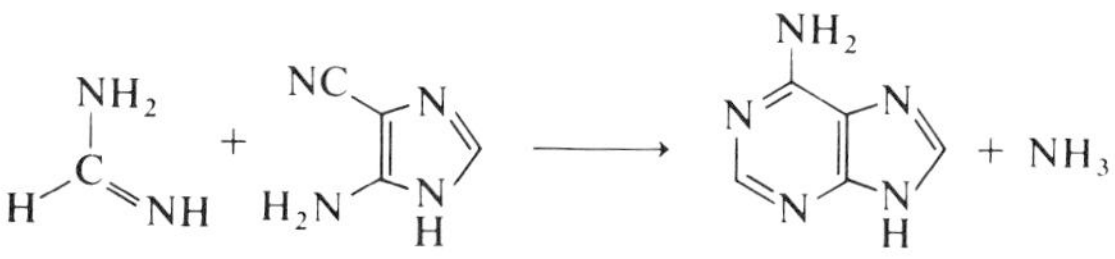

[12]   adenine

above compounds except the HCN dimer have been identified in the aqueous solution. There is little doubt that many of the units of biopolymers were present under prebiotic conditions and it is not difficult to visualize the formation of proteins and nucleic acids taking place also. There is still, of course, an enormous gap in our understanding of how these substances became organized into the first living cell able to replicate itself.

summary

Of the 24 α-amino acids that are important constituents of proteins, all except glycine, $NH_2CH_2CO_2H$, are optically active. Eight of them are essential to human nutrition in the sense that the body cannot synthesize them. Four of the remainder are formed by conversion of other amino acids only after the protein has been synthesized.

Amino acids can be prepared from α-halo acids or by the Strecker synthesis ($RCHO \rightarrow RCHNH_2CN \rightarrow RCHNH_2CO_2H$).

Amino acids with one carboxyl and one amino group (neutral amino acids) exist in the dipolar (zwitterionic) form, $RCHCO_2{}^\ominus$, which is converted by $\underset{NH_3{}^\oplus}{}$ acids to a cation $RCHCO_2H$, and by bases to an anion $RCHCO_2{}^\ominus$.
$\underset{NH_3{}^\oplus}{}$ $\underset{NH_2}{}$

The isoelectric point is the pH at which the concentration of the zwitterion is at a maximum and is near pH 6 for many simple amino acids. Basic amino acids such as lysine ($NH_2CH_2CH_2CH_2CH_2CHNH_2CO_2H$), which have an excess of amino over carboxyl groups, have isoelectric points near pH 9, while acidic amino acids such as glutamic acid ($HO_2CCH_2CH_2CHNH_2CO_2H$) with an excess of carboxyl over amino groups have isoelectric points near pH 3.

Analysis and detection of amino acids can be carried out with nitrous acid (Van Slyke method), by the ninhydrin color test, or by chromatography. Paper chromatography involves the partitioning of compounds caused by differences in their rates of migration on the surface of moist filter paper. These are expressed as Rf values, the distances that compounds migrate relative to that of the solvent front. Thin-layer chromatography (tlc) is similar except that the filter paper is replaced by a thin layer of absorbent, such as silica gel, on glass plates.

Cyclization of esters of γ- and δ-amino acids (amino at C-4 or C-5) produces lactams (cyclic amides) whereas α-amino esters form six-membered rings by dimeric cyclization.

Peptides (polypeptides) are polyamides formed by the condensation of α-amino acids. Synthesis of peptides in the laboratory normally requires the use of a protective group, such as $RO\overset{\displaystyle O}{\overset{\|}{C}}-$, on the amino group of the amino acid that is being linked to the chain to prevent it from reacting with its own carboxyl function.

$$RO\overset{O}{\overset{\|}{C}}-NH\underset{R_1}{CH}CO_2H + NH_2\underset{R_2}{CH}\overset{O}{\overset{\|}{C}}NH\sim\!\!\sim \longrightarrow RO\overset{O}{\overset{\|}{C}}-NH\underset{R_1}{CH}\overset{O}{\overset{\|}{C}}-NH\underset{R_2}{CH}\overset{O}{\overset{\|}{C}}-NH\sim\!\!\sim$$

Formation of the peptide linkage can be brought about by mild dehydrating agents, such as $RN{=}C{=}NR$, or via the acid chloride. The protective group can be removed and the process continued. Solid-phase peptide synthesis can be achieved by attaching the first amino acid in the chain to a polystyrene resin and then using this granular material in all subsequent chemical and washing operations. In the final step, the peptide is liberated from the resin by a suitable reaction.

Proteins are peptides with special structural features beyond the primary structure, which refers to the sequence of amino acids in the chain. Proteins have a secondary structure, which refers to the way the chain is coiled; a tertiary structure, which refers to the manner of folding of the coiled chain; and a quaternary structure, which refers to the association of the folded units by noncovalent links.

Many proteins, such as hemoglobin, contain non-amino acid functions called prosthetic groups. Viruses consist of protein-nucleic acid combinations.

Deoxyribonucleic acid (DNA) is a polymer of 2-deoxyribose and phosphoric acid, with nitrogen bases (adenine, guanine, cytosine, and thymine) attached to the sugar units. The combination of an individual sugar and a base is called a nucleoside; the combination of a sugar, a base, and phosphoric acid is a nucleotide. Coded genetic information is contained in the sequence of bases along the polymer chains, which are coiled around one another in the form of a double-stranded helix.

Ribonucleic acid (RNA) differs from DNA in the following respects: it contains ribose rather than deoxyribose; it contains uracil rather than thymine; and it has a much greater variation in molecular weight (corresponding to the three different functional types, tRNA, mRNA, and rRNA). The genetic information coded in the base triplets of DNA becomes manifest in protein synthesis through the action of RNA.

The appearance of life on Earth was presumably preceded by the synthesis of rather complex organic molecules. The effects of radiation on the highly reduced atmosphere believed to exist in prebiotic times can be duplicated in the laboratory and shown to give rise to compounds such as amino acids and nucleic acid bases.

exercises

17·1   Pick out the amino acids in Table 17·1 which have more than one asymmetric center and draw projection formulas for all the possible stereoisomers of each which possess the L configuration for the α carbon.

17·2   Which of the amino acids in Table 17·1 are "acidic" amino acids and which "basic" amino acids? Which of the structures shown would have the most basic nitrogen? The least basic amino nitrogen? The most acidic and least acidic carboxyl group? Give the reasons for your choices.

17·3   Show the sequence of steps involved in the Strecker synthesis of α-amino acids.

17·4   Show how the following amino acids can be prepared from the indicated starting materials by the methods described above or earlier.

    a. leucine from 2-methyl-1-propanol
    b. lysine from 1,4-dibromobutane
    c. proline from hexanedioic acid (adipic acid)
    d. glutamic acid from α-ketoglutaric acid

17·5   Devise physical or chemical ways to determine directly or calculate the equilibrium constant between neutral glycine and its dipolar ion. Arguing from substituent effects on the ionization of carboxylic acids and amines, would you expect the equilibrium constant to be closer to 0.1, 1.0, or 10? Explain.

17·6   Suppose one were to titrate an equimolal mixture of ammonium chloride and acetic acid with two equivalents of sodium hydroxide. How would the titration curve be expected to differ from that of glycine hydrochloride shown in Figure 17·1? Take K_{HA} for acetic acid equal to 2×10^{-5} and $K_{BH^{\oplus}}$ for ammonium ion to be 5×10^{-10}.

17·7   Write mechanisms based insofar as possible on analogy for each of the steps involved in the ninhydrin test using glycine as an example. Would you expect ammonia or methylamine to give the blue color?

17·8   Arrange the following amino acids in the order in which you would expect each to move in a paper chromatogram with the weak organic base 2,4,6-collidine as the organic phase: glycine, phenylalanine, arginine, and glutamic acid. Show your reasoning.

2,4,6-collidine

17·9   Draw out the complete structure (using projection formulas) of the important hormonal peptide oxytocin.

$$\text{H·CyS·Tyr·Ile·Gln·Asn·CyS·Pro·Leu·Gly·NH}_2$$

17·10   On what theoretical grounds can we expect the C—O bonds of benzyloxy groups to undergo hydrogenolysis more readily than ethoxy groups?

17·11   Show how each of the following substances can by synthesized starting with the individual amino acids.

  a.   glycylalanylcysteine
  b. $HO_2C(CH_2)_2CH(NH_2)CONHCH_2CO_2H$
  c.   glutamine from glutamic acid

17·12   Most nonfatty tissue is about 80% water and 15% protein by weight with the remainder being made up of carbohydrates, lipids, nucleic acids, inorganic salts, and so on. Assuming an average molecular weight of protein of 10^5 calculate the molar ratio of water to protein in such tissue.

17·13   Hemoglobin, the protein responsible for carrying oxygen from the lungs to the body tissues, contains 0.355% of iron. Hydrolysis of 100 g of hemoglobin gives 1.48 g of tryptophan; calculate the minimum molecular weight of hemoglobin which is consistent with these results.

17·14   Write equations for the steps involved in hydrolysis of adenine deoxyribonucleoside to deoxyribose and adenine. Would you expect the reaction to occur more readily in acidic or basic solution?

17·15   *Escherichia coli* bacteria grown in a medium containing ^{15}N-labeled ammonium chloride produce ^{15}N-containing DNA. This can be distinguished from ordinary ^{14}N-DNA by ultracentrifugation in concentrated cesium chloride solution—at equilibrium ^{14}N-DNA and ^{15}N-DNA form separate bands of differing density. When the bacteria grown in an ^{15}N medium are transferred to a ^{14}N medium, DNA replication continues but, after one generation, all the DNA present appears to be of one kind, containing equal amounts of ^{15}N and ^{14}N; after two generations, the DNA is now of two kinds present in equal amounts—all ^{14}N-DNA and ^{14}N,^{15}N-DNA. What do these results tell about the replication of DNA and its stability in the cell?

17·16 Draw structures for the tautomeric forms of uracil (formula [11], Section 17·7) and show how a nucleotide of uracil can form hydrogen bonds with adenine.

17·17 Propynonitrile (cyanoacetylene), which is a product of CH_4–N_2 irradiation, has been suggested as a precursor for the amino acid aspartic acid (2-aminobutanedioic acid) under "primitive Earth" conditions. Write a reaction path for this conversion making use only of NH_3, HCN, and H_2O as reactants.

17·18 Write reasonable mechanisms for the cyclization steps shown in Section 17·8 for the conversion of HCN to its pentamer, adenine. (Two of the reactions involved bear resemblance to reactions met earlier, the condensation of aldehydes with amines, Section 11·4D, and the addition of nucleophiles to nitriles. Section 16·2B.)

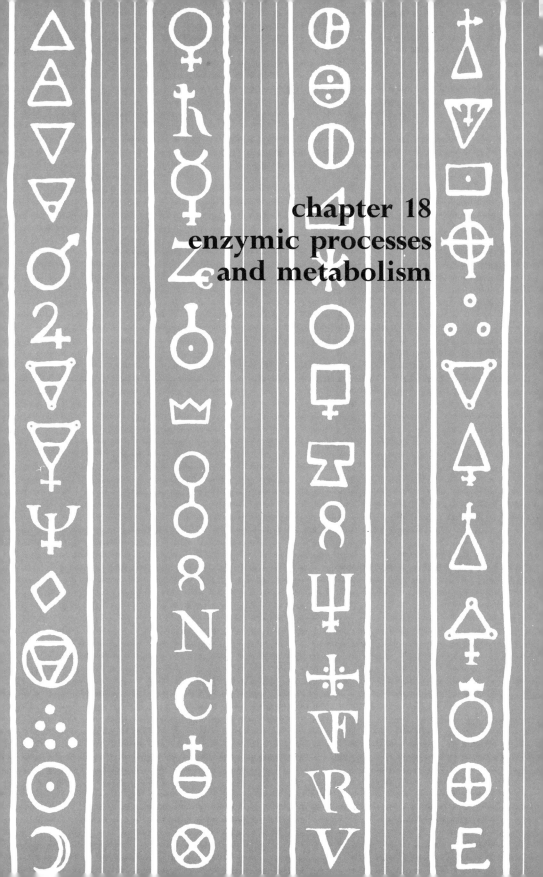

chapter 18
enzymic processes
and metabolism

The time scale of man's awareness ranges from about 10^{10} seconds to possibly 10^{-2} second. The former is a lifetime; the latter is the relaxation period of the eye. A person's reaction time—the time between observation and action — is measured in tenths of a second and we might well wonder how the complex physiological processes that result in a particular response— the batter's swing, the fencer's parry—can possibly occur in such brief periods of time. How fast can chemical reactions occur? Is a few tenths of a second long enough for nerve impulses to be translated into muscle action, a process essentially chemical in nature?

The fastest chemical reactions that can occur in solution are those that are diffusion controlled. This means that, if the rate of the reaction of A and B depends only on their encounter rate, then every encounter produces product. For solvents of normal viscosity at room temperature, the rate of diffusion, expressed as a bimolecular rate constant, is 10^{10} liters mole^{-1} sec^{-1}. This means that if the reactants A and B are each 1 M, the initial rate of production of product will be 10^{10} moles liter^{-1} sec^{-1}, a staggeringly high rate. Put another way, the reaction between A and B would be 99% complete in 10^{-8} second.

A number of diffusion-controlled reactions are known; one simple example is $H^{\oplus} + OH^{\ominus} \rightarrow H_2O$. Such reactions require no activation of the reactants for the reaction to occur. At the other extreme are countless reactions with heats of activation greater than 50 kcal, which means that their half-lives (the time for half of the reactants to be consumed) at room temperature would be measured in thousands or millions of years.

If the fastest known chemical reactions can be substantially complete in 10^{-8} second or so at room temperature, a 10^{-2}-second period does not appear to be quite so short, even though the chemistry of physiological processes is clearly much more complicated than the $H^{\oplus} + OH^{\ominus}$ reaction.

The study of enzymes and the way in which they accelerate and control biological processes is a fascinating area of study that combines the disciplines of organic chemistry, physical chemistry, biochemistry, and physiology. Because enzymes are essentially catalysts which operate by lowering the activation energy of what are ordinarily slow processes, we shall begin with a discussion of catalysis in simple organic systems.

18·1 catalysis in organic systems

A catalyst is a substance that will increase the rate of a reaction without itself being consumed. We saw in Chapter 8 that the rate of a reaction is governed by the energy difference between reactants and transition state, the latter being the highest point on the lowest energy path from reactants to products. Catalysis simply provides another path from reactants to products with a lower-energy transition state. A simple example should suffice to illustrate the point.

The reaction between chloromethane and hydroxide ion to give methanol and chloride ion is accelerated by the addition of small amounts of iodide ion.

$$CH_3Cl + OH^\ominus \xrightarrow{I^\ominus} CH_3OH + Cl^\ominus$$

The uncatalyzed reaction is a one-step S_N2 displacement and its rate is determined by the free-energy difference between the reactants and the transition state having a configuration roughly like the following:

$$HO^{\delta\ominus}\text{---}\overset{\overset{\displaystyle H}{|}}{\underset{/\ \backslash}{C}}\text{---}Cl^{\delta\ominus}$$
$$H\ \ H$$

(The free energy of activation, $\Delta G^{\ddagger}$, is made up of the heat of activation, $\Delta H^{\ddagger}$, and the entropy of activation, $\Delta S^{\ddagger}$, Section 8·9.)

The addition of iodide ion to the system provides another pathway—a two-stage route—to products. Iodide ion is a large polarizable ion and is both a good nucleophile and a good leaving group in displacement reactions. Accordingly, it reacts rapidly with chloromethane to give iodomethane but this, in turn, suffers rapid displacement by hydroxide ion. The iodide ion is thus regenerated and is a true catalyst.

$$CH_3Cl + I^\ominus \longrightarrow CH_3I + Cl^\ominus$$

$$CH_3I + OH^\ominus \longrightarrow CH_3OH + I^\ominus$$

The energetics of this process are shown in Figure 18·1. (The analysis of the activation process in terms of $\Delta H^{\ddagger}$ and $\Delta S^{\ddagger}$ need not concern us at this point.)

Figure 18·1   Energy profiles for the reaction of chloromethane with hydroxide ion in the presence (solid line) and absence (dashed line) of iodide ion.

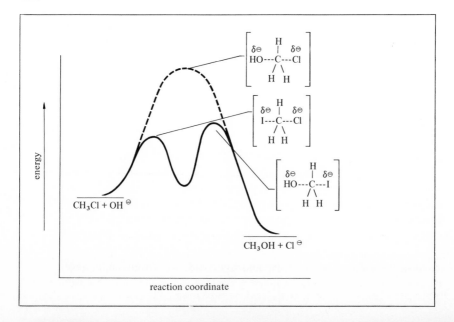

The two-step reaction has two transition states that correspond to energy maxima, but only the higher of the two determines the rate of the overall reaction. If the second transition state is the higher one, the overall rate of the reaction will be proportional to the concentrations of the catalyst (iodide ion) and hydroxide ion. If the first transition state is the higher one, the rate will be proportional to the concentration of iodide ion and not the concentration of hydroxide. Thus, in either case, iodide ion is a catalyst for the overall reaction. Catalysts have no influence on the position of equilibrium of a system[1] and it follows that iodide ion must catalyze the reverse reaction also. The rate of interconversion of chloromethane and methanol will be increased by the presence of iodide even though their equilibrium concentrations are unchanged.

There are two main categories of catalysis: homogeneous catalysis, in which all the components are in a single phase as in the above example, and heterogeneous catalysis, in which interactions occur at a solid surface. The hydrogenation of alkenes catalyzed by finely divided metal surfaces (Section 2·6A) is an example of heterogeneous catalysis. Most enzymic processes can be considered to be homogeneous although the way in which some high-molecular-weight enzymes orient small reactant molecules on their surfaces bears a strong resemblance to the action of heterogeneous catalysts.

The iodide ion in the example above is a nucleophilic catalyst and we shall see that some enzymes also operate this way. Many other organic processes are catalyzed by acids and bases. Since all bases are also nucleophiles it is sometimes difficult to tell if catalytic action is due to a molecule or ion acting as a base (removing a proton) or as a nucleophile (supplying the electrons to form a bond to carbon). Furthermore, acid catalysis and nucleophilic catalysis often go together, as we shall see in the following sections.

A. ACID CATALYSIS

A number of acid-promoted reactions have been met previously, such as the hydration of alkenes and dehydration of alcohols (Sections 4·4 and 10·5B), the formation and hydrolysis of hemiacetals (Section 11·4B), the formation and hydrolysis of esters (Section 10·4C), and the acid hydrolysis of amides. The course of these reactions is shown in Equations 18·1 to 18·4.

$$RCH=CH_2 + H^{\oplus} \; \rightleftharpoons \; R\overset{\oplus}{C}H-CH_3 \; \underset{-H_2O}{\overset{+H_2O}{\rightleftharpoons}} \; \underset{\overset{|}{RCH-CH_3}}{\overset{\overset{\oplus}{O}H_2}{}} \; \rightleftharpoons \; RCHOHCH_3 + H^{\oplus}$$

$$(18\cdot1)$$

$$R-\overset{O}{\overset{\|}{C}}{\diagdown}_H + H^{\oplus} \; \rightleftharpoons \; R-\overset{\overset{\oplus}{O}H}{\overset{\|}{C}}{\diagdown}_H \; \underset{-EtOH}{\overset{+EtOH}{\rightleftharpoons}} \; R-\overset{\overset{OH}{|}}{\underset{\overset{|}{H}\;\overset{|}{H}}{C}}-\overset{\oplus}{O}Et \; \rightleftharpoons \; R-\overset{\overset{OH}{|}}{\underset{\overset{|}{H}}{C}}-OEt + H^{\oplus}$$

$$(18\cdot2)$$

[1] The only exception would be where the catalyst forms a complex with one or more of the reactants or products and is present in such high concentration as to change appreciably the concentrations from the values they would otherwise have. An effect of this kind will change the position of equilibrium but not the equilibrium constant.

$$R-\overset{O}{\underset{OH}{C}} + H^{\oplus} \;\rightleftharpoons\; R-\overset{OH}{\underset{OH}{C^{\oplus}}} \xrightarrow[-EtOH]{+EtOH} R-\overset{OH}{\underset{\overset{|}{OH}\;H}{\overset{|}{C}}-OEt}$$

$$R-\overset{OH}{\underset{\overset{\oplus}{OH}_2}{\overset{|}{C}}-OEt} \xrightarrow[+H_2O]{-H_2O} R-\overset{OH}{\underset{OEt}{C^{\oplus}}} \;\rightleftharpoons\; R-\overset{O}{\underset{OEt}{C}} + H^{\oplus} \qquad (18\cdot3)$$

$$R-\overset{O}{\underset{NH_2}{C}} + H^{\oplus} \;\rightleftharpoons\; R-\overset{OH}{\underset{NH_2}{C^{\oplus}}} \xrightarrow[-H_2O]{+H_2O} R-\overset{OH}{\underset{\overset{\oplus}{OH}_2}{\overset{|}{C}}-NH_2} \;\rightleftharpoons\; R-\overset{OH}{\underset{OH}{\overset{|}{C}}-\overset{\oplus}{N}H_3}$$

$$R-\overset{OH}{\underset{OH}{C^{\oplus}}} + NH_3 \;\rightleftharpoons\; RCO_2H +$$

The dual role of the proton in each of the four reactions should be clear. At one stage, a carbon atom is activated toward an attacking nucleophile by protonation of the adjacent atom; at another stage, protonation increases the leaving ability of a substituent group. Proton transfers between oxygen atoms have low activation energies, and most of the protolytic equilibria shown in Equations 18·1 to 18·4 are fast. Despite the mechanistic similarity between these four processes, only the first three are examples of simple catalysis. In the fourth, the acid-promoted hydrolysis of amides, acid is consumed instead of regenerated as the reaction proceeds. Thus, although a catalytic quantity of acid would initiate the hydrolysis of an amide, it would not be sufficient to carry the reaction to completion.

If we examine the esterification reaction as a function of the concentration of reactants we find that the reaction has the following kinetic form (rate $= k[RCO_2H][EtOH][H^{\oplus}]$. The rate is proportional to the first power of the concentration of each of the two reactants and the catalyst. If the concentration of catalyst is doubled the rate doubles. Can the rate be indefinitely increased by addition of more and more catalyst? Only up to a point. When most of the carboxylic acid that is present in the system is already in the protonated form, further increases in acidity can have only a marginal effect on the concentration of protonated acid. Furthermore, protonation of the alcohol gives a non-nucleophilic species and therefore decreases the alcohol concentration. Carboxylic acids and alcohols are rather weak bases and it requires a considerable amount of acid to reach this point. Amides, however, are less weakly basic, and the rate of acid-induced hydrolysis of amides reaches a plateau much earlier as the acid concentration is increased than for esterification.

B. BASE CATALYSIS

Base-promoted reactions already met include the aldol addition (Section 12·2A), hemiacetal (but not acetal) formation and hydrolysis (Section 11·4B), and alkylation of ketones (Section 12·2B). The course of these reactions is shown in Equations 18·5 to 18·7.

$$HO^{\ominus} + CH_3-C\underset{H}{\overset{O}{\diagup\!\!\!\diagdown}} \longrightarrow H_2O + {}^{\ominus}CH_2-C\underset{H}{\overset{O}{\diagup\!\!\!\diagdown}}$$

$$\xrightarrow{CH_3CHO} CH_3-\overset{O^{\ominus}}{\underset{|}{CH}}-CH_2-C\underset{H}{\overset{O}{\diagup\!\!\!\diagdown}}$$

$$\Big/\!\!\Big/ H_2O$$

$$CH_3-\overset{OH}{\underset{|}{CH}}-CH_2-C\underset{H}{\overset{O}{\diagup\!\!\!\diagdown}} + OH^{\ominus} \tag{18·5}$$

$$RO^{\ominus} + CH_3CH_2OH \rightleftharpoons ROH + CH_3CH_2O^{\ominus}$$

$$\xrightarrow{RCHO} R-\overset{O^{\ominus}}{\underset{|}{CH}}-OCH_2CH_3$$

$$\Big/\!\!\Big/ ROH$$

$$R-\overset{OH}{\underset{|}{CH}}-OCH_2CH_3 + RO^{\ominus} \tag{18·6}$$

$$\overset{\ominus}{N}H_2 + R-\overset{O}{\overset{\|}{C}}-CH_3 \longrightarrow NH_3 + R-\overset{O}{\overset{\|}{C}}-CH_2^{\ominus}$$

$$\xrightarrow{CH_3I} R-\overset{O}{\overset{\|}{C}}-CH_2CH_3 + I^{\ominus} \tag{18·7}$$

For these reactions, the added base (hydroxide ion, alkoxide ion, and amide ion) generates an organic anion which undergoes further reaction to give the product. In the last reaction (18·7), however, the base is consumed as the reaction proceeds, so this reaction does not qualify as an example of base catalysis. In the other two reactions, base is regenerated in the final steps, so only catalytic amounts of base are required.

C. NUCLEOPHILIC CATALYSIS

The chloromethane–hydroxide ion reaction catalyzed by iodide ion (Section 18·1) is an example of nucleophilic catalysis.

$$CH_3Cl + OH^\ominus \xrightarrow{\quad I\ominus \quad} CH_3OH + Cl^\ominus$$

The catalyst forms a covalent bond to the substrate during the course of the reaction (CH_3I is a discrete intermediate). This type of reaction, particularly when it involves an enzyme, is sometimes called "covalent catalysis."

Bases are also nucleophiles and it is reasonable to ask how we distinguish base catalysis from nucleophilic catalysis. A reagent is a base when it removes a proton, and a nucleophile when it bonds to any atom other than H. We pointed out earlier that nucleophilicity does not always parallel basicity. A number of polarizable ions such as $I^\ominus$, $N_3{}^\ominus$, $HS^\ominus$, and $HOO^\ominus$ have much greater nucleophilicities than their basicities would indicate.

The molecules of the heterocyclic compound imidazole (Section 25·3) are neutral and possess high nucleophilicity.

imidazole

Although the basicity of imidazole is low ($pK_B = 7$), it is effective in catalyzing the hydrolysis of certain esters in neutral solution. These reactions follow the course shown in Equation 18·8.

$$R = -C_6H_4NO_2\text{-}p \tag{18·8}$$

The intermediate N-acetylimidazole [1] can be isolated and there is no doubt that the imidazole is acting here as a nucleophile rather than as a base.

The imidazole ring is present in the amino acid histidine, which is a key constituent of enzymes catalyzing hydrolytic reactions. This, of course, has led to speculation that the enzyme operates in the same general manner as shown in Equation 18·8. It is doubtful, however, that the catalysis is this simple. Thus, in enzyme-catalyzed hydrolyses of acid derivatives, the acyl group often becomes attached to the alcohol hydroxyl group of the amino acid serine in the enzyme. Nonetheless, the imidazole ring in the enzyme plays an important role in the hydrolysis and we shall examine this reaction further in Section 18·3.

D. GENERAL ACID AND BASE CATALYSIS

It might be expected that the rate of an acid-catalyzed reaction in buffered aqueous solution would depend only on the pH of the solution and that the concentration of buffer would be unimportant, except possibly for a small salt effect. Some reactions are indeed like this. For example, the rate of the acid-catalyzed hydrolysis of acetals (or its reverse) depends only on the pH of the solution. This is called specific-acid catalysis.

$$CH_3CH(OEt)_2 + H_2O \underset{H^\oplus}{\rightleftharpoons} CH_3\overset{\overset{\displaystyle OH}{|}}{C}HOEt + EtO$$

pH dependent
(specific acid catalysis)

Other acid-catalyzed reactions depend on the nature and the concentration of the buffer solution as well as on the pH. For example, the rate of the acid-catalyzed bromination of ketones, which takes place through the enol form, varies with the identity and concentration of the buffers used to control the pH.

$$R-\overset{\overset{\displaystyle O}{\|}}{C}-CH_3 \underset{H^\oplus}{\rightleftharpoons} R-\overset{\overset{\displaystyle OH}{|}}{C}=CH_2$$

$$\downarrow Br_2$$

$$R-\overset{\overset{\displaystyle O}{\|}}{C}-CH_2Br + HBr$$

pH and buffer dependent
(general acid catalysis)

It is difficult to see the cause of the difference without a complete kinetic analysis of the mechanisms in the two cases. Suffice it to say here that specific-acid catalysed reactions are those in which the substrate reacts in an equilibrium step with a proton and then suffers a rate-controlling unimolecular decomposition.

$$Z + H^\oplus \rightleftharpoons ZH^\oplus$$

$$ZH^\oplus \xrightarrow{slow} products$$

In the case of acid-catalyzed acetal hydrolysis, the protonated acetal de-

composes slowly to the cation $R-C\overset{\displaystyle \oplus OEt}{\underset{\displaystyle H}{\diagup}}$, which then undergoes a rapid

reaction with water to give the hemiacetal. The rate now depends simply and directly on the pH because the concentration of $ZH^\oplus$ depends on the pH.

General acid catalysis results when the intermediate ion, $ZH^\oplus$, can only decompose with the help of a base or a nucleophile.

$$Z + H^\oplus \rightleftharpoons ZH^\oplus$$

$$ZH^\oplus + :B \xrightarrow{slow} products$$

For acid-catalyzed enolization, the protonated ketone, $R-\overset{\overset{\displaystyle \oplus OH}{\|}}{C}-CH_3$, requires a base to remove a proton from the methyl group. The base might be a water molecule or a hydroxide ion (if present in significant concentrations), or it might be the anion $A^\ominus$ of the acid used as buffer. The intervention of the base $A^\ominus$ alters the kinetic form of the equation from one containing $[H^\oplus]$ to one containing $[H^\oplus][A^\ominus]$. Because $[H^\oplus][A^\ominus]$ is kinetically equivalent to $[HA]$,[1] we will have contributions to the rate which appear to depend on all

[1] $K_{HA} = \dfrac{[H^\oplus][A^\ominus]}{[HA]}$; therefore $[H^\oplus][A^\ominus] = K_{HA}[HA]$ and $[H^\oplus][A^\ominus] \propto [HA]$.

of the undissociated acids (HA, HA′, etc.) which are present, provided that $A^{\ominus}$, $A'^{\ominus}$, and so on are effective bases in removing a proton from the carbon of the protonated ketone.

A number of enzymic processes are known to be subject to general acid catalysis, but it is not always easy to distinguish between the action of a base and a nucleophile in the second step. In an enzyme, the proton source is often a protonated free amino group in the protein chain. The base or nucleophile is often an imidazole ring on a histidine unit, also in the protein chain.

The situation with respect to base catalysis is similar and examples of both specific and general base catalysis are known.

E. INTRAMOLECULAR CATALYSIS

One of the great advantages that enzymes have in accelerating reactions is that their precisely coiled and folded protein chains place two or more groups in a position where they can simultaneously interact with the substrate(s). In some simple molecules, a neighboring group to the reaction site can behave similarly and cause rate enhancements.

The conversion of 2-bromopropanoic acid to lactic acid can be accomplished in strong base in the normal way, with the product having the inverted configuration expected for an S_N2 reaction.

$$CH_3CHBrCO_2^{\ominus} + OH^{\ominus} \longrightarrow CH_3CHOHCO_2^{\ominus} + Br^{\ominus}$$

2-bromopropanoate ion   lactate ion
D series   L series

However, if the concentration of hydroxide ion is lowered by the use of appropriate buffers, this reaction becomes slower and is eventually superseded by a process that has a moderate rate, *independent of pH*. The resulting product is lactate ion as before, but it now has the *same* configuration as the starting material.

The explanation is that the bromide is displaced by the neighboring carboxylate group in an internal nucleophilic substitution reaction (called $S_N i$). The intermediate then suffers a second displacement by a water molecule, which restores the original configuration.

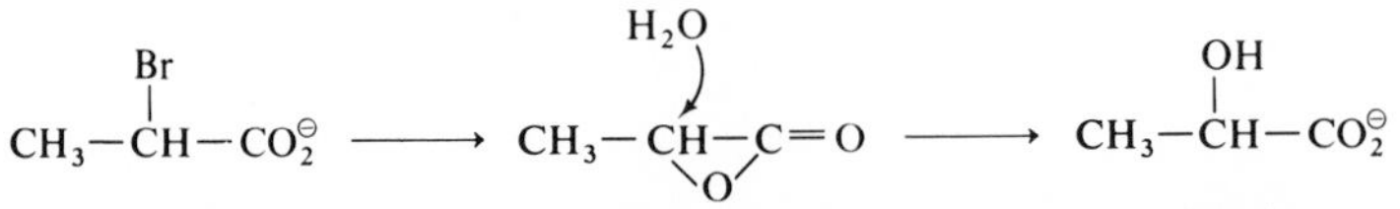

The intervention of a neighboring group this way is called *anchimeric assistance*. Because the reaction illustrated here is accelerated by the neighboring carboxylate group, and because this group emerges from the reaction intact, it is, in effect, an intramolecular catalyst.

Many other examples of intramolecular catalysis are known. The two phosphonate esters [2] and [3] differ enormously in their hydrolysis rates. The difference is clearly due to intramolecular catalysis by the neighboring carboxyl group in [2].

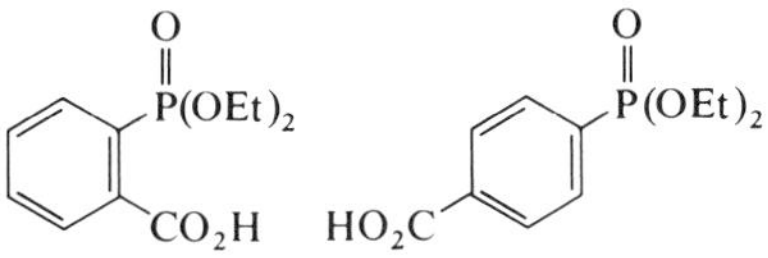

$$\underset{\text{[2]}}{\underset{\text{15 minutes}}{\text{(o-P(OEt)}_2\text{, CO}_2\text{H)}}} \qquad \underset{\text{[3]}}{\underset{> 10 \text{ years}}{\text{(p-P(OEt)}_2\text{, HO}_2\text{C)}}}$$

half-time for hydrolysis in
30% aq. dimethyl sulfoxide
at 36°

In nonhydroxylic solvents, molecules that can change from one tautomeric form to another by donating a proton at one site and accepting a proton at another are effective catalysts for enolization and other processes. α-Pyridone [4] is such a molecule because it exists in equilibrium with its tautomer [5].

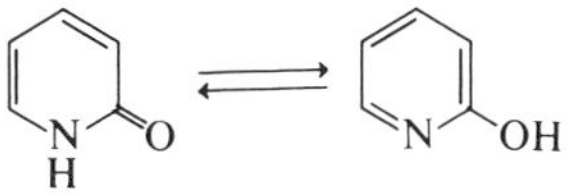

[4] ⇌ [5]

The mutarotation of tetramethylglucose in chloroform solution and a number of other reactions in which hydrogen shifts are important are catalyzed by this reagent (Equation 18·9).

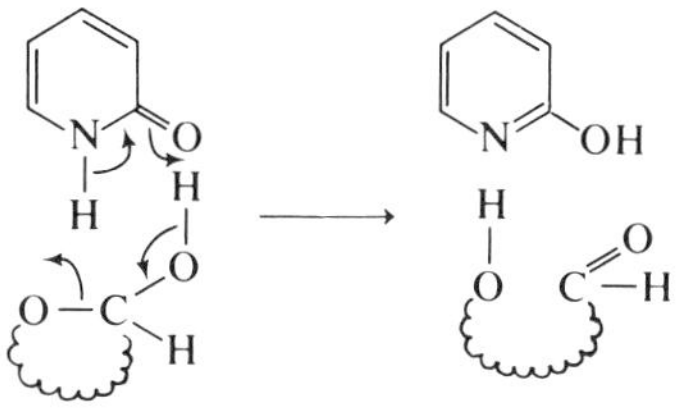

$$(18\cdot9)$$

A carboxylic acid can also act as a catalyst of this type; it exists in two

tautomeric forms that are exactly equivalent, $\text{R—C}\begin{smallmatrix}\text{O}\\\text{OH}\end{smallmatrix}$ and $\text{R—C}\begin{smallmatrix}\text{OH}\\\text{O}\end{smallmatrix}$

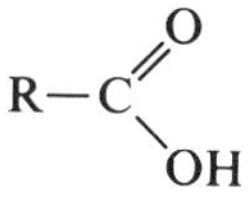

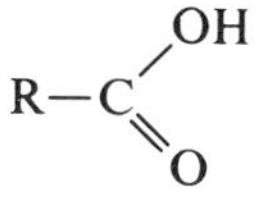

Even though Equation 18·9 shows proton shifts, these are concerted so as not to give free ions at any stage of the reaction. Tautomeric catalysis of the type shown above appears to be important only in nonhydroxylic media. In hydroxylic solvents, it is likely that separate protonation and deprotonation steps occur.

18·2   enzymes and coenzymes

Enzymes are invariably proteins. Some enzymes consist only of peptide chains and others require the presence of non-amino acid groups or molecules as well. If these other groups are attached directly to the peptide chain they are often called prosthetic groups (Section 17·3). If they are complexed to the enzyme in a looser fashion, they are called **coenzymes**. In some ways the coenzyme resembles a reagent which undergoes a chemical change under the influence of the enzyme, just as does the substrate. The difference is that a coenzyme is restored to its original condition in a subsequent step. Although all biological oxidation systems make use of coenzymes, many hydrolytic systems do not.

The most remarkable characteristics of enzymes are their catalytic effectiveness and their specificity. A striking example of their effectiveness is provided by the way in which the enzyme urease catalyzes the hydrolysis of urea, a product of protein metabolism. The nonenzymic reaction under neutral con-

$$NH_2\!-\!\underset{\underset{\text{urea}}{}}{\overset{\overset{O}{\|}}{C}}\!-\!NH_2 + H_2O \xrightarrow{\text{urease}} 2\,NH_3 + CO_2$$

ditions in water is so slow that the reaction is virtually undetectable at room temperature. The rate can be measured at high temperatures, however, and extrapolated to room temperature. This reveals that at low concentrations of urea the enzymic hydrolysis is about 10^{14} *times* faster than the uncatalyzed reaction.

There is an important limitation on the catalytic effectiveness of enzymes; it is commonly observed that as the concentration of substrate is increased the rate of reaction tends to level off. The explanation for this is that the substrate and enzyme form a complex which then decomposes to products. Despite the large sizes of enzyme molecules, there are usually only a few sites (often only one) at which reaction occurs; these are called the **active sites**. The function of the rest of the molecule is normally to bring substrate(s) and active site together. With a large excess of substrate, the active sites are continually being filled and the rate or decomposition to products and their removal from the active sites is the rate-limiting factor. Increasing the number of substrate molecules awaiting reaction increases the rate of product formation only up to the point where the enzyme becomes saturated with substrate. This phenomenon is called the **Michaelis-Menten effect**.

The reasons for the high specificity of enzymes have been the subjects of lively debate. According to one view—the " induced-fit " theory—the catalytic groups at the active site in an enzyme only take up positions in which they can interact with a substrate as a result of a conformational change that forces the enzyme into a slightly less energetically favorable, but catalytically active, spatial arrangement. This theory accounts for the observation that certain compounds, even though they may bind to the active site of an enzyme, do not undergo further reaction. They do not have the necessary structural features to induce the critical conformation at the active site.

18·3 hydrolytic enzymes

A large number of hydrolytic enzymes that catalyze esters and amide hydrolysis are known. Undoubtedly the most intensively studied of these is **chymotrypsin**, an enzyme of the digestive tract. It is a protein molecule with a molecular weight of 24,500, consisting of three peptide chains. There are two amino acid units in the enzyme that are known to be intimately involved in the bond-breaking steps of ester hydrolysis. These are histidine [6] and serine [7].

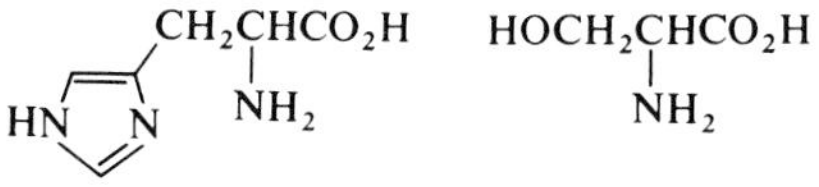

$$CH_2CHCO_2H$$
(with NH_2 and imidazole ring)
$$HOCH_2CHCO_2H$$
$$NH_2$$

histidine
[6]

serine
[7]

When an ester such as phenyl acetate, $CH_3-C\underset{OC_6H_5}{\overset{O}{\parallel}}$, is hydrolyzed

by the action of chymotrypsin, the acetyl group, $CH_3-C\overset{O}{\diagdown}$, is actually

transferred to the enzyme. In a subsequent step the acetylated enzyme is hydrolyzed to acetic acid and the enzyme is regenerated. The hydroxyl group

$$E-H + CH_3-C\underset{OC_6H_5}{\overset{O}{\diagup}} \longrightarrow E-\overset{O}{\overset{\parallel}{C}}-CH_3 + C_6H_5OH$$

enzyme

acetylated
enzyme

$$E-\overset{O}{\overset{\parallel}{C}}-CH_3 + H_2O \longrightarrow EH + CH_3C\overset{O}{\underset{OH}{\diagup}}$$

in the serine unit in the chain has been identified as the group that becomes acetylated. The imidazole ring of the histidine unit is known to aid this transfer, possibly by acting as a base. In the mechanism shown in Figure 18·2, the

Figure 18·2 Possible mechanism for the chymotrypsin-catalyzed hydrolysis of phenyl acetate; E = enzyme.

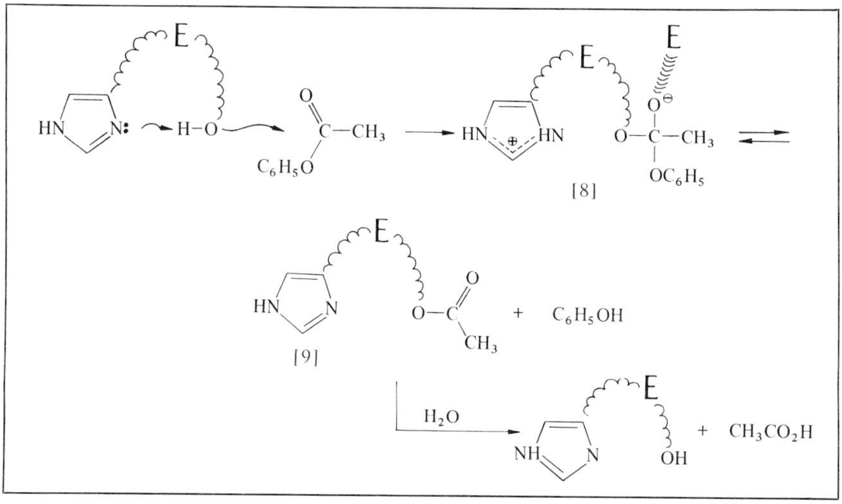

imidazole accepts a proton from the serine hydroxyl as the latter attacks the carbonyl carbon of the ester.

The ester must be held in position at the active site of the enzyme by complex formation. This presumably involves hydrogen bonds to the carbonyl oxygen atom, thus avoiding a full negative charge being generated at this site in the intermediate [8]. The cleavage of the phenoxy group in [8] and the deacylation of [9] that restores the enzyme to its original state also seem to be assisted by the imidazole ring, acting as a base in each case. There are, in fact, two histidine units in the peptide chain of chymotrypsin, and it is possible that both are involved in one or more of these steps.

Another important hydrolytic enzyme is **acetylcholinesterase**. Nerve cells contain the molecule acetylcholine [10] in a bound state. Stimulation of the cell releases acetylcholine, which stimulates the neighboring cell to release acetylcholine and this, in turn, its neighbor, thus transmitting the nerve impulse. Deactivation of the stimulant must be done very quickly once the impulse is transmitted. Deactivation is achieved by the enzyme acetylcholinesterase, which catalyzes the hydrolysis.

$$\underset{\substack{\text{acetylcholine} \\ [10]}}{CH_3-\overset{\overset{\textstyle O}{\|}}{C}-OCH_2CH_2\overset{\oplus}{N}(CH_3)_3} + H_2O \xrightarrow{\text{acetylcholinesterase}} CH_3CO_2H + \underset{\text{choline}}{HOCH_2CH_2\overset{\oplus}{N}(CH_3)_3}$$

A nerve poison such as diisopropyl fluorophosphate, $[(CH_3)_2CHO]_2POF$, forms a stable ester with the serine hydroxyl at the active site in the enzyme, thus preventing the deactivation step from occurring.

18·4 oxidative enzymes

The groups ordinarily present in a peptide chain do not undergo facile oxidation or reduction and, as a consequence, the enzymes involved in biological oxidation and reduction processes utilize a coenzyme which serves as the actual oxidant or reductant. One of the most important coenzymes in this regard is the molecule nicotinamide-adenine dinucleotide (Figure 18·3), abbreviated $NAD^\oplus$. [This substance is often called "diphosphopyridine nucleotide" ($DPN^\oplus$). The name used here is that approved by the International Union of Biochemistry.] The structure of this molecule is not unlike that of adenosine triphosphate (ATP) met earlier (Section 15·5). It contains the adenosine ring (upper right in Figure 18·3) attached to a ribose molecule which in turn has a phosphate link. In $NAD^\oplus$, this is diphosphate, not triphosphate, and is further linked through another ribose ring to a nicotinamide unit (upper left in the formula). The pyridinium ring in the latter unit is the active oxidant. Since the molecule contains two nitrogen bases, two sugar units, and two phosphates it is a dinucleotide.

Ethanol is oxidized in the liver by $NAD^\oplus$ under the influence of the enzyme **alcohol: NAD oxidoreductase**. (This enzyme is often called alcohol dehydrogenase, but such a name implies that the enzyme acts in one direction only. Like all catalysts, enzymes increase the rates of both forward and reverse

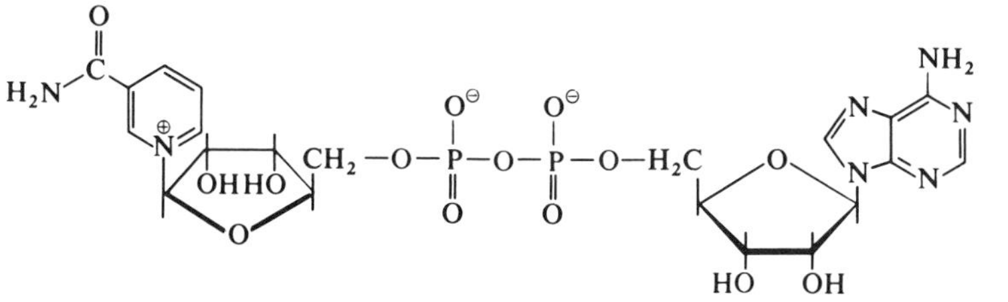

Figure 18·3 The coenzyme nicotinamide-adenine dinucleotide (NAD⊕). Although it is anionic at neutral pH, because of the ionization of the diphosphate linkage, the reactive part of the coenzyme bears a positive charge, hence the abbreviation NAD⊕.

reactions). In the oxidation of ethanol to acetaldehyde a hydride ion is transferred from C-1 to the pyridinium ring in the coenzyme at the same time as a proton is lost by the hydroxyl group.

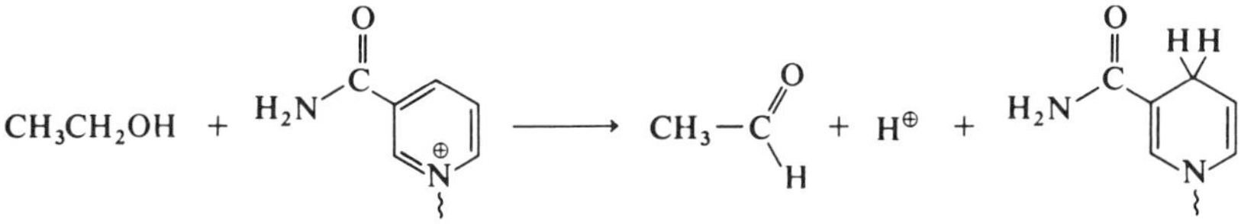

There is extensive evidence in support of this mechanism which will not be covered here. Instead we will consider three important general questions. First, what is the function of the remainder of the coenzyme molecule? Second, what is the function of the enzyme itself? And third, how is the reduced form of the coenzyme (abbreviated NADH) oxidized back to NAD⊕ so that it can be used again?

The coenzyme contains a number of hydrogen-bonding groups that must function to bind the coenzyme to the enzyme in such a way that the pyridinium ring is in a favorable position to react. For its part, the enzyme functions to complex both the coenzyme and the substrate. But it must also be involved in removing the hydroxyl hydrogen as a proton because otherwise the energetically unfavorable species $CH_3CHOH^⊕$ (protonated acetaldehyde) would be formed.

Either a carboxylate ion or an amino group in the coiled protein chain of the enzyme might be hydrogen bonded to the hydroxyl group of the alcohol and be able to accept the proton completely at the critical stage of C—H bond rupture. We saw in the previous chapter that a number of amino acids contain such additional groups. Because amino groups are extensively protonated at physiological pH, we show a carboxylate ion as the proton acceptor in Figure 18·4, which shows a plausible, but rather simplified, view of the enzyme-catalyzed oxidation of ethanol by NAD⊕.

The NADH that is formed is reoxidized by another enzyme-coenzyme system. The ultimate oxidizing agent for most physiological oxidations is, of course, molecular oxygen, but its reaction with NADH is extremely slow.

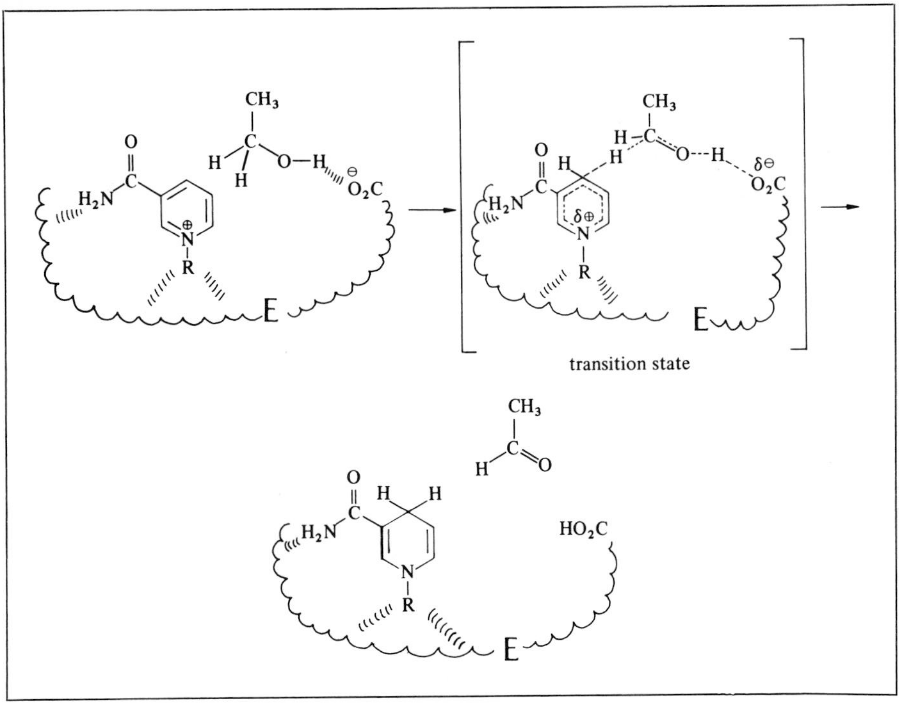

Figure 18·4 Possible mechanism for the NAD$^\oplus$ oxidation of ethanol under the influence of the enzyme alcohol:NAD oxidoreductase; E = enzyme.

A whole battery of enzymes is required to catalyze the overall reaction:

$$CH_3CH_2OH + 3\,O_2 \longrightarrow 2\,CO_2 + 3\,H_2O$$

We have seen that NAD$^\oplus$, a hydride acceptor, reacts directly with ethanol. The enzyme that reacts with oxygen must have rather different characteristics because oxygen is a substance which invariably reacts by one-electron steps. (Transfer of hydride ion, H$^\ominus$, amounts to a two-electron or two-equivalent group oxidation-reduction step. Transfer of H$^\oplus$ is neither oxidation nor reduction, transfer of H· is a one-electron step, and transfer of H:$^\ominus$ is a two-electron step.)

The enzyme systems that react directly with oxygen in these reactions are called **cytochromes**. They contain an iron atom complexed in a cyclic system that resembles that in hemoglobin (Section 25·4). Whereas the ferrous ion in hemoglobin complexes with oxygen, the ferrous ion in the cytochromes is oxidized to the ferric state, each iron atom undergoing a one-electron change.

$$4\,Fe_{cyt}^{II} + O_2 + 4\,H^\oplus \longrightarrow 4\,Fe_{cyt}^{III} + 2\,H_2O$$

Between Fe_{cyt}^{III} and NADH come a number of other enzyme systems, one of which must be capable of reacting both with a one-equivalent couple such as Fe^{II}-Fe^{III} and with a two-equivalent couple such as NAD$^\oplus$-NADH. The enzyme systems that play this role are known as **flavins**.

Batteries of enzymes able to bring about the overall oxidation of ethanol to acetaldehyde (and similar processes) are located in the **mitochondria**. These are subcellular, oblong bodies found in the oxygen-consuming cells of plants and animals. They are reponsible for oxidizing carbohydrates and fats to carbon dioxide and water and supplying the energy for processes such as muscle action, nerve impulses, and chemical synthesis. The sequence of re-actions is often called the **electron-transport chain**, although this name ob-scures the fact that most of the reactions, including the oxidation steps, are not, in fact, simple electron transfer processes.

18·5   the energetics of metabolic processes

The mitochondrial enzymes not only speed up the rate of the overall reaction of oxygen with say, glucose, by an enormous factor (probably in excess of 10^{20}), but they also control the energy release so that it can be used for a multitude of purposes and not simply appear as heat. This is done by har-nessing the many oxidation steps to the synthesis of adenosine triphosphate (ATP) from adenosine diphosphate (ADP) and inorganic phosphate (Equa-tion 18·10). Hydrolysis of ATP releases this energy in such a way that the system can utilize it as work. Neither the mechanisms of the coupling of the oxidation steps to ATP synthesis (oxidative phosphorylation) nor the coupling of the hydrolysis step to production of work are very well understood at present.

$$\Delta G = +7 \text{ kcal (at pH 7.0, 25°)}$$

ATP and ADP are shown in Equation 18·10 in the ionic forms which predominate at pH 7.

The complete oxidation of one mole of glucose releases 673 kcal of heat and the standard free energy change for the reaction is almost the same. It is

Table 18·1   Heats of combustion of various substances

compound	state	formula	ΔH, kcal[a] per mole	per gram
ethane	g	CH_3CH_3	370	12.3
octane	l	$CH_3(CH_2)_6CH_3$	1303	11.4
cetane	s	$CH_3(CH_2)_{14}CH_3$	2560	11.3
ethanol	l	C_2H_5OH	328	7.1
glyceryl tri-stearate (a typical fat)	s	$CH_2O_2CC_{17}H_{35}$ $\mid$ $CHO_2CC_{17}H_{35}$ $\mid$ $CH_2O_2CC_{17}H_{35}$	8290	9.3
glucose	s	$C_6H_{12}O_6$	673	3.7
starch	s	$(C_6H_{10}O_5)_x$	$x \cdot 678$	4.2
glycine	s	$NH_2CH_2CO_2H$	235 / 159[b]	3.1 / 2.1[b]
protein	s	$(-NHCH\overset{\displaystyle O}{\overset{\displaystyle \|}{C}}-)_x$ $\mid$ R	—	< 4[b]

[a] To give carbon dioxide, liquid water, and nitrogen. (Some of these values differ from those given in Chapter 2, where all the products were assumed to be gases.)
[b] To give carbon dioxide, liquid water, and urea.

clear that such a process, even if it could occur rapidly in a cell, has to be partitioned into small packets of energy for ATP synthesis ($\Delta G = +7$ kcal) to be accomplished.

$$C_6H_{12}O_6 + 6\,O_2 \longrightarrow 6\,CO_2 + 6\,H_2O \qquad \begin{array}{l} \Delta G = -686 \text{ kcal} \\ \Delta H = -673 \text{ kcal} \end{array}$$

Oxidation (in effect combustion) of fats, carbohydrates, and proteins provides the energy for metabolic processes of animals. A comparison of the heats of combustion of these classes of compounds reveals that fats release far more heat on a weight basis than do either carbohydrates or proteins. Table 18·1 gives the heats of combustion of compounds of each type and includes for comparison those of some other fuels. The combustion energy clearly decreases as the degree of oxidation of the compound increases. Thus, hydrocarbons ($\Delta H \sim -11$ kcal g^{-1}) release the most energy, followed by fats ($\Delta H \sim -9.3$ kcal g^{-1}) which contain long hydrocarbon-like chains. Carbohydrates ($\Delta H \sim -4.0$ kcal g^{-1}) are already in a partly oxidized state and so their available combustion energy is less. (This is reflected in the smaller amounts of oxygen they consume during combustion.)

Why are proteins ($\Delta H \sim -4$ kcal g^{-1} or less), which contain less oxygen than carbohydrates, not better sources of energy? To a great extent because they do not undergo complete combustion. In man and other terrestrial verte-brates most of the nitrogen in proteins is converted to urea and excreted as such or as its hydrolysis product, ammonia. This is rather wasteful energetic-ally because the combustion of urea with formation of nitrogen would release an additional 2.5 kcal g^{-1}.

$$\underset{\text{urea}}{NH_2-\overset{\overset{\textstyle O}{\|}}{C}-NH_2} + \tfrac{3}{2}O_2 \longrightarrow CO_2 + N_2 + 2\,H_2O \qquad \begin{array}{l} \Delta H = -152\text{ kcal} \\ (2.5\text{ kcal g}^{-1}) \end{array}$$

However, having urea as the end product of protein metabolism provides those organisms that are unable to fix N_2 with a source of nitrogen for chemical synthesis.

The fixation of N_2 by certain bacteria is a biological reduction reaction of great interest. Very few nonbiochemical systems are known which will react with N_2 at room temperature and atmospheric pressure. Lithium metal com-bines slowly with nitrogen to form lithium nitride Li_3N. Another is the titanium(II) compound titanocene, whose simplest formula is $(C_5H_5)_2Ti$, sug-gesting that it might be a sandwich compound like ferrocene $(C_5H_5)_2Fe$ (Section 9·9F). Titanocene appears to be a dimer, however, and its true struc-ture has yet to be established. It reacts with nitrogen at room temperature to give a compound $(C_5H_5)_2TiN_2$ (again apparently dimeric) which can be reduced to ammonia.

summary

The fastest chemical reactions are those which occur at each encounter be-tween reactants. The controlling factors for such reactions are the rates of diffusion of the reactant molecules; in solution at room temperature, these have rate constants of about 10^{10} liters mole^{-1} sec^{-1}. The rates of other chemical reactions depend on the energy differences between reactants and transition states (the activation energy). A catalyst speeds up a reaction by providing an alternate path from reactants to products via a lower-energy transition state. Heterogeneous catalysts operate by providing a favorable surface for the re-action to occur on, while homogeneous catalysts form reactive combinations in solution which subsequently give the reaction products and regenerate the catalyst.

Many acid-catalyzed reactions of carbonyl compounds take place by way of this general path:

The rate of such a reaction is proportional to $[RCOZ][HY][H^{\oplus}]$, provided the concentration of acid catalyst is not so great as to substantially protonate the carbonyl compound.

Many base-catalyzed reactions of carbonyl compounds occur by this general path:

$$ZH + RO^{\ominus} \rightleftharpoons \overset{\ominus}{Z} + ROH$$

$$R-\overset{O}{\underset{Y}{C}} \longrightarrow R-\overset{O^{\ominus}}{\underset{\underset{Z}{|}}{\overset{|}{C}}}-Y \xrightarrow{ROH} R-\overset{OH}{\underset{\underset{Z}{|}}{\overset{|}{C}}}-Y + RO^{\ominus}$$

Closely related to base catalysis is nucleophilic catalysis, in which the catalyst forms a bond to the substrate rather than removing a proton from it. Imidazole is particularly effective in this regard.

General acid catalysis occurs when the reaction rate depends on the concentration of all the acids present in the system, not simply on the hydrogen ion concentration. Most reactions of this type involve attack of a base on a protonated intermediate. The combined effect of the proton $H^{\oplus}$ and the base $A^{\ominus}$ appears in the kinetic expression as the function $[HA]$.

Some reactions are subject to neighboring group (anchimeric) assistance. If the neighboring group is regenerated in a subsequent step, this can be thought of as intramolecular catalysis.

$$X \rightsquigarrow CO_2^{\ominus} \xrightarrow{-X^{\ominus}} \overset{O}{\underset{}{C}} \xrightarrow{Y^{\ominus}} Y \rightsquigarrow CO_2^{\ominus}$$

Tautomeric catalysts are those which can donate and accept protons simultaneously, such as α-pyridone, which is especially effective for catalysis of mutarotation of sugars.

Enzymes are highly efficient biological catalysts. They are protein molecules that sometimes have smaller units such as coenzymes associated with them. The active site is the place in the protein chain where the substrate becomes bound and where reaction actually occurs.

A hydrolytic enzyme such as chymotrypsin does not require a coenzyme. Instead, histidine and serine units in the protein chain appear to function together to effect the hydrolytic cleavage of esters and amides. Histidine contains an imidazole ring which probably acts as a base in removing a proton from the serine hydroxyl group at the same time that the oxygen of the latter bonds to the carbonyl carbon of the ester. The acylated serine that is thus formed is subsequently cleaved to give the free acid.

$$\underset{HN \quad N:\rightsquigarrow H-O}{\overset{E}{\diagdown}} \longrightarrow \overset{O}{\underset{OR}{\overset{\|}{C}}}-R$$

Oxidative enzymes and coenzymes include nicotinamide-adenine dinucleo-tide, $NAD^{\oplus}$; the flavins; and the cytochromes. $NAD^{\oplus}$ is a coenzyme that behaves as a two-equivalent oxidant by removing hydride ion from com-pounds such as ethanol. The pyridinium ring is thereby reduced and the com-pound NADH is formed. The function of the enzyme is to orient the co-enzyme and substrate in such a way as to facilitate the reaction.

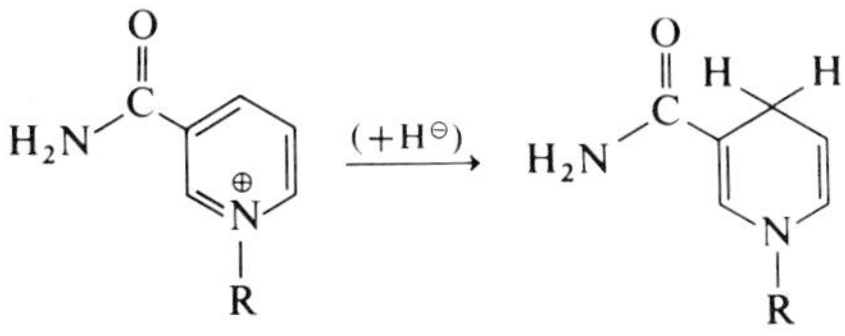

In those parts of living cells called mitochondria, the biological oxidation chain includes $NAD^{\oplus}$ at one end (oxidants for various covalent organic compounds) and the cytochromes at the other (systems that are oxidized by molecular oxygen). These disparate kinds of redox systems are linked by a number of other enzyme-coenzyme systems.

Much of the energy released by virtue of combustion of organic compounds in living cells is stored by synthesis of adenosine triphosphate (ATP) from the diphosphate (ADP) and inorganic phosphate, and subsequently used to drive a multitude of physiological processes.

Hydrocarbons, fats, carbohydrates, and proteins release on combustion about 11, 9, 4, and less than 4 kcal per gram, respectively. This order reflects to a great extent the state of oxidation of the compounds themselves.

exercises

18·1   Will the rate of a diffusion-controlled reaction be affected by a change in temperature of the system?

18·2   The reaction of 1-chlorobutane with sodium hydroxide to give n-butyl alcohol is catalyzed by sodium iodide. Work out the stereochemistry to be expected for *both* the catalyzed and the uncatalyzed reactions if right-handed 1-chlorobutane-1-D

$(CH_3CH_2CH_2{-}\overset{\overset{\displaystyle H}{|}}{\underset{\underset{\displaystyle D}{|}}{C}}{-}Cl)$ were used as the starting material. Show your

reasoning.

18·3   Is the hydrolysis of amides brought about by hydroxide ion an example of a base-catalyzed reaction?

18·4   Why do the laws of conservation of energy require that a catalyst increase both the forward and reverse rates of a chemical reaction? Is there a viola-tion of this principle in the system used for the preparation of diacetone alcohol? (See Figure 12·1.)

18·5   Draw resonance structures for the cation and for the anion of imidazole (formed by protonation and deprotonation, respectively).

18·6   What might one conclude about the active site of α-chymotrypsin from the fact that negatively charged inhibitors are less effective in reducing catalytic activity than neutral molecules of the same type of structure?

18·7   Is important conjugation possible between the amide group and the ring nitrogen in the dihydropyridine ring of NADH? (See Figure 18·4).

18·8   Which of the following reagents are likely to be one-equivalent oxidants and which two-equivalent oxidants?

$$Co^{III}, Tl^{III}, Pd^{II}, (CH_3)_3C^{\oplus}, {}^{\ominus}OCl, Fe(CN)_6^{3\ominus},$$

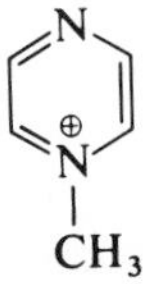

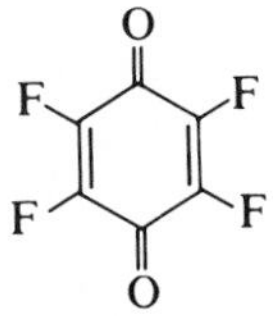

18·9   Assuming the carboxylate group shown in Figure 18·4 belongs to a non-terminal amino acid in the enzyme, which amino acids could fill this role?

18·10   Arrange the following compounds in the order of their expected heats of combustion (on a per gram basis): 1,4-butanediol, 1,3-butadiene, 1,2-butadiene, 2-methylpropanoic acid.

18·11   Let us assume that memory depends on proteins with particular amino acid sequences being deposited in the brain. Calculate the approximate number of amino acid molecules that would be deposited per second if one gram (0.04 ounce) of protein is added to the brain in this way in one year. In your opinion is this number sufficiently high that the source of memory could be explained on this basis?

chapter 19
organic compounds of sulfur, phosphorus, silicon, and boron

The four elements we shall consider in this chapter occupy positions in the periodic table that are adjacent to carbon, nitrogen, and oxygen, the three elements whose compounds have been our chief concern up to this point. Figure 19·1 shows the locations of these seven elements and the number of valence-shell electrons that each possesses.

A similarity is to be expected between the bonding pattern exhibited by a second-row element and by the element immediately above it, because both possess the same number of valence electrons. However, a second-row element has an additional degree of freedom since it is *not* necessarily restricted to a maximum of eight electrons in its bonding shell. The compounds SF_6 and PF_5 are both stable gaseous compounds, and it is clear that sulfur and phosphorus in these molecules have a share in 12 and 10 bonding electrons, respectively. The electron configurations of atomic oxygen and sulfur are shown in Figure 19·2. It appears that sulfur must make use of its 3d orbitals in forming SF_6, as does phosphorus in forming PF_5. Although silicon can also use its d orbitals in bonding ($SiF_6^{2\ominus}$ is known), it generally tends to be tetracovalent like carbon. Boron is different from any of the elements we have been discussing and we shall consider its pattern of bonding in Section 19·5.

19·1 d orbitals and chemical bonds

The maximum number of s electrons is two, of p electrons six, and of d electrons 10 in any atomic shell. Although s orbitals are spherical and p orbitals dumbbell shaped, it was shown in Chapter 1 that the shape of the bonding orbitals in a *molecule* may bear little resemblance to these atomic precursors. Thus, CH_4 has a tetrahedral configuration for its bonds because this is the arrangement in which repulsion between the bonding electrons is at a minimum.

The three p orbitals on an isolated atom run along the three geometric axes, *x*, *y*, and *z*, and are all clearly equivalent. The four bonding orbitals in a molecule such as CH_4 are tetrahedrally arranged and, again, all four are clearly equivalent. When we come to the five d orbitals that assume importance in the bonding of second-row elements, we encounter a new situation. If five bonds around a central atom are separated to the maximum extent they cannot be equivalent. This may not seem obvious at first glance. One might

Figure 19·1   The first two rows of the periodic table showing the relative positions of boron, silicon, phosphorus, and sulfur with respect to carbon, nitrogen, and oxygen, and the numbers of valence electrons of each.

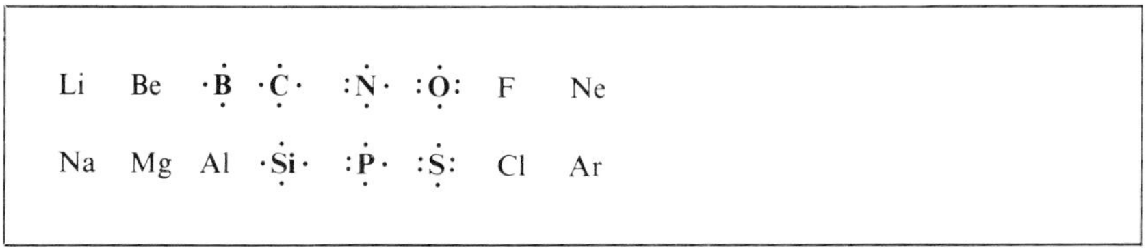

Li	Be	·B	·Ċ·	:N̈·	:Ö:	F	Ne
Na	Mg	Al	·Si·	:P̈·	:S̈:	Cl	Ar

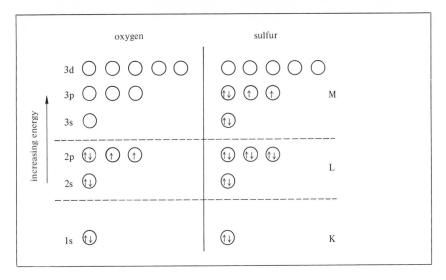

Figure 19·2   Electronic configurations of oxygen and sulfur.

expect that five lines can be drawn radiating from a central point so that all are equivalent, just as four lines can.

Solid geometry shows us that this is not so. There are only five regular polyhedra, the tetrahedron (four sides, four apexes), the cube (six sides, eight apexes), the octahedron (eight sides, six apexes), the dodecahedron (12 sides, 20 apexes), and the eicosahedron (20 sides, 12 apexes). This means that only those three-dimensional spatial arrangements with four, six, eight, 12, and 20 apexes have their apexes in identical and equivalent positions. Since the five atomic d orbitals are, in fact, exactly equivalent in energy, what shapes do they assume? If they are all completely filled or half-filled, the resulting electron cloud is spherically symmetrical. But this does not help to provide us with a picture of the five component orbitals. A mathematical solution to the electronic wave equation, however, provides the shapes of the five d orbitals as shown in Figure 19·3. Despite the different appearance of the d_{z^2} orbital, it is *equivalent in energy* to the other four rosette-shaped d orbitals.

Should we assume that the bonds in molecules such as SF_6 or $HO-\overset{\overset{\displaystyle O}{\|}}{\underset{\underset{\displaystyle O}{\|}}{S}}-OH$

point in directions corresponding to the directions of maximum extent of the d orbitals? The same problem arises here as in inferring the tetrahedral arrangement of bonds in methane from the shapes of s or p orbitals. The maximum number of electrons that are found in the valence shell of sulfur is 12 and, if the bonds are all equivalent (as they are in SF_6), then the six pairs of electrons will on the average be located at the corners of a regular octahedron.

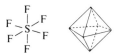

The six bonds are sometimes designated d^2sp^3 hybrids, or octahedral bonds, just as the four single bonds to carbon are designated sp^3 or tetrahedral bonds.

Double bonds to tetravalent or hexavalent sulfur, as in $(CH_3)_2S{=}O$ or

$CH_3{-}\overset{\overset{O}{\|}}{\underset{\underset{O}{\|}}{S}}{-}CH_3$, differ from double bonds to carbon in that the π bonds are

formed not by p orbitals on sulfur but by something close to d orbitals. Divalent sulfur compounds, on the other hand, such as thioketones, $R_2C{=}S$, are formed by interaction of p orbitals on both carbon and sulfur. Such compounds are relatively uncommon and often are unstable with respect to polymerization, which can be ascribed to low effectiveness of π-type interacaction involving 3p orbitals. In this connection we may note that S_2, unlike O_2, is highly unstable and that elemental sulfur is most stable in the cyclic S_8 form. The reluctance of sulfur to form double bonds to carbon is also exhibited by phosphorus and silicon, and no stable compounds are known with $C{=}Si$ or $C{=}P$ bonds.

Dimethyl sulfoxide, $(CH_3)_2S{=}O$, has an unshared pair of electrons on sulfur and, unlike acetone, $(CH_3)_2C{=}O$, is nonplanar.

Figure 19·3   The five atomic d orbitals; all are equivalent in energy.

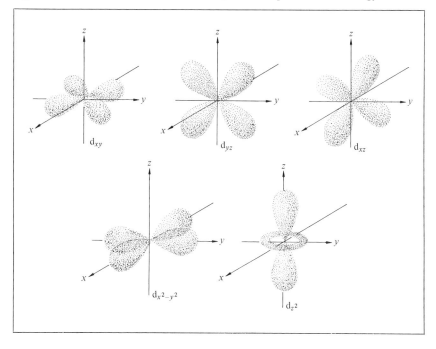

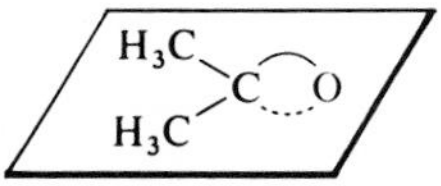

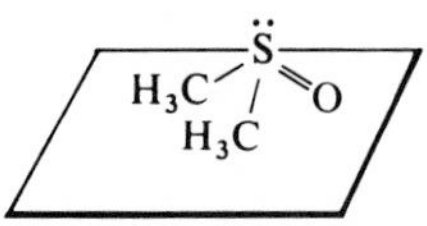

Some persons prefer to write $\diagup\!\!\!\diagdown\!\!S{=}O$ bonds as $\overset{\oplus}{\diagup}\!\!\!\diagdown\!\!S{-}\overset{\ominus}{O}$ and $-\overset{\overset{O}{\|}}{\underset{\|}{\underset{O}{S}}}-$ bonds as $-\overset{O^{\ominus}}{\underset{O^{\ominus}}{\overset{|}{\underset{|}{S}}}}\!\!^{2\oplus}$, thus preserving an octet arrangement about sulfur. The difference in electronegativity between oxygen and sulfur suggests that such structures should make important contributions to the resonance hybrid. Nonetheless, we shall use the double-bonded formulas in this book because they emphasize the d-orbital participation in the bonding. It is important to recognize that drawing S=O does not imply any necessary correspondence to carbon-oxygen or carbon-nitrogen double bonds.

19·2 types and nomenclature of organic compounds of sulfur[1]

A number of typical sulfur compounds with their common and IUPAC names are listed in Table 19·1. It can be seen that the divalent sulfur derivatives are structurally analogous to oxygen compounds of types discussed in earlier chapters. These sulfur derivatives are often named by using the prefix *thio* in conjunction with the name of the corresponding oxygen analog. The prefix *thia* is occasionally used when sulfur replaces carbon in an organic compound.

CH_3CH_2SH

ethanethiol

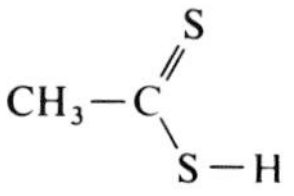

dithioacetic acid
(ethanethionthioic acid)

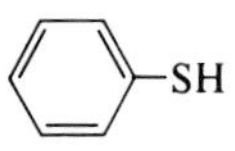

thiophenol

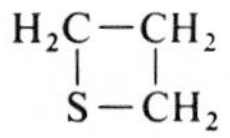

thiacyclobutane
(trimethylene sulfide)
(thietane)

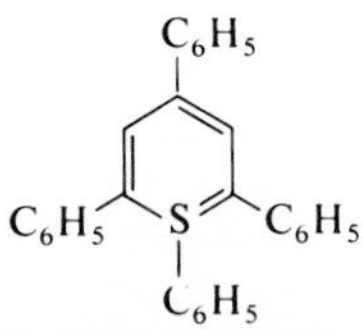

1,2,4,6-tetraphenylthiabenzene

---

[1] Terms such as organosulfur, organophosphorus, and so on actually refer to those compounds containing the bonds C—S, C—P, and so on. Just as sodium acetate is not regarded as an organometallic compound, so dimethyl sulfate, $(CH_3O)_2SO_2$, is not regarded as an organosulfur compound; the links between carbon and the other element are through oxygen in both cases.

Table 19·1   Typical organic compounds of sulfur

compound	oxygen analog	common name	IUPAC name
CH_3SH	ROH	methyl mercaptan	methanethiol
$C_2H_5SC_2H_5$	ROR	diethyl sulfide diethyl thioether	ethylthioethane
$C_6H_5SSC_6H_5$	R—O—O—R	diphenyl disulfide	phenyldithio- benzene
$(CH_3)_3\overset{\oplus}{S}$ $\overset{\ominus}{Br}$	$R_3\overset{\oplus}{O}$ $\overset{\ominus}{X}$	trimethylsulfonium bromide	
$(C_6H_5)_2C{=}S$	$R_2C{=}O$	thiobenzophenone	
$O_2N{-}\!\!\bigcirc\!\!{-}S{-}Cl$ (with NO_2)	ROCl	2,4-dinitrobenzene- sulfenyl chloride	2,4-dinitrobenzene- sulfenyl chloride
$C_2H_5{-}\overset{\overset{O}{\|}}{\underset{..}{S}}{-}OH$		ethanesulfinic acid	ethanesulfinic acid
$CH_3{-}\overset{\overset{O}{\|}}{\underset{\underset{O}{\|}}{S}}{-}OH$		methanesulfonic acid	methanesulfonic acid
$CH_3{-}\overset{\overset{O}{\|}}{\underset{\underset{O}{\|}}{S}}{-}Cl$		methanesulfonyl chloride	methanesulfonyl chloride
$CH_3{-}\overset{\overset{O}{\|}}{\underset{..}{S}}{-}C_2H_5$		ethyl methyl sulfoxide	methylsulfinyl- ethane
$C_6H_5{-}\overset{\overset{O}{\|}}{\underset{\underset{O}{\|}}{S}}{-}C_6H_5$		diphenyl sulfone	phenylsulfonyl- benzene
$CH_3O{-}\overset{\overset{O}{\|}}{\underset{\underset{O}{\|}}{S}}{-}OCH_3$		dimethyl sulfate	dimethyl sulfate

A. THIOLS

The thiols (or mercaptans) are derivatives of hydrogen sulfide in the same way that alcohols are derivatives of water. The volatile thiols, both aliphatic and aromatic, are like hydrogen sulfide in possessing characteristically disagreeable odors.

A variety of thiols occurs along with other sulfur compounds to the extent of several percent in crude petroleum. Besides having objectionable odors, these substances cause difficulties in petroleum refining, particularly by poisoning metal catalysts. The odors from pulp mills arise from volatile sulfur compounds formed during the digestion operation (Section 15·7).

Thiols also have animal and vegetable origins; notably, butanethiol is a component of skunk secretion; propanethiol is evolved from freshly chopped onions, and, as we have seen in Chapters 17 and 18, the thiol groups of cysteine are important to the chemistry of proteins and enzymes.

In many respects, the chemistry of thiols is like that of alcohols. Thus thiols can be readily prepared by the reaction of sodium hydrosulfide (NaSH) with those alkyl halides, sulfates, or sulfonates which undergo S_N2 displacements. This synthesis parallels the preparation of alcohols from similar substances and hydroxide ion (Chapter 8).

$$C_2H_5Br + SH^\ominus \longrightarrow C_2H_5SH + Br^\ominus$$

Since thiols are acids with strength comparable to hydrogen sulfide ($K_{HA} = 6 \times 10^{-8}$), some thioethers may be produced by the following sequence of reactions, unless the sodium hydrosulfide is used in large excess:

$$C_2H_5SH + SH^\ominus \rightleftharpoons C_2H_5S^\ominus + H_2S$$
$$C_2H_5S^\ominus + C_2H_5Br \longrightarrow (C_2H_5)_2S + Br^\ominus$$

Thiols can also be prepared by the reaction of Grignard reagents with sulfur (Section 9·9C).

cyclohexyl
bromide

cyclohexane-
thiol

Thiols do not form as strong hydrogen bonds as do alcohols, and consequently the low-molecular-weight thiols have lower boiling points than alcohols; thus ethanethiol boils at 35° compared to 78.5° for ethanol. The difference in boiling points diminishes with increasing chain length.

The lack of extensive hydrogen bonding is also evident from the infrared spectra of thiols, wherein a weak band characteristic of S—H linkages appears in the region 2600 to 2550 cm^{-1}. In contrast to the O—H absorption of alcohols, the frequency of this band does not shift significantly with concentration, physical state (gas, solid, or liquid), or the nature of the solvent.

It is perhaps surprising, in view of the smaller electronegativity of sulfur than oxygen, that thiols are considerably stronger acids than the corresponding alcohols. Thus K_{HA} of ethanethiol is about 10^{-11}, compared to 10^{-17} for ethanol. However, this behavior is not unusual, in that H_2O is a weaker acid than H_2S, HF is weaker than HCl, and NH_3 is a weaker acid than PH_3.

Thiols form insoluble salts with heavy metals, particularly mercury. This behavior is the origin of the common name (now out of favor), for thiols, **mercaptan**. As mentioned above, alkali metal salts of thiols react readily in

S_N2-type displacements to yield thioethers, and this provides a general method of synthesis of these substances. The pronounced nucleophilicity of sulfur combined with its relatively low basicity makes for rapid reaction with little competition from elimination, except for those compounds where S_N2-type displacements are quite unfavorable and E2-type elimination is favorable.

Thiols react with carboxylic acids and acid chlorides to yield thioesters and with aldehydes and ketones to yield dithioacetals and dithioketals, respectively.

$$CH_3CH_2SH + CH_3-\overset{O}{\overset{\|}{C}}-Cl \longrightarrow CH_3\overset{O}{\overset{\|}{C}}-S-C_2H_5 + HCl$$
$$\text{ethyl thioacetate}$$

$$HSCH_2CH_2CH_2SH + CH_3-\overset{O}{\overset{\|}{C}}-CH_3 \xrightarrow{HCl}$$
$$\text{1,3-propanedithiol}$$

$$\begin{array}{c} H_3C \quad S-CH_2 \\ \diagdown \diagup \quad \diagdown \\ C \qquad CH_2 \\ \diagup \diagdown \quad \diagup \\ H_3C \quad S-CH_2 \end{array}$$

$$\text{acetone trimethylene}$$
$$\text{dithioketal}$$

An important difference between thiols and alcohols is their behavior toward oxidizing agents. In general, oxidation of alcohols occurs with increase of the oxidation level of carbon rather than that of oxygen; carbonyl groups, not peroxides, are formed. It takes a powerful oxidizing agent (e.g., Co^{III}) to achieve one-electron oxidation of oxygen by removing a hydrogen atom from the hydroxyl group of an alcohol.

$$R-O-H + \cdot X \longrightarrow RO\cdot + HX \text{ (a generally unfavorable reaction)}$$

In addition, the hydroxyl oxygen of an alcohol does not accept an oxygen atom from reagents like hydrogen peroxide, although these same reagents readily donate an oxygen atom to nitrogen of amines to form amine oxides (see Section 16·1F5). Why does the oxidation of thiols take a different course?

$$\left[R\overset{..}{O}H + H_2O_2 \xrightarrow{\quad\not\quad} R:\overset{\overset{:\overset{\ominus}{O}:}{}}{\underset{\oplus}{O}:}H \longrightarrow R-O-O-H \right]$$

$$R\overset{..}{N}(CH_3)_2 + H_2O_2 \longrightarrow R\underset{\oplus}{N}(CH_3)_2 \overset{\overset{O^{\ominus}}{|}}{} + H_2O$$

First, because the strength of S—H bonds (83 kcal) is considerably less than that of O—H bonds (111 kcal); there is therefore good reason to expect that reaction mechanisms that are unfavorable with alcohols might well occur with sulfur. Thus we find that oxidation of thiols with a variety of mild oxidizing agents, such as atmospheric oxygen, halogens, sulfuric acid, and so on, produces disulfides, probably by way of thiyl radicals. The coupling of the amino acid cysteine to give cystine is an important example of this reaction (Section 17·1).

$$R-S-H + [O] \longrightarrow R-S\cdot + H[O]$$
$$2\,RS\cdot \longrightarrow RS-SR$$
$$\text{disulfide}$$

The second reason for the difference between alcohol and thiol oxidations is that compounds in which sulfur is in a higher oxidation state are frequently stable. Thus, vigorous oxidation of thiols with nitric acid, permanganate, or hydrogen peroxide gives sulfonic acids, possibly by way of the disulfides, or else through intermediate formation of the sulfenic and sulfinic acids, which are themselves too readily oxidized to be isolated under these conditions.

$$
R-S-S-R \longrightarrow R-\underset{\underset{O}{\parallel}}{\overset{\overset{O}{\parallel}}{S}}-S-R \longrightarrow R-\underset{\underset{O}{\parallel}}{\overset{\overset{O}{\parallel}}{S}}-\underset{\underset{O}{\parallel}}{\overset{\overset{O}{\parallel}}{S}}-R
$$

disulfide   thiosulfonate ester   disulfone

R—SH

R—S—OH
sulfenic acid

$\longrightarrow$

RSO$_3$H
sulfonic acid

$$
R-\underset{}{\overset{\overset{O}{\parallel}}{S}}-OH
$$
sulfinic acid

B. ALKYL SULFIDES

Organic sulfides or thioethers, R—S—R′, are readily obtained by displacement reactions between alkyl compounds and salts of thiols (Section 19·2A).

$$
HOCH_2CH_2SH + (CH_3)_2SO_4 \xrightarrow[60°-70°]{\text{aq. 25\% NaOH}} HOCH_2CH_2SCH_3
$$

ethan-1-ol-2-thiol   2-(methylthio)ethanol

Sulfides undergo two important reactions involving the electron pairs on sulfur. They are rather easily oxidized to sulfoxides and sulfones (see next section), and they act as nucleophilic agents toward substances that undergo nucleophilic displacement readily to give sulfonium salts. The formation of sulfonium salts from alkyl halides is reversible, and heating of the salt

$$
\underset{\underset{CH_3}{}}{\overset{CH_3}{\diagdown}}\ddot{S}: + CH_3-I \rightleftharpoons \underset{\underset{CH_3}{}}{\overset{CH_3}{\diagdown}}\overset{\oplus}{S}-CH_3 \overset{\ominus}{I}
$$

trimethylsulfonium iodide

causes dissociation into its components. Sulfonium salts are analogous in structure and properties to quaternary ammonium salts; sulfonium hydroxides, $R_3S^{\oplus}OH^{\ominus}$, like quaternary ammonium hydroxides, $R_4N^{\oplus}OH^{\ominus}$ (Section 16·1E1), are strong bases.

A noteworthy feature of sulfonium ions is that, when substituted with three different groups, they can usually be separated into optical enantiomers. Thus the reaction of methyl ethyl sulfide with bromoacetic acid gives a sulfonium ion that is separable into dextro- and levorotatory forms by crystallization as the salt of an optically active amine. The asymmetry of these ions stems from the nonplanar configuration of the bonds formed by sulfonium

$$\underset{\overset{|}{CH_2CO_2H}}{H_3C \diagdown \overset{\overset{\cdot\cdot}{S}^{\oplus}}{|} \diagup CH_2CH_3} \qquad \underset{HO_2CH_2C \diagup}{CH_3CH_2 \diagup \overset{\overset{\cdot\cdot}{S}^{\oplus}}{|} \diagdown CH_3}$$

enantiomers of methylethyl(carboxymethyl)-sulfonium ion

sulfur. The optically active forms of unsymmetrically substituted sulfonium ions are quite stable—surprisingly so, in view of the very low configurational stability of analogously constituted amines. Apparently, nonplanar compounds of the type $R_3Y:$, where Y is an element in the second row of the periodic table, undergo inversion much less readily than similar compounds for which Y is a first-row element. Thus phosphorus compounds resemble sulfur compounds in this respect, and several asymmetric phosphines $(R_1R_2R_3P:)$ have been successfully resolved into enantiomeric forms.

C. SULFOXIDES AND SULFONES

Oxidation of sulfides, preferably with hydrogen peroxide in acetic acid, yields sulfoxides and sulfones. The degree of oxidation is determined by the ratio of the reagents, and either the sulfoxide or the sulfone can be obtained in good yield.

$$\underset{\text{methionine}}{\underset{\overset{|}{NH_2}}{CH_3SCH_2CH_2CHCO_2H}}$$

30% H_2O_2, 1.5 moles / CH_3CO_2H

$$\underset{\text{methionine sulfoxide}}{\overset{\overset{O}{\|}}{CH_3S}-CH_2CH_2\overset{\overset{|}{NH_2}}{C}HCO_2H}$$

30% H_2O_2, 3.2 moles / CH_3CO_2H

$$\underset{\text{methionine sulfone}}{\overset{\overset{O}{\|}}{\underset{\overset{\|}{O}}{CH_3S}}-CH_2CH_2\overset{\overset{|}{NH_2}}{C}HCO_2H}$$

Dimethyl sulfoxide (DMSO) is a particularly useful substance in the laboratory, both as a solvent and as a reagent. It is a polar substance with a

$$\underset{\text{dimethyl sulfoxide}}{\overset{\overset{O}{\|}}{CH_3-S-CH_3}}$$
mp 18°, bp 189°

fairly high dielectric constant ($\varepsilon = 48$) and hence it dissolves polar and ionic substances quite well. It lacks hydrogen-bonding protons, however, and the activity of anions, particularly those whose charge is not dispersed, is high in DMSO solution. We have seen how this property greatly enhances S_N2 reactivity (Section 8·11D). It is also responsible for the powerfully basic character of solutions of hydroxide or alkoxide ions in DMSO. Judging by their ability to remove protons from feeble acids such as aromatic amines (Table 22·1, footnote) and hydrocarbons these solutions are about 10^{14} times more basic than the corresponding aqueous solutions. DMSO itself is very weakly acidic ($pK_{HA} = 33$). Its anion, $CH_3SOCH_2^\ominus$, called the dimsyl ion, has found wide use as a powerful base in elimination and other reactions.

One of DMSO's most unusual solvent properties is its extraordinary ability to penetrate through cell membranes. When this property was discovered it was thought that DMSO might provide a vehicle for introducing medicinals directly into cells through the skin. However, large doses of DMSO have been found to cause retinal damage and this plan has been discarded.

DMSO can also function as a mild but effective oxidant for alcohols. Treatment of an alcohol with DMSO and dicyclohexylcarbodiimide (a mild nonacidic dehydrating agent) produces high yields of aldehydes or ketones.

$$RCH_2OH + CH_3\overset{O}{\underset{\|}{S}}CH_3 + C_6H_{11}N{=}C{=}NC_6H_{11}$$

$$\longrightarrow \quad RCHO + CH_3SCH_3 + C_6H_{11}NH\overset{O}{\underset{\|}{C}}NHC_6H_{11}$$

This reaction is particularly useful if the alcohol is sensitive to acid rearrangement (Section 10·5B) or if, as in the case of the secondary hydroxyl groups in many carbohydrates, the alcohol resists oxidation by conventional means.

D. SULFENIC, SULFINIC, AND SULFONIC ACIDS

The sulfenic acids, $RSOH$, are unstable with respect to self-oxidation and reduction and generally cannot be isolated. However, certain derivatives of sulfenic acids are relatively stable, notably the acid halides $RSCl$.

Sulfinic acids, RSO_2H, are more stable than sulfenic acids but are nonetheless easily oxidized to sulfonic acids, RSO_3H. They are moderately strong acids with K_{HA} values comparable to the first ionization of sulfurous acid ($K_{HA} \sim 10^{-2}$).

Many sulfonic acids, RSO_3H, have considerable commercial importance as detergents in the form of their sodium salts, RSO_3Na. Many commercial detergents are sodium alkylarylsulfonates of types which are readily synthesized from petroleum by reactions discussed in the next chapter.

$$C_{9\text{-}15}H_{19\text{-}31}{-}\!\!\left\langle\!\!\bigcirc\!\!\right\rangle\!\!{-}\overset{\ominus}{S}\overset{\oplus}{O_3}Na$$

The resistance of highly branched alkyl chains of arylalkylsulfonates to biochemical degradation and the water pollution that results led to their elimination as detergents for domestic purposes. Sodium arylalkylsulfonates with nonbranched side chains or sodium alkylsulfonates derived from long-chain alcohols are more easily degraded by bacteria. The principal advantage that sodium sulfonates have as detergents over the sodium salts of fatty acids (Section 13·1) used in ordinary soaps is that the corresponding calcium and magnesium salts are much more soluble, and hence the sulfonates do not produce scum (bathtub ring) when used in hard water.

Sulfonic acid groups are often introduced into organic molecules to increase water solubility. This is particularly important in the dye industry, where it is desired to solubilize colored organic molecules for use in aqueous dye baths (see Section 28·7A).

Aliphatic sulfonic acids can be prepared by the oxidation of thiols (Section 19·2A).

$$
\underset{\substack{\text{4-chloro-2-methyl-}\\\text{2-butanethiol}}}{\overset{\displaystyle CH_3\atop\displaystyle |}{ClCH_2CH_2\overset{\displaystyle |}{C}-SH}}+3\,H_2O_2 \xrightarrow{CH_3CO_2H} \underset{\substack{\text{4-chloro-2-methyl-}\\\text{butane-2-sulfonic acid}\\92\%}}{\overset{\displaystyle CH_3\atop\displaystyle |}{ClCH_2CH_2\overset{\displaystyle |}{C}-SO_3H}}+3\,H_2O
$$

α-Hydroxysulfonate salts result from the addition of sodium bisulfite to aldehydes (Section 11·4I). The free sulfonic acid $RCHOHSO_3H$ is unstable since addition of acid to the salt drives the reaction back to aldehyde by converting $HSO_3{}^{\ominus}$ to SO_2.

$$
\underset{\substack{}}{R-\overset{\displaystyle O}{\underset{\displaystyle H}{C}}} + NaHSO_3 \rightleftharpoons \underset{}{R-\overset{\displaystyle OH}{\underset{}{CH}}-SO_3^{\ominus}\ Na^{\oplus}}
$$

Arylsulfonic acids are almost always prepared by sulfonation of the corresponding hydrocarbon (see next chapter). They are strong acids, comparable in strength to sulfuric acid. Furthermore, the sulfonate group is an excellent leaving group from carbon in nucleophilic displacement reactions and, in consequence, conversion of an alcohol to a sulfonate ester is a means of activating alcohols for replacement of the hydroxyl group by a variety of nucleophilic reagents. A sulfonate ester is best prepared from a sulfonyl chloride and an alcohol, and many sulfonyl chlorides that can be used for this purpose are available commercially. The use of p-toluenesulfonyl chloride (often called tosyl chloride) is illustrated in Equation 19·1.

$$
(CH_3CH_2)_2CHOH \xrightarrow{CH_3-\langle\rangle-SO_2Cl} (CH_3CH_2)_2CHO-\overset{\displaystyle O}{\underset{\displaystyle O}{\overset{\|}{\underset{\|}{S}}}}-\langle\rangle-CH_3
$$

$$
\Big\downarrow C_2H_5S^{\ominus}
$$

$$
(CH_3CH_2)_2CH-S-C_2H_5 + CH_3-\langle\rangle-SO_3^{\ominus} \tag{19·1}
$$

A number of important antibiotic drugs, the so-called sulfa drugs, are sulfonamide derivatives.

$$
H_2N-\langle\rangle-SO_2NH-\langle\overset{N}{\underset{N}{\rangle}}
$$

sulfadiazine

$$
H_2N-\langle\rangle-SO_2NH-\underset{\substack{\\ NH_2}}{\overset{\substack{NH\\ \|}}{C}}
$$

sulfaguanidine

E. SULFATE ESTERS

Sulfate esters such as dimethyl sulfate lack a sulfur-carbon bond and as mentioned earlier are not classified as organosulfur compounds. Dimethyl

$$CH_3-O-\overset{\overset{O}{\|}}{\underset{\underset{O}{\|}}{S}}-O-CH_3$$

dimethyl sulfate, bp 188°

sulfate is a good methylating agent; the methyl carbon easily undergoes attack by the substance being methylated because the group being displaced is a good leaving group. The leaving group in this reaction is the anion of a strong acid CH_3-O-SO_3H, methylsulfuric acid or methyl hydrogen sulfate. (It should not be confused with the compound methanesulfonic acid, CH_3-SO_3H, also a strong acid.)

$$\overset{\ominus}{Nu} + CH_3-O-\overset{\overset{O}{\|}}{\underset{\underset{O}{\|}}{S}}-O-CH_3 \longrightarrow Nu-CH_3 + CH_3-O-SO_3^{\ominus}$$

Dimethyl sulfate on hydrolysis produces sulfuric acid.

$$(CH_3O)_2SO_2 + 2\,H_2O \longrightarrow H_2SO_4 + 2\,CH_3OH$$

Like most volatile esters of inorganic acids, dimethyl sulfate is toxic and should be handled with care. Contact of the vapors with the eye can cause permanent corneal damage.

19·3 phosphorus compounds

The two important groups of organic compounds of phosphorus are the phosphate esters, which contain oxygen-phosphorus bonds, and the organophosphorus compounds, which contain carbon-phosphorus bonds.

A. PHOSPHATE ESTERS

Phosphoric acid, H_3PO_4, has a tendency (absent in nitric acid) to exist in polymeric forms, such as diphosphoric acid, $H_4P_2O_7$, and triphosphoric acid, $H_5P_3O_{10}$.

$$\underset{\substack{\text{phosphoric acid}\\\text{(mono)}}}{HO-\overset{\overset{O}{\|}}{\underset{\underset{OH}{|}}{P}}-OH} \qquad \underset{\text{diphosphoric acid}}{HO-\overset{\overset{O}{\|}}{\underset{\underset{OH}{|}}{P}}-O-\overset{\overset{O}{\|}}{\underset{\underset{OH}{|}}{P}}-OH} \qquad \underset{\text{triphosphoric acid}}{HO-\overset{\overset{O}{\|}}{\underset{\underset{OH}{|}}{P}}-O-\overset{\overset{O}{\|}}{\underset{\underset{OH}{|}}{P}}-O-\overset{\overset{O}{\|}}{\underset{\underset{OH}{|}}{P}}-OH}$$

Polyphosphate salts such as the sodium salts of triphosphoric acid are used in large amounts (up to 40%) in detergents to bring clay and similar particles into suspension. Because of their high phosphorus content, detergents are believed to be a major contributor to eutrophication of lakes—

overfertilization caused by nutrient abundance. Runoff from fertilized agricultural land is also an important factor. Phosphorus being a nutrient for plant life stimulates the growth of algae to such an extent that other forms of marine life may be extinguished. Unlike nitrogen, which also contributes to eutrophication, phosphorus does not enter into biochemical reactions that allow it to escape from water as a gas.

We have already met extremely important derivatives of each of the three acids, monophosphoric acid, diphosphoric acid, and triphosphoric acid. Nucleic acids are derivatives of monophosphoric acid (Figure 17·9) while adenosine diphosphate, ADP, and adenosine triphosphate, ATP (Section 15·5), are derivatives of diphosphoric acid and triphosphoric acid, respectively.

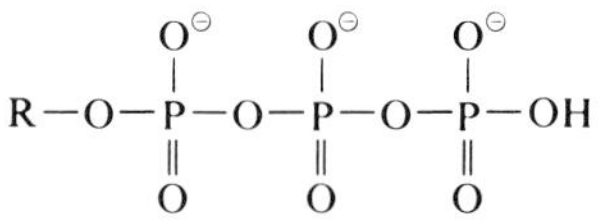

adenosine triphosphate (ATP) 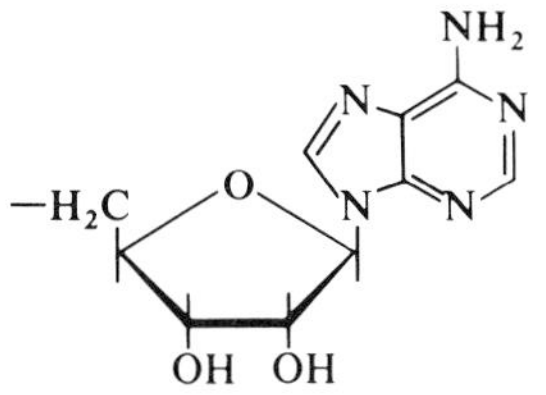   adenosine group

At pH 7, only one of the four phosphate hydroxyl groups in ATP remains un-ionized in the cell. The resulting triple negative charge on the triphosphate group is considerably reduced, however, by complex formation with magnesium ions.

The energies of the ADP-ATP system have been extensively studied because it is the link between high-energy phosphate donors, formed during the oxidation of foods (Section 18·5), and low-energy phosphate acceptors. The latter are activated by phosphorylation and can then perform cellular work: muscle contraction, biological transport, biosynthesis, and so on.

The hydrolysis of ATP has a negative free energy; that is, hydrolysis is favored at equilibrium. The free energy is more negative still in living cells, because of magnesium complexing in the cell.

$$ATP + H_2O \longrightarrow ADP + HPO_4^{2\ominus} \qquad \begin{array}{l} \Delta G_{standard} = -7 \text{ kcal} \\ \Delta G_{cellular} \sim -12 \text{ kcal} \end{array}$$

Thus ATP is a *high-energy phosphate compound*. The frequently used phrase "high-energy bond" in connection with the ATP-phosphate link is a misnomer. We saw in Chapter 2 that the higher the energy of a bond, the more stable it is. The sense of this is opposite to the hydrolysis of ATP, which is energetically favorable.

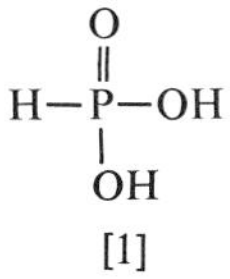

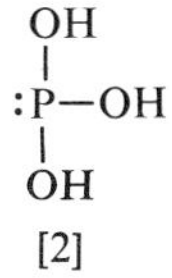

Phosphorous acid, H_3PO_3, has the structure [1], not [2], although organic derivatives of *both* of these structures are known. Ironically, it is the esters of [2] rather than the esters of [1] that are known as phosphites. The latter are called phosphonates.

$$
\begin{array}{cc}
\underset{\text{diethyl phenylphosphonate}}{
\begin{array}{c}
\overset{\displaystyle O}{\overset{\displaystyle \|}{C_6H_5-P-OC_2H_5}} \\
\underset{\displaystyle O-C_2H_5}{|}
\end{array}}
&
\underset{\text{triethyl phosphite}}{
\begin{array}{c}
\overset{\displaystyle OC_2H_5}{|} \\
:P-OC_2H_5 \\
\underset{\displaystyle OC_2H_5}{|}
\end{array}}
\end{array}
$$

B. ORGANOPHOSPHORUS COMPOUNDS

These compounds contain carbon-phosphorus bonds and resemble to some extent their nitrogen analogs. Thus trimethylphosphine is a weak base that can form phosphonium compounds analogous to ammonium compounds.

$$(CH_3)_3P: + HCl \longrightarrow (CH_3)_3\overset{\oplus}{P}H \overset{\ominus}{Cl}$$
trimethylphosphonium chloride

$$(CH_3)_3\overset{..}{P}: + CH_3Cl \longrightarrow (CH_3)_4P^{\oplus} Cl^{\ominus}$$
tetramethylphosphonium chloride

Despite being weaker bases than the corresponding amines the phosphines are actually more nucleophilic, probably because phosphorus is a larger, more electropositive atom than nitrogen, and its outer-shell electrons are consequently less firmly held and more polarizable.

C. REACTIONS OF QUATERNARY PHOSPHONIUM COMPOUNDS

There are interesting differences in behavior of quaternary ammonium and quaternary phosphonium salts toward basic reagents. Whereas tetraalkylammonium salts with hydroxide or alkoxide ions generally form alkenes and trialkylamines by E2-type elimination (Section 8·12), corresponding reactions of tetraalkyl- or arylphosphonium salts lead to phosphine oxides and hydrocarbons.

$$(CH_3)_3\overset{\oplus}{N}CH_2CH_3 + {}^{\ominus}OH \longrightarrow (CH_3)_3N + CH_2{=}CH_2 + H_2O$$

$$(C_6H_5)_3\overset{\oplus}{P}CH_2CH_3 + {}^{\ominus}OH \longrightarrow (C_6H_5)_2\overset{O}{\overset{\|}{P}}CH_2CH_3 + C_6H_6$$

There is an alternative course of reaction of quaternary phosphonium salts with basic reagents. It involves attack of a base, usually phenyllithium, at a hydrogen α to phosphorus. The product [3] is called an alkylidenephosphorane.

$$\underset{X^{\ominus}}{R_3\overset{\oplus}{P}-CH_2R'} + C_6H_5Li \longrightarrow \underset{[3]}{R_3\overset{\oplus}{P}{=}\overset{\ominus}{C}HR'} + C_6H_6 + Li\,X$$

Compounds of this type are frequently written as dipolar structures such as

[4a]. However, they are better considered as hybrids of the contributing structures [4a] and [4b], the latter involving $p_\pi\text{-}d_\pi$ bonding.

$$R_3P\overset{\oplus}{-}\overset{\ominus}{\underset{\cdot\cdot}{C}}HR \quad \longleftrightarrow \quad R_3P{=}CHR$$
$$\quad [4a] \qquad\qquad\qquad [4b]$$

Compounds in which two adjacent atoms bear opposite formal charges[2] are called **ylids** (pronounced "illids."). Although [4a] is only a contributor to the hybrid, alkylidenephosphoranes are often regarded as ylids.

Alkylidenephosphoranes are reactive, often highly colored substances, that rapidly react with oxygen, water, acids, alcohols, and carbonyl compounds—in fact, with most oxygen-containing compounds. Two of these reactions are illustrated here for methylenetriphenylphosphorane and again the driving force is formation of a phosphorus-oxygen bond at the expense of a phosphorus-carbon bond.

$$(C_6H_5)_3\overset{\oplus}{P}CH_3 \ Br^{\ominus} \quad \xrightarrow[-HBr]{C_6H_5Li} \quad (C_6H_5)_3P{=}CH_2$$

methyltriphenylphosphonium
bromide

methylenetriphenyl-
phosphorane

$$(C_6H_5)_3P{=}CH_2 + H_2O \quad \longrightarrow \quad \underset{\underset{CH_3}{|}}{(C_6H_5)_2P{=}O} + C_6H_6$$

methyldiphenylphosphine
oxide

$$(C_6H_5)_3P{=}CH_2 + \bigcirc{=}O \quad \longrightarrow \quad (C_6H_5)_3P{=}O + \bigcirc{=}CH_2$$

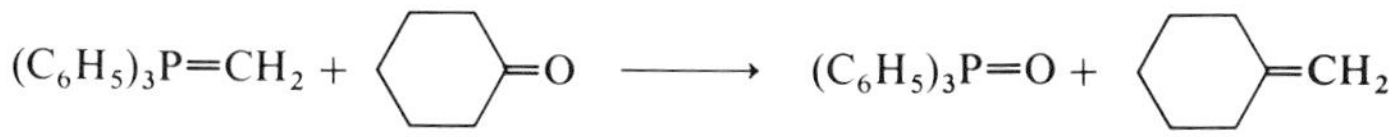

triphenylphosphine   methylene-
oxide   cyclohexane

The preparation of alkenes from the reactions of alkylidenetriphenylphosphoranes with aldehydes and ketones is known as the **Wittig reaction**. The example given here probably proceeds by way of the following intermediate.

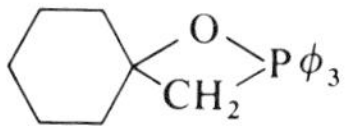

19·4 organosilicon compounds

Silicon, like carbon, normally has a valence of four and forms reasonably stable bonds to other silicon atoms, carbon, hydrogen, oxygen, and nitrogen. Compounds of some of these types are listed in Table 19·2, together with the

---

[2] **Betaine** is a term given to compounds in which two *nonadjacent* atoms bear opposite charges. An amino acid zwitterion (Section 17·1B) is an example of a betaine.

Table 19·2   Principal types of silicon compounds and their carbon analogs

silicon compound		carbon compound	
silanes and organosilanes		*alkanes*	
$H_3Si-SiH_3$	disilane	CH_3-CH_3	ethane
CH_3-SiH_3	methylsilane	CH_3-CH_3	ethane
$(CH_3)_4Si$	tetramethylsilane	$(CH_3)_4C$	neopentane
organosilyl halides (halosilanes)		*alkyl halides (haloalkanes)*	
$(CH_3)_3SiCl$	trimethylsilyl chloride	$(CH_3)_3CCl$	*t*-butyl chloride
H_2SiCl_2	dichlorosilane	CH_2Cl_2	dichloromethane
silanols		*alcohols*	
H_3SiOH	silanol	H_3COH	methanol (carbinol)
$(CH_3)_3SiOH$	trimethylsilanol	$(CH_3)_3COH$	trimethylcarbinol (*t*-butyl alcohol)
$(CH_3)_2Si(OH)_2$	dimethylsilanediol	$(CH_3)_2C(OH)_2$	acetone hydrate (unstable)
$CH_3Si(OH)_3$	methylsilanetriol	$CH_3C(OH)_3$	orthoacetic acid (unstable)
siloxanes and alkoxysilanes		*ethers*	
$(CH_3)_3SiOSi(CH_3)_3$	hexamethyldisiloxane	$(CH_3)_3COC(CH_3)_3$	di-*t*-butyl ether
$(CH_3)_3SiOCH_3$	trimethylmethoxy- silane	$(CH_3)_3COCH_3$	methyl *t*-butyl ether
$(CH_3)_2Si(OCH_3)_2$	dimethyldimethoxy- silane	$(CH_3)_2C(OCH_3)_2$	acetone dimethyl ketal
$CH_3Si(OCH_3)_2$	methyltrimethoxy- silane	$CH_3C(OCH_3)_3$	methyl orthoacetate

corresponding carbon compounds. Some idea of the strength of bonds to silicon relative to analogous bonds to carbon may be obtained from the average bond energies shown in Table 19·3. Significantly, the Si—Si bond is *weaker* than the C—C bond by some 30 kcal/mole, whereas the Si—O bond

Table 19·3   Average bond energies

bond	bond energy, kcal/mole	bond	bond energy, kcal/mole
Si—Si	53	C—C	83
Si—C	76	C—Si	76
Si—H	76	C—H	99
Si—O	108	C—O	86

is *stronger* than the C—O bond by some 22 kcal/mole. These bond energies account for several differences in the chemistry of the two elements. Thus, while carbon forms a great many compounds having linear and branched chains of C—C bonds, silicon is less versatile; the silanes of formula Si_nH_{2n+2} analogous to the alkanes of formula C_nH_{2n+2} are relatively unstable and react avidly with oxygen. On the other hand, the silicone polymers have chains of Si—O—Si bonds and have a high thermal stability as corresponds to the considerable strength of the Si—O bond.

No compounds containing silicon double bonds of the type

$$\Si=Si\diagdown, \quad \Si=C\diagdown, \quad \Si=O, \quad \text{or} \quad \Si=N—$$

have been prepared to date. Thus, there are no organosilicon compounds that are structurally analogous to alkenes, alkynes, arenes, aldehydes, ketones, carboxylic acids, esters, or imines. One clear illustration is the formation of silanediols of the type $R_2Si(OH)_2$. The silanediols do not lose water to form "silicones" of structure $R_2Si=O$ in the way the alkanediols, $R_2C(OH)_2$, which are normally unstable, lose water to form the corresponding ketones, $R_2C=O$. Loss of water from silanediols results in formation of Si—O—Si bonds, and this is the basic reaction by which silicon polymers are formed.

$$
\begin{array}{ccc}
\text{R} & & \text{R} \quad\ \text{R} \\
| & -H_2O & |\qquad\ | \\
2\ \text{HO—Si—OH} & \longrightarrow & \text{HO—Si—O—Si—OH} \\
| & & |\qquad\ | \\
\text{R} & & \text{R} \quad\ \text{R}
\end{array}
$$

In its inability to form the p_π-p_π type of double bond, silicon resembles other second-row elements of the periodic table, such as sulfur and phosphorus.

A. BONDING INVOLVING d ORBITALS IN ORGANOSILICON COMPOUNDS

Silicon is normally tetracovalent in organosilicon compounds and, by analogy with carbon, we may reasonably suppose the bonds involved to be of the sp^3 type and the substituent groups to be tetrahedrally disposed in space. Evidence that this is so comes from the successful resolution of several silicon compounds having a center of asymmetry at the silicon atom; for example, both enantiomers of 1-naphthylphenylmethylsilane [5] have been isolated.

[5]

$$[\alpha]_D = \pm 32°$$

X-Ray and electron-diffraction studies of silicon tetraiodide, silicon tetrachloride, and tetramethylsilane also indicate tetrahedral structures. Substances with hexacovalent silicon such as hexafluosilicate ion, $SiF_6{}^{2\ominus}$, are known, however, and this shows that silicon can expand its valence shell to accommodate 10 electrons by utilizing the 3d orbitals. The silicon 3d orbitals may also be involved in the bonds of compounds of the type $\overset{\diagdown}{\underset{\diagup}{Si}}-\overset{\cdot\cdot}{X}$, where

X is an atom or group having electrons in a p orbital so situated as to be able to overlap with an empty 3d orbital of silicon. The result would be a Si—X bond with partial double-bond character of the d_π-p_π type, in which the silicon has an expanded valence shell. The bonding can be symbolized by these resonance structures (examples of X include oxygen, nitrogen, and the halogens, as well as unsaturated groups such as the vinyl and phenyl groups):

$$\overset{\diagdown}{\underset{\diagup}{Si}}-\overset{\cdot\cdot}{X} \quad\longleftrightarrow\quad \overset{\diagdown}{\underset{\diagup}{Si}}\overset{\ominus}{=}\overset{\oplus}{X}$$

B. PREPARATION AND PROPERTIES OF ORGANOSILICON COMPOUNDS

Organosilicon compounds are prepared from elementary silicon or the silicon halides. A particularly valuable synthesis of organochlorosilanes involves heating an alkyl chloride or even an aryl chloride with elementary silicon in the presence of a copper catalyst. A mixture of products usually results; nonetheless, the reaction is employed commercially for the synthesis of organochlorosilanes, particularly the methylchlorosilanes.

$$CH_3Cl + Si \xrightarrow[300°]{Cu(10\%)} \underset{9\%}{SiCl_4} + \underset{12\%}{CH_3SiHCl_2} + \underset{37\%}{CH_3SiCl_3} + \underset{42\%}{(CH_3)_2SiCl_2}$$

$$\text{⬡}-Cl + Si \xrightarrow[420°]{Cu(50\%)} \text{⬡}-SiCl_3 + \left(\text{⬡}\right)_2\!\!-SiCl_2$$

The physical properties of some organosilanes may be seen from Table 19·4 to be roughly similar to those of the analogously constituted carbon compounds.

C. SILANOLS, SILOXANES, AND POLYSILOXANES

The silanols are generally prepared by hydrolysis of silyl halides and sometimes by hydrolysis of hydrides and alkoxides.

$$R_3SiCl + H_2O \longrightarrow R_3SiOH + HCl$$

$$R_2SiCl_2 + 2\,H_2O \longrightarrow R_2Si(OH)_2 + 2\,HCl$$

$$R_3SiH + H_2O \xrightarrow{\overset{\ominus}{O}H} R_3SiOH + H_2$$

The reaction conditions have to be controlled to avoid condensation of the

Table 19·4   Physical properties of some representative silicon compounds and their carbon analogs

silicon compound	bp, °C	mp, °C	carbon compound	bp, °C	mp, °C
SiH_4[a]	−112	−156.8	CH_4	−162	−183
SiH_3SiH_3[a]	−14.5	−133	CH_3CH_3	−88.6	−172
CH_3SiH_3	−57.5	−156.8	CH_3CH_3	−88.6	−172
$(CH_3)_4Si$	27		$(CH_3)_4C$	9.5	−20
$(CH_3)_3SiC_6H_5$	172		$(CH_3)_3CC_6H_5$	169	−58
$(C_6H_5)_4Si$	430	237	$(C_6H_5)_4C$	431	285
$SiCl_4$	57.6	−70	CCl_4	76.8	−22.8
$SiHCl_3$	33	−134	$CHCl_3$	61	−63.5
SiH_2Cl_2	8.3	−122	CH_2Cl_2	40	−96.7
CH_3SiCl_3	65.7		CH_3CCl_3	74	
$C_6H_5SiCl_3$	201		$C_6H_5CCl_3$	214	−5
$(CH_3)_3SiOH$	98.6		$(CH_3)_3COH$	82.8	25.5
$(CH_3)_2Si(OH)_2$		100			

[a] Spontaneously flammable in air.

silanols to siloxanes, especially when working with silanediols. This may necessitate working in neutral solution at high dilution.

$$R_2Si(OH)_2 + R_2Si(OH)_2 \xrightarrow{-H_2O} \underset{\underset{R}{|}}{\overset{\overset{R}{|}}{HO-Si}}-O-\underset{\underset{R}{|}}{\overset{\overset{R}{|}}{Si}}-OH$$

The silanols are less volatile than the halides and siloxanes because of intermolecular association through hydrogen bonding, and the diols, $R_2Si(OH)_2$, are more soluble in water than the silanols, R_3SiOH. Compared to alcohols, silanols are more acidic and form stronger hydrogen bonds. This can be ascribed to d_π-p_π bonding of the Si—O bond.

$$R_3Si-O-H \longleftrightarrow R_3\overset{\ominus}{Si}=\overset{\oplus}{O}-H$$

In the presence of either acids or bases, most silanols are unstable and condense to form siloxanes. The ease with which these reactions occur compared to corresponding reactions of alcohols is likely to be associated with the ease of formation of pentacoordinate silicon intermediates.

$$Nu^\ominus + X-\overset{|}{\underset{|}{Si}}- \;\rightleftharpoons\; \overset{Nu}{\underset{X}{\diagdown}}\overset{|\ominus}{\underset{\diagup}{Si}}- \;\rightleftharpoons\; Nu-\overset{|}{\underset{|}{Si}}- + X^\ominus$$

Acid-catalyzed condensation:

$$R_3SiOH + H^\oplus \;\rightleftharpoons\; R_3Si\overset{\oplus}{O}H_2$$

$$R_3Si\overset{\underset{|}{H}}{O} + R_3Si\overset{\oplus}{-OH_2} \longrightarrow R_3Si\overset{\oplus}{O}SiR_3 + H_2O \longrightarrow R_3SiOSiR_3 + H_3\overset{\oplus}{O}$$

Base-catalyzed condensation:

$$R_3SiOH + \overset{\ominus}{O}H \; \rightleftharpoons \; R_3Si\overset{\ominus}{O} + H_2O$$

$$R_3Si\overset{\ominus}{O} + R_3Si-OH \; \longrightarrow \; R_3SiOSiR_3 + \overset{\ominus}{O}H$$

The same type of condensation reaction, when carried out with the silane-diols, leads to linear chains and cyclic structures with Si—O and Si—C bonds which are called polysiloxanes.

$$(CH_3)_2Si(OH)_2 \xrightarrow{\;H^{\oplus}\; or\; ^{\ominus}OH\;}$$

The higher-molecular-weight products are the "silicone polymers."

The linear silicone polymers are liquids of varying viscosity depending on the chain length. They remain fluid to low temperatures and are very stable thermally, which makes them useful as hydraulic fluids and lubricants.

Cross-linking results in hard and sometimes brittle resins, depending upon the ratio of methyl groups to silicon atoms in the polymer.

19·5 organoboron compounds

Boron has three valence shell electrons available for bonding and it utilizes these to form trigonal (sp^2) bonds in compounds of the type BX_3. Typical examples are boron trifluoride, BF_3; trimethylborane, $B(CH_3)_3$; and boric acid, $B(OH)_3$. In such compounds the boron normally has only six electrons in three of the four available bonding orbitals and therefore is said to be "electron deficient." There is a considerable tendency for boron to acquire an additional electron pair to fill the fourth orbital and so attain an octet of electrons. The boron halides and the organoboranes (BR_3) are Lewis acids and may accept an electron pair from a base to form tetracovalent boron compounds in which the boron atom has a share of eight electrons.

trimethylborane
(planar)

ammonia trimethylborane
(tetrahedral)

A change in configuration at boron occurs in these reactions because tetracovalent boron is tetrahedral (sp³ hybrid orbitals), whereas tricovalent boron is trigonal and planar (sp²).

A particularly interesting class of compounds is the **borazines**. These compounds are six-membered heterocycles with alternating boron and nitrogen atoms. They are formally analogous to benzene in that there are six electrons—one pair at each nitrogen—which could be delocalized over six orbitals, one from each boron and nitrogen in the ring.

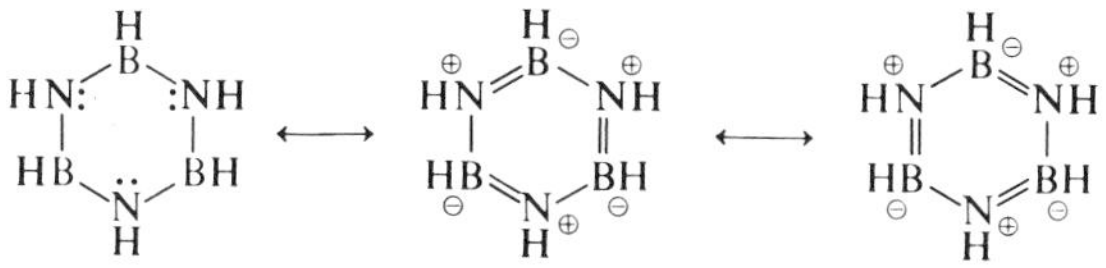

[6a]   [6b]   [6c]

The similarity between benzene and borazine is obvious from the Kekulé structures [6b] and [6c]. The degree to which these structures can be regarded as contributing to the actual structure of the borazine molecule, however, has been a topic of controversy. The borazine molecule has a planar ring with 120° bond angles and six equivalent B—N bonds of length 1.44 A, which is shorter than the expected value of 1.54 A for a B—N single bond and longer than the calculated value of 1.36 A for a B=N double bond.

A. MULTICENTER BONDING AND BORON HYDRIDES

The simple hydride of boron, BH_3, is not stable, and the simplest known hydride is diborane, B_2H_6. Higher hydrides exist, the best known of which are tetraborane, B_4H_{10}; pentaborane, B_5H_9; dihydropentaborane, B_5H_{11}; hexaborane, B_6H_{10}; and decaborane, $B_{10}H_{14}$. These compounds are especially interesting with regard to their structures and bonding. They are referred to as "electron deficient" because there are insufficient electrons with which to form all normal electron-pair bonds. This will become clear from the following description of the structure of diborane.

The configuration and molecular dimensions of diborane resemble ethene in that the central B—B bond and four of the B—H bonds form a planar framework. However, the remaining two hydrogens are centered above and below this framework and form bridges across the B—B bond, as shown in Figure 19·4. The presence of two kinds of hydrogens in diborane is also consistent with its infrared and nmr spectra.

If we try to write a conventional electron-pair structure for diborane, we see at once that there are not enough valence electron pairs for six normal B—H bonds and one B—B bond. Seven normal covalent bonds require 14 bonding electrons, but diborane has only 12 bonding electrons. The way the atoms of diborane are held together would therefore appear to be different from any we have thus far encountered, except perhaps in some carbonium ions (Section 4·4B). Nonetheless, it is possible to describe the bonds in diborane in terms of electron pairs if we adopt the concept of having *three* (or more) atomic centers bonded by an electron pair in contrast to the usual

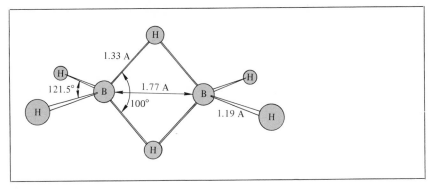

Figure 19·4   Configuration of diborane.

bonding of *two* atomic centers by an electron pair. We can formulate diborane as having two three-center bonds, each involving an electron pair, the two boron atoms, and a bridge hydrogen.

The three-center bonds can be represented in different ways—one possible way being with dotted lines, as in [7].

H⟍   ͵H⟍   ͵H
    B⟜⟜⟜B
H͵   ⟍H͵   ⟍H

[7]

The structures of many of the higher boron hydrides, such as B_4H_{10}, B_5H_9, B_5H_{11}, B_6H_{10}, and $B_{10}H_{14}$, have been determined by electron and(or) X-ray diffraction. These substances resemble diborane in having an overall deficiency of electrons for the total number of bonds formed unless some are formulated as multicenter bonds.

The structure of pentaborane is shown in Figure 19·5. This molecule has 24

Figure 19·5   Structure of pentaborane.

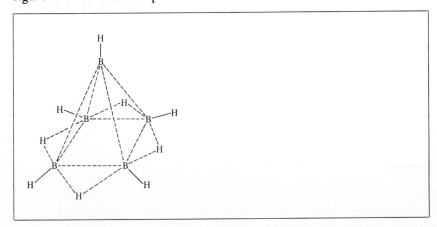

valence electrons; of these, 10 can be regarded as utilized in forming five *two-center* B—H bonds (solid lines), and eight in forming four *three-center* BHB bonds (dashed lines). The remaining six electrons can be taken to contribute to *multicenter* binding of the boron framework (dashed lines).

A number of alkylated diboranes are known, and their structures are similar to diborane.

sym-tetramethyldiborane

However, when a boron atom carries three alkyl groups, three-center bonding does not occur, and the compound is most stable in the monomeric form. Apparently, alkyl groups are unable to form very strong three-center bonds with boron.

B. NOMENCLATURE OF ORGANOBORON COMPOUNDS

The literature on organoboron compounds is inconsistent as to nomenclature, and many compounds are called by two or more names. For example, the simple substance of formula $B(CH_3)_3$ is called variously trimethylborane, trimethylborine, or trimethylboron. Insofar as possible, we will name organoboron compounds as derivatives of borane, BH_3. Thus, substitution of all the B—H hydrogens by methyl groups gives $B(CH_3)_3$, trimethylborane. Several more examples follow:

$B(C_6H_5)_3$	B_2H_6	$C_6H_5BCl_2$
triphenylborane	diborane	phenyldichloroborane

$(CH_3)_2BCl$	$(CH_3)_3\overset{\oplus}{N}-\overset{\ominus}{B}H_3$	$(CH_3)_2N-BH_2$
dimethylchloroborane	trimethylamine borane	dimethylaminoborane

C. HYDROBORATION

Trialkylboranes can be prepared by addition of boron hydrides to multiple bonds. In general, these reactions of boron hydrides conform to a pattern of cleavage of B—H bonds in the direction $\overset{\oplus}{B} : \overset{\ominus}{H}$, with boron acting as an electrophile.

Addition of a B—H linkage across the double bond of an alkene is known as **hydroboration** and has been discussed earlier (Section 4·4F). Cleavage of the B—C bond with a carboxylic acid gives an alkane, with alkaline hydrogen peroxide, an alcohol. (Note that the alcohol that is formed is the anti-Markownikoff product.)

$$CH_3CH=CH_2 + BH_3 \longrightarrow CH_3CH_2CH_2BH_2 \xrightarrow{CH_3CH=CH_2} (CH_3CH_2CH_2)_2BH$$

$$(CH_3CH_2CH_2)_3B \xleftarrow{\overline{CH_3CH=CH_2}}$$

$RCO_2H \swarrow \qquad HO^{\ominus} \searrow H_2O_2.$

$$CH_3CH_2CH_3 \qquad CH_3CH_2CH_2OH$$

summary

Sulfur, phosphorus, and silicon, being second-row elements in the periodic table, have low-lying d orbitals available and are not restricted to an octet of bonding electrons as are the elements in the first row. Sulfur can have as many as 12 bonding electrons (six covalent bonds), and phosphorus 10 bonding electrons (five covalent bonds). Silicon is usually tetravalent although even here there is often some d orbital participation in bond formation. Boron is unique in having only three electrons in its valence shell. Neutral boron can form either three covalent bonds and be electron deficient or four covalent bonds and be anionic, as in $BH_4^{\ominus}$. Many compounds are known with three-center bonds between two boron atoms and a hydrogen atom.

Sulfur in its divalent state is analogous to oxygen. Thiols, also called mercaptans (RSH), correspond to alcohols (ROH); sulfides, also called thioethers (RSR), correspond to ethers (ROR); and disulfides (RSSR) correspond to peroxides (ROOR). There are no oxygen analogs for the sulfur compounds with four and six bonds, the most important of which are sul-

foxides, $R-\overset{\overset{\displaystyle O}{\|}}{S}-R$, sulfones, $R-\overset{\overset{\displaystyle O}{\|}}{\underset{\underset{\displaystyle O}{\|}}{S}}-R$, and sulfonic acids, $R-\overset{\overset{\displaystyle O}{\|}}{\underset{\underset{\displaystyle O}{\|}}{S}}-OH$.

Thiols are more acidic than alcohols and also more nucleophilic. Oxidation of thiols produces disulfides.

$$RSH \xrightarrow{[O]} RS-SR \quad \text{(disulfide)}$$

Alkylation of thiols, RSH, gives sulfides, RSR, which can be converted to sulfonium salts, $R_3S^{\oplus}X^{\ominus}$. If the R groups are all different the salts can be resolved into optical enantiomers.

Oxidation of sulfides gives sulfoxides and sulfones.

$$R-S-R \begin{cases} \nearrow R-\overset{\overset{\displaystyle O}{\|}}{S}-R \quad \text{(sulfoxide)} \\ \searrow R-\overset{\overset{\displaystyle O}{\|}}{\underset{\underset{\displaystyle O}{\|}}{S}}-R \quad \text{(sulfone)} \end{cases}$$

Dimethyl sulfoxide (DMSO) is an example of a polar aprotic solvent. It enhances the reactivity of small anions and is often used as a solvent for S_N2 reactions. It is also an excellent mild oxidant for alcohols.

There are three kinds of organosulfur acids: sulfenic acids (RSOH), sulfinic acids (RSO_2H), and sulfonic acids (RSO_3H). The last are strong acids, and are the most important of the series. They will be met again in the next chapter.

Sulfate esters, $RO-\overset{\overset{O}{\|}}{\underset{\underset{O}{\|}}{S}}-OR$, lack a carbon-sulfur bond and hence are not classed as organosulfur compounds. They are useful alkylating agents.

Organic compounds of phosphorus include phosphate esters, $R-O-PO(OH)_2$, phosphonic acids, $R-PO(OH)_2$, and organophosphines, R_3P. Phosphate esters may exist as polyphosphates, an important example of which is adenosine triphosphate, ATP.

Phosphines can form phosphonium salts, $R_4P^{\oplus}X^{\ominus}$, analogous to ammonium salts. When treated with phenyllithium, a methylphosphonium ion loses a proton to give a methylenephosphorane.

$$\overset{\oplus}{R_3P}-CH_3 \xrightarrow{-H^{\oplus}} R_3P=CH_2 \quad \text{(methylenephosphorane)}$$

These compounds can convert ketones to ethene derivatives as a result of the exchange of a carbonyl and a methylene group (the Wittig reaction).

$$R_3P=CH_2 + R'_2C=O \longrightarrow R'_2C=CH_2 + R_3P=O$$

Silicon, like carbon, has four valence electrons but, unlike carbon, it forms only single bonds. Compounds containing only silicon and hydrogen (silane SiH_4, disilane Si_2H_6, etc.) ignite spontaneously in air. Alkylsilanes, such as R_4Si, are more stable. Silanediols, $R_2Si(OH)_2$, can be prepared whereas their carbon analogs can not. They are made from alkyl chlorides via the chlorosilanes.

$$RCl + Si \xrightarrow{300^\circ} R_2SiCl_2 \quad (+ \text{ other chlorosilanes})$$
$$\downarrow H_2O$$
$$\longrightarrow R_2Si(OH)_2$$

Silanediols tend to polymerize to form siloxanes, compounds of extremely high thermal stability.

$$R_2Si(OH)_2 \longrightarrow -O-\underset{\underset{R}{|}}{\overset{\overset{R}{|}}{Si}}-O-\underset{\underset{R}{|}}{\overset{\overset{R}{|}}{Si}}-O-\underset{\underset{R}{|}}{\overset{\overset{R}{|}}{Si}}-O-$$

Boron possesses only three valence electrons and as a result its tricovalent compounds, such as BF_3 and $B(CH_3)_3$, are electron deficient and highly reactive as electron-pair acceptors—that is, Lewis acids. When an electron pair is accepted an octet arrangement is achieved, for example, $BF_4^{\ominus}$. In the borazines π bonding tends to complete the octet of boron.

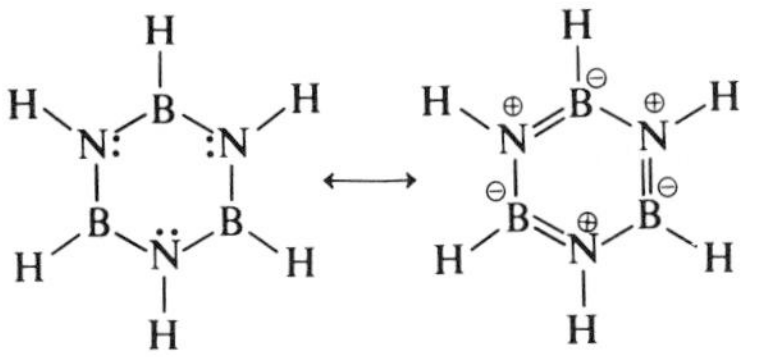

(borazine)

Diborane and higher boranes are constructed with three-center bonds, each consisting of an electron pair, two boron atoms, and a hydrogen bridge.

Hydroboration is the addition of boron hydrides, particularly BH_3, to multiple bonds. Treatment of an alkene with diborane results in the addition of BH_3 to the double bond. The reaction continues and finally gives a trialkylborane. These compounds can then be converted to alkanes or alcohols.

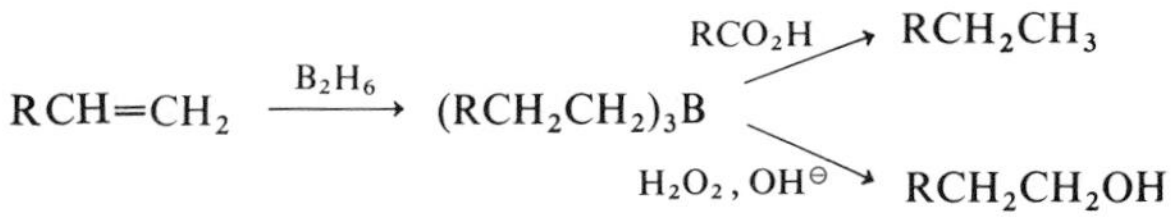

$$RCH{=}CH_2 \xrightarrow{\ B_2H_6\ } (RCH_2CH_2)_3B \begin{array}{c} \xrightarrow{\ RCO_2H\ } RCH_2CH_3 \\ \\ \xrightarrow{\ H_2O_2,\,OH^\ominus\ } RCH_2CH_2OH \end{array}$$

exercises

19·1   Write structural formulas for the following substances:

a.   di-s-butyl thioketone
b.   ethyl sulfide
c.   methyl thioacetate
d. β,β'-dichloroethyl sulfide
      (mustard gas)

e.   tris-(methylsulfonyl)-methane
f.   trimethylene disulfide
g.   5-thia-1,3-cyclopentadiene
      (thiophene)

19·2   Formulate each of the following substances in terms of electronic structure, types of bonds (i.e., σ and π) and probable molecular geometry (i.e., linear, angular, planar, pyramidal, etc.) with rough estimates of bond angles.

a. H_2S
b. SO_2
c. SF_4
d. H_2SO_4
e. Na_2SO_3

f. S_6 (six-membered ring)
g. CS_2
h. $SOCl_2$
i. S_8 (eight-membered ring)

19·3   Thiols are unlike alcohols in that they do not react readily with hydrogen bromide to yield bromides. Explain how a difference in behavior in this respect might be expected.

19·4   Write mechanisms for the conversion of a thiol to a disulfide by oxidation with air or iodine which are in accord with the observation that the reaction with either oxidizing agent is accelerated by alkali.

19·5   Dimethyl sulfide reacts with bromine in the absence of water to produce a

crystalline addition compound which reacts with water to produce dimethyl
sulfoxide. What is the likely structure of the addition compound and the
mechanism of its formation and reaction with water?

19·6   How many and what kinds of stereoisomers would you expect for each of the
following compounds?

    a.   methylethyl-*s*-butylsulfonium bromide
    b. $[CH_3(C_2H_5)SCH_2CH_2S(CH_3)C_2H_5]^{2\oplus}\ 2Br^{\ominus}$

$$\begin{array}{c} H_2C-CH_2 \\ \overset{\oplus}{CH_3S} \qquad \overset{\oplus}{S}CH_3 \quad 2\ Br^{\ominus} \\ H_2C-CH_2 \end{array}$$

    c.

19·7   Unsymmetrically substituted sulfoxides, but not the corresponding sulfones,
exhibit optical isomerism. Write structures for the stereoisomers you
would expect for

    a.   methyl ethyl sulfoxide
    b.   the disulfoxide of 1,3-dithiacyclohexane

19·8   Write equations for a practical synthesis of each of the following substances
based on the specified starting materials. Give reagents and approximate
reaction conditions.

    a. $CH_3-\overset{\overset{\displaystyle O}{\|}}{C}-S-CH_2CH_2CH_3$ from *n*-propyl alcohol
    b.   optically active methylethyl-*n*-butylsulfonium bromide from *n*-butyl
alcohol
    c.   neopentanethiol from neopentyl chloride

19·9   Suppose it were desired to study the addition of bromine to an alkene double
bond in water in the absence of organic solvents. A possible substrate for
this purpose would be $CH_2{=}CHCH_2CH_2CH_2CH_2-X$, where $-X$ is a
solubilizing group. What would be the merits of having $-X = -SO_3^{\ominus}Na^{\oplus}$
over $X = -OH,\ -NH_2,\ -CO_2^{\ominus}Na^{\oplus},\ -\overset{\oplus}{N}(CH_3)_3Br^{\ominus}$?

19·10   Give for each of the following pairs of compounds a chemical test, preferably a test tube reaction, which would serve to distinguish one from the
other.

    a. CH_3CH_2SH and CH_3SCH_3
    b. $CH_3S(O)OCH_3$ and $CH_3CH_2SO_3H$
    c. $CH_3S(O)OCH_3$ and $CH_3S(O)_2CH_3$
    d. $CH_3SCH_2CH_2OH$ and $CH_3OCH_2CH_2SH$

19·11   Name the following compounds:

    a. $CH_3PHCH_2CH_3$
    b. $CH_3\underset{\overset{\|}{O}}{P}(C_6H_5)_2$

c. $P(OC_2H_5)_3$

d. $O=P(OC_2H_5)_3$

e. 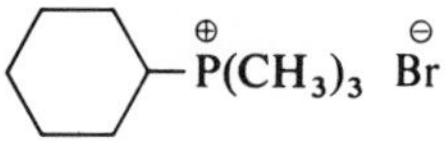 $\overset{\oplus}{P}(CH_3)_3$ $\overset{\ominus}{Br}$

f. 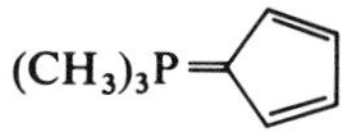 $(CH_3)_3P=$

19·12   Write structures for the following compounds:

<table>
<tr><td>a.</td><td>methyl diphosphate</td><td>c.</td><td>diisopropyl methylphosphonate</td></tr>
<tr><td>b.</td><td>tricyclohexyl phosphate</td><td>d.</td><td>tetraphenylphosphonium iodide</td></tr>
</table>

19·13   Using the Wittig reaction (Section 19·3C) in one of the steps, show how you could convert 1,1-dicyclopropylpropene to 1,1-dicyclopropylethene.

19·14   Name the following compounds according to the nomenclature used in Table 19·2.

a. $(C_6H_5)_4Si$ c. $(C_6H_5)_2Si(OH)_2$

b. $(C_2H_5)_2SiBr_2$ d. $(CH_3)_3SiOSiH_3$

19·15   Write resonance structures for trimethylsilanol and vinylsilane involving silicon d orbitals, that is, with five bonds to silicon.

19·16   Explain why trisilylamine, $(SiH_3)_3N$, is a weaker base than trimethylamine and why trimethylsilanol, $(CH_3)_3SiOH$, is a stronger acid than t-butyl alcohol.

19·17   With reference to the discussion of reactivity of silicon compounds in Section 19·4C, explain how it is possible for the following reaction to occur readily by the rate law, $v = k[R_3SiCl][\overset{\ominus}{OH}]$.

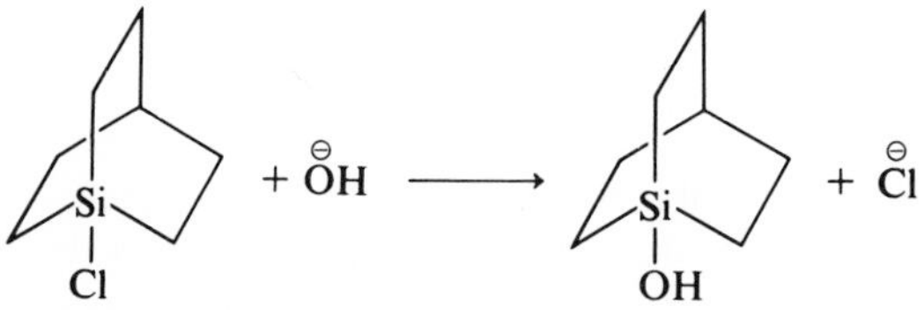

Refer also to Exercise 8·15.

19·18   Which compound in each of the following pairs would you expect to be more stable? Give your reasons.

a. B,B,B-trimethylborazine or N,N,N-trimethylborazine

b. borazine or B,B,B-trichloroborazine

c. B-methoxyborazine or B-(trifluoromethyl)-borazine

d. ammonia complex of $(CH_3)_2B-N(CH_3)_2$ or the ammonia complex of $(CH_3)_2B-P(CH_3)_2$

19·19   Write names for the following compounds:

a. $CH_2\!=\!CH\!-\!CH_2\!-\!B(CH_3)_2$

b. $(C_2H_5)_2BHBH_3$

c. 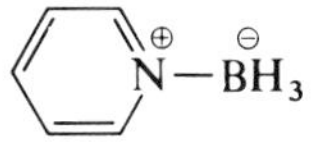 $\overset{\oplus}{N}\!-\!\overset{\ominus}{B}H_3$

d. $(CH_3)_2N\!-\!B(CH_3)_2$

e.

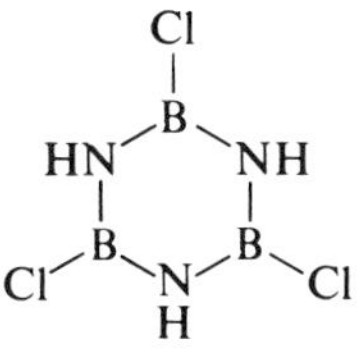

f.

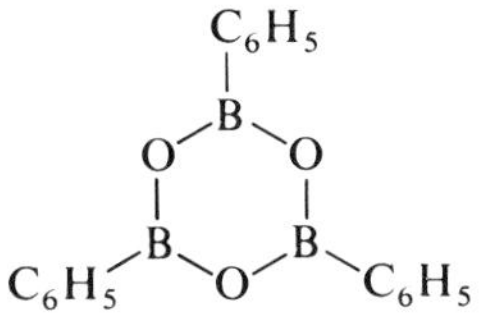

19·20   Write structures for the following:

a.   di-*n*-butyl-(*p*-dimethylaminophenyl)-borane
b.   di-*p*-tolylchloroborane
c.   dichloromethoxyborane
d.   tri-(dimethylphosphino)-borane

19·21   Would you expect boron-phosphorus analogs of borazines to have aromatic character?

19·22   Which would you expect to form a more stable addition compound with ammonia, trivinylborane or triethylborane? What all-carbon system has an electronic structure analogous to dimethylvinylborane?

chapter 20
arenes. electrophilic aromatic substitution

Benzene, C_6H_6, and the other aromatic hydrocarbons usually have such strikingly different properties from typical open-chain conjugated polyenes, such as 1,3,5-hexatriene, that it is convenient to consider them as a separate class of compounds called **arenes**. In this chapter we shall outline their salient features, and in subsequent chapters we shall discuss the chemistry of their halogen, oxygen, and nitrogen derivatives.

Some of the important properties of benzene were discussed in Chapter 6 in connection with the resonance method. Most noteworthy is the fact that benzene has a planar hexagonal structure in which all six carbon-carbon bonds are of equal length (1.397 A), and each carbon is bonded to one hydrogen. If each carbon is considered to form sp^2-σ bonds to its hydrogen and neighboring carbons, there remain six electrons, one for each carbon atom, which are termed π electrons. These electrons are not to be taken as localized in pairs between alternate carbon nuclei to form three conventional conjugated bonds. Rather, they should be regarded as delocalized symmetrically through the p_z orbitals of all six carbons (Section 6·1). The bonds between the carbons are therefore neither single nor double bonds. In fact, they are intermediate between single and double bonds in length.

However, there is more to the bonding than just the simple average of C—C single and double bonds, because benzene C—C bonds are substantially stronger than the average of the strengths of single and double bonds. This is reflected in the heat of combustion of benzene, which is substantially less than expected on the basis of bond energies; the extra stability of benzene by virtue of its stronger bonds is what we have called its **stabilization energy**. A large part of this stabilization energy can be ascribed to delocalization or **resonance energy** of the six carbon π electrons.

The choice of a suitable and convenient graphical formula to represent the structure of benzene presents a problem, since the best way to indicate delocalized bonding electrons is by dotted lines, which are quite time consuming to draw. Dotted-line structural formulas are preferred when it is necessary to show the fine details of an aromatic structure—as when the degree of bonding is *not* equal between different pairs of carbons, in phenanthrene, for example. Shorthand notations are usually desirable, however, and we shall most often use the conventional hexagon with alternating single and double bonds (i.e., Kekulé cyclohexatriene) despite the fact that benzene does not possess ordinary double bonds. Another and widely used notation for benzene is a hexagon with an inscribed circle to represent a closed shell of π electrons. However, as we have mentioned before (Section 6·1), this is fine for benzene but can be misleading for polynuclear hydrocarbons (Section 20·1B).

20·1   nomenclature of arenes

A. BENZENE DERIVATIVES

A variety of substituted benzenes are known with one or more of the hydrogen atoms of the ring replaced with other atoms or groups. In almost all of these compounds, the special stability associated with the benzene nucleus is retained. A few examples of "benzenoid" hydrocarbons follow, and it will be noticed that the hydrocarbon substituents include alkyl, alkenyl, alkynyl, and aryl groups.

toluene (methylbenzene)	ethylbenzene	cumene (isopropylbenzene)	styrene (vinylbenzene)

phenylacetylene (ethynylbenzene)	biphenyl (phenylbenzene)	diphenylmethane

The naming of these hydrocarbons is fairly straightforward. Each is named as an alkyl, alkenyl, or arylbenzene, unless for some reason the compound has a trivial name. The hydrocarbon group (C_6H_5-) from benzene itself is called a phenyl group and is sometimes abbreviated as the symbol ϕ or as Ph. Aryl groups in general are often abbreviated as Ar. Other groups that have trivial names include

benzyl	benzal	benzo	benzhydryl

When there are two or more substituents on a benzene ring, position isomerism arises. Thus, there are three possible isomeric disubstituted benzene derivatives according to whether the substituents have the 1,2, 1,3, or 1,4 relationship. The isomers are commonly designated as *ortho*, *meta*, and *para* (or *o*, *m*, and *p*) for the 1,2, 1,3, and 1,4 isomers, respectively. The actual symmetry of the benzene ring is such that only one 1,2-disubstitution product is found despite the fact that two would be predicted if benzene had the 1,3,5-cyclohexatriene structure.

ortho-xylene (1,2-dimethylbenzene)	*meta*-xylene (1,3-dimethylbenzene)	*para*-xylene (1,4-dimethylbenzene)

CH₃ structures — o-bromotoluene, m-bromotoluene, p-bromotoluene

o-bromotoluene   m-bromotoluene   p-bromotoluene

B. POLYNUCLEAR AROMATIC HYDROCARBONS

A wide range of polycyclic aromatic compounds are known that have benzene rings with common *ortho* positions. The parent compounds of this type are usually called **polynuclear** aromatic hydrocarbons. Three important examples are naphthalene, anthracene, and phenanthrene. In anthracene, the rings are connected *linearly*, while in phenanthrene they are connected *angularly*.

naphthalene   anthracene   phenanthrene

There are two possible monosubstitution products for naphthalene, three for anthracene, and five for phenanthrene. The accepted numbering system for these hydrocarbons is as shown in the formulas; however, the 1 and 2 positions of the naphthalene ring are frequently designated as α and β. Some illustrative substitution products are shown.

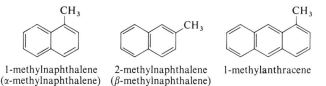

1-methylnaphthalene   2-methylnaphthalene   1-methylanthracene
(α-methylnaphthalene)   (β-methylnaphthalene)

Substances that can be regarded as partial or complete reduction products of aromatic compounds are often named as *hydro* derivatives of the parent system—the completely reduced derivatives being known as *perhydro* compounds.

9,10-dihydro-   1,2,3,4-tetrahydro-   decahydro-   perhydro-
anthracene   naphthalene   naphthalene   phenanthrene
                     (tetralin)   (decalin)

The names that have been given to the more elaborate types of polynuclear aromatic hydrocarbons are for the most part distressingly uninformative in relation to their structures. (A thorough summary of names and numbering systems has been published by A. M. Patterson, L. T. Capell, and D. F. Walker, " Ring Index," 2d Ed., American Chemical Society, 1960.) Two such compounds are shown here, with their systematic names given in parentheses.

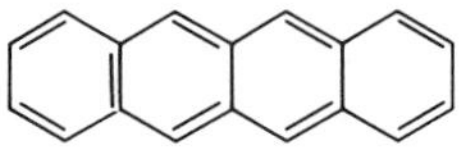

naphthacene
(benz[b]anthracene)

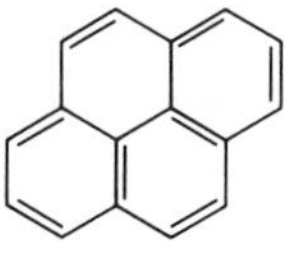

pyrene
(benz[d,e,f]phenanthrene)

These are named as derivatives of simpler polynuclear hydrocarbons such as naphthalene or phenanthrene, to which are fused additional rings. An extra ring, which adds only four carbons at the most, is designated by the prefix *benzo*[1] (or *benz* if followed by a vowel), and its positions of attachment either by numbers or, as shown, by letters. (The sides of the parent compound are lettered in sequence beginning with the 1,2 side, which is *a*.)

One can insert a Kekulé structure in any of the rings in the above compounds and be reasonably confident that alternating double and single bonds can be placed in the remaining rings. This is not true for the compound phenalenyl, a rather reactive hydrocarbon of formula $C_{13}H_9$ (Figure 20·1). Note that the Kekulé formula [1] reveals that one of the carbon atoms in the molecule has only three bonds to it whereas formula [2] does not. There are 10 contributing resonance structures for this molecule, each containing a three-bonded carbon atom having one unpaired electron. The molecule is thus a radical. The various Kekulé structures of other polynuclear hydrocarbons are discussed in Section 20·6.

---

[1] Confusion between the two meanings of *benzo* (see Section 20·1A) seldom arises since it is usually clear from the context whether it refers to a C_6H_5C- group or a fused ring.

Figure 20·1 Two ways [1] and [2] of representing phenalenyl, $C_{13}H_9$. The skeleton showing only the location of the carbon and hydrogen atoms is also given.

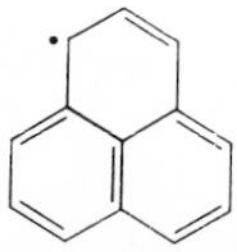

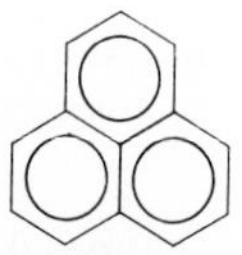

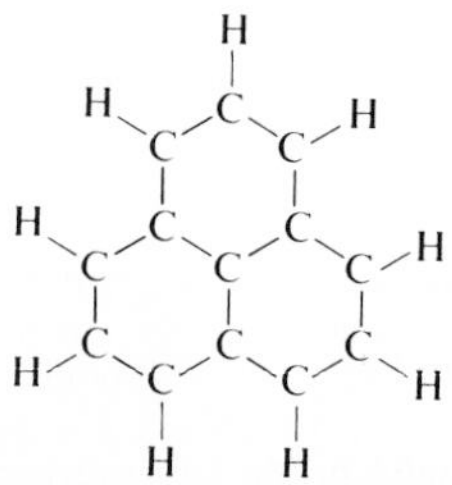

Many polynuclear hydrocarbons, like many aromatic amines (Section 22·9B), are carcinogens.

20·2 *physical properties of arenes*

The pleasant odors of the derivatives of many arenes are the reason they are often called **aromatic hydrocarbons**. The arenes themselves, however, are generally quite toxic and inhalation of their vapors should be avoided. The volatile arenes are highly flammable and burn with a luminous, sooty flame, in contrast to alkanes and alkenes, which burn with a bluish flame leaving little carbon residue.

A list of common arenes and their physical properties is given in Table 20·1. They are less dense than water and are highly insoluble. Boiling points are found to increase fairly regularly with molecular weight, but there is little correlation between melting point and molecular weight. The melting point is highly dependent on the symmetry of the compound; benzene thus melts 100° higher than toluene, and the more symmetrical *p*-xylene has a higher melting point than either the *o*- or the *m*-isomer.

Table 20·1   Physical properties of arenes

compound	mp, °C	bp, °C	density, d_4^{20}
benzene	5.5	80	0.8790
toluene	−95	111	0.866
ethylbenzene	−94	136	0.8669
n-propylbenzene	−99	159	0.8617
isopropylbenzene (cumene)	−96	152	0.8620
t-butylbenzene	−58	168	0.8658
o-xylene	−25	144	0.8968
m-xylene	−47	139	0.8811
p-xylene	13	138	0.8541
mesitylene (1,3,5-trimethylbenzene)	−50	165	0.8634
durene (1,2,4,5-tetramethylbenzene)	80	191	
naphthalene	80	218	
anthracene	216	340	
phenanthrene	101	340	

20·3 spectroscopic properties of arenes

A. INFRARED SPECTRA

The presence of a phenyl group in a compound can be ascertained with a fair degree of certainty from its infrared spectrum. Furthermore, the number and positions of substituent groups on the ring can also be determined from the spectrum. For example, in Figure 20·2, we see the individual infrared spectra of four compounds: toluene and o-, m-, and p-xylene. That each spectrum is of a benzene derivative is apparent from certain common features, notably the two bands near 1600 cm^{-1} and 1500 cm^{-1} which, although of variable intensity, have been correlated with the stretching vibrations of the carbon-carbon bonds of the aromatic ring. In some compounds, there is an additional band around 1580 cm^{-1}. The sharp bands near 3030 cm^{-1} are characteristic of aromatic C—H bonds. Other bands in the spectra, especially those between 1650 and 2000 cm^{-1}, between 1225 and 950 cm^{-1}, and below 900 cm^{-1}, have been correlated with the number and positions of ring substituents. Although we shall not document all these various bands in detail, each of the spectra in Figure 20·2 is marked to show some of the types of correlations that have been made.

B. ELECTRONIC ABSORPTION SPECTRA

Compared to straight-chain conjugated polyenes, aromatic compounds have relatively complex absorption spectra with several bands in the ultraviolet region. Benzene and the alkylbenzenes possess two bands in which we shall be primarily interested, one lying near 2000 A and the other near 2600 A.

The 2000 A band is of fairly high intensity and corresponds to excitation of a π electron of the conjugated system to a π* orbital (i.e., a π → π* transition). The excited state has significant contributions from dipolar structures such as [3]. This is analogous to the absorption bands of conjugated dienes (Section

[3]

7·5) except that the wavelength of absorption of benzene is shorter. In fact, benzene and the alkylbenzenes absorb just beyond the range of most commercial quartz spectrometers. However, this band (which we say is due to the benzene **chromophore**) is intensified and shifted to longer wavelengths when the conjugated system is extended by replacement of the ring hydrogens by unsaturated groups (e.g., —HC=CH$_2$, —C≡CH, —HC=O, and —C≡N; see Table 20·2). The absorbing chromophore now embraces the electrons of the unsaturated substituent as well as those of the ring. In the specific case

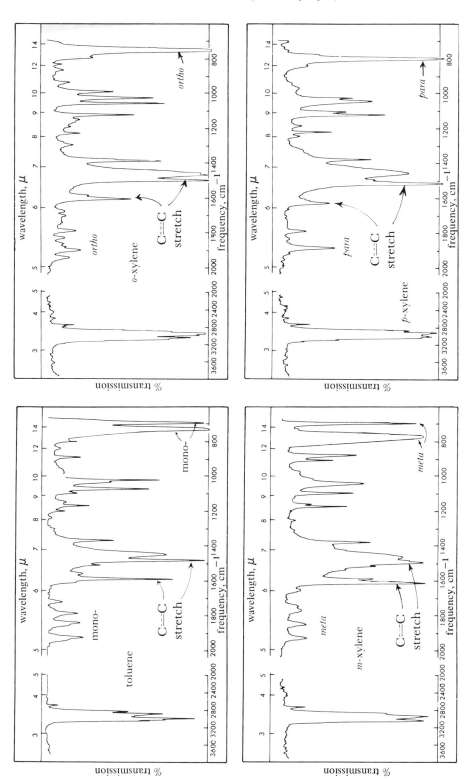

Figure 20·2 Infrared spectra of toluene, *o*-, *m*-, and *p*-xylenes. The number and positions of ring substituents determine the pattern of the low-intensity bands in the region 2000 to 1650 cm⁻¹ and the positions of the stronger bands in the region 800 to 690 cm⁻¹.

Table 20·2   Effect of conjugation on the ultraviolet spectrum of the benzene chromoph

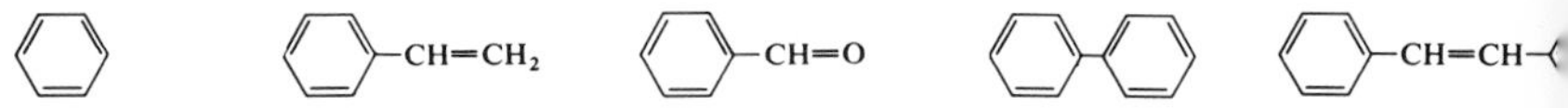

	benzene	styrene	benzaldehyde	biphenyl	stilbene
λ_{max}, A	1980	2440	2440	2500	2950
ε_{max}	8000	12,000	15,000	18,000	27,000

Table 20·3   Effect of substituents on the ultraviolet spectrum of the benzene chromophore

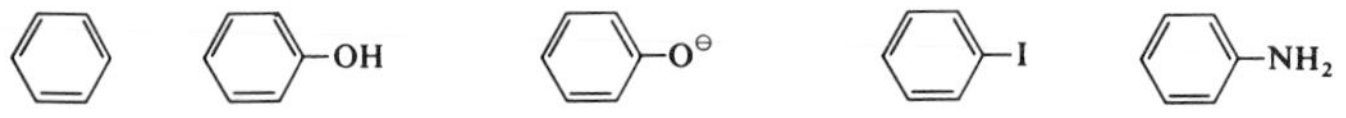

	benzene	phenol	phenoxide ion	iodobenzene	aniline
λ_{max}, A	1980	2100	2350	2260	2300
ε_{max}	8000	6200	9400	13,000	8600

of styrene, the excited state is a hybrid structure, composite of [4a] and [4b] and other related dipolar structures.

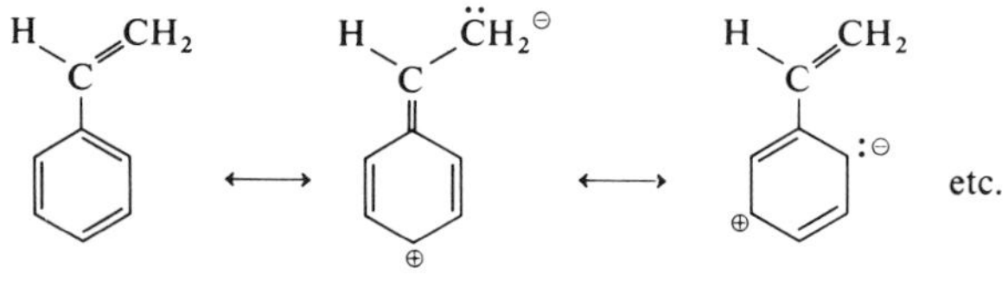

[4a]   [4b]   etc.

Similar effects are observed for benzene derivatives in which the substituent has unshared electron pairs in conjugation with the benzene ring (e.g., $-\ddot{N}H_2$, $-\ddot{O}H$, $-\ddot{C}l$:). An unshared electron pair is to some extent delocalized to become a part of the aromatic π-electron system in both the ground and excited states, but more importantly in the excited state. This may be illustrated for aniline by the following structures, which can be regarded as contributing to the hybrid structure of aniline. (The data of Table 20·3 show the effect on the benzene chromophore of this type of substituent.)

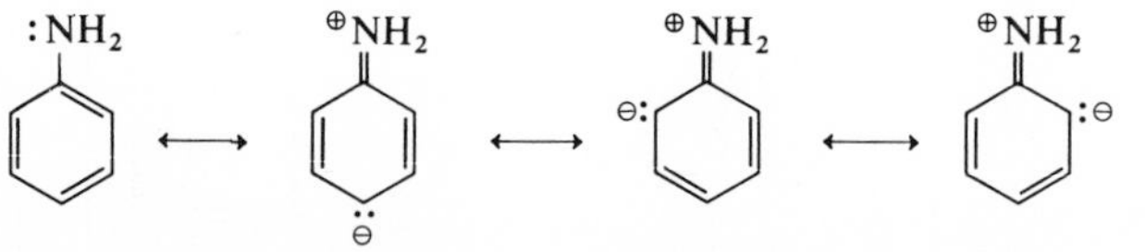

As already mentioned, the benzene chromophore gives rise to a second band at longer wavelengths, as shown in Figure 20·3. This band, which is of low intensity, is found to be a composite of several equally spaced (1000

Table 20·4   The effect of substituents on absorption corresponding to the benzenoid band

	benzene	toluene	styrene	iodobenzene	aniline
λ_{max}, A	2550	2610	2820	2560	2800
ε_{max}	230	300	450	800	1430

Table 20·5   Benzenoid band of linear polycyclic aromatics

	benzene	naphthalene	anthracene	naphthacene	pentacene
λ_{max}, A	2550	3140	3800	4800	5800
ε_{max}	230	316	7900	11,000	12,600

cm^{-1}) narrow peaks. It is remarkably characteristic of aromatic hydro-carbons, for no analogous band is found in the spectra of conjugated polyenes. For this reason, it is often called the *benzenoid band*. The position and intensity of this band, like the one at shorter wavelengths, are affected by the nature of the ring substituents, particularly by those which extend the conjugated system, as may be seen from the data in Table 20·4 and Table 20·5.

Figure 20·3   Ultraviolet absorption spectrum of benzene (in cyclohexane) showing the "benzenoid" band.

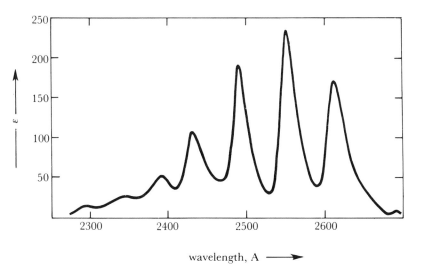

wavelength, A ⟶

C. NUCLEAR MAGNETIC RESONANCE SPECTRA

The chemical shifts of aromatic protons (6.5 to 8.0 ppm) are characteristically toward lower magnetic fields than those of protons attached to ordinary double bonds (4.6 to 6.9 ppm). The difference is usually about 2 ppm and has special interest because we have already formulated the hydrogens in both types of systems as being bonded to carbon through sp^2-σ bonds.

In general, the spin-spin splittings observed for phenyl derivatives are extremely complex. An example is given by nitrobenzene (Figure 20·4), which has different chemical shifts for its *ortho*, *meta*, and *para* hydrogens and six *different* spin-spin interaction constants: J_{23}, J_{24}, J_{25}, J_{26}, J_{34}, J_{35} (the subscripts correspond to position numbers of the protons).

Such a spectrum is much too complex to be analyzed by any very simple procedure. Nonetheless, as will be seen from Exercise 20·7, nuclear magnetic resonance can be useful in assigning structures to aromatic derivatives, particularly in conjunction with integrated line intensities and approximate values of the coupling constants between the ring hydrogens, as shown here.

Figure 20·4   Nuclear magnetic resonance spectrum of nitrobenzene at 60 MHz with reference to tetramethylsilane at 0.00 ppm.

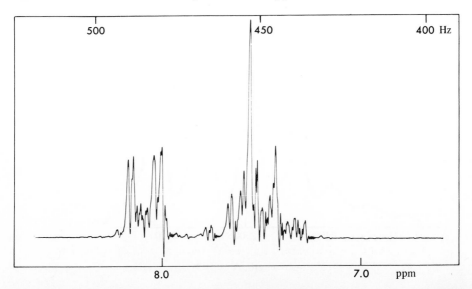

20·4 reactions of aromatic hydrocarbons

A. ELECTROPHILIC AROMATIC SUBSTITUTION

In this section we shall be mainly interested in the reactions of arenes that involve attack on the aromatic ring. We shall not at this point elaborate on the reactions of substituent groups around the ring, although, as we shall see later, these and reactions at the ring are not always independent.

The principal types of reactions involving aromatic rings are substitution, addition, and oxidation. Of these, the most common are electrophilic substitution reactions. A summary of the more important substitution reactions of benzene is given in Figure 20·5 and includes halogenation, nitration, sulfonation, alkylation, and acylation.

There are certain similarities between the aromatic substitution reactions listed in Figure 20·5 and electrophilic addition reactions of alkenes (Section 4·4). Indeed, many of the reagents that commonly add to the double bonds of alkenes also substitute an aromatic nucleus (e.g., Cl_2, Br_2, H_2SO_4, HOCl, HOBr). Furthermore, both types of reaction are polar, stepwise processes involving electrophilic reagents. The key step for either is considered to be the attack of an electrophile at carbon to form a cationic intermediate. We may represent this step by the following general equations in which the attacking reagent is represented either as a formal cation, $X^\oplus$, or as a neutral but polarized $\overset{\delta\oplus}{X}{-}\overset{\delta\ominus}{Y}$ molecule.

Electrophilic aromatic substitution (first step):

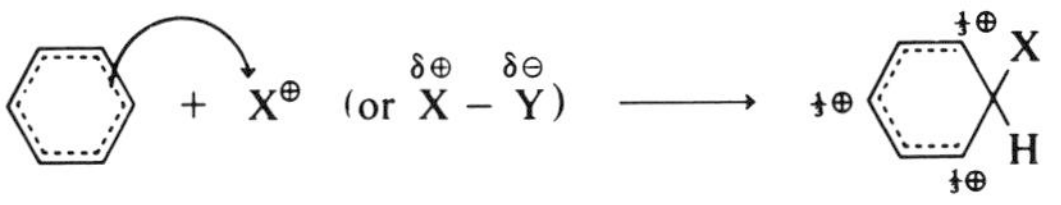

Electrophilic addition to alkenes (first step):

$$H_2C{=}CH_2 + X^\oplus \text{ (or } \overset{\delta\oplus}{X} - \overset{\delta\ominus}{Y}) \longrightarrow H_2\overset{\oplus}{C}{-}CH_2X$$

The intermediate depicted for aromatic substitution no longer has an aromatic structure; rather, it is an unstable cation with four π electrons delocalized over five carbon nuclei, the sixth carbon being a saturated carbon forming sp^3-hybrid bonds. It may be formulated in terms of the following contributing structures, which are assumed here to contribute essentially equally. (Note that the partial charges are at *three* positions, the two *ortho*

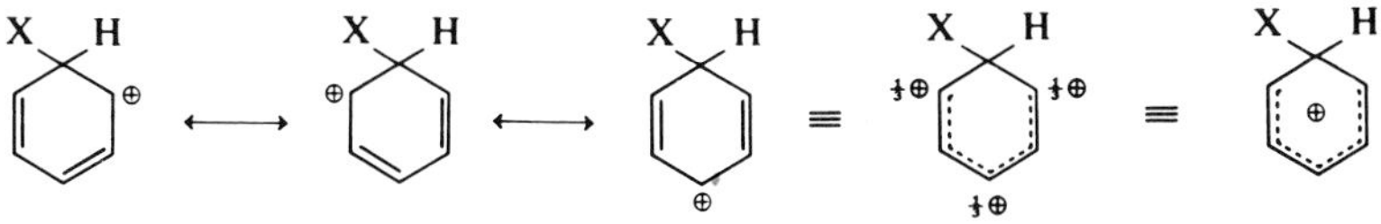

positions and the *para* position.)

Loss of a proton from this intermediate to $Y^\ominus$ results in regeneration of an aromatic ring, which is now a substitution product of benzene.

Figure 20·5   Typical benzene substitution reactions.

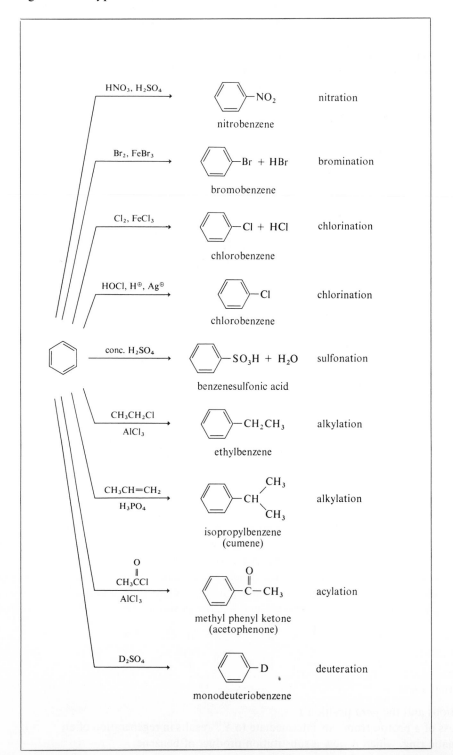

Electrophilic aromatic substitution (second step):

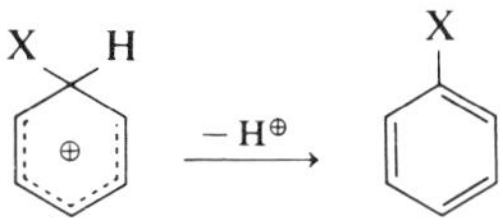

The gain in stabilization attendant on regeneration of the aromatic ring is sufficiently advantageous that this, rather than combination of the cation with $Y^{\ominus}$, is the actual course of reaction. Here is the difference between aromatic substitution and alkene addition. With alkenes, there is usually no substantial resonance energy to be gained by loss of a proton from the intermediate, which tends instead to react by combination with a nucleophilic reagent.

Electrophilic addition to alkenes (second step):

$$\overset{\oplus}{C}H_2 - CH_2X + Y^{\ominus} \longrightarrow YCH_2 - CH_2X$$

B. NATURE OF THE SUBSTITUTING AGENT

It is important to realize that in aromatic substitution the electrophilic substituting agent, $X^{\oplus}$ or $\overset{\delta\oplus \quad \delta\ominus}{X-Y}$, is not necessarily the reagent that is initially added to the reaction mixture. For example, nitration in mixtures of nitric and sulfuric acids is not usually brought about by attack of the nitric acid molecule on the aromatic compound, but by attack of a more electrophilic species, the *nitronium ion*, $NO_2{}^{\oplus}$. There is good evidence to show that this ion is formed from nitric acid and sulfuric acid according to the following equation:

$$HNO_3 + 2\,H_2SO_4 \rightleftharpoons NO_2{}^{\oplus} + H_3O^{\oplus} + 2\,HSO_4{}^{\ominus}$$

The nitronium ion so formed then attacks the aromatic ring to give an aromatic nitro compound.

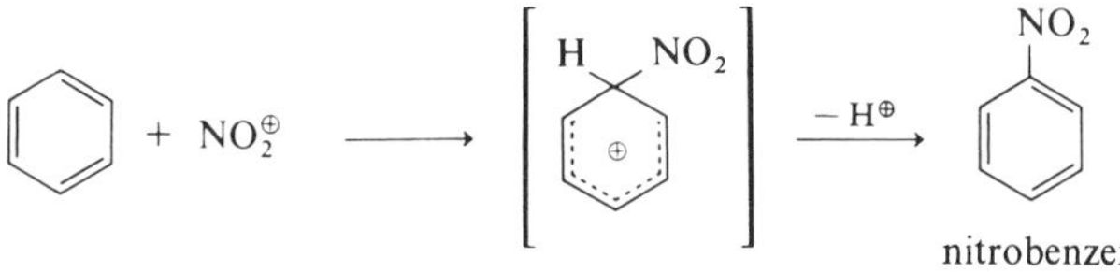

nitrobenzene

In general, the function of a catalyst (which is so often necessary to promote aromatic substitution) is to generate an electrophilic substituting agent from the given reagents.

C. NITRATION

We have already mentioned that the nitronium ion, $NO_2{}^{\oplus}$, is the active nitrating agent in nitric acid–sulfuric acid mixtures. The nitration of toluene is a fairly typical example of a nitration that proceeds well using nitric acid in a $1:2$ mixture with sulfuric acid. The nitration product is a mixture of *o*-, *m*-, and *p*-nitrotoluenes.

| 62% | 5% | 33% |

The presence of any appreciable concentration of water in the reaction mixture is deleterious since water tends to reverse the reaction by which nitronium ion is formed.

$$HNO_3 + H_2SO_4 \rightleftharpoons NO_2^{\oplus} + HSO_4^{\ominus} + H_2O$$

It follows that the potency of the mixed acids can be increased by using fuming nitric and fuming sulfuric acids, which have almost negligible water contents. With such mixtures, nitration of relatively unreactive compounds can be achieved. For example, *p*-nitrotoluene is far less reactive than toluene but when heated with an excess of nitric acid in fuming sulfuric acid ($H_2SO_4 + SO_3$), it can be converted successively to 2,4-dinitrotoluene and to 2,4,6-trinitrotoluene (TNT).

p-nitrotoluene   2,4-dinitrotoluene   2,4,6-trinitrotoluene

There are several interesting features about the nitration reactions thus far discussed. In the first place, the conditions required for nitration of *p*-nitrotoluene would, in contrast, rapidly oxidize an alkene by cleavage of the double bond.

adipic acid

We may also note that the nitration of toluene does not lead to equal amounts of the three possible mononitrotoluenes. The methyl substituent apparently orients the entering substituent preferentially to the *ortho* and *para* positions. This aspect of aromatic substitution will be discussed later in the chapter in conjunction with the effect of substituents on the reactivity of aromatic compounds.

D. HALOGENATION

The mechanism of halogenation is complicated by the fact that molecular halogens, Cl_2, Br_2, and I_2, form complexes with aromatic hydrocarbons.

Although complex formation assists substitution by bringing the reactants in close proximity, it does not always follow that a substitution reaction will occur. A catalyst is usually necessary. The catalysts most frequently used are metal halides that can act as Lewis acids ($FeBr_3$, $AlCl_3$, and $ZnCl_2$). Their catalytic activity may be attributed to their ability to polarize the halogen-halogen bond:

$$\overset{\delta\oplus}{Br}\text{---}\overset{\delta\ominus}{Br}\text{---}FeBr_3$$

The positive end of the halogen dipole attacks the aromatic compound while the negative end is complexed with the catalyst. We may then represent the reaction sequence as in Figure 20·6, with the slow step being formation of a σ bond between $Br^\oplus$ and a carbon of the aromatic ring.

The order of reactivity of the halogens is $F_2 > Cl_2 > Br_2 > I_2$. Fluorine is too reactive to be of practical use for the preparation of aromatic fluorine compounds and indirect methods are necessary (see Chapter 21). Iodine is usually unreactive and, in fact, its reaction with some arenes is energetically unfavorable. Use of iodine monochloride instead of iodine usually improves both the rate and the equilibrium condition to the point where good yields of iodination products are obtained: $C_6H_6 + ICl \rightarrow C_6H_5I + HCl$. Alternatively, molecular iodine can be converted to a more active species (perhaps $I^\oplus$) with an oxidizing agent such as nitric acid. With combinations of this kind, good yields of iodination products are obtained.

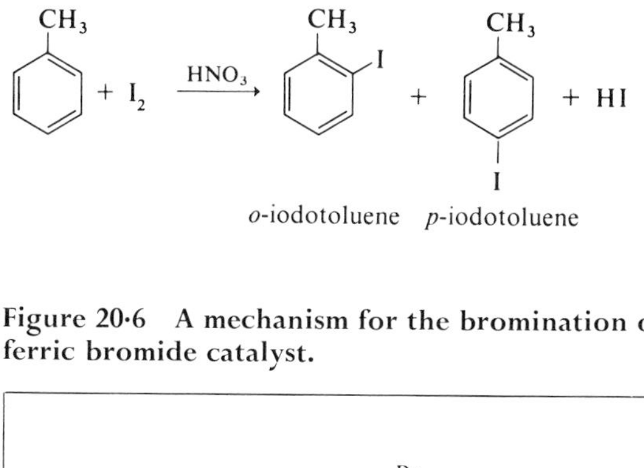

o-iodotoluene   p-iodotoluene

Figure 20·6   A mechanism for the bromination of benzene in the presence of ferric bromide catalyst.

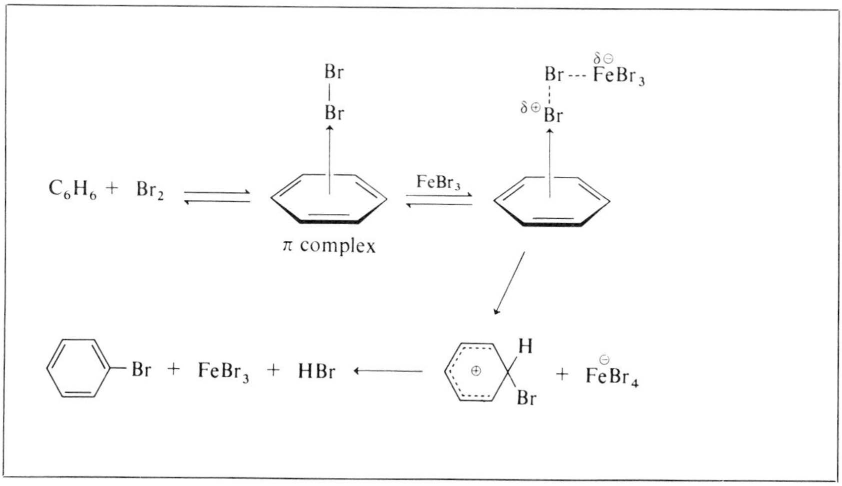

E. ALKYLATION

An important method of synthesizing alkylbenzenes utilizes an alkyl halide as the alkylating agent together with a metal halide catalyst, usually aluminum chloride.

benzene   ethyl bromide   ethylbenzene
(large excess)   83%

The class of reaction is familiarly known as **Friedel-Crafts alkylation**. The metal-halide catalyst functions much as it does in halogenation reactions; that is, it provides a source (real or potential) of a positive substituting agent, which in this case is a carbonium ion.

cumene
(isopropylbenzene)

Alkylation is not restricted to alkyl halides; any combination of reagents giving carbonium ions will serve. Frequently used combinations are alcohols and alkenes in the presence of acidic catalysts, such as H_3PO_4, H_2SO_4, HF, BF_3, or $HF\text{-}BF_3$. Ethylbenzene is made commercially from benzene and ethene using phosphoric acid as the catalyst. Cumene is made similarly from benzene and propene.

Under these conditions, the carbonium ion, which is the active substituting agent, is generated by protonation of the alkene.

$$CH_2{=}CH_2 + H^\oplus \rightleftharpoons CH_3CH_2{}^\oplus$$

$$CH_3CH{=}CH_2 + H^\oplus \rightleftharpoons CH_3\overset{\oplus}{C}HCH_3$$

It is not possible to make *n*-propylbenzene satisfactorily by direct alkylation of benzene because the *n*-propyl cation rearranges to the isopropyl cation as quickly as it is formed. Thus, cumene is the product of the reaction of benzene with either *n*-propyl chloride or isopropyl chloride.

A serious drawback to Friedel-Crafts alkylation is the tendency for poly-substitution to occur. This is because the alkyl group enhances further substitution (Section 20·5). The use of a large excess of arene is helpful in favoring monosubstitution.

F. ACYLATION

Acylation and alkylation of arenes are closely related. **Friedel-Crafts acylation** introduces an acyl group, $RCO{-}$, into an aromatic ring, and the product is an aryl ketone. Acylating reagents commonly used are acid halides, $RCOCl$, or anhydrides, $(RCO)_2O$. The catalyst is usually aluminum chloride, and its function is to generate the active substituting agent, which potentially is an acyl cation.

$$CH_3COCl + AlCl_3 \rightleftharpoons CH_3CO^\oplus{\cdots}\overset{\ominus}{Cl}{-}\overline{Al}Cl_3$$

methyl phenyl ketone
(acetophenone)

Acylation differs from alkylation in that the reaction is usually carried out in a solvent, commonly carbon disulfide or nitrobenzene. Furthermore, acylation requires more catalyst than alkylation because much of the catalyst is effectively removed by complex formation with the product ketone.

$$C_6H_5COCH_3 \ + \ AlCl_3 \ \rightleftharpoons \ \underset{CH_3}{\overset{C_6H_5}{\diagdown}}C=O\text{---}AlCl_3$$

1 : 1 complex

When an acylating reagent such as carboxylic anhydride is used, still more catalyst is required because some is consumed in converting the acyl compound to the acyl cation.

$$(RCO)_2O + 2\,AlCl_3 \ \longrightarrow \ R\overset{\oplus}{C}O\ \overset{\ominus}{AlCl_4} + RCO_2AlCl_2$$

Unlike alkylation, acylation is easily controlled to give monosubstitution because, once an acyl group is attached to a benzene ring, it is not possible to introduce a second acyl group into the same ring. For this reason, arenes are sometimes best prepared by acylation, followed by reduction of the carbonyl group with amalgamated zinc and hydrochloric acid (Section 11·4F). For example, n-propylbenzene is best prepared by this two-step route since, as we have noted, the direct alkylation of benzene with n-propyl chloride will give considerable amounts of cumene and polysubstitution products.

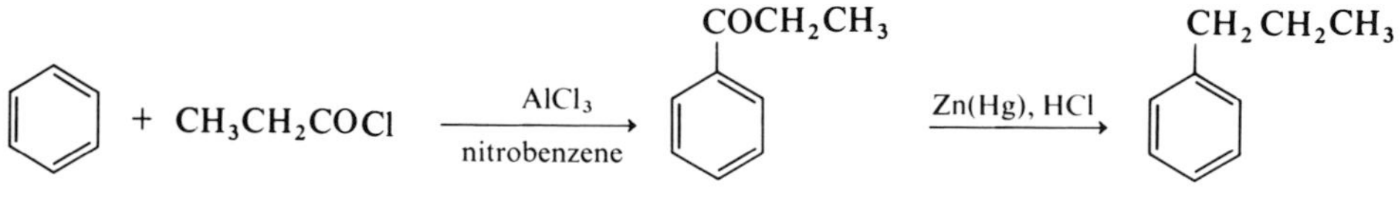

propanoyl chloride

n-propylbenzene

G. SULFONATION

Substitution of the sulfonic acid ($-SO_3H$) group for a hydrogen of an aromatic hydrocarbon is usually carried out by heating the hydrocarbon with a slight excess of concentrated or fuming sulfuric acid.

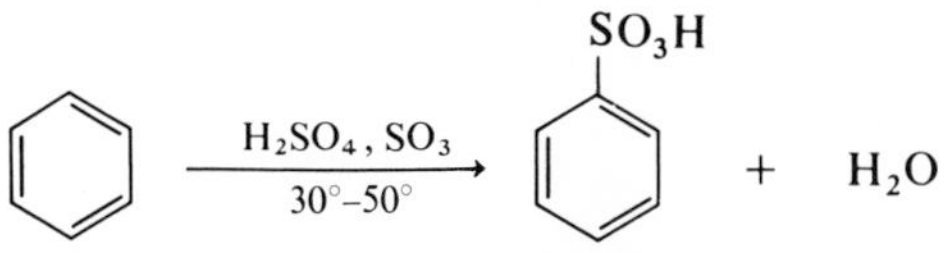

benzenesulfonic acid

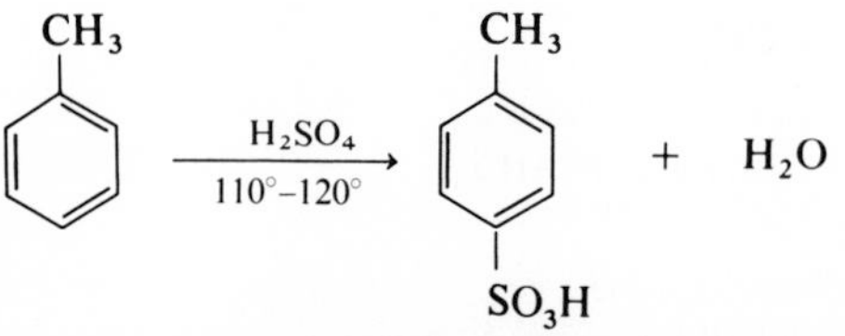

p-toluenesulfonic acid

The actual sulfonating agent is normally the SO_3 molecule, which, although it is a neutral reagent, has a powerfully electrophilic sulfur atom.

H. DEUTERATION

It is possible to replace the ring hydrogens of many aromatic compounds by exchange with deuteriosulfuric acid. The mechanism is analogous to other electrophilic substitutions.

Perdeuteriobenzene can be made from benzene in good yield if a sufficiently large excess of deuteriosulfuric acid is used. Sulfonation, which might appear to be a competing reaction, requires considerably more vigorous conditions.

20·5   effect of substituents on reactivity and orientation in electrophilic aromatic substitution

In planning syntheses based on substitution reactions of mono- or polysubstituted benzenes, you must be able to predict in advance which of the available positions of the ring are most likely to be substituted. This is now possible with a rather high degree of certainty, thanks to the work of many chemists over the last 100 years. Few, if any, other problems in organic chemistry have received so much attention, and there is now accumulated enough data on the orienting and reactivity effects of ring substituents in electrophilic substitution to permit the formulation of some valuable generalizations.

Basically, three problems are involved in the substitution reactions of aromatic compounds: (a) proof of the structures of the possible isomers, o, m, and p, that are formed; (b) the percentage of each isomer formed, if the product is a mixture; and (c) the reactivity of the compound being substituted relative to some standard substance, usually benzene.

Originally, the identity of each isomer formed was established by **Körner's absolute method**, which involves determining how many isomers each will give on further substitution, this number being diagnostic of the particular isomer (see Exercise 20·1). In practice, Körner's method is often very tedious and lengthy, and it is now primarily of historical interest except in its application to substitution reactions of unusual types of aromatic systems. For benzenoid compounds, structures can usually be established with the aid of correlations between spectroscopic properties and positions of substitution, as we have indicated earlier in this chapter. Also, it is often possible to convert the isomers to compounds of known structure by reactions that do not lead to rearrangement. For example, trifluoromethylbenzene on nitration gives only one product, which has been shown to be the *meta*-nitro derivative by conversion to the known *m*-nitrobenzoic acid.

A. THE PATTERN OF ORIENTATION IN AROMATIC SUBSTITUTION

The reaction most studied in connection with the orientation problem is nitration, but the principles established also apply for the most part to the related reactions of halogenation, sulfonation, alkylation, and acylation. Some illustrative data for the nitration of a number of monosubstituted benzene derivatives are given in Table 20·6. The orientation data are here expressed as the percentage of *ortho*, *meta*, and *para* isomers formed, and the rate data are

Table 20·6 Orientation and rate data for nitration of some monosubstituted benzene derivatives

| substituent, R | orientation | | | relative reactivity | partial rate factors | | |
	% o	% m	% p		f_o	f_m	f_p
—CH$_3$	56.5	3.5	40	24	42	2.5	58
—C(CH$_3$)$_3$	12.0	8.5	79.5	15.7	5.5	4.0	75
—CH$_2$Cl	32.0	15.5	52.5	0.302	0.29	0.14	0.951
—Cl	29.6	0.9	68.9	0.033	0.029	0.0009	0.137
—Br	36.5	1.2	62.4	0.030	0.033	0.0011	0.112
—NO$_2$	6.4	93.2	0.3	$\sim 10^{-7}$	1.8×10^{-6}	2.8×10^{-5}	2×10^{-7}
—CO$_2$C$_2$H$_5$	28.3	68.4	3.3	0.0003	2.5×10^{-4}	6×10^{-4}	5×10^{-5}
—CF$_3$		100		low			
—$\overset{\oplus}{N}$(CH$_3$)$_3$		89	11	low			

overall rates relative to benzene. Rates are also expressed as **partial rate factors**, symbolized as f_o, f_m, and f_p, which are, respectively, the rate of substitution at *one* of the *ortho, meta,* and *para* positions relative to *one* of the six equivalent positions in benzene. Consideration of the partial rate factors is particularly useful, since it lets you tell at a glance if, for example, a substituent gives *ortho,para* substitution with activation ($f_o, f_p > 1$), but *meta* substitution with deactivation ($f_m < 1$).

Inspection of the data in Table 20·6 shows that each substituent falls into one of three categories:

1. Those substituents [e.g., CH_3 and $-C(CH_3)_3$] which **activate all** the ring positions relative to benzene ($f > 1$), but are more activating for the *ortho* and *para* positions than for the *meta* position. These substituents lead to predominance of the *ortho* and *para* isomers. As a class, they give ***ortho,para* orientation with activation**. Other examples, in addition to those included in Table 20·6, are $-OH$, $-OCH_3$, $-NR_2$, and $-NHCOCH_3$.

2. Those substituents (e.g., Cl, Br, and CH_2Cl) which **deactivate all** of the ring positions ($f < 1$) but deactivate the *ortho* and *para* positions less than the *meta* position so that formation of the *ortho* and *para* isomers is favored. These substituents are classified as giving ***ortho,para* orientation with deactivation**.

3. Those substituents [e.g., $-NO_2$, $-CO_2C_2H_5$, $-\overset{\oplus}{N}(CH_3)_3$, and $-CF_3$] that deactivate **all** the ring positions ($f < 1$) but deactivate the *ortho* and *para* positions more than the *meta* position. Hence, mostly the *meta* isomer is formed. These substituents give ***meta* orientation with deactivation**.

There is no known example of a substituent that activates the ring and, at the same time, directs an electrophilic reagent preferentially to the *meta* position.

A more comprehensive list of substituents which fall into one of the three main categories is given in Table 20·7. It may be convenient to refer to this table when in doubt as to the orientation characteristics of particular substituents. An explanation of these substituent effects follows, which should make clear the criteria whereby predictions of the behavior of other substituents can be made with considerable confidence. First, however, we must examine more closely the energetics of electrophilic substitution.

The distribution of products in most aromatic electrophilic substitutions of benzene derivatives is determined not by the relative stabilities of the products but by the *rates* at which they are formed. Thus nitration of chlorobenzene gives mostly *o*- and *p*-nitrochlorobenzene, whereas chlorination of nitrobenzene produces mostly the *meta* isomer. This means that benzene can be converted to one or the other set of products depending on the sequence of the nitration and chlorination reactions (Figure 20·7). Furthermore, there is virtually no isomerization of the products.

To rationalize the orientation effects of ring substituents, then, we should compare the transition states leading to the various products. The rate-controlling step in electrophilic aromatic substitution is normally the first step— the attack of the electrophile at the activated position—not the second step in which a proton is lost from the intermediate ion. The energy profile for the attack of an electrophile $Z^\oplus$ on benzene is shown in Figure 20·8.

Table 20·7   Orientation and reactivity effects of ring substituents

o,p orientation with activation	o,p orientation with deactivation	m orientation with deactivation
—OH	—CH$_2$Cl	—NO$_2$
—O$^\ominus$	—F	—$\overset{\oplus}{N}H_3$
—OR	—Cl	—$\overset{\oplus}{N}R_3$
—OC$_6$H$_5$	—Br	—$\overset{\oplus}{P}R_3$
—NH$_2$	—I	—$\overset{\oplus}{S}R_2$
—NR$_2$	—CH=CHNO$_2$	—$\overset{\oplus}{I}C_6H_5$
—NHCOCH$_3$		—CF$_3$
—alkyl (e.g., CH$_3$)		—CCl$_3$
—aryl (e.g., C$_6$H$_5$)		—SO$_3$H
		—SO$_2$R
		—CO$_2$H
		—CO$_2$R
		—CONH$_2$
		—CHO
		—COR
		—C≡N

The transition states are closer in energy to the intermediate ion than they they are to either the products or the reactants. It is convenient to take the intermediate as equivalent to the transition states in the discussion that follows.

B. ELECTRICAL EFFECTS

An important effect of substituent groups on aromatic substitution is the inductive effect which we have encountered previously in connection with the ionization of carboxylic acids (Section 13·4B). An electron-attracting group ($-I$ effect) will exert an electrostatic effect such as to destabilize a positively charged intermediate, while an electron-donating group ($+I$ effect) will have the opposite effect. We shall illustrate this simple principle, using the (CH$_3$)$_3\overset{\oplus}{N}$— group as an example. This group is strongly electron-attracting. If we write the hybrid structure of the substitution intermediate with the group X representing some electrophilic substituting agent, we see at once that the charge produced in the ring is unfavorable when the (CH$_3$)$_3\overset{\oplus}{N}$— substituent is

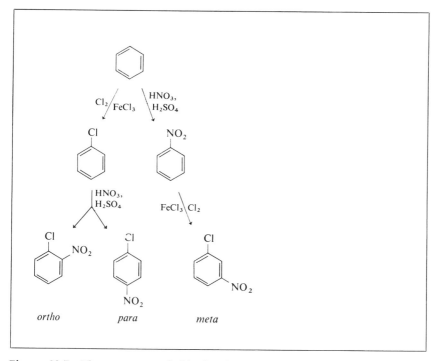

Figure 20·7 The sequence of chlorination and nitration reactions required to give the three isomers of nitrochlorobenzene.

Figure 20·8 Energetics of the reaction of an electrophile $Z^{\oplus}$ with benzene showing the formation of the intermediate, $C_6H_6Z^{\oplus}$, and its decomposition to products. The transition state which determines the rate of the overall reaction is that of the *first* step.

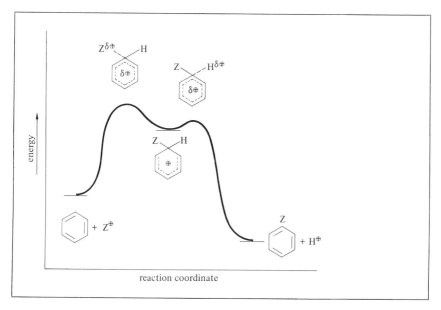

present, particularly for substitution at the *ortho* and *para* positions where adjacent atoms would carry *like* charges. Thus, although all three intermediates should then be less stable than the corresponding intermediate for benzene, the *ortho* and *para* intermediates should be less favorable than the one for *meta* substitution. This should lead to *meta* orientation with deactivation, as indeed is observed. (We show the charge distribution in the intermediate ions in these examples.)

ortho substitution   *meta* substitution   *para* substitution

Other substituents that are strongly electron attracting and that also orient *meta* with deactivation include $-NO_2$, $-CF_3$, $-\overset{\oplus}{P}(CH_3)_3$, $-SO_3H$, $-CO_2H$, $-CO_2CH_3$, $-CONH_2$, $-CHO$, $-COC_6H_5$, and $-C\equiv N$.

The activating and *ortho, para*-orienting influence of alkyl substituents can also be rationalized on the basis of inductive effects. Thus, the substitution intermediates for *ortho, para*, and *meta* substitution of toluene are stabilized by the capacity of a methyl group to release electrons ($+I$ effect) and partially compensate for the positive charge.

ortho substitution   *meta* substitution   *para* substitution

Furthermore, the stabilization is most effective in *ortho* and *para* substitution where part of the positive charge is adjacent to the methyl substituent. (For other examples of stabilization of positive carbon by alkyl groups see Section 4·4C). The result is *ortho,para* orientation with activation.

In addition to the inductive effects of substituents, conjugation effects may be a factor in orientation and are frequently decisive. This is especially true of substituents that carry one or more pairs of unshared electron pairs on the atom immediately attached to the ring (e.g., $-\overset{..}{O}H$, $-\overset{..}{O}{:}^{\ominus}$, $-\overset{..}{O}CH_3$, $-\overset{..}{N}H_2$, $-\overset{..}{N}HCOCH_3$, $-\overset{..}{C}l{:}$). An electron pair so situated helps to stabilize the positive charge of the substitution intermediate, as the extra resonance forms [5] and [6] will indicate for *ortho* and *para* substitution of anisole (methyl phenyl ether).

ortho substitution

[5]

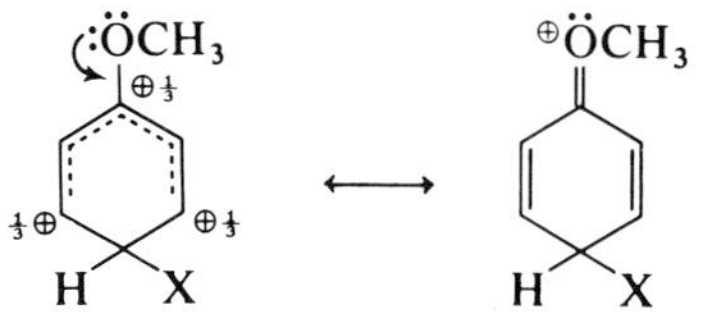

para substitution

[6]

In *meta* substitution, however, the charge is not similarly stabilized as no resonance structures analogous to [5] or [6] can be written. Accordingly, the favored orientation is *ortho,para*, but whether substitution proceeds with activation or deactivation depends on the magnitude of the inductive effect of the substituent. For example, halogen substituents are strongly electronegative and deactivate the ring at all positions; yet they strongly orient *ortho* and *para* through conjugation of the unshared electron pairs. Apparently the inductive effect is strong enough to reduce the overall reactivity, but not powerful enough to determine the orientation. Thus for *para* substitution of chlorobenzene the intermediate stage is formed less readily than in the substitution of benzene itself.

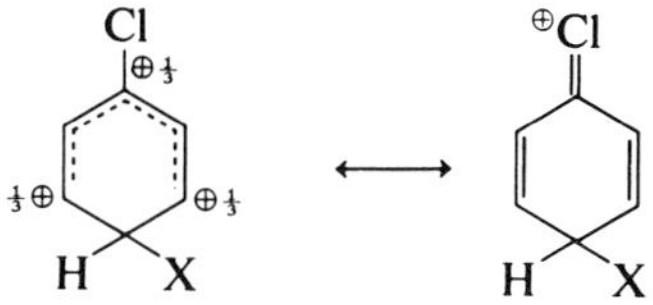

(unfavorable, because positive
carbon is next to chlorine)

Other groups such as $-NH_2$, $-NHCOCH_3$, and $-OCH_3$ are electron attracting but much less so than the halogens, and the inductive effect is completely overshadowed by the conjugation effect. Therefore, substitution proceeds with *ortho,para* orientation and activation. The most activating common substituent is $-\ddot{O}:^{\ominus}$, which combines a large electron-donating inductive effect with a conjugation effect.

C. ORIENTATION IN DISUBSTITUTED BENZENES

The orientation and reactivity effects of substituents discussed for the substitution of monosubstituted benzenes also hold for disubstituted benzenes except that the directing influence now comes from two groups. Qualitatively, the effects of the two substituents are additive. We would therefore expect *p*-nitrotoluene to be less reactive than toluene because of the deactivating effect of a nitro group. Also, the most likely position of substitution should be, and is, *ortho* to the methyl group and *meta* to the nitro group.

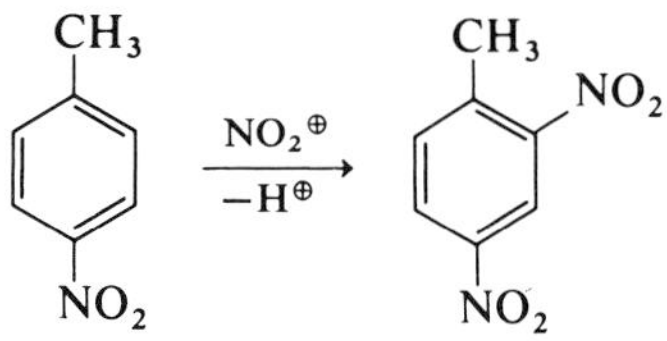

When the two substituents have opposed orientation effects, it is not always easy to predict what products will be obtained. For example, 2-methoxy-acetanilide has two powerful *ortho,para*-directing substituents, $-OCH_3$ and $-NHCOCH_3$. Nitration of this compound gives mainly the 4-nitro derivative, which indicates that the $-NHCOCH_3$ exerts a stronger influence than OCH_3.

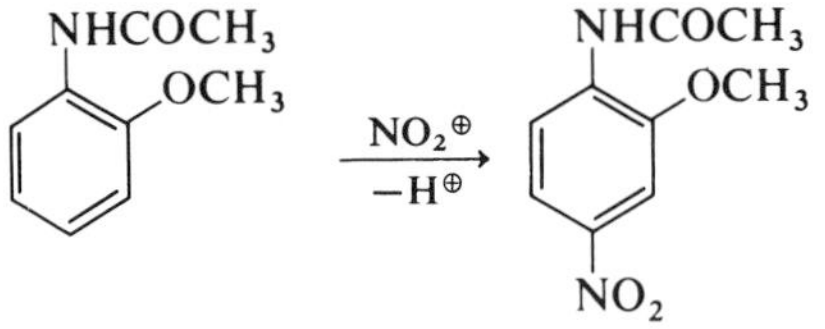

20·6 *substitution reactions of polynuclear aromatic hydrocarbons*

Although naphthalene, phenanthrene, and anthracene resemble benzene in many respects, they are more reactive than benzene in both substitution and addition reactions. This is expected theoretically because quantum mechanical calculations show that the loss in stabilization energy for the first step in electrophilic substitution or addition decreases progressively from benzene to anthracene; therefore the reactivity in substitution and addition reactions should increase from benzene to anthracene.

In considering the properties of the polynuclear hydrocarbons relative to benzene, it is important to recognize that the carbon-carbon bonds in poly-nuclear hydrocarbons are not all alike nor do they correspond exactly to benzene bonds. This we may predict from the hybrid structures of these molecules, derived by considering all of the electron-pairing schemes having normal bonds, there being three such structures for naphthalene, four for anthracene, and five for phenanthrene. See Figure 20·9. If we assume that each structure contributes equally to its resonance hybrid, then, in the case of naphthalene, the 1,2 and 2,3 bonds have $\frac{2}{3}$ and $\frac{1}{3}$ double-bond character, re-spectively. Accordingly, the 1,2 bond should be shorter than the 2,3 bond, and this has been verified by X-ray diffraction studies of crystalline naphtha-lene.

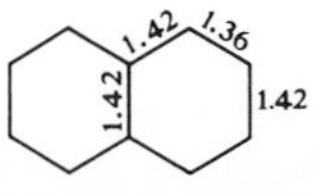

bond lengths of naphthalene, A units

Similarly, the 1,2 bond of anthracene should have $\frac{3}{4}$ double-bond character and should be shorter than the 2,3 bond, which has only $\frac{1}{4}$ double-bond character. The 1,2 bond is indeed shorter than the 2,3 bond.

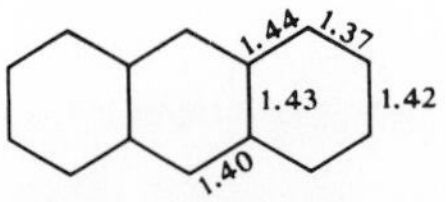

bond lengths of anthracene, A units

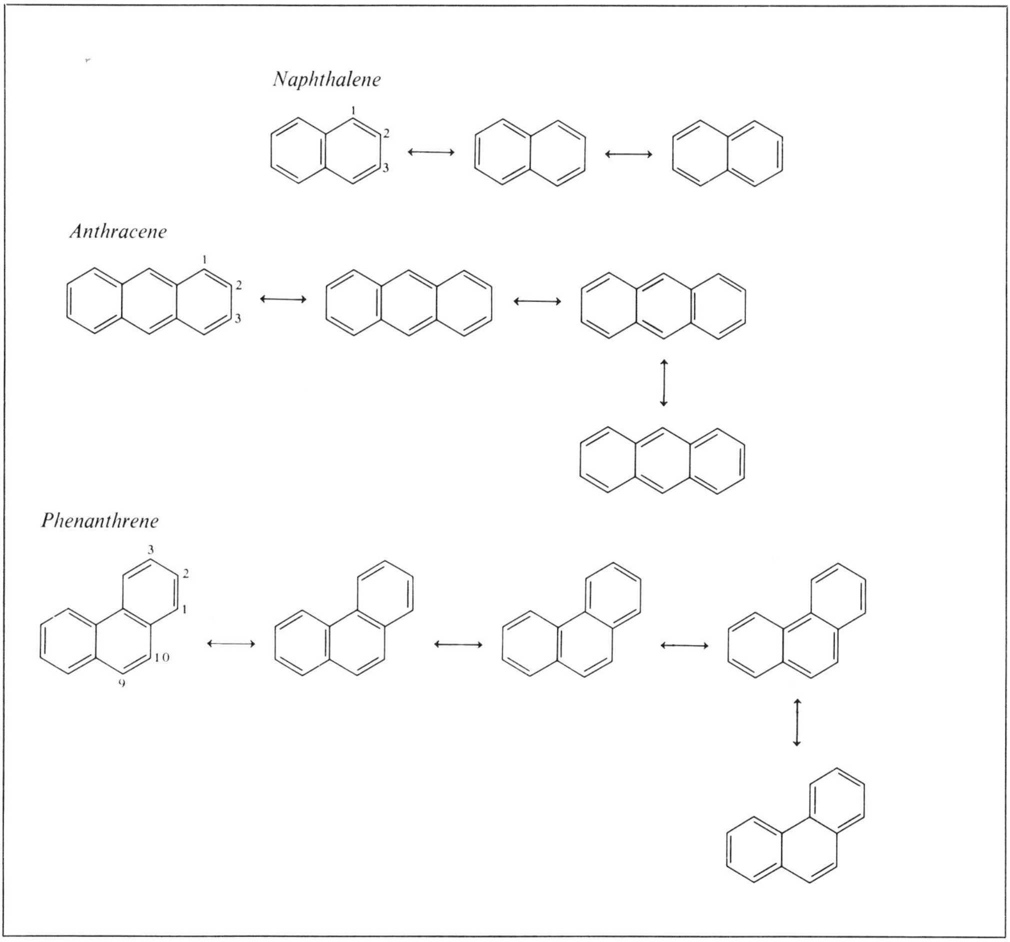

Naphthalene

Anthracene

Phenanthrene

Figure 20·9   Resonance structures for naphthalene, anthracene, and phenanthrene.

The trend toward greater inequality of the carbon-carbon bonds in poly-nuclear hydrocarbons is very pronounced in phenanthrene. Here, the 9,10 bond is predicted to have $\frac{4}{5}$ double-bond character, and experiment verifies that this bond does resemble an alkene double bond, as we shall see in subsequent discussions.

A. NAPHTHALENE

In connection with orientation in the substitution of naphthalene, the picture is often complex, although the 1 position is the more reactive (Figure 20·10). Sometimes, relatively small changes in the reagents and conditions change the pattern of orientation. One example is sulfonation, a reversible reaction leading to 1-naphthalenesulfonic acid at 120° but to the 2 isomer on prolonged reaction or at temperatures above 160°C. Another example is supplied by Friedel-Crafts acylation: the major product in carbon disulfide is the 1 isomer, while in nitrobenzene it is the 2 isomer.

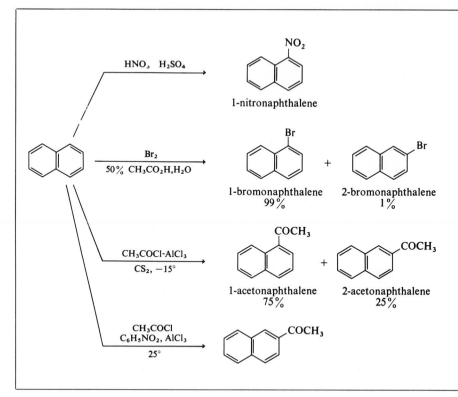

Figure 20·10 Electrophilic substitution pattern of naphthalene.

Normally, substitution of naphthalene occurs more readily at the 1 position than at the 2 position. This may be accounted for on the basis that the most favorable resonance structures for either the 1- or the 2-substituted intermediate are those which have one ring fully aromatic. We see then that 1 substitution is favored over 2 substitution since the positive charge in the 1 intermediate can be distributed over two positions, leaving one aromatic ring unchanged; but this is not possible for the 2 intermediate without affecting the benzenoid structure of both rings.

1 substitution:

2 substitution:

B. PHENANTHRENE AND ANTHRACENE

The substitution patterns of the higher hydrocarbons are more complex than for naphthalene. For example, phenanthrene can be nitrated and sulfonated, but the products are mixtures of 1-, 2-, 3-, 4-, and 9-substituted phenanthrenes.

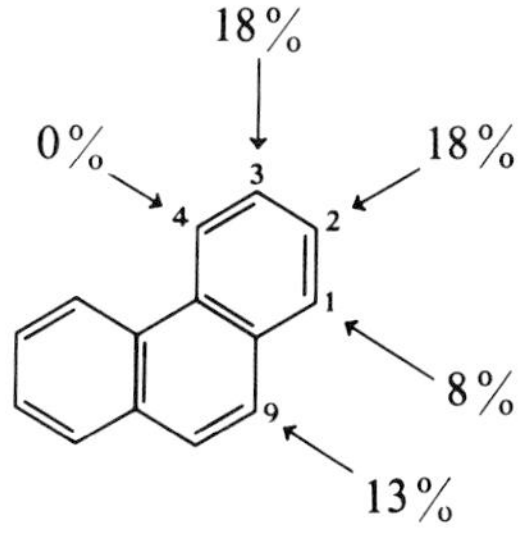

sulfonation

nitration

(percentages are yields of sulfonic acids with H_2SO_4 at 60°. At 120°, mostly the 2- and 3-sulfonic acids are obtained)

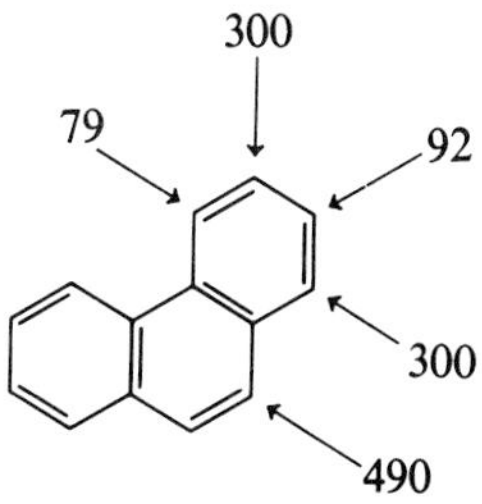

(figures at the 9, 1, 2, 3, and 4 positions are partial rate factors)

The 9,10 bond in phenanthrene is quite reactive; in fact, almost as much so as an alkene double bond. Addition therefore occurs readily, giving both 9,10 addition and 9-substitution products (Scheme I).

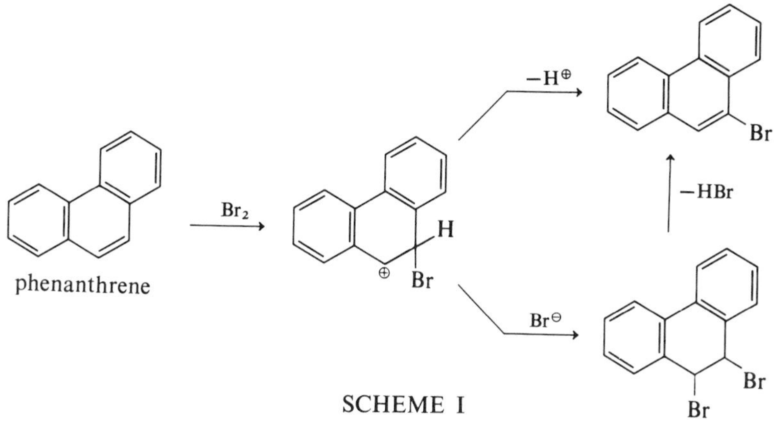

phenanthrene

$-H^\oplus$

$-HBr$

$Br^\ominus$

SCHEME I

Anthracene is even more reactive than phenanthrene and has a great tendency to add various reagents to the 9,10 positions. The addition products of nitration and halogenation readily give the 9-substitution products on warming.

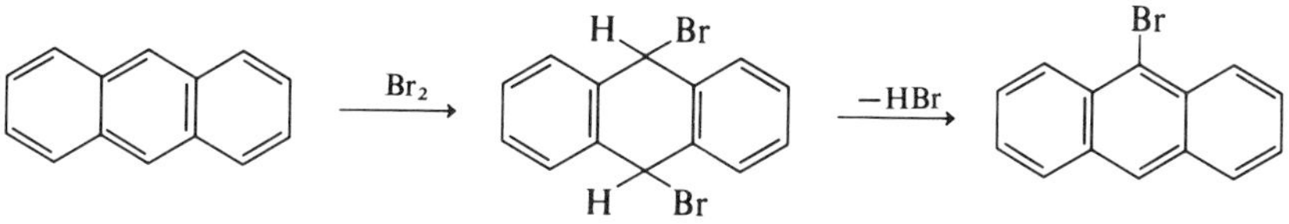

20·7 nonbenzenoid conjugated cyclic compounds

A. AZULENE

There are a number of compounds that possess some measure of aromatic character typical of benzene, but that do not possess a benzenoid ring. Appropriately, they are classified as nonbenzenoid aromatic compounds. One example of interest is azulene, and, like benzene, it tends to react by substitution, not addition. It is isomeric with naphthalene and has a five- and a seven-membered ring fused through adjacent carbons. As the name implies, it is

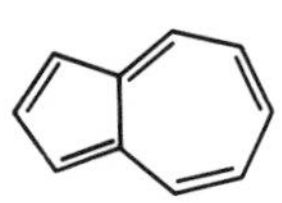

azulene

deep blue in color. It is less stable than naphthalene and isomerizes quantitatively on heating above 350° in the absence of air.

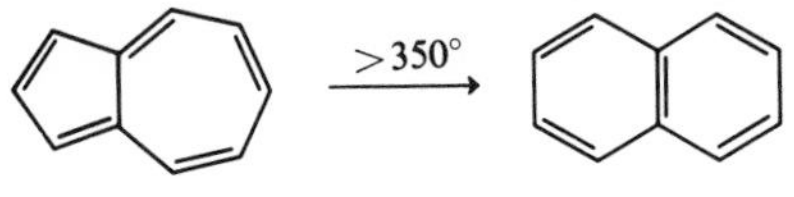

Azulene can be represented as a hybrid of neutral and ionic structures.

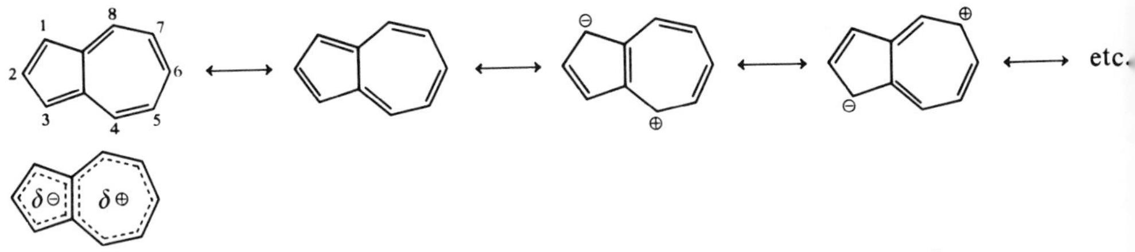

The polarization shown above puts weight on those ionic structures having six electrons in both the five- and seven-membered rings (see Section 6·7).

B. CYCLOOCTATETRAENE

Of equal interest to azulene is cyclooctatetraene, which is a bright yellow, nonbenzenoid, *nonaromatic* compound with alternating single and double bonds. If the carbons of cyclooctatetraene were to occupy the corners of a regular planar octagon, the C—C—C bond angles would have to be 135°. Cyclooctatetraene does not conform to the Hückel $4n + 2$ rule (Section 6·7) and it is not surprising that the resonance energy gained in the planar structure is not sufficient to overcome the unfavorable angle strain. Cyclooctatetraene, instead, exists in a "tub" structure with alternating single and double bonds.

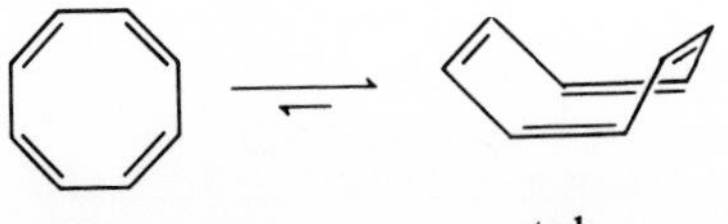

planar   tub

There is, however, nmr evidence that indicates that the tub form is in quite rapid equilibrium with a very small amount of the planar form at room temperature. Probably there is not much more than a 10-kcal energy difference between the two forms.

summary

The rules of nomenclature for arenes (aromatic hydrocarbons) are similar to those for aliphatic systems except that pairs of substituents at different ring positions may be designated *ortho, meta,* and *para*. A number of important arenes are C_6H_6 (benzene), $C_6H_5CH_3$ (toluene), $C_6H_5CH(CH_3)_2$ (cumene), and $C_6H_5CH=CH_2$ (styrene). A number of important aryl or aralkyl groups are C_6H_5- (phenyl), $C_6H_5CH_2-$ (benzyl), $C_6H_5CH\Big\langle$ (benzal), C_6H_5C- (benzo), and $(C_6H_5)_2CH-$ (benzhydryl).

Polynuclear aromatic hydrocarbons have aromatic rings fused together so that the rings have one or more sides in common. Important examples of these are naphthalene, anthracene, and phenanthrene. Fusing an additional ring to an arene normally adds C_4H_2 to the molecular formula; the extra ring is designated benzo or benz.

naphthalene ($C_{10}H_8$) anthracene ($C_{14}H_{10}$) phenanthrene ($C_{14}H_{10}$)

Aromatic rings have characteristic absorption bands in the infrared (near 1500, 1600, and just above 3000 cm^{-1}), in the ultraviolet (near 2000 A but shifting to higher wavelengths with conjugation), and in nmr spectra (6.5 to 8.0 ppm for aromatic protons).

Electrophilic substitution serves to introduce the following groups into an aromatic ring: $-NO_2$, $-Cl$ (or Br or I), $-SO_3H$, $-R$ (alkyl), $R-\overset{\overset{\displaystyle O}{\|}}{C}-$ (acyl), and $-D$. The actual electrophilic reagents in these cases are electron-deficient cations (except for SO_3). Substituents already present in the ring determine the position taken by the incoming group. Some important substituents that direct the incoming electrophile to the *ortho* and *para* positions are $-R$ (alkyl), $-OR$, $-NH_2$, and X (halogen). Those that direct toward the *meta* position include $-NO_2$, $-\overset{\oplus}{N}H_3$, $-\overset{\overset{\displaystyle O}{\|}}{C}-$, and $-C{\equiv}N$.

The orienting effect of a substituent Y on an electrophile $Z^{\oplus}$ is determined by how Y affects the dispersal of the positive charge in the transition state, a reasonable model for which is the intermediate ion [1] (shown for the case of *para* substitution).

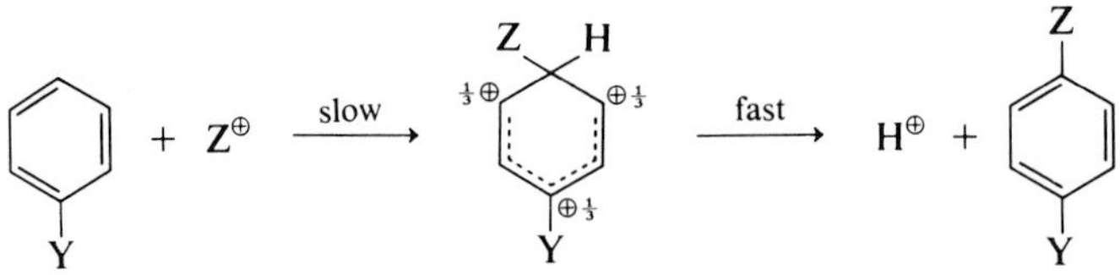

[1]

All of the common *ortho,para*-directing substituents, with the exception of halogen, activate the ring toward substitution and all the *meta*-directing substituents deactivate the ring; nitro to such an extent that the Friedel-Crafts reaction cannot be applied to nitrobenzene.

Naphthalene is normally substituted at the 1 position (α) but sulfonation at high temperatures and Friedel-Crafts acylation in nitrobenzene give substitution at the 2 position (β). Phenanthrene gives mixtures of substitution products but anthracene tends to react by addition at the 9,10 positions. Other cyclic hydrocarbons that have been considered are phenalenyl [2], a resonance-stabilized radical; azulene [3], which has aromatic character; and cyclooctatetraene [4], which does not. There are a number of other resonance structures for [2] and [3].

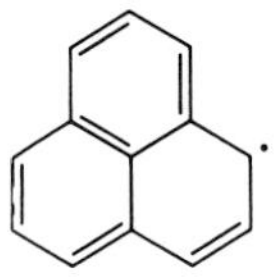

[2] 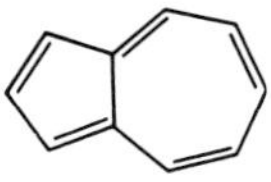   [3]    [4]

exercises

20·1   How many isomeric products could each of the xylenes give on introduction of a third substituent? Name each isomer using chlorine as the third substituent.

20·2   Name each of the following compounds by an accepted system:

a. $(C_6H_5)_2CHCl$

b. $C_6H_5CHCl_2$

c. $C_6H_5CCl_3$

d.

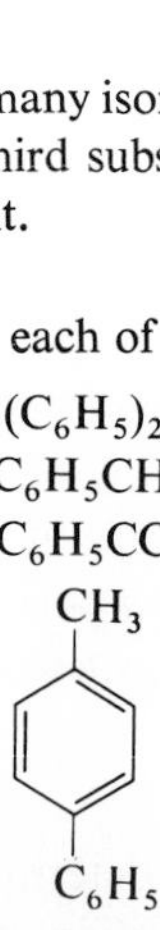

e.

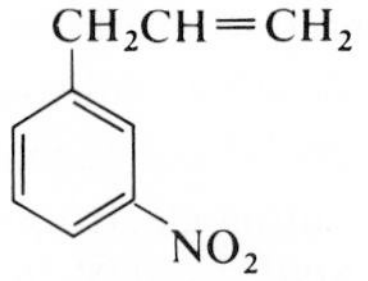

f.

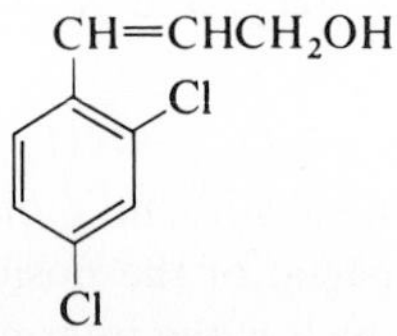

20·3   How many possible disubstitution (X,X and X,Y) products are there for naphthalene, phenanthrene, anthracene, and biphenyl? Name each of the possible dimethyl derivatives.

20·4   A number of polynuclear hydrocarbons are shown below with their conjugated rings shown as hexagons with inscribed circles.

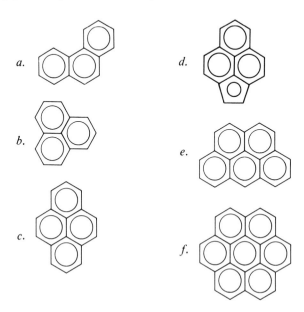

(i) Determine which of these compounds are radicals by drawing Kekulé structures. (ii) Three of the structures above represent compounds whose structures have been given earlier in the chapter in a somewhat different form. Identify them.

20·5   Identify the two compounds with molecular formula C_7H_7Cl from their infrared spectra in Figure 20·11.

20·6   Predict the effect on the ultraviolet spectrum of a solution of aniline in water when hydrochloric acid is added. Explain why a solution of sodium phenoxide absorbs at longer wavelengths than a solution of phenol (see Table 20·3).

20·7   Establish the structures of the following benzene derivatives on the basis of their empirical formulas and nmr spectra as shown in Figure 20·12. Remember that equivalent protons do not normally split each other's resonances (Section 7·6B).

  a. C_8H_{10} c. $C_9H_{10}O_2$
  b. C_8H_7OCl d. C_9H_{12}

20·8   Calculate from appropriate bond and stabilization energies the heats of reaction of chlorine with benzene to give (a) chlorobenzene and (b) 5,6-dichloro-1,3-cyclohexadiene. Your answer should indicate that substitution is energetically more favorable than addition.

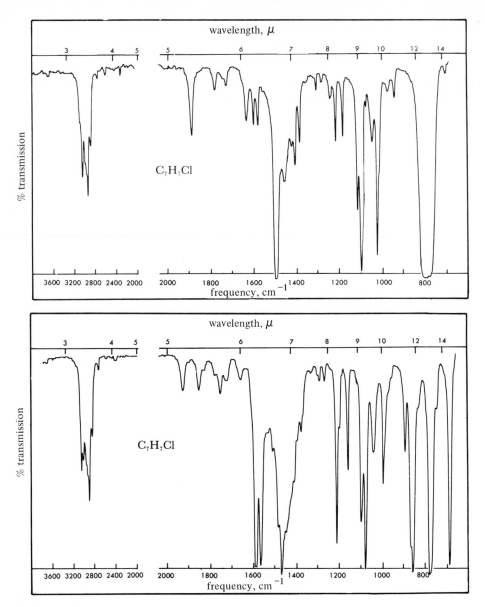

Figure 20·11   Infrared spectra of two isomeric compounds of formula C_7H_7Cl (see Exercise 20·5).

20·9   On what basis (other than the thermodynamic one suggested in Exercise 20·8) could we decide whether or not the following addition-elimination mechanism for bromination of benzene actually takes place?

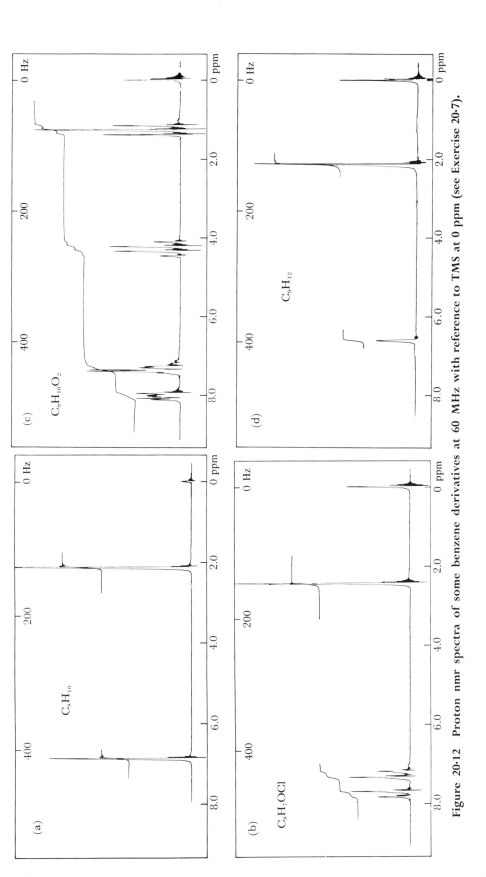

Figure 20-12 Proton nmr spectra of some benzene derivatives at 60 MHz with reference to TMS at 0 ppm (see Exercise 20-7).

20·10   Explain with the aid of an energy diagram for aromatic nitration how one can account for the fact that hexadeuteriobenzene undergoes nitration with nitric acid at the same rate as ordinary benzene.

20·11   From the fact that nitrations in concentrated nitric acid are strongly retarded by added nitrate ions and strongly accelerated by small amounts of sulfuric acid, deduce the nature of the actual nitrating agent.

20·12   Account for the fact that fairly reactive arenes (e.g., benzene, toluene, and ethylbenzene) are nitrated with excess nitric acid in nitromethane solution at a rate that is *independent* of the concentration of the arene (i.e., zeroth order). Does this mean that nitration of an equimolal mixture of benzene and toluene would necessarily give an equimolal mixture of nitrobenzene and nitrotoluenes? Why or why not?

20·13   Write a mechanism for the alkylation of benzene with isopropyl alcohol catalyzed by boron trifluoride.

20·14   Suggest possible routes for the synthesis of the following compounds:

a.   *c.*

b.

20·15   Calculate the partial rate factors for each different position in the mononitration of biphenyl, given that the overall reaction rate relative to benzene is 40, and the products are 68% *o*-, 1% *m*-, and 31% *p*-nitrobiphenyl. (Remember, there are *two* benzene rings in biphenyl.)

20·16   Explain why the $-CF_3$, $-NO_2$, and $-CHO$ groups should be *meta* orienting with deactivation.

20·17   Explain why the nitration and halogenation of biphenyl goes with activation at the *ortho* and *para* positions but with deactivation at the *meta* position. Suggest a reason why biphenyl is more reactive than 2,2′-dimethylbiphenyl in nitration.

20·18   Explain why the bromination of aniline gives 2,4,6-tribromoaniline, whereas the nitration of aniline with mixed acids gives *m*-nitroaniline.

20·19   Predict the favored positions of substitution in the nitration of the following compounds:

a.

b.

c.

Cl
⟨benzene ring⟩—CH₃

f.

F
⟨benzene ring⟩—OCH₃

d.

Br
⟨benzene ring⟩—Br

g.

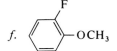

e.

Br
⟨benzene ring⟩—Br

(consider the character of the various resonance structures for substitution in the 1- and 2- positions)

20·20 Predict the orientation in the following reactions:

    a. 1-methylnaphthalene + Br₂
    b. 2-methylnaphthalene + HNO₃
    c. 2-naphthoic acid + HNO₃

20·21 How would you go about proving that the acylation of naphthalene in the 2 position in nitrobenzene solution is not the result of thermodynamic control?

20·22 Show how you can predict qualitatively the character of the 1,2 bond in acenaphthylene.

⟨structure of acenaphthylene with positions 1 and 2 labeled⟩

20·23 Write structural formulas for all of the possible isomers of C_8H_{10} containing one benzene ring. Show how many different mononitration products each could give if no carbon skeleton rearrangements occur but nitration is considered possible either in the ring or side chain. Name all of the mononitration products by an accepted system.

20·24 Write structural formulas (more than one might be possible) for aromatic substances that fit the following descriptions:

    a. C_8H_{10}, which can give only one theoretically possible ring nitration product
    b. $C_6H_3Br_3$, which can give three theoretically possible nitration products
    c. $C_6H_3Br_2Cl$, which can give two theoretically possible nitration products
    d. $C_8H_8(NO_2)_2$, which can give only two theoretically possible different ring monobromo substitution products

20·25 1,3-Cyclohexadiene cannot be isolated from reduction of benzene by hydrogen over nickel. The isolable reduction product is always cyclohexane.

a. Explain why the hydrogenation of benzene is difficult to stop at the 1,3-cyclohexadiene stage, even though 1,3-butadiene is relatively easy to reduce to butenes.

b. How could an apparatus for determining heats of hydrogenation be used to obtain an accurate ΔH value for the reaction?

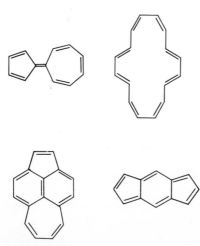

$$ \text{⬡} + H_2 \longrightarrow \text{⬡} $$

c. Calculate a ΔH of combustion for benzene as 1,3,5-cyclohexatriene (no resonance) from bond energies and compare it with a calculated value for heat of combustion of benzene obtained from the experimental ΔH, $+5.9$ kcal, for the hydrogenation in (*b*).

20·26 Predict the most favorable position for mononitration for each of the following substances. Indicate whether the rate is greater or less than for the nitration of benzene. Give your reasoning in each case.

a. fluorobenzene
b. trifluoromethylbenzene
c. acetophenone
d. nitrosobenzene
e. benzyldimethylamine oxide
f. diphenylmethane
g. p-methoxybromobenzene

h. diphenyl sulfone
i. p-t-butyltoluene
j. $(C_6H_5)_2\overset{\oplus\ominus}{I}NO_3$
k. m-diphenylbenzene (m-terphenyl)
l. 4-acetylaminobiphenyl

20·27 Predict which of the following compounds have some aromatic character. Give your reasons.

tropylium bromide

aceplieadylene

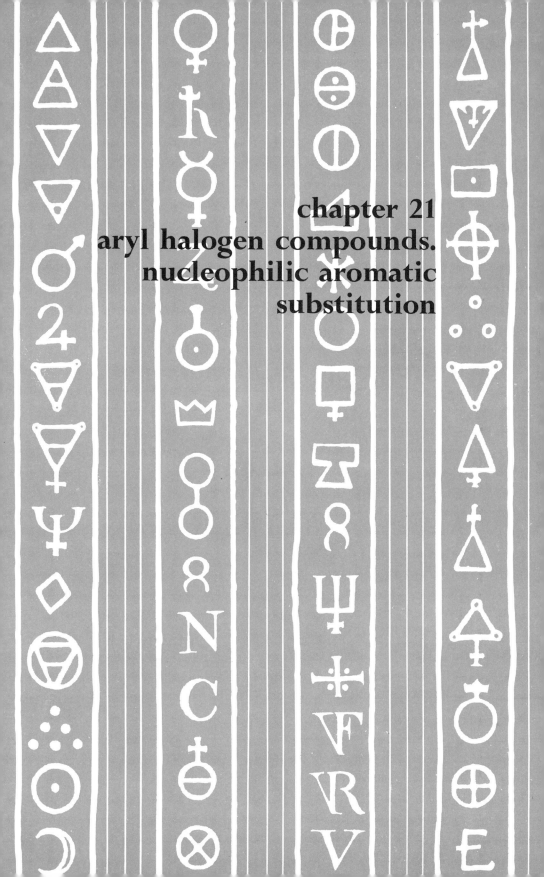

chapter 21
aryl halogen compounds.
nucleophilic aromatic
substitution

The chemical behavior of aromatic halogen compounds depends largely on whether the halogen is attached to carbon of the aromatic ring, as in bromobenzene, C_6H_5Br, or to carbon of an alkyl substituent, as in benzyl bromide, $C_6H_5CH_2Br$. Compounds of the former type are referred to as aryl halides, and those of the latter as arylalkyl halides.

Aryl halides are expected to resemble vinyl halides to some extent since both have their halogen atoms attached to unsaturated carbon.

bromobenzene	vinyl bromide
(phenyl bromide)	(bromoethene)

$$CH_2=CH-Br$$

Consequently, it is no surprise to find that most aryl halides are usually much less reactive than alkyl or allyl halides toward nucleophilic reagents in either S_N1 or S_N2 reactions. Whereas ethyl bromide reacts easily with sodium methoxide in methanol to form methyl ethyl ether, vinyl bromide and bromobenzene completely fail to undergo nucleophilic displacement under similar conditions. Also, neither bromobenzene nor vinyl bromide reacts appreciably with boiling alcoholic silver nitrate solution even after many hours.

In contrast to phenyl halides, benzyl halides are quite reactive. In fact, they are analogous in reactivity to allyl halides (Section 9·6).

$$CH_2=CH-CH_2-Br$$

benzyl bromide   allyl bromide

Benzyl halides are readily attacked by nucleophilic reagents in both S_N1 and S_N2 displacement reactions. The ability to undergo S_N1 reactions is clearly related to the stability of the benzyl cation, the positive charge of which is expected, on the basis of the resonance structures [1a] through [1d], to be extensively delocalized.

| [1a] | [1b] | [1c] | [1d] |

When the halogen substituent is located two or more carbons from the aromatic rings—as in 2-phenylethyl bromide, $C_6H_5CH_2CH_2Br$—the pronounced activating effect evident in benzyl halides disappears, and the reactivity of the halide is essentially that of a primary alkyl halide (e.g., $CH_3CH_2CH_2Br$). Since, in general, the chemistry of arylalkyl halides is related more closely to that of aliphatic derivatives than to aryl halides, we shall defer further discussion of arylalkyl halides to Chapter 24, which is concerned with the chemistry of aromatic side-chain derivatives.

Table 21·1   Physical properties of aryl halides

name	bp, °C	mp, °C	$d^{20/4}$	n_D^{25}
fluorobenzene	85	−42	1.024	1.4646[22.8]
chlorobenzene	132	−45	1.1066	1.5248
bromobenzene	155	−31	1.4991[15/15]	1.5598
iodobenzene	189	−31	1.832	1.6214[18.5]
o-chlorotoluene	159	−34	1.0817	1.5238
m-chlorotoluene	162	−48	1.0732	1.5214[19]
p-chlorotoluene	162	8	1.0697	1.5199[19]
1-chloronaphthalene	263		1.1938	1.6332[20]
2-chloronaphthalene	265	55		

21·1 physical properties of aryl halogen compounds

There is nothing unexpected about most of the physical properties of aryl halides. They are slightly polar substances and accordingly have boiling points approximating those of hydrocarbons of the same molecular weights; their solubility in water is very low, whereas their solubility in nonpolar organic solvents is high. In general, they are colorless, oily, highly refractive liquids with characteristic aromatic odors and with densities greater than that of water. A representative list of halides and their physical properties is given in Table 21·1.

With respect to the infrared spectra of aryl halides, correlations between structure and absorption bands of aromatic carbon-halogen bonds have not proved to be useful.

21·2 preparation of aryl halides

Many of the methods that are commonly used for the preparation of alkyl halides simply do not work when applied to the preparation of aryl halides. Thus, it is not possible to convert phenol to chlorobenzene by reagents such as $HCl-ZnCl_2$, $SOCl_2$, and PCl_3 which convert ethanol to chloroethane. In fact, there is no very practical route at all for conversion of phenol to chlorobenzene. In this situation, it is not surprising that some of the methods by which aryl halides are prepared are not often applicable to the preparation of alkyl halides. One of these methods is direct halogenation of benzene or its derivatives with chlorine or bromine in the presence of a metal halide catalyst, as discussed in Section 20·4C.

Direct halogenation of monosubstituted benzene derivatives often gives a mixture of products, which may or may not contain practical amounts of the desired isomer. A more useful method of introducing a halogen substituent into a particular position of an aromatic ring involves the reaction of an aromatic primary amine with nitrous acid under conditions that lead to the formation of an aryldiazonium salt. Decomposition of the diazonium salt to an aryl chloride or bromide is effected by warming a solution of the diazonium salt with cuprous chloride or bromide in an excess of the corresponding halogen acid. The method is known as the **Sandmeyer reaction**.

o-toluidine

HCl, NaNO$_2$, H$_2$O
0°–5°

o-methylbenzenediazonium
chloride
(not isolated)

(CuCl)
HCl, 60°

o-chlorotoluene
74–79%

For the formation of aryl iodides from diazonium salts, the cuprous catalyst is not necessary since iodide ion is sufficient to cause decomposition of the diazonium salt. Both cuprous ion and iodide ion appear to be involved in an oxidation-reduction process at the diazo group that promotes the decomposition.

1-phenanthrylamine

1.   NaNO$_2$, H$_2$SO$_4$, H$_2$O
2.   KI–H$_2$O

1-iodophenanthrene
53%

Aryl fluorides may also be prepared from diazonium salts if the procedure is slightly modified. The amine is diazotized in the usual way; then fluoboric acid or a fluoborate salt is added, which usually causes precipitation of a sparingly soluble diazonium fluoborate. The salt is collected and thoroughly dried, then carefully heated to the decomposition point, the products being an aryl fluoride, nitrogen, and boron trifluoride.

$$C_6H_5N_2\overset{\oplus}{}\overset{\ominus}{BF_4} \xrightarrow{\text{heat}} C_6H_5F + N_2 + BF_3$$

The reaction is known as the **Schiemann reaction**. An example (which gives a rather better than usual yield) follows:

4-bromo-1-
naphthylamine

1. NaNO$_2$, H$_2$SO$_4$
2. HBF$_4$

4-bromonaphthalene
-1-diazonium fluoborate

150°–155°

1-fluoro-4-
bromonaphthalene
97%

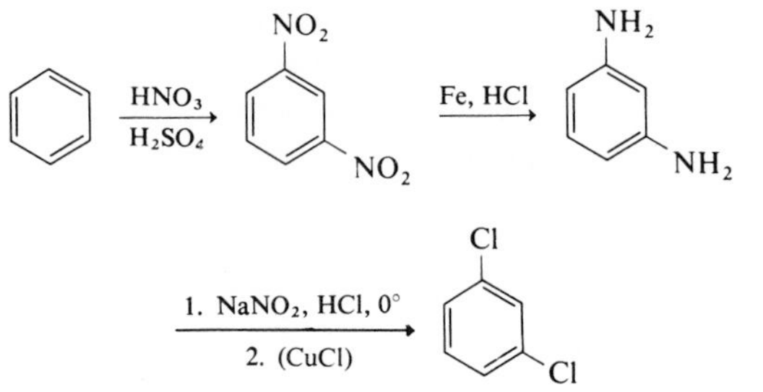

Figure 21·1   Preparation of *m*-dichlorobenzene from benzene. The nitration reaction gives very largely *meta* substitution (see Table 20·6) and the *m*-dinitro product is easily purified by crystallization.

The arylamines necessary for the preparation of aryl halides by the Sandmeyer and Schiemann reactions are usually prepared by reduction of the corresponding nitro compounds (see Chapter 22), which in turn are usually obtained by direct nitration of an aromatic compound. For example, although *m*-dichlorobenzene cannot be prepared conveniently by direct chlorination of benzene, it can be made by dinitration of benzene followed by reduction and the Sandmeyer reaction (Figure 21·1). In connection with this synthesis, it should be noted that tetrazotization (double diazotization) of 1,2- and 1,4-diaminobenzene derivatives is not as easy to achieve as with the 1,3 compound, because the 1,2- and 1,4-diaminobenzenes are very easily oxidized.

21·3   reactions of aryl halides

A. ORGANOMETALLIC COMPOUNDS FROM ARYL HALIDES

Grignard reagents can be prepared with fair ease from aryl bromides or iodides and magnesium metal.

$$C_6H_5Br + Mg \xrightarrow{\text{ether}} C_6H_5MgBr$$
$$\text{phenylmagnesium bromide}$$

Chlorobenzene and other aryl chlorides are usually unreactive unless added to the magnesium admixed with a more reactive halide. 1,2-Dibromoethane is particularly useful as the second halide because it is converted to ethene, which does not then contaminate the products, and it continually produces a fresh magnesium surface, which is sufficiently active to be able to react with the aryl chloride.

The reactions of arylmagnesium halides are analogous to those of alkylmagnesium halides (see Chapter 9) and require little further comment.

Aryllithiums can usually be prepared by direct reaction of lithium metal with chloro or bromo compounds.

$$C_6H_5Cl + 2 Li \xrightarrow{\text{ether}} C_6H_5Li + LiCl$$
phenyllithium

As with the Grignard reagents, aryllithiums react as you might expect by analogy with alkyllithiums.

B. NUCLEOPHILIC DISPLACEMENT REACTIONS OF ACTIVATED ARYL HALIDES

While the simple aryl halides are inert to the usual nucleophilic reagents, considerable activation is produced by strongly electron-attracting substituents, provided these are located in either the *ortho* or *para* positions, or both. As one example, the displacement of chloride ion from 1-chloro-2,4-dinitrobenzene by dimethylamine occurs measurably fast in ethanol solution at room temperature. Under the same conditions, chlorobenzene completely fails to react; thus, the activating influence of the two nitro groups easily amounts to a factor of at least 10^8.

A related reaction is that of 2,4-dinitrofluorobenzene with peptides and proteins, which is used for analysis of the N-terminal amino acids in polypeptide chains. (See Section 17·3A.)

In general, the reactions of activated aryl halides bear a close resemblance to S_N2 displacement reactions of aliphatic halides. The same nucleophilic reagents are effective (e.g., $CH_3O^\ominus$, $HO^\ominus$, and RNH_2); the reactions are second order overall—first order in halide and first order in nucleophile. For a given halide, the more nucleophilic the attacking reagent, the faster is the reaction. There must be more than a subtle difference in mechanism, however, since an aryl halide is unable to pass through the same type of transition state as an alkyl halide in S_N2 displacements.

A generally accepted mechanism of nucleophilic aromatic substitution visualizes the reaction as proceeding in two steps closely analogous to those postulated for electrophilic substitution (Chapter 20). The first step involves attack of the nucleophile $Y:^\ominus$ at the carbon bearing the halogen substituent to form an intermediate anion [2]. The aromatic system is of course destroyed on forming the anion, and the hybridization of carbon at the reaction site changes from sp^2 to sp^3.

[2]

In the second step, loss of an anion, $X^\ominus$ or $Y^\ominus$, regenerates an aromatic system, and, if $X^\ominus$ is lost, the reaction is one of overall nucleophilic displacement of X for Y.

In the case of a neutral nucleophilic reagent, Y or HY, the reaction sequence would be the same except for the necessary adjustments in charge of the intermediate.

Formation of [2] is highly unfavorable for the simple phenyl halides, even with the most powerful nucleophilic reagents. It should be clear how electron-attracting groups, $-NO_2$, $-NO$, $-C\equiv N$, $-N_2^\oplus$, and so on, can facilitate nucleophilic substitution by this mechanism through stabilization of the intermediate. The effect of such substituents can be illustrated in the case of p-bromonitrobenzene and its reaction with methoxide ion. The structure of the reaction intermediate can be described in terms of the resonance structures [3a] through [3d]. Of these [3d] is especially important because the negative charge can be located on oxygen, an electronegative atom.

[3b]   [3c]   [3d]

The reason that substituents in the *meta* positions have much less effect on the reactivity of an aryl halide is the substituent's inability to contribute directly to the delocalization of the negative charge in the ring; no structures can be written analogous to [3d].

C. ELIMINATION-ADDITION MECHANISM OF NUCLEOPHILIC AROMATIC SUBSTITUTION

The reactivity of aryl halides such as the halobenzenes and halotoluenes is exceedingly low toward nucleophilic reagents that normally effect smooth displacements with alkyl halides and activated aryl halides. Substitutions, however, do occur under sufficiently forcing conditions involving either high temperatures or very strong bases. For example, the reaction of chlorobenzene with sodium hydroxide solution at temperatures around 340° is an important commercial process for the production of phenol.

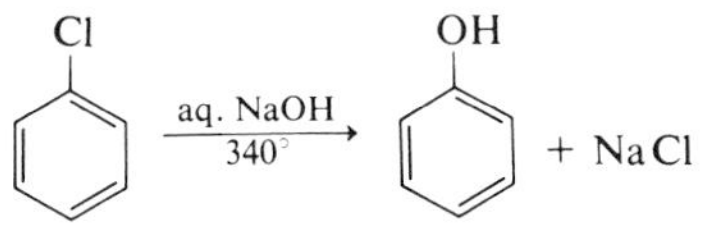

Also, aryl chlorides, bromides, and iodides can be converted to arylamines by amide ions, which are very strong bases. In fact, the reaction of potassium amide with bromobenzene is extremely rapid, even at temperatures as low as −33°, with liquid ammonia as solvent.

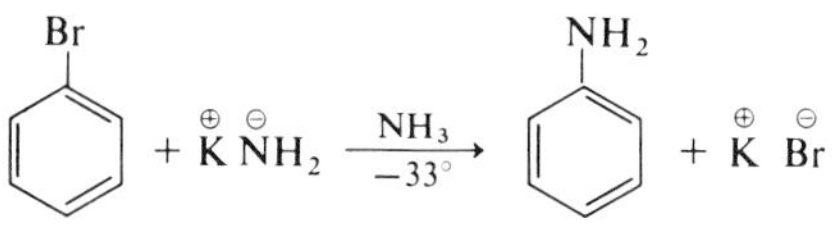

Displacement reactions of this type, however, differ from the previously discussed displacements of activated aryl halides in that rearrangement often occurs. That is to say, the entering group does not always take up the same position on the ring as that vacated by the halogen substituent. For example, the hydrolysis of p-chlorotoluene at 340° gives an equimolar mixture of m- and p-cresols.

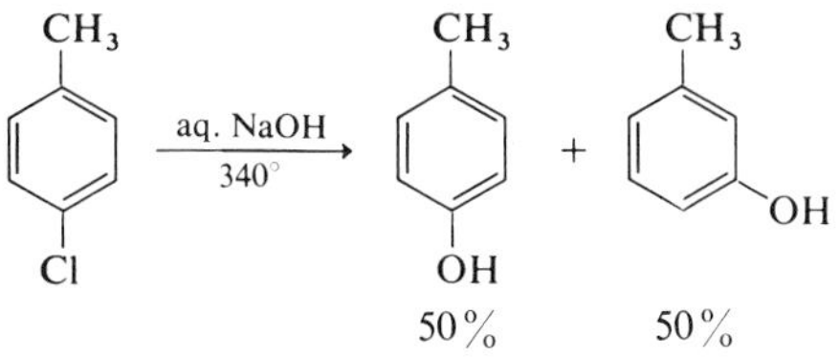

Even more striking is the exclusive formation of m-aminoanisole in the amination of o-chloroanisole.

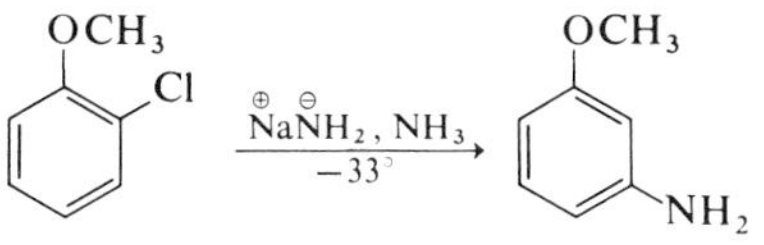

Mechanisms of this type have been widely studied, and much evidence has accumulated in support of a stepwise process, which proceeds first by base-catalyzed elimination of hydrogen halide (HX) from the aryl halide. This first reaction resembles the E2 elimination reactions of alkyl halides discussed earlier (Section 8·12) except that the abstraction of the proton appears to precede loss of the bromide ion. The reaction is illustrated below for the amination of bromobenzene.

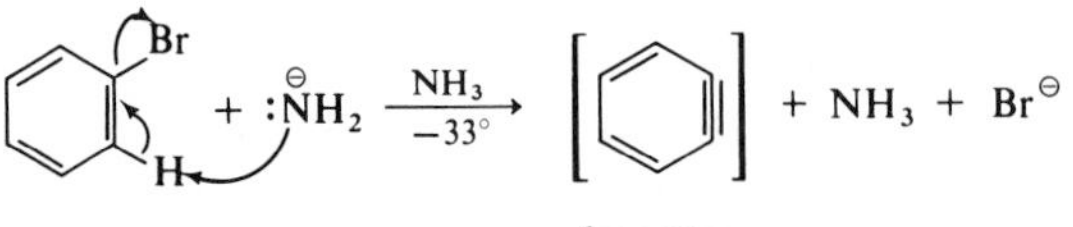

benzyne
[4]

The product of the elimination reaction is a highly reactive intermediate [4] called **benzyne**, or **dehydrobenzene**. Its formula is C_6H_4 and it differs from benzene in having an extra bond between two *ortho* carbons. Benzyne reacts rapidly with any available nucleophile, in this example the solvent ammonia, to give an addition product.

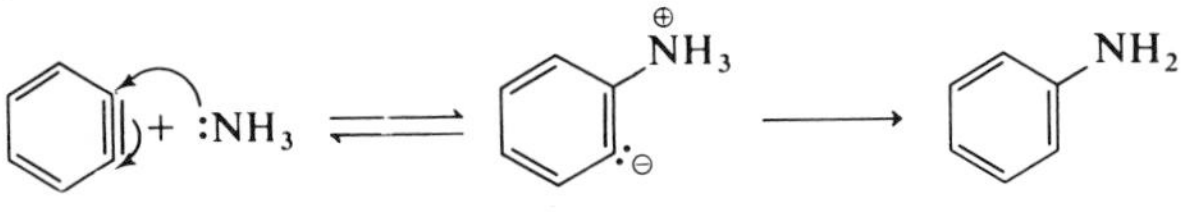

[4]   aniline

The occurrence of rearrangements in these reactions follows from the possibility of the nucleophile's attacking the intermediate at one or the other of the carbons of the extra bond. With benzyne itself, the symmetry of the molecule is such that no rearrangement would be detected. However, this symmetry is destroyed if one of the ring carbons is labeled with ^{14}C isotope, so that two isotopically different products can be formed. Studies of the amination of halobenzenes labeled with ^{14}C at the 1 position have demonstrated that essentially equal amounts of 1- and 2-^{14}C-labeled anilines are produced, as predicted by the elimination-addition mechanism.

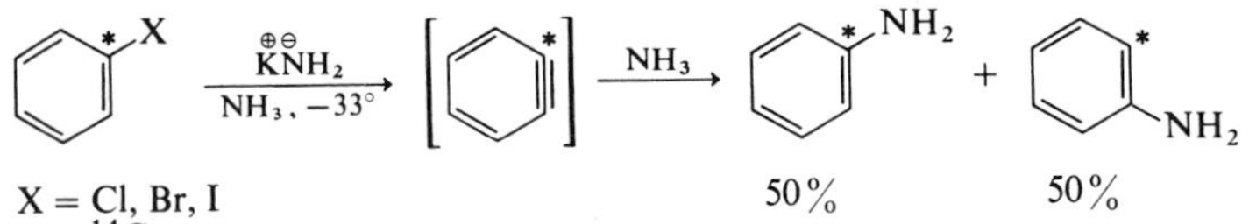

X = Cl, Br, I   50%   50%
* = ^{14}C

21·4 organochlorine pesticides

The general term *pesticide* includes insecticides, herbicides, and fungicides. A number of the most important pesticides are chlorinated aromatic hydrocarbons or their derivatives (Figure 21·2). Prodigious quantities have been used throughout the world in the past 25 years with, as we now know, tragic consequences.

Chlorinated hydrocarbons such as DDT have low water solubility but high solubility in nonpolar media such as fatty tissue. Their slow rate of decomposition causes them to accumulate in nature, and predatory birds and animals are particularly vulnerable. The food chain running from plankton to small fish to bigger fish to predatory birds results in a magnification of the residue concentration at each stage. As a result the world's population of falcons, hawks, and eagles has dropped drastically in the past decade. A remarkable

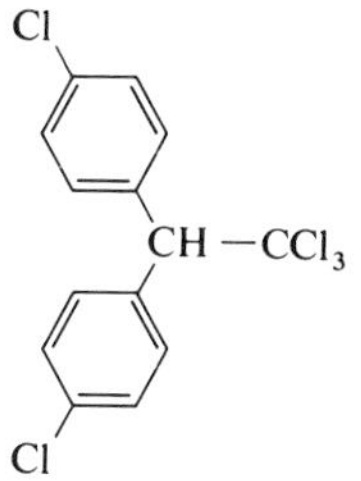

1,1,1-trichloro-2,2-
bis(*p*-chlorophenyl)ethane (DDT)
an insecticide

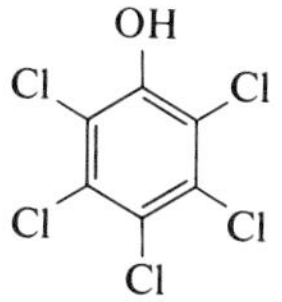

pentachlorophenol (PCP)
a fungicide

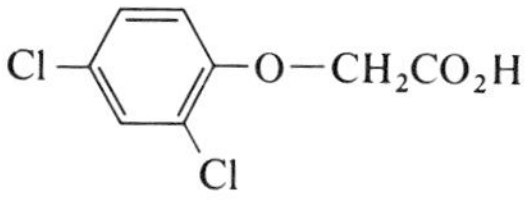

2,4-dichlorophenoxyacetic acid
a herbicide

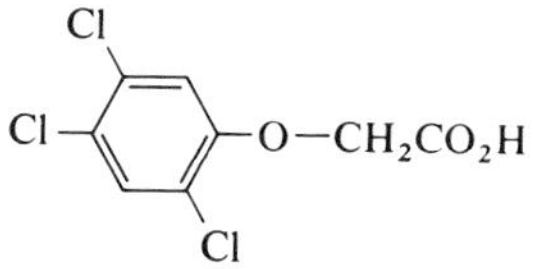

2,4,5-trichlorophenoxyacetic acid
a herbicide

Figure 21·2   Some organochlorine pesticides. The abbreviation DDT arises from the semisystematic name *dichlorodiphenyltrichloroethane*. *Bis, tris,* and *tetrakis* are used in place of *di, tri,* and *tetra* for substituents whose *names* contain two parts; thus, the compound *p*-CH₃C₆H₄CH₂C₆H₄CH₃-*p* can be named either di-*p*-tolylmethane or bis (*p*-methylphenyl)methane.

effect of high pesticide residues in these birds is extreme fragility of the shells of their eggs. Experiments have shown that DDE [5], the principal decomposition product of DDT, causes this effect when present in very small amount. It is believed to inhibit the action of the enzyme carbonic anhydrase which controls the supply of calcium available for shell formation.

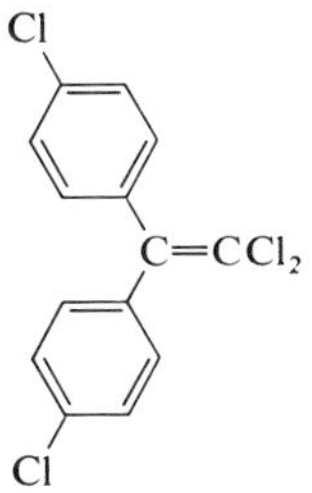

DDE, 1,1-dichloro-2,2-bis(*p*-chlorophenyl)ethene
[5]

It has been estimated that there are now a billion pounds of DDE spread throughout the world ecosystem and traces of it have been found in animals everywhere, including the Arctic and Antarctic. Even though the use of DDT has now been severely curtailed by legislation it will take many years for the level of DDE to decrease to tolerable levels. Man, like predatory birds, is at the top of a food chain and human beings now carry in their fatty tissue 10 to 20 ppm of chlorinated hydrocarbon insecticides and their conversion products. The effect on human health is still not known with certainty.

The herbicides 2,4-D[6] and 2,4,5-T[7] have come under fire recently because their indiscriminate use as defoliants threatens the ecology of large areas. Furthermore, 2,4,5-T is suspected of being a teratogen (a fetus-deforming agent). Mice given 2,4,5-T in the early stages of pregnancy have a high incidence of fetal mortality and there is a high incidence of abnormalities in the survivors. There is some indication that 2,3,7,8-tetrachlorodibenzodioxin [8], sometimes present as an impurity in commercial samples of 2,4,5-T, may actually be the teratogenic agent.

[6]   [7]   2,3,7,8-tetrachlorodibenzodioxin
                      [8]

summary

Aryl halides such as bromobenzene, C_6H_5Br, are unreactive to most nucleophiles unless activating groups are present in the ring. Benzyl halides such as $C_6H_5CH_2Br$, on the other hand, react readily by nucleophilic displacement.

Aryl halides can be prepared from benzene by direct halogenation or from aniline by the Sandmeyer reaction.

Grignard reagents can be prepared from aryl halides and their reactions are analogous to those of alkylmagnesium compounds.

A halogen which is *ortho* or *para* to one or more nitro groups is activated toward nucleophilic substitution.

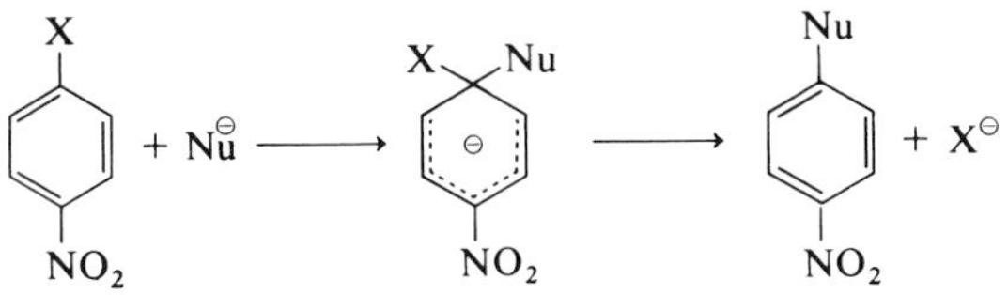

Those aryl halides that lack activating groups may suffer displacement of halogen under forcing conditions via an elimination-addition reaction.

$$C_6H_5Br \xrightarrow[\text{(}-H\oplus\text{)}]{NH_2\ominus} C_6H_4Br\ominus \xrightarrow[\text{(}-Br\ominus\text{)}]{} C_6H_4 \xrightarrow{NH_3} C_6H_5NH_2$$

The amino group does not necessarily occupy the position vacated by the bromine atom since the intermediate, benzyne (C_6H_4), is symmetrical and ammonia can add to it in either direction.

Many chlorinated aromatic hydrocarbons or their derivatives are widely used as pesticides.

exercises

21·1 Suggest a feasible synthesis of each of the following compounds based on benzene as the starting material:

a. 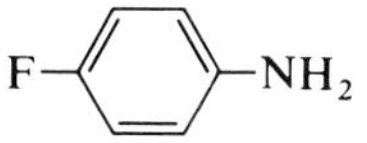 F—⟨benzene⟩—NH$_2$

b. 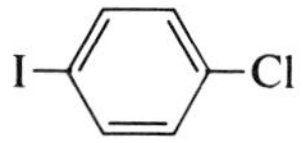 I—⟨benzene⟩—Cl

c. 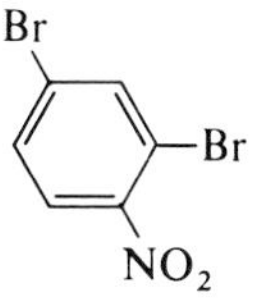 ⟨benzene with Br top, Br right, NO$_2$ bottom⟩

d. 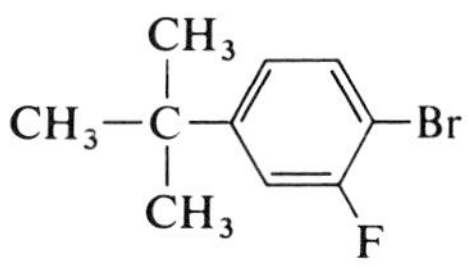 CH_3—C(CH$_3$)(CH$_3$)—⟨benzene with Br right, F bottom⟩

21·2 Suggest a method for preparing the following compounds from the indicated starting materials and any other necessary reagents:

    a. $p\text{-ClC}_6H_4C(CH_3)_2OH$ from benzene
    b. 1-naphthoic acid from naphthalene

    c. 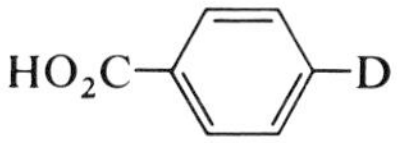 HO_2C—⟨benzene⟩—D from toluene

21·3 Why is the following mechanism of S_N2 substitution of an alkyl halide unlikely for aryl halides?

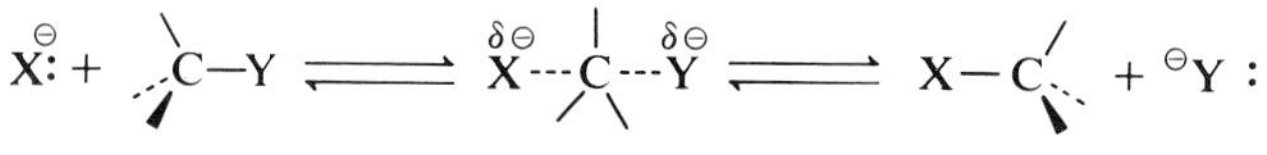

$$X:^\ominus + \underset{\diagdown}{\overset{\diagup}{C}}\text{—}Y \rightleftharpoons X^{\delta\ominus}\text{---}\underset{\diagup}{\overset{\diagdown}{C}}\text{---}Y^{\delta\ominus} \rightleftharpoons X\text{—}\underset{\diagdown}{\overset{\diagup}{C}} + {}^\ominus Y:$$

transition state

21-4 *a.* Write resonance structures analogous to structures [3a] through [3d] to show the activating effect of $-C\equiv N$, $-SO_2R$, and $-CF_3$ groups in nucleophilic substitution of the corresponding *p*-substituted chlorobenzenes.

   b. How would you expect the introduction of methyl groups *ortho* to the activating group to affect the reactivity of *p*-bromonitrobenzene and *p*-bromocyanobenzene toward ethoxide ion?

21-5 Would you expect *p*-bromonitrobenzene or (*p*-bromophenyl)-trimethylammonium chloride to be more reactive in bimolecular replacement of bromine by ethoxide ion? Why?

21-6 Would you expect *p*-chloroanisole to be more or less reactive than chlorobenzene toward methoxide ion? Explain.

21-7 Devise a synthesis of each of the following compounds from the indicated starting materials:

   a. $H_2N-\!\!\left\langle\bigcirc\right\rangle\!\!-O-C_2H_5$ from *p*-nitrochlorobenzene

   b.

   from toluene

   c. $O_2N-\!\!\left\langle\bigcirc\right\rangle\!\!-N\!\!\left\langle\bigcirc\right\rangle$ from benzene

21-8 In the hydrolysis of chlorobenzene-1-^{14}C with 4 M aqueous sodium hydroxide at 340°, the products are 58% phenol-1-^{14}C and 42% phenol-2-[14]C. Calculate the percentage of reaction proceeding (*a*) by an elimination-addition mechanism, and (*b*) by direct nucleophilic displacement. (You may disregard the effect of isotopic substitution on the reaction rates.) Would you expect the amount of direct displacement to increase or decrease if the reaction were carried out (*a*) at 240°, and (*b*) in aqueous sodium acetate in place of aqueous sodium hydroxide? Give the reasons on which you base your answers.

21-9 Explain the following observations:

   a. 2,6-Dimethylchlorobenzene does not react with potassium amide in liquid ammonia.

   b. Fluorobenzene, labeled with deuterium in the 2 and 6 positions, undergoes rapid exchange of deuterium for hydrogen in the presence of potassium amide in liquid ammonia, but does not form aniline.

21·10   Predict the principal product of the following reaction:

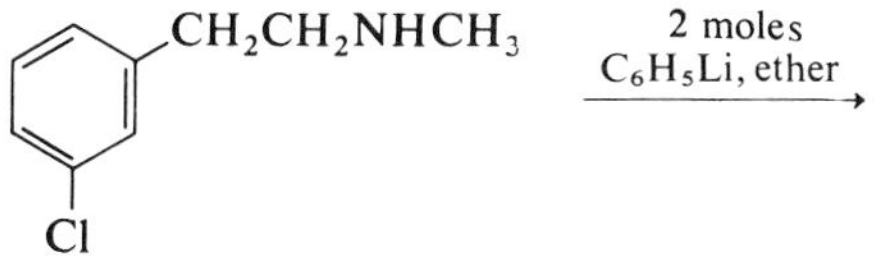

$$\underset{\text{C}_6\text{H}_5\text{Li, ether}}{\xrightarrow{\text{2 moles}}}$$

21·11   Give for each of the following pairs of compounds a chemical test, preferably a test tube reaction, that will distinguish between the two compounds. Write a structural formula for each compound and equations for the reactions involved.

   a.   chlorobenzene and benzyl chloride
   b.   *p*-nitrochlorobenzene and *m*-nitrochlorobenzene
   c.   *p*-chloroacetophenone and α-chloroacetophenone
   d.   *p*-ethylbenzenesulfonyl chloride and ethyl *p*-chlorobenzenesulfonate
   e.   *p*-bromoaniline hydrochloride and *p*-chloroaniline hydrobromide

21·12   Show by means of equations how each of the following substances might be synthesized starting from the indicated materials. Specify reagents and approximate reaction conditions. Several steps may be required.

   a.   1,3,5-tribromobenzene from benzene
   b.   *p*-fluorobenzoic acid from toluene
   c.   *m*-bromoaniline from benzene
   d.   *p*-nitrobenzoic acid from toluene
   e.   *m*-dibromobenzene from benzene
   f.   *m*-nitroacetophenone from benzene
   g.   2,4,6-trinitrobenzoic acid from toluene
   h.   benzyl *m*-nitrobenzoate from toluene

21·13   Write a structural formula for a compound that fits the following description:

   a.   an aromatic halogen compound that reacts with sodium iodide in acetone but not with aqueous silver nitrate solution
   b.   an aryl bromide that cannot undergo substitution by the elimination-addition (benzyne) mechanism
   c.   the least reactive of the monobromomononitronaphthalenes toward ethoxide ion in ethanol

21·14   Explain why the substitution reactions of α-halonaphthalenes in Equations 21·1 through 21·3 show no significant variation in the percentage of α- and β-naphthyl derivatives produced either with the nature of the halogen substituent or with the nucleophilic reagent.

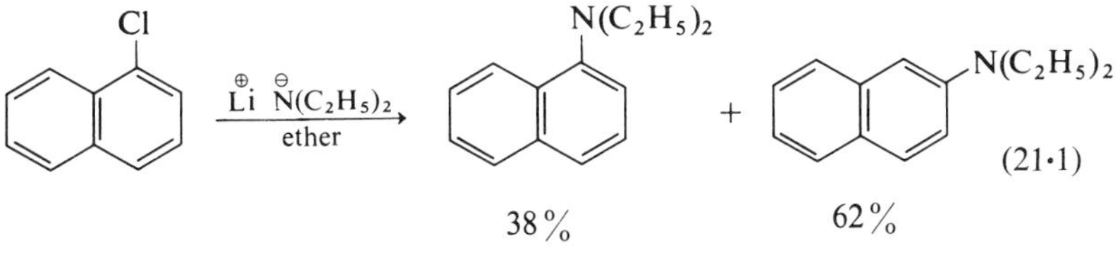

$$38\% \qquad\qquad 62\%$$

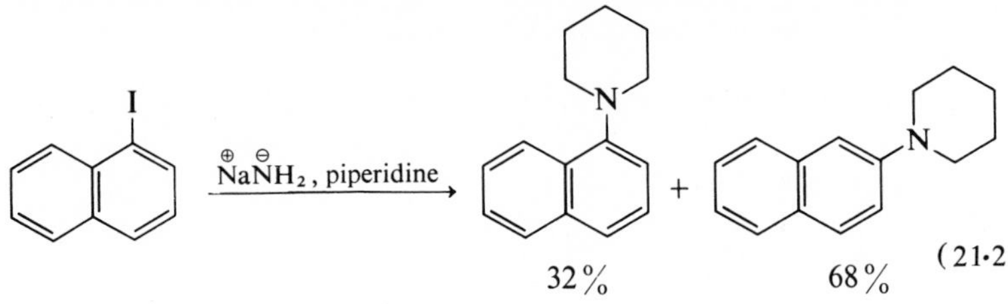

(21·2)

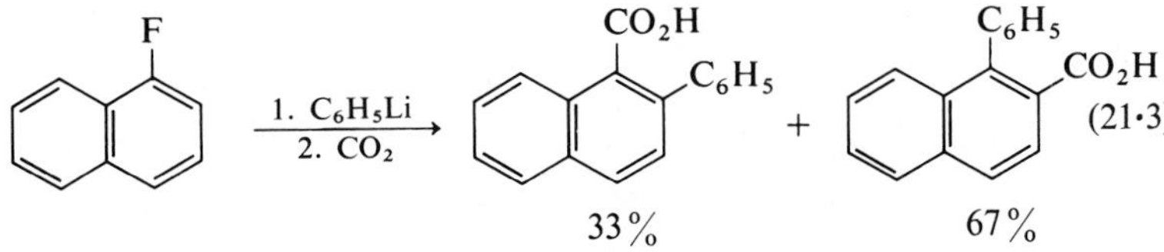

(21·3)

21·15   The conversion of DDT to DDE (Section 21·4) is catalyzed by the enzyme
DDT dehydrochlorinase, which, as you might expect, is a protein. What
groups normally present as substituents on protein chains (Table 17·1) might
aid the simultaneous removal of a proton and a chloride ion?

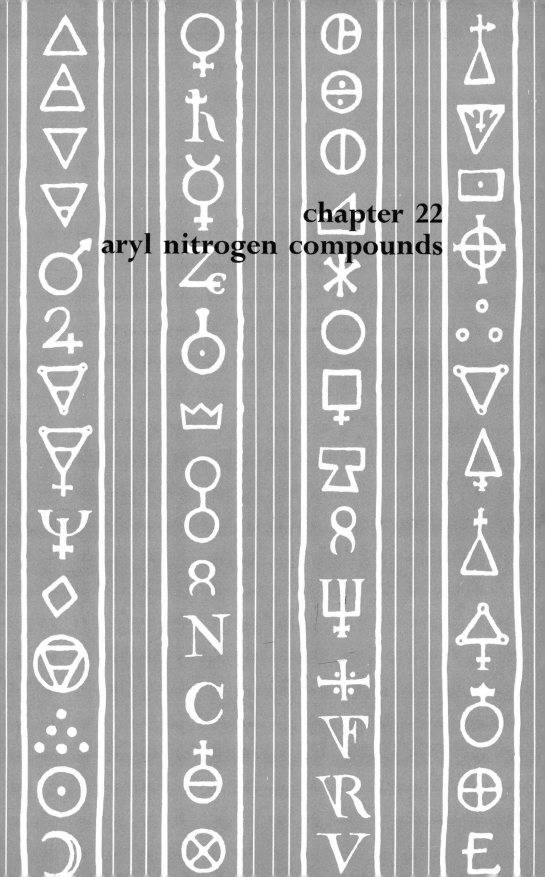

chapter 22
aryl nitrogen compounds

Many of the properties of aryl halides, such as their lack of reactivity in nucleophilic substitution reactions, are closely related to the properties of vinyl halides. Attempts to make similar comparisons between vinyl oxygen and nitrogen compounds and the related aryl oxygen and nitrogen compounds are often thwarted by the unavailability of suitable vinyl analogs. Thus, while vinyl ethers are easily accessible, most vinyl alcohols and primary or secondary amines are unstable with respect to their tautomers with $C=O$ and $C=N$ bonds. (The enol forms of 1,3-dicarbonyl compounds are notable exceptions; see Sections 12·6 and 16·1D.)

$$\overset{\backslash}{\underset{/}{C}}=\overset{/}{\underset{\backslash}{C}}\!\!-\!\!N\!\!-\!\!H \longrightarrow -\overset{|}{\underset{|}{C}}-\overset{H}{\underset{}{\overset{|}{C}}}\!=\!\!N\overset{/}{} \qquad \Delta H = -16 \text{ kcal}$$

$$\overset{\backslash}{\underset{/}{C}}=\overset{/}{\underset{\backslash}{C}}\!\!-\!\!O\!\!-\!\!H \longrightarrow -\overset{|}{\underset{|}{C}}-\overset{H}{\underset{}{\overset{|}{C}}}\!=\!\!O \qquad \Delta H = -18 \text{ kcal}$$

That the same situation does not hold for most aromatic amino and hydroxy compounds is a consequence of the stability of the benzene ring. This stability would be almost completely lost by tautomerization. For aniline, the stabilization energy based on its heat of combustion is 41 kcal/mole, and we can expect a stabilization energy (S.E.) of about 5 kcal/mole for its tautomer, 2,4-cyclohexadienimine. Thus the ΔH of tautomerization is unfavorable by $(41 - 16 - 5) = 20$ kcal/mole.

$$\Delta H_{(calc.)} = 20 \text{ kcal}$$

S.E. = 41 kcal   S.E. ~ 5 kcal

Phenol is similarly more stable than the corresponding ketone by about 17 kcal/mole.

$$\Delta H_{(calc.)} = 17 \text{ kcal}$$

S.E. = 40 kcal   S.E. ~ 5 kcal

Since aromatic amino and hydroxy compounds have special stabilization, their behavior is not expected to parallel in all respects that of the less stable vinylamines and vinyl alcohols. Nonetheless, similar reactions are often encountered. Both enols and phenols are acidic; they react readily with halogens, and their anions undergo either C or O alkylation with organic halides. The qualitative differences observed in these reactions will be considered in more detail later in this chapter (see also Chapter 23); but, as already indicated, such differences can usually be accounted for in terms of the stabilization of the aromatic ring.

aromatic nitro compounds

22·1   synthesis of nitro compounds

The most generally useful way to introduce a nitro group into an aromatic nucleus is by direct nitration, as previously discussed (Section 20·4B). This method is obviously unsatisfactory when the orientation determined by substituent groups does not lead to the desired isomer. Thus, *p*-dinitrobenzene and *p*-nitrobenzoic acid cannot be prepared by direct nitration, since nitrations of nitrobenzene and benzoic acid give practically exclusively *m*-dinitrobenzene and *m*-nitrobenzoic acid, respectively. To prepare the *para* isomers, less direct routes are necessary. The usual stratagem is to use benzene derivatives with substituent groups that produce the desired orientation on nitration and then to make the necessary modifications in these groups to produce the final product. Thus, *p*-dinitrobenzene can be prepared from aniline by nitration of acetanilide (acetylaminobenzene), followed by hydrolysis to *p*-nitroaniline and replacement of amino by nitro through the action of nitrite ion, in the presence of cuprous salts, on the corresponding diazonium salt (see Section 22·8). Alternatively, the amino group of *p*-nitroaniline can be oxidized to a nitro group by trifluoroperacetic acid. In this synthesis, acetanilide is nitrated in preference to aniline itself, since not only is aniline easily oxidized by nitric acid, but the reaction leads to extensive *meta* substitution by nitration involving the anilinium ion. Another route to *p*-nitroaniline is to nitrate chlorobenzene and subsequently replace the chlorine with ammonia. See Figure 22·1 for representation of these reactions.

The nitrations mentioned give mixtures of *ortho* and *para* isomers, but these are usually easy to separate by distillation or crystallization. The same approach can be used to synthesize *p*-nitrobenzoic acid. The methyl group of toluene directs nitration preferentially to the *para* position, and subsequent oxidation with chromic acid yields *p*-nitrobenzoic acid.

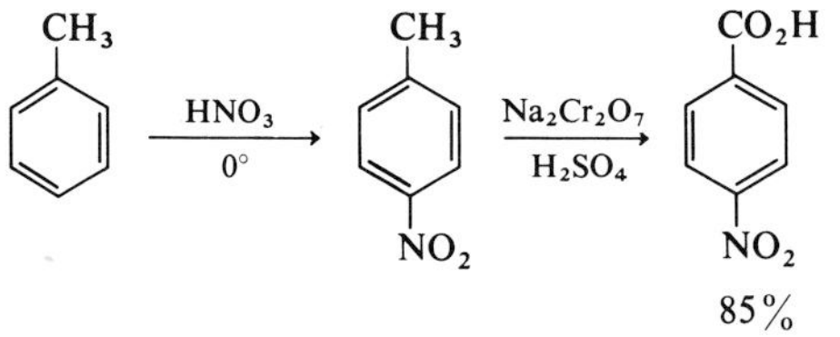

In some cases, it may be necessary to have an activating group to facilitate substitution, which would otherwise be very difficult. The preparation of 1,3,5-trinitrobenzene provides a good example—direct substitution of *m*-dinitrobenzene requires long heating with nitric acid in fuming sulfuric acid. However, toluene is more readily converted to the trinitro derivative and this substance, on oxidation (Section 24·1) and decarboxylation (Section 13·6), yields 1,3,5-trinitrobenzene.

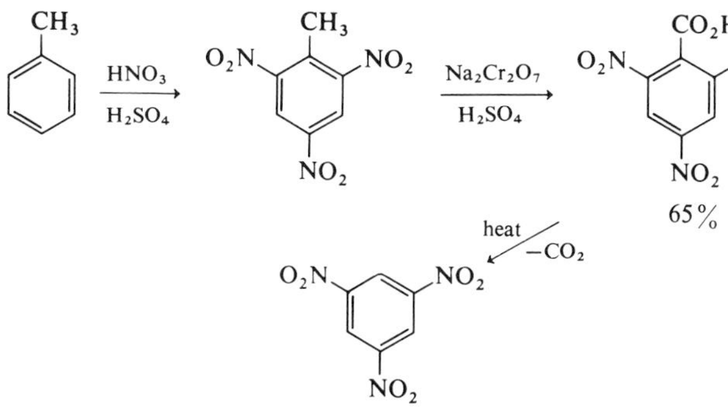

Acylamino groups are also useful activating groups and have the advantage that the amino groups obtained after hydrolysis of the acyl function can be

Figure 22·1   Schemes for the preparation of *p*-dinitrobenzene from aniline or chlorobenzene.

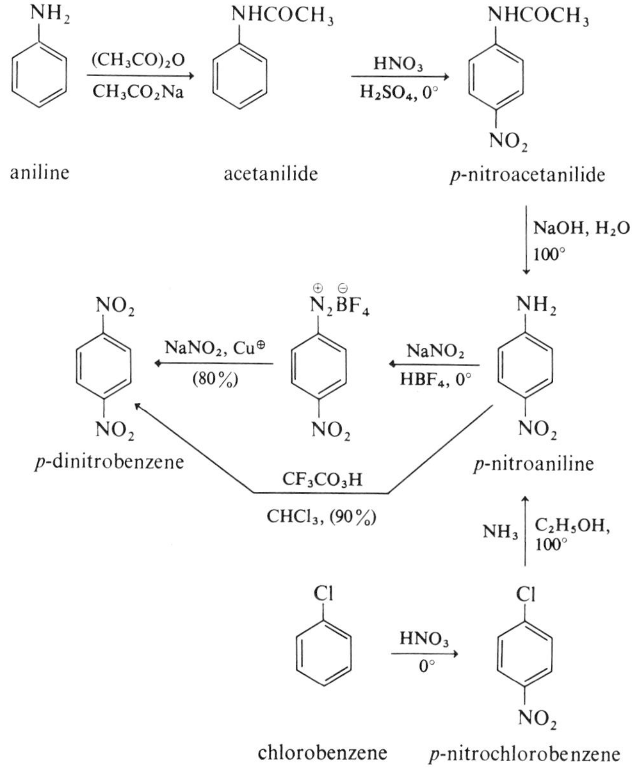

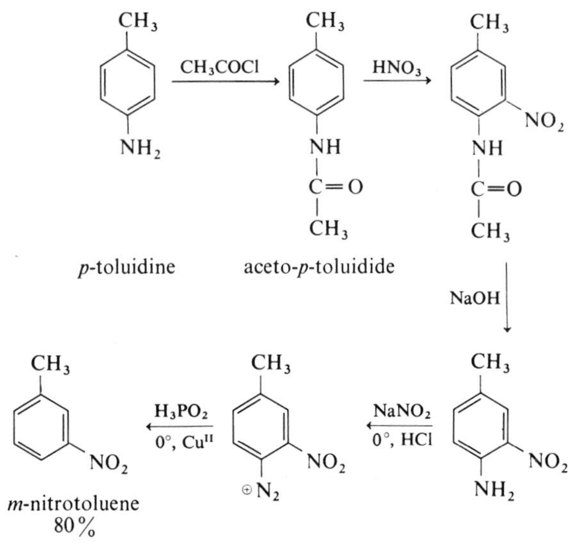

Figure 22·2 Preparation of *m*-nitrotoluene starting with *p*-aminotoluene (*p*-toluidine).

removed from an aromatic ring by reduction of the corresponding diazonium salt with hypophosphorous acid, preferably in the presence of copper ions. An example is the preparation of *m*-nitrotoluene from *p*-aminotoluene (*p*-toluidine) via 4-acetylaminotoluene (aceto-*p*-toluidide) as shown in Figure 22·2.

The acetylamino derivatives of the amines are usually used in the nitration step in preference to the amines themselves because, as mentioned in connection with the formation of *p*-nitroaniline, they are less susceptible to oxidation by nitric acid and give the desired orientation.

The physical properties and spectra of aliphatic and aromatic nitro compounds were touched on briefly (Section 16·5). Nitrobenzene itself is a pale-yellow liquid (bp 210°), which should be handled with care because like many nitro compounds it is toxic when inhaled or when absorbed through the skin.

A nitro group usually has a rather strong influence on the properties and reactions of other substituents on an aromatic ring, particularly when it is in an *ortho* or *para* position. A strong activating influence in displacement reactions of aromatic halogens was discussed in the preceding chapter (Section 21·3B). We shall see later how nitro groups make aromatic amines weaker bases and phenols stronger acids.

22·2 *reduction of aromatic nitro compounds*

The most important synthetic reactions of nitro groups involve reduction, particularly to the amine level. In fact, aromatic amines are normally prepared by nitration followed by reduction. They may also be prepared by halogenation followed by amination. But since amination of halides requires the use of either amide salts or ammonia and high temperatures, which often lead to rearrangements (Section 21·3C), the nitration-reduction sequence is usually preferred. Direct amination of aromatic compounds is not generally feasible.

A. REDUCTION OF NITRO COMPOUNDS TO AMINES

The reduction of nitrobenzene to aniline requires six equivalents of reducing agent and appears to proceed through the following principal stages:

| nitrobenzene | nitrosobenzene | N-phenylhydroxylamine |

aniline

Despite the complexity of the reaction, reduction of aromatic nitro compounds to amines occurs smoothly in *acid* solution with a variety of reducing agents of which tin metal and hydrochloric acid or stannous chloride are often favored on a laboratory scale. Hydrogenation is also useful but is strongly exothermic and must be carried out with care.

Ammonium (or sodium) sulfide has the interesting property of reducing one nitro group in a dinitro compound much faster than the other. It is

not always easy to predict which of two nitro groups will be reduced more readily.

In contrast to the reduction of 2,4-dinitroaniline, reduction of 2,4-dinitrotoluene leads to preferential reduction of the 4-nitro group.

B. REDUCTION OF NITRO COMPOUNDS IN NEUTRAL AND ALKALINE SOLUTION

In neutral or alkaline solution, the reducing power of some of the usual reducing agents toward nitrobenzene is less than in acid solution. A typical reagent is zinc, which gives aniline in the presence of excess acid, but produces N-phenylhydroxylamine when buffered with ammonium chloride.

Nitrosobenzene is too easily reduced to be prepared by direct reduction of nitrobenzene and is usually made by oxidation of N-phenylhydroxylamine with chromic acid.

Nitrosobenzene exists as a colorless dimer in the crystalline state. When the solid is melted or dissolved in organic solvents, the dimer undergoes reversible dissociation to the green monomer (see Section 16·4).

Reduction of nitrobenzene with methanol in the presence of sodium hydroxide produces azoxybenzene. The methanol is oxidized to formaldehyde.

azoxybenzene

The reason that azoxybenzene is produced instead of aniline is partly because methanol in alkali is a less powerful reducing agent than tin and hydrochloric acid. Also, in the presence of alkali, the intermediate reduction products can condense with one another; thus azoxybenzene probably arises in the reduction by a base-induced reaction of nitrosobenzene with N-phenylhydroxylamine. In fact, azoxybenzene can be prepared separately from these same reagents. This condensation reaction does not occur readily in acid

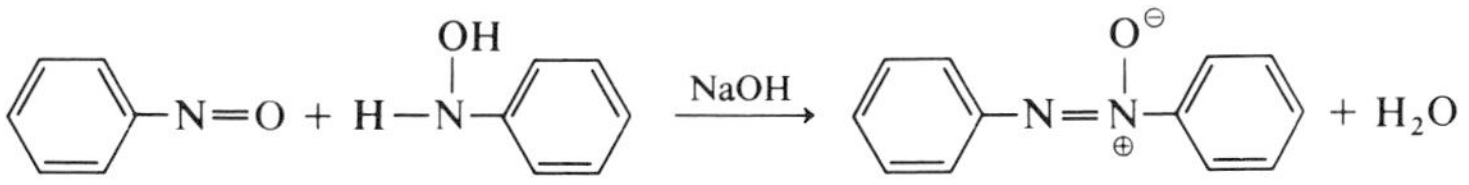

solution; furthermore, azoxybenzene is reduced to aniline by tin and hydrochloric acid.

Reduction of nitrobenzene in the presence of alkali with stronger reducing agents than methanol produces azobenzene and hydrazobenzene. Both of these compounds are reduction products of azoxybenzene and can be formed from azoxybenzene as well as from nitrobenzene by the same reducing reagents (Scheme I).

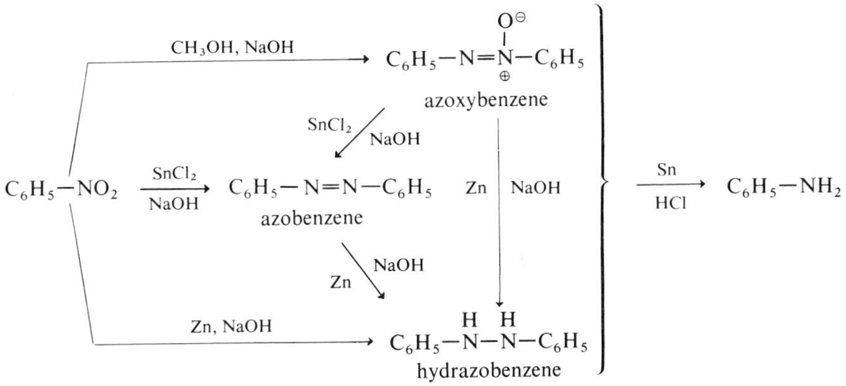

SCHEME I

When hydrazobenzene is allowed to stand in strong acid solution, it undergoes an extraordinary rearrangement to form the technically important dye intermediate, benzidine (4,4'-diaminobiphenyl).

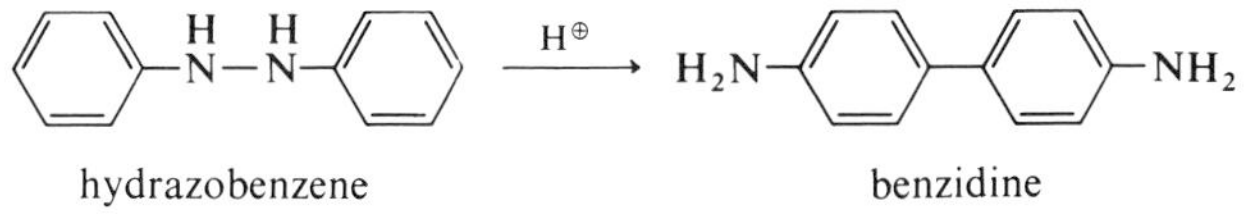

hydrazobenzene   benzidine

22·3 polynitro compounds

A number of aromatic polynitro compounds have important uses as high explosives (Section 16·5). Of these 2,4,6-trinitrotoluene (TNT), 2,4,6-trinitrophenol (picric acid), and N,2,4,6-tetranitro-N-methylaniline (tetryl) are particularly important. 1,3,5-Trinitrobenzene has excellent properties as an explosive but is difficult to prepare by direct nitration of benzene (Section 22·1).

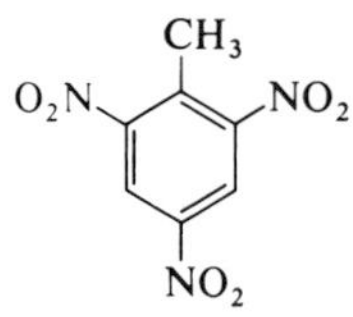

2,4,6-trinitrotoluene   2,4,6-trinitrophenol   N,2,4,6-tetranitro-
(TNT)   (picric acid)   N-methylaniline
                                                          (tetryl)

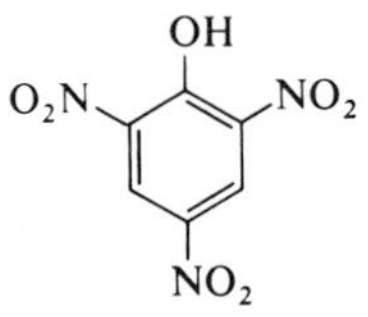

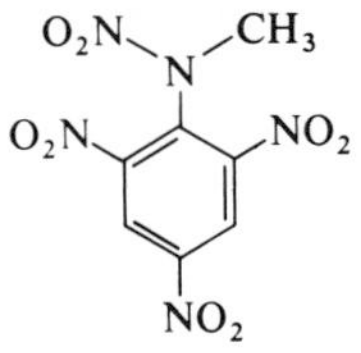

The trinitro derivatives of 3-*t*-butyltoluene and 1,3-dimethyl-5-*t*-butyl-benzene possess musklike odors and have been used as ingredients of cheap perfumes and soaps.

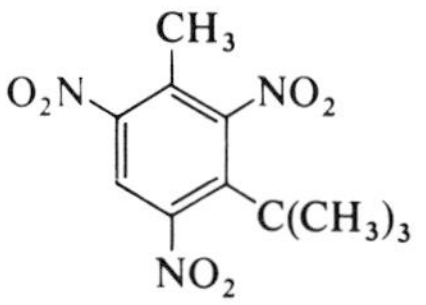

1-methyl-3-*t*-butyl-   1,3-dimethyl-5-*t*-butyl-
2,4,6-trinitrobenzene   2,4,6-trinitrobenzene

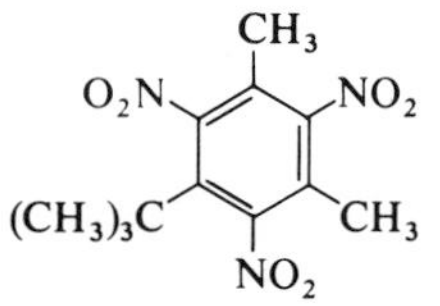

22·4 *charge-transfer and* π *complexes*

An important characteristic of polynitro compounds is their ability to form more or less stable complexes with aromatic hydrocarbons, especially those that are substituted with alkyl groups or are otherwise expected to have electron-donating properties. The behavior is very commonly observed with picric acid, and the complexes therefrom are often nicely crystalline solids, which are useful for the separation, purification, and identification of aromatic hydrocarbons. These substances are often called "hydrocarbon picrates" but the name is misleading since they are not ordinary salts; furthermore, similar complexes are formed between aromatic hydrocarbons and trinitrobenzene, which shows that the strongly electron-attracting nitro groups rather than the acidic hydroxyl group are essential to complex formation. The binding in these complexes results from attractive forces between electron-rich and electron-poor substances. The designation **charge-transfer complex** originates from a resonance description in which the structure of the complex receives contributions from resonance forms involving transfer of an electron from the donor (electron-rich) molecule to the acceptor (electron-poor) molecule. However, the name π complex is also used because usually at least one component of the complex has a π-electron system. Charge-transfer complexes between polynitro compounds and aromatic hydrocarbons appear to have sandwich-type structures with the aromatic rings in parallel planes, although not necessarily coaxial. (See Figure 22·3.)

Charge-transfer complexes are almost always more highly colored than their individual components. A spectacular example is shown by benzene and tetracyanoethene, each of which separately is colorless, but which give a bright-orange complex when mixed. A shift toward longer wavelengths of absorption is to be expected for charge-transfer complexes relative to their components because of the enhanced possibility for resonance stabilization of the excited state involving both components. (See Sections 7·5 and 26·2.)

With good electron donors such as carbanions, nitrobenzene itself will undergo charge transfer by adding an electron (Equation 22·1). The resulting radical anion [1] has both the negative charge and the spin of the odd electron distributed over the nitro group and the phenyl ring.

$$R\overset{\ominus}{:} + C_6H_5NO_2 \; \rightleftharpoons \; R\cdot + C_6H_5\overset{\ominus}{NO_2}\cdot \tag{22·1}$$
$$[1]$$

A few of the many contributing structures for [1] are shown below.

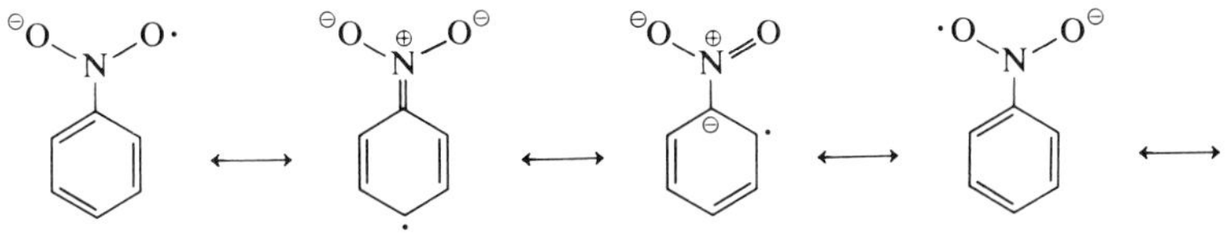

etc.

Many autoxidation reactions occur under basic conditions and are catalyzed by nitroarenes. The base generates a carbanion which is converted to a radical as in Equation 22·1 and this combines with molecular oxygen to form a peroxyradical, ROO·. The next step produces the hydroperoxide and regenerates more radical. Thus production of one radical can account for the consumption of many molecules of substrate. The initiation and propagation steps of this, a typical chain reaction, are shown below.

$$RH + OH^{\ominus} \; \rightleftharpoons \; R^{\ominus} + H_2O$$
$$R^{\ominus} + C_6H_5NO_2 \; \rightleftharpoons \; R\cdot + C_6H_5\overset{\ominus}{NO_2}\cdot$$
initiation

$$R\cdot + O_2 \; \longrightarrow \; R-O-O\cdot$$
$$R-O-O\cdot + RH \; \longrightarrow \; ROOH + R\cdot$$
propagation

Figure 22·3   Formulation of charge-transfer complex between 1,3,5-trinitrobenzene (acceptor) and 1,3,5-trimethylbenzene (donor).

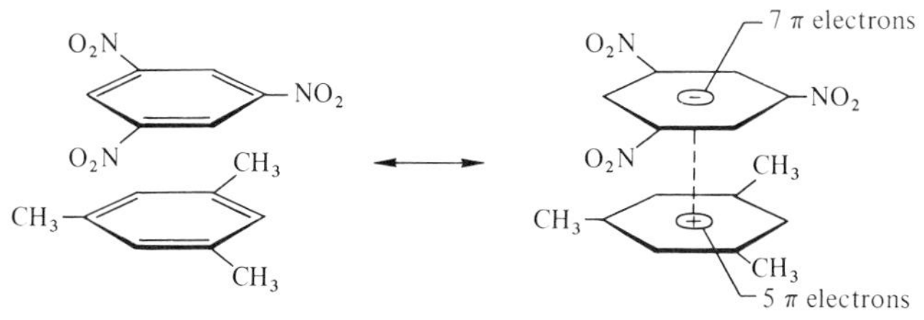

aromatic amines

22·5 general properties

Aniline, $C_6H_5NH_2$, is a rather musty smelling liquid which is only slightly soluble in water. It solidifies at $-6°$, boils at $184°$, and is colorless when pure. Like most aromatic amines, however, it tends to discolor on standing because

Table 22·1 Physical properties of some representative aromatic amines

name	formula	basicity,[a] K_B H_2O, 25°C	ultraviolet absorption			
			λ_{max}	ε	λ_{max}	ε
aniline	$C_6H_5NH_2$	4.6×10^{-10}	2300	8600	2800	1430
N-methylaniline	$C_6H_5NHCH_3$	2.5×10^{-10b}	2450	11,600	2950	1800
N, N-dimethylaniline	$C_6H_5N(CH_3)_2$	2.42×10^{-10b}	2510	14,000	2980	1900
p-toluidine	$H_3C-\!\!\langle\ \rangle\!\!-NH_2$	1.48×10^{-9}	2320	8900	2860	1600
m-nitroaniline	O_2N structure $-NH_2$	4.0×10^{-13}	2800	4800	3580	1450
p-nitroaniline	$O_2N-\!\!\langle\ \rangle\!\!-NH_2$	1.1×10^{-12}	3810	13,500		
p-phenylenediamine	$H_2N-\!\!\langle\ \rangle\!\!-NH_2$				3210	1550
benzidine[c]	$H_2N-\!\!\langle\ \rangle\!\!-\!\!\langle\ \rangle\!\!-NH_2$	1.4×10^{-12}	2840	24,500		
diphenylamine	$(C_6H_5)_2NH$	$\sim 10^{-14}$	2850	20,600		
triphenylamine	$(C_6H_5)_3N$	$-^d$	2950	23,000		
1-naphthylamine	naphthalene-NH_2	9.9×10^{-11}			3200	5000
2-naphthylamine[c]	naphthalene-NH_2	2.0×10^{-10}			3400	2000

[a] Often given as $K_{BH\oplus}$, the dissociation constant of the conjugate acid, $ArNH_3^\oplus + H_2O \rightleftharpoons ArNH_2 + H_3O^\oplus$. $K_B = 10^{-14}/K_{BH\oplus}$ and $K_{BH\oplus}$ for aniline is 2.2×10^{-5}. The K_{HA} values for aromatic amines, corresponding to the reaction $ArNH_2 + H_2O \rightleftharpoons ArNH^\ominus + H_3O^\oplus$, are low, but measurable, e.g., K_{HA} for aniline is 10^{-27}.
[b] At 18°C.
[c] Hazardous substances; see Section 22·9B.
[d] Not measurably basic in water solution.

of air oxidation. Table 22·1 gives the basicities and the ultraviolet spectral properties of aniline and many of its derivatives.

The chemical properties of the aromatic amines are in many ways similar to those of aliphatic amines. Alkylation and acylation, for example, occur in the normal manner (Sections 16·1E1 and 16·1F2). We have noted before (Section 16·1D) that aniline is a weaker base than cyclohexylamine by a factor of 10^6. The stabilization which can be ascribed to delocalization of the unshared electron pair over the aromatic ring is lost in the cation because the electron pair must be *localized* when the nitrogen-proton bond is formed. The changes that occur in terms of the principal electron-pairing schemes for the aniline and anilinium ion are shown in Figure 22·4.

A hybrid structure [4] for aniline, deduced from the structures [2a] through [2e], has some degree of double-bond character between the nitrogen and the ring, and some degree of negative charge at the *ortho* and *para* positions.

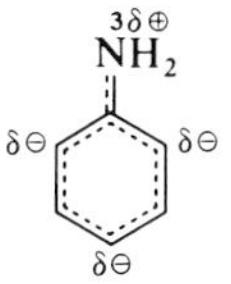

[4]

Accordingly, the ability of the amine nitrogen to add a proton should be particularly sensitive to the electrical effects of substituent groups on the aromatic ring, when such are present. Many substituents such as nitro, cyano, and carbethoxy have the ability to stabilize an electron pair on an adjacent

Figure 22·4   Electron-pairing schemes for aniline and anilinium ion.

[2a]   [2b]   [2c]   [2d]   [2e]

3 kcal extra stabilization attributed to delocalization of unshared electron pair

[3a]   [3b]

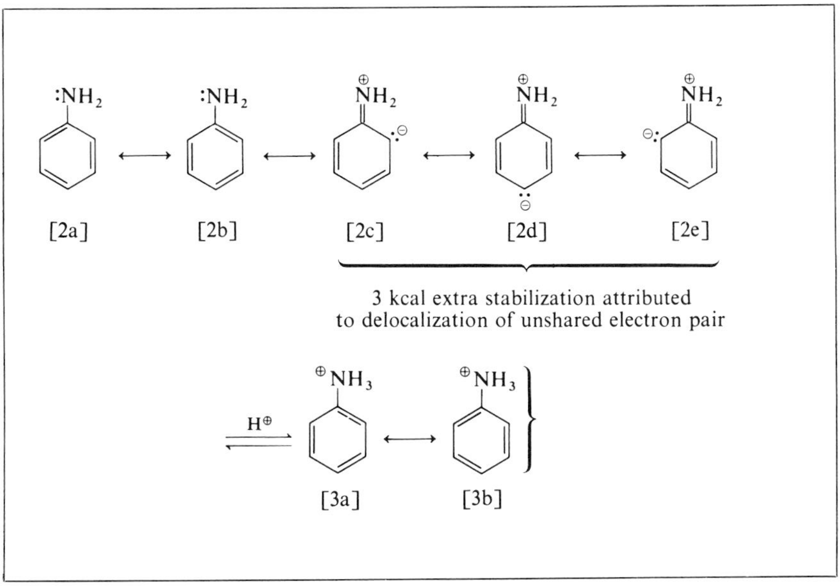

carbon (see Section 21·3B). Such groups, located in the *ortho* or *para* position, should reduce substantially the base strength of the amine nitrogen. The reason is that the substituted aniline, but not the anilinium ion, is stabilized by contributions of electron-pairing schemes such as [5].

[5]

To gain some idea of the magnitude of this effect, we first note that aniline as a base is 90 times stronger than *m*-nitroaniline and 4000 times stronger than *p*-nitroaniline. In contrast the acid-strengthening effect of a nitro group on benzoic acid is only 5.1 times for *meta* nitro and 6.0 for *para* nitro. Clearly, the nitro groups in the nitroanilines exert a more powerful electrical effect than in the nitrobenzoic acids. This is reasonable because the site at which ionization occurs is closer to the benzene ring in the anilines than in the acids. Even when this factor is taken into account, however, *p*-nitroaniline is much weaker than expected, unless forms such as [5] are important.

The contribution made by the polar form [5] becomes even more important on excitation of *p*-nitroaniline by ultraviolet radiation (see Section 7·5). The necessary excitation energies are therefore lower than for aniline, with the result that the absorption bands in the electronic spectrum of *p*-nitroaniline are shifted to much longer wavelengths and are of higher intensity than are those of aniline (cf. Table 22·1). Since no counterpart to [5] can be written for *m*-nitroaniline, the absorption bands of *m*-nitroaniline are not as intense and occur at shorter wavelengths than those of *p*-nitroaniline.

The —NH_2 group of aniline leads to very easy substitution by electrophilic agents (Section 20·5A) and high reactivity toward oxidizing agents. Bromine reacts rapidly with aniline in water solution to give 2,4,6-tribromoaniline in good yield. Introduction of the second and third bromines is so fast that it is difficult to obtain the monosubstitution products in aqueous solution.

Other facets of the substitution of aromatic amines were discussed in connection with the orientation effects of substituents (see Section 20·5).

22·6   *aromatic amines with nitrous acid*

Primary aromatic amines react with nitrous acid at 0° in a way different from aliphatic amines in that the intermediate diazonium salts are much more stable and can, in most cases, be isolated as nicely crystalline fluoborate salts

(Section 21·2). Other salts can often be isolated, but some of these, such as benzenediazonium chloride, are not very stable and may decompose with considerable violence.

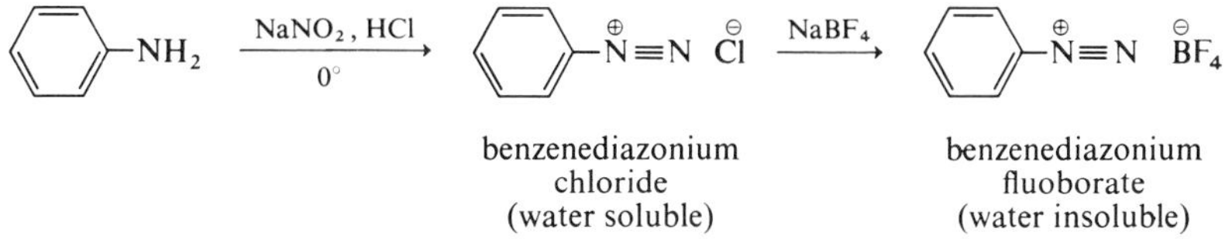

benzenediazonium
chloride
(water soluble)

benzenediazonium
fluoborate
(water insoluble)

The reason for the greater stability of aryldiazonium salts compared with alkyldiazonium salts seems to be related to the difficulty of achieving S_N1 reactions with aryl compounds (Section 21·3C). Even the gain in energy, associated with formation of nitrogen by decomposition of a diazonium ion, is not sufficient to make production of aryl cations occur readily at less than 100°.

This reaction has considerable general utility for replacement of aromatic amino groups by hydroxyl groups. In contrast to the behavior of aliphatic amines, no rearrangements occur.

Secondary aromatic amines react with nitrous acid to form N-nitroso compounds in the same way as do aliphatic amines (Section 16·1F3).

Tertiary aromatic amines normally behave differently from aliphatic tertiary amines with nitrous acid in that they undergo C-nitrosation, preferably in the *para* position. It is possible that an N-nitroso compound is formed first, which subsequently isomerizes to the *p*-nitroso derivative.

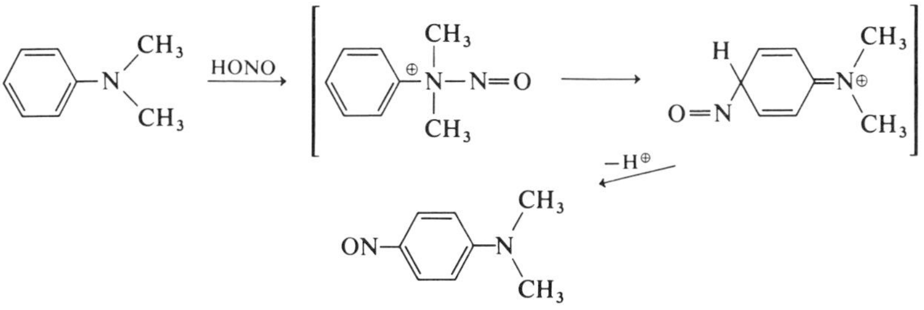

p-nitroso-N,N-dimethylaniline

diazonium salts

22·7 preparation and general properties

The formation of diazonium salts from amines and nitrous acid has been described in the previous section. Most aromatic amines react readily, unless strong electron-withdrawing groups are present.

Tetrazotization of aromatic diamines is usually straightforward if the amino groups are located on different rings, as with benzidine, or are *meta* to each other on the same ring. Tetrazotization of amino groups *para* to one another, or diazotization of *p*-aminophenols, has to be conducted carefully to avoid oxidation to quinones (Section 23·3).

Diazonium salts are normally stable only if the anion is one derived from a reasonably strong acid. Diazonium salts of weak acids usually convert to covalent forms from which the salts can usually be regenerated by strong acid. Benzenediazonium cyanide provides a good example in being unstable and forming two isomeric covalent benzenediazocyanides, one with the $N{=}N$ bond *trans* and the other with the $N{=}N$ bond *cis*. Of these, the *trans* isomer is the more stable.

$$C_6H_5\overset{\oplus}{N}{\equiv}\overset{\ominus}{N}{:}\ \overset{\ominus}{C}N \rightleftharpoons \underset{cis\text{-benzenediazocyanide}}{\overset{\displaystyle C_6H_5\diagdown\quad\diagup CN}{N{=}N}} + \underset{trans\text{-benzenediazocyanide}}{\overset{\displaystyle C_6H_5\diagdown}{N{=}\overset{..}{N}\diagdown_{CN}}}$$

In strong acid, the covalent diazocyanides are unstable with respect to benzenediazonium ion and hydrogen cyanide.

The covalent forms are sometimes significant in the reactions of diazonium salts, since they offer a convenient path for the formation of free radicals (see Section 16·6B).

$$C_6H_5\overset{\oplus}{N}{\equiv}\overset{\ominus}{N} + \overset{\ominus}{O}_2CCH_3 \rightleftharpoons C_6H_5N{=}N{-}O{-}\overset{\overset{\displaystyle O}{\|}}{C}{-}CH_3$$

$$\xrightarrow{\text{slow}} C_6H_5\cdot + N_2 + \cdot O{-}\overset{\overset{\displaystyle O}{\|}}{C}{-}CH_3$$

22·8   *replacement reactions of diazonium salts*

The utility of diazonium salts in synthesis is largely due to the fact that they provide the only readily accessible substances that undergo nucleophilic substitution reactions on the aromatic ring under mild conditions without the necessity of having activating groups, such as nitro or cyano, in the *ortho* or *para* position.

A. THE SANDMEYER REACTION

The replacement of diazonium groups by halogen is the most important reaction of this type and some of its uses for the synthesis of aryl halides were discussed previously (Section 21·2). Two helpful variations on the Sandmeyer reaction employ sodium nitrite with cuprous ion as catalyst for the synthesis of nitro compounds (Section 22·1), and cuprous cyanide for the synthesis of cyano compounds.

B. THE SCHIEMANN REACTION

The replacement of diazonium groups by fluorine was also covered earlier (Section 21·2). This reaction, like the replacement of the diazonium group by hydroxyl (Section 22·6), may well involve aromatic cations as intermediates. One strong piece of evidence for this is the fact that benzenediazonium fluoborate yields 3-nitrobiphenyl along with fluorobenzene when heated in nitrobenzene. Formation of 3-nitrobiphenyl is indicative of an electrophilic attack on nitrobenzene.

22·9   reactions of diazonium compounds that occur without loss of nitrogen

A. REDUCTION TO HYDRAZINES

Reduction of diazonium salts to arylhydrazines can be carried out smoothly with sodium sulfite or stannous chloride, or by electrolysis.

B. DIAZO COUPLING

A very important group of reactions of diazonium ions involves aromatic substitution by the diazonium salt acting as an electrophilic agent to yield azo compounds.

This reaction is highly sensitive to the nature of the substituent (X), and coupling to benzene derivatives normally occurs only when X is a strongly activating group such as $-O^{\ominus}$, $-N(CH_3)_2$, and $-OH$; however, coupling with $X = OCH_3$ may take place with particularly active diazonium compounds. Diazo coupling has considerable technical value, because the azo compounds that are produced are colored and often useful as dyes and coloring matters. A typical example of diazo coupling is afforded by formation of p-dimethylaminoazobenzene from benzenediazonium chloride and N,N-dimethylaniline.

p-dimethylaminoazobenzene
(yellow)

The product was once used to color edible fats and was therefore known as "Butter Yellow" but its use in foods and cosmetics has been banned by many countries because of its ability to cause cancer in rats. There are indications, but no firm evidence, that it causes cancer in humans.

Certain other nitrogen-containing compounds, particularly aromatic amines, have been definitely shown to be carcinogenic for man. One of the most dangerous of these is 2-aminonaphthalene, formerly used as an antioxidant to protect the insulation on electric cables. In Britain a study showed that men continually exposed to this amine during its manufacture had a bladder cancer incidence of 50% at 30 years from first exposure. One particularly unfortunate group of 15 men involved in its distillation showed a 100% incidence. Other dangerous amines are 4-aminobiphenyl and benzidine.

2-aminonaphthalene
(2-naphthylamine)

4-aminobiphenyl

benzidine
(4,4'-diaminobiphenyl)

summary

Aryl nitrogen compounds include amines, such as aniline, $C_6H_5NH_2$; nitro compounds, such as nitrobenzene, $C_6H_5NO_2$; and a number of substances with nitrogen-nitrogen bonds, benzenediazonium salts, $C_6H_5N_2^{\oplus}X^{\ominus}$;

azoxybenzene, $C_6H_5\overset{\overset{\displaystyle O^{\ominus}}{|}}{\underset{\oplus}{N}}=NC_6H_5$; azobenzene, $C_6H_5N=NC_6H_5$; and

hydrazobenzene, $C_6H_5NHNHC_6H_5$.

Aromatic nitro compounds are prepared by direct nitration using HNO_3-H_2SO_4 mixtures. Polynitration is difficult because of the deactivating effect of the nitro group, and use is often made of acylamino or alkyl substituents to counteract this effect. The groups are removed at a later stage.

Reduction of aromatic nitro compounds in acid solution (route A) gives amines directly, but in neutral or basic solution (route B), a number of compounds with nitrogen-nitrogen bonds can be isolated as intermediates.

$$C_6H_5NO_2 \xrightarrow{\quad(A)\quad} C_6H_5NH_2$$

$$\downarrow (B)$$

$$C_6H_5\underset{\oplus}{\overset{\overset{\displaystyle O^{\ominus}}{|}}{N}}=NC_6H_5 \longrightarrow C_6H_5N=NC_6H_5 \longrightarrow C_6H_5NHNHC_6H_5$$

Nitroarenes abstract electrons from certain electron donors. Some good donors such as carbanions convert the nitrobenzene to a radical anion and this reaction can be important in initiating radical processes.

$$R^{\ominus} + C_6H_5NO_2 \rightleftharpoons R\cdot + C_6H_5\overset{\ominus}{N}O_2\cdot$$

Polynitroarenes form complexes with many neutral donors such as alkylbenzenes or polynuclear hydrocarbons by charge transfer. Such complexes are usually highly colored and can be described as two radical ions held together by electrostatic attraction

Aromatic amines resemble aliphatic amines in most of their reactions but are considerably weaker bases because of resonance interaction between the amino group and the ring. Aromatic amines also differ in that they give fairly stable diazonium ions on treatment with nitrous acid; these undergo a number of useful synthetic reactions.

$$ArNH_2 \longrightarrow ArN_2^{\oplus} \begin{cases} ArX \\ ArCN \\ ArNHNH_2 \\ ArN=NAr \end{cases}$$

Certain aromatic amines, such as 2-aminonaphthalene, are carcinogenic.

exercises

22·1 Show how the following compounds could be synthesized from the indicated starting materials. (It may be necessary to review parts of Chapters 20 and 21 to work this exercise.)

a.   from toluene

b.   from *p*-toluenesulfonic acid

c.   from chlorobenzene

d.   from chlorobenzene

e.   from *p*-chlorobenzenesulfonic acid

22·2   Tetracyanoethene in benzene forms an orange solution, but when this solution is mixed with a solution of anthracene in benzene, a brilliant blue-green color is produced, which fades rapidly; colorless crystals of a compound of composition $C_{14}H_{10} \cdot C_2(CN)_4$ are then deposited. Explain the color changes that occur and write a structure for the crystalline product.

22·3   Anthracene (mp 217°) forms a red crystalline complex (mp 164°) with 1,3,5-trinitrobenzene (mp 121°). If you were to purify anthracene as this complex, how could you regenerate the anthracene free of trinitrobenzene?

22·4   N,N,4-Trimethylaniline has $K_B = 3 \times 10^{-9}$; quinuclidine, $K_B = 4 \times 10^{-4}$; and benzoquinuclidine, $K_B = 6 \times 10^{-7}$. What conclusions may be drawn from these results as to the cause(s) of the reduced base strength of aromatic amines relative to saturated aliphatic or alicyclic amines? Explain.

benzoquinuclidine

Would you expect a nitro group *meta* or *para* to the nitrogen in benzo-quinuclidine to have as large an effect on the base strength of benzoquinu-clidine as the corresponding substitution in aniline?

22·5   Pure secondary aliphatic amines can often be prepared free of primary and tertiary amines by cleavage of a *p*-nitroso-N,N-dialkylaniline with strong alkali to *p*-nitrosophenol and the dialkylamine. Why does this cleavage occur readily? Show how the synthesis might be used for preparation of di-*n*-butylamine starting with aniline and *n*-butyl bromide.

22·6 N,N-Dimethylaniline, but not N,N,2,6-tetramethylaniline, couples readily with diazonium salts in neutral solution. Explain the low reactivity of N,N,2,6-tetramethylaniline by consideration of the geometry of the transition state for the reaction.

22·7 Some very reactive unsaturated hydrocarbons, such as azulene (Section 20·7A), couple with diazonium salts. At which position would you expect azulene to couple most readily? Explain.

22·8 1-Naphthol couples with benzenediazonium chloride in the 2 position; 2-methyl-1-naphthol, in the 4 position; and 2-naphthol, in the 1 position. However, 1-methyl-2-naphthol does not couple at all under the same conditions. Why?

22·9 Give for each of the following pairs of compounds a chemical test, preferably a test tube reaction, that will distinguish the two compounds. Write a structural formula for each compound and equations for the reactions involved:

    a. *p*-nitrotoluene and benzamide
    b. aniline and cyclohexylamine
    c. N-methylaniline and *p*-toluidine
    d. N-nitroso-N-methylaniline and *p*-nitroso-N-methylaniline

22·10 Show by equations how each of the following substances might be synthesized starting from the indicated materials. Specify reagents and approximate reaction conditions.

    a. *o*-dinitrobenzene from benzene
    b. 2,6-dinitrophenol from benzene
    c. 2-amino-4-chlorotoluene from toluene
    d. *p*-cyanonitrobenzene from benzene
    e. 2-amino-4-nitrophenol from phenol
    f. *m*-cyanotoluene from toluene

22·11 Write structural formulas for substances (one for each part) that fit the following descriptions:

    a. an aromatic amine that is a stronger base than aniline
    b. a substituted phenol that would not be expected to couple with benzenediazonium chloride in acidic, alkaline, or neutral solution
    c. a substituted benzenediazonium chloride that would be a more active coupling agent than benzenediazonium chloride itself

22·12 Explain why triphenylamine is a much weaker base than aniline and why its absorption spectrum is shifted to longer wavelengths compared with the spectrum of aniline (see Table 22·1). Would you expect N-phenylcarbazole to be a stronger or weaker base than triphenylamine? Explain.

N-phenylcarbazole

chapter 23
aryl oxygen compounds

In the previous chapter, we indicated that, although there are considerable structural similarities between vinyl alcohols (enols) and phenols, and between vinylamines (enamines) and aromatic amines, the enols and enamines are generally unstable with respect to their keto and imine tautomeric forms, whereas the reverse is true of phenols and aromatic amines because of the stability associated with the aromatic ring.

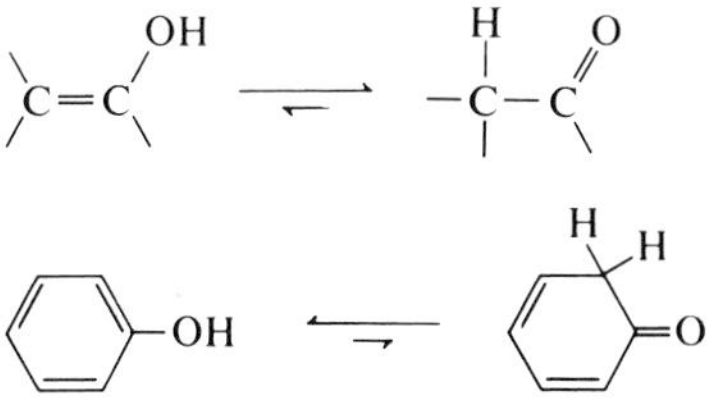

In this chapter, after considering some of the more general procedures for the preparation of phenols, we shall take up the effect of the aromatic ring on the reactivity and reactions of the hydroxyl group of phenols and the effect of the hydroxyl group on the properties of the aromatic ring. The chapter concludes with discussions of the chemistry of quinones and of some non-benzenoid seven-membered ring substances with aromatic properties.

23·1 synthesis and physical properties of phenols

Considerable amounts of phenol and cresols (o-, m-, and p-methylphenols) can be isolated from coal tar, which is formed in the destructive distillation of coal. Phenol itself is used commercially in such large quantities that alternate methods of synthesis are necessary. Direct oxidation of benzene is unsatisfactory because phenol is much more readily oxidized than is benzene. The more usual procedures are to sulfonate or chlorinate benzene and then introduce the hydroxyl group by nucleophilic substitution using strong alkali.

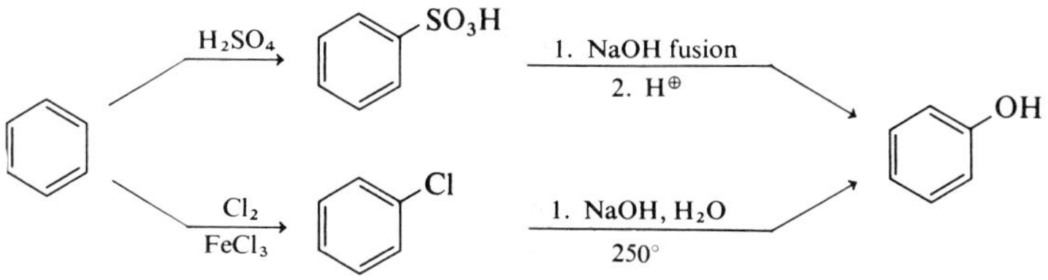

These reactions are general for introduction of hydroxyl substituents on aromatic rings; however, in some cases, they proceed by way of benzyne intermediates (Section 21·3C) and may lead to rearrangement.

A more recent commercial synthesis of phenol involves oxidation of isopropylbenzene (cumene). This is made more commercially attractive by virtue of acetone being formed at the same time. The sequence of reactions starting with benzene and propene is shown in Figure 23·1. Some interesting chemistry is involved in this process. The first step, conversion of benzene to cumene, is a Friedel-Crafts alkylation (Section 20·4D). The second step,

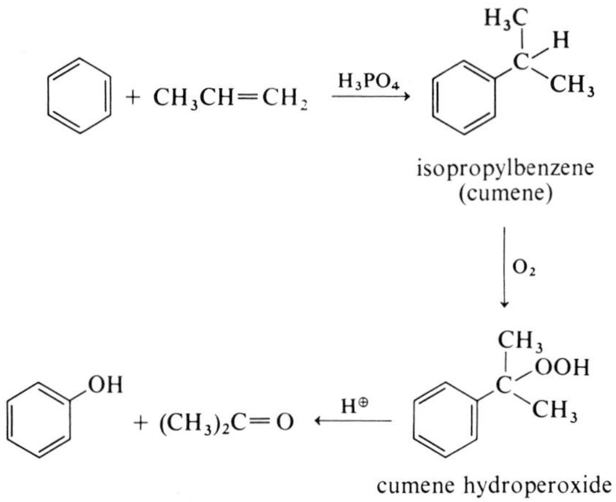

Figure 23·1   Commercial preparation of phenol and acetone starting with benzene and propene.

conversion of cumene to the hydroperoxide, is a radical chain reaction (Section 2·5B). The third step is an acid-catalyzed rearrangement that resembles the Beckmann rearrangement (Section 16·1E2). (For more on the mechanism, see Exercises 23·13 and 23·14.)

Phenol is a colorless crystalline solid when pure, but samples of it are often pink or brown because, like aniline, it is subject to air oxidation. Phenols are more polar and are able to form stronger hydrogen bonds than the corresponding saturated alcohols. A comparison of the physical properties of phenol and cyclohexanol shown in Table 23·1 shows that phenol has the higher melting point, higher boiling point, and higher water solubility, and is the more acidic.

The acid dissociation constants and the ultraviolet spectral properties of phenols are shown in Table 23·2. There is a considerable effect of substituents on the wavelength and intensity of the absorption maxima.

Table 23·1   Comparative physical properties of phenol and cyclohexanol

	phenol	cyclohexanol
mp	43°	26°
bp	181°	161°
water solubility, g/100 g, 20°	9.3	3.6
K_{HA}	1.0×10^{-10}	$\sim 10^{-18}$

Table 23·2   Physical properties of some representative phenols

name	formula	K_{HA}, H$_2$O, 25°C	λ_{max}	ε	λ_{max}	ε
phenol	C$_6$H$_5$OH	1.3×10^{-10}	2105	6200	2700	1450
p-cresol	H$_3$C—⟨C$_6$H$_4$⟩—OH	1.5×10^{-10}	2250	7400	2800	1995
p-nitrophenol	O$_2$N—⟨C$_6$H$_4$⟩—OH	6.5×10^{-8}	3175	10,000		
picric acid	O$_2$N—⟨C$_6$H$_2$(NO$_2$)$_2$⟩—OH	6×10^{-1}	3800	13,450		
catechol	⟨C$_6$H$_4$⟩(OH)(OH) (1,2)	3.3×10^{-10a}	2140	6300	2755	2300
resorcinol	HO—⟨C$_6$H$_4$⟩—OH (1,3)	3.6×10^{-10a}	2160	6800	2735	1900
hydroquinone	HO—⟨C$_6$H$_4$⟩—OH	1×10^{-10}			2900	2800
p-aminophenol	H$_2$N—⟨C$_6$H$_4$⟩—OH	6.6×10^{-9a}	2330	8000	2800	3200
salicylaldehyde	⟨C$_6$H$_4$⟩(OH)(CHO) (1,2)	3.0×10^{-9}	2560	12,600	3240	3400
p-hydroxybenzal-dehyde	HO—⟨C$_6$H$_4$⟩—CHO	2.2×10^{-8}	2835	16,000		
1-naphthol	naphthalene-1-OH	4.9×10^{-10}	2325	33,000	2950	5000
2-naphthol	naphthalene-2-OH	2.8×10^{-10}	2260	76,000	2735	4500

[a] At 18°C.

23·2 some chemical properties of phenols

A. REACTIONS INVOLVING O—H BONDS

The acidity of phenols compared to alcohols can be accounted for by an argument similar to that used to explain the acidity of carboxylic acids (Section 13·4). There is a small amount of resonance stabilization in phenol that is due to delocalization of one of the unshared electron pairs on oxygen over the aromatic ring, as can be described in terms of the resonance structures [1a] through [1c].

Conversion of phenol by loss of the hydroxyl proton to phenoxide anion leads to much greater delocalization of the unshared pair because, as can be seen from the resonance structures [2a] through [2c], no charge separation is involved of the type apparent in [1a] through [1c].

The greater stabilization energy of the anion makes the ionization process energetically more favorable than for a saturated alcohol such as cyclohexanol.

The reactions of the hydroxyl groups of phenols that involve breaking the O—H bonds and formation of new bonds from oxygen to carbon are generally similar to those of alcohols. It is possible to prepare esters with carboxylic acid anhydrides and to prepare ethers by reaction of phenoxide anions with halides, sulfate esters, sulfonates, and so on, which react well by S_N2 mechanisms.

Phenols are sufficiently acidic to be converted to methoxy derivatives with diazomethane (Section 16·6C) with no need for an acidic catalyst.

$$\text{C}_6\text{H}_5\text{-OH} + \text{CH}_2\text{N}_2 \xrightarrow[-\text{N}_2]{\text{ether}} \text{C}_6\text{H}_5\text{-OCH}_3$$

However, they are weaker than carboxylic acids (by a factor of 10^5) and this is the basis for separating phenols and carboxylic acids by extraction with aqueous bicarbonate solution. Carboxylic acids can be extracted from ether or benzene solution by this reagent whereas phenols can not (Section 13·1).

Almost all phenols and enols (such as those of 1,3-diketones) give colors with ferric chloride in dilute water or alcohol solutions. Phenol itself produces a violet coloration with ferric chloride and the cresols give a blue color. The products are apparently ferric phenoxide salts, which absorb visible light to give an excited state having electrons delocalized over both the iron atom and the unsaturated system.

B. C- vs. O-ALKYLATION OF PHENOLS

The same type of problem with respect to O- and C-alkylation is encountered with phenoxide salts as with enolate anions (Section 12·2B). Normally, only O-alkylation is observed. However, with allyl halides either reaction can be made essentially the exclusive reaction by proper choice of solvent. With sodium phenoxide, more polar solvents such as acetone tend to lead to phenyl allyl ether while in nonpolar solvents, such as benzene, *o*-allylphenol is the favored product.

$$\text{C}_6\text{H}_5\text{-OCH}_2\text{CH}=\text{CH}_2$$

phenyl allyl ether

polar ↑ solvents

$$\text{C}_6\text{H}_5\text{-}\overset{\ominus}{\text{O}}\ \overset{\oplus}{\text{Na}} + \text{CH}_2\text{=CH}-\text{CH}_2\text{Br}$$

nonpolar │ solvents

o-allylphenol

Apparently, in nonpolar solvents, the lack of dissociation of the $\overset{\ominus}{\text{—O}}\overset{\oplus}{\text{Na}}$ part of the phenoxide salts tends to increase the steric hindrance at oxygen and makes attack on the ring more favorable.

The C-allylation product is thermodynamically more stable than the O-allylation product, as shown by the fact that phenyl allyl ether rearranges to *o*-allylphenol above 200°. Such rearrangements are quite general and are called **Claisen rearrangements**.

It should be noted that C-allylation of sodium phenoxide as observed in nonpolar solvents is not the result of O-allylation followed by rearrangement, because the temperature of the allylation reaction is far too low to obtain the observed yield of *o*-allylphenol by rearrangement.

C. REACTIONS INVOLVING THE C—O BONDS

It is very difficult to break the aromatic C—O bond in reactions involving phenols or phenol derivatives. Thus, concentrated halogen acids do not convert phenols to aryl halides, and cleavage of phenyl alkyl ethers with hydrogen bromide or hydrogen iodide produces the phenol and an alkyl halide, not an aryl halide and an alcohol. Diaryl ethers, such as diphenyl ether, do not react with hydrogen iodide even at 200°.

Such behavior is very much in line with the difficulty of breaking aromatic halogen bonds in nucleophilic reactions (Chapter 21). There is no very suitable way for converting phenols to aryl halides, except when activation is provided by *ortho* or *para* nitro groups. Thus, 2,4-dinitrophenol is smoothly converted to 2,4-dinitrochlorobenzene with phosphorus pentachloride.

D. REACTIONS OF THE AROMATIC RING

The —OH and —O$^\ominus$ groups of phenol and phenoxide ion make for easy electrophilic substitution. The situation here is very much like that in aniline (see Section 22·5; see also Section 20·5A). Phenols react rapidly with bromine in aqueous solution to substitute the positions *ortho* or *para* to the hydroxyl group, phenol itself giving 2,4,6-tribromophenol in high yield.

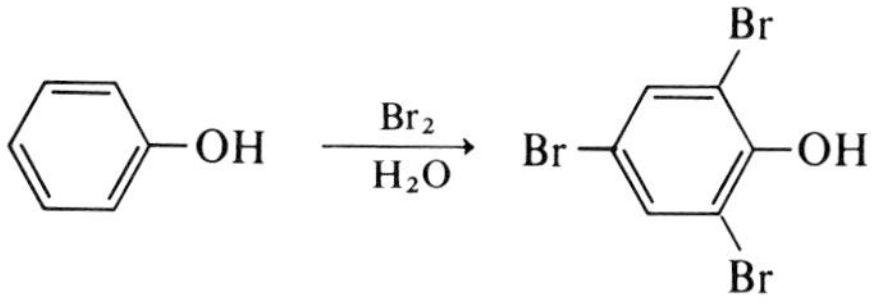

A number of important reactions of phenols involve electrophilic aromatic substitution of phenoxide ions. One example, which we have discussed in the previous chapter, is the diazo coupling reaction (Section 22·9B). Another example, which looks quite unrelated, is the **Kolbe reaction** (Figure 23·2) in which carbon dioxide reacts with sodium phenoxide to give the sodium salt of *o*-hydroxybenzoic acid (salicylic acid).

Sodium phenoxide absorbs carbon dioxide at room temperature to form sodium phenyl carbonate and, when this is heated to 125° under a pressure of several atmospheres of carbon dioxide, it rearranges to sodium salicylate. However, there is no reason to expect that this reaction is anything other than a dissociation-recombination process, in which the important step involves electrophilic attack by carbon dioxide on the aromatic ring of phenoxide ion.

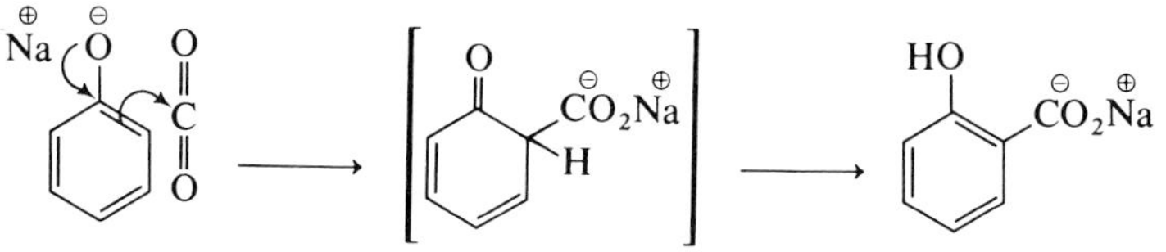

With sodium phenoxide and temperatures of 125° to 150°, *ortho* substitution occurs; at higher temperatures (250° to 300°) and particularly with the potassium salt, the *para* isomer is favored.

Figure 23·2 The reaction of sodium phenoxide with carbon dioxide (the Kolbe reaction).

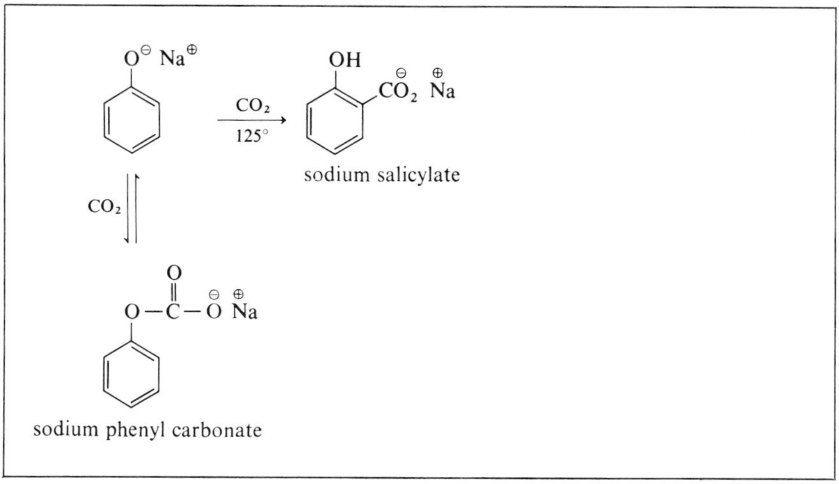

sodium salicylate

sodium phenyl carbonate

Many substances such as salicylaldehyde, salicylic acid, and *o*-nitrophenol that have hydroxyl groups *ortho* to some substituent to which they can form hydrogen bonds have exceptional physical properties compared with the *meta* or *para* isomers. This is because formation of intra- rather than intermolecular hydrogen bonds reduces intermolecular attraction, thus reducing boiling points, increasing solubility in nonpolar solvents, and so on. Compounds with intramolecular hydrogen bonds are often said to be **chelated** (Gk. *chele*, claw) and the resulting ring is called a **chelate ring**.

intramolecular   only intermolecular
hydrogen bond   hydrogen bonds

Table 23·3   Physical properties of some *o*, *m*, and *p* disubstituted benzene derivatives

compound		bp, °C	mp, °C	volatility with steam
OH / CH$_3$	ortho	191	31	$++$
	meta	203	12	$++$
	para	202	35	$++$
OH / CHO	ortho	196.5	-7	$+$
	meta	240	108	$-$
	para		117	$-$
OCH$_3$ / CHO	ortho	244	38	$+$
	meta	230		$+$
	para	248	2.5	$+$
OH / CO$_2$H	ortho	211^{20mm}	158	$+$
	meta		201	$-$
	para		215	$-$
OH / NO$_2$	ortho	216	45	$+$
	meta	194^{70mm}	97	$-$
	para		114	$-$

The physical constants for the different isomers of some substances that can and cannot form reasonably strong intramolecular hydrogen bonds are given in Table 23·3. It will be seen that intramolecular hydrogen bonding between suitable *ortho* groups has the effect of reducing both the melting and boiling points. An important practical use of this is often made in isomer separations, because many of the substances which can form intramolecular hydrogen bonds turn out to be volatile with steam, whereas the corresponding *meta* and *para* isomers are much less so.

Formation of intramolecular hydrogen bonds shows up clearly in nmr spectra, as we have seen before in the case of the enol forms of 1,3-dicarbonyl compounds (Section 12·6). Figure 23·3 shows that there is a difference of 2.3 ppm between the O—H resonance positions of *o*-nitrophenol and *p*-nitrophenol. Intramolecular hydrogen-bond formation also influences the OH stretching frequencies in the infrared.

Phenols generally can be successfully reduced with hydrogen over nickel catalysts to the corresponding cyclohexanols. A variety of alkyl-substituted cyclohexanols can be prepared in this way.

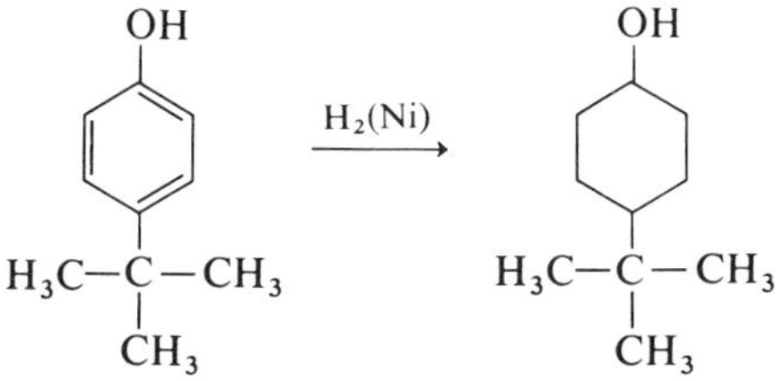

23.3 *polyhydric phenols*

A number of important aromatic compounds have more than one phenolic hydroxyl group. These are most often derivatives of the following dihydric and trihydric phenols, all of which have commonly used but poorly descriptive names.

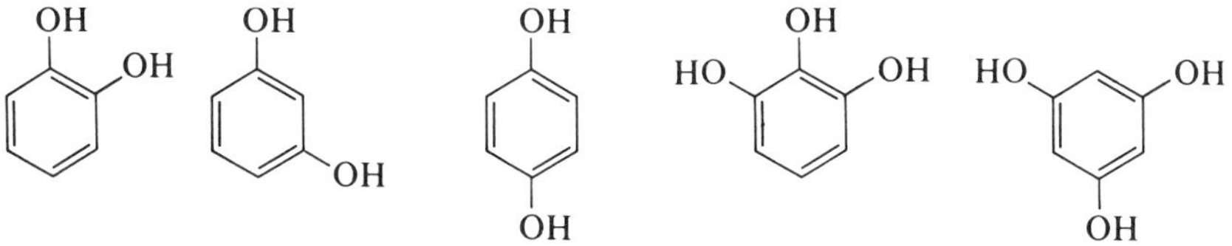

catechol   resorcinol   hydroquinone   pyrogallol   phloroglucinol

The polyhydric phenols with the hydroxyls in the *ortho* or *para* relationship are normally easily oxidized to quinones—the chemistry of which substances will be discussed shortly.

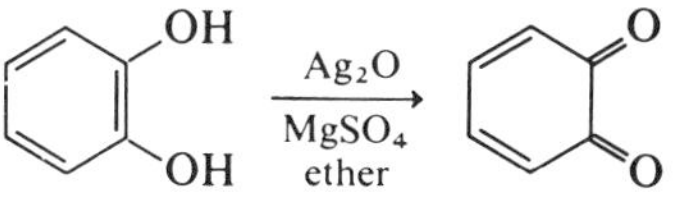

o-benzoquinone

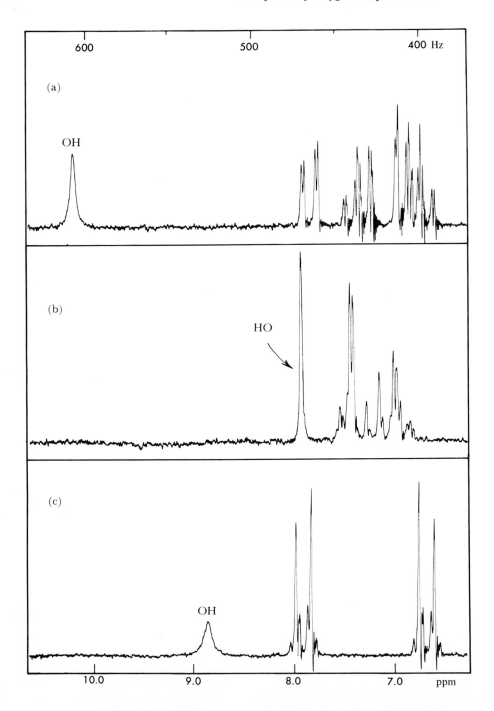

Figure 23·3 Nmr spectra at 60 MHz of *o*-nitrophenol (a), *m*-nitrophenol (b), and *p*-nitrophenol (c) in diethyl ether solution (the solvent bands are not shown).

p-benzoquinone

The m-dihydroxybenzenes undergo oxidation but do not give m-quinones, since these are substances for which no single unstrained planar structure can be written. Oxidation of resorcinol gives complex products—probably by way of attack at the 4 position, which is activated by being *ortho* to one hydroxyl and *para* to the other. The use of hydroquinone and related substances as reducing agents for silver bromide in photography will be discussed later.

Substitution of more than one hydroxyl group on an aromatic ring tends to make the ring particularly susceptible to electrophilic substitution, especially when the hydroxyls are *meta* to one another, in which circumstance their activating influences reinforce one another. For this reason, resorcinol and phloroglucinol are exceptionally reactive toward electrophilic reagents, particularly in alkaline solution.

23·4 quinones

Strictly speaking, quinones are conjugated cyclic diketones rather than aromatic compounds; hence a discussion of the properties of quinones is, to a degree, out of place in a chapter covering aromatic oxygen compounds, even though quinones have more stability than expected on the basis of bond energies alone. Thus, p-benzoquinone has a stabilization energy of 5 kcal, which can be ascribed largely to resonance structures such as [3], there being a total of four polar forms equivalent to [3]. The fact that quinones and poly-

[3]

hydric phenols are normally very readily interconvertible results in the chemistry of either class of compound being difficult to disentangle from the other; consequently, we shall discuss quinones at this point.

A variety of quinones have been prepared, the most common of which are the 1,2- and 1,4-quinones as exemplified by o-benzoquinone and p-benzoquinone. Usually the 1,2-quinones are more difficult to make and are more reactive than the 1,4-quinones. A few 1,6- and 1,8-quinones are also known.

1,5-dichloro-2,6-naphthoquinone   3,10-pyrenequinone

A. REDUCTION OF QUINONES

The most characteristic and important reaction of quinones is reduction to the corresponding dihydroxyaromatic compounds.

$$\text{(23·1)}$$

These reductions are sufficiently rapid and reversible to give easily repro- ducible electrode potentials in an electrolytic cell. The position of the quinone- hydroquinone equilibrium (Equation 23·1) is proportional to the square of the hydrogen ion concentration. The electrode potential is therefore sensitive to pH, a change of one unit of pH in water solution changing the potential by 0.059 volt. Before the invention of the glass electrode pH meter, the half-cell potential developed by the quinone-hydroquinone equilibrium was widely used to determine pH values of aqueous solutions. The method is not very good above pH 9 or 10 because quinone reacts irreversibly with alkali.

Numerous studies have been made of half-cell potentials for the reduction of quinones. As might be expected, the potentials are greatest when the greatest gain in resonance stabilization is associated with formation of the aromatic ring.

The hydroquinone-quinone oxidation-reduction system is actually some- what more complicated than presented above. This is evident in one way from the fact that mixing alcoholic solutions of hydroquinone and quinone gives a brown-red solution, which then deposits a crystalline green-black 1 : 1 complex known as **quinhydrone**. This substance is apparently a charge-transfer complex (of the type discussed in Section 22·4) with the hydroquinone acting as the electron donor and the quinone as the electron acceptor. Quinhydrone is not very soluble and dissociates considerably to its components in solution.

The reduction of quinone requires two electrons, and it is of course possible that these electrons could be transferred either together or one at a time. The product of a single electron transfer leads to what is appropriately called a **semiquinone** [4] with both a negative charge and an odd electron. The forma-

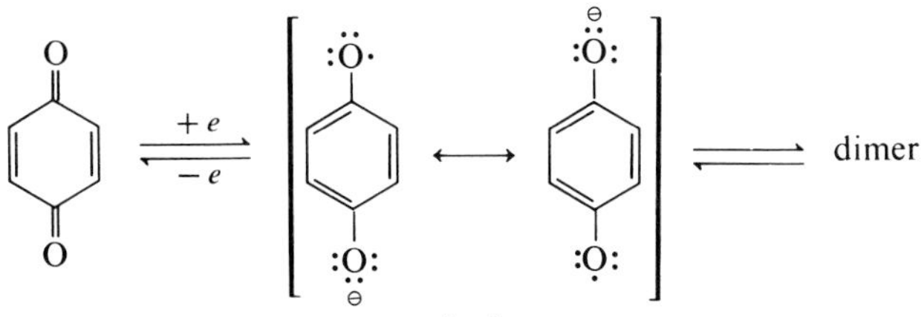

$$\underset{\text{[4]}}{\underset{\text{semiquinone}}{\left[\overset{:\ddot{O}\cdot}{\underset{:\ddot{O}:^\ominus}{\bigcirc}} \longleftrightarrow \overset{:\ddot{O}:^\ominus}{\underset{:\underset{\ominus}{O}:}{\bigcirc}} \right]}} \underset{-e}{\overset{+e}{\rightleftharpoons}} \cdots \rightleftharpoons \text{dimer}$$

tion of relatively stable semiquinone radicals by electrolytic reduction of quinones has been established by a variety of methods. Some semiquinone radicals undergo reversible dimerization reactions to form peroxides.

B. PHOTOGRAPHIC DEVELOPERS

A particularly important practical use of the hydroquinone-quinone oxida-tion-reduction system is in photography. Exposure of the minute grains of silver bromide in a photographic emulsion to blue light (or any visible light in the presence of suitable sensitizing dyes; see Chapter 26) produces a stable activated form of silver bromide, the activation probably involving generation of some sort of crystal defect. Subsequently, when the emulsion is brought into contact with a developer, which may be an alkaline aqueous solution of hydroquinone and sodium sulfite, the particles of activated silver bromide are reduced to silver metal much more rapidly than the ordinary silver bromide. Removal of the unreduced silver bromide with sodium thiosulfate ("fixing") leaves a suspension of finely divided silver in the emulsion in the form of the familiar photographic negative.

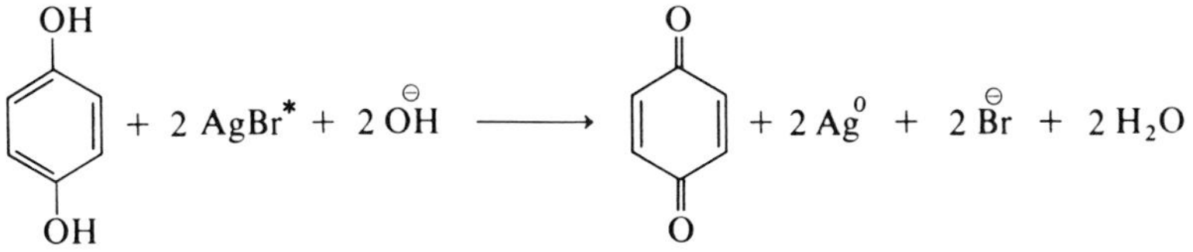

$$\underset{\text{OH}}{\overset{\text{OH}}{\bigcirc}} + 2\,AgBr^* + 2\,\overset{\ominus}{OH} \longrightarrow \underset{\text{O}}{\overset{\text{O}}{\bigcirc}} + 2\,Ag^0 + 2\,\overset{\ominus}{Br} + 2\,H_2O$$

AgBr* = activated silver bromide

C. ADDITION REACTIONS OF QUINONES

Being α,β-unsaturated ketones, quinones are expected to have the possibility of forming 1,4-addition products in the same way as their open-chain analogs (Section 12·3). p-Benzoquinone itself undergoes such additions rather readily. Two examples are provided in Figure 23·4 by the addition of hydrogen chloride and the acid-catalyzed addition of acetic anhydride. In the second reaction, the hydroxyl groups of the hydroquinone are acetylated by the acetic anhydride. Hydrolysis of the product affords hydroxyhydroquinone.

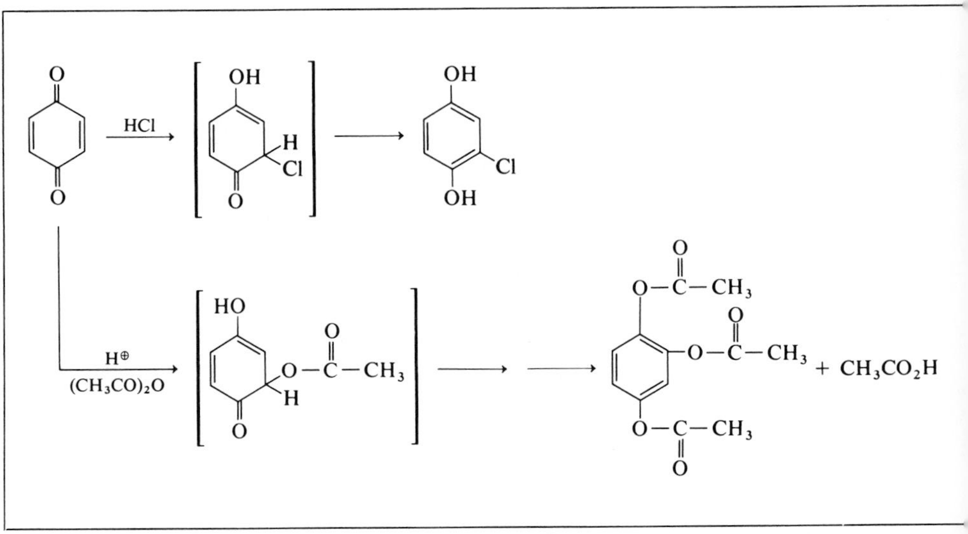

Figure 23·4   Some addition reactions of p-benzoquinone.

D. NATURALLY OCCURRING QUINONES

Many naturally occurring substances have quinone-type structures, one of the most important being the blood antihemorrhagic factor, vitamin K_1, which occurs in green plants and is a substituted 1,4-naphthoquinone. The structure of vitamin K_1 has been established by degradation and by synthesis. Surprisingly, the long alkyl side chain of vitamin K_1 is not necessary for its action in aiding blood clotting because 2-methyl-1,4-naphthoquinone is almost equally active on a molar basis.

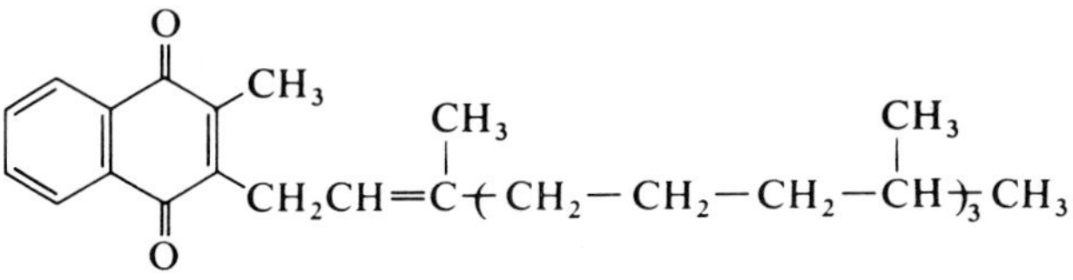

vitamin K_1

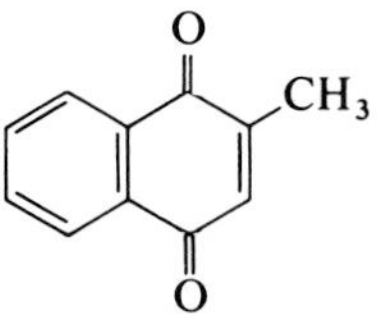

2-methyl-1, 4-naphthoquinone
(menadione)

A molecule that is structurally similar to vitamin K_1 is coenzyme Q. There are, in fact, several of these differing in the length of the side chain. Coenzyme Q_{10} is shown below, the subscript in the name revealing the number of repeating C_5 units in the side chain. The Q coenzymes are widely distributed in nature and are particularly important constituents of mitochondria. They are links in the so-called **electron-transport chain** (Section 18·4), appearing between the flavins and the cytochromes, and seem to be able to function both as one- and two-equivalent oxidants.

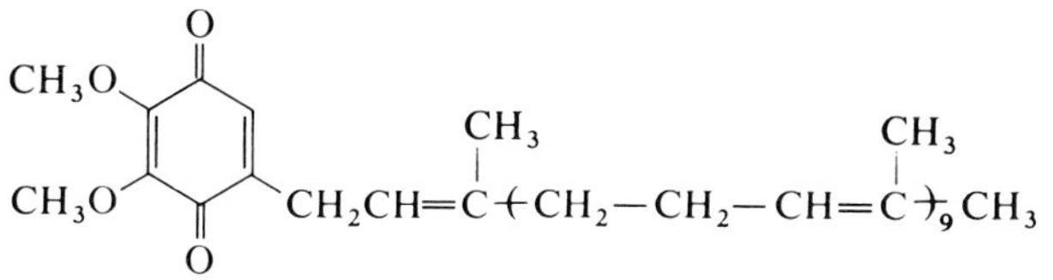

coenzyme Q_{10}

The repeating C_5 moieties in the side chains of vitamin K_1 and coenzyme Q are referred to as **isoprenoid** units. These will be met again in Chapter 29.

23·5 tropolones and related compounds

The tropolones make up a very interesting class of nonbenzenoid aromatic compounds which were first encountered in several quite different kinds of natural products. As one example of a naturally occurring tropolone, the substance called β-thujaplicin or hinokitiol has been isolated from the oil of the western red cedar. The wood of these trees rots extremely slowly and this characteristic has been traced to the presence of this compound, and its γ isomer, which are natural fungicides. The outer butt heartwood of older cedars contains as much as 1% thujaplicins whereas young trees lay down very little of these materials. This accounts for the hollow center often seen in very old cedars—the core, which has a low thujaplicin content, rots.

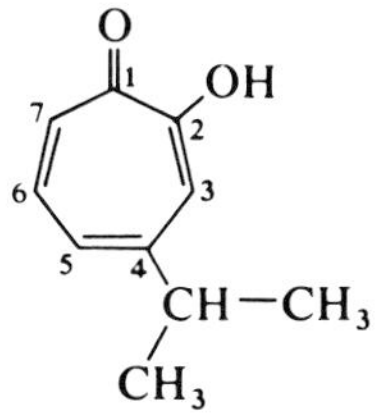

β-thujaplicin
(4-isopropyltropolone)

Tropolone itself can be prepared in a number of ways, the most convenient of which involves oxidation of 1,3,5-cycloheptatriene ("tropilidene") with alkaline potassium permanganate. The yield is low but the product is readily isolated as the copper salt.

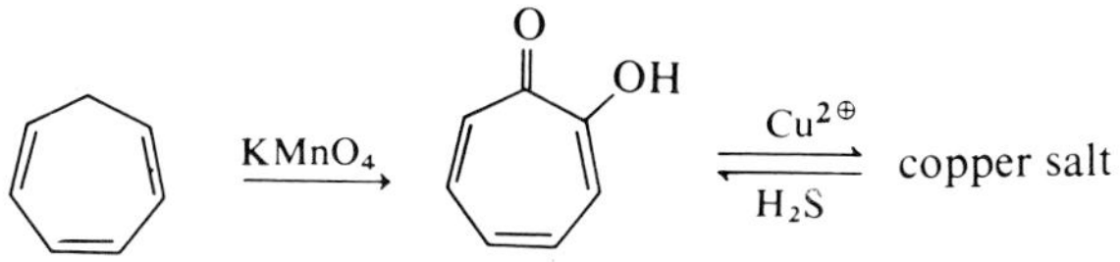

tropilidene   tropolone

Tropolone is an acid with an ionization constant of 10^{-7}, which is intermediate between that of acetic acid and that of phenol. Like phenols, tropolones form colored complexes with ferric chloride solution. Tropolone has many properties which suggest that it has some aromatic character. Thus, it resists hydrogenation, undergoes diazo coupling, and can be nitrated, sulfonated, and substituted with halogens. Its stability can be attributed to resonance involving the two nonequivalent structures [5] and [6] and to the several structures such as [7] and [8] which correspond to the stable tropylium cation with six π electrons (Section 6·7). There is a strong intramolecular hydrogen bond between the carbonyl oxygen and the hydroxylic proton and this fact reflects the importance of structure [6].

The tropylium cation itself is easily prepared by transfer of hydride ion from tropilidine to triphenylmethyl cation in sulfur dioxide solution.

$$\text{H} \quad \text{H} \qquad + (C_6H_5)_3C^\oplus \xrightarrow{\;SO_2\;} \qquad + (C_6H_5)_3CH$$

tropylium cation

Seven equivalent resonance structures can be written for the cation so that only one-seventh the positive charge is expected to be on each carbon. Since the cation also has just six π electrons, it is anticipated to be unusually stable for a carbonium ion.

hybrid structure for
   tropylium ion

summary

Phenols, ArOH, although enols, are stable because of the stabilization energy of the benzene ring. Phenol can be prepared from benzene via benzenesulfonic acid or via halobenzenes.

$$C_6H_6 \nearrow \begin{array}{c} C_6H_5SO_3H \\ \\ C_6H_5X \end{array} \searrow C_6H_5OH$$

Phenols resemble alcohols in forming esters and ethers but their considerably greater acidity (midway between alcohols and carboxylic acids) allows them to form salts with sodium hydroxide, though not with sodium bicarbonate.

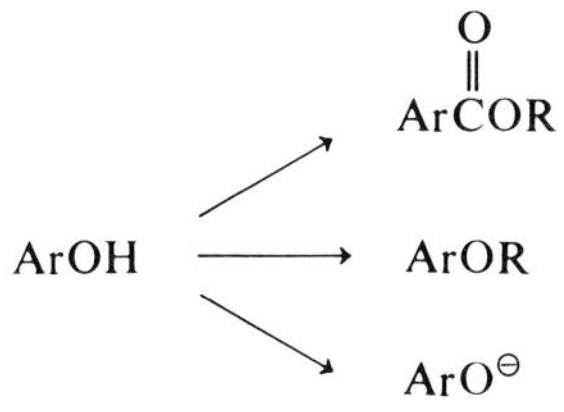

$$
\text{ArOH} \quad
\begin{cases}
\nearrow & \overset{\overset{\text{O}}{\parallel}}{\text{ArCOR}} \\
\longrightarrow & \text{ArOR} \\
\searrow & \text{ArO}^{\ominus}
\end{cases}
$$

Ether formation via phenoxide ion may be accompanied by C-alkylation. Cleavage of an aryl alkyl ether with hydrogen halide always gives alkyl halide and a phenol.

The hydroxyl group in phenols activates the ring toward electrophilic attack. Ionization of the hydroxyl causes further activation and enables feeble electrophiles such as carbon dioxide to react (Kolbe reaction).

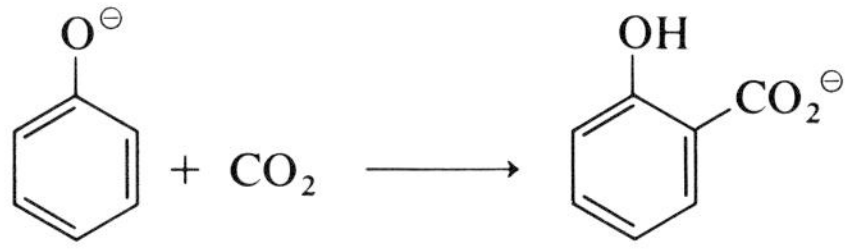

Intramolecular hydrogen bonding in *ortho*-substituted phenols is revealed by downfield nmr spectral shifts and by higher vapor pressures in comparison to analogous *para* compounds.

A number of polyhydric phenols are known; those with two hydroxyl groups *ortho* or *para* to one another can usually be oxidized to quinones. A quinone can undergo a number of addition reactions.

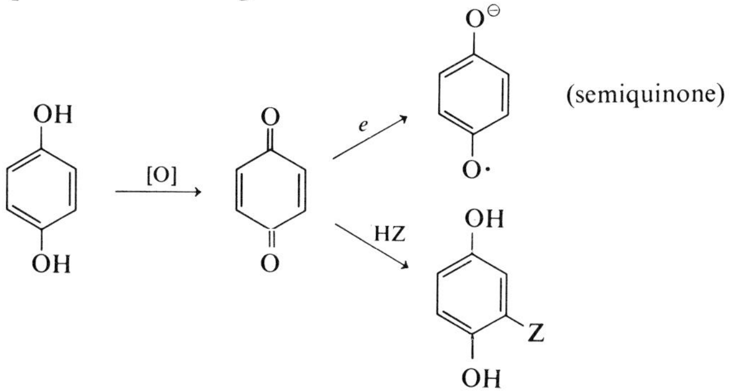

Two important naturally occurring quinones are vitamin K_1 and coenzyme Q. Tropolones, including the natural product β-thujaplicin, are seven-membered cyclic enols. A major factor in stabilizing the enol form is intramolecular hydrogen bonding. Resonance stabilization as in the tropylium ion may also be important.

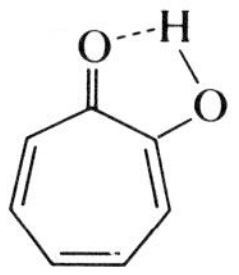

(tropolone) 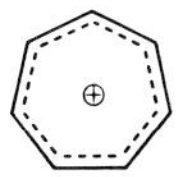   (tropylium ion)

exercises

23·1   Would you expect phenyl acetate to be hydrolyzed more readily or less readily than cyclohexyl acetate in alkaline solution? Use reasoning based on the mechanism of ester hydrolysis (Section 13·8).

23·2   Rearrangement of phenyl allyl-3-^{14}C ether at 200° gives o-allyl-1-^{14}C-phenol. What does this tell you about the rearrangement mechanism? Can it be a dissociation-recombination process? What product(s) would you expect from a para Claisen rearrangement of 2,6-dimethylphenyl allyl-3-^{14}C ether? From 2,6-diallylphenyl allyl-3-^{14}C ether?

23·3   Explain why phenol with bromine gives tribromophenol readily in water solution and o- and p-monobromophenols in nonpolar solvents. Note that 2,4,6-tribromophenol is at least a 300-fold stronger acid than phenol in water solution.

23·4   The herbicide 2,4-D is 2,4-dichlorophenoxyacetic acid (Figure 21·2). Show how this substance might be synthesized starting from phenol and acetic acid.

23·5   How much difference in physical properties would you expect for o- and p-cyanophenol isomers? Explain.

23·6   Resorcinol (m-dihydroxybenzene) can be converted to a carboxylic acid with carbon dioxide and alkali. Would you expect resorcinol to react more or less readily than phenol? Why? Which is the most likely point of monosubstitution? Explain.

23·7   Arrange the following quinones in order of increasing half-cell potential expected for reduction: p-benzoquinone, 4,4′-diphenoquinone, cis-2,2′-diphenoquinone, 9,10-anthraquinone, and 1,4-naphthoquinone. Your reasoning should be based on difference in stabilization of the quinones and the hydroquinones, including steric factors (if any).

23·8   Tropone (2,4,6-cycloheptatrienone) is an exceptionally strong base for a ketone. Explain.

23·9   At which position would you expect tropolone to substitute most readily with nitric acid? Explain.

23·10   Give for each of the following pairs of compounds a chemical test, preferably a test tube reaction, that will distinguish between the two compounds. Write a structural formula for each compound and equations for the reactions involved.

   a.   phenol and cyclohexanol
   b.   methyl p-hydroxybenzoate and p-methoxybenzoic acid
   c.   hydroquinone and resorcinol
   d.   hydroquinone and tropolone

23·11   Show by means of equations how each of the following substances might be synthesized, starting from the indicated materials. Specify reagents and approximate reaction conditions.

    a.   methyl 2-methoxybenzoate from phenol
    b.   2,6-dibromo-4-*t*-butylanisole from phenol
    c.   2-hydroxy-5-nitrobenzoic acid from phenol
    d.   4-cyanophenoxyacetic acid from phenol
    e.   cyanoquinone from hydroquinone

23·12   Write structural formulas for substances (one for each part) that fit the following descriptions:

    a.   a phenol that would be a stronger acid than phenol itself
    b.   that isomer of dichlorophenol that is the strongest acid
    c.   the Claisen rearrangement product from α-methylallyl-2,6-dimethyl-phenyl ether
    d.   the Claisen-type rearrangement product from allyl 2,6-dimethyl-4-(β-methylvinyl)-phenyl ether.
    e.   a quinone that would be a better charge-transfer agent than quinone itself
    f.   the expected product from addition of hydrogen cyanide to mono-cyanoquinone
    g.   a nonbenzenoid, quinone-like substance with its carbonyl groups in a 1,3 relationship

23·13   The chain reaction involved in the conversion of isopropylbenzene (cumene) to its hydroperoxide (Figure 23·1) can be written as follows, using a *t*-butoxy radical (formed by the decomposition of di-*t*-butyl peroxide) as the initiator.

$$C_6H_5CH(CH_3)_2 + t\text{-BuO}\cdot \longrightarrow A + t\text{-BuOH} \quad \text{initiation step}$$

$$A + O_2 \longrightarrow B$$

$$B + C_6H_5CH(CH_3)_2 \longrightarrow A + C_6H_5\overset{\overset{\displaystyle OOH}{|}}{C}(CH_3)_2$$

$$\left. \right\} \text{propagation steps}$$

    a.   Deduce the structure of A and B and suggest a reason for A, rather than one of its structural isomers, being formed in the initiation step.
    b.   Suggest a termination step (Section 2·5B) for the chain.

23·14   The acid-catalyzed rearrangement involved in the conversion of cumene hydroperoxide to phenol and acetone (Figure 23·1) can be written as follows:

$$C_6H_5\overset{\overset{\displaystyle OOH}{|}}{C}(CH_3)_2 + H^\oplus \rightleftharpoons C_6H_5\overset{\overset{\displaystyle O\overset{\oplus}{O}H_2}{|}}{C}(CH_3)_2 \xrightarrow{-H_2O} C_6H_5\overset{\oplus}{O}=C(CH_3)_2$$

$$\xrightarrow{+H_2O} C \xrightarrow{-H^\oplus} D \longrightarrow C_6H_5OH + (CH_3)_2C=O$$

    a.   Write a structure for the transition state for the rearrangement that occurs in the second step.
    b.   What are the structures of the cation C and the neutral molecule D and to what class of compounds does D belong?

23·15 Reduction of 9,10-anthraquinone with tin and hydrochloric acid in acetic acid produces a solid, light-yellow ketone, mp 156°, which has the formula $C_{14}H_{10}O$. This ketone is not soluble in cold alkali but does dissolve when heated with alkali. Acidification of cooled alkaline solutions of the ketone precipitates a brown-yellow isomer of the ketone of mp 120°, which gives a color with ferric chloride, couples with diazonium salts, reacts with bromine, and slowly is reconverted to the ketone.

What are the structures of the ketone and its isomer? Write equations for the reactions described.

23·16 Devise syntheses of each of the following photographic developing agents based on benzene as the aromatic starting material. Give approximate reaction conditions and reagents.

    a. hydroquinone
    b. *p*-aminophenol
    c. *p*-amino-N,N-diethylaniline
    d. (*p*-hydroxyphenyl)-aminoacetic acid
    e. 2,4-diaminophenol

23·17 Addition of hydrogen chloride to *p*-benzoquinone yields some 2,3,5,6-tetrachloroquinone. Explain how the latter could be formed in the absence of an external oxidizing agent.

23·18 Consider the possibility of benzilic acid-type rearrangements of 9,10-phenanthrenequinone and anthraquinone. Give your reasoning.

23·19 When quinone is treated with hydroxylamine and phenol is treated with nitrous acid, the same compound of formula $C_6H_5O_2N$ is produced. What is the likely structure of this compound and how would you establish its correctness?

23·20 How would you expect the properties of 3- and 4-hydroxy-2,4,6-cycloheptatrienone to compare with those of tropolone? Explain.

23·21 Make an atomic orbital model of phenol, showing in detail the orbitals and electrons at the oxygen atom (it may be desirable to review Chapters 6 and 20 in connection with this problem). From your model, would you expect either or both pairs of unshared electrons on oxygen to be delocalized over the ring? What would be the most favorable orientation of the hydrogen of the hydroxyl group for maximum delocalization of an unshared electron pair?

chapter 24
aromatic side-chain derivatives

The pronounced modification in the reactivity of halogen, amino, and hydroxyl substituents when linked to aromatic carbon rather than saturated carbon was discussed in Chapters 21, 22, and 23. Other substituents, particularly those linked to an aromatic ring through a carbon-carbon bond, are also influenced by the ring, although usually to a lesser degree. Examples include $-CH_2OH$, $-CH_2OCH_3$, $-CH_2Cl$, $-CHO$, $-COCH_3$, $-CO_2H$, and $-CN$, and we shall refer to aromatic compounds containing substituents of this type as **aromatic side-chain derivatives.**

preparation of aromatic side-chain compounds

Since the utility of any method of synthesis is limited by the accessibility of the starting materials, we may anticipate that the most practical methods for the preparation of benzenoid side-chain compounds will start from benzene or an alkylbenzene. These methods may be divided into two categories—those that modify an existing side chain, and those by which a side chain is introduced through substitution of the aromatic ring. We shall consider first the reactions that modify a side chain and for which the obvious starting materials are the alkylbenzenes, especially toluene and the xylenes.

24·1   aromatic carboxylic acids

An alkylbenzene can be converted to benzoic acid by oxidation of the side chain with reagents such as potassium permanganate, potassium dichromate, or nitric acid.

benzoic acid

Under the conditions of oxidation, higher alkyl or alkenyl groups are degraded and ring substituents, other than halogen and nitro groups, often fail to survive.

In fact, the presence of a hydroxyl or amino substituent causes the whole ring to be degraded long before the alkyl group undergoes appreciable oxidation.

By contrast, prolonged oxidation of 5-nitro-2-indanone gives a good yield of product with the substituent untouched and the ring intact.

5-nitro-2-indanone   4-nitrophthalic acid

To retain a side-chain substituent, selective methods of oxidation are required. For example, *p*-toluic acid may be prepared from *p*-tolyl methyl ketone by the haloform reaction (Section 12·1C).

$$H_3C-\!\!\!\bigcirc\!\!\!-COCH_3 \xrightarrow{Br_2,\,OH^\ominus} H_3C-\!\!\!\bigcirc\!\!\!-CO_2H$$

The Cannizzaro reaction (Section 11·4H) is sometimes useful for the preparation of substituted benzoic acids and (or) benzyl alcohols, provided that the starting aldehyde is available.

2-iodo-3-hydroxy-
benzaldehyde

$\xrightarrow{H_2O,\ ^\ominus OH}$

2-iodo-3-hydroxy-
benzoic acid
80%

+

2-iodo-3-hydroxy-
benzyl alcohol
80%

24·2 *preparation of side-chain aromatic halogen compounds*

Although many side-chain halogen compounds can be synthesized by reactions that are also applicable to alkyl halides, there are several other methods especially useful for the preparation of arylmethyl halides. The most important of these are the radical halogenation of alkylbenzenes and chloromethylation of aromatic compounds (Section 24·4B).

The light-induced, radical chlorination or bromination of alkylbenzenes with molecular chlorine or bromine gives substitution on the side chain rather than on the ring. Thus, toluene reacts with chlorine to give successively benzyl chloride, benzal chloride, and benzotrichloride.

$$C_6H_5CH_3 \xrightarrow[h\upsilon]{Cl_2} C_6H_5CH_2Cl \xrightarrow[h\upsilon]{Cl_2} C_6H_5CHCl_2 \xrightarrow[h\upsilon]{Cl_2} C_6H_5CCl_3$$

toluene

benzyl
chloride

benzal
chloride

benzo-
trichloride

This reaction was met when the chlorination of methane was discussed in Chapter 2. The major effect of the phenyl ring is to facilitate the reaction by making the intermediate benzyl radicals more stable.

24·3 *side-chain compounds derived from arylmethyl halides*

Arylmethyl halides, such as benzyl chloride ($C_6H_5CH_2Cl$), benzal chloride ($C_6H_5CHCl_2$), and benzotrichloride are quite reactive compounds. They are

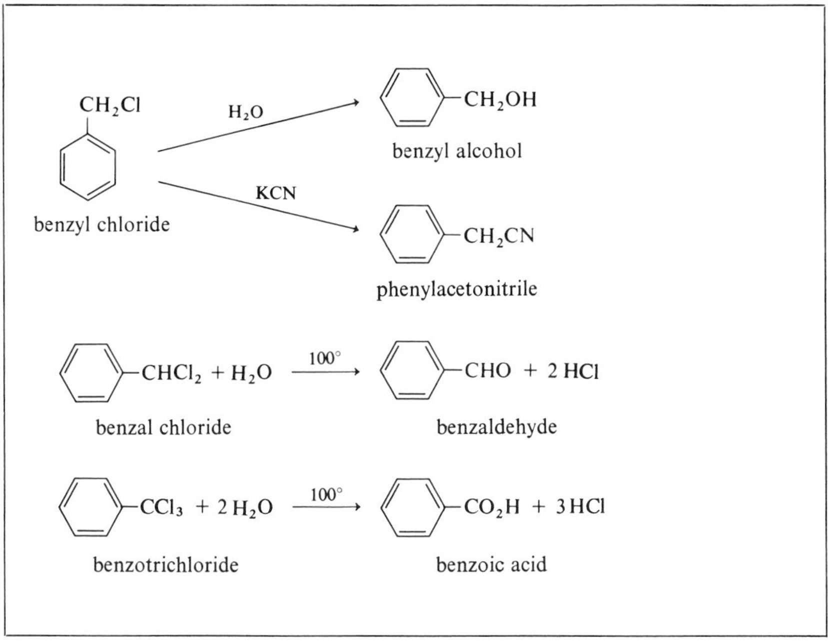

Figure 24·1   Reactions of benzyl chloride, benzal chloride, and benzotrichloride.

readily available or easily prepared and are useful intermediates for the synthesis of other side-chain derivatives. See Figure 24·1 for examples.

24·4 preparation of aromatic side-chain compounds by ring substitution

A. FRIEDEL-CRAFTS REACTION

The Friedel-Crafts alkylation and acylation reactions have been discussed (Sections 20·4D and 20·4E). For alkylation, catalytic amounts of $AlCl_3$ are

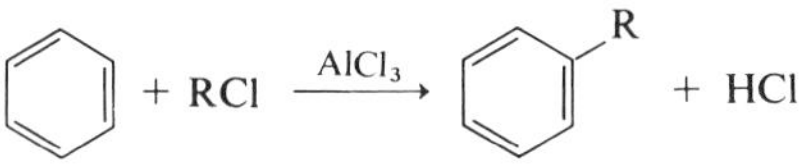

usually sufficient and polysubstitution may be an important side reaction because of the activating effect of the R group.

For acylation, large amounts of $AlCl_3$ are required and only monosubstitution occurs because of the deactivating effect of the $-\overset{O}{\overset{\|}{C}}-R$ group.

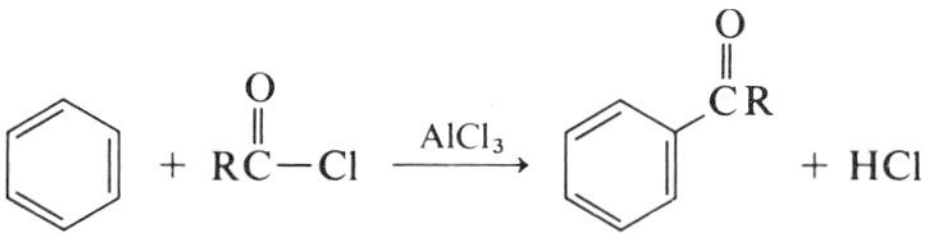

B. CHLOROMETHYLATION

The reaction of an aromatic compound with formaldehyde and hydrogen chloride in the presence of zinc chloride as catalyst results in the substitution of a chloromethyl group, $-CH_2Cl$, for a ring hydrogen.

$$C_6H_6 + CH_2O + HCl \xrightarrow{\text{ZnCl}_2} C_6H_5CH_2Cl + H_2O$$

The mechanism of the chloromethylation reaction is related to that of Friedel-Crafts alkylation and acylation and probably involves an incipient chloromethyl cation, $^{\oplus}CH_2Cl$.

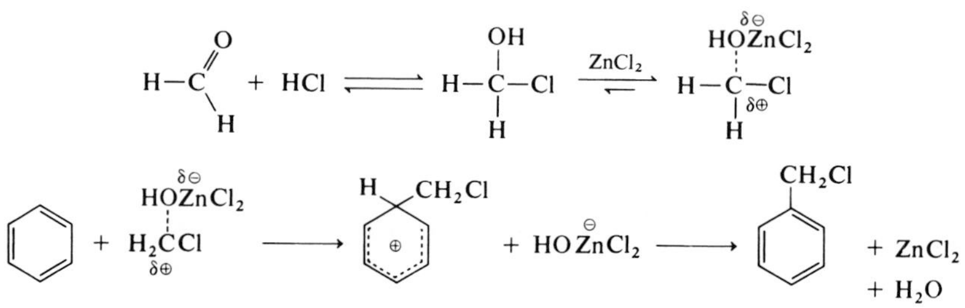

C. ALDEHYDES BY FORMYLATION

Substitution of the carboxaldehyde group ($-CHO$) into an aromatic ring is known as **formylation**. This is accomplished by reaction of an aromatic hydrocarbon with carbon monoxide in the presence of hydrogen chloride and aluminum chloride. Cuprous chloride is also required for reactions proceeding at atmospheric pressure but is not necessary for reactions at elevated pressures.

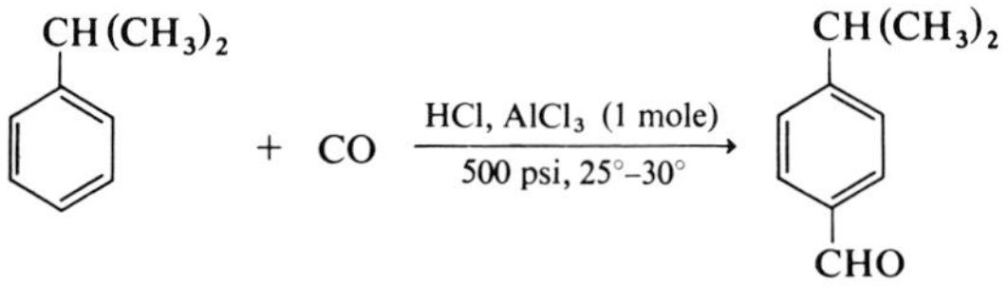

p-isopropylbenzaldehyde
60%

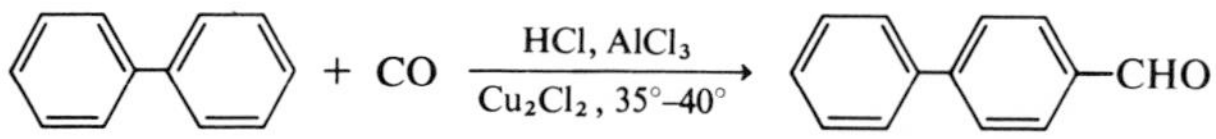

p-phenylbenzaldehyde
73%

Formylation of *reactive* aromatic compounds such as phenols, phenolic ethers, and certain hydrocarbons can be brought about by the action of hydrogen cyanide, hydrogen chloride, and a catalyst, usually zinc chloride or aluminum chloride. A convenient alternative is to use zinc cyanide and hydrogen chloride. The product is then hydrolyzed to an aldehyde.

2-naphthol   2-hydroxy-1-naphthaldehyde

properties of aromatic side-chain derivatives

24·5 arylmethyl halides. stable carbonium ions, carbanions, and radicals

The arylmethyl halides of particular interest are those having both halogen and aryl substituents bonded to the same saturated carbon. Typical examples and their physical properties are listed in Table 24·1.

We noted in Chapter 21 that benzyl halides ($C_6H_5CH_2X$) are comparable in both S_N1 and S_N2 reactivity to allyl halides ($CH_2=CHCH_2X$) and, because high reactivity in S_N1 reactions is associated primarily with exceptional carbonium ion stability, the reactivity of benzyl derivatives can be ascribed mainly to resonance stabilization of the benzyl cation. Diphenylmethyl or benzhydryl halides, $(C_6H_5)_2CHX$, are still more reactive than benzyl halides in S_N1 reactions, and this is reasonable because the diphenylmethyl cation has two phenyl groups over which the positive charge can be delocalized and is, therefore, more stable relative to the starting halide than is the benzyl cation.

diphenylmethyl cation

Table 24·1   Physical properties of arylmethyl halides

compound	formula	bp, °C	mp, °C	$d^{20/4}$, g/ml
benzyl fluoride	$C_6H_5CH_2F$	140	−35	$1.0228^{25/4}$
benzyl chloride	$C_6H_5CH_2Cl$	179	−43	$1.1026^{18/4}$
benzyl bromide	$C_6H_5CH_2Br$	198	−4.0	$1.438^{22/0}$
benzyl iodide	$C_6H_5CH_2I$	93^{10mm}	24	$1.733^{25/4}$
benzal chloride	$C_6H_5CHCl_2$	207	−16	1.2557^{14}
benzotrichloride	$C_6H_5CCl_3$	214	−22	1.38
benzotrifluoride	$C_6H_5CF_3$	103	−29.1	1.1886^{20}
benzhydryl chloride (diphenylmethyl chloride)	$(C_6H_5)_2CHCl$	173^{19mm}	20.5	
triphenylmethyl chloride (trityl chloride)	$(C_6H_5)_3CCl$		112.3	

Accordingly, we might expect triphenylmethyl or trityl halides, $(C_6H_5)_3C$ —X, to be more reactive yet. In fact, the C—X bonds of such compounds are sufficiently labile that reversible ionization occurs in solvents that have reasonably high dielectric constants but do not react irreversibly with the carbonium ion. An example of such a solvent is liquid sulfur dioxide, and the degrees of ionization of a number of triarylmethyl halides in this solvent have been determined by electrical-conductance measurements, although the equilibria are complicated by ion-pair association.

$$(C_6H_5)_3C-Cl \xrightarrow{SO_2,\,0°} \underset{\text{ion pair}}{(C_6H_5)_3C^\oplus Cl^\ominus} \rightleftharpoons \underset{\text{dissociated ions}}{(C_6H_5)_3C^\oplus + Cl^\ominus}$$

Triarylmethyl cations are among the most stable carbonium ions known. They are intensely colored and are readily formed when the corresponding triarylcarbinol is dissolved in strong acids.

$$\underset{\substack{\text{triphenylcarbinol} \\ \text{(colorless)}}}{(C_6H_5)_3C-OH} \underset{H_2SO_4}{\rightleftharpoons} (C_6H_5)_3C-\overset{\oplus}{O}H_2 \overset{(-H_2O)}{\rightleftharpoons} \underset{\substack{\text{triphenylmethyl cation} \\ \text{(orange-yellow)}}}{(C_6H_5)_3C^\oplus}$$

If electron-donating *para* substituents such as amino groups are placed in each ring [1] the energy of the carbonium ion is lowered to such an extent that it is stable in water at pH 7.

$(p\text{-}NH_2C_6H_4)_3C^\oplus$

[1]

In addition to forming stable cations, triarylmethyl compounds form stable carbanions. Because of this, the corresponding hydrocarbons are relatively acidic compared to simple alkanes. They react readily with strong bases such as sodamide, and the resulting carbanions are usually intensely colored.

$$\underset{\substack{\text{triphenylmethane} \\ \text{(colorless)}}}{(C_6H_5)_3CH + Na^\oplus NH_2{}^\ominus} \overset{\text{ether}}{\rightleftharpoons} \underset{\substack{\text{sodium triphenylmethide} \\ \text{(blood red)}}}{(C_6H_5)_3C{:}^\ominus Na^\oplus + NH_3}$$

This carbanion can also be generated by the action of less basic reagents such as sodium ethoxide, provided polar aprotic solvents such as dimethyl sulfoxide or hexamethylphosphoramide are used (Sections 8·11D and 19·2C). Just as the positive charge in triarylmethyl cations can be distributed over the *ortho* and *para* positions of each ring, so can the negative charge in the triphenylmethide ion.

Triarylmethyl compounds also form stable triarylmethyl radicals, and indeed the first stable carbon radical to be reported was the triphenylmethyl radical, $(C_6H_5)_3C\cdot$, prepared inadvertently by Gomberg in 1900. Gomberg's objective was to prepare hexaphenylethane by a Wurtz coupling reaction of triphenylmethyl chloride with metallic silver; but he found that no hydrocarbon was formed unless air was carefully excluded from the system.

$$2\,(C_6H_5)_3C-Cl + 2\,Ag \xrightarrow{\text{benzene}} \underset{\text{hexaphenylethane }(C_{38}H_{30})}{(C_6H_5)_3C-C(C_6H_5)_3 + 2\,AgCl}$$

In the presence of atmospheric oxygen, the product is triphenylmethyl peroxide, $(C_6H_5)_3COOC(C_6H_5)_3$, rather than hexaphenylethane. In the absence of oxygen a compound, $C_{38}H_{30}$, assumed to be hexaphenylethane, was obtained and shown to dissociate slightly to triphenylmethyl radicals at room temperature in inert solvents ($K = 2.2 \times 10^{-4}$ at 24° in benzene). However, equilibrium between this compound and triphenylmethyl radicals is rapidly established so that oxygen readily converts the ethane into the relatively stable triphenylmethyl peroxide.

$$C_{38}H_{30} \underset{K=2.2 \times 10^{-4}}{\overset{\text{benzene } 24°}{\rightleftharpoons}} 2(C_6H_5)_3C\cdot$$
triphenylmethyl radical

$$(C_6H_5)_3C\cdot + O_2 \rightleftharpoons (C_6H_5)_3COO\cdot \xrightarrow{(C_6H_5)_3C\cdot} (C_6H_5)_3COOC(C_6H_5)_3$$
triphenylmethyl
peroxide

While these reactions may now seem entirely reasonable, Gomberg's suggestion that the triphenylmethyl radical could exist as a fairly stable species was not well received at the time. Today, the stability of the radical has been established beyond question by a variety of methods such as electron paramagnetic resonance (epr) spectroscopy, which is discussed briefly at the end of this chapter (Section 24·8). This stability can be attributed to stabilization of the odd electron by the attached phenyl groups.

A curious sequel to Gomberg's work has occurred. The compound $C_{38}H_{30}$ that is in equilibrium with the radical was shown in 1968 to be not hexaphenylethane [2] but its structural isomer [3] resulting from coupling of two radicals through a *para* carbon in one of them. Presumably [3] is more

[2]   [3]

stable than [2] because of lower steric strain. It is interesting that the difference is sufficient to overcome the loss of the resonance energy of one benzene ring. Some strain undoubtedly remains in [3] and is relieved by dissociation, although the main driving force for this is the resonance stabilization of the radical so formed.

The stability of a carbon radical, $R_3C\cdot$, is reflected in the ease with which the C—H bond of the corresponding hydrocarbon, R_3CH, is broken homolytically. A hydrogen atom bonded to a tertiary carbon is replaced in radical chlorination faster than hydrogen at a secondary or primary position (see Section 3·3B) showing that the order of stability of the resulting carbon radicals is tertiary > secondary > primary. Hydrogen-abstraction reactions by radicals other than chlorine atoms have been investigated to obtain some measure of hydrocarbon reactivity and radical stability.

24·6 aromatic aldehydes

Most of the reactions of aromatic aldehydes involve nothing new or surprising in view of our earlier discussion on the reactions of aldehydes (Chapters 11 and 12). One reaction, which is rather different and is usually regarded as being characteristic of aromatic aldehydes (although, in fact, it does occur with other aldehydes having no α hydrogens), is known as the **benzoin condensation**. It is essentially a dimerization of two aldehyde molecules through the catalytic action of sodium or potassium cyanide.

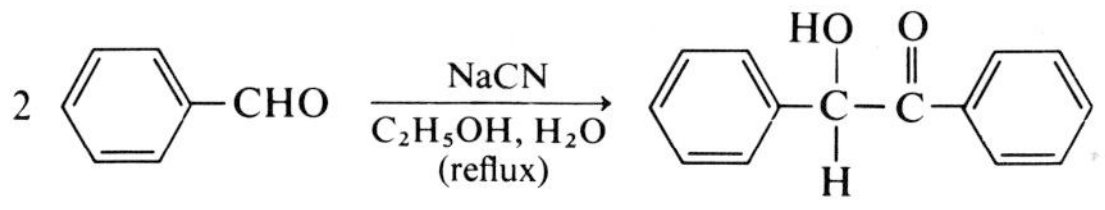

benzoin
90%

The dimer so formed from benzaldehyde is an α-hydroxy ketone and is called benzoin. Unsymmetrical or mixed benzoins may often be obtained in good yield from two different aldehydes.

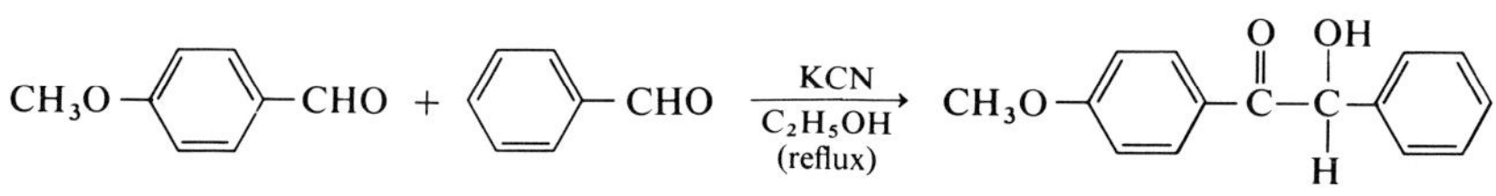

anisaldehyde   benzaldehyde   4-methoxybenzoin

In naming an unsymmetrical benzoin, substituents in the ring attached to the carbonyl group are numbered in the usual way while primes are used to number substituents in the ring attached to the carbinol carbon.

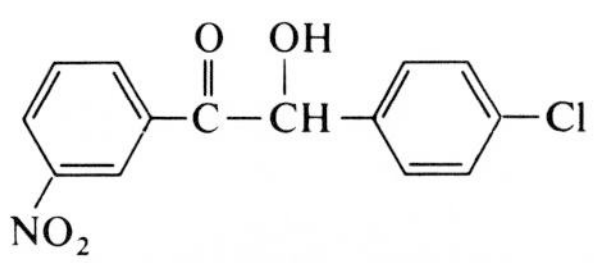

3-nitro-4'-chlorobenzoin

The first step in the benzoin condensation involves conversion of the aldehyde to the cyanohydrin by attack of cyanide ion at the carbonyl group.

The cyanohydrin [4] thus formed has a relatively acidic α hydrogen because the resulting carbanion is stabilized by both a phenyl and a cyano group. At the pH of a cyanide solution, a benzyl-type carbanion [5] is readily formed and, in a subsequent slow step, attacks the carbonyl carbon of a second aldehyde molecule. Loss of HCN from the addition product [6] leads to benzoin.

$$C_6H_5C\underset{H}{\overset{O}{\diagdown}} + CN^{\ominus} \rightleftharpoons C_6H_5-\underset{C\equiv N}{\overset{O^{\ominus}}{\underset{|}{C}}}-H \rightleftharpoons C_6H_5-\underset{C\equiv N}{\overset{OH}{\underset{|}{C}}}:^{\ominus}$$

$$[4] \qquad\qquad [5]$$

$$C_6H_5-\underset{C\equiv N}{\overset{OH}{\underset{|}{C}}}:^{\ominus} + \overset{O}{\underset{H}{\diagup}}C-C_6H_5 \longrightarrow C_6H_5-\underset{NC}{\overset{HO}{\underset{|}{C}}}-\underset{H}{\overset{O^{\ominus}}{\underset{|}{C}}}-C_6H_5$$

$$[6]$$

$$C_6H_5-\underset{NC}{\overset{O^{\ominus}}{\underset{|}{C}}}-\underset{H}{\overset{OH}{\underset{|}{C}}}-C_6H_5 \xrightarrow{-CN^{\ominus}} C_6H_5-\overset{O}{\overset{\|}{C}}-\underset{}{\overset{OH}{\underset{|}{CH}}}-C_6H_5$$

$$\text{benzoin}$$

The unique catalytic effect of cyanide ion is due to its high nucleophilicity which leads to the production of an adduct such as [4]; the electron-withdrawing power of the cyano group that stabilizes ion [5]; and the ease with which the cyanide ion can be eliminated in the final step.

The benzoin condensation is a useful synthetic reaction when you want to prepare a compound with the Ar-C-C-Ar skeleton. The carbonyl and hydroxyl groups in benzoins are subject to the usual reactions of ketones and alcohols.

24·7 natural occurrence and uses of aromatic side-chain derivatives

Derivatives of aromatic aldehydes occur naturally in the seeds of plants. For example, amygdalin is a substance occurring in the seeds of the bitter almond; it is a derivative of gentiobiose, which is a disaccharide made up of two glucose units. One of the glucose units is bonded through the OH group of benzaldehyde cyanohydrin by a β-glucoside linkage.

amygdalin

The flavoring vanillin occurs naturally as glucovanillin (a glucoside) in the vanilla bean, although it is also obtained commercially as a byproduct from the treatment of lignin waste liquor (Section 15·7) and by oxidation of eugenol, a constituent of several essential oils.

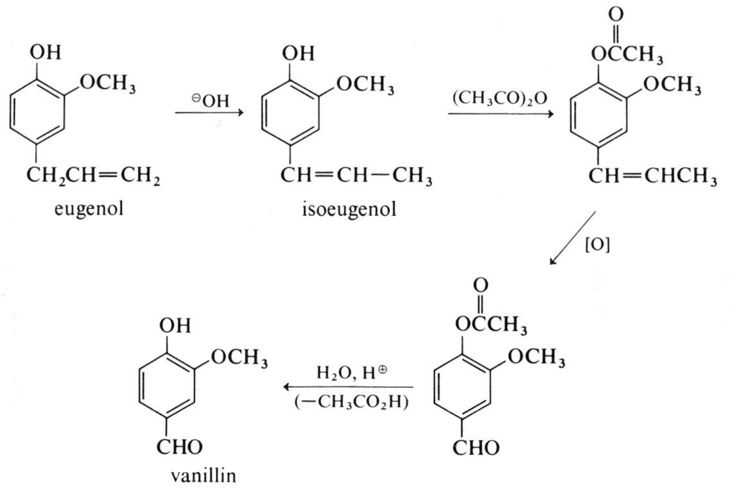

eugenol   isoeugenol

vanillin

Methyl salicylate, the major constituent of oil of wintergreen, occurs in many plants, but it is also readily prepared synthetically by esterification of salicylic acid, which in turn is made from phenol (see Section 23·2D).

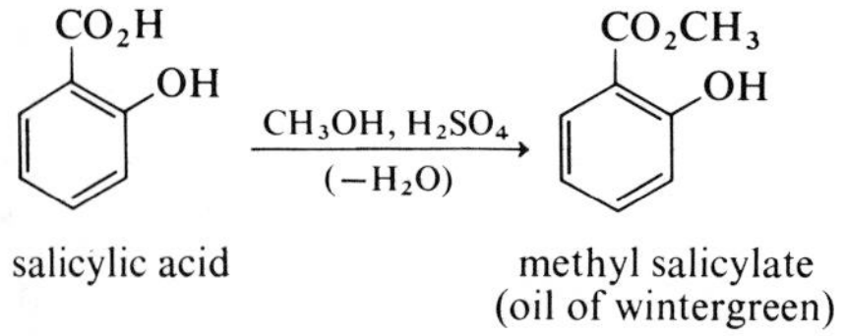

salicylic acid   methyl salicylate (oil of wintergreen)

The acetyl derivative of salicylic acid is better known as aspirin and is prepared from the acid with acetic anhydride using sulfuric acid as catalyst.

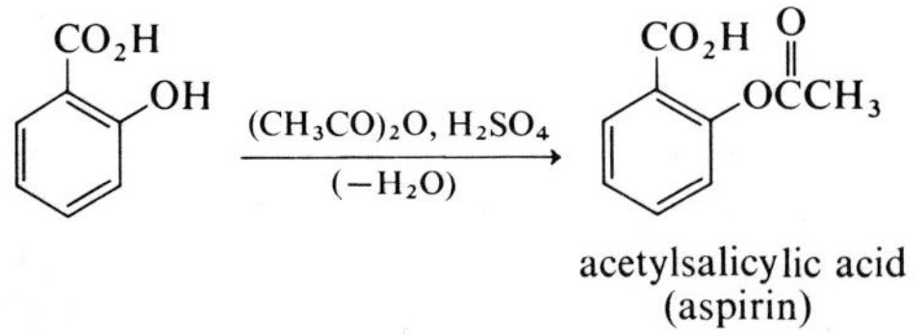

acetylsalicylic acid (aspirin)

The structures of several other side-chain compounds used as flavorings, perfumes, or drugs are shown in Figure 24·2.

Numerals are used to indicate positions both on an alkane chain and in a benzene ring and this can sometimes be awkward, as in the systematic name for adrenaline shown in Figure 24·2. With a single substituent on a ring this difficulty can be avoided by using the symbol o, m, or p.

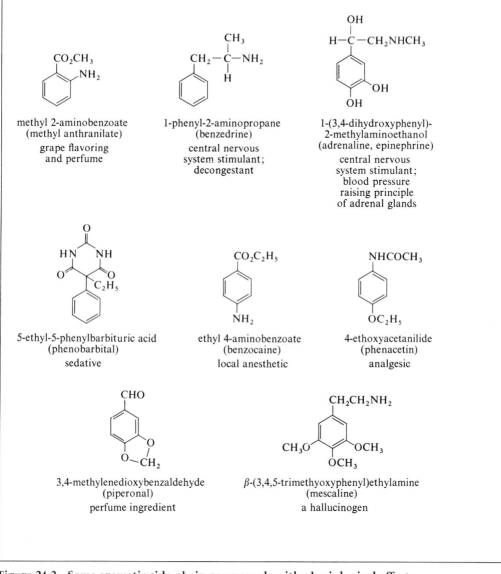

Figure 24·2   Some aromatic side-chain compounds with physiological effects.

24·8   electron paramagnetic resonance (epr) spectroscopy

One of the most important methods of studying radicals that has yet been developed is electron paramagnetic resonance (epr) or, as it is sometimes called, electron-spin resonance (esr) spectroscopy. The principles of this form of spectroscopy are in many respects similar to nmr spectroscopy, even though the language used is often quite different. The important point is that an *unpaired* electron, like a proton, has a spin and a magnetic moment such that it has two possible orientations in a magnetic field corresponding to magnetic quantum numbers $+\frac{1}{2}$ and $-\frac{1}{2}$. The two orientations define two energy states which differ in energy by about 1000 times the energy difference between corresponding states for protons, and therefore the frequency of absorption of electrons is about 1000 times that of protons at the same magnetic field. At magnetic fields of 3600 gauss, the absorption frequency of free electrons is about 10,000 MHz, which falls in the microwave, rather than the radiowave, region.

The basic apparatus for epr spectroscopy differs from that shown in Figure 7·11 for nmr spectroscopy by having the sample located in the resonant cavity of a microwave generator. The spectrum produced by epr absorption of unpaired electrons is similar to that shown in Figure 24·3a, except that epr spectrometers are normally so arranged as to yield a plot of the first derivative of the curve of absorption against magnetic field, rather than the absorption curve itself, as shown in Figure 24·3b. This arrangement is used because it gives a better signal-to-noise ratio than a simple plot of absorption against magnetic field.

The sensitivity of epr spectroscopy for detection of radicals is high. Under favorable conditions, a concentration of radicals as low as 10^{-12} M can be readily detected. Identification of simple hydrocarbon free radicals is often possible by analysis of the fine structure in their spectra. This fine structure

Figure 24·3   Plots of absorption (a) and derivative (b) epr curves.

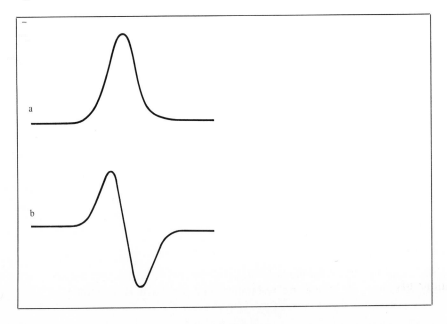

arises from spin-spin splittings involving protons, which are reasonably close to the centers over which the unpaired electron is distributed. The multiplicity of hydrogens and their location in the *ortho*, *meta*, and *para* positions of the triphenylmethyl radical produces an extremely complex epr spectrum with at least 21 observable absorption lines. Other radicals may give simpler spectra. Methyl radicals generated by X-ray bombardment of methyl iodide at $-196°$ show four $(n + 1)$ resonance lines, as expected, for interaction of the electron with three (n) protons (see Section 7·6B).

One of the most exciting uses of epr is in the study of radical intermediates in organic reactions. Thus, in the oxidation of hydroquinone in alkaline solution by oxygen, the formation of the semiquinone radical (Section 23·4) can be detected by epr. The identity of the intermediate is shown by the fact that its electron spectrum is split into five equally spaced lines by the four equivalent ring protons. The radical disappears by disproportionation reactions and has a half-life of about 3 seconds.

Similar studies have shown that radicals are generated and decay in oxidations brought about by enzymes. Radicals have been detected by epr measurements in algae "fixing" carbon dioxide in photosynthesis. The character of the radicals formed has been found to depend on the wavelength of the light supplied for photosynthesis.

24·9   linear free-energy relations

Can we predict the effect a substituent on a benzene ring will have on the rate or the position of equilibrium of a reaction taking place elsewhere in the molecule? Yes, to a very considerable degree, provided the substituent is in a *meta* or *para* position and certain other information is available. Some idea of the regularity of substituent effects can be seen in Figure 24·4, which shows a plot of the logarithm of the equilibrium constants for the dissociation of a series of benzoic acids against the logarithm of the rate constants for the alkaline hydrolysis of the corresponding ethyl benzoates (Equations 24·1 and 24·2).

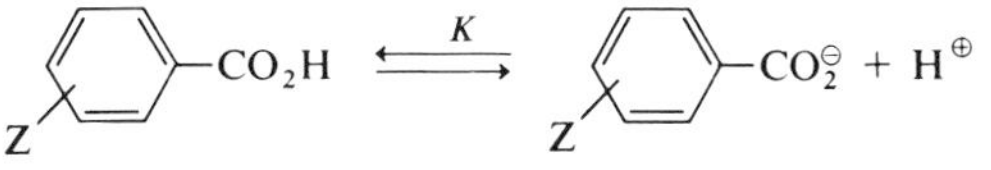

$$Z{-}\langle\ \rangle{-}CO_2H \overset{K}{\rightleftharpoons} Z{-}\langle\ \rangle{-}CO_2^{\ominus} + H^{\oplus} \qquad (24·1)$$

$$Z{-}\langle\ \rangle{-}CO_2Et + OH^{\ominus} \overset{k}{\longrightarrow} Z{-}\langle\ \rangle{-}CO_2^{\ominus} + EtOH \qquad (24·2)$$

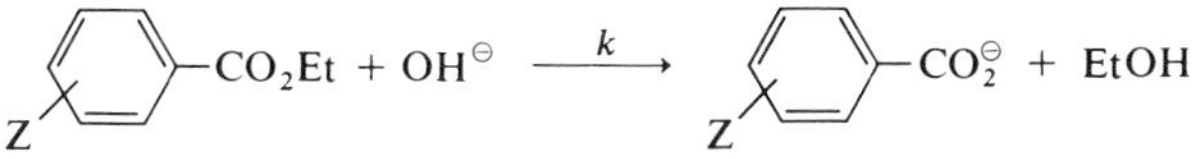

A plot of $\log k$ against $\log K$ is really a plot of free energies since $\log k \propto \Delta G^{\ddagger}$ and $\log K \propto \Delta G$. Thus, we can say that the two reaction series (the *meta* and *para* compounds, at least) obey a "linear free-energy relation."

Relations like this are not usually observed with *ortho*-substituted compounds (see Figure 24·4) or with aliphatic systems because of steric and other

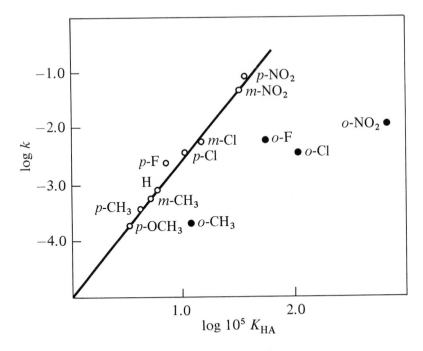

Figure 24·4 Plot of log k for the rates of alkaline hydrolysis of substituted ethyl benzoates in 85% ethanol at 30° against log $10^5\,K_{HA}$ for the dissociation of substituted benzoic acids in water at 25°.

Table 24·2   Substituent constants

substituent	σ meta	σ para	substituent	σ meta	σ para
$O^{\ominus}$	−0.708	−1.00	SH	+0.25	+0.15
NH_2	−0.161	−0.660	Cl	+0.373	+0.227
OH	+0.121	−0.37	CO_2H	+0.355	+0.406
OCH_3	+0.115	−0.268	$COCH_3$	+0.376	+0.502
CH_3	−0.069	−0.170	CF_3	+0.43	+0.54
$(CH_3)_3Si$	−0.121	−0.072	NO_2	+0.710	+0.778
C_6H_5	+0.06	−0.01	$\overset{\oplus}{N}(CH_3)_3$	+0.88	+0.82
H	0.000	0.000	$\overset{\oplus}{S}(CH_3)_2$	+1.00	+0.90
SCH_3	+0.15	0.00	$\overset{\oplus}{N_2}$	+1.76	+1.91
F	+0.337	+0.062			

proximity effects. *Meta-* and *para*-substituted series can be related this way because the substituents are far enough away from the reaction sites so that steric and proximity effects are diminished and only the electrical effect of the substituent is important. A *p*-nitro group is always electron withdrawing and a *p*-amino group always electron donating and we can assign to these and other substituents a value that represents their electron-donating or electron-withdrawing ability relative to hydrogen taken as zero. These **substituent constants**, symbol σ, are obtained from the ionization constants of substituted benzoic acids. If a substituent increases the acidity of benzoic acid, σ is positive; if it decreases the acidity of benzoic acid, σ is negative. The larger the effect of the substituent on the benzoic acid ionization, the larger is the absolute value of σ. Table 24·2 lists the substituent constants for a number of common groups.

To predict the effect of a substituent on a given rate or equilibrium constant, a further factor must be considered—the sensitivity of the reaction site to electrical effects of the substituents. The slope of the line in Figure 24·4 is $+2.2$. The positive sign means that the reaction sites in both ester hydrolysis and acid ionization have the same kind of response to substituent electrical effects. Thus, *p*-nitro speeds up the hydrolysis of the ester and also increases the degree of dissociation of the acid. For the ester hydrolysis, the electron-withdrawing group helps to make the carbonyl carbon more positive and hence better able to attract hydroxide ion (Section 13·8); in ionization, it helps to stabilize the anion by electron attraction. Since the slope is greater than unity (2.2) the ester hydrolysis is *more sensitive* to the effects of substituents than is the acid dissociation.

The sensitivity of a reaction to substituents is given by the **reaction constant**, symbol ρ, and is obtained by measuring the slope of the line when $\log k$ or $\log K$ is plotted against $\log K_{HA}$ for benzoic acids. If, as for the benzoic acid dissociation, the reaction is facilitated by electron-withdrawing groups, ρ is positive. If the reaction is more sensitive than the benzoic acid dissociation (slope > 1), then ρ is greater than unity; if it is less sensitive, ρ is less than unity. A reaction with the opposite electronic requirements has a negative ρ.

Values of ρ are obtained by plots such as that in Figure 24·4, and a number of these reaction constants are listed in Table 24·3.

The combination of the two independent variables ρ and σ defines the effect of the *meta* or *para* substituent on the rate constant—that is, the difference between $\log k$ and $\log k_0$, where k_0 refers to the unsubstituted compound.

$$\log k = \rho\sigma + \log k_0$$

This equation (or its analog for equilibrium constants) is known as the Hammett equation. It describes in a quantitative way the effect of substituents on reaction rates (or equilibrium constants) of *meta* or *para* substituted aromatic compounds.

Table 24·3   Reaction constants

	ρ
equilibria	

$$R\!-\!C_6H_4\!-\!CO_2H \underset{25°}{\overset{H_2O}{\rightleftharpoons}} R\!-\!C_6H_4\!-\!CO_2^{\ominus} + H^{\oplus}$$ 1.00

$$R\!-\!C_6H_4\!-\!CH_2CO_2H \underset{25°}{\overset{H_2O}{\rightleftharpoons}} R\!-\!C_6H_4\!-\!CH_2CO_2^{\ominus} + H^{\oplus}$$ 0.489

$$R\!-\!C_6H_4\!-\!CHO + HCN \overset{95\% \; C_2H_5OH}{\rightleftharpoons} R\!-\!C_6H_4\!-\!CH(OH)CN$$ 1.492

$$R\!-\!C_6H_4\!-\!OH \underset{25°}{\overset{H_2O}{\rightleftharpoons}} R\!-\!C_6H_4\!-\!O^{\ominus} + H^{\oplus}$$ 2.113[a]

| *reaction rates* | |

$$R\!-\!C_6H_4\!-\!CO_2C_2H_5 + OH^{\ominus} \underset{30°}{\overset{85\% \; C_2H_5OH}{\longrightarrow}} R\!-\!C_6H_4\!-\!CO_2^{\ominus} + C_2H_5OH$$ 2.431

$$R\!-\!C_6H_4\!-\!\underset{Cl}{CH}\!-\!C_6H_5 + C_2H_5OH \underset{25°}{\longrightarrow} R\!-\!C_6H_4\!-\!\underset{OC_2H_5}{CH}\!-\!C_6H_5 + HCl$$ -5.090^{b}

$$R\!-\!C_6H_4\!-\!COCH_3 + Br_2 \overset{CH_3CO_2H, \; 35°}{\underset{CH_3CO_2^{\ominus}}{\longrightarrow}} R\!-\!C_6H_4\!-\!COCH_2Br + HBr$$ 0.417

$$R\!-\!C_6H_5 + NO_2^{\oplus} \underset{18°}{\overset{(CH_3CO)_2O}{\longrightarrow}} R\!-\!C_6H_4\!-\!NO_2 + H^{\oplus}$$ -5.926^{b}

[a] Nitro and similar groups have somewhat exalted σ_{para} values in reactions such as this in which direct resonance interaction is possible between the anionic reaction site and the *para* position.

[b] Amino and similar groups have somewhat exalted σ_{para} values in reactions such as this in which direct resonance interaction is possible between the cationic reaction site (in the transition state in this case) and the *para* position.

summary

Aromatic side chains are joined by carbon-carbon bonds to the aromatic ring. Such compounds have reactions that are very like those of their aliphatic analogs, but their methods of preparation are usually different. Vigorous oxidation of any of these compounds (including those with longer side chains) produces benzoic acid, [1]–[8] → [9], although the presence of hydroxyl or amino substituents on the ring causes the ring to be degraded.

$$ArCH_3 \quad ArCH_2X \quad ArCHX_2 \quad ArCX_3 \quad ArCH_2OH \quad ArCHO \quad Ar\overset{O}{\overset{\|}{C}}CH_3 \quad ArC\equiv N \quad ArCO_2H$$
[1]   [2]   [3]   [4]   [5]   [6]   [7]   [8]   [9]

X = halogen

Side-chain halogenation occurs readily, [1] → [2] + [3] + [4], and the resulting halo compounds can be readily hydrolyzed to [5], [6], and [9].

Friedel-Crafts methylation of arenes gives [1] (RX gives ArR) but poly-substitution also occurs; Friedel-Crafts acylation by $CH_3\overset{O}{\overset{\|}{C}}Cl$ gives [7] (R$\overset{O}{\overset{\|}{C}}$Cl gives Ar$\overset{O}{\overset{\|}{C}}$R) and only monosubstitution occurs. Introduction of the formyl group, −CHO, is only successful with activated rings. Aromatic aldehydes undergo the benzoin condensation to give benzoins, ArCHOHC$\overset{O}{\overset{\|}{}}$Ar.

Multiple substitution of aryl rings on one carbon atom allows carbonium ions, carbanions, and radicals to be formed.

$$Ar_3C-Z + Y \longrightarrow
\begin{cases}
Ar_3C^{\oplus} & Z = OH, Y = H^{\oplus} \\
Ar_3C^{\ominus} & Z = H, Y = NH_2^{\ominus} \\
Ar_3C\cdot & Z = Cl, Y = Ag
\end{cases}$$

Steric and electronic effects are important in stabilizing these three entities. All absorb light in the visible region of the spectrum. Radicals, in addition, can be detected and identified by epr spectroscopy.

The reactions of *meta*- and *para*-substituted aromatic systems obey linear free-energy relationships, one of which is the Hammett equation, $\log k = \rho\sigma + \log k_0$. This expresses a rate constant for the reaction of a *meta*- or *para*-substituted aryl compound in terms of k_0 (the rate constant for the rate of the unsubstituted compound), ρ (the reaction constant, which is independent of the substituent), and σ (the substituent constant, which is independent of the reaction). A similar relationship holds for equilibrium constants.

exercises

24·1 Suggest a practical synthesis of each of the following compounds from a readily available aromatic hydrocarbon:

a. 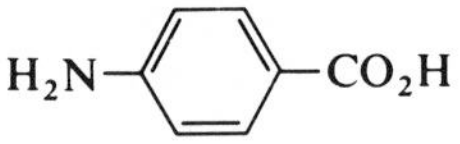
H₂N
CO₂H

c. 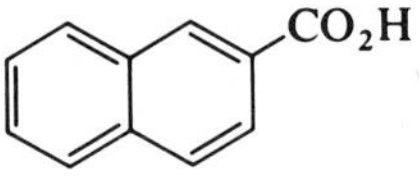
CO₂H

b. 
HO₂C
CO₂H

d. 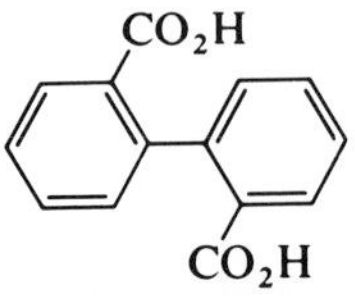
CO₂H
CO₂H

24·2 Write a mechanism for the formation of benzyl chloride by photochemical chlorination of toluene with molecular chlorine. What other products would you anticipate being formed? At what position would you expect ethylbenzene to substitute under similar conditions?

24·3 Outline a suitable synthesis of each of the following compounds, starting with benzene:

a. $C_6H_5CH_2COC_6H_5$

b. 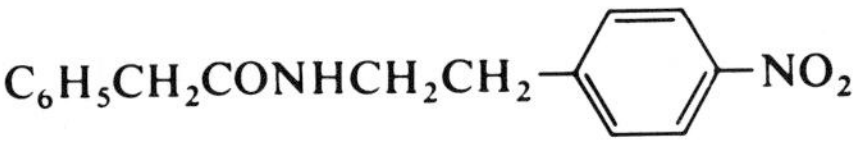
C₆H₅CH₂CONHCH₂CH₂
NO₂

c. 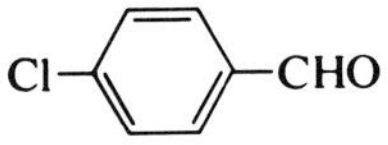
Cl
CHO

24·4 Suggest a reason why zinc chloride is used in preference to aluminum chloride as a catalyst for chloromethylation reactions.

24·5 Give the principal product(s) of chloromethylation of the following compounds:

a. 1-methylnaphthalene
b. 1-nitronaphthalene
c. *p*-methoxybenzaldehyde
d. anisole (using acetaldehyde in place of formaldehyde)

24·6 Suggest a possible mechanism for formylation of arenes by carbon monoxide (Section 24·4C).

24·7 Formulate the steps that are probably involved in the formylation of a phenol by the action of HCN, HCl, and $ZnCl_2$.

24·8 How would you synthesize the following compounds from the indicated starting materials?

a. 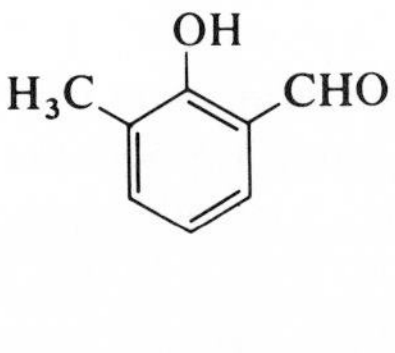
OH
H₃C
CHO
from toluene

b. 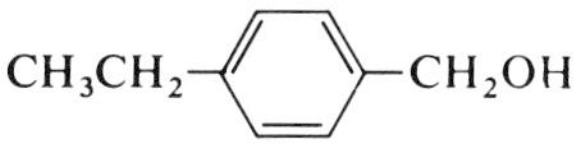 CH₃CH₂—⟨benzene ring⟩—CH₂OH   from benzene

c. 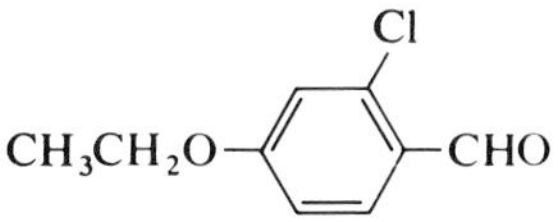 CH₃CH₂O—⟨benzene ring with Cl⟩—CHO   from benzene

24·9   Write resonance structures for $(p\text{-}NH_2C_6H_4)_3C^{\oplus}$. Would *meta* amino groups be as effective in stabilizing the ion?

24·10 *a.* Suggest why the extent of ionic dissociation of triarylmethyl chlorides in liquid sulfur dioxide decreases for compounds [1], [2], and [3] in the order [1] > [2] > [3]. Use of models may be helpful here.

$(C_6H_5)_3C\text{—}Cl$

[1]   [2] 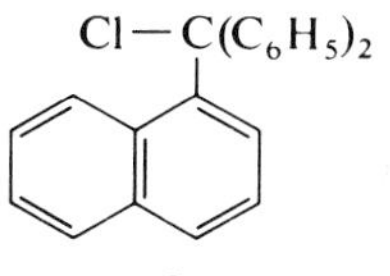   [3]

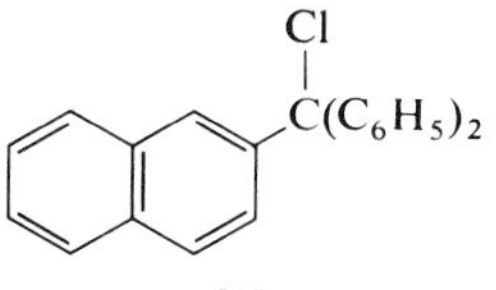

b. Which alcohol would you expect to give the more stable carbonium ion in sulfuric acid, 9-fluorenol [4] or 2,3,6,7-dibenzotropyl alcohol [5]? Explain.

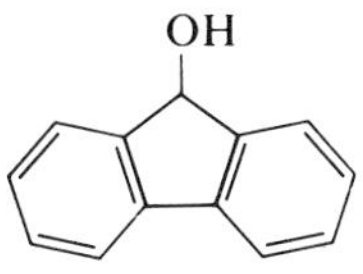

[4] 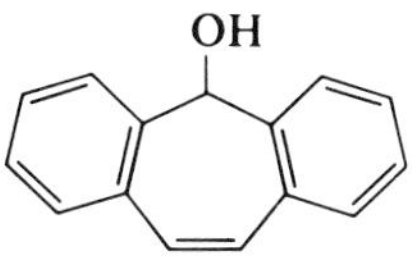   [5]

c. When triphenylcarbinol is dissolved in 100% sulfuric acid, it gives a freezing-point depression that corresponds to formation of 4 moles of particles per mole of carbinol. Explain.

24·11 Write the important resonance structures for the triphenylmethide ion and for the carbanion formed by proton loss from 4-cyanophenyldiphenyl-methane.

24·12 Which of the following pairs of compounds would you expect to be the more reactive under the specified conditions? Give your reasons and write equations for the reactions involved.

   a. $p\text{-}NO_2C_6H_4CH_2Br$ or $p\text{-}CH_3OC_6H_4CH_2Br$ on hydrolysis in aqueous acetone
   b. $(C_6H_5)_3CH$ or $C_6H_5CH_3$ in the presence of phenyllithium
   c. $(C_6H_5)_3C\text{—}C(C_6H_5)_3$ or $(C_6H_5)_2CH\text{—}CH(C_6H_5)_2$ on heating
   d. $(C_6H_5)_2N\text{—}N(C_6H_5)_2$ or $(C_6H_5)_2CH\text{—}CH(C_6H_5)_2$ on heating

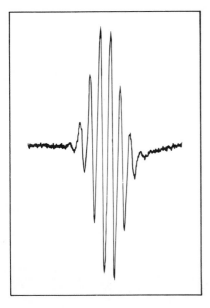

Figure 24·5   Electron paramagnetic resonance spectrum of cycloheptatrienyl radical produced by X-irradiation of 1,3,5-cycloheptatriene.

24·13   Draw structures and name all the possible benzoins that could be formed from a mixture of (*a*) *p*-tolualdehyde and *o*-ethoxybenzaldehyde, and (*b*) 8-methyl-1-naphthaldehyde and anisaldehyde. An unsymmetrical benzoin such as 4-methoxybenzoin is rather readily equilibrated with its isomer, 4′-methoxybenzoin, under the influence of bases. Explain.

24·14   The epr spectrum shown in Figure 24·5 is of a first-derivative curve of the absorption of a radical produced by X-irradiation of 1,3,5-cycloheptatriene present as an impurity in crystals of naphthalene. Make a sketch of this spectrum as it would look as an *absorption* spectrum and show the structure of the radical to which it corresponds. Show how at least one isomeric structure for the radical can be eliminated by the observed character of the spectrum.

24·15   The ionization constants of *m*- and *p*-cyanobenzoic acids at 20° are 2.51×10^{-4} and 2.82×10^{-4}, respectively. Benzoic acid has K_{HA} of 6.76×10^{-5} at 20°. Calculate σ_{meta} and σ_{para} for the cyano substituent.

24·16   The effects produced by substituents are explained in terms of inductive, conjugative (resonance), and steric influences. Show how it is possible, within this framework, to account for the following facts:

a.   The σ constant of the methoxy group ($-OCH_3$) in the *meta* position is positive and in the *para* position negative.

b.   The $\overset{\oplus}{-N(CH_3)_3}$ group has a larger positive σ constant in the *meta* position than in the *para* position, but the reverse is true for the $-N_2^{\oplus}$ group.

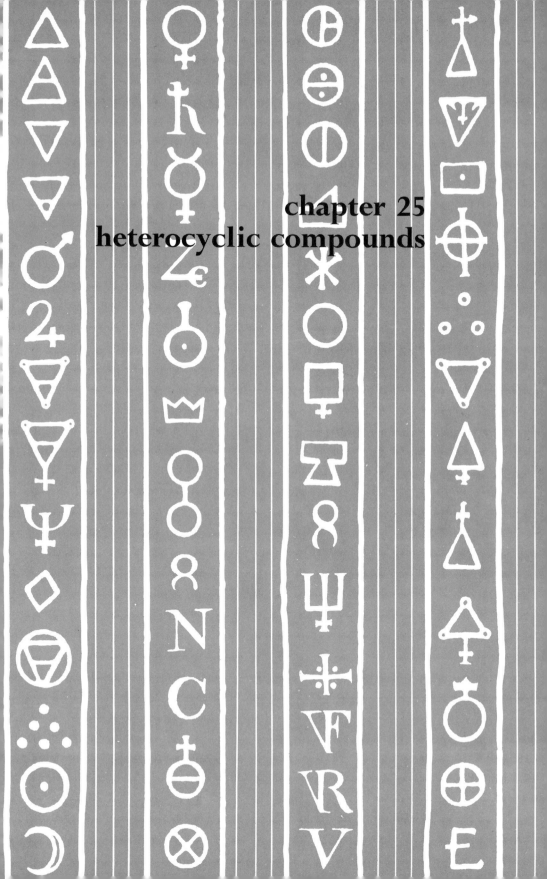

chapter 25
heterocyclic compounds

Heterocyclic organic compounds have cyclic structures in which one or more of the ring atoms are elements other than carbon. In this chapter we shall confine our attention to a discussion of the chemistry of heterocyclic nitrogen, oxygen, and sulfur compounds, and of these we shall be concerned primarily with the aromatic heterocycles rather than their saturated analogs. The chemistry of saturated heterocycles, such as ethylene oxide and the other compounds shown in Figure 25·1, has been dealt with in earlier chapters. In general, the properties of such substances can be correlated with those of their open-chain analogs, provided appropriate account is taken of the strain and conformational effects that are associated with ring compounds.

The importance of heterocyclic compounds is apparent from the wealth and variety of such compounds that occur naturally or are prepared on a commercial scale by the dye and drug industries. Many of these compounds fulfill important physiological functions in plants and animals. We have already encountered some of the important naturally occurring heterocycles in earlier chapters. Thus, the carbohydrates may be classified as oxygen heterocycles, whereas the nucleic acids and some amino acids, peptides, and proteins possess nitrogen-containing ring systems.

We shall begin with a discussion of four important unsaturated heterocyclic compounds: pyrrole, furan, thiophene, and pyridine (Figure 25·2; their systematic names are shown in parentheses). The prefixes **az-**, **ox-**, and **thi-** refer, respectively, to nitrogen, oxygen, and sulfur heterocycles. Suffixes indicate the size of the ring, for example, **-ole** for five-membered unsaturated rings, and **-ine** for six-membered unsaturated rings.

These four compounds are all liquid at room temperature; their boiling points range from 32° for furan to 130° for pyrrole. The fairly high boiling point of the latter is presumably the result of intermolecular hydrogen bonding.

The conjugated bonding in pyridine bears an obvious resemblance to that in benzene and it is no surprise to find that pyridine is an " aromatic " compound; for instance, it reacts with electrophiles by substitution rather than by addition. It is less obvious that pyrrole, furan, and thiophene should have aromatic character and yet we shall see that these compounds, too, resemble benzene in many ways.

Figure 25·1   Some important saturated heterocycles.

ethylene oxide   tetrahydrofuran   1, 4-dioxane   lactones   lactams

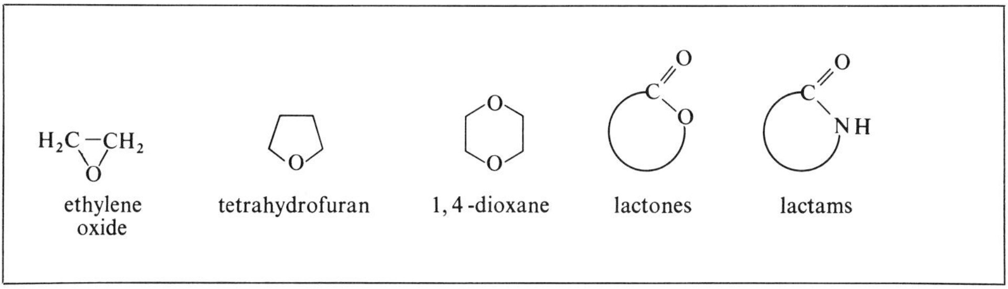

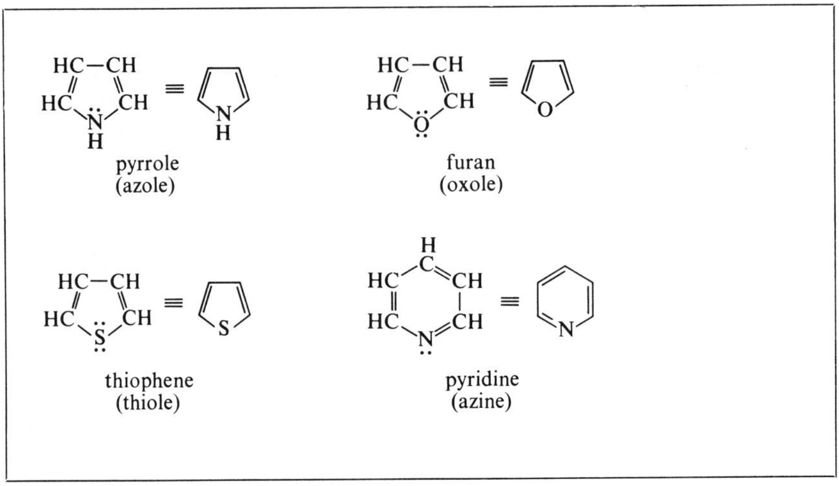

Figure 25·2   The structures of four important unsaturated heterocycles.

25·1   aromatic character of pyrrole, furan, and thiophene

The five-membered heterocyclic compounds, pyrrole, furan, and thiophene, possess some degree of aromatic character because of the delocalization of four carbon π electrons and the two unshared electrons of the heteroatom. This combination constitutes a *sextet* of delocalized electrons. We learned earlier (Section 6·7) that cyclic systems with this electronic arrangement tend to have special stabilization—for example, benzene, cyclopentadienide anion, and cycloheptatrienyl (tropylium) cation.

The structure of each heterocycle can be described as a hybrid of several electron-pairing schemes, as shown here for pyrrole. We shall have more to say later about the degree of contribution of the dipolar resonance forms, [1b] to [1e].

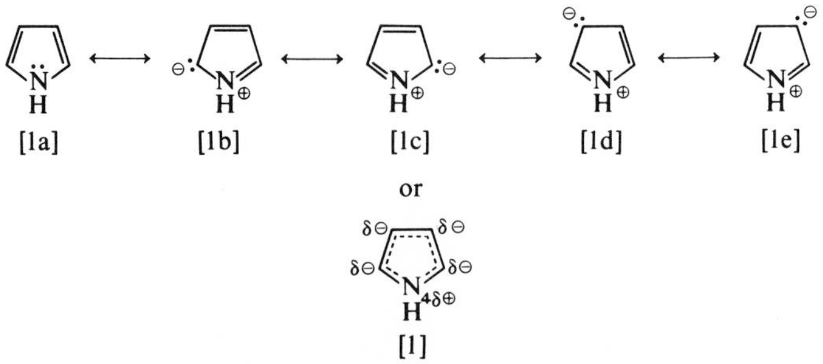

In terms of atomic orbitals, the structure of each of these heterocycles may be regarded as a planar pentagonal framework of C—H, C—C, and C—Y σ bonds (Y being the heteroatom) made up of trigonally bonded (sp^2) atoms, each with one p orbital perpendicular to the plane of the ring. The π system formed by overlap of the p orbitals perpendicular to the plane contains four

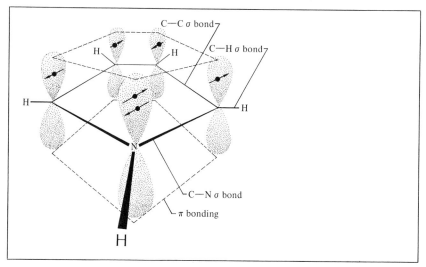

C—C σ bond

C—H σ bond

H

H

H

H

C—N σ bond

π bonding

H

Figure 25·3   Atomic orbital description of pyrrole.

electrons from the carbons and two from the heteroatom. The overall formulation is illustrated in Figure 25·3 for pyrrole.

The stabilization energies of pyrrole, furan, and thiophene obtained from experimental and calculated heats of combustion are only about half of the stabilization energy of benzene. However, the heterocycles differ from benzene in that each has only one resonance structure with no formal bonds or charge separation. Furthermore, on the basis of relative electronegativities of sulfur, nitrogen, and oxygen, we may anticipate that the structures analogous to [1b] to [1e] should be important in the order thiophene > pyrrole > furan. As a result, it is reasonable to expect furan to be the least aromatic of the three heterocycles, and indeed it is.

25·2 chemical properties of pyrrole, furan, thiophene, and pyridine

In discussing the reactivity of these heterocycles, we shall be interested primarily in their degree of aromatic character, as typified by their ability to exhibit electrophilic and nucleophilic substitution reactions rather than undergo addition reactions. First, however, we shall consider their acidic and basic properties.

A. ACIDIC AND BASIC PROPERTIES

Pyrrole, furan, thiophene, and pyridine are potential bases because each can accept a proton at the heteroatom. Thiophene and furan, however, are too weak to form salts with aqueous acid. Pyrrole and pyridine are somewhat stronger bases, as might be expected from the lower electronegativity of nitrogen. Pyrrole, however, polymerizes in acid solution (as does furan).

Pyridine ($K_B = 1.7 \times 10^{-9}$) is thus the only one of these heterocycles which forms stable salts with aqueous acid.

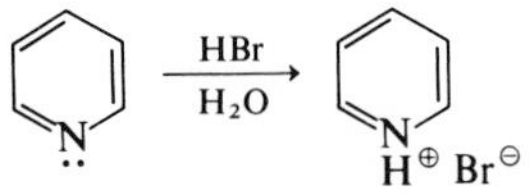

pyridine   pyridinium bromide

Turning to the acidic properties of these four compounds, a glance at their structures tells us that pyrrole is the only one that is likely to be acidic because it is the only one in which there is a hydrogen attached to the heteroatom. Pyrrole is a rather weak acid ($K_{HA} = 10^{-15}$) and reacts completely only with strong bases such as hydroxide ion or Grignard reagents.

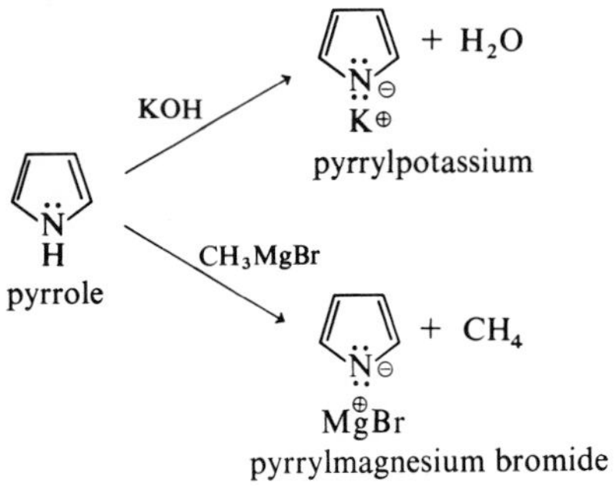

Although pyrrole is only weakly acidic it is a stronger acid than aliphatic amines by a factor of about 10^{18} (see Section 16·1D) and stronger than aromatic amines by a factor of about 10^{12} (see Table 22·1, footnote). This reflects the stability of the π-electron system of the resultant anion [2] relative to that of pyrrole itself [1] where charge separation is associated with all but one of the resonance structures.

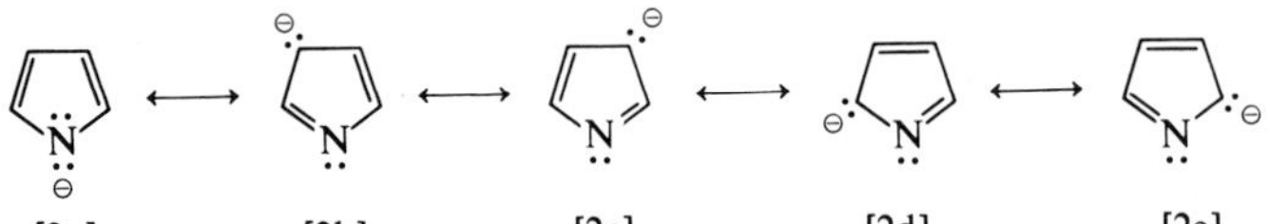

[2a]   [2b]   [2c]   [2d]   [2e]

The resonance structures [2a]–[2e] are useful for indicating charge dispersal in the anion but do not reveal the special stabilization that is associated with delocalization of six π electrons.

B. ELECTROPHILIC SUBSTITUTION REACTIONS

Electrophilic substitution of pyrrole is rapid at the 2 position, although if this site (and the 5 position) is blocked, the 3 position is attacked readily. As with electrophilic substitution in benzene (Figure 20·8) a convenient model for the transition state is the intermediate cation formed by addition of an electrophile $X^{\oplus}$ to the pyrrole ring.

The stability that the heteroatom confers on the intermediate and, by analogy, on the transition state for substitution is illustrated in [3a]–[3c] for the case of 2 substitution.

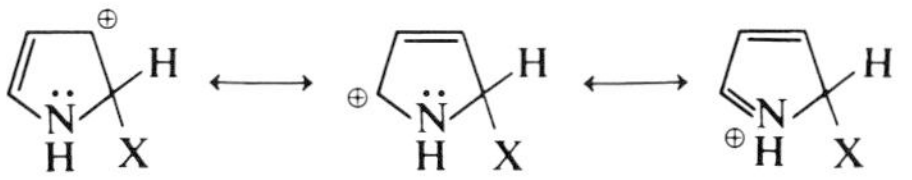

[3a]   [3b]   [3c]

The positive charge is located on nitrogen in [3c] and this is the most important contributor to the resonance hybrid, even though nitrogen is more electronegative than carbon. It is important to recognize the reason for this, which is simply that there is more bonding in [3c] than in [3a] or [3b]—two π bonds instead of one.

The analogous intermediates [4] or [5] that result from electrophilic attack on benzene or pyridine do not have structures in which there are different numbers of bonds.

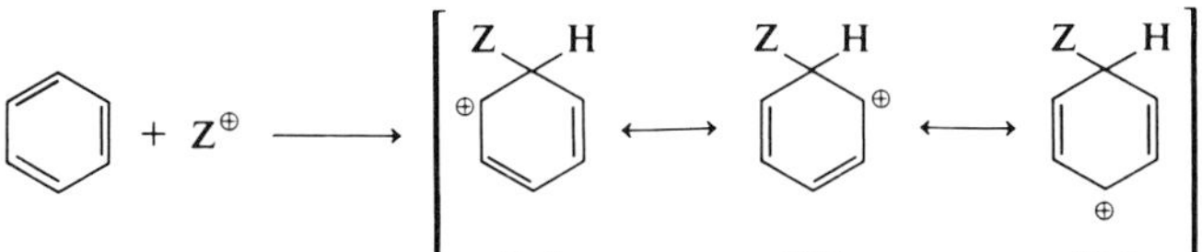

[4a]   [4b]   [4c]

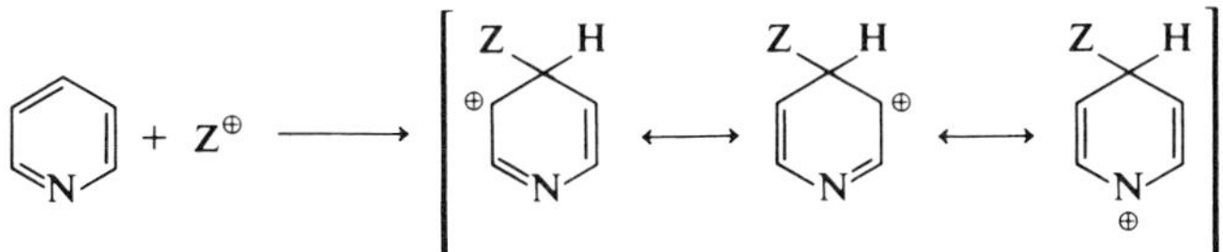

[5a]   [5b]   [5c]

Although the nitrogen atoms in [3c] and [5c] are each cationic, that in [3c] has an octet and that in [5c] only a sextet of electrons. Because nitrogen is more electronegative than carbon, [5c] will make only a small contribution to the resonance hybrid and, for this reason, electrophilic substitution in pyridine occurs at the 3 position (although very slowly).

The principal electrophilic substitution reactions of pyrrole are summarized in Figure 25·4 and a study of these reactions provides an opportunity to review the reactions discussed earlier in our study of benzene. Note that 2 substitution predominates; nitration and sulfonation of pyrrole are possible, but only if strongly acidic conditions which would lead to polymerization are avoided; and pyrrole is sufficiently reactive for halogenation and Friedel-Crafts acylation to proceed without a catalyst.

Furan resembles pyrrole in its behavior toward electrophilic reagents, and its principal reactions of this type are summarized in Figure 25·5. Direct chlorination and bromination of furan are hard to control and can lead to violent reaction, possibly caused by the halogen acid that is formed.

Related reactions of thiophene are summarized in Figure 25·6. Because thiophene is less subject to acid-induced polymerization than either pyrrole or furan, it can be sulfonated or nitrated under strongly acidic conditions. In fact, sulfonation and extraction are used as a means of freeing commercial

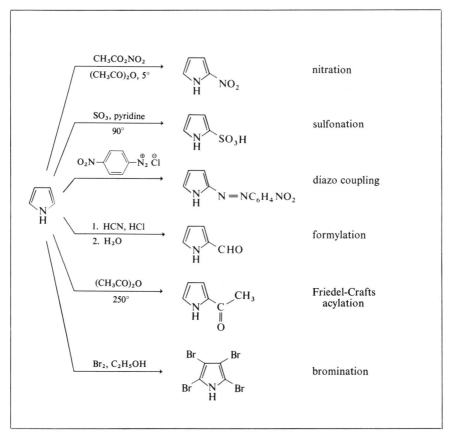

Figure 25·4   Electrophilic substitution reactions of pyrrole.

Figure 25·5   Electrophilic substitution reactions of furan.

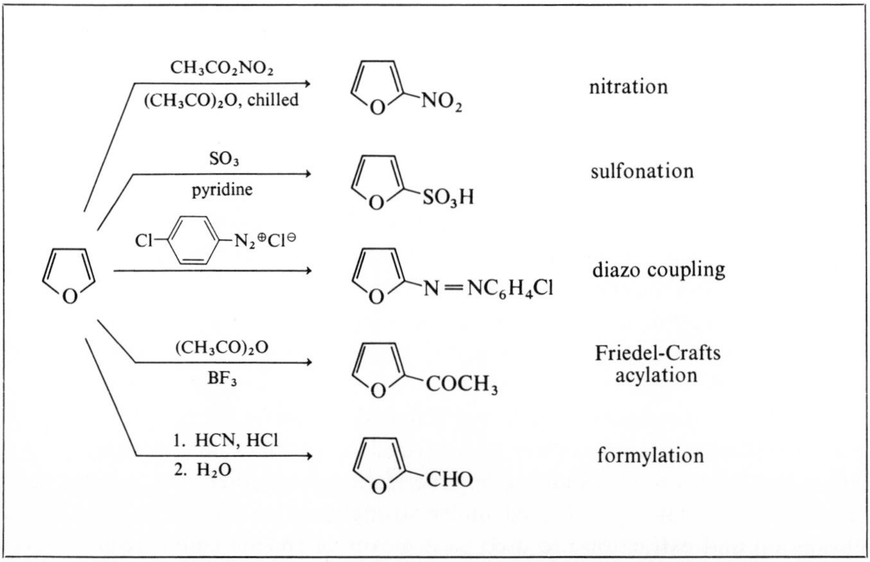

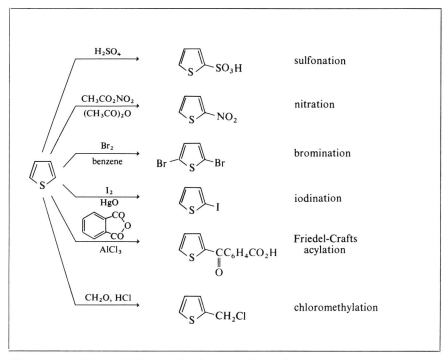

Figure 25·6   Electrophilic substitution reactions of thiophene.

Figure 25·7   Electrophilic substitution reactions of pyridine. In most of these reactions the yields are low.

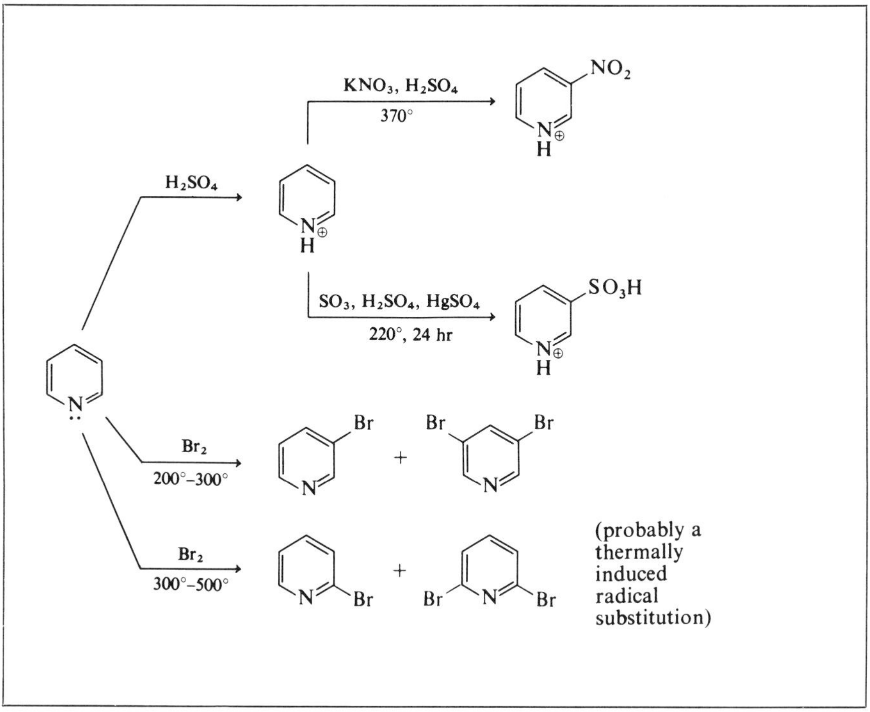

benzene from thiophene, with which it is often contaminated. Thiophene is sulfonated much more readily than benzene and the resulting product, being acidic, can be extracted by aqueous base.

Electrophilic substitution of pyridine is hard to achieve, partly because of deactivation of the ring by the heteroatom and partly because under acidic conditions, as in sulfonation and nitration, the ring is further deactivated by formation of the pyridinium ion. Three pertinent substitution reactions are listed in Figure 25·7; their most striking feature is the vigorous conditions necessary for successful reaction. Note that the Friedel-Crafts reaction does not take place with pyridine.

C. NUCLEOPHILIC SUBSTITUTION REACTIONS

The most important substitution reactions of the pyridine ring are effected by nucleophilic reagents. Thus, pyridine can be aminated on heating with soda-mide, hydroxylated with potassium hydroxide, and alkylated and arylated with alkyl- and aryllithiums (Figure 25·8). Since related reactions with benzene either do not occur or are relatively difficult, we can conclude that the ring nitrogen in pyridine has a pronounced activating effect for nucleophilic attack at the ring analogous to the activation produced by the nitro group in nitrobenzenes. The reason for this activation is that addition to the

Figure 25·8   Nucleophilic substitution reactions of pyridine.

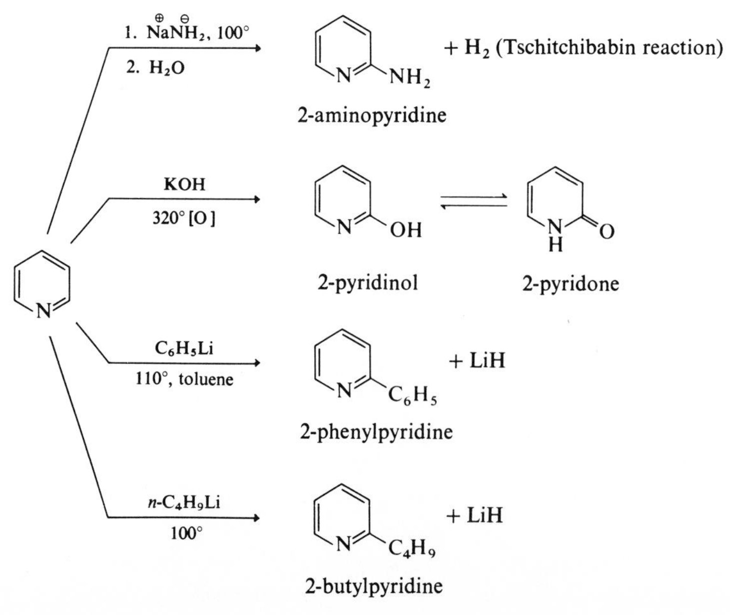

2 or 4 but not the 3 position permits the charge to reside at least partially on nitrogen rather than on carbon (see Equations 25·1 and 25·2).

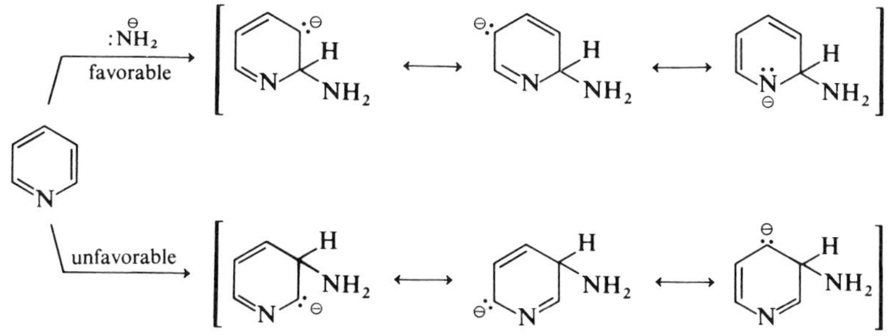
favorable
unfavorable

(25·1)

(25·2)

In the case of amination, the reaction is completed by loss of hydride ion and subsequent formation of hydrogen (Equation 25·3).

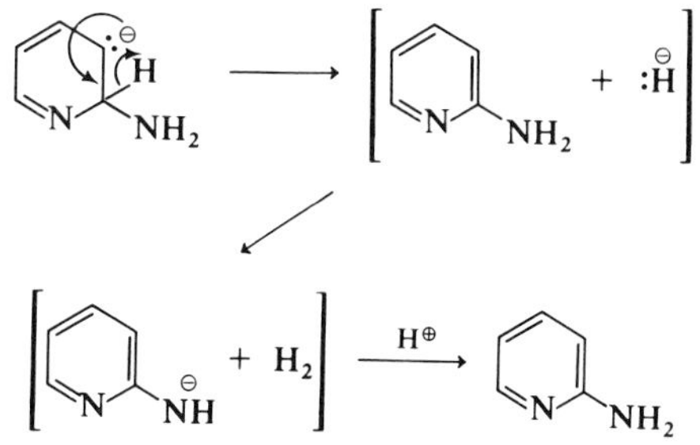

(25·3)

25·3 *polycyclic and polyhetero systems*

A number of heterocycles that have fused benzene rings attached are shown in Figure 25·9. As might be expected, electrophilic substitution occurs in the

Figure 25·9 Some important polycyclic and polyhetero ring systems.

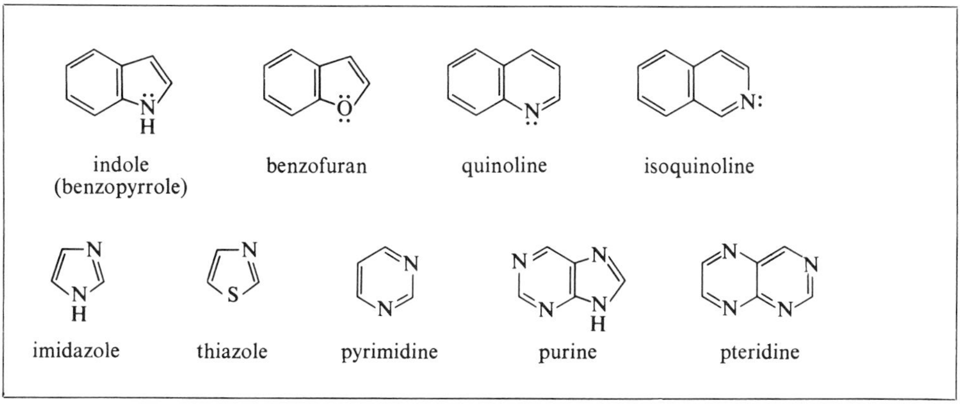
indole
(benzopyrrole)
benzofuran
quinoline
isoquinoline
imidazole
thiazole
pyrimidine
purine
pteridine

hetero ring in the case of indole and benzofuran but in the benzenoid ring in the case of quinoline and isoquinoline.

There are several five- and six-membered heterocyclic ring systems containing two or more heteroatoms within the ring that are particularly important in that they occur in many natural products and in certain synthetic drugs and synthetic dyes. The parent compounds of the most commonly encountered ring systems are shown in Figure 25·9.

Each five- and six-membered ring compound has a delocalized sextet of π electrons; the bicyclic compounds, purine and pteridine, resemble naphthalene in having 10 delocalized π electrons.

heterocyclic natural products

Some of the heterocyclic ring systems mentioned in this chapter are of special interest and importance because certain of their derivatives are synthesized naturally as part of the life cycles of plants and animals. The structures of these naturally occurring compounds are often extremely complex and elucidation of their structures has been and continues to be a major challenge to organic chemists and biochemists alike. The approach to solving the structure of a complex natural product is discussed in some detail in Chapter 29; at this point we shall briefly describe only a few natural products of known structure which can be classified as heterocyclic compounds and which are of some biological or physiological importance.

25·4 natural products related to pyrrole

An interesting compound having a fully conjugated cyclic structure of four pyrrole rings linked together through their 2 and 5 positions by four methine (=CH—) bridges is known as *porphyrin* [6].

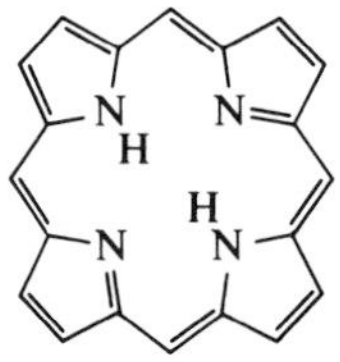

[6]

Although porphyrin itself does not exist in nature, the porphyrin or related ring system is found in several very important natural products, notably hemoglobin, chlorophyll, and vitamin B_{12}.

Hemoglobin is present in the red corpuscles of blood and functions to carry oxygen from the lungs to the body tissue; it consists of a protein called *globin* bound to an iron-containing prosthetic group called *heme*. Acid hydrolysis of hemoglobin liberates the prosthetic group as a complex iron(III) salt called *hemin* [7]. The structure of hemin was established by 1929 after years of work, notably by W. Küster, R. Willstätter, and H. Fischer. A complete synthesis of hemin was achieved by Fischer in 1929, and his contributions were rewarded with a Nobel Prize (1930). The structure of hemin [6] shows that the iron (as Fe^{III}) is complexed to all four of the pyrrole nitrogens.

The poisonous action of carbon monoxide is due to its reaction with hemoglobin to form carboxyhemoglobin. Carbon monoxide makes up about 4% of undiluted cigarette smoke and can produce up to 15% carboxyhemoglobin in the blood.

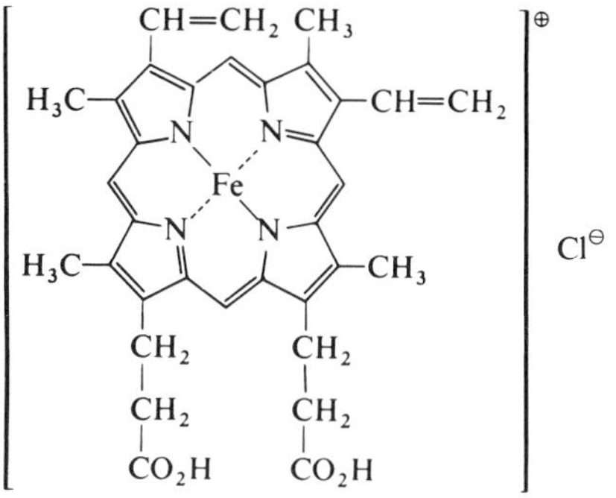

hemin
[7]

Certain pigments in the bile of mammals, the so-called bile pigments, are pyrrole derivatives. They contain four pyrrole rings linked in a chain through a methine bridge between the 2 position of one ring and the 5 position of another. As one might suspect, bile pigments are degradation products of hemoglobin.

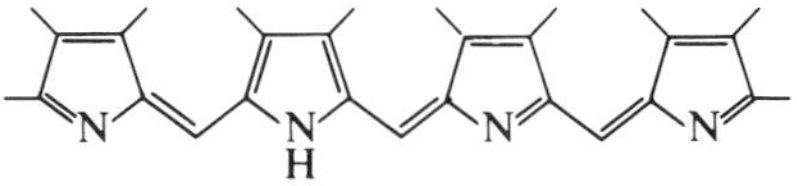

basic structure of a bile pigment

Chlorophyll was briefly mentioned in connection with photosynthesis, and its structure is shown in Figure 15·1. It is a porphyrin derivative in which the four pyrrole nitrogens are complexed with magnesium (as Mg^{II}). The structure was established largely through the work of R. Willstätter, H. Fischer, and J. B. Conant. A total synthesis was completed by R. B. Woodward and co-workers in 1960.

The structure of **vitamin B_{12}** [8], known also as the antipernicious anemia factor and as cyanocobalamin, was finally established in 1955 as the result of both X-ray diffraction and chemical studies. The vitamin has a reduced porphyrin ring in which one methine bridge is absent and the nitrogen heteroatoms are complexed with a cyanocobalt group. It also has a ribofuranoside ring and a benzimidazole ring. Intensive efforts have been underway for some time to achieve a synthesis of vitamin B_{12} in the laboratory.

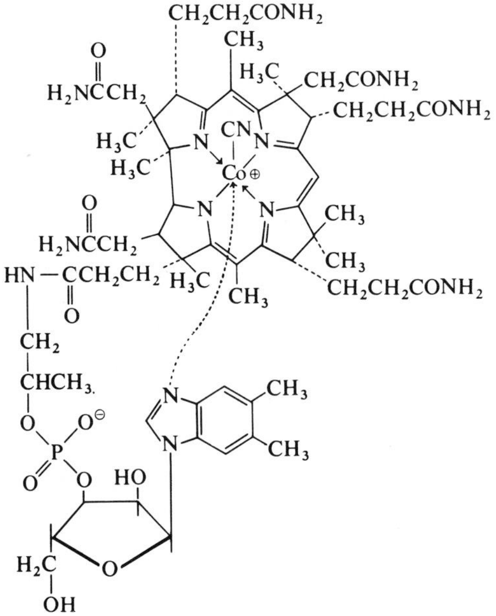

vitamin B$_{12}$

[8]

25·5   natural products related to indole

The indole ring system is common to many naturally occurring compounds, for
example, the essential amino acid tryptophan which is a constituent of almost
all proteins.

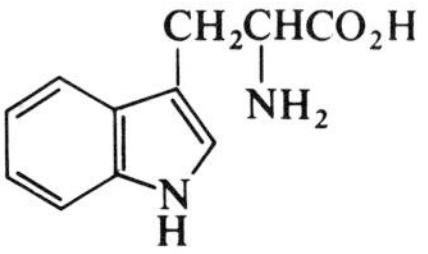

tryptophan

There are also many compounds related to indole that occur in plants. They
are part of a class of natural products known as alkaloids—the term being
used to designate nitrogen-containing compounds of vegetable origin commonly having heterocyclic ring systems and one or more basic nitrogen atoms.
Their physiological activity is often pronounced and their structures complex.
Alkaloids related to indole are called indole alkaloids, and some of these are
described here.

An indole derivative commonly known as serotonin, which is actually
5-hydroxytryptamine, is of interest because of its apparent connection with
mental processes. It occurs widely in plant and animal life, but its presence in
the brain and the schizophrenic state that ensues when its normal concen-

tration is disturbed indicates that it may have an important function in establishing a stable pattern of mental activity.

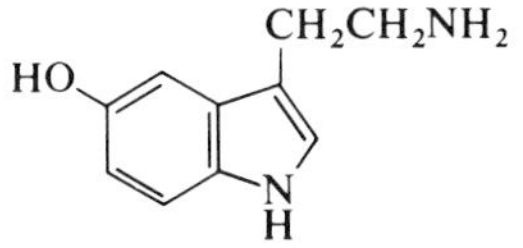

serotonin

The *ergot alkaloids* are produced by a fungus known as ergot, which grows as a parasite on cereals, particularly rye. They are amides of the indole derivative known as lysergic acid and their levorotatory forms are physiologically active in minute amounts. Ergot poisoning, or St. Anthony's fire, has been known for centuries and still occurs occasionally. Several deaths following fits of madness were reported in a village in France a few years ago and were traced to bread baked with ergot-containing rye.

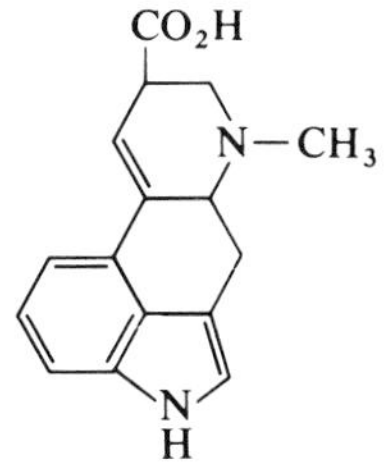

lysergic acid

The diethylamide of lysergic acid, while not itself a naturally occurring compound, has achieved notoriety as a drug (LSD) that can produce a temporary schizophrenic state, although permanent damage to the brain can also result. Current theory suggests that the diethylamide of lysergic acid upsets the balance of serotonin in the brain.

Another indole alkaloid called reserpine has important clinical use in the treatment of high blood pressure (hypertension) and also as a tranquilizer for the emotionally disturbed. The tranquilizing action is thought to be the result of a reduction in the concentration of brain serotonin.

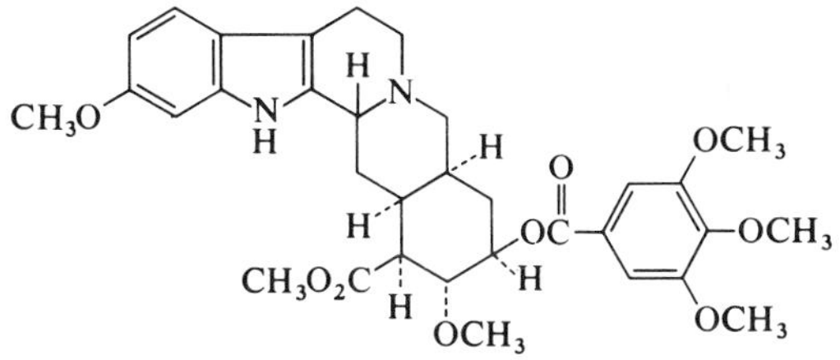

reserpine

Two other alkaloids, strychnine and brucine, have been discussed (Section 14·6). The problem of elucidating their structures was solved only after more than a century of research, the major contributions in recent years being made by R. Robinson and R. B. Woodward.

25·6 natural products related to pyridine, quinoline, and isoquinoline

Among the natural products related to pyridine, we have already mentioned the coenzyme nicotinamide-adenine dinucleotide (NAD$^\oplus$, Figure 18·3). Other important pyridine derivatives include nicotine, nicotinic acid (niacin, anti-pellagra factor), and pyridoxine (vitamin B$_6$). Coniine is a toxic alkaloid which occurs in the shrub poison hemlock; it has a reduced pyridine (piperidine) ring.

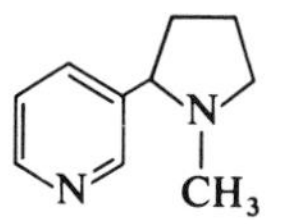

nicotine
(from tobacco)

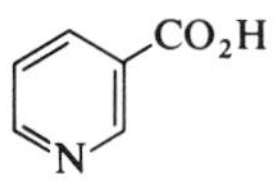

nicotinic acid
(niacin)

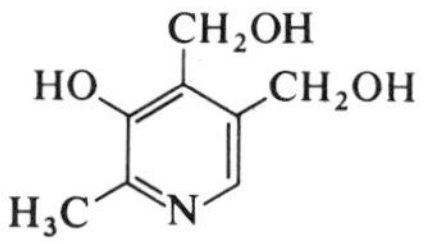

pyridoxine

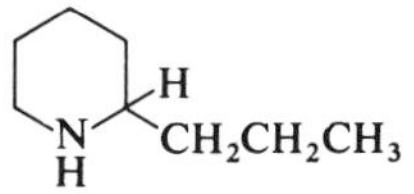

coniine
(poisonous component
of hemlock)

A group of related and rather poisonous compounds known as *the tropane alkaloids* are derivatives of reduced pyrroles and reduced pyridines. Two of the more important tropanes are atropine and cocaine.

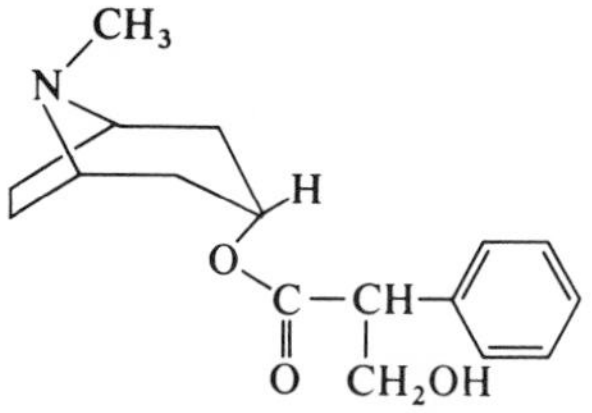

atropine
(from *Atropa belladonna* plant,
"deadly nightshade"

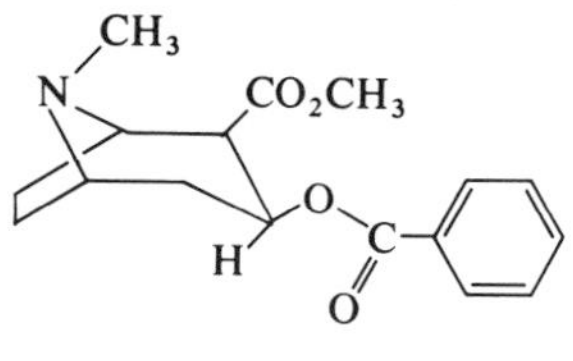

(−)-cocaine
(from coca plant)

The cinchona alkaloids are quinoline derivatives which occur in cinchona bark and have medicinal value as antimalarials. The most notable example is quinine, the structure of which is shown in Section 14·6.

Many alkaloids have isoquinoline and reduced isoquinoline ring systems. *The opium alkaloids* are prime examples, and include the compounds nar-cotine, papaverine, morphine, codeine, and several others, all of which occur in the seed of the opium poppy.

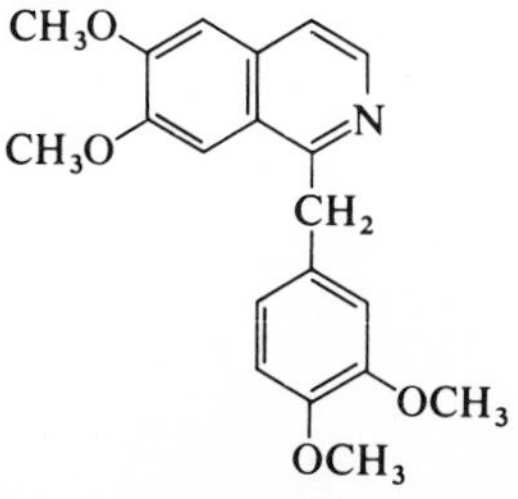

papaverine

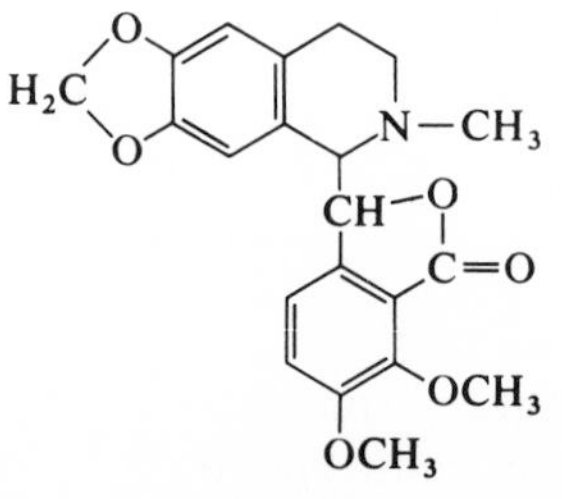

narcotine

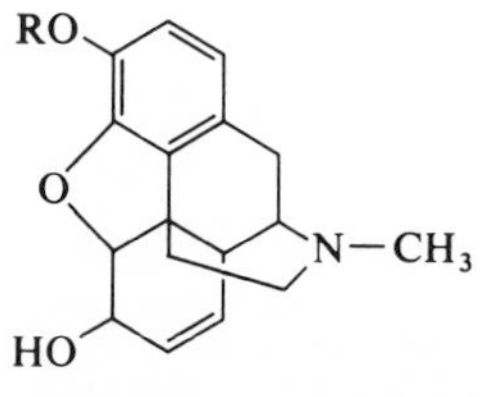

morphine, R = H
codeine, R = CH$_3$

25·7 natural products related to pyrimidine

The pyrimidine ring system occurs in thymine, cytosine, and uracil, which are component structures of the nucleic acids and certain coenzymes. A detailed account of the structures of nucleic acids is given in Section 17·7. Thiamine [9] is both a pyrimidine and a 1,3-thiazole derivative. The pyrophosphate of thiamine is the coenzyme of carboxylase—the enzyme that decarboxylates α-ketoacids; thiamine is also known as vitamin B_1, and a deficiency of it in the diet is responsible for the disease known as beri-beri.

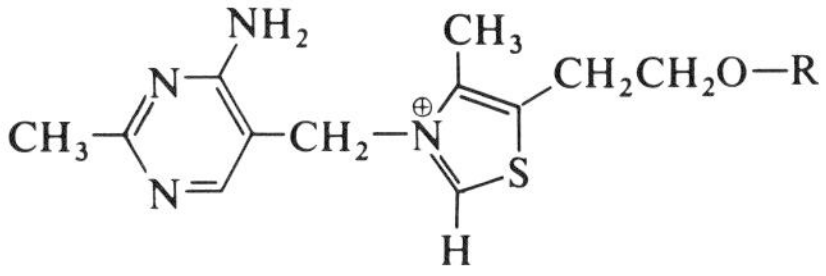

thiamine, R = H
thiamine pyrophosphate, $R = -\overset{OH}{\underset{O}{P}} - O - \overset{OH}{\underset{O}{P}} - OH$

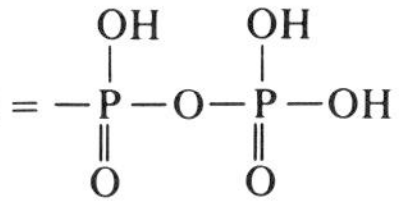

[9]

There are, in addition to the above-mentioned naturally occurring pyrimidine derivatives, many pyrimidines of synthetic origin which are widely used as therapeutic drugs. Of these, we have already mentioned the sulfonamide drug, sulfadiazine (see Section 19·2D). Another large class of pyrimidine medicinals is based on 2,4,6-trihydroxypyrimidine. Most of these substances are 5-alkyl or aryl derivatives of 2,4,6-trihydroxypyrimidine—which is better known as barbituric acid and can exist in several tautomeric forms.

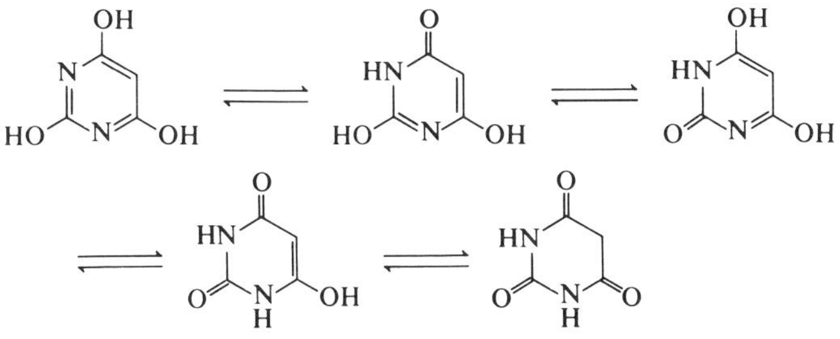

(predominant form)

barbituric acid

For simplicity we shall represent barbituric acid as the triketo tautomer. Two of the more important barbituric acids are known as veronal (5,5-diethylbarbituric acid) and phenobarbital (5-ethyl-5-phenylbarbituric acid).

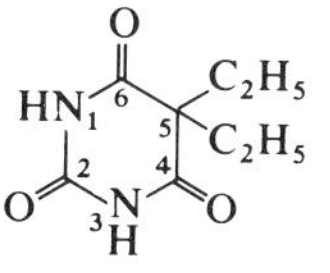

veronal

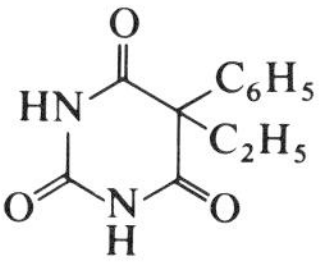

phenobarbital

Barbituric acids are readily synthesized by the reaction of urea with substituted malonic esters.

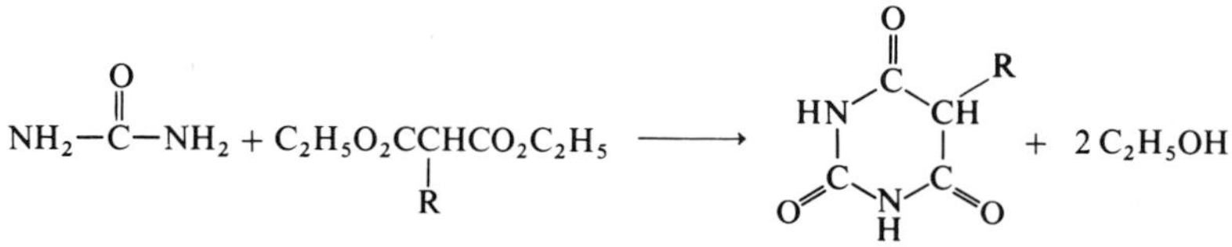

$$NH_2-\overset{\overset{O}{\|}}{C}-NH_2 + C_2H_5O_2CCHCO_2C_2H_5 \longrightarrow$$

with R substituent below the CH, giving the cyclic product + 2 C$_2$H$_5$OH

25·8 natural products related to purine and pteridine

Heterocyclic nitrogen bases (other than pyrimidines) present in nucleic acids are the purine derivatives adenine and guanine (Section 17·6). Adenine is also a component of the trinucleotide adenosine triphosphate (ATP), whose structure is shown in Section 15·5. Nicotinamide-adenine dinucleotide (NAD$^{\oplus}$, Figure 18·3) is also a derivative of adenine.

A number of alkaloids are purine derivatives. Examples include caffeine, which occurs in the tea plant and coffee bean, and theobromine, which occurs in the cocoa bean. The physiological stimulation derived from beverages such as tea, coffee, and many soft drinks is due to the presence of caffeine.

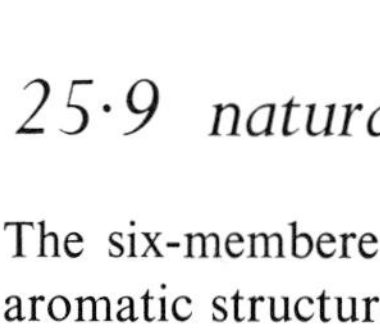

caffeine 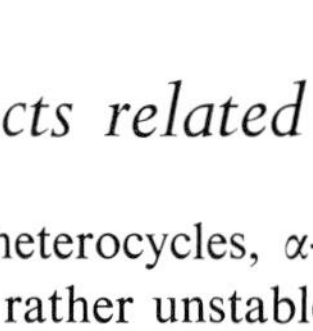   theobromine

25·9 natural products related to pyran

The six-membered oxygen heterocycles, α-pyran and γ-pyran, do not have aromatic structures and are rather unstable. Of more interest are the α- and γ-pyrones, which differ from the corresponding pyrans in having a carbonyl group at the α- and γ-ring positions, respectively.

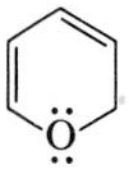

α-pyran 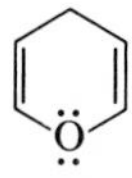   γ-pyran 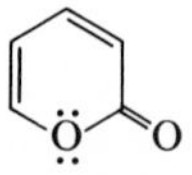   α-pyrone 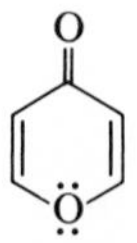   γ-pyrone

The pyrones may be regarded as pseudoaromatic compounds—they are expected to have considerable electron delocalization through π overlap of orbitals of the double bond, the ring oxygen, and the carbonyl group. Thus,

γ-pyrone should have at least some stabilization associated with contributions of the electron-pairing schemes [10a] to [10e].

It is significant in this connection that γ-pyrone behaves quite differently than
might be expected from consideration of structure [10a] alone. For example,
it does not readily undergo those additions characteristic of α,β-unsaturated
ketones and does not form carbonyl derivatives.

The benzo derivatives of the pyrones are known as *coumarin* for benzo-α-
pyrone and *chromone* for benzo-γ-pyrone.

coumarin   chromone

Coumarins occur in grasses, citrus peel, and the leaves of certain vegetables.
Coumarin itself occurs in clover and is used as a perfume; it can be prepared
by condensation of salicylaldehyde with acetic anhydride.

Chromones or benzo-γ-pyrones are widely distributed in plant life, mostly
as pigments in plant leaves and flowers. Particularly widespread are the
flavones (2-phenylchromones), quercetin being the flavone most commonly
found.

flavone   quercetin

The beautiful and varied colors of many flowers, fruits, and berries are due
to the pigments known as *anthocyanins*. Their structures are closely related
to the flavones, although they occur as glycosides, from which they are
obtained as salts on hydrolysis with hydrochloric acid. The salts are called
anthocyanidins. Two examples follow:

OH

HO

OH

$\overset{\ominus}{Cl}$

OH

OH

pelargonidin chloride

OH

OH

HO

OH

OH

$\overset{\ominus}{Cl}$

OH

OH

delphinidin chloride
(delphinium)

Glycoside formation is through the 3-hydroxy group of the anthocyanidin.

25·10   polyhetero natural products

Of the many important polyhetero natural products with two or more different heteroatoms in one ring we have already mentioned penicillin (Section 17·2) and thiamine (Section 25·7). Another interesting example is luciferin, which is a benzothiazole derivative.

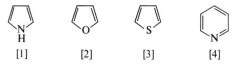

HO

luciferin

Enzymic oxidation of luciferin is responsible for the characteristic luminescence of the firefly. The luminescence arises because the oxidation product is formed in an excited state which liberates its excess energy as light rather than as heat. The relation between ground states and excited states of molecules will be pursued in the next chapter.

summary

In heterocyclic compounds at least one of the ring members is an atom other than carbon. Some of the important unsaturated heterocyclic ring systems containing nitrogen, oxygen, and sulfur are pyrrole [1], furan [2], thiophene [3], and pyridine [4].

N H	O	S	N
[1]	[2]	[3]	[4]

All have aromatic character, [4] because of its benzenoid bonding, and [1], [2], and [3] because their heteroatoms have unshared pairs of electrons that can interact with the π electrons in the ring, giving a stable aromatic sextet.

Strong acids cause polymerization of [1] and [2] and form salts with [4]. Strong bases form salts only with [1]. Electrophilic substitution occurs rapidly with [1], [2], and [3] and substitution occurs preferentially at the 2 position.

The activation of the ring results because the unshared pair of electrons on the heteroatom is able to stabilize the cationic intermediate [5].

[5]

All of the substitution reactions of activated benzene compounds, such as aniline and phenol, also occur with pyrrole and furan. Thiophene is not quite so reactive. Pyridine [4], on the other hand, is deactivated toward electrophilic substitution because in the analogous intermediate [6] the electronegative nitrogen atom has a share in only six valence electrons.

[6]

Substitution under vigorous conditions occurs at the 3 position. Pyridine, however, is subject to nucleophilic attack at the 2 position, and if hydride can be removed, either directly or by oxidation, substitution is achieved.

Some important polycyclic and polyhetero compounds are indole, benzofuran, quinoline, isoquinoline, imidazole, thiazole, pyrimidine, purine, and pteridine.

A number of important natural products contain heterocyclic rings. Hemoglobin, bile pigments, chlorophyll, and vitamin B_{12} all contain pyrrole rings.

Virtually all alkaloids contain heterocyclic rings. The indole ring is present in serotonin, lysergic acid, and reserpine, all of which affect mental processes. Pyridine, quinoline, and isoquinoline are present in the structures of the tropane, cinchona, and opium alkaloids. The pyrimidine ring is present in barbituric acid and its derivatives. The purine ring system (fused pyrimidine and imidazole rings) occurs in nucleic acids and in caffeine.

The six-membered unsaturated oxygen heterocycles (pyrans) are not aromatic. Their keto derivatives (pyrones) are present in a number of natural products, many of which are highly colored.

Compounds with two different heteroatoms in the same ring are also known and include penicillin, thiamine, and luciferin.

exercises

25·1 Suggest a feasible synthesis of each of the following compounds from the indicated starting material:

a. 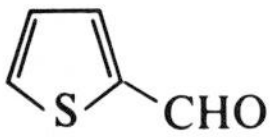 from thiophene

b. 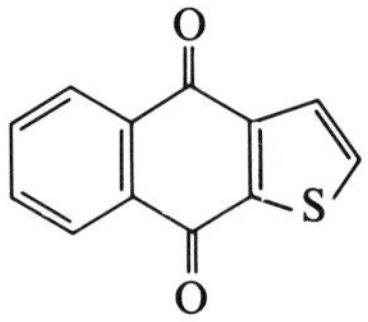 from thiophene

c. 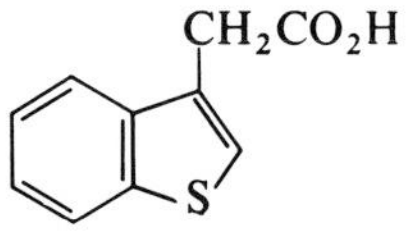 from benzothiophene

d. 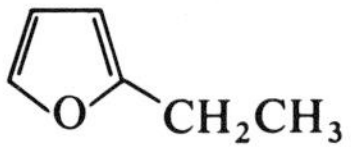 from furan

25·2   *m*-Dinitrobenzene in the presence of potassium hydroxide and oxygen yields potassium dinitrophenoxide. Write a reasonable mechanism for this reaction with emphasis on determining the most likely arrangement of groups in the product.

25·3   Predict the product(s) of the following reactions:

a.

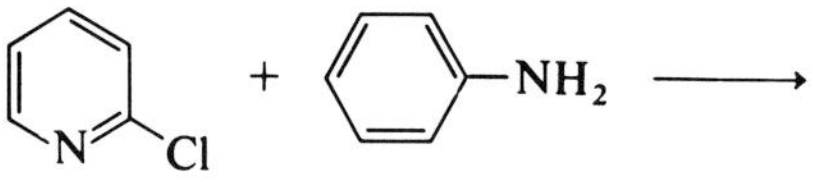

b.

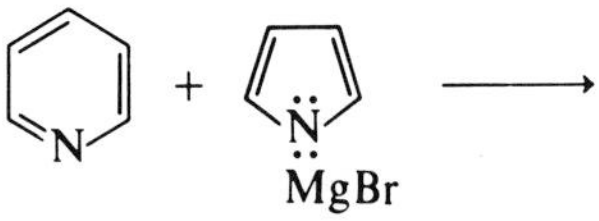

c.   indole $\xrightarrow{\text{KOH}}$ $\xrightarrow{\text{CH}_3\text{I}}$

d.   quinoline $\xrightarrow{\text{KNH}_2}$

e.   isoquinoline $\xrightarrow{\text{KNH}_2}$

25·4   Would you expect porphyrin to possess aromatic character and to what degree would you expect the four N-Fe bonds to be equivalent? Explain.

25·5   The dextrorotatory ergot alkaloids are amides of *isolysergic* acid. Hydrolysis of these amides with aqueous alkali gives lysergic acid. What is the most likely structure of isolysergic acid? Why does rearrangement occur on basic hydrolysis?

25·6   Uric acid, a purine derivative found mainly in the excrement of snakes and birds, has the molecular formula $C_5H_4N_4O_3$. On nitric acid oxidation it breaks down to urea and a hydrated compound called alloxan of formula $C_4H_2N_2O_4 \cdot H_2O$. Alloxan is readily obtained by oxidation of barbituric acid. What is the probable structure of alloxan and uric acid? Why is alloxan hydrated?

25·7   2,6-Dimethyl-γ-pyrone is converted by treatment with dimethyl sulfate and then with perchloric acid to $[C_8H_{11}O_2]^{\oplus}ClO_4^{\ominus}$. Simple recrystallization of this salt from ethanol converts it to $[C_9H_{13}O_2]^{\oplus}ClO_4^{\ominus}$. What are the structures of these salts, and why does the reaction with ethanol occur so readily?

25·8   Show the probable mechanistic steps involved in the preparation of coumarin by the condensation of acetic anhydride with salicylaldehyde in the presence of sodium acetate as catalyst (Section 25·9).

chapter 26
photochemistry

Photochemistry deals with the chemical changes that are brought about by the action of visible or ultraviolet light. In Chapter 7 we discussed organic spectroscopy—how radiation from the various regions of the electromagnetic spectrum interacts with organic molecules. In that chapter and in subsequent references to light absorption we have dealt with it primarily as an analytical tool. We turn now to the chemical changes that sometimes result from the absorption of radiation. We shall see that the chemistry of electronically excited states is often quite different from that of ground states and that we can sometimes change the course of a reaction completely by activating the reactants by light rather than by heat.

The regions of the electromagnetic spectrum that we described in Chapter 7 and the changes they bring about in organic molecules are listed in Table 26·1.

Absorption of infrared or microwave radiation produces vibrationally or rotationally excited molecules whose chemistry is almost unchanged. After all, in any sample of compound at room temperature, there will be a distribution of molecules among the various vibrational and rotational states. As the temperature is increased, the higher states become more and more populated. Although molecules do have more energy at higher temperatures and chemical reactions do occur at faster rates, it should be clear that we will not expect to encounter much new or unusual chemistry as a result of absorption of radiation quanta of such low energy as to only duplicate the effects of increasing temperature.

As we proceed to higher-energy radiation we reach the visible and then the ultraviolet region of the spectrum. Here we find activation of a sort that cannot be duplicated by heat. Absorption of the higher-energy light quanta produces electronically excited states, and even the lowest of these are normally so far above the electronic ground states in energy that they are essentially completely unpopulated, even at temperatures of 100° or more. Although the lifetimes of excited states are normally short they are often quite long enough for important chemical reactions to ensue.

The energy of quanta of visible light—light of wavelength 7500 to 4000 A— varies between 38 and 71 kcal/mole. These are energies of the same order of magnitude as bond energies (Section 2·4 A). Although red light (λ near 7500 A) is able to produce little in the way of chemical activation, the greater

Table 26·1   Effects of various kinds of radiation

	type of radiation	effect on absorbing molecule
↑ increasing energy	X-rays and γ-rays	bond rupture, decomposition[a]
	ultraviolet and visible light	electronic excitation
	infrared radiation	vibrational excitation
	microwaves and radio waves	rotational excitation

[a] The results of X-ray absorption, not X-ray diffraction.

energy of blue light (λ near 4000 A) is often able to induce chemical change. Ultraviolet light is, of course, still more effective. As we pass to still higher energy quanta, such as X rays, we find more and more molecular disintegration occurring as bonding electrons are not merely excited but are completely removed from the influence of the molecule's nuclei. We shall, therefore, concentrate on the effects of visible and ultraviolet light on organic molecules in the remainder of the chapter. Before beginning our discussion of the chemical reactions of excited states, however, we will review the principles of spectroscopy since activation can only occur if the light is actually absorbed. We will also examine more closely the ordinary fate of excited states; that is, when their deactivation does not produce chemical change.

26·1 light absorption, fluorescence, and phosphorescence

When a quantum of visible or ultraviolet light is absorbed by a molecule, the time required to produce the new electronic arrangement is extremely short ($\sim 10^{-15}$ sec) and consequently the electronically excited state will be formed with the atoms essentially in their original positions (Franck-Condon principle). (The absorption of rf radiation in nmr spectroscopy is quite different. The time required to absorb such low-energy quanta is actually much longer than the vibrational times and is even longer than the reaction times of some chemical processes—see Section 7·6D.)

What is the fate of the electronically excited molecule? We have seen that in the first instant it is produced, it is just like the ground-state molecule as far as positions and kinetic energies of the atoms go, but has a very different electronic configuration. What happens at this point depends on several factors, some of which can be best illustrated by energy diagrams. We shall talk in terms of diatomic molecules, but the argument is easily extended to more complicated systems.

Consider the diagram of Figure 26·1, which shows schematic potential energy curves for a molecule A—B in the ground state (A—B) and in an excited electronic state (A—B*). Each curve represents the energy of the molecule A—B as a function of the distance r between the two atoms. At very large values of r there is no interaction; at very small values of r there is enormous repulsion and the energy of these configurations is very high; and at intermediate values there are energy minima which correspond to bonding between A and B. The vibrational levels of the bonds are represented by horizontal lines in the figure.

The two curves in Figure 26·1 do not have identical shapes. The weaker bonding in the excited state tends to make the average distance r_e between the nuclei at the bottom of the "potential well" greater in the excited state than in the ground state.

The high-energy transition marked 1 in Figure 26·1 corresponds to absorption of energy by an A—B molecule existing in a relatively high vibrational level. The energy change occurs with no change in r (Franck-Condon principle), and the electronic energy of the A—B* molecule so produced is

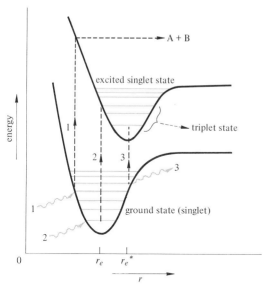

Figure 26·1   Schematic potential energy diagram for ground and excited electronic singlet states of a diatomic molecule, A—B and A—B*, respectively. The horizontal lines represent vibrational energy levels. The wavy lines represent the arrival or departure of light quanta.

seen to be *above* the level required for dissociation of A—B*. The vibration of the excited molecule therefore has no restoring force and leads to dissociation to A and B atoms. On the other hand, the somewhat lower-energy transition marked 2 leads to an excited vibrational state of A—B* which is not expected to dissociate but which can lose vibrational energy to the surroundings and come down to a lower vibrational state. This is called "vibrational relaxation" and usually requires about 10^{-12} sec. The vibrationally "relaxed" excited state can now undergo several processes. It can return to ground state with emission of radiation (transition 3); this is known as **fluorescence**, the wavelength of fluorescence being different from that of the original light absorbed. Normally, fluorescence, if it occurs at all, occurs in 10^{-9} to 10^{-7} sec after absorption of the original radiation. In many cases, the excited state can also return to the ground state by nonradiative processes, the electronic excited state being converted to a vibrationally excited ground state of the original molecule which by vibrational relaxation proceeds to the ground state. This means, in effect, that the excess energy is shuffled into vibrational modes and thence by molecular collisions to the system as a whole. Sometimes, however, decay to a **triplet** state occurs before either complete vibrational relaxation or fluorescence takes place. Formation of a triplet state is of particular chemical interest because triplet states, even though of high energy, are often relatively long lived, up to a second or so, and can lead to important reaction products. To understand these processes we must consider in more detail the nature of singlet and triplet electronic states.

We have already noted that in the ground states of ordinary molecules all the electrons are paired; we can also have excited states with all electrons paired. States with paired electrons are called singlet states. A schematic representation of the ground state (S_0) and lowest excited singlet (S_1) electronic configurations of a molecule with four electrons and two bonding and two antibonding molecular orbitals is shown in Figure 26·2. The π-electron system of butadiene (Section 6·7) provides a concrete example of this type of system.

A triplet state has two *unpaired* electrons and is normally more stable than the corresponding excited singlet state because, by Hund's rule, less interelectronic repulsion is expected with unpaired than paired electrons. An example of the lowest energy triplet electronic configuration (T_1) is shown in Figure 26·2. The name "triplet" arises from the fact that two unpaired electrons turn out to have *three* possible energy states in an applied magnetic field. "Singlet" means that there is only one possible energy state in a magnetic field.

Conversion of the lowest singlet excited state to the lowest triplet state $(S_1 \rightarrow T_1)$ is energetically favorable but usually occurs rather slowly, in accord with the so-called spectroscopic selection rules, which predict that spontaneous changes of electronic configuration of this type should have very low probabilities. Nonetheless, if the singlet state is sufficiently long lived, the singlet-triplet change, $S_1 \rightarrow T_1$ (often called **intersystem crossing**), may occur for a very considerable proportion of the excited singlet molecules. The triplet and singlet states are actually different chemical entities.

The triplet state, like the singlet state, can return to the ground state by a nonradiative process or by a radiative transition $(T_1 \rightarrow S_0)$. Such radiative transitions result in emission of light of considerably longer wavelength than either that absorbed originally or that emitted by fluorescence. This type of radiative transition is called **phosphorescence**. Because phosphorescence is a process with a low probability, the T_1 state may persist from fractions of a second to many seconds. For benzene at $-200°$, absorption of light at 2540 A leads to fluorescence centered on 2900 A and phosphorescence at 3400 A with a half-life of 7 sec.

There are a number of possible fates for excited singlet or triplet molecules.

Figure 26·2 Schematic representation of the electronic configurations of ground and lowest excited singlet and triplet states of a molecule with four electrons and four molecular orbitals (ψ_1, ψ_2, ψ_3, and ψ_4).

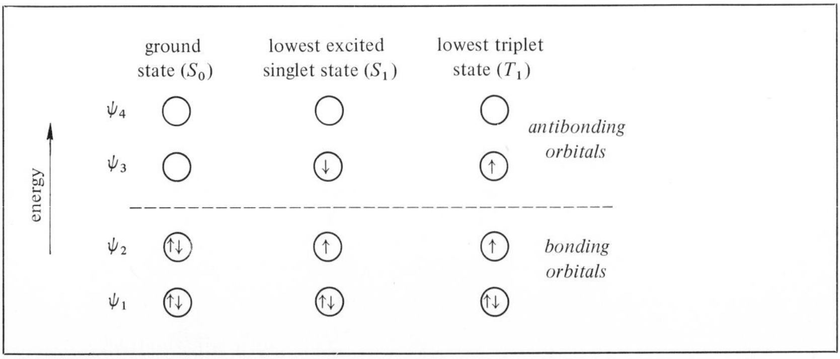

A singlet state can lose some vibrational energy and radiate the remainder (fluoresce); decay to a high vibrational state of the electronic ground state and then undergo vibrational relaxation to dissipate its energy; undergo a chemical reaction; lose energy by vibrational relaxation and come down to a lower singlet state (if there is one); or decay to a triplet state. A triplet state can undergo similar changes except that intersystem crossing to an excited singlet state is seldom possible because the latter is usually of higher energy. We are chiefly concerned in this chapter with the chemical reactions of excited states, but we must first examine more closely the relation between molecular structure and the wavelength and intensity of absorption of ultraviolet and visible light, because photochemical changes depend on the system first being activated by the absorption of light quanta.

26·2 light absorption and structure

In Chapter 7 it was shown how the changes in wavelength of absorption of conjugated systems could be accounted for in terms of differences in the degree of resonance stabilization between ground and excited states. If the conjugated system of multiple bonds is long enough the absorption occurs in the visible part of the spectrum. Thus, 1,2-diphenylethene is colorless (λ_{max} 3190 A), whereas 1,10-diphenyl-1,3,5,7,9-decapentaene is orange (λ_{max} 4240 A).

colorless
(λ_{max} 3190A)

orange
(λ_{max} 4240 A)

In general, the more extended a planar system of conjugated bonds is, the smaller is the energy difference between the ground and excited states. The importance of having the bonds coplanar should be obvious from consideration of preferred geometries of the resonance structures with formal bonds and (or) charge separations. The contribution of such structures to stabilization of the ground state increases with an increase in length of the conjugated system; but stabilization of the excited state increases even more rapidly, so that the overall energy difference between ground and excited states decreases and hence the wavelength required for excitation shifts to longer wavelengths.

The effect of substituents on the colors associated with conjugated systems is of particular interest in the study of dyes because, with the exception of compounds such as β-carotene, which is an orange-red conjugated polyene occurring in a variety of plants and which is commonly used as a food color, most dyes have relatively short conjugated systems and would not be intensely colored in the absence of substituent groups.

β-carotene (all *trans* double bonds)
(λ_{max} 4500 A, ε 140,000)

A typical dyestuff is 2,4-dinitro-1-naphthol (Martius Yellow), a substance that is used to dye wool and silk. (In addition to possessing color, dyes must be able to interact with the fibers of these substances. The chemistry of dyestuffs is considered in Chapter 28, which deals with polymers.)

Martius Yellow

Although naphthalene is a conjugated system it is colorless to the eye, as is pure 1-naphthol. 2,4-Dinitronaphthalene is pale yellow, so the red-orange color of crystalline Martius Yellow is clearly due to a special combination of substituents with a conjugated system.

Substitution of a group on a conjugated system which is capable of either donating or accepting electrons usually has the effect of extending the conjugation. This is particularly true if an electron-attracting group is connected to one end of the system and an electron-donating group to the other. Thus, with p-nitrophenolate ion, we can expect considerable stabilization because of interaction between the strongly electron-donating $-O^{\ominus}$ group and the strongly electron-accepting $-NO_2$ group.

The high degree of electron delocalization which can be associated with this system is clearly related to its absorption spectrum because, while p-nitrophenolate ion in water gives a strongly yellow solution (λ_{max} 4000 A, ε 15,000), p-nitrophenol produces a less intensely colored greenish-yellow solution (λ_{max} 3200 A, ε 9000). The important structural difference here is that the $-OH$ group is not nearly so strong an electron-donating group as an $-O^{\ominus}$ group, and electron delocalization is therefore likely to be less important.

There are several connections in which changes of color resulting from interconversions of such substances as *p*-nitrophenol and the *p*-nitrophenolate ion are important, including the practical one of the colors of acid-base indicators as a function of pH. However, before discussing some of these, it will be well to make clear that, in visual comparisons of the colors of substances, it must be remembered that both wavelength and absorption coefficient are involved in judgments of color intensities. The change from *p*-nitrophenolate ion to *p*-nitrophenol provides an excellent example of how both wavelength and absorption coefficient are affected by a structural change. It is possible for wavelength to shift without changing the degree of absorption and vice versa, so in speaking of one substance as being more "highly colored" than another we must be careful as to which features of the spectra we are actually comparing.

Furthermore, a compound with an absorption maximum in the ultraviolet may be colored if the absorption band extends into the visible (Figure 26·3). It should be remembered that colored substances remove part of the white light spectrum and the color that registers in the eye is complementary to that which was absorbed. Thus compounds that absorb violet light (light of wavelength near 4000 A) appear green-yellow and those that absorb red light (light of wavelength near 7000 A) appear blue-green.

The problems of correlating wavelength and absorption coefficient with structure can be approached in a number of ways. In an earlier discussion (Section 7·5), the excited electronic states were considered to have hybrid structures with important contributions from dipolar electron-pairing schemes. Thus for the first excited singlet state of butadiene, we may write these contributing structures:

$$\overset{\oplus}{C}H_2-CH=CH-\overset{\ominus}{\ddot{C}}H_2 \longleftrightarrow \overset{\ominus}{\ddot{C}}H_2-CH=CH-\overset{\oplus}{C}H_2$$
$$\qquad\quad [1] \qquad\qquad\qquad\qquad\qquad [2]$$

$$\longleftrightarrow\; CH_2=CH-\overset{\ominus}{\ddot{C}}H-\overset{\oplus}{C}H_2 \longleftrightarrow \text{ etc.}$$
$$\qquad\qquad\qquad [3]$$

Extension of this approach to benzene suggests the importance of resonance structures such as [4], [5], and so on for the excited singlet state of benzene.

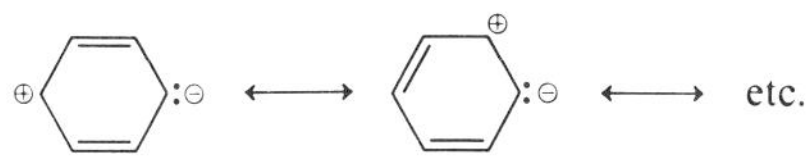

$$[4] \qquad\qquad\qquad [5]$$

It is not unreasonable to suppose that substitution of an electron-attracting group at one end of such a system and an electron-donating group at the other end should be particularly favorable for stabilizing the excited state relative to the ground state wherein [4], [5], and so on are of negligible importance. At the same time, we would not expect that two electron-attracting (or two electron-donating) groups at opposite ends would be nearly as effective.

The problem of predicting the absorption intensities is a difficult and complicated one. An important factor is the ease of displacement of charge

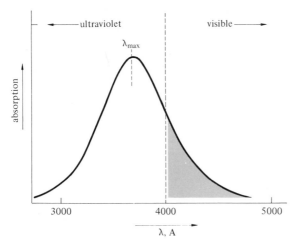

Figure 26·3   Absorption in the visible region by a substance that has λ_{max} in the ultraviolet.

during the transition. On this account we expect substances such as *p*-nitrophenolate ions, which have roughly equivalent electron-donating and electron-attracting groups in each of their principal resonance structures, to absorb particularly strongly.

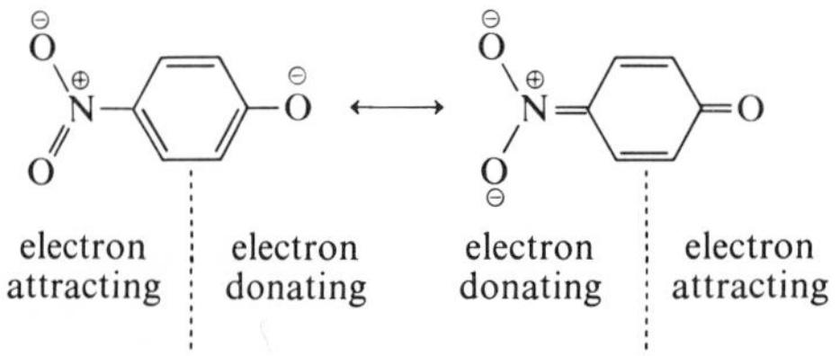

electron   electron   electron   electron
attracting   donating   donating   attracting

Figure 26·4   Two of the many resonance structures of the dye Crystal Violet.

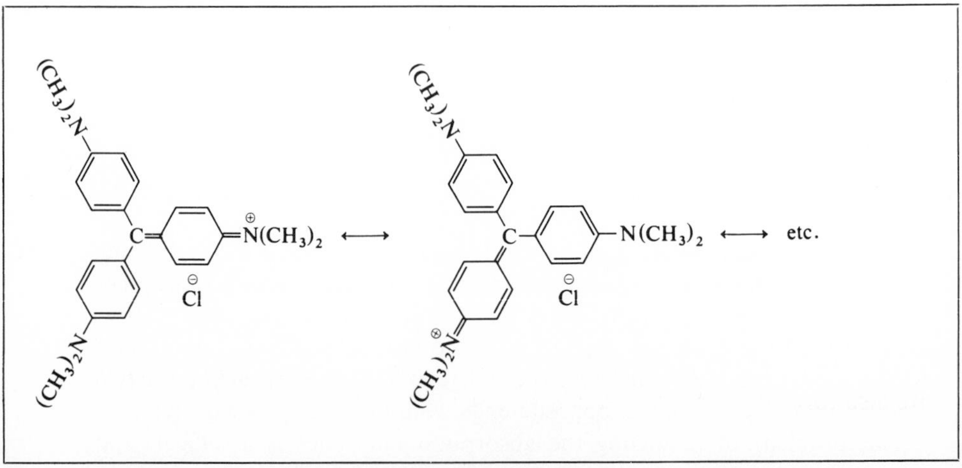

We expect this factor to be especially favorable where equivalent resonance structures may be written. Many useful and intensely colored dyes have resonance structures of this general sort. A typical example is Crystal Violet, shown in Figure 26·4.

26·3 photodissociation reactions

We have already mentioned (Section 2·5B) that the chlorine molecule undergoes dissociation with near-ultraviolet light to give chlorine atoms and thereby initiates the radical chain chlorination of saturated hydrocarbons. Photochemical chlorination is an example of a photochemical reaction which can have a high *quantum yield*—that is, many molecules of chlorination product can be generated per quantum of light absorbed. The quantum yield, Φ, of a reaction is said to be unity when 1 mole of reactant(s) is converted to product(s) per mole of photons absorbed. (This quantity of light is called one **einstein**.)

Acetone vapor undergoes a photodissociation reaction with 3130-A light with Φ somewhat less than unity and is of interest in illustrating some of the things which are taken into account in the study of photochemical processes.

Absorption of light by acetone results in the formation of an excited state which has sufficient energy to undergo cleavage of a C—C bond (the weakest bond in the molecule) and form a methyl radical and an acetyl radical.

$$CH_3-\overset{\overset{\displaystyle O}{\|}}{C}-CH_3 \xrightarrow{h\upsilon} \left[CH_3-\overset{\overset{\displaystyle O}{\|}}{C}-CH_3\right]^* \longrightarrow CH_3-\overset{\overset{\displaystyle O}{\|}}{C}\cdot + CH_3\cdot$$

At temperatures much above room temperature, the acetyl radical breaks down to give another methyl radical and carbon monoxide.

$$CH_3-\overset{\overset{\displaystyle O}{\|}}{C}\cdot \longrightarrow CH_3\cdot + C{=}O$$

If this reaction goes to completion, the principal reaction products are ethane and carbon monoxide.

$$2\,CH_3\cdot \longrightarrow CH_3-CH_3$$

If the acetyl radical does not decompose completely, then some biacetyl is also formed. This reaction is quite important at room temperature or below.

$$2\,CH_3-\overset{\overset{\displaystyle O}{\|}}{C}\cdot \longrightarrow CH_3-\overset{\overset{\displaystyle O}{\|}}{C}-\overset{\overset{\displaystyle O}{\|}}{C}-CH_3$$
biacetyl

Lesser amounts of methane, hydrogen, ketene (see Section 12·4), and so on are also formed in the photochemical dissociation of acetone.

A variety of dissociation-type photochemical reactions has been found to take place with other carbonyl compounds. Two examples are

26·4 photochemical reduction

One of the classic photochemical reductions of organic chemistry is the formation of benzopinacol, as brought about by the action of light on a solution of benzophenone in isopropyl alcohol. The yield is quantitative.

The light functions to energize the benzophenone, and the activated ketone removes a hydrogen from isopropyl alcohol.

benzhydrol radical
[6]

Benzopinacol results from dimerization of benzhydrol radicals [6].

The initial light absorption process involves excitation of one of the unshared electrons on the carbonyl oxygen atom ($n \to \pi^*$). However, the excited singlet state undergoes facile intersystem crossing to give the longer-lived triplet state ($S_1 \to T_1$) and it is the latter that abstracts the hydrogen atom from the alcohol.

Because the quantum yields of acetone and benzopinacol are both nearly unity when the light intensity is not high, it is clear that *two* benzhydrol radicals [6] must be formed for each molecule of benzophenone that becomes activated. This is possible if the hydroxyisopropyl radicals formed by Equation 26·1 react with benzophenone to give benzhydrol radicals.

$$\begin{array}{c} CH_3 \\ | \\ \cdot C-OH \\ | \\ CH_3 \end{array} + \longrightarrow \begin{array}{c} CH_3 \\ | \\ C=O \\ | \\ CH_3 \end{array} + \tag{26·1}$$

This reaction is energetically favorable because of the greater possibility for delocalization of the odd electron in the benzhydrol radical than in the hydroxyisopropyl radical.

Photochemical formation of benzopinacol can also be achieved from benzophenone and benzhydrol.

The mechanism is similar to that for isopropyl alcohol as the reducing agent except that now two benzhydrol radicals are formed.

benzopinacol

The reduction is believed to involve the triplet state of benzophenone by the following argument. Benzopinacol formation is reasonably efficient even when the benzhydrol concentration is low; therefore, whatever excited state of benzophenone accepts a hydrogen atom from benzhydrol, it must be a fairly long-lived one. Because benzophenone in solution shows no visible fluorescence, it must be converted to another state in something like 10^{-10} sec, but this is not long enough to seek out benzhydrol molecules in dilute solution. The long-lived state is then most reasonably a triplet state.

26·5 photochemical oxidation

Molecular oxygen, O_2, is unusual in that its most stable electronic configuration is that of a triplet, $\cdot O-O\cdot$, in which the spins of the odd electrons are the same. The reactions of oxygen are in accord with this arrangement, for example, rapid reaction with radicals (Sections 2·5B and 22·4) or paramagnetic metal ions (Section 18·4). When oxygen is raised to its excited state by absorption of energy we find a different set of reactions entirely. The first excited state is a singlet and corresponds to the structure O=O. Because oxygen does not absorb light in the accessible region of the visible or ultra-violet spectrum we cannot easily obtain singlet oxygen by simply irradiating oxygen. However, it is possible to obtain this chemical species if there is a sensitizer present in the system. A sensitizer is a compound which can absorb a light quantum and then transfer some of this energy to a second substance. Benzophenone is particularly useful for this purpose. We saw in the previous section how the excited singlet state of benzophenone changes to the excited triplet which can then abstract a hydrogen atom from alcohols. The triplet is also extremely efficient at transferring energy to oxygen. The sequence of reactions is shown.

$$(C_6H_5)_2C=O \xrightarrow[3665A]{h\nu} (C_6H_5)_2C=O^* \text{ (singlet)}$$

$$(C_6H_5)_2C=O^* \text{ (singlet)} \longrightarrow (C_6H_5)_2C=O^* \text{ (triplet)}$$

$$(C_6H_5)_2C=O^* \text{ (triplet)} + O_2 \longrightarrow (C_6H_5)_2C=O + O=O \text{ (singlet)}$$

The reactions of the excited state of oxygen, O=O, are characteristic of a molecule with paired electrons rather than of a diradical. It reacts with alkenes in a concerted manner by attaching itself to one carbon atom of the double bond while abstracting a hydrogen from the allylic position.

The concerted nature of the reaction is shown by the fact that the abstracted hydrogen is always *cis* to the position of oxygen attack; see Exercise 26·10. This suggests that the reaction proceeds through a cyclic transition state such as the following:

Singlet oxygen reacts with conjugated dienes to form bicyclic compounds.

We shall encounter this type of cyclization reaction again in the next chapter and we shall see that there is a distinct resemblance between the reactions of O=O and $CH_2=CH_2$.

Singlet oxygen can also be generated chemically by the oxidation of hydrogen peroxide in alkaline solution with two-electron oxidizing agents (Section 18·4) able to remove hydride ion from hydrogen peroxide. Hypochlorite is useful for this purpose.

$$^{\ominus}O-O-H + ^{\ominus}OCl \longrightarrow O=O + HO^{\ominus} + Cl^{\ominus}$$

26·6 photochemical isomerization of cis- and trans-unsaturated compounds

An important problem in many syntheses of unsaturated compounds is to produce the desired isomer of a *cis-trans* pair. In many cases, it is necessary to utilize an otherwise inefficient synthesis because it affords the desired isomer, even though an efficient synthesis of the unwanted isomer or of an isomer mixture may be available. An alternative way of attacking this problem is to use the most efficient synthesis and then to isomerize the undesired isomer to the desired isomer. In many cases this can be done photochemically.

A typical example is given by *cis*- and *trans*-stilbene.

$$\text{trans} \xrightarrow{h\nu} \text{cis}$$

Here the *trans* form is easily available by a variety of reactions and is much more stable than the *cis* isomer because it is less sterically hindered. However, it is possible to produce a mixture containing mostly the *cis* isomer by irradiating a solution of the *trans* isomer in the presence of a suitable photosensitizer. This process in no way contravenes the laws of thermodynamics, because the input of radiant energy permits the equilibrium point to be shifted from what it would be normally.

Another example is provided by the equilibration of 1-bromo-2-phenyl-1-propene. The *trans* isomer is formed to the extent of 95% in the dehydrohalogenation of 1,2-dibromo-2-phenylpropane.

$$\text{Br}-\underset{\text{H}_3\text{C}}{\overset{\text{Br}}{\text{C}}}-\underset{\text{H}}{\overset{}{\text{C}}}-\text{H} \xrightarrow[\text{HOCH}_3]{\text{NaOCH}_3} \underset{\substack{trans \\ 95\%}}{\text{C}=\text{C}} + \underset{\substack{cis \\ 5\%}}{\text{C}=\text{C}}$$

Photoisomerization of the elimination product with 2-naphthyl methyl ketone as sensitizer produces a mixture containing 85% of the *cis* isomer.

In the practical use of the sensitized photochemical equilibrium of *cis* and *trans* isomers, it is normally necessary to carry out pilot experiments to determine what sensitizers are useful and the equilibrium point which each gives.

26·7 photochemical cycloadditions

In the next chapter cyclization reactions of various kinds will be discussed, including those resulting from absorption of light. We shall only point out here how photochemistry has in recent years enabled some cyclic compounds with unusual structures to be prepared.

R = *t*-butyl   [7]   [8]   [9]

Compounds [8] and [9] are moderately stable at room temperature although they are clearly of higher energy than benzene derivatives. They will be recognized as two of the structures that were suggested a century ago for the structure of benzene by Dewar and Ladenburg (Chapter 6). The terms Dewar benzene and Ladenburg benzene are often used for [8] and [9], respectively; [9] is also called prismane, because of its resemblance to a prism. Although the structure of Dewar benzene is often drawn as in [8] it is preferable to show the molecule's partly folded geometry and the closeness of the bridgehead carbons, as in [10]. Thus [10] should not be regarded as contributing to the resonance hybrid of benzene because the geometries of [10] and benzene are very different.

[10]

summary

Absorption of visible or ultraviolet light by an organic molecule in a ground singlet state, S_0, produces a short-lived electronically excited singlet state, S (S_1 if the lowest singlet state), which may undergo a chemical reaction or return to the ground state by one of the following means: it may fluoresce (lose some energy by vibrational relaxation and then radiate the remainder); it may undergo vibrational relaxation to a lower singlet state, if there is one, or all the way to the ground state (S_0); or it may undergo intersystem crossing to produce a longer-lived triplet state ($S_1 \rightarrow T_1$) which may, in turn, either phosphoresce (lose energy by vibrational relaxation and then radiate the remainder), undergo a chemical reaction, or act as a photosensitizer by transferring its energy to a second molecule.

Photoactivation requires that light be absorbed; photosensitizers (e.g., benzophenone) are useful for activating other compounds that do not absorb light in an accessible part of the spectrum.

Conjugation stabilizes excited states more than ground states and conjugated compounds thus tend to absorb at the longer wavelengths.

Some of the reactions undergone by compounds that have been raised to their excited electronic states (either by direct light absorption or by energy transfer from a photosensitizer) include dissociation, oxidation or reduction, *trans-cis* isomerization, and cycloaddition. Many of the sensitized reactions involve the triplet state of aromatic ketones such as benzophenone.

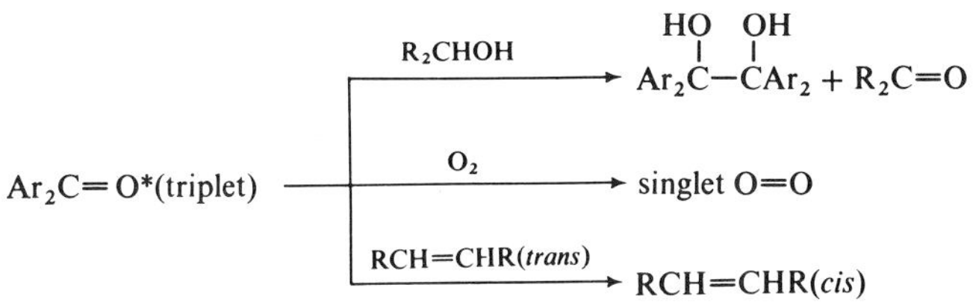

$$Ar_2C=O^*(triplet) \quad
\begin{cases}
\xrightarrow{R_2CHOH} & Ar_2\overset{HO}{\underset{|}{C}}-\overset{OH}{\underset{|}{C}}Ar_2 + R_2C=O \\
\xrightarrow{O_2} & \text{singlet } O=O \\
\xrightarrow{RCH=CHR(trans)} & RCH=CHR(cis)
\end{cases}$$

Singlet oxygen ($O=O$), which can also be generated chemically, undergoes a number of reactions unknown to ground-state (triplet) oxygen, including the following:

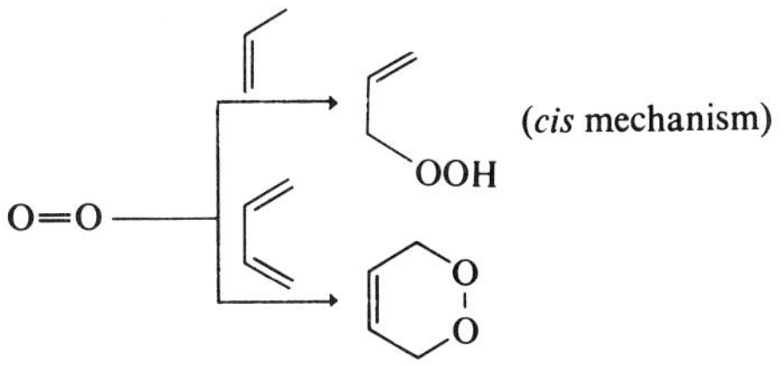

Derivatives of both Dewar benzene and Ladenburg benzene (prismane) have been prepared by photochemical isomerization of derivatives of ordinary benzene.

exercises

26·1   The fluorescence of many substances can be "quenched" (diminished or even prevented) by a variety of means. Explain how concentration, temperature, viscosity, and presence of dissolved oxygen and impurities might affect the degree of fluorescence observed for solutions of a fluorescent material. Would you expect similar effects on phosphorescence? Explain.

26·2 Explain qualitatively how temperature could have an effect on the appearance of the absorption spectrum of a system such as shown in Figure 26·1, knowing that most molecules are usually in their lowest vibrational state at room temperature.

26·3 Make diagrams of at least five different singlet states and three different triplet states of the system shown in Figure 26·2.

26·4 What visible color would you expect the substance to have whose spectrum is shown in Figure 26·3?

26·5 The $\pi \rightarrow \pi^*$ absorption spectra of *trans,trans*-, *trans,cis*-, and *cis,cis*-1,4-diphenylbutadiene show maxima and ε values (in parentheses) at about 3300 A (5.5×10^4), 3100 A (3×10^4), and 3000 A (3×10^4), respectively. What is the difference in energy between the transitions of these isomers in kilocalories per mole? Why should the *trans,trans* isomer have a different λ_{max} than the other isomers? (It may be helpful to make scale drawings or models.)

26·6 How would you expect the spectra of compounds [11] and [12] to compare with each other and with the spectra of *cis*- and *trans*-1,2-diphenylethene (stilbene)? Explain.

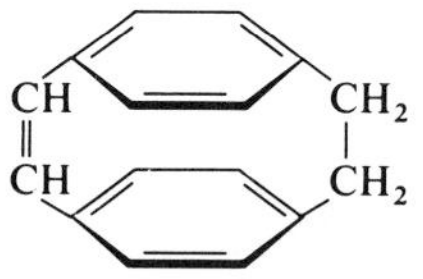

[11] 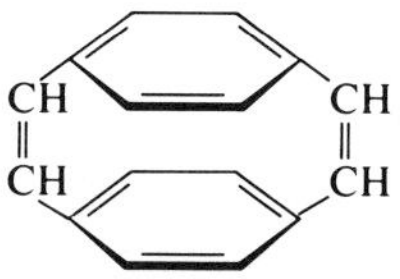   [12]

26·7 Why must the resonance forms [1], [2], [3], etc., for butadiene correspond to a singlet state? Formulate the hybrid structure of a triplet state of butadiene in terms of appropriate contributing resonance structures.

26·8 *a.* *p*-Nitrodimethylaniline gives a yellow solution in water which fades to colorless when made acidic. Explain.

b. *p*-Dimethylaminoazobenzene (Section 22·9B) is bright yellow in aqueous solution (λ_{max} 4200A) but turns intense red (λ_{max} 5300 A) if dilute acid is added. If the solution is then made very strongly acid, the red color changes to a different yellow (λ_{max} 4300 A) than the starting solution. Show how one proton could be added to *p*-dimethylaminoazobenzene to cause the absorption to shift to *longer* wavelengths and how addition of a second proton could shift the absorption back to shorter wavelengths.

26·9 The well-known indicator and laxative, phenolphthalein, undergoes the following changes as a neutral solution is made successively more basic:

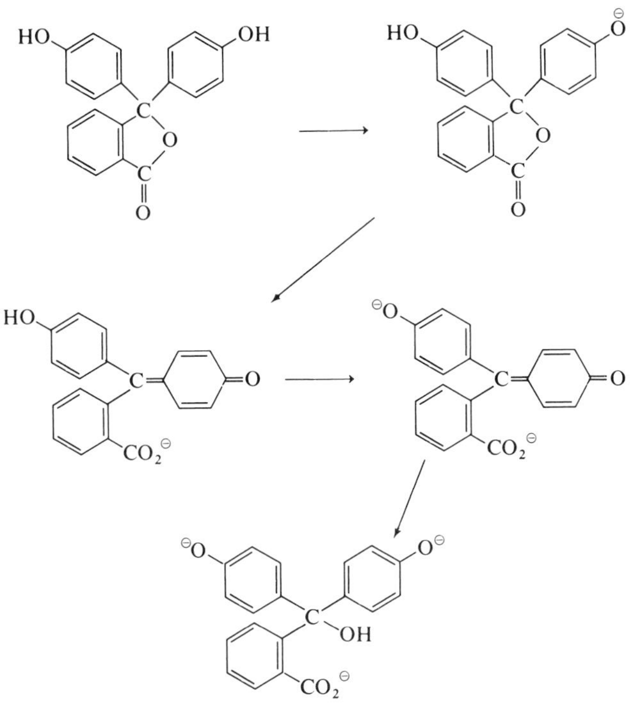

Some of these forms are colorless, some intensely colored. Which would you expect to absorb at sufficiently long wavelengths to be visibly colored? Give your reasoning.

26·10 A steroid molecule, only part of whose structure is shown below, contained one atom of deuterium in a position *cis* to the hydroxyl group. On irradiation of a mixture of this compound, oxygen, and an aryl ketone sensitizer, one of the following hydroperoxides was obtained in high yield and the other in very small yield. Identify the major product. Give your reasoning.

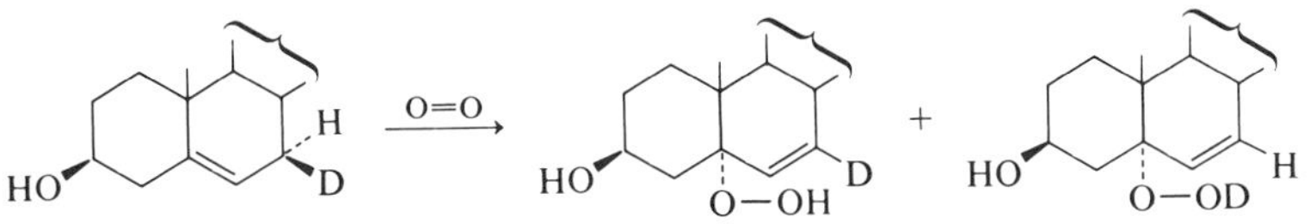

chapter 27
cyclization reactions

Ring formation can take place if functional groups in the same molecule react intramolecularly. Cyclic structures can also be formed by the addition reaction of two unsaturated molecules with one another. In this chapter we shall first examine intramolecular ring closure, especially as it involves carbonyl compounds, and then examine the addition reactions of alkenes and polyenes that lead to cyclic structures. The first group of reactions enables us to review some familiar chemistry; the second introduces new reactions and new concepts and takes us deeper into molecular orbital theory than we have hitherto gone. Those whose interests are less theoretical may not wish to pursue this subject beyond Section 27·4.

27·1 cyclization reactions of carbonyl compounds

Carboxylic acids react with alcohols and amines to form esters and amides.

$$RCO_2H + HOR \longrightarrow RCO_2R + H_2O$$

$$RCO_2H + H_2NR \longrightarrow RCONHR + H_2O$$

Hydroxy acids and amino acids undergo the same reactions to give cyclic structures (lactones and lactams, Sections 13·10B and 17·2), provided that the functional groups are favorably situated with respect to one another.

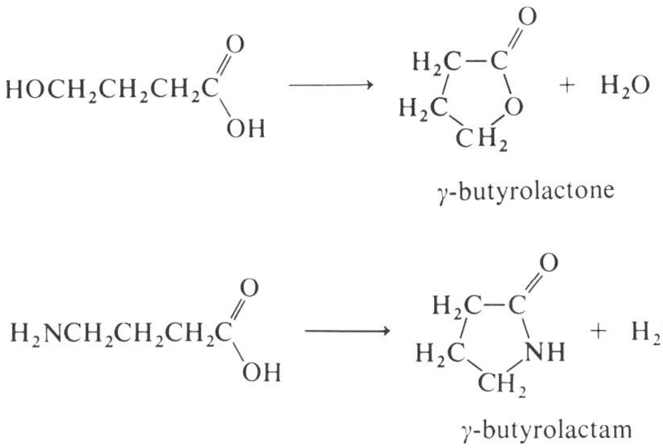

γ-butyrolactone

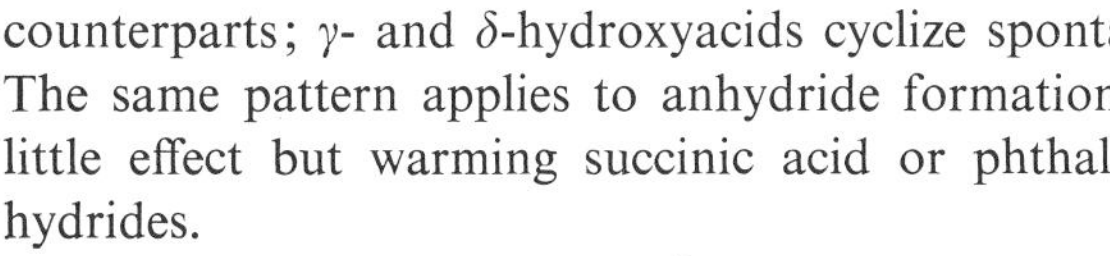

γ-butyrolactam

Indeed, these reactions occur much more readily than their intermolecular counterparts; γ- and δ-hydroxyacids cyclize spontaneously to give lactones. The same pattern applies to anhydride formation; heating acetic acid has little effect but warming succinic acid or phthalic acid produces the anhydrides.

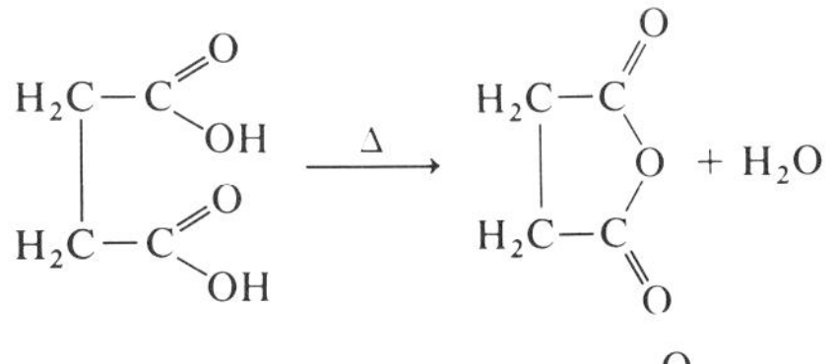

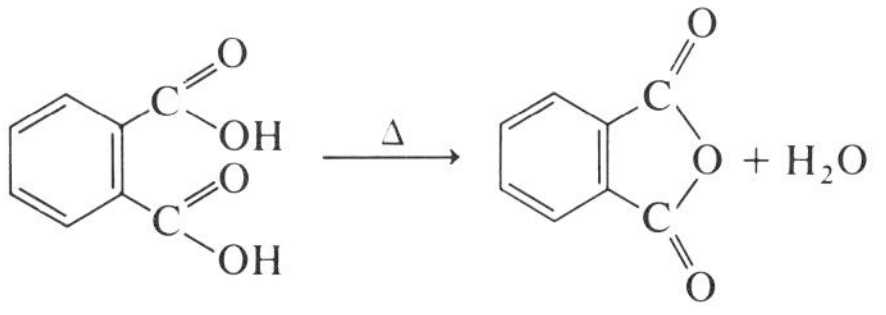

When more than three carbon atoms intervene between the carboxyl groups of a dicarboxylic acid, pyrolysis of the acid (or its thorium salt) produces ketones (Section 13·11B).

$$n > 3$$

Spontaneous cyclization occurs with γ- and δ-hydroxyaldehydes and ketones to give hemiacetals (Section 11·4B).

The best known examples are provided by carbohydrates (Section 15·3).

The Claisen condensation of esters (Section 13·9B) has its intramolecular counterpart in the **Dieckmann reaction**.

The course of this cyclization reaction is the same as that of the Claisen reaction. Ethoxide ion abstracts a proton from one of the two activated methylene groups in the diester to give an anion.

The highly nucleophilic anion thus formed attacks a carbonyl group and, particularly in dilute solution, this is likely to be the group in the same molecule. Loss of ethoxide ion gives the product.

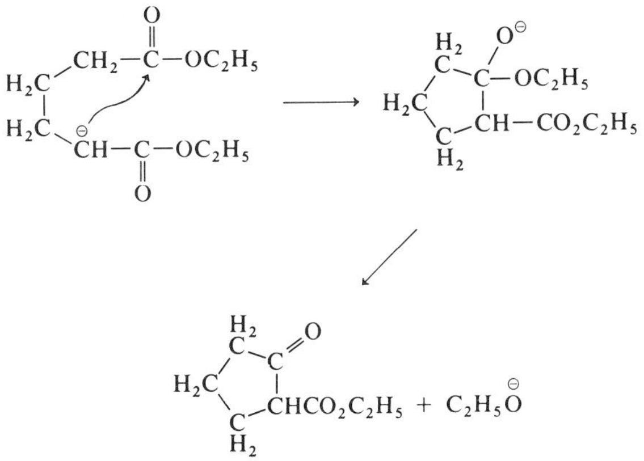

Another very useful ring closure reaction that bears a superficial resemblance to the above reaction is the **acyloin condensation**. The reactant is again a dicarboxylic ester but the reagent is sodium dispersed in a hydrocarbon solvent instead of sodium ethoxide dissolved in ethanol. This seemingly small difference in the reagent changes the course of the reaction completely. Sodium is unable to function as a base in a hydrocarbon solvent and instead it reacts as a one-electron reducing reagent to produce a radical anion at each carbonyl group. Ring closure followed by elimination of ethoxide ions and further reduction produces the dianion [1] which on addition of water yields the hydroxy ketone [2] (an **acyloin**).

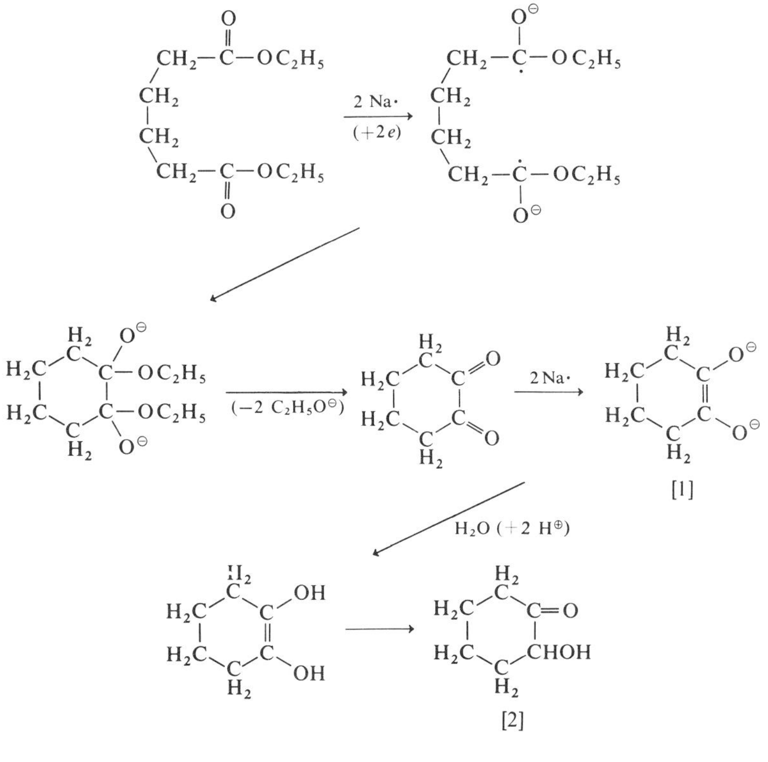

This reaction, which works very well for large rings, has been used in an ingenious synthesis of a **catenane**, a compound whose two rings are not joined by bonds but are held together like links in a chain. A large-ring compound [5] was prepared by the acyloin condensation followed by Clemmensen reduction (Section 11·4F) using deuterated reagents. This produced a large carbocyclic ring containing some deuterium label. (Partial exchange of the α hydrogens occurred and produced a compound containing on the average five deuterium atoms per molecule.)

The labeled compound was then dissolved in xylene, more [3] added, and the acyloin condensation repeated. If the long chain of [3] happens to be threaded through a molecule of [5] when ring closure occurs the catenane [6] will be produced.

The product was purified by chromatography and after all traces of [5] were removed, it was found that some deuterium label remained, suggesting the presence of about 2% [6] mixed with [4]. Cleavage of the hydroxy ketone ring by oxidation produced a dicarboxylic acid containing no deuterium and the large-ring deuterium-containing hydrocarbon [5].

27·2 cycloaddition reactions of carbon-carbon multiple bonds

The tendency of an alkene such as ethene to undergo a cycloaddition reaction with another unsaturated molecule depends on two important factors: whether the other molecule contains isolated or conjugated double bonds, and whether the system is activated by heat or by light. For example, most alkenes show little tendency to dimerize to cyclobutanes thermally (Δ), but the reaction can usually be brought about readily by the action of light ($h\nu$).

On the other hand, substituted alkenes usually react readily on being warmed with conjugated dienes to give cyclohexenes. Light ($h\nu$) is not required for this reaction.

The reaction of a conjugated diene with an alkene is known as the Diels-Alder reaction and is described in some detail in the next section.

A. DIELS-ALDER REACTION

Although the Diels-Alder reaction can be conducted with ethene as the alkene (often referred to as the **dienophile**), addition occurs much more readily if the alkene contains electron-withdrawing groups such as $-\overset{\overset{\displaystyle O}{\|}}{C}-$, $-C{\equiv}N$, or $-NO_2$.

One of the reasons that the reaction has proved of value, especially in the synthesis of natural products, is that it is highly stereospecific. First, and most obvious, the diene reacts in the *s-cis*[1] conformation of its double bonds because the double bond in the product (a six-membered ring) necessarily has the *cis* configuration.

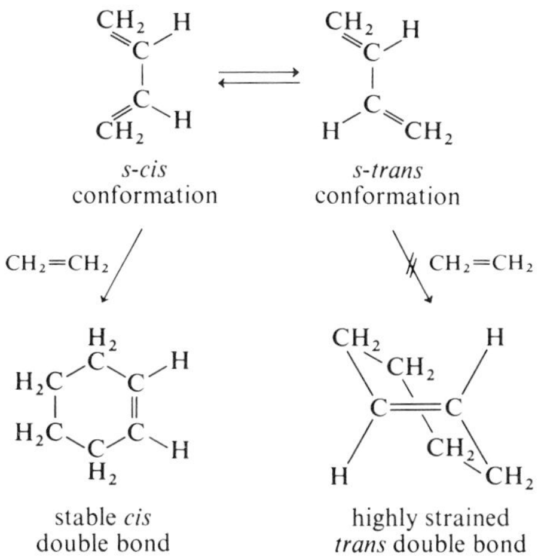

s-cis
conformation

s-trans
conformation

stable *cis*
double bond

highly strained
trans double bond

Cyclic dienes with five- and six-membered rings usually react readily because they are fixed in *s-cis* configurations.

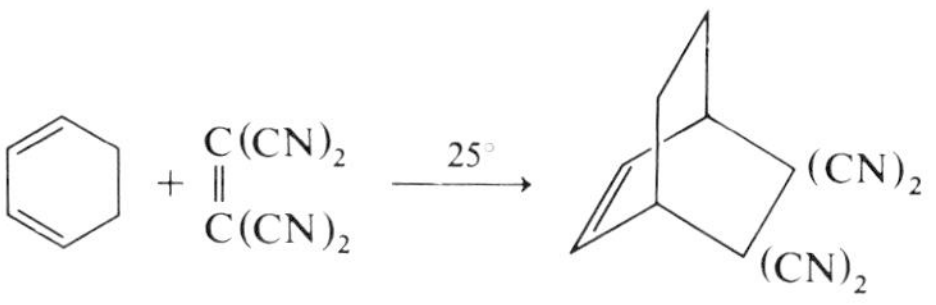

Second, the configurations of the diene and the dienophile are *retained* in the adduct. This means that the reactants (or addends) come together to give *cis* addition. Two illustrative examples follow which are drawn to emphasize how *cis* addition occurs. In the first example, dimethyl maleate, which has *cis*

---

[1] The designation *s-cis* means that the double bonds lie in a plane on the same side (*cis*) of the single bond connnecting them. The opposite and usually somewhat more stable conformation is called *s-trans*.

ester (CO_2CH_3) groups, adds to 1,3-butadiene to give a *cis*-substituted cyclohexene.

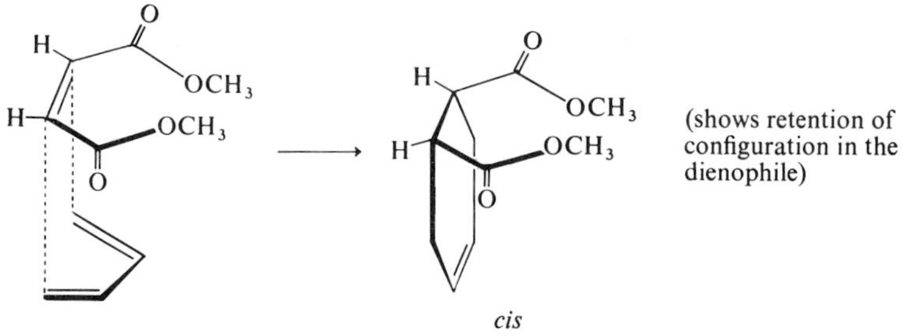

(shows retention of configuration in the dienophile)

cis

In the second example, *cis* addition of a dienophile to *trans,trans*-2,4-hexadiene is seen to yield the product with the two methyl groups on the same side of the cyclohexene ring.

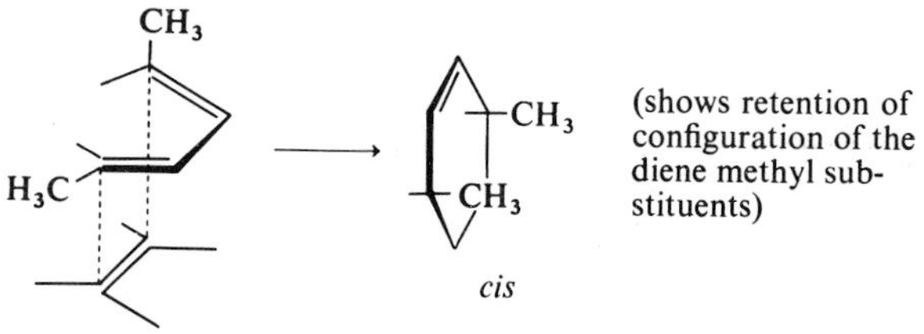

(shows retention of configuration of the diene methyl substituents)

cis

The Diels-Alder reaction is believed to occur by a one-step synchronous process in which bonds form simultaneously between each end of the diene and the dienophile.

The difference between thermal activation and photoactivation of dienes is shown in Figure 27·1.

The thermal process is a Diels-Alder reaction between two molecules of 1,3-butadiene, one of which acts as the diene and the other as the dienophile. The photochemical reaction is analogous to a reaction between two alkenes. The absorption of a photon by 1,3-butadiene is expected to activate the

Figure 27·1   Dimerization of 1,3-butadiene by thermal activation and photoactivation.

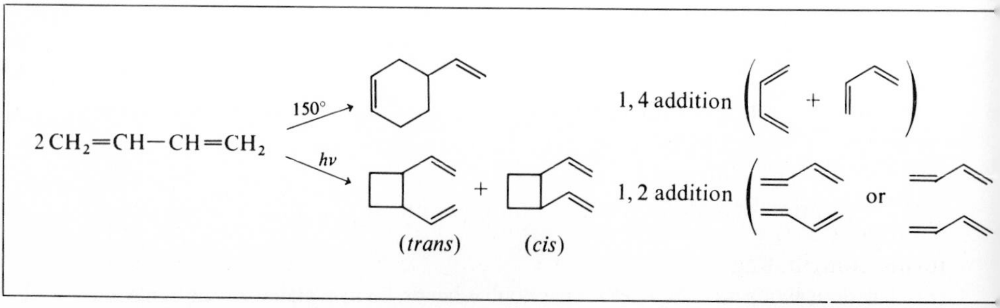

molecule, but it is less obvious why the excited state prefers to react by the 1,2-addition route rather than by the usual 1,4-path. There is no reason, how-ever, to expect electronically excited states, particularly those with different arrangements of electron spin, to undergo the same reactions as ground states. A rationale for the different routes has been developed recently based on orbital symmetry considerations and is discussed in Section 27·5.

B. CYCLIZATION REACTIONS OF ALKYNES

Alkynes can act as dienophiles in the Diels-Alder reaction to produce non-conjugated cyclohexadienes.

Acetylene can be readily polymerized to cyclooctatetraene by the action of nickel cyanide.

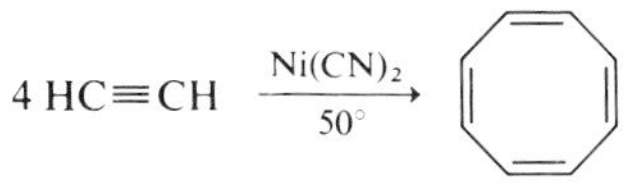

$$4\ HC\!\equiv\!CH \xrightarrow[50^\circ]{Ni(CN)_2}$$

80 90%

With this reaction, cyclooctatetraene could be manufactured easily on a large scale; however, profitable commercial uses of the substance have yet to be developed.

It is easy to become confused about the reactions of alkynes with transition-metal ions. Acetylene, for example, is hydrated under the influence of Hg^{II} (Section 5·4); it forms salts with Ag^I (Section 5·5); it is dimerized to vinyl-acetylene by Cu^I (Section 5·4); it is polymerized to cyclooctatetraene by Ni^{II} (above); and we shall see later in this chapter that it and other alkynes can be oxidatively coupled by the action of Cu^{II}.

C. 1,3-DIPOLAR ADDITIONS

Alkenes and some other compounds with multiple bonds undergo 1,3-cyclo-addition with a variety of substances which can be formulated as 1,3-dipolar molecules of the type $\overset{\oplus}{X}\!-\!Y\!-\!\overset{\ominus}{Z}$.

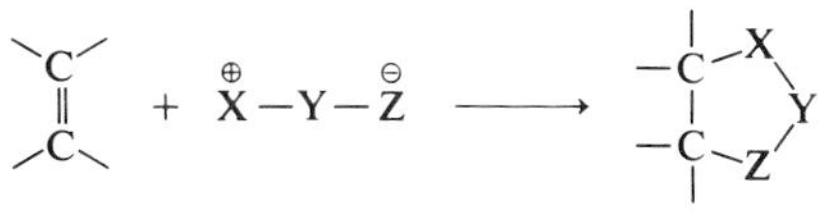

The 1,3-dipolar compounds seldom carry full formal charges on the terminal atoms and, indeed, in the list of these reagents shown in Figure 27·2, the 1,3-dipolar form is not the one we would regard as the most important of the forms contributing to the resonance hybrid. (Each of the 1,3-dipolar struc-tures shown in Figure 27·2 has an atom with an incomplete octet whereas in

ozone	$\overset{\oplus}{O}-O-\overset{\ominus}{O}$ ⟷ $O=\overset{\oplus}{O}-\overset{\ominus}{O}$
organic azides	$R-\overset{\oplus}{N}-N=\overset{\ominus}{N}$ ⟷ $R-N=\overset{\oplus}{N}=\overset{\ominus}{N}$ ⟷ $R-\overset{\ominus}{N}-\overset{\oplus}{N}≡N$
nitrile oxides	$R-\overset{\oplus}{C}=N-\overset{\ominus}{O}$ ⟷ $R-C≡\overset{\oplus}{N}-\overset{\ominus}{O}$
diazoalkanes	$R_2\overset{\oplus}{C}-N=\overset{\ominus}{N}$ ⟷ $R_2C=\overset{\oplus}{N}=\overset{\ominus}{N}$

Figure 27·2   Some 1,3-dipolar reagents.

the 1,2-dipolar structures each atom has a filled octet.) Nonetheless, alkenes add 1,3 to these substances to give five-membered rings.

A simple example is the addition of phenyl azide to norbornene. Here the azide is written to correspond to the resonance form that appropriately accounts for the occurrence of the addition.

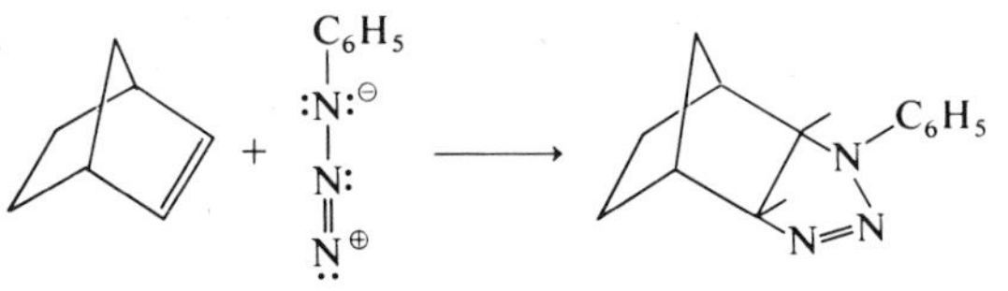

norbornene   phenyl azide

In all of these reactions heterocyclic compounds are formed, although the ozone adduct undergoes further reaction (Section 4·4G). The basis for the names shown was given earlier (Chapter 25).

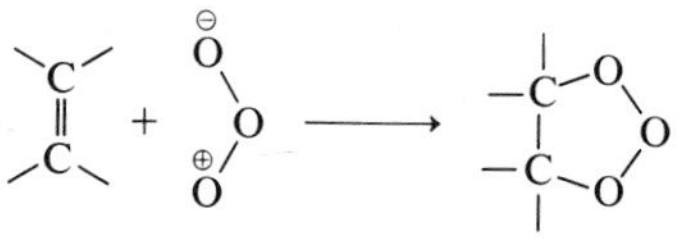

a trioxole

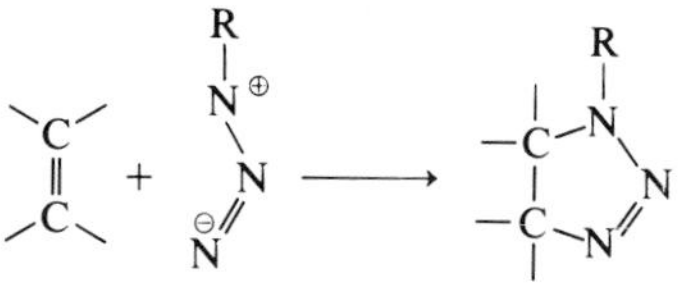

a triazole

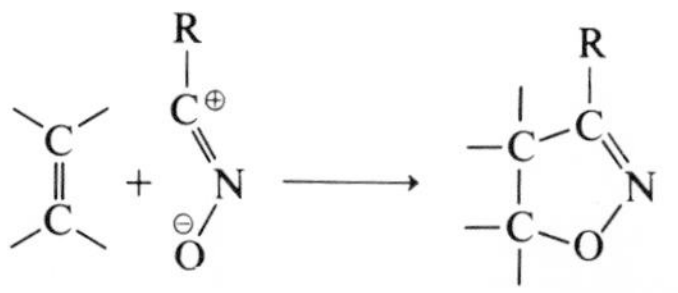

an oxazole

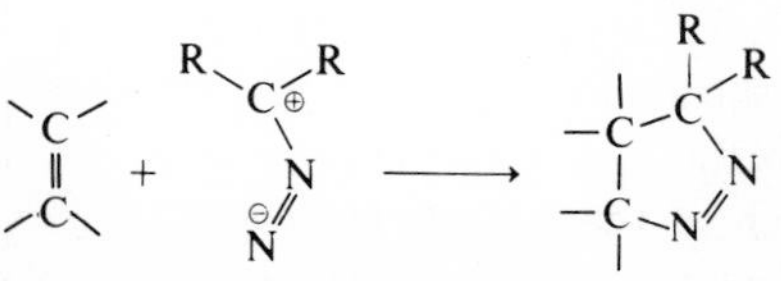

a diazole

These reactions, which are believed to be one-step synchronous processes like the Diels-Alder reaction, also take place with alkynes.

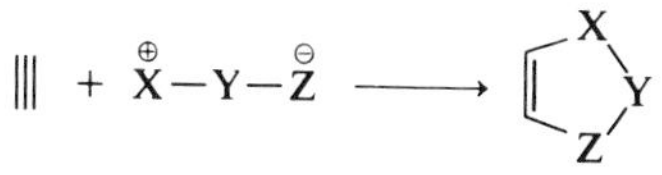

$$ ||| \ + \ \overset{\oplus}{X} - Y - \overset{\ominus}{Z} \ \longrightarrow $$

27·3 *fluxional systems*

In earlier chapters we frequently encountered the phenomenon of tautomerism, the rapid equilibration of structural isomers.

2,4-pentanedione and its enol form (Section 12·6)

$$ \underset{\displaystyle}{CH_3-\overset{O}{\overset{||}{C}}-CH_2-\overset{O}{\overset{||}{C}}-CH_3} \ \rightleftharpoons \ CH_3-\overset{O}{\overset{||}{C}}-CH=\overset{OH}{\overset{|}{C}}-CH_3 $$

2-hydroxypyridine and α-pyridone (Section 18·1E)

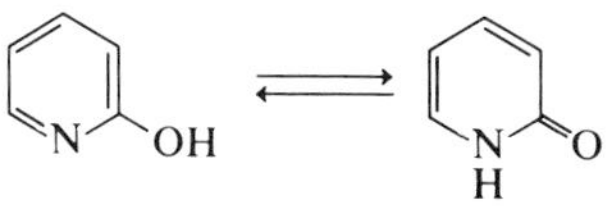

barbituric acid, keto and enol forms (Section 25·7)

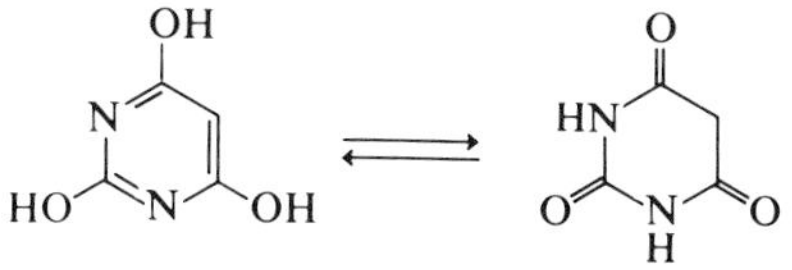

All of the above examples involve proton shifts but there is nothing in the definition that restricts us to this kind of process. For example, a rapid equilibrium exists at 100° between 1,3,5-cyclooctatriene and the bicyclic compound shown here, which is also an example of tautomerism. (The term "valence tautomerism" or "valence isomerism" is sometimes used to describe such equilibria and the reactions are sometimes called Cope rearrangements.)

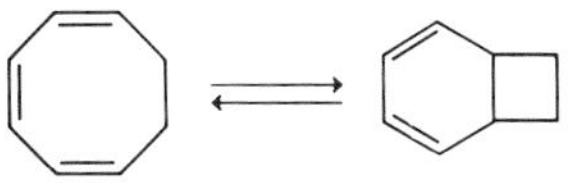

85%   15%

The nmr spectra of systems such as this clearly reveal the position of equilibrium and even the rate at which the forward and reverse reactions occur. (See Section 7·6D for a discussion of how nmr can be used to measure the rates of conformational change.)

The situation with cyclooctatetraene is similar. Although the eight-membered ring is the major form in the equilibrium mixture some of its reactions are those of the bicyclic tautomer.

Tautomerism, which involves the relocation of atoms, should not be confused with resonance, which is formulated as a dispersal of electrons over several nuclei and which can be represented by drawing two or more valence structures in which the atomic locations are the same. Tautomers are thus distinctly different chemical entities with different atomic locations. It is also possible to have equilibria between molecules with the same formal structure—for example, the rapid shifting of a hydrogen atom between the two oxygens of the carboxyl group in acetic acid or the slow equilibration of the methylene groups in 1,5-hexadiene.

This situation is very different from resonance because the atomic locations are different, and it is not strictly tautomerism because the molecules are not isomers. The term **fluxional molecules** has been coined to describe the participants in such equilibria. In the absence of some sort of label it is not possible to distinguish the two forms; nonetheless, a pathway between the fluxional molecules must exist and this has become a matter of interest to many chemists.

A facile pathway for the 1,5-hexadiene equilibration exists in which bond rupture and bond formation occur at the same time and which has the cyclic transition state shown.

transition state

A curious fluxional molecule, called **barbaralane** [7], is shown by its nmr spectrum to exist in two equivalent forms that are in rapid equilibrium at room temperature.

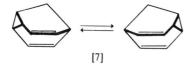

[7]

If the CH_2 group is replaced by a $CH=CH$ group the number of fluxional forms rises dramatically (see Exercise 27·4). The latter compound has been given the name **bullvalene**. (The classical languages have heretofore provided the basis for naming new compounds but this approach is now in some danger of being replaced by whimsy.)

The ease with which the two forms of barbaralane interconvert reflects the importance of synchronous bond breaking and bond making in lowering the energy of a transition state. An important part of this is the fact that the reacting atoms are held in favorable positions by the ring structure.

The similarity between the equilibrium in 1,5-hexadiene and in barbaralane can be seen if we draw the latter so that the hexadiene portion of the molecule is clearly displayed.

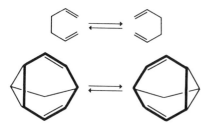

27·4 annulenes

There has been considerable interest for many years in the synthesis of conjugated cyclic polyalkenes with a large enough number of carbons in the ring to permit attainment of a strainless planar structure. Inspection of models shows that a strainless structure can only be achieved with two or more of the double bonds in *trans* configurations, and then only with a large enough ring that the "inside" hydrogens do not interfere with one another.

In discussing compounds of this type, it will be convenient to use the name [*n*]annulene to designate the simple conjugated cyclic polyalkenes, with *n* referring to the number of carbons in the ring—benzene being [6]annulene. The simplest conjugated cyclic polyolefin that could have a strainless planar ring containing *trans* double bonds, except for interferences between the inside hydrogens, is [10]annulene. Inside-hydrogen interferences are likely to be of at least some importance in all annulenes up to [30]annulene.

[10]annulene

Several annulenes have been synthesized and found to be reasonably stable
—at least much more so than could possibly be expected for the corresponding
open-chain conjugated polyenes. An elegant synthesis of [18]annulene provides an excellent illustration of some of the more useful steps for preparation
of annulenes. The key reaction is oxidative coupling of alkynes by cupric
acetate in pyridine solution.

$$2 \; RC{\equiv}CH \xrightarrow[C_5H_5N]{Cu^{II}} RC{\equiv}C{-}C{\equiv}CR$$

This type of oxidative coupling with 1,5-hexadiyne gives a 6% yield of the
cyclic trimer [8], which rearranges in the presence of potassium t-butoxide
to the brown, fully conjugated 1,2,7,8,13,14-tridehydro[18]annulene [9].

$$3 \; HC{\equiv}C{-}CH_2{-}CH_2{-}C{\equiv}CH \xrightarrow[C_5H_5N]{Cu^{II}}$$

[8]

$K^{\oplus} \; {}^{\ominus}OC(CH_3)_3$

$\xrightarrow[Pd(Pb)]{H_2}$

[9]   [18]annulene

Hydrogenation of [9] over a lead-poisoned palladium on calcium carbonate
catalyst (the Lindlar catalyst, of general utility for hydrogenation of alkynes
to alkenes) gives [18]annulene as a brown-red crystalline solid, reasonably
stable in the presence of oxygen and light.

27·5 orbital symmetry and cycloaddition

We pointed out earlier that an alkene cyclodimerization[2] usually requires
photoactivation whereas the Diels-Alder reaction between an alkene and a
conjugated diene occurs thermally. A rationale for this difference and for the
stereochemistry of a large number of cyclization and ring-opening reactions
has been developed recently by several theorists, including Longuet-Higgins,
Fukui, Woodward, and Hoffmann, using molecular orbital theory. In
Chapter 6 we described the four π molecular orbitals in 1,3-butadiene that
result from interaction of four p orbitals, one on each carbon atom. The

[2] A few alkenes such as tetrafluoroethene, $CF_2{=}CF_2$, cyclodimerize thermally but these
reactions are known to go by a radical, not a concerted, pathway.

σ-bonded skeleton of the molecule is ignored in this treatment and only the π electrons are considered.

The wave functions that describe the energies of an electron in each of the four p orbitals of butadiene can be combined algebraically to give us an approximation set of four molecular orbitals with different energies. (These molecular orbitals are linear combinations of atomic orbitals and the procedure is thus known as the LCAO approach.) Two of these molecular orbitals are bonding (energy lower than that of the isolated p orbitals) and two are antibonding (energy higher than that of the isolated orbitals). In a crude analogy the molecular energy levels can be compared with the energies of the standing waves of a vibrating string. The energy of a standing wave with a given amplitude increases with the number of nodes as shown on the left side of Figure 27·3.

In a molecular orbital made up of a linear combination of p orbitals, the coefficients of the p-orbital functions can have positive or negative values. If the signs of the coefficients of two adjacent p orbitals overlapping in the π manner are the same, then the positive parts of the atomic orbital lobes are pointed in the same direction and we say that there is no node between the atoms and that the molecular orbital is *bonding*. If the signs of the coefficients for the two adjacent orbitals are different, the arrangement has a node and is antibonding between these atoms. Figure 27·4 shows schematically the bonding and antibonding arrangements for the two p-π orbitals in ethene.

A schematic representation showing the nodes for the simple LCAO molecular orbitals of butadiene is given on the right side of Figure 27·3. Here, the relative sizes of the orbitals are drawn to reflect the values obtained by numerical calculations. The first two molecular orbitals are bonding (zero and one node) and the second two are antibonding (two and three nodes) (see Section 6·7). In the ground state of butadiene, the first two orbitals are doubly occupied whereas in the excited state an electron is raised from molecular orbital ψ_2 to ψ_3 (see Figure 26·3).

A rule for determining whether or not cycloadditions are allowed can be stated as follows: The orbitals that overlap in the transition state between the *highest occupied* level of one reactant and the *lowest unoccupied* level of the other reactant must be of the same symmetry (sign). The π orbitals of ethene and 1,3-butadiene are shown in Figure 27·5.

This rule predicts that concerted combination will not occur between two molecules of ethene in their ground states because the lobes of the lowest unoccupied level in one molecule and the highest occupied level in the other do not have corresponding signs. However, if one of the ethene molecules is raised to its first excited state by light absorption the situation is altered. The lobes of the orbitals of the excited state and those of the lowest unoccupied level of the second ethene molecule now correspond and combination can occur (see Figure 27·6).

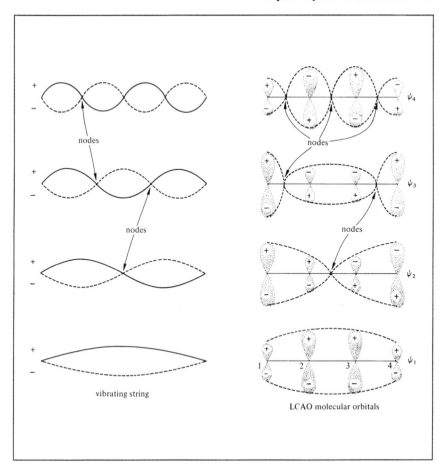

Figure 27·3   Nodes in a vibrating string in comparison with nodes in the LCAO π molecular orbitals of butadiene.

Figure 27·4   Interaction of p orbitals in ethene.

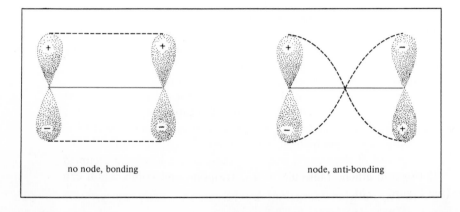

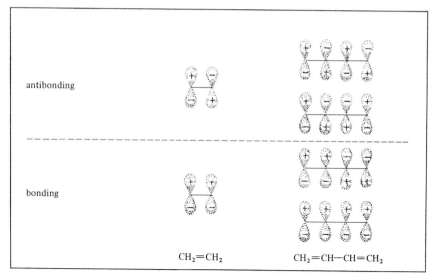

Figure 27·5 The molecular orbitals of ethene and 1,3-butadiene showing their p-orbital precursors.

The Diels-Alder reaction is quite different. When both 1,3-butadiene and ethene are in their ground states, the 1,4 lobes of the highest occupied level of the diene match in sign those of the lowest unoccupied level of the alkene and thermal reaction is allowed (see Figure 27·5). (This conclusion is also reached if the lowest unoccupied level of the diene and highest occupied level of the alkene are considered.) Photoexcitation of the reactants, however, de-

Figure 27·6 Orbital symmetries and cycloaddition pathways for ethene.

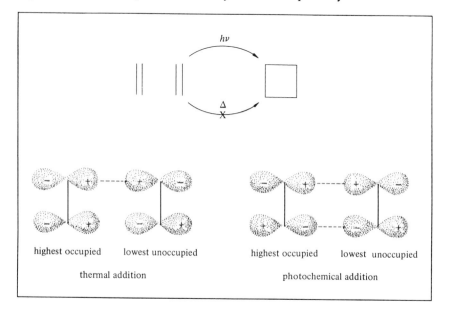

highest occupied   lowest unoccupied   highest occupied   lowest unoccupied

thermal addition   photochemical addition stroys this correspondence and 1,4-addition does not occur. Instead, 1,2 addition takes place.

The 1,2 addition is allowed because the 1,2 lobes of the highest occupied level in the excited state of the diene (the first antibonding level) match in sign the lobes of the lowest unoccupied level of the alkene (the antibonding level, also).

Many other cycloaddition reactions have been examined recently from the point of view of orbital symmetry principles and these principles have been found to predict not only the effect of thermal activation and photoactivation but also the correct stereochemistry of the addition compounds. Furthermore, many cyclization reactions, such as the Diels-Alder reaction, are reversible and the same considerations are found to apply to the reverse reactions also.

summary

Intramolecular ring closure of bifunctional compounds occurs readily with hydroxy or amino acids, with hydroxy aldehydes or ketones, with dicarboxylic acids, and with diesters, provided the reacting groups are favorably situated with respect to each other.

$$RO_2C(CH_2)_nCO_2R$$

$$(CH_2)_{n-1} \quad \overset{O}{\underset{CHCO_2R}{\overset{\|}{C}}}$$

$$(CH_2)_n \quad \overset{O}{\underset{CHOH}{\overset{\|}{C}}}$$

Formation of five- and six-membered rings is favored, but in the case of the conversion of diesters to hydroxy ketones (acyloin condensation) very large rings can also be produced. This reaction has enabled a chain-link compound called a catenane to be synthesized.

Alkenes dimerize to cyclobutanes under the influence of light, whereas the reaction of an alkene and a conjugated diene to produce a cyclohexene (the Diels-Alder reaction) occurs thermally.

$$+ \quad \overset{CHZ}{\underset{CHZ}{\|}} \longrightarrow \overset{Z}{\underset{Z}{}}$$

The reaction has the following characteristics: electron-withdrawing substituents Z in the alkene (the dienophile) increase the reaction rate; the configurations of the diene and dienophile are retained in the product showing that *cis* addition occurs; and the reaction occurs via a one-step concerted mechanism.

Photoactivation of a conjugated diene results in preferential formation of a four-membered ring rather than the six-membered Diels-Alder product.

$$\| + \| \quad \overset{hv}{\longrightarrow} \quad \square$$

$$2 \nearrow\!\!\diagup \quad \overset{\Delta}{\longrightarrow} \quad \text{(cyclohexene with vinyl)}$$

$$\overset{hv}{\longrightarrow} \quad \text{(cyclobutane with vinyl)} + \text{(cyclobutane with vinyl)}$$

Alkenes react with 1,3-dipolar compounds to form five-membered heterocyclic rings.

$$\| + \quad \overset{\oplus X}{\underset{\ominus Z}{\diagup}}\!\!Y \longrightarrow \overset{X}{\underset{Z}{}}Y$$

The 1,3-dipolar compounds include ozone (O_3), organic azides (RN_3), nitrile oxides (RCNO), and diazoalkanes (R_2CN_2).

Fluxional molecules are those that have identical structures and configurations but that can be distinguished either by means of isotopic labeling or by the effect of their interconversion on their nmr spectrum. A number of these systems involve the rearrangement of 1,5-dienes via six-membered cyclic transition states.

This type of reaction is greatly accelerated if the reacting atoms are held in favorable positions by a network of bonds such as are present in barbaralane [1] or bullvalene [2].

[1]   [2]

Oxidative coupling of alkynes, followed by base-catalyzed prototropic rearrangement and partial hydrogenation, gives large-ring conjugated polyalkenes called annulenes.

$$ n \cdot \begin{matrix} CH \\ \| \\ CH \end{matrix} \longrightarrow \longrightarrow \longrightarrow \left(\begin{matrix} CH \\ \| \\ CH \end{matrix} \right)_n $$

Alkynes can act as dienophiles in the Diels-Alder reaction and acetylene, itself, can be polymerized to give cyclooctatetraene.

Whether a cycloaddition will be subject to thermal activation or photoactivation can be predicted using rules based on orbital symmetry arguments. The π molecular orbitals of alkenes and alkadienes can be formulated as combinations of p orbitals, the lobes of which have either a positive or negative sign. Reaction is allowed only between atoms whose lobes have the same sign when the highest occupied level of one of the reactants and the lowest unoccupied level of the other reactant are considered.

The allowed reactions are the following:

(1) Thermal alkene-alkadiene cyclization (Diels-Alder reaction).

highest occupied   lowest unoccupied level
level of ethene   of 1,3-butadiene

(or lowest unoccupied level of ethene +
highest occupied level of 1,3-butadiene)

(2) Alkene photodimerization.

highest occupied   lowest unoccupied
level of the excited   level of the ground
state of ethene   state of ethene

Reactions that are not allowed include thermally activated concerted alkene cyclodimerization and the photoactivated Diels-Alder reaction. When the latter reaction is attempted, cyclobutanes are formed.

exercises

27·1 What products would you expect from the Diels-Alder addition of tetra-cyanoethene to *cis,trans*-2,4-hexadiene and *cis,cis*-2,4-hexadiene? Explain.

27·2 Write structures for the products of the following reactions:

a. $C_6H_5N-N \atop | \atop N=N$ C—C_6H_5 $\xrightarrow[-N_2]{150°}$ C_6H_5CHO

b. $2 \quad \underset{Cl}{\overset{C_6H_5}{\diagup}} C=N-NHC_6H_5 \xrightarrow[-HCl]{(C_2H_5)_3N} \xrightarrow{CS_2}$

c. $\underset{Cl}{\overset{C_6H_5}{\diagup}} C=N-OH \xrightarrow[-HCl]{(C_2H_5)_3N} \xrightarrow{C_6H_5CN}$

27·3 The rate of the Diels-Alder addition between cyclooctatetraene and tetra-cyanoethene is proportional to the tetracyanoethene concentration $[C_2(CN)_4]$ at low concentrations of the addends but becomes independent of $[C_2(CN)_4]$ at high concentrations. Write a mechanism which accounts for this behavior.

27·4 The compound bullvalene, $C_{10}H_{10}$, has the following structure:

    a. Write several fluxional forms of this molecule (the total number is greater than 10^6).

    b. At 100° equilibration is rapid and at 0° it is slow. How many different kinds of proton would you expect to be seen in a well-resolved nmr spectrum at each of these temperatures?

27·5 Work out a synthesis of [20]annulene from the coupling product of allyl-magnesium bromide with 1,4-dibromo-2-butene, which is reported to be 1,5,9-decatriene.

chapter 28
polymers

Polymers are substances made up of recurring structural units, each of which can be regarded as derived from a specific compound called a monomer. The number of monomeric units is usually large and variable, a given polymer sample being characteristically a mixture of molecules with different molecular weights. The range of molecular weights encountered may be either small or very large.

The properties of a polymer, both physical and chemical, are in many ways as sensitive to changes in the structure of the monomer as are the properties of the monomer itself. This means that to a very considerable degree the properties of a polymer can be tailored to particular practical applications. We have already considered several methods of synthesis of monomers and polymers and mechanisms of polymerization reactions in earlier chapters, and much of the emphasis in this chapter will be on how the properties of polymers can be related to their structures.

The thermal polymerization of cyclopentadiene by way of the Diels-Alder reaction provides a simple concrete example of how a monomer and a polymer are related.

monomer   dimer   trimer

tetramer   polymer

The first step in this polymerization is formation of the dimer, which involves cyclopentadiene's acting as both diene and dienophile. This step occurs readily on heating but slowly at room temperature. In subsequent steps, cyclopentadiene adds to the relatively strained double bonds of the first-formed polymer. These additions require higher temperatures (180° to 200°). If cyclopentadiene is heated to 200° until substantially no further reaction occurs, the product is a waxy solid having a *degree of polymerization n* ranging from two to greater than six.

Polycyclopentadiene molecules have double bonds for *end groups* and a complicated *backbone* of saturated fused rings. The polymerization is reversible, and on strong heating the polymer reverts to cyclopentadiene.

28·1 types of polymers

Polymers can be classified several different ways: according to their structures, the types of reactions by which they are prepared, their physical properties,

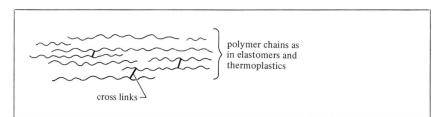

Figure 28·1 Schematic representation of a polymer with few cross links.

or their technological uses. However, these classifications are not all mutually exclusive.

From the standpoint of general physical properties, we recognize three types of solid polymers: **elastomers** (rubbers or rubberlike elastic substances), **thermoplastic** polymers, and **thermosetting** polymers. These categories overlap considerably but are nonetheless helpful in defining general areas of use and types of structures. Elastomers (uncured) and thermoplastics typically have long polymer chains with few, if any, chemical bonds acting as **cross links** between the chains. This is shown schematically in Figure 28·1.

Such polymers, when heated, normally become soft and more or less fluid and can then be molded into useful shapes. The main difference between an elastomer and a thermoplastic polymer is in the degree of attractive forces between the polymer chains, as discussed in the next section. Thus, although elastomers, which are not cross-linked, are normally thermoplastic, not all thermoplastics are elastomers.

Cross links are extremely important in determining physical properties because they increase the molecular weight and limit the motion of the chains with respect to one another. Only two cross links per polymer chain are required to connect together all the polymer molecules in a given sample to produce one gigantic molecule. As a result, introduction of only a few cross links acts to greatly reduce solubility and tends to produce a gel polymer, which, although insoluble, will usually absorb (be swelled by) solvents in which the uncross-linked polymer is soluble. The tendency to absorb solvents decreases as the degree of cross linking is increased.

Thermosetting polymers are normally made from relatively low molecular weight, usually semifluid substances which, when heated in a mold, become highly cross linked, thereby forming hard, infusible, and insoluble products having a three-dimensional *space network* of bonds interconnecting the polymer chains (Figure 28·2).

Figure 28·2 Schematic representation of the conversion of an uncross-linked polymer to a highly cross-linked polymer.

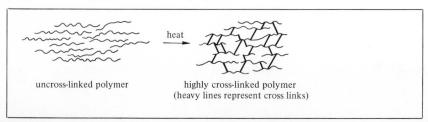

physical properties of polymers

28·2 forces between polymer chains

Polymers are produced on an industrial scale primarily, although not exclusively, for use as structural materials. Their physical properties are particularly important in determining their usefulness, be it as rubber tires, sidings for buildings, or solid rocket fuels.

Polymers that are not highly cross-linked have properties that depend upon the degree and kind of forces that act between the chains. By way of example, consider a polymer such as Polythene (polyethene) which, in a normal commercial sample, will be made up of molecules having 1000 to 2000 CH_2 groups in continuous chains. Since the material is a mixture of different molecules, it is not expected to crystallize in a conventional way.[1] Nonetheless, X-ray diffraction shows polyethene to have very considerable crystalline character, there being regions as large as several hundred angstrom units in length, which have ordered, zigzag chains of CH_2 groups oriented with respect to one another like the chains in crystalline low-molecular-weight hydrocarbons. These crystalline regions are often called *crystallites*. Between the crystallites of polyethene are amorphous, noncrystalline regions in which the polymer chains are more randomly ordered with respect to one another (Figure 28·3). These regions essentially constitute crystal defects.

The forces between the chains in the crystallites of polyethene are the so-called **van der Waals** or **dispersion** forces, which are the same forces acting between hydrocarbon molecules in the liquid and solid states and, to a lesser extent, in the vapor state. These forces are relatively weak and arise through synchronization of the motions of the electrons in the separate atoms as they approach one another. The attractive force that results is rapidly overcome by repulsive forces when the atoms get very close to one another.

In other kinds of polymers, much stronger intermolecular forces can be produced by hydrogen bonding. This is especially important in the polyamides, such as the nylons, of which nylon (66) or polyhexamethyleneadipamide is most widely used.

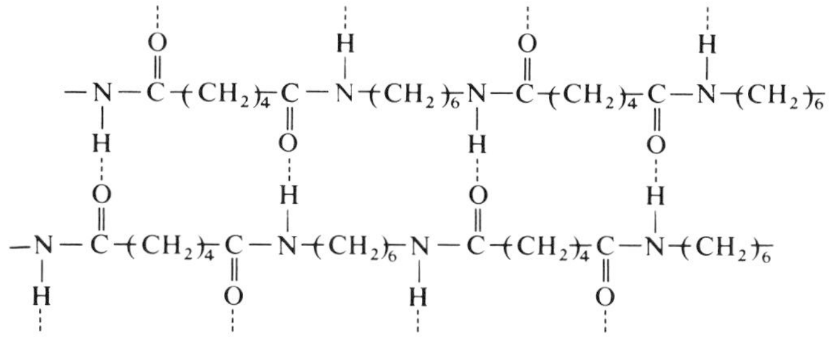

possible hydrogen-bonded structure for
crystallites of nylon (66), polyhexamethyleneadipamide

---

[1] Quite good platelike crystals have been formed from dilute solutions of certain polymers such as polyethene. In the crystals, the polymer chains seem to run back and forth in folds between the large surfaces of the plates.

The effect of temperature on the physical properties of polymers is very important to their practical uses. At low temperatures, polymers become hard and glasslike because the motion of the polymer chains in relation to each other is slow. The approximate temperature below which glasslike behavior is apparent is called the **glass temperature** and is symbolized by T_g. When a polymer containing crystallites is heated, the crystallites ultimately melt; this temperature is usually called the **melting temperature**, symbolized as T_m. Usually, the molding temperature will be above T_m and the mechanical strength of the polymer will diminish rapidly as the temperature approaches T_m.

Obviously, another temperature of great importance in the practical use of polymers is the temperature near which thermal breakdown of the polymer chains occurs. Decomposition temperatures will obviously be sensitive to impurities, such as oxygen, and will be influenced strongly by the presence of inhibitors, antioxidants, and so on. Nonetheless, there will be a temperature (usually rather high, $200°$ to $400°$) at which uncatalyzed scission of the bonds in a chain will take place at an appreciable rate, and, in general, you cannot expect to prevent this type of reaction from causing degradation of the polymer. Clearly, if this degradation temperature is comparable to T_m, as it is for polyacrylonitrile, difficulties are to be expected in simple thermal molding of the plastic. This difficulty is overcome in making polyacrylonitrile (Orlon) fibers by dissolving the polymer in N,N-dimethylformamide and forcing the solution through fine holes into a heated air space where the solvent evaporates.

Physical properties such as tensile strength, X-ray diffraction pattern, resistance to plastic flow, softening point, and elasticity of most polymers can be understood in a general way in terms of crystallites, amorphous regions, the degree of flexibility of the chains, and the strength of the forces acting between the chains (dispersion forces, hydrogen bonding, etc.). One way to approach the problem is to make a rough classification of properties of solid polymers according to the way the chains are disposed in relation to each other.

1. An **amorphous** polymer is one with no crystallites. If the forces between the chains are weak and if the motions of the chains are not in some way severely restricted, such a polymer would be expected to have low tensile strength and be subject to plastic flow in which the chains slip by one another.

2. An **unoriented crystalline** polymer is one which is considerably crystallized but has the crystallites essentially randomly oriented with respect to one another as in Figure $28 \cdot 3$. Such polymers, when heated, often show rather sharp T_m points, which correspond to the melting of the crystallites. Above T_m, these polymers are amorphous and undergo plastic flow, which permits them to be molded. Other things being the same, we expect T_m to be higher for the polymers with stiff chains (high barriers to internal rotation).

3. An **oriented crystalline** polymer is one in which the crystallites are oriented with respect to one another, usually as the result of a **cold-drawing** process. Consider a polymer such as nylon, which has strong intermolecular forces and is in an unoriented state like the one represented by Figure $28 \cdot 3$. If the material is subjected to strong stress, say along the horizontal axis, at some temperature (most easily above T_g) where at least some plastic flow can

occur, elongation will take place and the crystallites will be drawn together and oriented along the direction of the applied stress (Figure 28·4).

An oriented crystalline polymer usually has a much higher tensile strength than the unoriented polymer. Cold drawing is an important step in the production of synthetic fibers.

4. **Elastomers** are intermediate in character between amorphous and crystalline polymers. The key to elastic behavior is to have a polymer that has either sufficiently weak forces between the chains or a sufficiently irregular structure to be very largely amorphous. The tendency for the chains to orient can often be considerably reduced by random introduction of methyl groups which, by steric hindrance, inhibit ordering of the chains. An elastomer needs to have some crystalline (or cross-linked) regions to prevent plastic flow and, in addition, should have rather flexible chains (which means T_g should be low). The structure of a polymer of this kind is shown schematically in Figure 28·5. The important difference between this elastomer and the crystalline polymer of Figure 28·3 is the size of the amorphous regions. When tension is applied and the material elongates, the chains in the amorphous regions straighten

Figure 28·3   Schematic diagram of crystallites (enclosed by dotted lines) in a largely crystalline polymer.

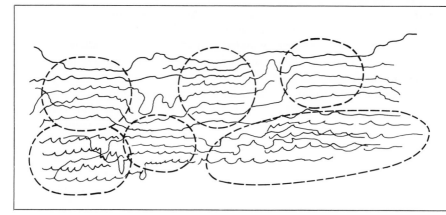

Figure 28·4   Schematic representation of an oriented crystalline polymer produced by drawing in the horizontal direction. The crystalline regions are enclosed with dotted lines.

out and become more nearly parallel. At the elastic limit, a semicrystalline state is reached, which is different from the one produced by cold drawing a crystalline polymer in that it is stable only while under tension. The forces between the chains are too weak in the absence of tension to maintain the crystalline state. Thus, when tension is released, contraction occurs and the original, nearly amorphous, polymer is produced.

Probably the best known elastomer is natural rubber, which is a polymer of 2-methyl-1,3-butadiene (isoprene) with virtually all the double bonds in the *cis* configuration.

$$CH_2=\overset{\overset{\displaystyle CH_3}{|}}{C}-CH=CH_2$$

isoprene   natural rubber (*cis*-polyisoprene)

Figure 28·5   Schematic representation of an elastomer in relaxed and stretched configurations. The crystalline regions are enclosed by dotted lines.

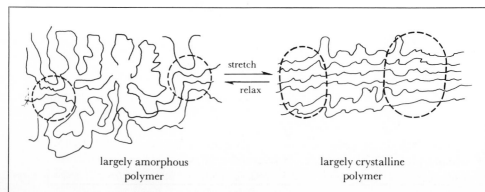

largely amorphous
polymer

largely crystalline
polymer

When pure isoprene is polymerized in the laboratory with the help of radical initiators the product is hard and brittle, quite unlike natural rubber. This material is similar to a naturally occurring substance known as **gutta percha** that is used to make covers for golf balls. It owes its properties to its *trans* arrangement of double bonds which allow the chains to lie alongside one another in a semicrystalline array.

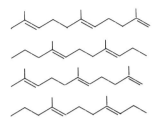

When the double bonds are *cis*, as in natural rubber, steric hindrance keeps the chains from assuming a similar ordered structure and the bulk of the material exists in an amorphous state with randomly oriented chains. When the *cis* polymer is stretched, the chains are straightened and tend to become oriented; but since this is an unfavorable state, the material snaps back to the amorphous state when released. Although radical polymerization of isoprene produces gutta percha, Ziegler polymerization (Section 28·5A) gives a *cis* polymer that is identical with natural rubber. The correlation between polymer structure and properties are examined further in the next section.

A good elastomer should not undergo plastic flow in either the stretched or relaxed state, and when stretched should have a "memory" of its relaxed state. These conditions are best achieved with natural rubber (*cis*-polyisoprene) by *curing* (*vulcanizing*) with sulfur. Natural rubber is tacky and undergoes plastic flow rather readily, but when heated with 1 to 8% by weight of elemental sulfur in the presence of an *accelerator*, sulfur cross links are introduced between the chains. These cross links reduce plastic flow and provide a sort of reference framework for the stretched polymer to return to when it is allowed to relax. Too much sulfur completely destroys the elastic properties and gives hard rubber of the kind used in cases for storage batteries.

28·3 correlation of polymer properties with structure

With the aid of the concepts developed in the previous section, it is possible to correlate the properties of many of the technically important thermoplastic and elastic polymers with their chemical structures. We can understand why the simple linear polymers such as Polythene (polyethene), polyformaldehyde, and Teflon (polytetrafluoroethene) are crystalline polymers with rather high melting points. Polyvinyl chloride, polyvinyl fluoride, and polystyrene as usually prepared are much less crystalline and have lower melting points; with these polymers, the stereochemical configuration is very important in determining the physical properties. Polystyrene, made by radical polymerization in solution, is **atactic**. This means that, if we orient the carbons in the polymer chain in the form of a regular zigzag, the phenyl groups will be randomly distributed on one side or the other when we look along the chain, as shown in Figure 28·6. Polymerization of styrene with Ziegler catalysts (Sections 4·4H and 28·5A) produces **isotactic** polystyrene, which is different from the atactic polymer in that all of the phenyl groups are located on one side of the chain. The difference in properties between the atactic and isotactic materials is considerable. The atactic polymer can be molded at much lower temperatures and is much more soluble in most solvents than is the isotactic product. There are many other possible types of stereoregular polymers, one of which is called **syndiotactic** and has the side-chain groups oriented alternately on one side and then the other, as shown in Figure 28·6.

Polypropene, made by polymerization of propene with Ziegler catalysts, appears to be isotactic and highly crystalline with a melting point of 175°. It can be drawn into fibers that resemble nylon fibers although, as might be expected, they do not match the 270° melting point of nylon and are much more difficult to dye.

Figure 28·6 Configurations of atactic, isotactic, and syndiotactic polystyrene. The conformations are drawn to show the stereochemical relations of the substituent groups and are not meant to represent necessarily the stable conformations of the polymer chains.

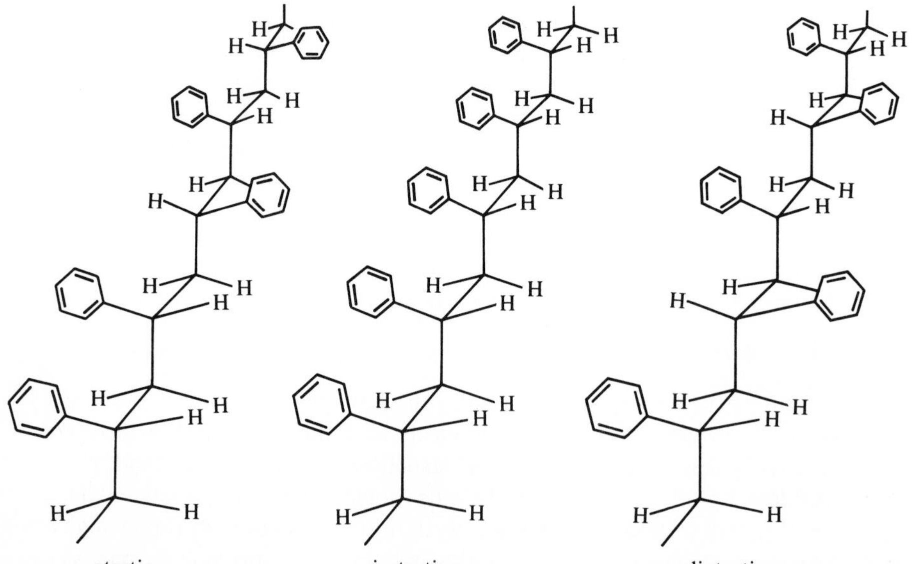

atactic   isotactic   syndiotactic

Table 28·1   Representative synthetic thermoplastic and elastic polymers and their uses[a]

monomer(s)	formula	type of polymerization	physical type	T_g, °C	T_m, °C	trade names	uses
ethene	$CH_2=CH_2$	radical (high pressure)	semi-crystalline	≪0	110	Polythene	film, containers, etc.
		Ziegler	crystalline	−120	130	Alathon	
vinyl chloride	$CH_2=CHCl$	radical	atactic, semi-crystalline	80	180	polyvinyl chloride, Geon	film, insulation, piping, etc.
vinyl fluoride	$CH_2=CHF$	radical	atactic, semi-crystalline	45		Tedlar	coatings[b]
vinyl chloride vinylidene chloride	$CH_2=CHCl$ $CH_2=CCl_2$	radical	crystalline	variable		Saran	tubing, fibers, film, structural materials
chlorotrifluoroethene	$CF_2=CFCl$	radical	atactic, semi-crystalline	≪0	210	Kel-F	gaskets, insulation[c]
tetrafluoroethene	$CF_2=CF_2$	radical	crystalline	<−100	330	Teflon	gaskets, valves, insulation, filter felts, coatings[d]
propene	$CH_2=CHCH_3$	Ziegler	isotactic, crystalline	−20	175		fibers, molded articles
hexafluoropropene vinylidene fluoride	$CF_2=CFCF_3$ $CH_2=CF_2$	radical	amorphous	−23		Viton	rubber articles[c]

Table 28·1   Representative synthetic thermoplastic and elastic polymers and their uses[a] (*continued*)

monomer(s)	formula	type of polymerization	physical type	T_g, °C	T_m, °C	trade names	uses
2-methylpropene	$CH_2{=}C(CH_3)_2$	cationic	amorphous	−70		Vistanex, Oppanol	pressure-sensitive adhesives
2-methylpropene	$CH_2{=}C(CH_3)_2$	cationic	amorphous			butyl rubber	inner tubes
chloroprene	$CH_2{=}C(Cl)CH{=}CH_2$	radical	amorphous	−40		Neoprene	rubber articles[e]
isoprene	$CH_2{=}C(CH_3)CH{=}CH_2$	Ziegler, Li	amorphous (*cis*-1,4)	−70	28	natural rubber, Ameripol, Coral rubber	rubber articles,
styrene	$CH_2{=}CHC_6H_5$	radical	atactic, semi-crystalline	85	<200	Styron, Lustron	molded articles, foam
styrene	$CH_2{=}CHC_6H_5$	Ziegler	isotactic	100	230		
vinyl acetate	$CH_2{=}CHO_2CCH_3$	radical	amorphous	40		polyvinyl acetate	adhesives
vinyl alcohol	$(CH_2{=}CHOH)^f$	hydrolysis of polyvinyl acetate	crystalline		dec.	polyvinyl alcohol	water-soluble adhesives, paper sizing
vinyl butyral		polyvinyl alcohol and butanal	amorphous			polyvinyl butyral	safety-glass laminate

Table 28·1 (*continued*)

monomer(s)	formula	type of polymerization	physical type	T_g, °C	T_m, °C	trade names	uses
formaldehyde	$CH_2{=}O$	anionic	crystalline		179	Delrin	molded articles
acrylonitrile	$CH_2{=}CHCN$	radical	crystalline	100[g]	>200	Orlon	fiber
methyl methacrylate	$CH_2{=}C(CH_3)CO_2CH_3$	radical	atactic, amorphous	105		Lucite, Plexiglas	coatings, molded articles
		anionic	isotactic, crystalline	115	200		
		anionic	syndiotactic, crystalline	45	160		
ethylene glycol terephthalate	$HO_2C{-}\langle\bigcirc\rangle{-}CO_2C_2H_4OH$	ester interchange between dimethyl terephthalate and ethylene glycol	crystalline	56	260	Dacron, Mylar, Cronar, Terylene	fiber, film
hexamethylenediamine and hexanedioic acid (adipic acid)	$NH_2(CH_2)_6NH_2$ $HO_2C(CH_2)_4CO_2H$	anionic condensation	crystalline	50	270	nylon, Zytel	fibers, molded articles

[a] Much useful information on these and related polymers is given by F. W. Billmeyer, Jr., *A Textbook of Polymer Chemistry*, Interscience, New York, 1957; J. K. Stille, *Introduction to Polymer Chemistry*, Wiley, New York, 1962; F. Bueche, *Physical Properties of Polymers*, Interscience, New York, 1962; and W. R. Sorenson and T. W. Campbell, *Preparative Methods of Polymer Chemistry*, Interscience, New York, 1961.
[b] Exceptional outdoor durability.
[c] Used where chemical resistance is important.
[d] Excellent self-lubricating and electrical properties.
[e] Used particularly where ozone resistance is important.
[f] These monomers are not the starting materials used to make the polymers, which are actually synthesized from polyvinyl acetate.
[g] T_g is 60° when water is present.

Although both linear polyethene and isotactic polypropene are crystalline polymers, ethene-propene copolymers prepared with the aid of Ziegler catalysts are excellent elastomers. Apparently, a more or less random introduction of methyl groups along a polyethene chain reduces the crystallinity sufficiently drastically to lead to a largely amorphous polymer.

Polyvinyl chloride, as usually prepared, is atactic and not very crystalline. It is relatively brittle and glassy. The properties of polyvinyl chloride can be improved by copolymerization, as with vinyl acetate, which produces a softer polymer (Vinylite) with better molding properties. Polyvinyl chloride can also be *plasticized* by blending it with substances of low volatility such as tricresyl phosphate and di-*n*-butyl phthalate, which, when dissolved in the polymer, tend to break down its glasslike structure. Plasticized polyvinyl chloride is reasonably elastic and is widely used as electrical insulation, plastic sheeting, and so on.

Table 28·1 contains information about a number of representative important polymers and their uses.

preparation of synthetic polymers

A prevalent but erroneous notion has it that useful polymers, such as those given in Table 28·1, can be, and are, made by slap-dash procedures applied to impure starting materials. In actual fact the monomers used in most large-scale polymerizations are among the purest known organic substances. Furthermore, to obtain uniform, commercially useful products, extraordinary care must be used in controlling the polymerization reactions. The reasons are simple—namely, that formation of a high-molecular-weight polymer (high polymer) requires a reaction that proceeds in very high yields, and purification of the product by distillation, crystallization, and so on, is difficult, if not impossible. Even a minute contribution of any side reaction that stops polymer chains from growing will seriously affect the yield of high polymer.

In this section, we shall discuss some of the more useful procedures for the preparation of high polymers, starting with examples involving condensation reactions.

28·4 condensation polymers

There is a very wide variety of condensation reactions[2] that, in principle, can be used to form high polymers. However, as explained above, high polymers can only be obtained in high-yield reactions, and this limitation severely restricts the number of condensation reactions having any practical importance. A specific example of an impractical reaction is the formation of polytetramethylene glycol by reaction of tetramethylene bromide with the sodium salt of the glycol.

---

[2] A condensation reaction is usually taken to mean one in which two molecules react to split out water or some other simple molecule.

$$\overset{\oplus}{Na}\overset{\ominus}{O}(CH_2)_4\overset{\ominus}{O}\overset{\oplus}{Na} + Br(CH_2)_4Br \longrightarrow +O(CH_2)_4O\}_n + \overset{\oplus}{Na}\overset{\ominus}{Br}$$

It is unlikely that this reaction would give useful yields of any very high polymer because E2 elimination, involving the dibromide, would give a double bond end group and prevent the chain from growing.

A. POLYESTERS

A variety of polyester-condensation polymers are made commercially. Ester interchange (Section 13·8) appears to be the most useful reaction for preparation of linear polymers (see Figure 28·7).

Figure 28·7 Reactions used to prepare the polymers Dacron and Lexan.

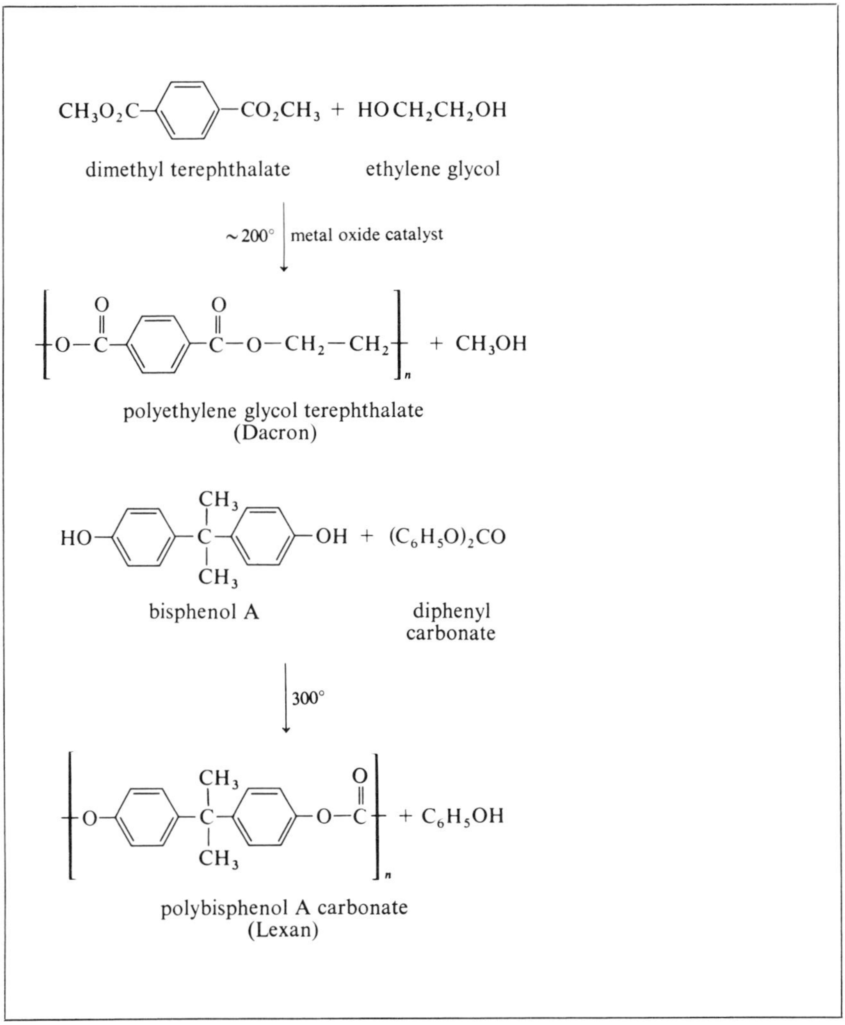

$$CH_3O_2C-\bigcirc-CO_2CH_3 + HOCH_2CH_2OH$$

dimethyl terephthalate   ethylene glycol

~200° | metal oxide catalyst

$$\left[O-\overset{O}{\underset{\|}{C}}-\bigcirc-\overset{O}{\underset{\|}{C}}-O-CH_2-CH_2\right]_n + CH_3OH$$

polyethylene glycol terephthalate
(Dacron)

$$HO-\bigcirc-\overset{CH_3}{\underset{CH_3}{\overset{|}{C}}}-\bigcirc-OH + (C_6H_5O)_2CO$$

bisphenol A   diphenyl
                             carbonate

300°

$$\left[O-\bigcirc-\overset{CH_3}{\underset{CH_3}{\overset{|}{C}}}-\bigcirc-O-\overset{O}{\underset{\|}{C}}\right]_n + C_6H_5OH$$

polybisphenol A carbonate
(Lexan)

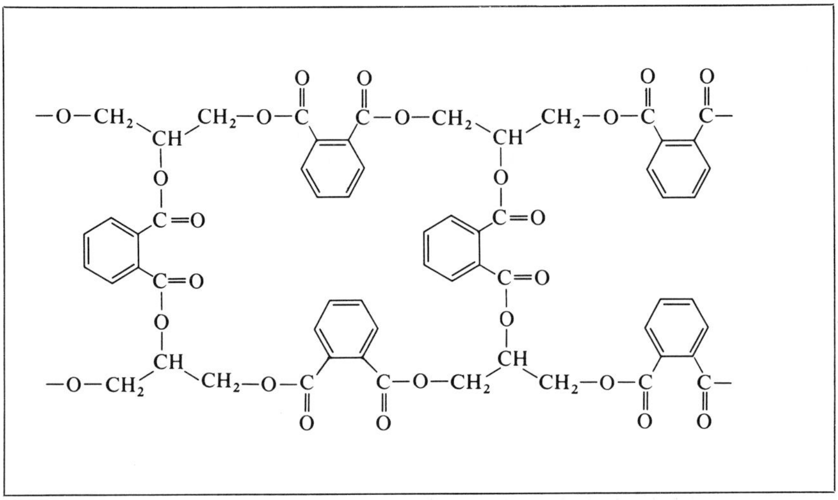

Figure 28·8 Glyptal resin.

Thermosetting space-network polymers are often prepared through the reaction of polybasic acid anhydrides with polyhydric alcohols. A linear polymer is obtained with a bifunctional anhydride and a bifunctional alcohol, but if either reactant has three or more reactive sites, then formation of a three-dimensional polymer is possible. For example, two moles of glycerol can react with three moles of phthalic anhydride to give a highly cross-linked resin, which is usually called a **glyptal** (Figure 28·8).

B. NYLONS

A variety of polyamides can be made by heating diamines with dicarboxylic acids. The most generally useful of these is nylon (66), the designation (66) arising from the fact that it is made from the six-carbon diamine hexamethylenediamine, and the six-carbon dicarboxylic acid, hexanedioic acid (adipic acid).

$$HO_2C(CH_2)_4CO_2H + NH_2(CH_2)_6NH_2 \xrightarrow{280°} \left[\overset{O}{\overset{\|}{C}}(CH_2)_4\overset{O}{\overset{\|}{C}} - \overset{H}{N} \\left(CH_2 \\right)_{\!6} \overset{H}{N} \right]_{n} + H_2O$$

The polymer can be converted into fibers by extruding it above its melting point through spinnerettes, then cooling and drawing the resulting filaments. It is also used to make molded articles. Nylon (66) is exceptionally strong and abrasion resistant.

The starting materials for nylon (66) manufacture can be made in many ways. Apparently, the best route to adipic acid is by air oxidation of cyclohexane by way of cyclohexanone.

Hexamethylenediamine is prepared from the addition product of chlorine to butadiene (Section 6·2) by the following steps:

Both the 1,2- and 1,4-chlorine addition products give the same dinitrile with sodium cyanide.

Nylon (6) is obtained by the polymerization of ε-caprolactam.

Note that here the intramolecular interaction between amino and carboxyl groups (lactam formation) is replaced by intermolecular interaction (poly-amide formation). ε-Caprolactam is prepared by the Beckmann rearrange-ment (Section 16·1E2) of cyclohexanone oxime, which can be made, in turn, from cyclohexanone.

C. PHENOL-FORMALDEHYDE (BAKELITE) RESINS

One of the oldest-known thermosetting synthetic polymers is made by con-densation of phenol with formaldehyde using basic catalysts. The resins that are formed are known as **Bakelites**. The initial stage in the base-induced re-action of phenol and formaldehyde yields a hydroxybenzyl alcohol. This part of the reaction closely resembles an aldol addition and can take place at either an *ortho* or the *para* position.

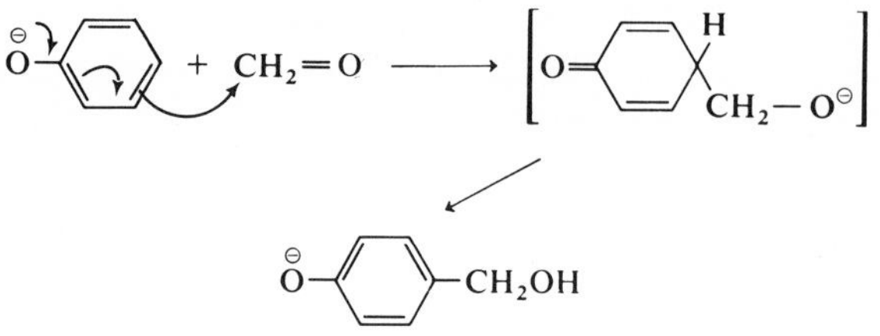

The next step in the condensation is formation of a dihydroxydiphenyl-methane derivative which for convenience is here taken to be the 4,4′ isomer.

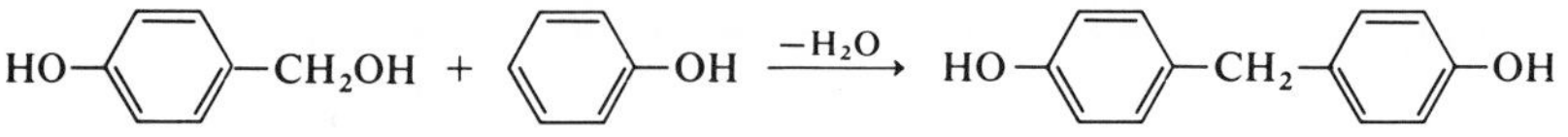

This reaction is likely to be an addition to a base-induced dehydration product of the hydroxybenzyl alcohol.

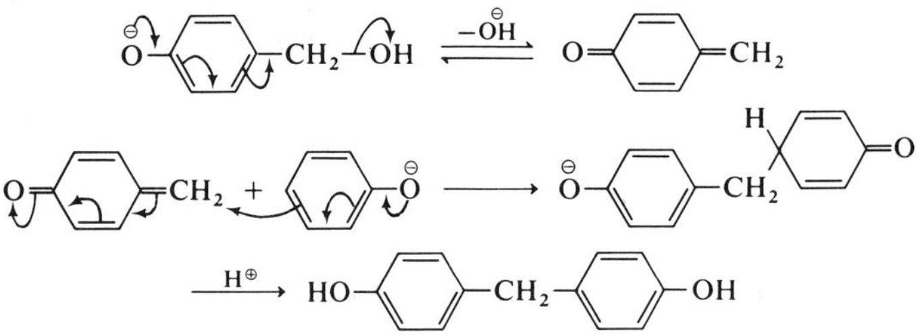

Continuation of these reactions to all of the available *ortho* and *para* positions of the phenol leads to a cross-linked three-dimensional polymer (Figure 28·9).

Figure 28·9   Phenol-formaldehyde resin.

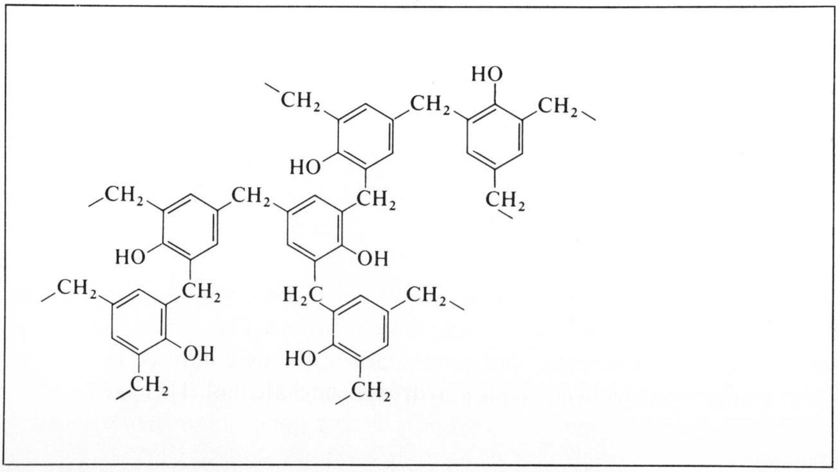

28·5   addition polymers

We have already discussed the synthesis and properties of a considerable number of addition polymers in this and earlier chapters. Our primary concern here will be with some aspects of the mechanism of addition polymerization that influence the character of the polymers formed.

A. VINYL POLYMERIZATION

The most important type of addition polymerization is that of the simple vinyl monomers such as ethene, propene, styrene, and so on. In general, we now recognize four basic kinds of polymerization of vinyl monomers—radical, cationic, anionic, and coordination. The elements of the mechanisms of the first three of these have been outlined earlier (Section 4·4H). The possibility, in fact the reality, of a fourth mechanism is forced on us by the discovery of the Ziegler and other (mostly heterogeneous) catalysts, which apparently do not involve "free" radicals, cations or anions, and which can and usually do lead to highly stereoregular polymers. Although a great deal of work has been done on the mechanism of coordination polymerization, the details of how each unit of monomer is added to the growing chains is mostly conjecture. With titanium-aluminum catalysts, the growing chain probably has a C—Ti bond; further monomer units are then added to the growing chain by coordination with titanium, followed by an intramolecular rearrangement to give a new growing-chain end and a new vacant site on titanium where a new molecule of monomer can coordinate.

$$-CH_2-CH_2-CH_2-CH_2\overset{Ti}{} \xrightarrow{\quad CH_2=CH_2 \quad} \quad H_2C\overset{CH_2}{\underset{-CH_2-CH_2-CH_2-CH_2}{\diagup}} Ti$$

$$\xrightarrow{\quad} \quad -CH_2-CH_2-CH_2-CH_2-CH_2-CH_2\overset{Ti}{}$$

In the coordination of the monomer with the titanium, the metal is probably behaving as an electrophilic agent and the growing-chain end may well be transferred to the monomer as an anion. Since this mechanism gives no explicit role to the aluminum, it is surely a considerable oversimplification. Ziegler catalysts polymerize most monomers of the type $RCH=CH_2$, provided the R group is one that does not react with the organometallic compounds present in the catalyst.

B. RADICAL POLYMERIZATION

In contrast to coordination polymerization, formation of vinyl polymers by radical chain mechanisms is reasonably well understood—at least for the kinds of procedures used on a laboratory scale. The first step in the reaction is the production of radicals; this can be achieved in a number of different ways, the most common being the thermal decomposition of an *initiator*, usually a peroxide or an azo compound.

$$\text{benzoyl peroxide} \xrightarrow{70°-80°} 2 \text{ } \bigcirc\text{-C} \longrightarrow 2 \text{ } \bigcirc\text{·} + 2 CO_2$$

benzoyl peroxide

$$CH_3-\underset{CN}{\overset{CH_3}{C}}-N=N-\underset{CN}{\overset{CH_3}{C}}-CH_3 \xrightarrow{40°-80°} 2 \text{ } CH_3-\underset{CN}{\overset{CH_3}{C}}\text{·} + N_2$$

2,2'-azobis(2-methylpropanonitrile)

Many polymerizations are carried out on aqueous emulsions of monomers. For these, water-soluble inorganic peroxides, such as persulfuric acid, are often employed.

Addition of the initiator radicals to monomer produces a growing-chain radical which combines with successive molecules of monomer until, in some way, the chain is terminated. It will be seen that addition to an unsymmetrical monomer, such as styrene, can occur in two ways.

$$X_2 \longrightarrow 2 X\text{·} \quad \text{initiation}$$

$$X\text{·} + \bigcirc\text{-CH=CH}_2 \begin{cases} \longrightarrow \bigcirc\text{-}\overset{\cdot}{C}H-CH_2X \\ \longrightarrow \bigcirc\text{-}\underset{X}{C}H-CH_2\text{·} \end{cases}$$

All evidence on the addition of radicals to styrene indicates that the process by which X· adds to the CH_2 end of the double bond is greatly favored over addition at the CH end. This direction of addition is in accord with the considerable stabilization of benzyl-type radicals relative to alkyl-type radicals (see Section 24·2). Polymerization will then result in the addition of styrene units to give phenyl groups only on alternate carbons ("head-to-tail" addition).

$$X-CH_2-\underset{C_6H_5}{\overset{}{C}}H\text{·} \longrightarrow X-CH_2-\underset{C_6H_5}{\overset{}{C}}H-CH_2-\overset{}{C}H\text{·}$$
$$\longrightarrow X-CH_2-\underset{C_6H_5}{C}H-CH_2-\underset{C_6H_5}{C}H-CH_2-\underset{C_6H_5}{C}H\text{·}$$

In general, we predict that the direction of addition of an unsymmetrical monomer will be such as to give always the most stable growing-chain radical.

The process of addition of monomer units to the growing chain can be interrupted in different ways. One is chain termination by combination or disproportionation of radicals. Explicitly, two growing-chain radicals can combine with formation of a carbon-carbon bond, or disproportionation can occur with a hydrogen atom being transferred from one chain to the other.

$$X\left(CH_2-\overset{\overset{\displaystyle C_6H_5}{|}}{CH}\right)_m CH_2-\overset{\overset{\displaystyle C_6H_5}{|}}{CH}\cdot \ + \ \cdot\overset{\overset{\displaystyle C_6H_5}{|}}{CH}-CH_2\left(\overset{\overset{\displaystyle C_6H_5}{|}}{CH}-CH_2\right)_n X$$

$$\xrightarrow{\text{combination}} X\left(CH_2-\overset{\overset{\displaystyle C_6H_5}{|}}{CH}\right)_m CH_2-\overset{\overset{\displaystyle C_6H_5}{|}}{CH}-\overset{\overset{\displaystyle C_6H_5}{|}}{CH}-CH_2\left(\overset{\overset{\displaystyle C_6H_5}{|}}{CH}-CH_2\right)_n X$$

$$\xrightarrow{\text{disproportionation}} X\left(CH_2-\overset{\overset{\displaystyle C_6H_5}{|}}{CH}\right)_m CH=\overset{\overset{\displaystyle C_6H_5}{|}}{CH} \ + \ \overset{\overset{\displaystyle C_6H_5}{|}}{CH_2}-CH_2\left(\overset{\overset{\displaystyle C_6H_5}{|}}{CH}-CH_2\right)_n X$$

The disproportionation reaction is the radical equivalent of the E2 reaction.

$$\cdot\overset{|}{C}\overset{\curvearrowright}{}\overset{|}{\underset{\underset{H}{|}}{C}}- \ + \ \cdot\overset{|}{\underset{|}{C}}- \ \longrightarrow \ \overset{/}{\underset{\backslash}{C}}{=}\overset{\backslash}{\underset{/}{C}} \ + \ H-\overset{|}{\underset{|}{C}}-$$

Which mode of termination occurs can be determined by measuring the number of initiator fragments per polymer molecule. If there are two initiator fragments in each molecule, termination must have occurred by combination. One initiator fragment per molecule indicates disproportionation. Apparently styrene terminates by combination; but, with methyl methacrylate, both reactions take place, disproportionation being favored.

C. CATIONIC AND ANIONIC POLYMERIZATION

Polymerization of alkenes by the cationic mechanism is most important for 2-methylpropene and α-methylstyrene, which do not polymerize well by other methods, and was discussed earlier in considerable detail (Section 4·4H).

In general, we expect that anionic polymerization (Section 4·4H) will occur when the monomer carries substituents that will tend to stabilize the anion formed when a basic initiator, such as amide ion, adds to the double bond of the monomer. Cyano and carbalkoxy groups are favorable in this respect and

$$H_2\overset{\ominus}{N}{:} \ + \ CH_2{=}\overset{\overset{\displaystyle R}{/}}{\underset{\underset{\displaystyle H}{\backslash}}{C}} \ \longrightarrow \ H_2N-CH_2-\overset{\overset{\displaystyle R}{\ominus/}}{\underset{\underset{\displaystyle H}{\backslash}}{C}}$$

it is reported that acrylonitrile and methyl methacrylate can be polymerized with sodium amide in liquid ammonia. Styrene and isoprene undergo anionic polymerization under the influence of powerful bases such as butyllithium and phenylsodium.

Ethylene oxide reacts readily with aqueous hydroxide ion to give either ethylene glycol or polymers of various chain length, depending on the quantity of water present.

$$\underset{\underset{CH_2}{\overset{CH_2}{|}}}{}\!\!\diagdown O \xrightarrow{\;OH^{\ominus}\;}
\begin{cases}
\xrightarrow[\text{H}_2\text{O}]{\text{excess}} \quad \underset{\text{ethylene glycol}}{HOCH_2CH_2OH} \\[3em]
\xrightarrow[\text{H}_2\text{O}]{\text{deficient}} \quad \underset{\text{polyethylene glycol}}{HOCH_2(CH_2OCH_2)_nCH_2OH}
\end{cases}$$

Polyethylene glycol polymers can be viscous liquids or waxy solids (Carbowax, Section $10\cdot11$) depending on the molecular weight, and all are water soluble. This property makes them valuable for preserving archeological relics. Water-logged wooden objects that would warp or disintegrate on being dried can be repeatedly saturated with polyethylene glycol, thus removing the water and adding a permanent filler simultaneously. The Swedish warship Vasa recently raised from the bottom of Stockholm harbor, where it lay for over three centuries, is being preserved in this way.

D. COPOLYMERS

When polymerization occurs in a mixture of monomers, there will be some competition between the different kinds of monomers to add to the growing chain and produce a *copolymer*. Such a polymer will be expected to have quite different physical properties than a mixture of the separate *homopolymers*. Many copolymers, such as butadiene-styrene, ethene-propene, Viton rubbers, and vinyl chloride-vinyl acetate plastics are of considerable commercial importance.

$28\cdot6$ *naturally occurring polymers*

There are a number of naturally occurring polymeric substances that have a high degree of technical or biological importance. Some of these, such as natural rubber, cellulose, and starch have regular structures and can be regarded as being made up of single monomer units. Others such as wool, silk, and deoxyribonucleic acid are copolymers. We have considered the chemistry of most of these substances in some detail earlier and we shall confine our attention here to silk, wool, and collagen.

A. SILK

Silk fibroin is a relatively simple polypeptide, the composition of which varies according to the larva by which it is produced. The commercial product, obtained from the cocoons of mulberry silk moths, contains glycine, L-alanine, L-serine, and L-tyrosine as its principal amino acids. Silk fibroin has an oriented-crystalline structure. The polypeptide chains occur in sheets, each chain with an extended configuration parallel to the fiber axis (not the α helix, Figure $17\cdot7$), and hydrogen bonded to two others in which the directions of the peptide chain are reversed (Figure $28\cdot10$).

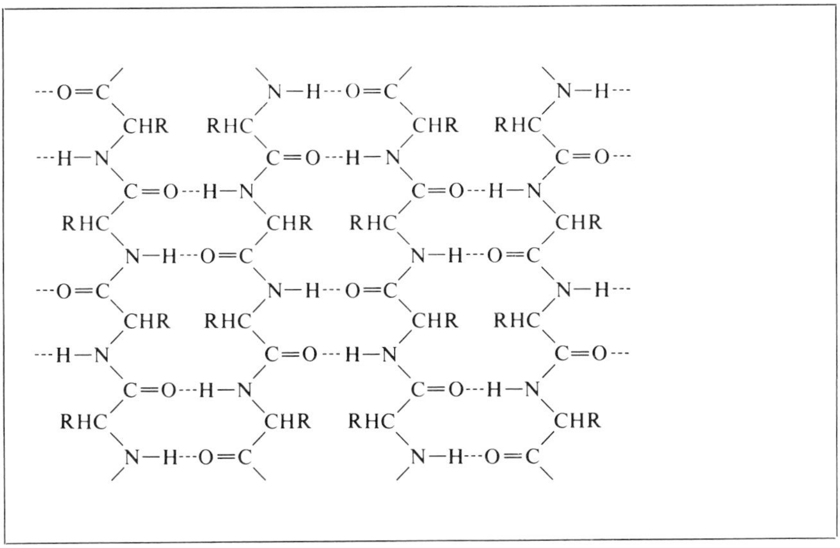

Figure 28·10   Hydrogen-bonded structure of silk fibroin. Note that the peptides run in different directions in alternate chains.

B. WOOL

The structure of wool is more complicated than that of silk fibroin, because wool, like insulin (Section 17·4), contains a considerable quantity of cystine (Table 17·1), which provides disulfide cross links between the peptide chains. These disulfide linkages play an important part in determining the mechanical properties of wool fibers because, if the disulfide linkages are reduced, as with ammonium thioglycolate solution, the fibers become much more pliable.

$$RCH_2-S-S-CH_2R + 2\, HSCH_2\overset{\ominus}{C}O_2\overset{\oplus}{N}H_4 \longrightarrow RCH_2SH + HSCH_2R$$
(wool disulfide cross link)
$$+ \overset{\oplus}{N}H_4\overset{\ominus}{O}_2CCH_2-S-S-CH_2\overset{\ominus}{C}O_2\overset{\oplus}{N}H_4$$

Advantage is taken of this in the curling of hair, thioglycolate reduction being followed by restoration of the disulfide linkages through treatment with a mild oxidizing agent while the hair is held in the desired, curled position.

C. COLLAGEN

The principal protein of skin and connective tissue is called collagen and is primarily constituted of glycine, proline, and hydroxyproline. Collagen molecules are very long and thin (14 A × 2900 A), and each appears to be made up of three twisted polypeptide strands. When collagen is boiled with water, the strands come apart and the product is ordinary cooking gelatin. Connective tissue and skin are made up of fibrils, 200 to 1000 A wide, which are indicated by X-ray diffraction photographs to be composed of collagen molecules running parallel to the long axis. Electron micrographs show regular bands, about 700 A apart, across the fibrils. It is believed that these correspond to

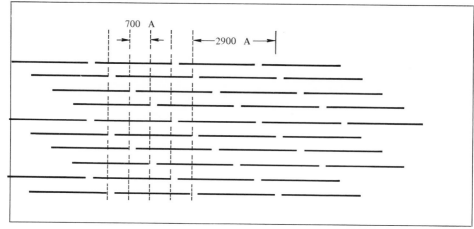

Figure 28·11   Schematic diagram of collagen molecules in a fibril so arranged as to give the 700-A spacing visible in electron micrographs.

collagen molecules, all heading in the same direction but regularly staggered by about a fourth of their length (Figure 28·11).

The conversion of collagen fibrils to leather presumably involves formation of cross links between the collagen molecules. Various substances can be used for the purpose, but chromium salts act particularly rapidly.

28·7   dyeing of fibrous polymers

Many fibrous polymers from synthetic and natural sources are used in the manufacture of fabrics, and the need for a variety of methods and a variety of dyes should be clear from the chemical diversity of these polymers. At the nonpolar extreme are substances such as polypropene, a long-chain hydrocarbon; in the middle is cotton, a polyglucoside with ether and hydroxyl linkages; at the polar end is wool, a polypeptide structure, cross-linked by cystine and containing free acid and amino groups.

In virtually all dyeing processes the dye must do more than color the surface of the fiber. It must also penetrate the fiber and not be removed during washing and cleaning operations. Thus, a water-soluble color applied directly to medium- or non-polar fibers normally is poorly wash-fast, and some stratagem has to be developed to keep it in the fiber. Some of the methods of producing wash-fast dyes follow.

A. DYES WITH POLAR GROUPS

Substitution of polar groups such as amino and sulfonic acid groups into colored molecules often improves wash-fastness by enabling the dye to combine with polar sites in the fiber. This is a particularly useful technique with wool and silk, both of which are polypeptides and contain many strongly polar groups. Martius Yellow (Section 26·2), which is strongly acidic, is a simple *direct* dye for wool and silk. For cotton, linen, and rayon, which are cellulose fibers, it is more difficult to achieve wash-fast colors by direct dyeing. Congo Red was the first reasonably satisfactory direct dye for cotton. It has polar amine and sulfonate groups which, in the fiber, can form hydrogen bonds to the cellulose ether and hydroxyl groups and to other dye molecules, thus reducing its tendency to be leached out in washing.

Congo Red

B. DISPERSE DYES

The use of water-insoluble, fiber-soluble ("disperse") dyes is helpful for many of the medium- and less-polar fibers. Such dyes usually give true solutions in the fiber—the absorption of the dye not being dependent on combination with a limited number of polar sites. Disperse dyes are usually applied in the form of a dispersion of finely divided dye in a soap solution in the presence of some solubilizing agent such as phenol, cresol, or benzoic acid. The process suffers from the fact that usually the absorption of dye in the fiber is slow and is best carried out at elevated temperatures in pressure vessels.

1-Amino-4-hydroxyanthraquinone is a typical dye which can be used in dispersed form to color Dacron (polyethylene glycol terephthalate). Absorption of this dye is a solution process, as indicated by the fact that, even up to high dye concentrations in the fiber, the amount of dye in the fiber is directly proportional to the equilibrium concentration of dye in the solution.

1-amino-4-hydroxyanthraquinone
(red-violet solid, used to dye fabrics pink)

C. MORDANT DYES

One of the oldest known methods of producing wash-fast colors is with the aid of metallic hydroxides to form a link between the fabric and the dye. The production of cloth dyed with "Turkey red," the coloring material of the root of the madder plant, using aluminum hydroxide as a binder or "mordant," has been carried out for many centuries. The principal organic ingredient of

Turkey red has been shown to be 1,2-dihydroxyanthraquinone ("alizarin") and this substance is now prepared synthetically from anthraquinone.

1,2-dihydroxyanthraquinone
(alizarin)

Mordant dyes are useful on cotton, wool, or silk, and are applied in a rather complicated sequence of operations whereby the cloth is treated with a solution of a metallic salt in the presence of mild alkali and a wetting agent for the purpose of forming a complex of the fiber with the metal cation. The dye is then introduced and an insoluble complex salt (often called a "lake") is formed in the fiber. With alizarin and aluminum hydroxide, it is probable that the binding to the dye involves salt formation at the 1-hydroxyl and coordination to aluminum at the adjacent carbonyl group.

Apparently, this chelated type of structure is important in contributing to the excellent light-fastness of most mordant dyes.

A variety of metals can be used as mordants, but aluminum, iron, and chromium are most commonly used. Mordant dyes normally have reasonably acidic phenolic groups and some kind of an adjacent complexing group which fills the function of the carbonyl group in alizarin.

D. VAT DYES

Another and very effective way of making fast colors is to introduce the dye in a soluble form (which may itself be colorless) and then generate the dye in an insoluble form within the fiber. Most commonly, the soluble form of the dye is a reduced form, the dye being produced by oxidation. The overall process is known as "vat dyeing," the name arising from the vats used in the reduction step.

The famous dyes of the ancients, indigo and Tyrian purple (royal purple), can be applied this way; reduced, soluble forms of these dyes occur naturally. In the case of indigo, this is a glycoside, indican, which occurs in the indigo plant. Enzymic or acid hydrolysis of indican gives 3-hydroxyindole ("indoxyl"), which exists in equilibrium with the corresponding keto form.

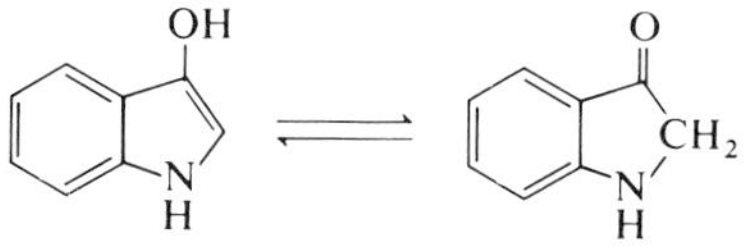

indoxyl

Air oxidation of indoxyl produces indigo probably by a radical mechanism (Figure 28·12).

Figure 28·12   Preparation of indigo from indoxyl.

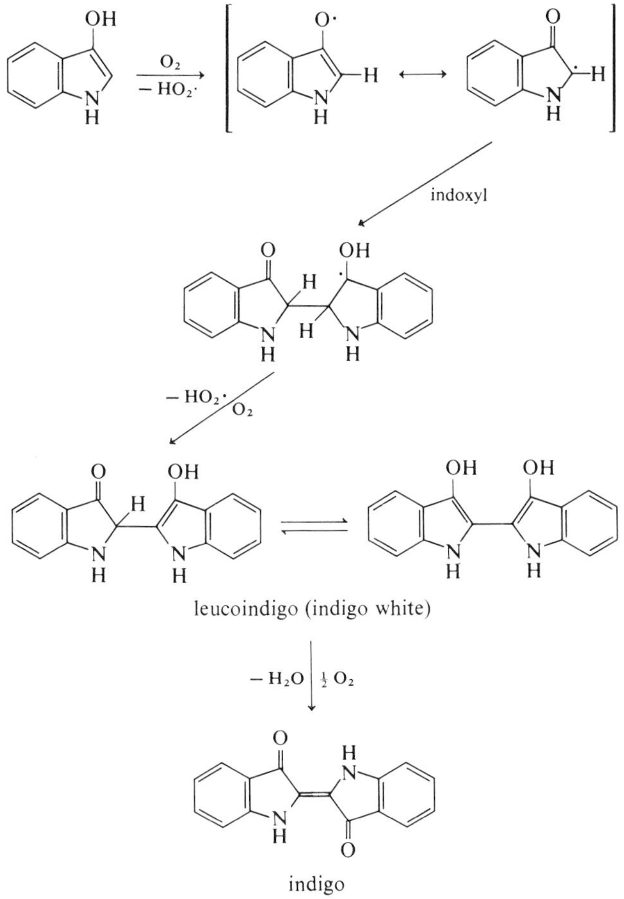

indoxyl

leucoindigo (indigo white)

indigo

The last stage of this reaction, the oxidation of leucoindigo, will be seen to resemble conversion of hydroquinone to quinone. X-Ray studies have shown that indigo has the *trans* configuration of the double bond. Indigo is very insoluble in water and most organic solvents. It absorbs strongly at 5900 A.

In the ordinary dyeing process, indigo is reduced to the colorless **leuco** form which, as an enol, is soluble in alkaline solution and is applied to fabric in this form. That alkaline solutions are required for solubilization of the leuco form of most vat dyes restricts the use of such dyes to fabrics such as cotton and rayon which, unlike wool and silk, are reasonably stable under alkaline conditions.

Oxidation of the leuco form to the dye in the fiber can be achieved simply with oxygen of the air; but this is slow, and it is more common to regenerate the dye by passing the fabric, which has absorbed the leuco form of the dye, into a solution containing chromic acid or perboric acid.

summary

Polymers can be classified on the basis of their physical properties as elastomers (elastic substances), thermoplastic polymers (substances that flow when heated), or thermosetting polymers (rigid, insoluble, amorphous substances possessing cross links between the polymer chains). Polymers that are not cross-linked may be partly crystalline by virtue of van der Waals forces or hydrogen bonds causing ordering of the chains. These substances become glasslike at low temperatures (T_g) and begin to liquefy when heated above the melting temperature (T_m).

Atactic polymers have a random orientation of groups along a chain whereas isotactic polymers have the groups oriented in the same direction. Syndiotactic polymers have a regular alternating orientation of the groups.

Synthetic polymers can be prepared by condensation reactions between:

(a) esters or anhydrides and alcohols

$$RO_2C-Z-CO_2R + HO-Y-OH$$

$$-\overset{O}{\overset{\|}{C}}-O-Y-O-\overset{O}{\overset{\|}{C}}-Z-\overset{O}{\overset{\|}{C}}-O-Y-O-\overset{O}{\overset{\|}{C}}-Z-$$

(b) carboxylic acids and amines

$$HO_2C-Z-CO_2H + H_2N-Y-NH_2$$

$$\longrightarrow -\overset{O}{\overset{\|}{C}}-NH-Y-NH-\overset{O}{\overset{\|}{C}}-Z-\overset{O}{\overset{\|}{C}}-NH-Y-$$

(c) phenols and formaldehyde

OH

$$\text{(phenol)} + CH_2O \longrightarrow -H_2C \underset{\overset{|}{CH_2}}{\overset{OH}{\underset{}{\bigcirc}}} CH_2-$$

Addition polymerization of a wide variety of vinyl compounds is brought about by radical initiators (peroxides or azo compounds). Chain growth is

$$CH_2{=}CHZ \xrightarrow{\;R\cdot\;} -CH_2-\underset{\overset{|}{Z}}{CH}-CH_2-\underset{\overset{|}{Z}}{CH}-CH_2-\underset{\overset{|}{Z}}{CH}-$$

terminated by radical disproportionation or by radical combination.

Cationic and anionic polymerization is also possible with certain monomers.

Naturally occurring polymers include cellulose and starch (polymers of glucose), rubber (a *cis* polymer of isoprene), nucleic acids (copolymers of substituted pentoses and phosphoric acid), wool, silk, and collagen and proteins in general (polypeptide copolymers).

Four general procedures for dyeing fibrous polymers are (a) direct dyeing— useful with silk and wool, which are proteins and contain highly polar groups, and sometimes with cellulose fibers such as cotton, linen, and rayon; (b) disperse dyeing, direct solution of the dye in the fiber—useful with Dacron; (c) mordant dyes, formation of a complex of a metal salt, dye, and fiber— useful with cotton, wool, or silk; (d) vat dyeing, oxidation of a soluble form of a dye to give an insoluble form within the fiber—useful with cotton and rayon.

exercises

28·1   Write a reasonable mechanism for the thermal depolymerization of cyclo-pentadiene tetramer. How could you chemically alter the tetramer to make thermal breakdown more difficult? Explain.

28·2   Suppose a bottle of cyclopentadiene were held at a temperature at which polymerization is rapid, but depolymerization is insignificant. Would the polymerization result in conversion of all of the cyclopentadiene into essentially one gigantic molecule? Why or why not? How would you carry on the polymerization so as to favor formation of polymer molecules with high molecular weights?

28·3   Show how each of the following polymer structures might be obtained from suitable monomers by either addition or condensation. More than one step may be involved.

    a. $-CH_2-CH_2-CH_2-CH_2-CH_2-CH_2-CH_2-$

    b. $-\underset{\overset{|}{CH_3}}{N}-CH_2-CH_2-\underset{\overset{|}{CH_3}}{N}-CH_2-CH_2-\underset{\overset{|}{CH_3}}{N}-CH_2-CH_2-$

c.
$$-CH-CH-CH-CH-CH-CH-$$
$$\quad\ |\quad\ \ |\quad\ \ |\quad\ \ |\quad\ \ |\quad\ \ |$$
$$\ \ \ CH_3\ CH_3\ CH_3\ CH_3\ CH_3\ CH_3$$

d.
$$-O-CH_2-CH_2-\overset{\overset{\textstyle O}{\|}}{C}-O-CH_2-CH_2-\overset{\overset{\textstyle O}{\|}}{C}-O-CH_2-CH_2-\overset{\overset{\textstyle O}{\|}}{C}-$$

e.
$$-CH_2-CH-CH_2-CH-CH_2-CH-$$
$$\qquad\quad\ |\qquad\qquad\ |\qquad\qquad\ |$$
$$\qquad\ \ O-C-CH_3\ \ O-C-CH_3\ \ O-C-CH_3$$
$$\qquad\qquad\ \|\qquad\qquad\ \|\qquad\qquad\ \|$$
$$\qquad\qquad\ O\qquad\qquad\ O\qquad\qquad\ O$$

f.
$$-CH_2-CH-CH_2-CH-CH_2-CH-$$
$$\qquad\quad\ |\qquad\qquad\ |\qquad\qquad\ |$$
$$\qquad\quad OH\qquad\quad OH\qquad\quad OH$$

g.

h.

28·4 High-pressure polyethene (p. 102) differs from polyethene made with the aid of Ziegler catalysts (p. 103) in having a lower density and lower T_m. It has been suggested that this is due to branches in the chains of the high-pressure material. Explain how such branches might arise in the polymerization process and how they would affect the density and T_m.

28·5 Radical-induced chlorination of polyethene in the presence of sulfur dioxide produces a polymer with many chlorine and a few sulfonyl chloride $(-SO_2Cl)$ groups, substituted more or less randomly along the chains. Write suitable mechanisms for these substitution reactions. What kind of physical properties would you expect the chlorosulfonated polymer to have if substitution is carried to the point of having one substituent group to every 25 to 100 CH_2 groups? How might this polymer be cross linked? (A useful product of this general type is marketed under the name of Hypalon.)

28·6 When polyethene (and other polymers) are irradiated with X rays, cross links are formed between the chains. What changes in physical properties would you expect to accompany such cross linking? Would the polyethene become more elastic? Explain.

Suppose polyethene were cross-linked by irradiation above T_m; what would happen if it were then cooled?

28·7 Answer the following questions in as much detail as you can, showing your reasoning:

   a. Why is atactic polymethyl methacrylate not an elastomer?
   b. How might one make a polyamide which is an elastomer?
   c. What kind of physical properties are to be expected for atactic poly-propene?
   d. What would you expect to happen if a piece of high-molecular-weight polyacrylic acid $+CH_2-CH+$ were placed in a solution of sodium hydroxide?
   $$\overset{|}{CO_2H}$$
   e. What kind of properties would you expect for high-molecular-weight poly-p-phenylene?

   $$H-\langle\;\rangle+\langle\;\rangle+_{n-2}\langle\;\rangle-H \quad \text{poly-}p\text{-phenylene}$$

   f. Are the properties, listed in Table 28·1, of polychloroprene as produced by radical polymerization of chloroprene (2-chlorobutadiene) such as to make it likely that *trans* 1,4 addition occurs exclusively?

28·8 The material popularly known as Silly Putty is a polymer having an $-O-Si(R)_2-O-Si(R)_2-O-$ backbone. It is elastic in that it bounces and snaps back when given a quick jerk but rapidly loses any shape it is given when allowed to stand. Which of the polymers listed in Table 28·1 is likely to be the best candidate to have anything like comparable properties? Explain. What changes would you expect to take place in the properties of Silly Putty as a function of time if it were irradiated with X rays (see Exercise 28·6)?

28·9 What kind of a polymer would you expect to be formed if p-cresol were used in place of phenol in the Bakelite process?

28·10 Polymerization of methyl methacrylate with benzoyl peroxide labeled with ^{14}C in the aromatic ring gives a polymer from which only 57% of the ^{14}C can be removed by vigorous alkaline hydrolysis. Correlation of the ^{14}C content of the original polymer with its molecular weight shows that, on the average, there are 1.27 initiator fragments per polymer molecule. Write mechanism(s) for this polymerization that are in accord with the experimental data, and calculate the ratios of the different initiation and termination reactions.

28·11 The radical polymerization of styrene gives atactic polymer. Explain what this means in terms of the mode of addition of monomer units to the growing-chain radical.

28·12 Polyvinyl alcohol prepared by hydrolysis of vinyl acetate (Table 28·1) does not consume measurable amounts of periodic acid or lead tetraacetate (Section 11·3). However, the molecular weight of a typical sample of the polymer decreases from 25,000 to 5000. Explain what these results mean in terms of the structure of polyvinyl alcohol and of polyvinyl acetate.

28·13   Ozonizations of natural rubber and gutta percha, which are both polyiso-
prenes, give high yields of levulinic aldehyde ($CH_3COCH_2CH_2CHO$) and
no 2,5-hexanedione ($CH_3COCH_2CH_2COCH_3$). What are the structures of
these polymers?

28·14   Devise a synthesis of polyvinylamine, remembering that vinylamine itself
is unstable.

28·15   How will the side chains on the L-amino acids of silk fibroin be oriented with
respect to the fiber sheets?

28·16   Apparently the economically important chain reaction wool + moths →
holes + more moths has, as a key step, scission of the disulfide linkages of
cystine in the polypeptide chains by the digestive enzymes of the moth larva.
Devise a method of mothproofing wool which would involve chemically
altering the disulfide linkages (review Chapter 19).

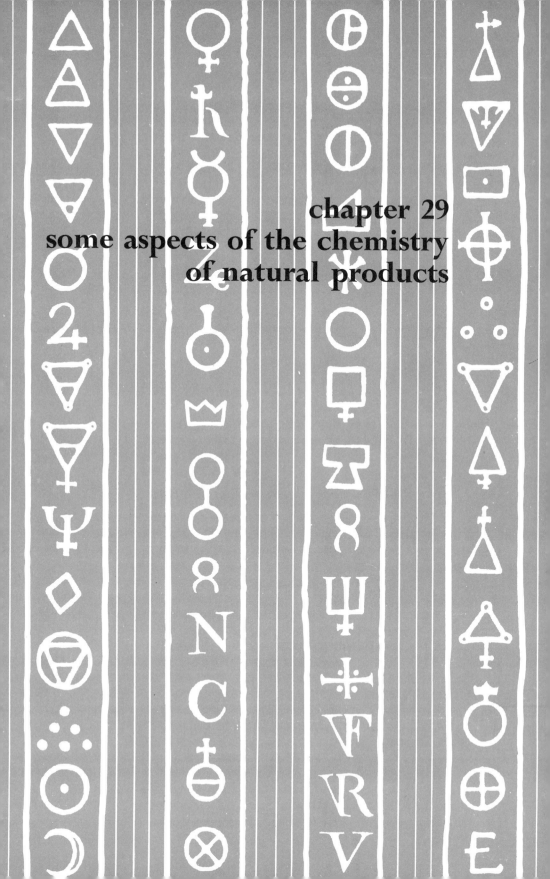

chapter 29
some aspects of the chemistry of natural products

The area of organic chemistry that deals primarily with the structures and chemistry of the compounds which are synthesized by living organisms is extremely large and highly variegated. Many types of natural products, including the carbohydrates, amino acids, proteins and peptides, and alkaloids (discussed in earlier chapters), have been investigated in such detail that whole volumes or series of volumes have been, or could be, devoted to their occurrence, isolation, analysis, structure proof, chemical reactions, synthesis, biological function, and the biogenetic reactions by which they are produced.

The chemistry of many classes of natural products is of general interest quite apart from their biochemical importance. Thus, the chemistry of the bicyclic terpenes contributed much to the interesting and unusual chemistry of such ring compounds long before satisfactory syntheses were available by the Diels-Alder reaction (Chapter 27). Similarly, studies of the chemistry of the steroids has added as much or more to our knowledge of conformations in cyclohexane rings as studies of cyclohexane derivatives themselves. Many other equally cogent examples could be cited.

Our plan in this chapter is to first consider in some detail how the structures of natural products are established, both by classical procedures and by modern instrumental methods. We shall then consider in an illustrative way two rather closely related classes of natural products, terpenes and steroids. Finally, we discuss some of the aspects and uses of biogenetic schemes for the syntheses carried on by living systems. Throughout, we attempt to show how much of the material covered earlier in this book is pertinent to the study of natural products.

29·1   civetone

The active principle of civet, a substance collected from the scent gland of the African civet cat, is called **civetone.** This compound and one of similar nature called **muscone**, isolated from a scent gland of the Tibetan musk deer, are used in preparation of perfumes. Although civetone and muscone do not themselves have pleasant odors, they have the property of markedly enhancing and increasing the persistence of the flower essences.

The structure of civetone was established in 1926 by the Swiss chemist Ruzicka. The starting material for his work was commercial civet imported from Abyssinia packed in buffalo horns—an inhomogeneous, yellow-brown unctuous substance, containing 10 to 15% water, intermixed with civet-cat hairs, and possessing a less-than-pleasant odor. Of several methods of isolation of the active principle, the most useful involved destruction of the glycerides present by hydrolysis with alcoholic potassium hydroxide, fractional distillation of the unsaponifiable neutral material under reduced pressure, and treatment of the distillate of bp 140° to 180° (3 mm) with semicarbazide hydrochloride in the presence of acetate ion (Section 11·4D). The crystalline product formed was the semicarbazone of civetone, and the yield indicated that the starting material contained 10 to 15% of the active principle. Decomposition of the purified semicarbazone with boiling oxalic acid solution gave, after reduced-pressure distillation, crystalline civetone of mp 31°. The pure substance showed no optical activity.

Civetone is a ketone (an aldehyde would hardly have survived the alkaline isolation procedure) which was shown by its elemental analysis and molecular weight to be $C_{17}H_{30}O$. Saturated open-chain ketones have the general formula $C_nH_{2n}O$ and civetone has four hydrogens less, which means that it must have a triple bond, or two double bonds, or one double bond and one ring, or two rings. Civetone reacts with permanganate, gives a dibromide, and absorbs one mole of hydrogen in the presence of palladium. The presence of one double bond and one ring is therefore indicated, and a partial structure can be written as follows:

$$O=C \left\{ C_{14}H_{30} \right\} \quad \begin{array}{c} >C \\ \| \\ >C \end{array}$$

Oxidation of civetone with cold potassium permanganate solution gave a dibasic keto acid which was at first thought to be $C_{16}H_{28}O_5$ (loss of a carbon) but later was shown to be $C_{17}H_{30}O_5$. The formation of this acid confirms the presence of a ring and shows that each of the double-bonded carbons carries a hydrogen, because otherwise a dibasic acid with the same number of carbons could not be formed.

$$O=C \left\{ C_{14}H_{28} \right\} \begin{array}{c} \diagdown CH \\ \| \\ \diagup CH \end{array} \xrightarrow{[O]} O=C \left\{ C_{14}H_{28} \right\} \begin{array}{c} -CO_2H \\ -CO_2H \end{array}$$

A key step in the determination of the structure of civetone was to find out how many carbon atoms separate the carbonyl group and the double bond. This was done by oxidation of civetone under conditions such as to lead to cleavage both at the double bond and at the carbonyl group. Different oxidation procedures gave somewhat different results but in all cases mixtures of dibasic acids were formed, the mildest conditions leading to formation of pimelic acid, $HO_2C(CH_2)_5CO_2H$; suberic acid, $HO_2C(CH_2)_6CO_2H$; and azelaic acid, $HO_2C(CH_2)_7CO_2H$. The formation of azelaic acid indicates that there is at least one continuous chain of seven CH_2 groups forming a bridge between the carbonyl group and double bond.

$$O=C \begin{array}{c} \diagup (CH_2)_7 \diagdown CH \\ \diagdown {}_{\{C_7H_{14}\}} \diagup CH \end{array} \xrightarrow{[O]} \begin{array}{c} HO_2C \diagdown ^{(CH_2)_7} \diagdown CO_2H \\ HO_2C \diagdown {}_{(C_6H_{12})} \diagup CO_2H \end{array}$$

Since all the dicarboxylic acids isolated from the oxidation had continuous chains, Ruzicka inferred that the other seven carbons were also linked up in a continuous chain and that civetone is actually 9-cycloheptadecenone.

$$O=C \begin{array}{c} \diagup (CH_2)_7 \diagdown CH \\ \| \\ \diagdown (CH_2)_7 \diagup CH \end{array}$$

9-cycloheptadecen-1-one

This was an exciting conclusion at a time when the largest known monocyclic compounds were cyclooctane derivatives, and, along with the demonstration in 1925 of the existence of *cis*- and *trans*-decalin (Section 29·4), provided decisive evidence against the Baeyer theory of angle strain in large carbocyclic rings (Section 3·4C).

The postulated presence of a cycloheptadecene ring in civetone was supported by oxidation of dihydrocivetone by chromic acid to heptadecanedioic acid.

dihydrocivetone

heptadecanedioic acid

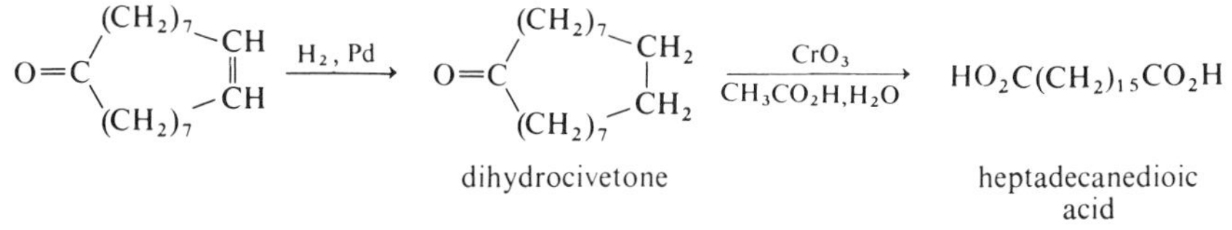

Further evidence was obtained in confirmation of the structure of civetone, one particularly interesting series of transformations being as follows:

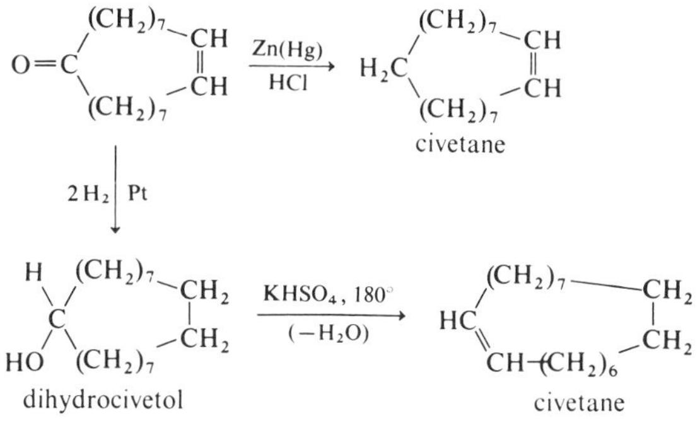

civetane

$2H_2$ | Pt

dihydrocivetol

civetane

The interest in these reactions is the demonstration that the symmetry of the civetone ring is such that civetane (cycloheptadecene) produced by the Clemmenson reduction (Section 11·4F) of civetone is identical with civetane obtained by reduction of civetone to dihydrocivetol and dehydration over an acidic catalyst.

In some quarters, the structure of a natural product is not regarded as really confirmed until a synthesis is achieved by an unambiguous route, and research aimed at such syntheses has been a fascinating and popular part of organic chemistry for many years. Syntheses of naturally occurring substances often yield very considerable benefits in the development of new synthetic reactions and furthermore may offer the possibility of preparing modified forms of the natural products which are of biochemical or medical interest.

In the case of civetone, a synthesis was not achieved until long after the structure was established, but the finding of the cycloheptadecene ring in civetone led Ruzicka to develop a method for the synthesis of large-ring compounds which, although now largely superseded by other procedures, gave the complete series of cyclic ketones from C_9 to C_{21} and a number of higher examples as well.

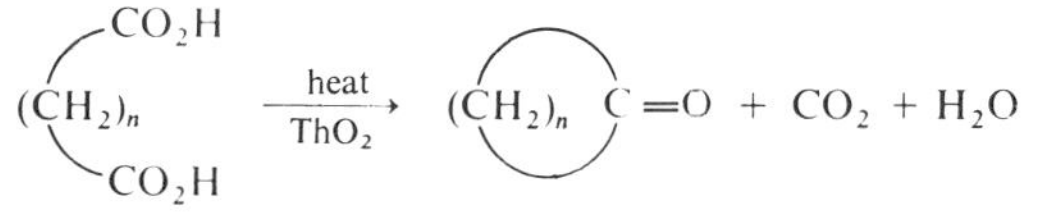

Ruzicka showed that pyrolyzing the appropriate dicarboxylic acid with thorium oxide gave 20% of cyclooctanone and 1 to 5% yields of the higher ketones. The yields are in the 1% range from C_9 to C_{12}, where conformational difficulties are to be expected during ring formation (Section 3·4C).

Musk-type odors are found to be associated with the C_{14} to C_{17} cycloalkanones, being particularly strong with cyclopentadecanone, which is available commercially under the name Exaltone. Interestingly, the odors of civetone and dihydrocivetone are the same. Further evidence for the presence of the 17-membered ring in civetone is supplied by the identity of synthetic cycloheptadecanone with dihydrocivetone. The synthesis of civetone was reported by Stoll and co-workers in 1948.

29·2 spectroscopic methods in the determination of the structures of natural products

The use of the types of spectroscopic methods described in Chapter 7 has greatly reduced the difficulty in determining the structures of the natural products of medium and low molecular weights. We have given many illustrations of the kind of information which is obtained from ultraviolet, infrared, and nmr spectroscopy in earlier chapters. Had these methods been available, their application to the problem of determining the structure of civetone would have been very helpful, but probably not decisive, for the reason that civetone is mostly saturated hydrocarbon and distinction between some of the possible isomers would be difficult if not impossible by spectroscopic methods.

Considerable difficulty can be expected in structure determinations of cyclic compounds which have several saturated rings with no functional groups to permit degradation by selective oxidation. A typical case is that of quebrachamine, an indole alkaloid with a complex polycyclic ring system.

quebrachamine

The ultraviolet spectrum of quebrachamine is typical of an indole and the nmr spectrum shows that the indole system is substituted at the 2 and 3 positions. Oxidation fails to open the saturated ring system, and the only very useful degradative reaction found so far is distillation with zinc dust at 400°, which yields a complex mixture of nitrogen compounds, including several pyridine derivatives.

Fortunately, mass spectrometry is showing great promise in handling structural problems of just this variety and, rather than try to review the application of the other forms of spectroscopy to natural products, we shall concentrate here on mass spectrometry, which has hardly been mentioned since Chapter 7.

One important use of mass spectrometry in the quebrachamine problem was in the identification of the components of the mixture of pyridine bases formed in the zinc-dust distillation. The mixture was separated by gas chromatography (Section 7·1) and the fractions identified by their mass spectra (Section 7·2B).

The procedure for identification of compounds by mass spectrometry is first to determine m/e for the intense peak of highest mass number. In most cases this peak corresponds to the positive ion $M^{\oplus}$ (a radical cation) formed by removal of just one electron from the molecule M being bombarded, and the m/e value of $M^{\oplus}$ is the molecular weight.

Removal of a nonbonding electron generally occurs more easily than removal of an electron from a chemical bond. In the case of compounds such as amines, ketones, and alcohols, all of which contain nonbonding electrons, the radical cation $M^{\oplus}$ can be expected to have the following structures:

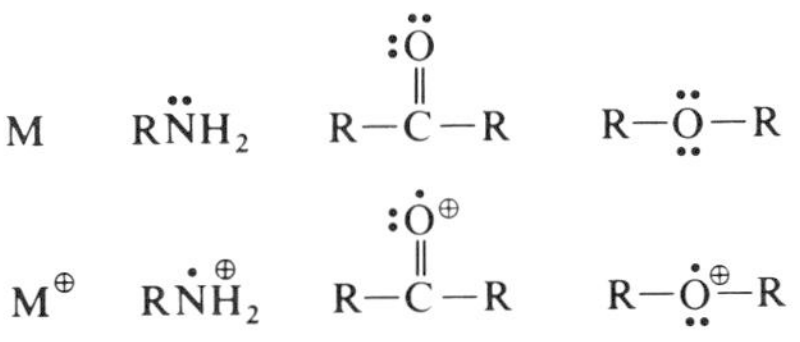

$$
\begin{array}{cccc}
 & & :\overset{\displaystyle\cdot\cdot}{\underset{\displaystyle\|}{O}} & \\[-4pt]
M & R\overset{\cdot\cdot}{N}H_2 & R-C-R & R-\overset{\cdot\cdot}{\underset{\displaystyle\cdot\cdot}{O}}-R \\[12pt]
 & & :\overset{\displaystyle\cdot}{\underset{\displaystyle\|}{O}}{}^{\oplus} & \\[-4pt]
M^{\oplus} & R\overset{\cdot\,\oplus}{N}H_2 & R-C-R & R-\overset{\cdot}{\underset{\displaystyle\cdot\cdot}{O}}{}^{\oplus}-R
\end{array}
$$

Incorrect molecular weights are obtained if the positive ion $M^{\oplus}$ becomes fragmented before it reaches the collector, or if two fragments combine to give a fragment heavier than $M^{\oplus}$. The peak of $M^{\oplus}$ is especially weak with alcohols and branched-chain hydrocarbons, which readily undergo fragmentation by loss of water or side-chain groups. With such compounds the peak corresponding to $M^{\oplus}$ may be 0.1% or less of the total ion intensity.

The pressure of the sample in the ion source of a mass spectrometer is usually about 10^{-5} mm, and, under these conditions, buildup of fragments to give significant peaks with m/e greater than $M^{\oplus}$ is rare. The only exception to this is the formation of (M + 1) peaks resulting from transfer of a hydrogen atom from M to $M^{\oplus}$. The relative intensities of such (M + 1) peaks are usually sensitive to the sample pressure and may be identified this way.

With the molecular weight available from the $M^{\oplus}$ peak with reasonable certainty, the next step is to study the cracking pattern to determine whether the m/e values of the fragments give any clue to the structure. In the mixture of pyridine derivatives obtained by zinc-dust distillation of quebrachamine, the principal substance present showed $M^{\oplus}$ at 107 and strong peaks at 106 and 92 (Figure 29·1). Loss of one m/e unit has to be loss of hydrogen, while loss of fifteen corresponds to NH or CH_3. Fragmentation of NH from a pyridine derivative seems to be a drastic change, but loss of a methyl radical, CH_3, is reasonable, particularly if it leads to a stabilized positive fragment. The m/e value of 107 corresponds to pyridine with one ethyl or two methyl groups. Using 3-ethylpyridine and 3,5-dimethylpyridine as specific examples, we could then have fragmentation reactions as follows:

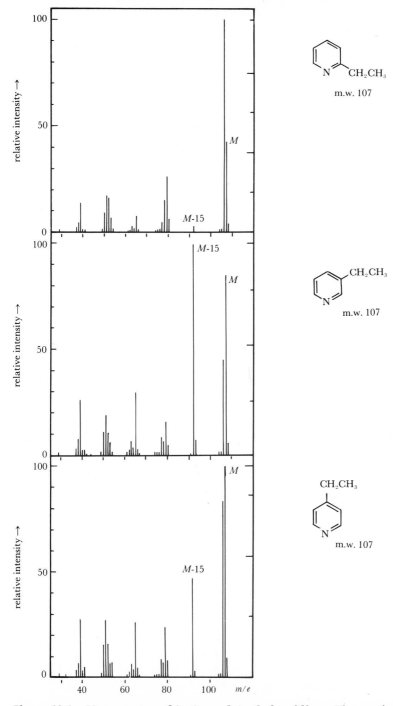

Figure 29·1   Mass spectra of 2-, 3-, and 4-ethylpyridines. The vertical scale is relative peak intensity. The spectrum of the C_7H_9N base from the zinc-dust distillation of quebrachamine is the same as that of 3-ethylpyridine. (By permission from K. Biemann, *Mass Spectrometry, Organic Chemical Applications,* **McGraw-Hill, New York, 1962.)**

For both compounds, the fragment of mass 106 is a benzylic-type cation which is expected to be stabilized by electron delocalization, which will distribute the positive charge over the ring. The fragment of mass 92 would be a stabilized benzylic cation in the one case and a high-energy phenyl-type cation in the other. The high intensity of the 92 peak suggests that the compound of mass 107 is 3-ethylpyridine and the identity of their mass spectra and other properties confirms this assignment.

Demonstration that the mixture of pyridines from zinc-dust distillation of quebrachamine contains 75% of 3-ethylpyridine provided strong support for the presence of a 3-ethylpiperidine grouping in the alkaloid.

Further evidence on the structure of quebrachamine was obtained by comparison of its mass spectrum with that of a transformation product [1] of a related alkaloid of known structure, aspidospermine.

[1]

It will be seen that formula [1] is actually that of a methoxyquebrachamine and, if the methoxy group could be replaced by hydrogen, a synthesis of quebrachamine would be achieved from aspidospermine, thus establishing the structure of quebrachamine. Comparison of the mass spectra of [1] and quebrachamine is much easier and no less definitive. The spectra (Figure 29·2) at first glance look rather different, but careful examination shows that they are actually very similar from $m/e = 138$ downward. Furthermore, virtually all of the peaks that appear in quebrachamine from 143 up to that of $M^{\oplus}$ (282) have counterparts in the spectrum of the methoxy compound just 30 units higher. This difference of 30 mass units is just the OCH_2 by which the molecular weight of the methoxyquebrachamine exceeds the molecular weight of quebrachamine itself.

Assuming the indole part of quebrachamine does not break up very easily, we would expect the *smallest* abundant fragments from that part of the molecule to have masses of 143 or 144.

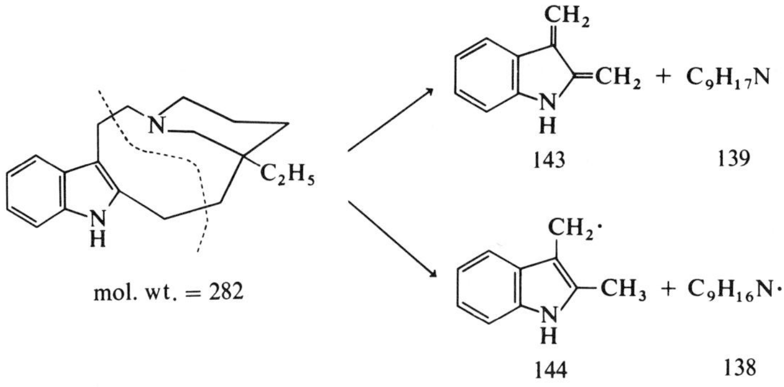

It is significant that the *largest* fragment from the saturated part of quebrachamine would then have m/e 138 or 139. From this we can see why substitution of the methoxyl group affects all peaks of 143 and over, but not those below this number.

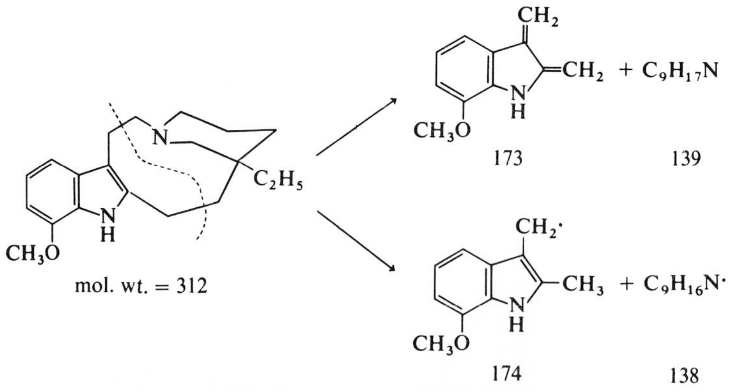

It would be a serious error to imagine that in mass spectra nothing is observed but simple fragmentation of organic molecules on electron impact. Actually, even though electron impact produces highly unstable molecular

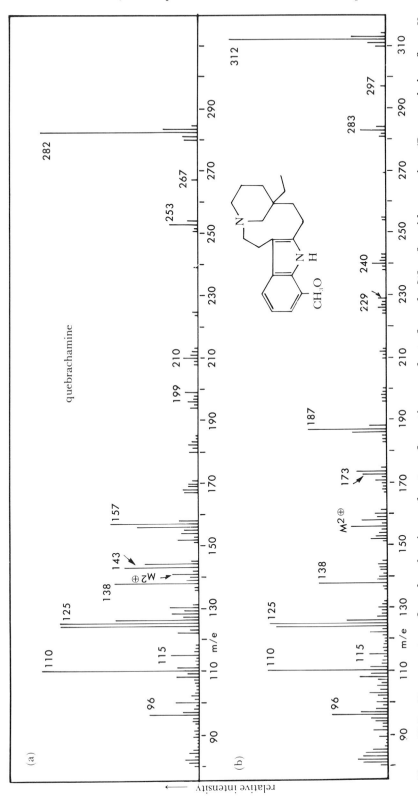

Figure 29·2   Mass spectra of quebrachamine and a transformation product, formula [1], of aspidospermine. (By permission from K. Biemann and *J. Am. Chem. Soc.*) The peaks at *m/e* 141 in quebrachamine and 156 in [1] correspond to parent ions which bear a double positive charge, that is, M²⁺.

ions, there is a strong tendency for breakdown to occur by chemically reasonable processes (as with the ethylpyridines), and this may involve rearrangement of atoms from one part of the molecule to another. An excellent example of such a rearrangement is provided by the $M^{\oplus}$ ion of ethyl butanoate, which breaks down to give ethene and a radical cation of the enol form of ethyl acetate.

The cyclic course of this fragmentation is revealed by studies of the mass spectra of 2-, 3-, and 4-deuterated ethyl butanoate. The 2,2-dideuterio compound gives the enol ion, now with mass 90; the 3,3-dideuterio isomer gives the enol ion of mass 88; while the 4,4,4-trideuterated ester produces an ion of mass 89.

29·3 terpenes

The odor of a freshly crushed mint leaf, like many plant odors, is due to the presence in the plant of volatile C_{10} and C_{15} compounds, which are called **terpenes**. Isolation of these substances from the various parts of plants, even from the wood in some cases, by steam distillation or ether extraction gives what are known as **essential oils**. These are widely used in perfumery, food flavorings, and medicines, or as solvents. Among the typical essential oils are those obtained from cloves, roses, lavender, citronella, eucalyptus, peppermint, camphor, sandalwood, cedar, and turpentine. Such substances are of interest to us here because, as was pointed out by Wallach in 1887, the components of the essential oils can be regarded as derived from isoprene.

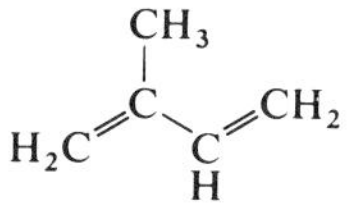

isoprene
(2-methyl-1,3-
butadiene, C_5H_8)

head   tail

Myrcene ($C_{10}H_{16}$), a typical terpene, occurs in the oil of the West Indian bay tree, whose leaves are used in the preparation of bay rum. The carbon skeleton is clearly divisible into two **isoprene units.**

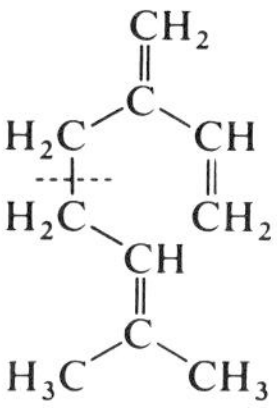

myrcene

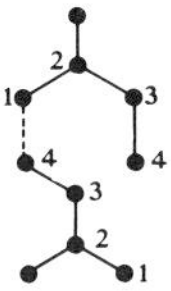

The isoprene units in myrcene (and in almost all other terpenes as well) are connected in a **head-to-tail** manner. Because it is time consuming to show all the carbon and hydrogen atoms of such substances, we shall represent the structures in a convenient short-hand notation in which the carbon-carbon bonds are represented by lines, carbon atoms being understood at the junctions or the ends of lines. By this notation, myrcene can be represented by formulas like the following.

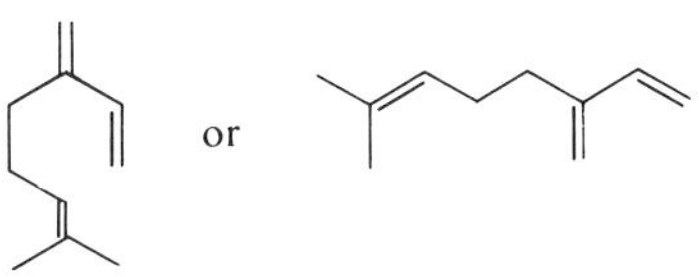

or

In the past the term *terpene* was reserved for C_{10} hydrocarbons such as myrcene. Current practice is to designate as terpenes (or isoprenoids or terpenoids) all compounds that are multiples of the C_5 isoprene skeleton including hydrocarbons, alcohols, aldehydes, and so on. The C_{10} compounds are monoterpenes, C_{15} are sesquiterpenes, C_{20} are diterpenes, C_{30} are triterpenes, and so on.

The empirical isoprene rule resulted from Ruzicka's observation that the majority of the terpene families could be considered as arising from head-to-tail combinations of isoprene units. Thus, the monoterpene (C_{10}) family represents two such units, the sesquiterpenes (C_{15}) three, the diterpenes (C_{20}) four, and so on. Some examples to illustrate this hypothesis are shown with the head-to-tail isoprene junctions indicated by dashed lines. In the cases of cyclic terpenes the thinner bonds indicate where subsequent cyclization has taken place.

Monoterpenes (C_{10})

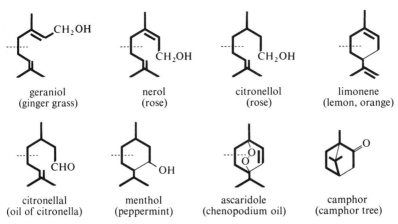

geraniol	nerol	citronellol	limonene
(ginger grass)	(rose)	(rose)	(lemon, orange)

citronellal	menthol	ascaridole	camphor
(oil of citronella)	(peppermint)	(chenopodium oil)	(camphor tree)

The terpene alcohols shown above have floral odors and are important perfume ingredients. The aldehydes have much stronger, citruslike odors and occur in many essential oils such as oil of citronella and oil of lemon. Ascaridole is interesting in being a naturally occurring peroxide. Camphor is a volatile solid substance which for centuries was believed to have medicinal properties. It is now used chiefly as a plasticizer for cellulose nitrate (Section 15·7) and is synthesized commercially from α-pinene (see Exercise 29·12).

camphor

Camphor has a very large molal freezing point depression constant which makes it useful for measuring molecular weights.

Camphor also produces large changes in the surface tension of water and a chip of wood with a piece of camphor embedded in one end will be propelled by the difference in surface pressure produced between the ends as the camphor spreads on the surface of the water (camphor boat). This effect is used in a defense mechanism of a tiny water beetle (*Stenus bipunctatus*), which when threatened by birds, streaks across the surface of the water by expelling a mixture of surface-active terpenes from the tip of its abdomen.

Sesquiterpenes (C_{15})

farnesol	β-selinene	santonin
(lily of the valley)	(oil of celery)	(*Artemisia*)

Farnesol, which occurs in lily of the valley and other plants, is a sex attractant for male insects. Santonin, extracted from the plant *Artemisia*, has been used for centuries in India as a medicinal because of its anthelmintic property (ability to destroy intestinal worms).

Diterpenes (C_{20})

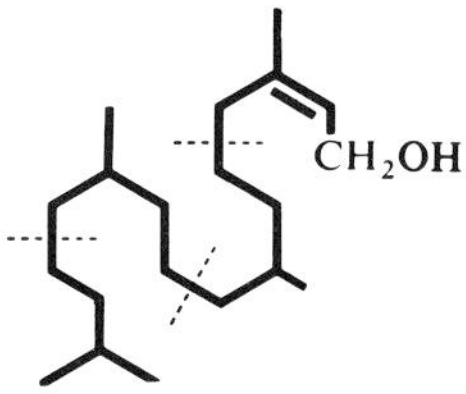

phytol
(chlorophyll)

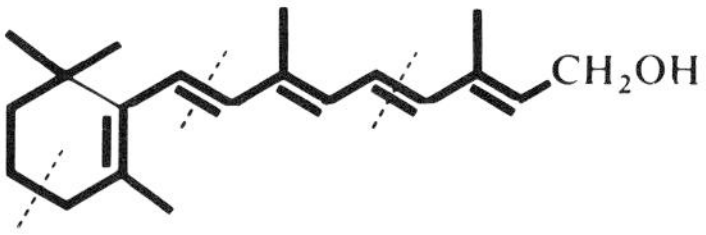

vitamin A

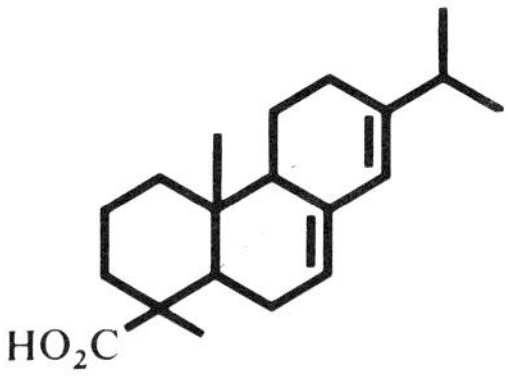

abietic acid
(pine rosin)

Whereas head-to-tail isoprene junctions can be readily picked out in phytol and vitamin A the situation with abietic acid and many of the higher cyclic isoprenoids is somewhat different because alkyl migrations have taken place during their formation.

Phytol occurs as an ester of the propanoic side chain of chlorophyll (Figure 15·1) and as a side chain in vitamin K_1 (Section 23·7). Abietic acid is a major constituent of rosin, which is obtained as a nonvolatile residue in the manufacture of turpentine by steam distillation of pine oleoresin or shredded pine stumps. Abietic acid is the cheapest organic acid by the pound and is used extensively in varnishes and as its sodium salt in laundry soaps).

Triterpenes (C_{30})

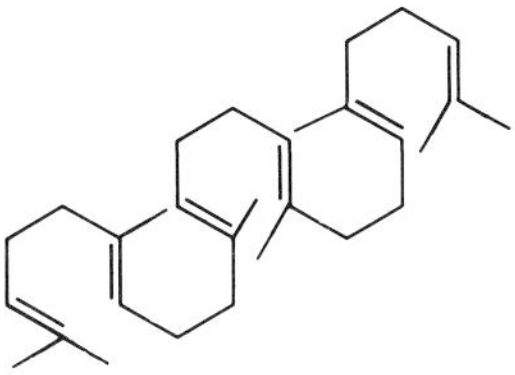

squalene
(shark liver oil)

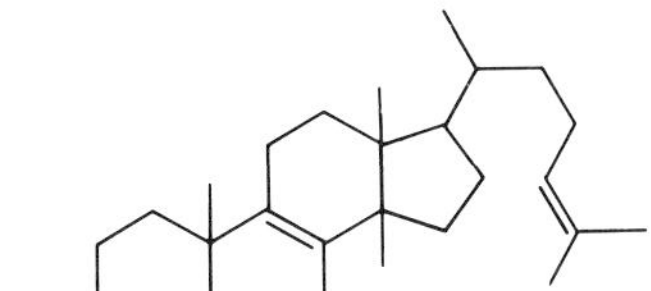

lanosterol
(wool fat)

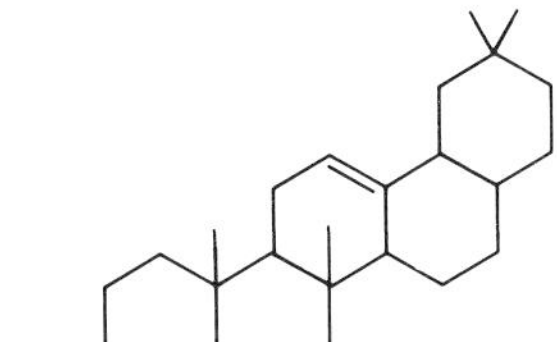

β-amyrin
(*manila elemi*)

The cyclic structures of β-amyrin and lanosterol and the folded conformation shown for squalene resembles the ring system of the steroids, an extremely important family of natural products to be discussed in the next section. The resemblance has a fundamental basis, as we shall see when we examine the biosynthesis of terpenes and steroids in Section 29·5.

Tetraterpenes (C$_{40}$)

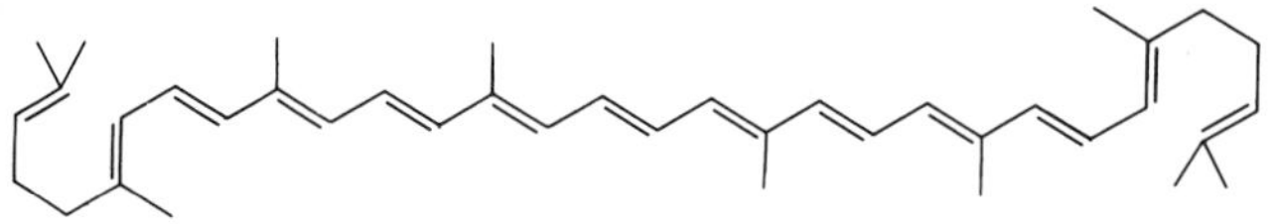

lycopene
(plant pigment, tomatoes, etc.)

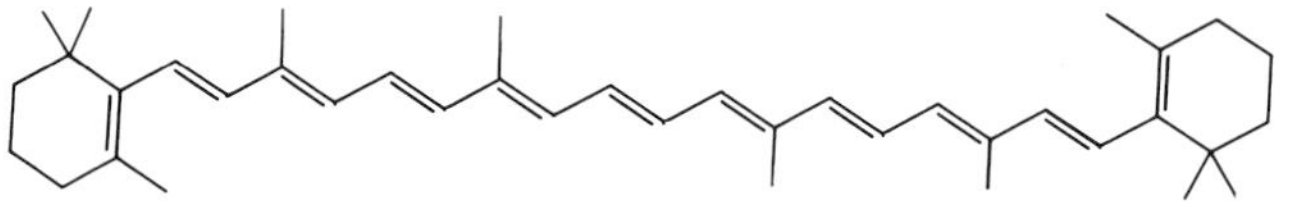

β-carotene
(plant pigment, carrots, etc.)

The long conjugated chains in these compounds are responsible for their color (Section 7·5).

29·4   steroids

In the discussion of the isoprenoid compounds it was our intention to show how the occurrence, structures, and properties of a large and important class of natural products can be correlated. In keeping the discussion within reasonable bounds it was not possible to show how the various structures were established, or give any one compound particular attention. With steroids, we shall take the opposite approach of considering one member of the class, cholesterol, in some detail and then show only the structures of some other representative steroids.

The term **steroid** is generally applied to compounds containing a hydrogenated cyclopentanophenanthrene carbon sketeton. Many of these com-

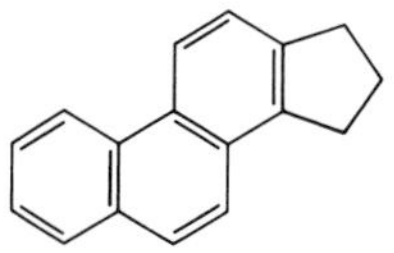

cyclopentanophenanthrene

pounds are alcohols, and sometimes the name **sterol** is used for the whole class. However, sterol is better reserved for the substances that are actually alcohols.

A. CHOLESTEROL

Cholesterol is an unsaturated alcohol of formula C$_{27}$H$_{45}$OH which has long been known to be the principal constituent of human gallstones. Cholesterol, either free or in the form of esters, is actually widely distributed in the body, particularly in nerve and brain tissue, of which it makes up about one sixth of the dry weight. The function of cholesterol in the body is not understood. Experiments with labeled cholesterol indicate that cholesterol in nerve and brain tissue is not rapidly equilibrated with cholesterol administered in the diet. Two things are clear: Cholesterol is synthesized in the body and its metabolism is regulated by a highly specific set of enzymes. The high specificity of these enzymes may be judged from the fact that the very closely related plant sterols, such as sitosterol, are not metabolized by the higher animals, even though they have the same stereochemical configuration of all groups in the ring and differ in structure only near the end of the side chain.

cholesterol   sitosterol

The cholesterol level in the blood generally rises with a person's age and body weight and is usually higher in populations whose diets are rich in animal fats. Atherosclerosis (hardening of the arteries) in man is often associated with high cholesterol levels in the blood and, indeed, it is possible to produce the disease in certain animals by feeding them diets high in cholesterol.

Although cholesterol was recognized as an individual chemical substance in 1812, all aspects of its structure and stereochemical configuration were not settled until about 1955. The structural problem was a very difficult one, because most of cholesterol is saturated and not easily degraded. Fortunately, cholesterol is readily available, so that it was possible to use rather elaborate degradative sequences which would have been quite out of the question with some of the more difficultly obtainable natural products.

The first step in the elucidation of the structure of cholesterol was the determination of the molecular formula, first incorrectly as $C_{26}H_{44}O$ in 1859 and then correctly as $C_{27}H_{46}O$ in 1888. The precision required to distinguish between these two formulas is quite high, since $C_{26}H_{44}O$ has 83.82% C and 11.90% H, whereas $C_{27}H_{46}O$ has 83.87% C and 11.99% H. Cholesterol was shown in 1859 to be an alcohol by formation of ester derivatives and in 1868 to possess a double bond by formation of a dibromide. By 1903 the alcohol function was indicated to be secondary by oxidation to a ketone rather than an aldehyde. The presence of the hydroxyl group and double bond when combined with the molecular formula showed the presence of four carbocyclic rings. Further progress was only possible by oxidative degradation.

There is but one point of unsaturation in the cholesterol molecule and oxidative reactions are not expected to proceed very well. However, chromic acid has the property of attacking tertiary hydrogens, probably by removal of $H:^{\ominus}$ and formation of a carbonium ion. Under these conditions, E1 elimination is expected, and this is likely to give the most highly substituted alkene which would then be cleaved by the chromic acid. With the side chain of cholesterol, two points of cleavage might be expected. Both processes occur, although the

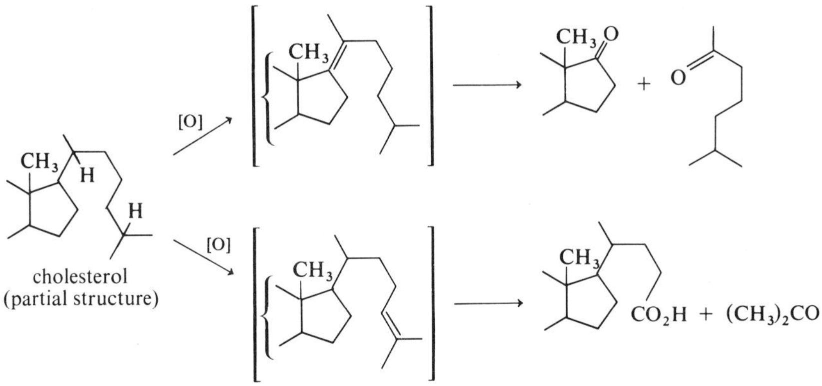

yields are poor. The observation that methyl isohexyl ketone was formed by cleavage of the side chain was important in that it gave the first identifiable fragment of known structure. The discovery of a second point of cleavage was even more significant, because it permitted correlation of cholesterol with another series of compounds, known as the **bile acids.** The principal bile acids are cholic acid [2] and desoxycholic acid [3].

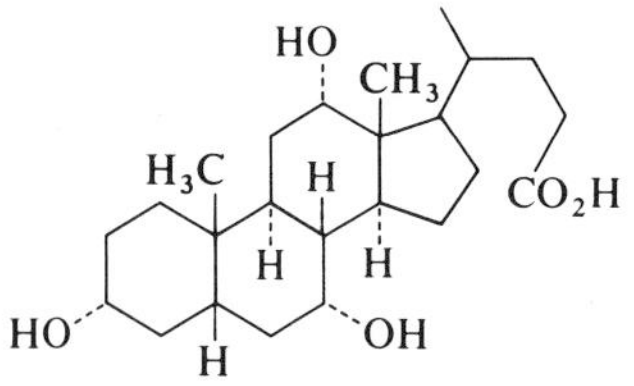

cholic acid
[2]

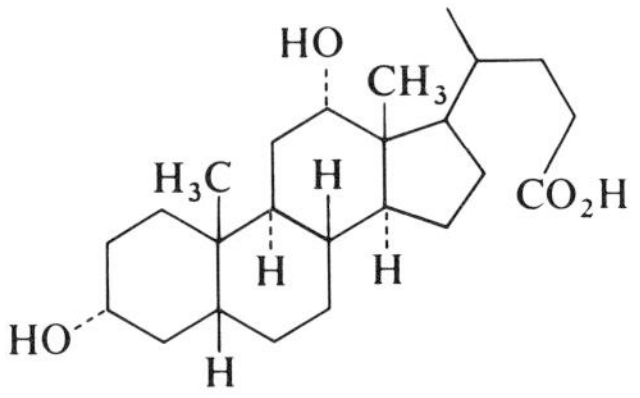

desoxycholic acid
[3]

The presence of a number of substituents on the cycloalkane rings of molecules such as cholic acid and cholesterol gives rise to various stereochemical possibilities. The three hydroxyl groups in cholic acid are said to occupy α positions; that is, they are directed away from the viewer when the skeleton of the molecule is oriented as shown above. On the other hand the hydroxyl group in cholesterol and the angular methyl groups in both cholesterol and cholic acid occupy β positions. (See Section 15·3 for a similar use of α and β in the carbohydrate series).

Both cholic acid and desoxycholic acid occur in bile as sodium salts of N-acyl derivatives of glycine ($RCONHCH_2CO_2{}^{\ominus}Na^{\oplus}$) and taurine, β-aminoethanesulfonic acid ($RCONHCH_2CH_2SO_3{}^{\ominus}Na^{\oplus}$). The function of the salts in bile is to aid in the solubilization and assimilation of fats and hydrocarbons, such as carotene. The bile acids are obtained by alkaline hydrolysis of the peptide bonds.

It will be seen that each of the six-membered rings in cholic acid carries a hydroxyl group, and this is most important, because it provides an entry into the rings by various kinds of oxidative processes. Furthermore, the side chain is seen to be the same length as in one of the chromic acid-oxidation products of cholesterol. The general similarity of the structures of the bile acids and cholesterol, including the stereochemical relations of the rings, strongly suggests that one is the precursor of the other in the body or that the two have a common precursor. Tracer experiments have shown that cholic acid can, in fact, be manufactured from dietary cholesterol.

stereochemical configuration and
numbering system of cholesterol

[4]

Proof that cholesterol and the bile acids have the same general ring system was achieved by reduction of cholesterol to two different hydrocarbons, *cholestane* and *coprostane*, which differ only in the stereochemistry of the junction between rings A and B.

cholestane   coprostane

The differing stereochemistry at the ring junction is shown in the following conformational formulas in which the A and B rings are shown in the chair conformations. (The symbol ⌇ indicates the ring junction with ring C in each case.)

cholestane   coprostane
[5]   [6]

The A and B rings of these compounds can be regarded as derivatives of the alicyclic compound decahydronaphthalene (decalin), $C_{10}H_{18}$, which exists in stable *cis* and *trans* forms.

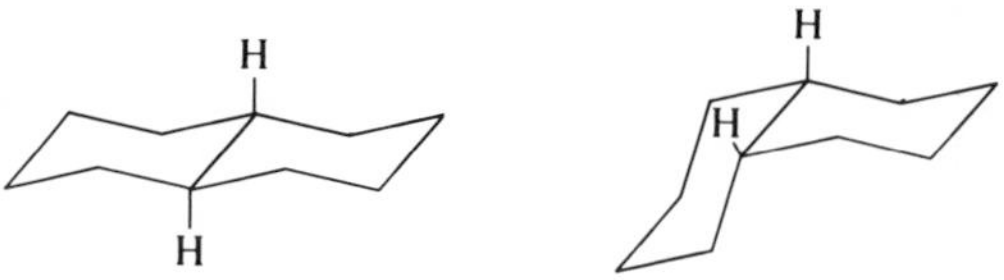

trans-decalin   *cis*-decalin

Oxidation of coprostane, but not cholestane, gave an acid which turned out to be identical with *cholanic acid* obtained by dehydration of cholic acid at 300° followed by hydrogenation.

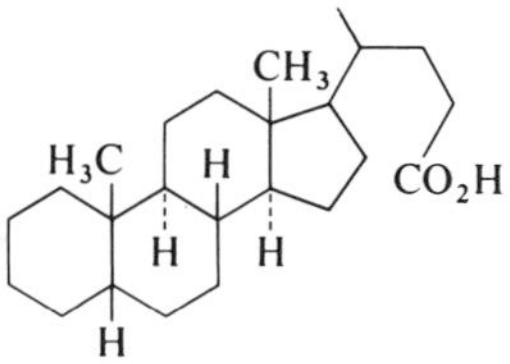

cholanic acid

Determination of the sizes of the rings in cholesterol and the bile acids was achieved in part by use of the so-called **Blanc rule**, which states that a six-carbon dicarboxylic acid on heating will give a ketone, whereas a five-carbon dicarboxylic acid will give an anhydride (Section 13·11B). Reduction of cholesterol to cholestanol followed by oxidation yielded a dibasic acid, which on heating formed a ketone. This indicated the ring on which the hydroxyl was located to be a six-membered ring.

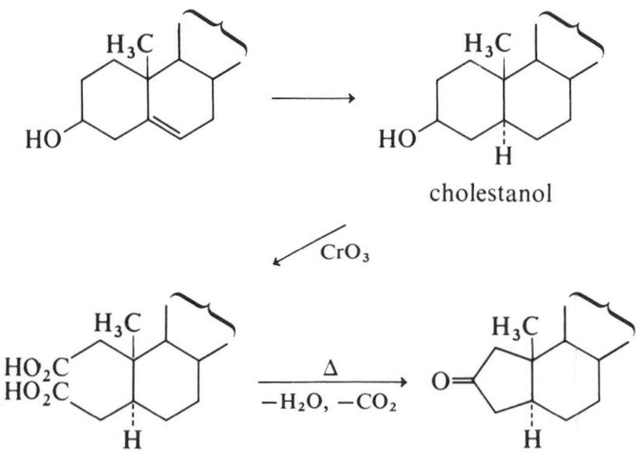

cholestanol

CrO_3

$$\xrightarrow[-H_2O,\ -CO_2]{\Delta}$$

Application of the Blanc rule to dicarboxylic acids obtained by opening the B ring indicated this ring to be six-membered but gave the wrong answer on ring C, an anhydride being formed in place of a ketone. The correct ring size was obtained for ring D by removing the side chain from cholanic acid, opening the ring by oxidation, and showing that an anhydride was formed on pyrolysis.

Location of the methyl groups was achieved by extended degradations—the methyl at C-10 being located by degradation of desoxycholic acid [7] to α-methyl-α-carboxyglutaric acid [8].

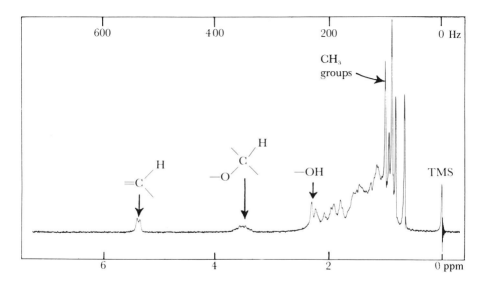

[7] [8]

With the wrong size for ring C, it was inevitable that at some stage incorrect structures would be proposed for cholesterol and the bile acids. Tentative structures [9] and [10] proposed in 1928 for desoxycholic acid and cholesterol, respectively, show a resemblance to the structures now known to be correct, but have a five-membered ring fused to ring A.

[9] [10]

Shortly thereafter, X-ray diffraction measurements indicated sterols to be extended rather than compact molecules. This evidence combined with the formation of chrysene and methylcyclopentanophenanthrene [11] from selenium dehydrogenation of cholesterol led to postulation of the correct ring structure in 1932.

Figure 29·3 Proton nmr spectrum of cholesterol at 100 MHz as a 10% solution in deuteriochloroform with reference to TMS at 0.00. At 60 MHz the chemical shifts are smaller and many of the features of the spectrum between 0.7 and 2.4 ppm are run together and less distinct. (Spectrum kindly furnished by Varian Associates.)

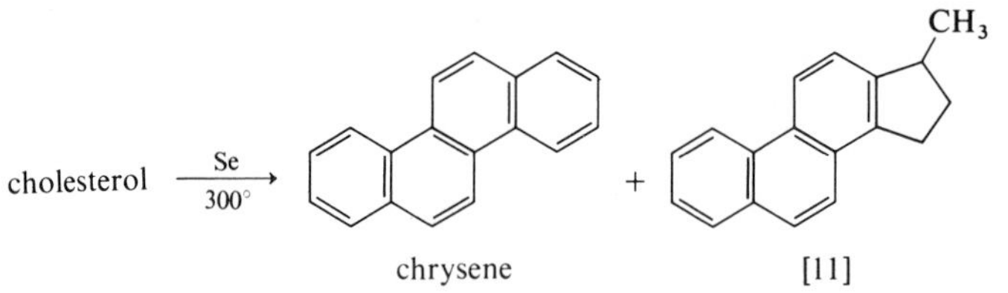

$$cholesterol \xrightarrow[300°]{Se}$$

chrysene   [11]

The absolute configuration of the sterols and bile acids was established in 1955. Cholesterol has eight asymmetric centers and therefore there are 256 possible stereoisomers, but only cholesterol itself occurs naturally.

The proton nmr spectrum of cholesterol at 100 MHz is shown in Figure 29·3. Such spectra are obviously of considerable value in the determination of the structures of even quite complex natural products. With cholesterol, many of the protons at or near the functional groups stand out quite clearly.

B. REPRESENTATIVE STEROIDS

The structures and physiological functions of a number of important steroids are shown in Table 29·1. Total syntheses have been achieved for the important sterols, sex hormones, and adrenal cortical hormones. The need for large quantities of cortisone and related substances for therapeutic use in treatment of arthritis and similar metabolic diseases has led to intensive research on synthetic approaches for methods of producing steriods with oxygen functions at C-11, which is not a particularly common point of substitution in steroids.

The most efficient way of doing this is by microbiological oxidation, and cortisone can be manufactured on a relatively large scale from the saponin diosgenin, which is isolated from tubers of a Mexican yam of the genus *Dioscorea*. Diosgenin is converted to progesterone, then by a high-yield (80 to 90%) oxidation with the mold *Rhizopus nigricans* to 11-hydroxyprogesterone, and finally to cortisone.

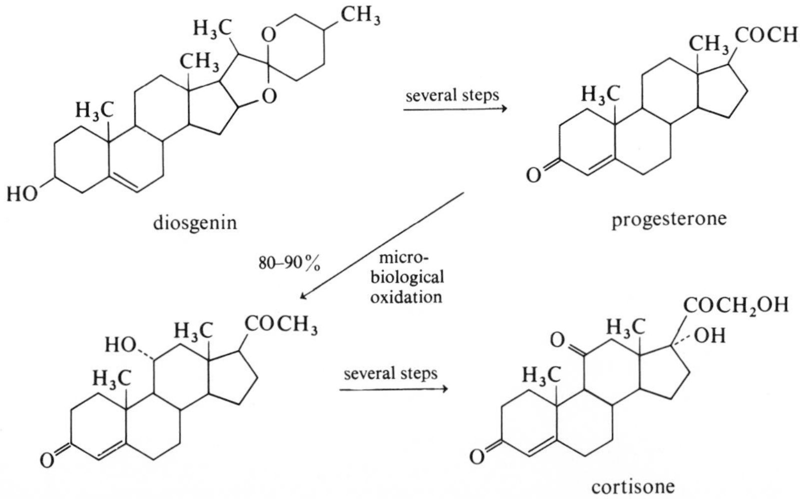

diosgenin

several steps

progesterone

80–90%   micro-biological oxidation

several steps

cortisone

Two synthetic steroids whose use has implications in the areas of physiology, economics, sociology, and religion are the compounds norethindrone [12] and mestranol [13]. These and a number of other compounds which are structurally related to the sex hormones (Table 29·1) can be used to control ovulation. Mixtures of such compounds are marketed as oral contraceptives under various names, Enovid, Ortho-Novum, and so on.

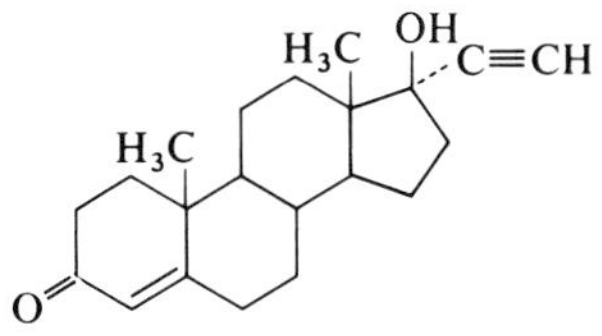

[12]

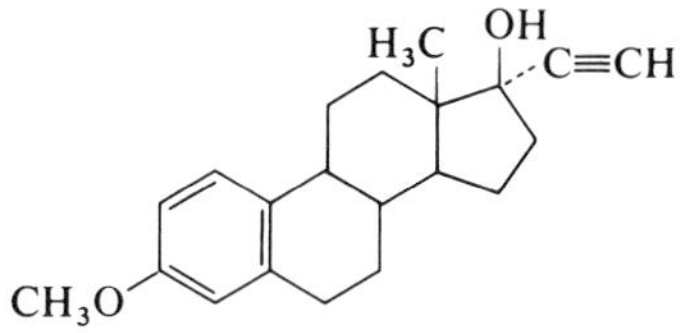

[13]

Vitamin D is of special interest as a photochemical transformation product of ergosterol.

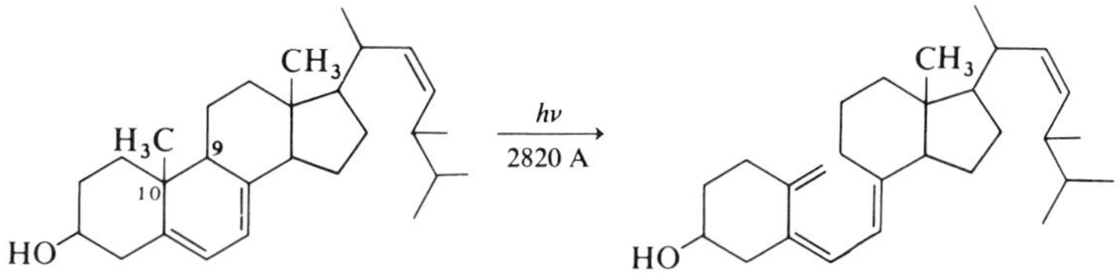

ergosterol

vitamin D₂
(X-ray diffraction studies indicate the *transoid* configuration of the 6,7 bond in the crystal)

29·5 biogenesis of terpenes and steroids

Inspection of the structures for the pentacyclic triterpene, β-amyrin, and cholesterol shows such a striking resemblance between the carbon skeletons that it is not hard to imagine that the way in which these substances are synthesized, their **biogenesis,** may be closely related.

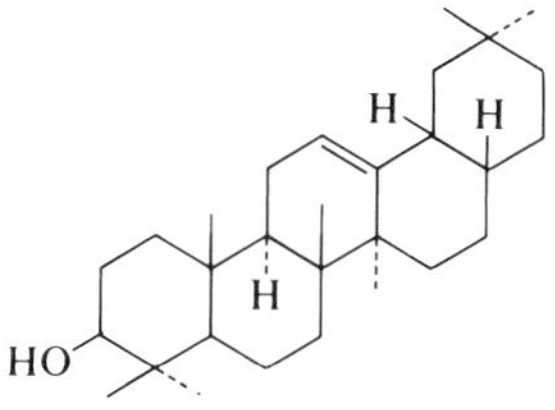

β-amyrin

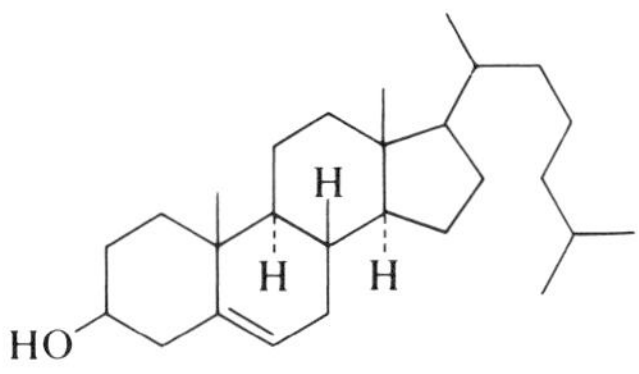

cholesterol

Table 29·1 Representative steroids

structure and name[a]	occurrence and physiological properties	structure and name[a]	occurrence and physiological properties
 ergosterol	sterol of yeast, gives vitamin D_2 when irradiated	 vitamin D_2	antirachitic factor, formed by ultraviolet irradiation of ergosterol
 stigmasterol	plant sterol, soybean oil	 equilenin	female sex hormone of horse, regulates sexual cycle
 estrone	human estrogenic hormone, the corresponding C-17 alcohol (OH *trans* to the C-13 methyl) is even more active (estradiol)	 progesterone	human pregnancy hormone, secreted by the corpus luteum

Table 29·1 Representative steroids (*continued*)

structure and name[a]	occurrence and physiological properties	structure and name[a]	occurrence and physiological properties
testosterone	male sex hormone, regulates development of reproductive organs and secondary sex characteristics	androsterone	androgenic hormone of less potency than testosterone
cortisone	hormone of adrenal cortex, used for treatment of arthritis; 6- and 9-fluoro derivatives have higher activity	digitoxigin	as a complex glycoside at the 3-hydroxyl in digitalis plants, potent cardiac poison, used in small doses to regulate heart action
digitogenin	a saponin, occurs as a complex glycoside (glucose, galactose, and xylose) in digitalis plants[b]	conessine	a representative alkaloid possessing a steroid nucleus

[a] The stereochemistry of the B/C and C/D ring junctions are as in cholesterol and the cholic acids; A/B stereochemistry is indicated where necessary.

[b] Digitogenin as the glycoside, digitonin, has the remarkable property of forming insoluble precipitates with the sterols having the 3-hydroxyl equatorial, but not those in which the hydroxyl is axial.

This idea is heightened by the structure of lanosterol, the tetracylic triterpene alcohol which occurs along with cholesterol in wool fat and has properties so typical of the sterols that it is better known as a sterol than a triterpene.

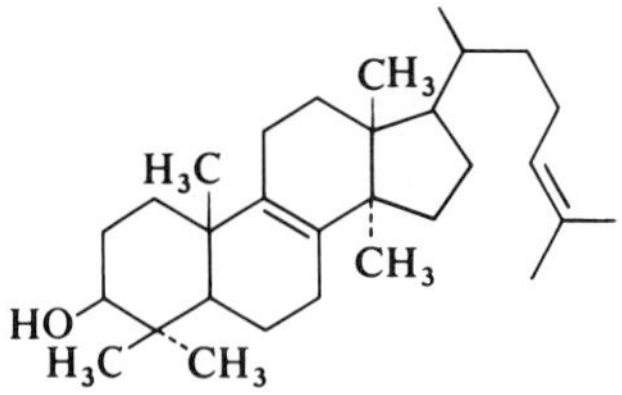

lanosterol

Positive evidence that terpene and steroid biogenesis are related has been provided by experiments with carbon-14 labels which show that acetic acid is their common biological precursor. The general biosynthetic pathway involving polymerization of C_5 units is shown in Figure 29·4.

Acetate is converted to 3,5-dihydroxy-3-methylpentanoic acid (mevalonic acid) by coenzyme A. Further enzymic action leads to the diphosphate, isopentenyl pyrophospate (IPP), the phosphoryl donor being ATP. IPP is the biological equivalent of isoprene which is not itself found in nature.

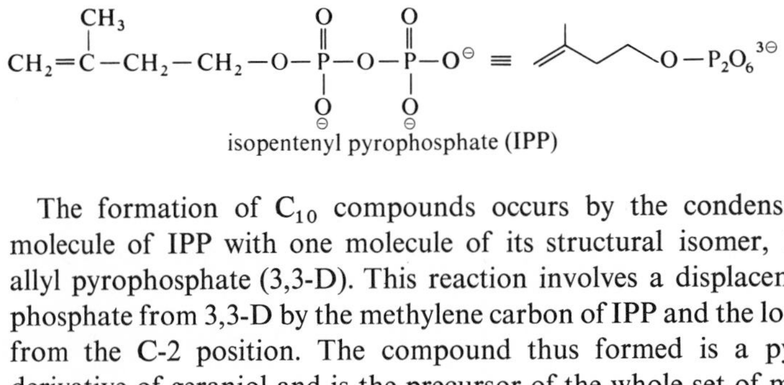

isopentenyl pyrophosphate (IPP)

The formation of C_{10} compounds occurs by the condensation of one molecule of IPP with one molecule of its structural isomer, 3,3-dimethylallyl pyrophosphate (3,3-D). This reaction involves a displacement of pyrophosphate from 3,3-D by the methylene carbon of IPP and the loss of a proton from the C-2 position. The compound thus formed is a pyrophosphate derivative of geraniol and is the precursor of the whole set of monoterpenes.

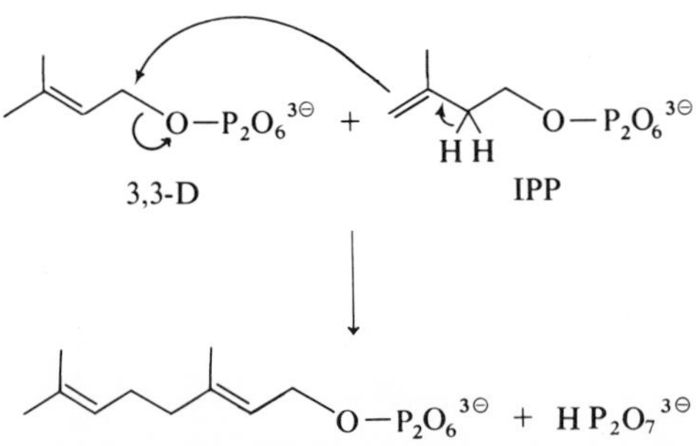

geranyl pyrophosphate

Further condensation with another molecule of IPP produces a C_{15} pyrophosphate, which turns out to be the precursor not only of the sesquiterpenes (C_{15}) but also squalene and lanosterol (C_{30}) and the steroids, as shown in Figure 29·4.

The conversion of squalene to lanosterol is particularly interesting because,

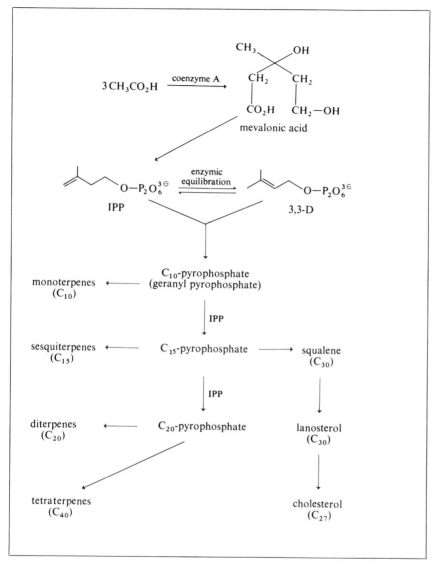

Figure 29·4   General biogenetic route to terpenes and steroids starting from acetic acid.

although squalene is divisible into isoprene units, lanosterol is not, a methyl being required at C-8 and not C-13.

lanosterol

Some kind of rearrangement is therefore required to get from squalene to lanosterol. The nature of this rearrangement becomes clearer if we write the squalene formula in the shape of lanosterol.

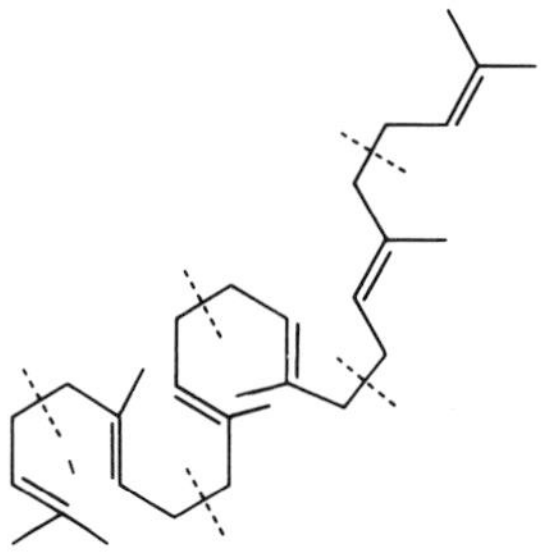

squalene

When written in this form, we see that squalene is beautifully constructed for cyclization to the ring system of lanosterol and this conversion has recently been shown to occur in both plants and animals via [14], the 2,3-epoxide of squalene. Acid-catalyzed opening of the epoxide ring and ring closure in the remainder of the molecule are essentially synchronous and

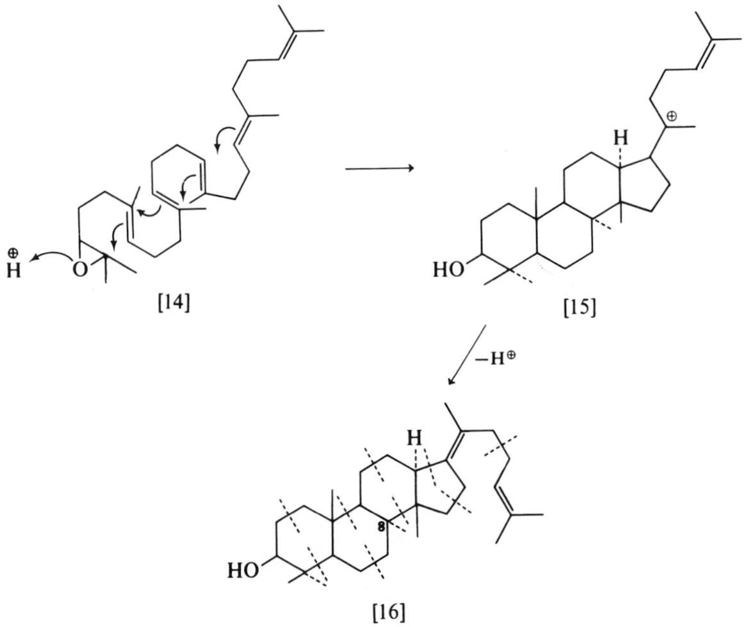

[14]

[15]

$-H^\oplus$

[16]

produce a carbonium ion [15] which eliminates a proton to give [16], an isomer of lanosterol. Now if a sequence of carbonium ion-type rearrangements occurs we can see how [16] could be readily converted to lanosterol.

The evidence is strong that the biogenesis of lanosterol actually proceeds by a route of this type. With squalene made from either methyl- or carboxyl-labeled acetate, all the carbons of lanosterol and cholesterol are labeled as predicted. Furthermore, ingenious double-labeling experiments have shown that the methyl at C-13 of lanosterol is the one that was originally located at C-14, whereas the one at C-14 is one that came from C-8.

The conversion of lanosterol to cholesterol involves removal of the three methyl groups at the 4, 4, and 14 positions, shift of the double bond at the B/C junction to between C-5 and C-6, and reduction of the C-24 to C-25 double bond. The methyl groups are indicated by tracer experiments to be eliminated by oxidation to carbon dioxide.

summary

Elucidation of the structure of a natural product usually involves degradation to smaller fragments that can be identified with known compounds. Mass spectrometry can be used to advantage both for producing fragments and for identifying them, and for determining molecular weights. Fragmentation patterns in the mass spectrometer are best interpreted by postulating that stabilized cations will tend to be produced either directly or by rearrangement.

Terpenes (isoprenoid compounds) contain carbon skeletons made by head-to-tail unions of C_5 isoprene units, for example.

Many terpenes contain oxygen, for example, camphor and vitamin A. The junctions of the isoprene units in these compounds are shown here by dashed lines and ring-closure positions with arrows.

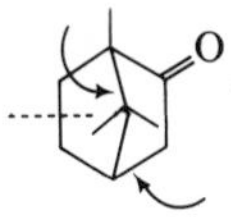

(camphor)

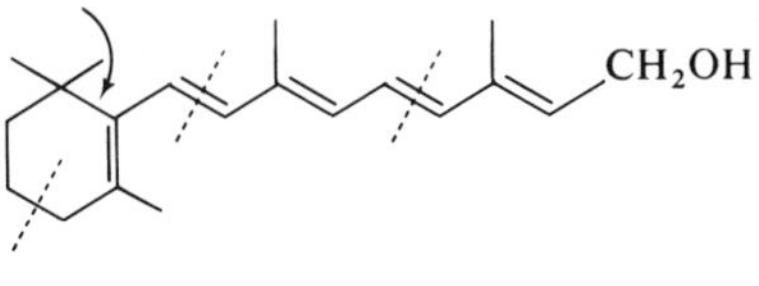

(vitamin A)

Steroids, which are derivatives of cyclopentanophenanthrene, include cholesterol (a sterol) and cholic acid (a bile acid). They have the same carbon

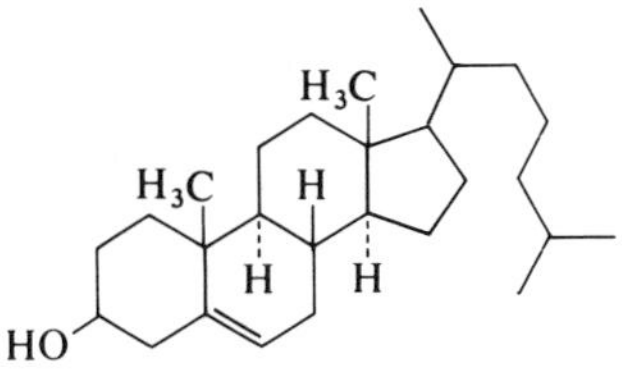

(cholesterol)

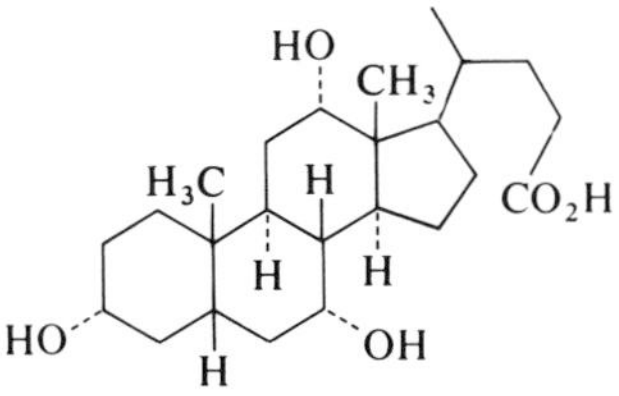

(cholic acid)

skeleton in the rings but differ in configuration as shown.

Studies using carbon-14 labels have shown that the biogenesis of cholesterol follows the sequence: acetic acid, mevalonic acid, several isoprenoid pyrophosphates, squalene, lanosterol, and cholesterol.

exercises

29·1   Muscone, the active principal of Tibetan musk, is an optically active ketone of formula $C_{16}H_{30}O$. On oxidation it gives a mixture of dicarboxylic acids. At least two acids of formula $C_{16}H_{30}O_4$ are formed, along with some dodecanedicarboxylic acid and suberic acid.

Clemmenson reduction of muscone gives an optically inactive hydrocarbon shown by synthesis to be methylcyclopentadecane. Muscone is not racemized by strong acids or strong bases, although it does form a benzylidene ($=CHC_6H_5$) derivative with benzaldehyde and sodium methoxide.

What structure(s) for muscone are consistent with the above experimental evidence? Give your reasoning. What additional evidence would be helpful?

29·2   Explain how use of ultraviolet, infrared, or nmr spectroscopy could be used to distinguish between the following possible structures for civetone.

    a.   9-cycloheptadecenone and 2-cycloheptadecenone
    b.   *cis*-9-cycloheptadecenone and *trans*-9-cycloheptadecenone
    c.   8-methyl-8-cyclohexadecenone and 9-cycloheptadecenone
    d.   8-cycloheptadecenone and 9-cycloheptadecenone

29·3   How could you use deuterium labeling to show that the fragmentation of 3-ethylpyridine which occurs in the mass spectrometer results in loss of the CH_3 group and not an NH fragment? Be as specific as possible.

29·4 The relative intensities of (M − 15) peaks for the 2- and 4-ethylpyridines are much less than for 3-ethylpyridine (see Figure 29·1). Suggest a reason for this. Can your explanation also account for the fact that intensity ratios (M − 15)/ (M − 1) for the different isomers fall in the ratio 3 > 4 > 2? Explain.

29·5 *a.* Identify the fragments in the mass spectrum of quebrachamine with m/e values of 267, 253, 157, and 125. Show your reasoning.
b. The very strong peak at 110 in the mass spectrum of quebrachamine has no counterpart at 172. How might a fragment of 110 mass units be reasonably formed by breakdown of the primary dissociation products?

29·6 The mass spectrum of 1-phenylpropane has a prominent peak at mass 92. With 3,3,3-trideuterio-1-phenylpropane, the peak shifts to 93. Write a likely mechanism for breakdown of 1-phenylpropane to give a fragment of mass 92.

29·7 The mass spectra of alcohols usually show peaks of (M − 18), which correspond to loss of water. What kind of mechanisms can explain the formation of (M − 18) peaks, and no (M − 19) peaks, from 1,1-dideuterio-ethanol and 1,1,1,3,3-pentadeuterio-2-butanol?

29·8 *a.* Write out all of the possible carbon skeletons for acyclic terpene and sesquiterpene hydrocarbons that follow the isoprene rule. Do not consider double-bond position isomers.
b. Do the same for monocyclic terpene hydrocarbons with a six-membered ring.

29·9 The terpene known as alloocimene ($C_{10}H_{16}$) shows λ_{max} at 2880 A and gives among other products 1 mole of acetone and 1 mole of acetaldehyde on ozonization. What is a likely structure for alloocimene? Show your reasoning.

29·10 Write structures for each of the optical and *cis-trans* isomers that are possible of the following isoprenoid compounds:

    a. myrcene   *e.* β-selinene
    b. farnesol   *f.* α-pinene
    c. limonene   *g.* camphor
    d. phytol

29·11 Nerol and geraniol cyclize under the influence of acid to yield α-terpineol. How could the relative ease of cylization of these alcohols, coupled with other reactions, be used to establish the configurations at the double bond of geraniol, nerol, and the corresponding aldehydes, geranial and neral? Write a mechanism for the cyclizations.

α-terpineol

29·12 Camphor can be made on an industrial scale from α-pinene (turpentine) by the following reactions, some of which involve carbonium ion rearrangements of a type particularly prevalent in the bicyclic terpenes and the scourge of the earlier workers in the field trying to determine terpene structures.

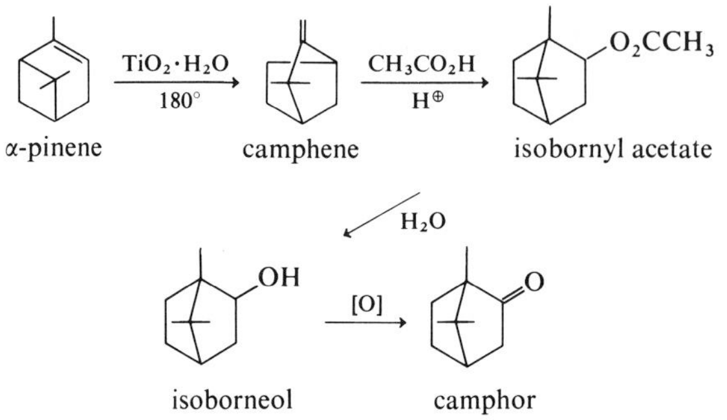

α-pinene   camphene   isobornyl acetate

isoborneol   camphor

Write mechanisms for the rearrangement reactions noting that hydrated titanium oxide is an acidic catalyst.

29·13   How many optical isomers of cholic acid are possible?

29·14   Assuming cholesterol has the stereochemical configuration shown below draw a similar configurational structure for cholic acid (including the hydroxyl groups).

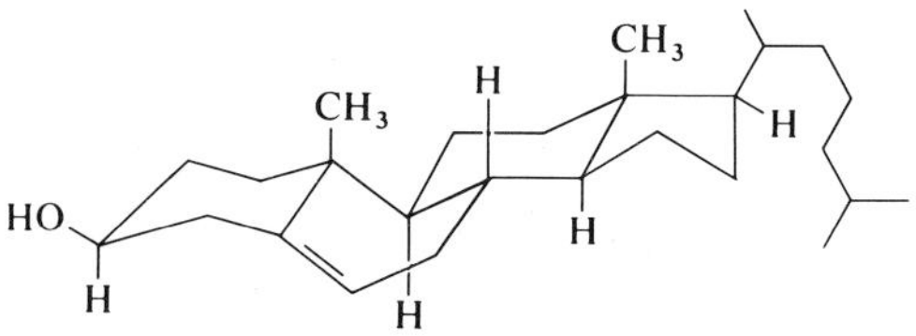

29·15   When the sodium salt of 12-ketocholanic acid is heated to 330°, 1 mole of water and 1 mole of carbon dioxide are evolved and a hydrocarbon "dehydronorcholene" is formed. Selenium dehydrogenation of this substance gives methylcholanthrene.

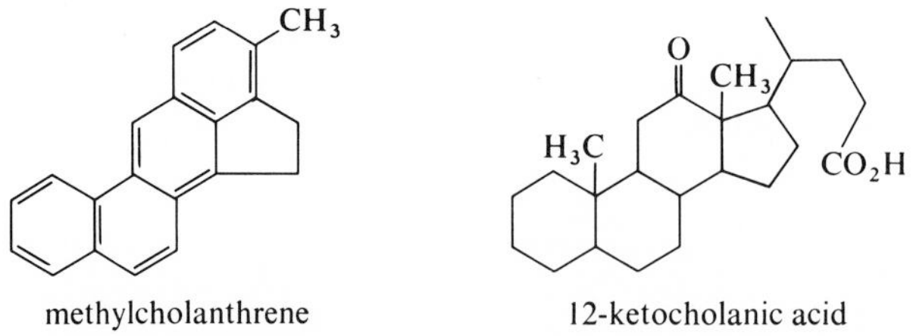

methylcholanthrene   12-ketocholanic acid

What is a likely structure for "dehydronorcholene" and how does the formation of methylcholanthrene help establish the location of the sterol side chain on ring D?

29·16 Using the stereochemical information shown in formulas [2], [4], and [5] decide whether the following substituents occupy equatorial or axial positions.

a. the C-19 methyl in cholestane
b. the C-5 hydrogen in cholestane
c. the C-3 hydroxyl in cholesterol
d. the C-3 hydroxyl in cholic acid
e. the C-7 hydroxyl in cholic acid

general index